Kirk-Othmer

ENCYCLOPEDIA OF CHEMICAL TECHNOLOGY

Second Edition

SUPPLEMENT VOLUME

Adamantane

to

Units

Interscience Publishers
a division of John Wiley & Sons, Inc.
New York · London · Sydney · Toronto

Kirk-Othmer

ENCYCLOPEDIA

OF CHEMICAL

TECHNOLOGY

Second completely revised edition

SUPPLEMENT VOLUME

**Adamantane
to
Units**

CONTENTS

v

EDITORIAL STAFF FOR SUPPLEMENT VOLUME

Leslie Holzer   Anna Klingsberg   Carolyn C. Wronker

CONTRIBUTORS TO SUPPLEMENT VOLUME

D. Arkin, *Chemical Projects Associates Inc.*, Olefins

R. L. Bebb, *Firestong Tire & Rubber Company*, Styrene–butadiene solution copolymers

Alan Beerbower, *Esso Research and Engineering Company*, Solubility parameters

N. Biederman, *Institute of Gas Technology,* Gas, natural

Francis K. Burr, *Fabric Research Labratories, Inc.*, Textile technology (Textile waste treatment)

E. J. Cairns, *Argonne National Laboratories*, Cells, high temperature

D. L. Caldwell, *The Lummus Company*, Ethylene

E. L. Carr, *Firestone Tire & Rubber Company*, Styrene–butadiene solution copolymers

J. R. Carruthers, *Bell Telephone Laboratories*, Nonlinear optical materials

A. D. Caunt, *Imperial Chemical Industries Ltd.*, Polymers of higher olefins

F. C. Cesare, *Uniroyal, Inc.,* Polypropylene fiber

S. G. Cottis, *The Carborundum Company*, Poly(hydroxybenzoic acid)

G. R. Cuthbertson, *Uniroyal Inc.*, Polypropylene fiber

E. Daby, *Ford Motor Co.*, Automobile exhaust control (Photochemical smog)

John D. A. Day, *Bechtel Corporation*, Microwaves

Geroge L. Drake, Jr., *U.S. Dept. of Agriculture*, Textile technology (Fire-resistant textiles)

G. Yale Eastman, *Radio Corportion of America*, Heat pipe

James Economy, *The Carborundum Company*, Phenolic fibers; Poly(hydroxybenzoic acid)

R. T. Eddinger, *FMC Corporation*, Coal (Synthetic crude oil from coal)

E. R. Elzinga, *Esso Research and Engineering Co.*, Proteins from petroleum

M. Farber, *Uniroyal, Inc.*, Polypropylene fiber

John R. Fenter, *Dept. of the Air Force*, Ceramic composite armor (Ceramic and adhesives)

Gerhard Flint, *Great Salt Lake Minerals & Chemicals Corporation*, Great Salt Lake chemicals

Galen R. Frysinger, *ESB Incorporated*, Fuel cells

Eugene Garfield, *Institute for Scientific Information*, Information retrieval services and methods

M. Garfinkel, *Chemical Projects Associates Inc.*, Olefins

David J. Goerz, Jr., *Bechtel Corporation*, Microwaves

Charles E. Granito, *Institute for Scientific Information,* Information retrieval services and methods

John W. E. Griemsmann, *Polytechnic Institute of Brooklyn,* Pipeline heating

James M. Hammack, *National Fire Protection Association,* Fire extinguishing agents

Jerome W. Hankin, *Bechtel Corporation,* Microwaves

Charles Hansen, *PPG Industries Inc.,* Solubility parameters

J. Happel, *New York University,* Methylacetylene

Edgar E. Hardy, *Monsanto Research Corporation,* Phosgene

Henry B. Hass, *Chemical Consultant,* Chlorine

T. A. Henrie, *Bureau of Mines, U.S. Dept. of the Interior,* Mercury, recovery by electrooxidation

N. Hiki, *Ford Motor Co.,* Automobile exhaust control (Photochemical smog)

Raymond Hindersinn, *Hooker Chemical Corporation,* Halogenated fire retardants

H. B. Huntington, *Rensselaer Polytechnic Institute,* Electromigration

R. W. Ingwalson, *Velsicol Chemical Corp.,* Nitriles

Edwin P. Kawasaki, *Republic Steel Corporation,* Pickling of steel

S. Klemantaski, *British Steel Corporation,* Slagceram

Robert Langguth, *Monsanto Company, Inorganic Chemicals Division,* Enzyme detergents

H. Lanier, *Essex International Inc.,* Copper

Theodore E. Lannefeld, *Fabric Research Laboratories, Inc.,* Textile technology (Adhesives for carpet backing and apparel.

A. I. Laskin, *Esso Research and Engineering Co.,* Proteins from petroleum

Harry G. Lassen, *Ford Motor Co.,* Automobile exhaust control

G. Fred Lee, *University of Wisconsin,* Eutrophication

W. Jared Leidigh, *Bechtel Corporation,* Microwaves

Gerd Leston, *Koppers Company,* Alkylphenols; Cresylic acids, synthetic

Henry R. Linden, *Institute of Gas Technology,* Coal (Coal gasification)

R. E. Lindstrom, *Bureau of Mines, U.S. Dept.of the Interior,* Mercury, recovery by electrooxidation

David L. McBride, *United States Steel Corporation,* Iron by direct reduction

M. L. McGlashan, *The University, Exeter, U.K.,* Units

Charles E. McGinn, *Allied Chemical Corporation,* Textile technology (Solvent dyeing)

Charles T. Masur, M.D., *Lederle Laboratories,* Cancer chemotherapy

J. W. Mausteller, *MSA Research Corporation,* Oxygen generation systems

S. G. Morley, *Wolfson Institute, University of Nottingham,* Carbon fibers

Robert E. Moore, *Sun Oil Company,* Adamantane

T. M. Muzyczko, *The Richardson Co.,* Chemical cleaning

Roy G. Neville, *Bechtel Corporation,* Microwaves

H. K. Nieuwenhuis, *Chemical Projects Associates, Inc.,* Olefins

Donald F. Othmer, *Polytechnic Institute of Brooklyn,* Pipeline heating

V. A. Pattison, *Hooker Chemical Corporation,* Halogenated fire retardants

Anthony E. Petrarca, *The Ohio State University,* Information retrieval services and methods

Jack Preston *Chemstrand Research Center, Inc., Monsanto Company,* Polyimides

J. B. Rose, *Imperial Chemical Industries Ltd.,* Polymers of higher olefins

George Rugger, *Dept. of the Army,* Ceramic composite armor (Fabrication and plastics)

Harold Schonhorn, *Bell Telephone Laboratories,* Adhesion

Arthur T. Schooley, *The B. F. Goodrich Co.*, Microplants

L. Seglin, *FMC*, Coal (Synthetic crude oil from coal)

S. H. Shapiro, *Armour Industrial Chemical Co.*, Amine oxides

G. Shell, *Envirotech. Corp.*, Pollution

H. Shimotake, *Argonne National Laboratory*, Cells, high temperature

Frederic L. Sievenpiper, *Allied Chemical Corporation*, Textile technology (Solvent dyeing)

A. V. Slack, *Tennessee Valley Authority*, Fertilizers

Samuel Smith, *Minnesota Mining and Manufacturing Company*, Textile technology (Soil-release finishes)

R. H. Stanley, *Titanium Intermediates Ltd.*, Nitrogen fixation

R. K. Steunenberg, *Argonne National Laboratory*, Cells, high temperature

A. Theodore Stewart, Jr., *Bechtel Corporation*, Microwaves

C. A. Stokes, *Consultant*, Carbon black; Research management

A. James Stonehouse, *The Brush Beryllium Company*, Beryllides

Edward A. Sullivan, *Ventron Corporation*, Hydrides

G. P. Sutton, *Envirotech Corp.*, Pollution

W. M. Tuddenham, *Kennecott Copper Corporation*, Copper

D. Walsh, *New York University*, Methylacetylene

Stuart Way, *Westinghouse Electric Corp.*, Coal (Power from coal by gasification and magnetohydrodynamics)

B. Weinstock, *Ford Motor Co.*, Automobile exhaust control (Photochemical smog)

Robert H. Wentorf, Jr., *General Electric Company*, Diamond

ABBREVIATIONS AND SYMBOLS

Å	Angstrom unit(s)	bp	boiling point
AATCC	American Association of Textile Chemists and Colorists	Btu	British thermal unit(s)
		C	centigrade; Celsius; coulomb(s)
ac	alternating current	C-	denoting attachment to carbon (eg, C-acetyl-indoline)
ACS	American Chemical Society		
AIChE	American Institute of Chemical Engineers	cal	calorie(s)
		calcd	calculated
AIP	American Institute of Physics	cg	centigram(s)
		cgs	centimeter-gram-second
amp	ampere(s)	Ci	curie(s)
amp-hr	ampere-hour(s)	CI	Colour Index
AOAC	Association of Official Analytical (formerly Agricultural) Chemists	cm	centimeter(s)
		cp	chemically pure
		cP	centipoise(s)
APHA	American Public Health Association	cps	cycles per second
		cSt	centistokes
API	American Petroleum Institute	cu	cubic
		d	density
approx	approximately	d-	*dextro*-, dextrorotatory
ar-	aromatic (eg, ar-vinylaniline)	D-	denoting configurational relationship (related to *dextro*-glyceraldehyde)
as-	asymmetric(al) (eg, as-trichlorobenzene)		
		D	Debye unit(s)
ASA	American Standards Association (now United States of America Standards Institute, USASI)	dB	decibel(s)
		dc	direct current
		dec pt	decomposition point
		dl-, DL-	racemic
		DTA	differential thermal analysis
ASTM	American Society for Testing and Materials		
		dyn	dyne(s)
atm	atmosphere(s)	ed.	edition, editor
at. no.	atomic number	emf	electromotive force
at. wt	atomic weight	emu	electromagnetic unit(s)
b	barn(s)	estd	estimated
b (as in b_{11})	boiling (at 11 mm Hg)	esu	electrostatic unit(s)
bbl	barrel(s)	eV	electron volt(s)
Bé	Baumé	exptl	experimental
beV	billion electron volt(s)	F	Fahrenheit; farad(s)
Bhn	Brinell hardness number	fl oz	fluid ounce(s)

Bi	biot	crit	critical
BP	*British Pharmacopoeia* (General Medical Council in London)	cryst	crystalline
		crystd	crystallized
		crystn	crystallization
Btu	British thermal unit	cSt	centistoke
bu	bushel	cu	cubic
C	Celsius; coulomb(s)	d	density
C-	denoting attachment to carbon	*d*	differential operator
		d-	*dextro-*, dextrorotatory
ca	circa, approximately	D	Debye unit(s)
CA	Chemical Abstracts	D-	denoting configurational relationship (as *dextro*-glyceraldehyde)
cal	calorie		
calcd	calculated		
cfm, ft³/min	cubic foot (feet) per minute	db	dry-bulb
		dB	decibel
cg	centigram	dc	direct current
cgs	centimeter-gram-second	dec, decomp	decompose(s)
Ci	curie		
CI	Colour Index (number); the CI numbers given in *ECT*, 2nd ed., are from the new *Colour Index* (1956) and Suppl. (1963), *Soc. Dyers Colourists*, Bradford, England, and *AATCC*, U.S.A.	decompd	decomposed
		decompn	decomposition
		den	denier
		den/fil	denier per filament
		deriv	derivative
		detd	determined
		detn	determination
		diam	diameter
		dielec	dielectric (adj.)
CIE	Commission Internationale de l'Eclairage (see also ICI)	dil	dilute
		DIN	Deutsche Industrienormen
		distd	distilled
cif	cost, insurance, freight	distn	distillation
cl	carload lots	dl	deciliter
cm	centimeter	*dl-*, DL	racemic
coeff	coefficient	dm	decimeter
compd, cpd	compound (noun)	DOT	Department of Transportation
compn	composition	dp	dewpoint
concd	concentrated	dyn	dyne
concn	concentration	*e*	electron; base of natural logarithms
cond	conductivity		
const	constant	ed.	edited, edition, editor
cont	continued	elec	electric(al)
cor	corrected	emf	electromotive force
cp	chemically pure	emu	electromagnetic unit
cP	centipoise	eng	engineering
cpd, compd	compound (noun)	equil	equilibrium
		equiv	equivalent
cps	cycles per second	esp	especially

esr, ESR	electron spin resonance	hyg	hygroscopic
est(d)	estimate(d)	Hz	hertz
estn	estimation	I	current
esu	electrostatic unit	i, insol	insoluble
eV	electron volt	^{i} (eg, Pr^i)	iso (eg, isopropyl)
expt(l)	experiment(al)	i-	inactive (eg, i-methionine)
ext(d)	extract(ed)	IACS	International Annealed
extn	extraction		Copper Standard
F	Fahrenheit; farad(s)	ibp	initial boiling point
F	faraday constant	ICC	Interstate Commerce
FAO	Food and Agriculture		Commission
	Organization of the	ICI	International Commission
	United Nations		on Illumination (see also
fcc	face-centered cubic		CIE); Imperial Chemical
Fed, fedl	federal		Industries, Ltd.
fl oz	fluid ounce	ICT	International Critical
fob	free on board		Tables
fp	freezing point	ID	inner diameter
frz	freezing	IEEE	Institute of Electrical and
ft	foot (feet)		Electronics Engineers
ft-lb	foot-pound	in.	inch
ft^3/min,		insol, i	insoluble
cfm	cubic foot (feet) per minute	IPT	Institute of Petroleum
g	gram		Technologists
g	gravitational acceleration	ir	infrared
G	gauss	ISO	International Organization
G	Gibbs free energy		for Standardization
Gal	gal (unit of acceleration;	IU	International Unit
	from Galileo)	IUPAC	International Union of
gal	gallon		Pure and Applied
gal/min,			Chemistry
gpm	gallon per minute	J	joule
g/den	gram per denier	K	Kelvin
gem-	geminal (attached to the	K	dissociation constant
	same atom)	kbar	kilobar
g-mol	gram-molecular	kc	kilocycle
g-mole	gram-mole	kcal	kilogram-calorie
G-Oe	gauss-oersted	keV	kilo electron volt
gpm,		kg	kilogram
gal/min	gallon per minute	kG	kilogauss
gr	grain	kgf	kilogram force
H	henry	kJ	kilojoule
h, hr	hour	kp	kilopond (equals kilo-
hl	hectoliter		gram force)
hmw	high-molecular-weight(adj.)	kV	kilovolt
hp	horsepower	kVA	kilovolt-ampere
hr, h	hour	kW	kilowatt
hyd	hydrated, hydrous	kWh	kilowatt-hour

l	liter	mM	millimole
l-	*levo-*, levorotatory	m*M*	millimolar
L-	denoting configurational relationship (as *levo-*glyceraldehyde)	mo	month
		mol	molecule, molecular
		mol wt	molecular weight
lb	pound	mp	melting point
LC_{50}	concentration lethal to 50% of the animals tested	mph	miles per hour
		MR	molar refraction
		mV	millivolt
lcl	less than carload lots	mμ	millimicron (10^{-9} m)
LD_{50}	dose lethal to 50% of the animals tested	Mx	maxwell
		^{n} (eg, Bu^n),	
liq	liquid	*n-*	normal (eg, normal butyl)
lmw	low-molecular-weight (adj.)	n (as, n_D^{20})	index of refraction (for 20°C and sodium light)
ln	logarithm (natural)		
log	logarithm (common)	*n-*, ^{n}	normal (eg, *n*-butyl, Bu^n)
m	meter	N	newton
m	molal	*N*	normal (as applied to concentration)
m-	meta (eg, *m*-xylene)		
M	metal	*N-*	denoting attachment to nitrogen
M	molar (as applied to concentration; not molal)	NASA	National Aeronautics and Space Administration
mA	milliampere	ND	*New Drugs* (NND changed to ND in 1965)
mAh	milliampere-hour		
manuf	manufacture	NF	*National Formulary* (American Pharmaceutical Association)
manufd, mfg	manufactured		
manufg, mfd	manufacturing	nm	nuclear magneton; nanometer (10^{-9} m)
max	maximum		
Mc	megacycle	nmr, NMR	nuclear magnetic resonance
MCA	Manufacturing Chemists' Association	NND	*New and Nonofficial Drugs* (AMA) (1958–1965). Later called ND
mcal	millicalorie		
mech	mechanical	NNR	*New and Nonofficial Remedies* (1907–1958). Later called NND
meq	milliequivalent		
MeV	million electron volt		
mfd, manufd	manufactured	no.	number
		NOIBN	not otherwise indexed by name (DOT specification for shipping containers)
mfg, manufg	manufacturing		
mg	milligram	*o-*	ortho (eg, *o*-xylene)
min	minimum; minute	*O-*	denoting attachment to oxygen
misc	miscellaneous		
mixt	mixture	Ω	ohm
ml	milliliter	Ω-cm	ohm-centimeter
MLD	minimum lethal dose	OD	outer diameter
mm	millimeter	Oe	oersted(s)

o/w	oil-in-water (eg, o/w emulsion)	resp	respectively
owf	on weight of fiber	rh	relative humidity
oz	ounce	Rhe	unit of fluidity (1/P)
p-	para (eg, *p*-xylene)	RI	Ring Index (number); from *The Ring Index*, Reinhold Publishing Corp., 1940. See also RRI
P	poise		
Pa	pascal		
pdr	powder		
PhI	*Pharmacopoeia Internationalis*, 2 vols. and Suppl., World Health Organization, Geneva, 1951, 1955, and 1959	rms	root mean square
		rpm	revolutions per minute
		rps	revolutions per second
		RRI	Revised Ring Index (number); from *The Ring Index*, 2nd ed., American Chemical Society, Washington, D.C., 1960
phr	parts per hundred of rubber or resin		
pos	positive (adj.)		
powd	powdered	RT	room temperature
ppb	parts per billion (parts per 10⁹)	s, sol	soluble
		ˢ (eg, Buˢ), *sec-*	secondary (eg, *sec*-butyl)
ppm	parts per million		
ppt(d)	precipitate(d)	*s-, sym-*	symmetrical (eg, *s*-dichloroethylene)
pptn	precipitation		
Pr. (no.)	Foreign prototype (number); dyestuff designation used in *AATCC Year Books* for dyes not listed in the old *Colour Index* (1924 ed.; 1928 Suppl.); obsolete since new *Colour Index* was published (1956 ed.; 1963 Suppl.)	*S-*	denoting attachment to sulfur
		S	Siemens
		SAE	Society of Automotive Engineers
		satd	saturated
		satn	saturation
		scf, SCF	standard cubic foot (feet) (760 mm Hg, 60°F)
		scfm	standard cubic feet per minute
prepd	prepared	Sch	Schultz number (designation for dyes from *Farbstofftabellen*, 4 vols., Akademie Verlag, Leipzig, 1931–1939)
prepn	preparation		
psi	pound per square inch		
psia (psig)	pound per square inch absolute (gage)		
pt	point		
pts	parts	sec	second
qual	qualitative	*sec-,* ˢ	secondary (eg, *sec*-butyl; Buˢ)
quant	quantitative		
qv	which see (quod vide)	SFs	Saybolt Furol second
R	Rankine; roentgen; univalent hydrocarbon radical	sl s, sl sol	slightly soluble
		sol, s	soluble
		soln	solution
rad	radian	soly	solubility
Rep	roentgen equivalent physical	sp	specific
		sp, spp	species (sing. and pl.)

$s-$ para para

Spec	specification	USP	(*The*) *United States*
sp gr	specific gravity		*Pharmacopeia* (Mack
SPI	Society of the Plastics		Publishing Co., Easton,
	Industry		Pa.)
sq	square	uv	ultraviolet
St	stokes	V	volt
STP	standard temperature and	*v-, vic-*	vicinal (attached to
	pressure (760 mm Hg,		adjacent atoms)
	0°C)	var	variety
subl	sublime(s), subliming	*vic-, v-*	vicinal (attached to
SUs	Saybolt Universal		adjacent atoms)
	second	vol	volume (not volatile)
sym, s-	symmetrical (eg, *sym-*	v s, v sol	very soluble
	dichloroethylene)	vs	versus
T	tesla	v/v	volume per volume
TAPPI	Technical Association of	W	watt
	the Pulp and Paper	We	weber
	Industry	Wh	watt-hour
tech	technical	w/o	water-in-oil (eg, w/o
temp	temperature		emulsion)
tert-, t-, ᵗ	tertiary (eg, *tert*-butyl,	wt	weight
	t-butyl)	w/v	weight per volume
theoret	theoretical	w/w	weight per weight
t	tonne	xu (ca	
Torr	torr	10^{-11}	
Twad	Twaddell	cm)	x unit(s)
USASI	United States of America	yd	yard(s)
	Standards Institute	yr	year(s)
	(ASA changed to USASI		
	in 1966)		

Quantities

Some standard abbreviations (prefixes) for very small and very large quantities are as follows:

deci (10^{-1})	d	atto (10^{-18})	a
centi (10^{-2})	c	deka (10^{1})	dk
milli (10^{-3})	m	hecto (10^{2})	h
micro (10^{-6})	μ	kilo (10^{3})	k
nano (10^{-9})	n	mega (10^{6})	M
pico (10^{-12})	p	giga (10^{9})	G (or B)
femto (10^{-15})	f	tera (10^{12})	T

A

ADAMANTANE

Adamantane is the trivial name assigned to tricyclo(3.3.1.1^{3,7})decane. The structural formula can be represented in different ways, as shown below:

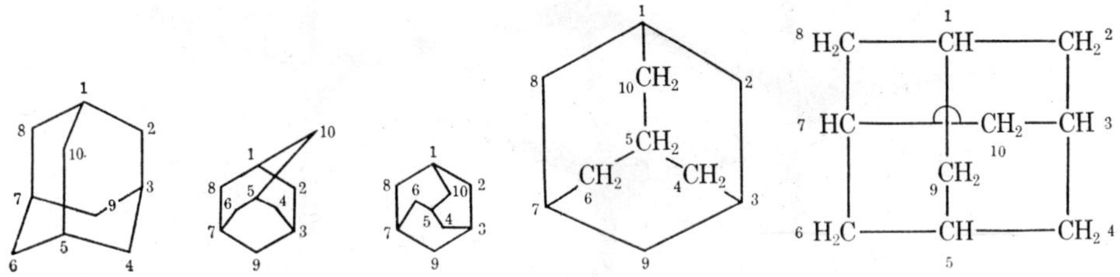

None of these two-dimensional representations, however, do justice to the symmetry of the molecule. Figure 1 is a photograph of an atomic model of adamantane; it can be seen that it consists of four six-carbon rings placed in a manner similar to the four planes of a regular tetrahedron (except that the six carbon atoms in one ring are not in a plane, but in the chair conformation; see Vol. 6, p. 677). The configuration of the carbon atoms is that of a portion of the diamond structure. The trivial name adamantane is taken from the obsolete word adamant (derived from Greek) meaning diamond.

Although four six-membered rings are clearly present (1,2,3,4,5,10; 1,10,5,6,7,8; 1,2,3,9,7,8; and 3,4,5,6,7,9) it can also be seen that no more than three "snips" would be necessary to destroy all rings; for example, if a snip were made between 1 and 2, and between 1 and 10, then atoms 8 and 1 would be left as a side chain to the ring 3,4,5,6,7,9 and so one more snip would destroy all rings. This is why the systematic name describes it as "tricyclo."

Adamantane is probably the most nearly spherical molecule known in its molecular-weight range. Its unique structure results in highly unusual physical and chemical properties.

The adamantane structure is actually quite common in chemistry. Phosphorus trioxide (**1**), arsenic trioxide (**2**), and hexamethylenetetramine (**3**), to name only a few, all have this structure.

Adamantane was isolated in 1933 from the petroleum of Hodinin, in Czechoslovakia, by Landa and Machacek (1). It has been isolated from various other petroleums where it is present to the extent of about 0.0004%. Also present are equally small

1

(1)   **(2)**   **(3)**

amounts of alkylated adamantanes, including 1-methyl-, 2-methyl-, 1-ethyl-, 1,3-dimethyladamantane, etc. Several excellent reviews of adamantane and its chemistry have been published (2–7).

Cilag Chemie and Aldrich Chemical Co. have offered research quantities of adamantane and several of its derivatives for years.

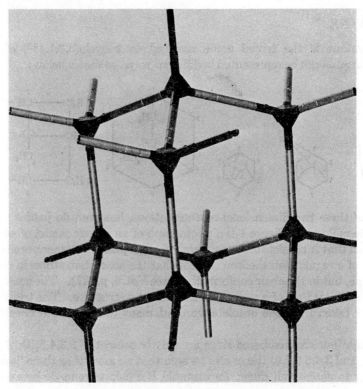

Fig. 1. Model of an adamantane molecule.

Sun Oil Company has been offering developmental quantities of 1,3-dimethyladamantane (1,3-DMA) and 5,7-dimethyl-1,3-adamantanediol (5,7-DMA-1,3-diol) since 1969. In the event that a sizeable use develops, the following prices have been projected:

Quantity, million lb/yr	$/lb	
	1,3-DMA	*5,7-DMA-1,3-diol*
0.5	2.50–5.00	5.00–10.00
1.0		2.50–5.00
10.0	0.50–1.00	

Syntheses

From about the turn of the century investigators had tried, without success, to synthesize the adamantane framework. The tricyclo(3.3.1.1^{3,7}) decane structure was synthesized first by Böttger in 1937 (8), as shown below, although he did not synthesize adamantane itself.

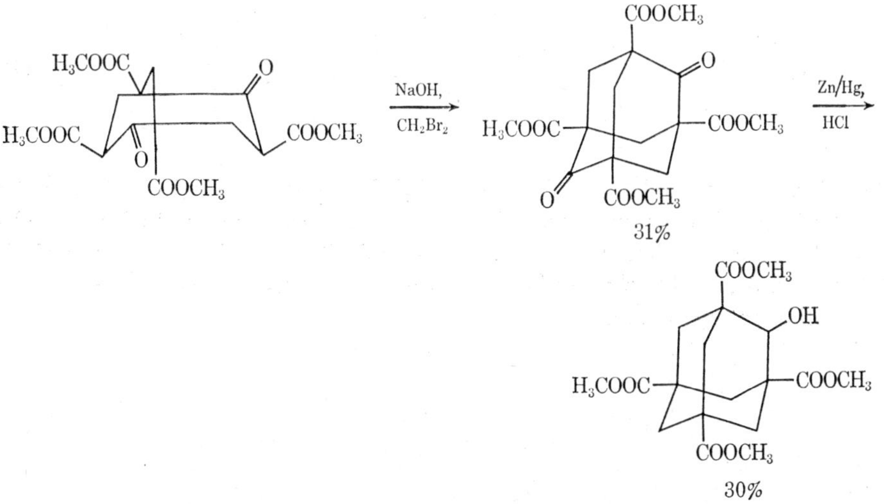

$$(1)$$

The unsubstituted hydrocarbon was first prepared by Prelog and Seiwerth in 1941 in an overall yield of 0.16% (9).

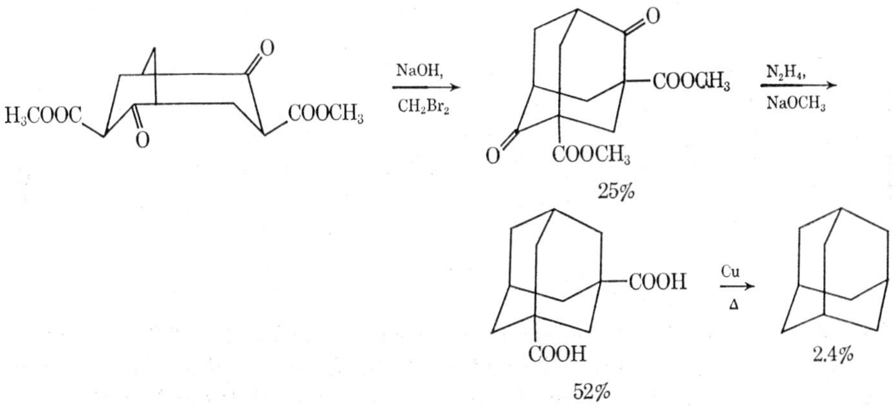

$$(2)$$

In 1956, Stetter, Bander, and Neumann modified this reaction, increasing the overall yield to 6.5% (10). Even at this yield, the preparation of large amounts of adamantane remained difficult. In the same year, however, this was changed by the discovery of a facile two-step synthesis. Schleyer and M. Donaldson, who were studying the AlCl₃-catalyzed isomerization of endo-tetrahydrodicyclopentadiene to its exo-isomer (eq. 3), observed that a small amount (12%) of adamantane was formed (11).

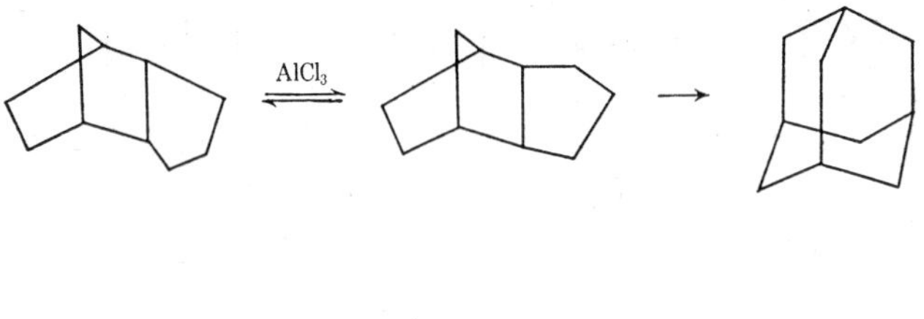

$$(3)$$

Upon further study, they found that a yield of 15–20% is readily obtained.   Modification of the simple AlCl$_3$-catalyzed reaction increased the yield of adamantane to 30–40% (12).   Yields are low due to fragmentation and other side reactions. Schleyer and Nicholas (13) also showed that methylnorbornanes isomerize to methyladamantanes (eq. 4), occasionally obtaining fairly high yields.

$$(4)$$

Schneider, Warren, and Janoski (14) extended this reaction to include all tricyclic perhydroaromatics with ten or more carbon atoms. For example, perhydroacenaphthene gives 1,3-dimethyladamantane (eq. 5); perhydrofluorene gives 1,3,5-trimethyladamantane (eq. 6); and perhydrophenanthrene or perhydroanthracene gives 1,3,5,7-tetramethyladamantane (eq. 7).

$$(5)$$

$$(6)$$

$$(7)$$

The yields of these alkylated adamantanes are on the order of 85–90%, in contrast to the 30–40% yields obtained for adamantane itself. Janoski and Moore (15) found that each of the isomerizations shown in equations 5–7 proceeds through an ethyl-substituted intermediate. That is, perhydroacenaphthene isomerizes to 1-ethyladamantane and then to 1,3-dimethyladamantane (eq. 8); perhydrofluorene isomerizes to 1-ethyl-3-methyladamantane (eq. 9); and perhydrophenanthrene or perhydroanthracene isomerizes to 1-ethyl-3,5-dimethyladamantane (eq. 10).

$$(8)$$

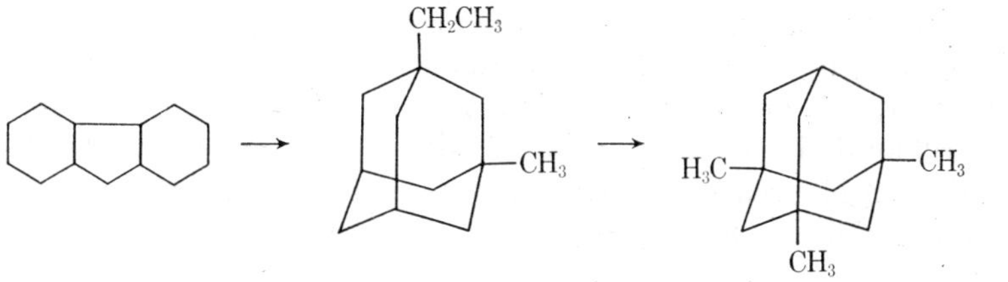

(9)

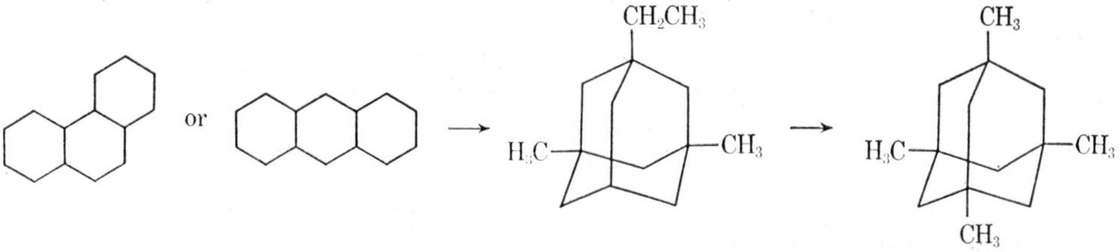

(10)

Each of the ethyl-substituted adamantanes can be obtained in 75–80% yield and good purity by interrupting the isomerization at the proper time, followed by distillation. Considerable control over the reaction products is possible, the most stable products, ie the bridgehead methyl derivatives, being favored by longer reaction times. The ethyl-substituted adamantanes boil about 15°C higher than their corresponding methyl isomers, allowing ready separation. These higher homologs are formed quite cleanly with very little of the fragmentation observed in the formation of adamantane itself. The reason for this is not fully understood; but it would appear that two different mechanisms are operative. Whitlock and Siefken (16) have speculated on the mechanisms by which adamantane is formed. In any event, adamantane, 1-methyl-adamantane, 1-ethyladamantane, 1,3-dimethyladamantane, 1-ethyl-3-methyladamantane, 1,3,5-trimethyladamantane, 1-ethyl-3,5-dimethyladamantane, and 1,3,5,7-tetramethyladamantane are all readily obtainable by isomerization of the appropriate perhydroaromatic hydrocarbon.

Properties

The highly symmetrical structure of adamantane is reflected in its high melting point (268°C in a sealed capillary), a density of 1.07, and the fact that it crystallizes in a face-centered cubic lattice (17). The properties of the homologs show strikingly what the symmetry of the molecule means to the ability to crystallize. With the exception of 1-methyladamantane, which melts at 104°C, the bridgehead lower-alkyl-substituted derivatives are liquids at room temperature. The alkyladamantane with the lowest melting point, 1-ethyladamantane, melts at −52°C.

REACTIONS OF ADAMANTANE

The reactivity of the bridgehead hydrogen atoms of adamantane and alkyl-adamantanes contrasts with the sluggishness of other bridgehead-type structures. The nucleus is easily derivatized both by ionic and radical-type reactions. The literature of the late 1960s includes numerous patents and publications concerning adamantane. The following reactions are chosen to be representative of adamantane chemistry and do not try to be all inclusive.

Halogenation. Treatment of adamantane with excess bromine produces 1-bromoadamantane in excellent yield (18). Introduction of a second bromine atom is more difficult; but with the proper choice of catalyst and reaction conditions, one to four bromines may be introduced into the adamantane molecule (19), all at the bridgehead positions 1, 3, 5, and 7, as shown in Scheme 1. A trace of aluminum bromide in the boron trifluoride is needed to obtain 1,3-dibromoadamantane. In the following representations, Ad is used for adamantane, or for radicals derived from it by abstraction of one or more bridgehead hydrogen atoms.

Scheme 1.

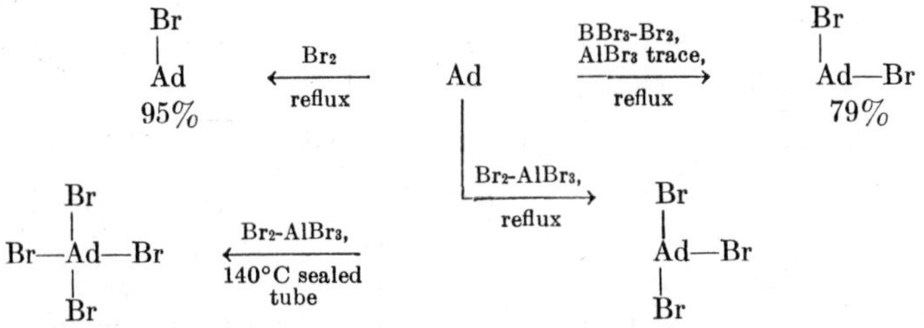

Similar results are obtained with chlorine in the presence of Friedel-Crafts catalysts (20). It is not possible to halogenate the nonbridgehead carbon atoms with these catalysts. When the usual conditions for radical-type halogenation are employed, halogenation of adamantane follows a nonspecific course (21). However, it has been reported that photochlorination of adamantane in CS_2 and *o*-xylene gives 82% of 1-chloroadamantane and 80% 1,3-dichloroadamantane, respectively (22). Adamantane can also be halogenated by halogenated hydrocarbons in the presence of Friedel-Crafts catalysts. Thus, treating adamantane with $AlCl_3$ in carbon tetrachloride (23) at room temperature gives a mixture of 1-chloroadamantane and 1,3-dichloroadamantane in 84% yield (eq. 11).

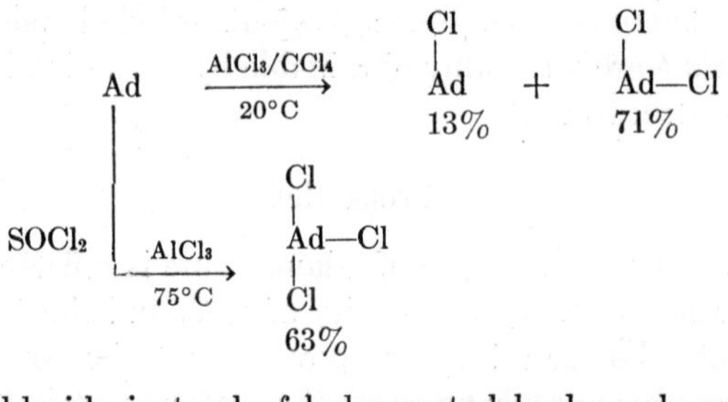

$$(11)$$

Using thionyl chloride instead of halogenated hydrocarbons also affords chlorinated adamantanes. At 75°C 1,3,5-trichloroadamantane is obtained in 63% yield. Halogenation of adamantane or alkyladamantanes can also be accomplished with sodium chloride or sodium bromide in fuming sulfuric acid (24). 1,3-Dimethyladamantane, for example, can lead to either the mono- or the dihaloadamantane by using the proper molar ratios of reagents.

Oxidation. The course of oxidation of adamantane is similar to halogenation; 1-adamantanol is obtained by the action of fuming sulfuric acid or chromium trioxide in aqueous acetic acid (25,26). Chromium trioxide in aqueous acetic acid can also be used to prepare 1,3-adamantanediols (27). The adamantane nucleus is ideally suited for oxidation by chromic acid. It contains tertiary hydrogens which are attacked quite readily despite their bridgehead position. Moreover, the structure of adamantane precludes dehydrogenation because of the geometrical requirements of bonding (Bredt's rule), and, therefore, secondary oxidative reactions, normally observed in chromic acid oxidations, are eliminated. 1-Adamantanol is obtained in 90% yield at a molar ratio of CrO_3 to hydrocarbon of 1.5:1; while at a 6:1 molar ratio 1,3-adamantanediol is obtained in 80% yield. Photo-induced hydroxylation using peroxyacetic acid gives a mixture of 1- and 2-adamantanols (28). A similar nonspecific course was observed in the oxidation of adamantane with oxygen in the presence of cobalt salts and organic peroxides (29–31). The nonbridgehead alcohols, however, can be easily isomerized to the bridgehead position (32).

Nitration. The direct nitration of adamantane with nitric acid in glacial acetic acid requires high temperature and pressure (33). Treatment with gaseous NO_2 at 175°C, on the other hand, gives the mononitro derivative (34). Dinitroadamantane may be prepared by treatment of mononitroadamantane with gaseous NO_2 at 200°C.

1-Substituted Derivatives. 1-Bromoadamantane does not react readily with lithium or magnesium (36), but it is highly reactive in nucleophilic substitutions (36). This is shown by a comparison of the solvolysis constants of 1-bromobicyclo(2,2,2)-octane and 1-bromonorbornane relative to *t*-butylbromide:

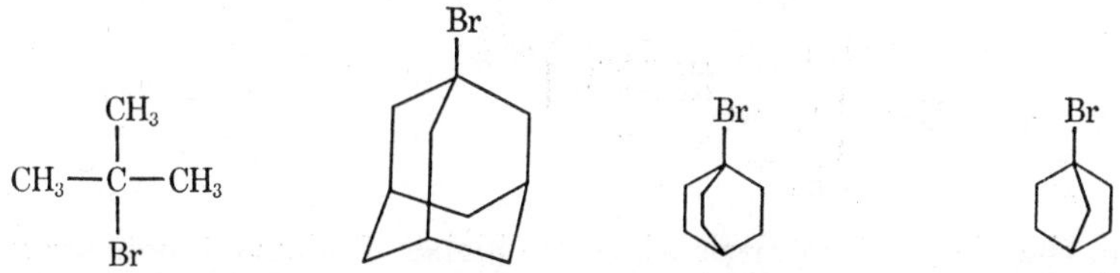

1.0	10^{-3}	10^{-6}	10^{-14}
t-butylbromide	1-bromoada-mantane	1-bromobicyclo-(2, 2, 2)octane	1-bromonorbornane

The high reactivity of 1-adamantanol makes it possible to prepare many 1-substituted adamantanes. The ready availability of 1-adamantanols and adamantane-diols makes them particularly attractive starting materials for the preparation of mono-functional and difunctional derivatives. The synthesis of carboxylic acids by the Koch reaction (Scheme 2) and the preparation of acylaminoadamantanes by the Ritter reaction (Scheme 3) are illustrative (37). Both 1-admantanecarboxylic acid and

Scheme 2.

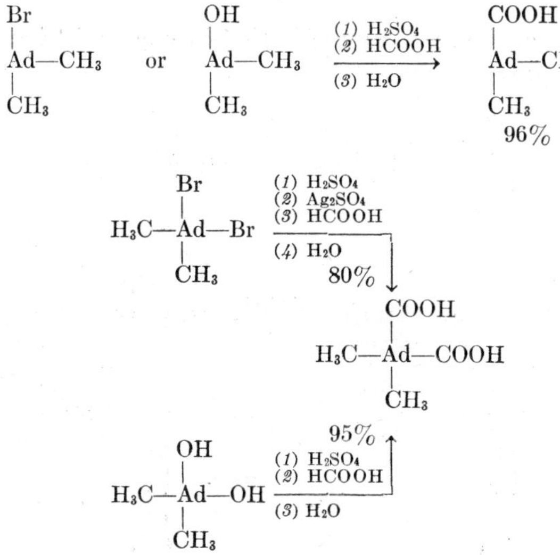

1,3-adamantanedicarboxylic acid can also be prepared by the reaction of adamantane with carbon monoxide in concentrated sulfuric acid under pressure (38).

Scheme 3.

$$
\begin{array}{ccc}
\text{Br} & \text{OH} & \text{NHCOCH}_3 \\
| & | & | \\
\text{Ad—CH}_3 \quad \text{or} \quad \text{Ad—CH}_3 & \xrightarrow[\substack{(1) \text{ H}_2\text{SO}_4 \\ (2) \text{ H}_3\text{CCN} \\ (3) \text{ H}_2\text{O}}]{} & \text{Ad—CH}_3 \\
| & | & | \\
\text{CH}_3 & \text{CH}_3 & \text{CH}_3
\end{array}
$$

$$
90\%
$$

$$
\begin{array}{c}
\text{Br} \\
| \\
\text{H}_3\text{C—Ad—Br} \\
| \\
\text{CH}_3
\end{array}
\xrightarrow[\substack{(1) \text{ H}_2\text{SO}_4 \\ (2) \text{ Ag}_2\text{SO}_4 \\ (3) \text{ H}_3\text{CCN} \\ (4) \text{ H}_2\text{O}}]{}
\Bigg\downarrow 70\%
$$

$$
\begin{array}{c}
\text{NHCOCH}_3 \\
| \\
\text{H}_3\text{C—Ad—NHCOCH}_3 \\
| \\
\text{CH}_3
\end{array}
$$

$$
\begin{array}{c}
\text{OH} \\
| \\
\text{H}_3\text{C—Ad—OH} \\
| \\
\text{CH}_3
\end{array}
\xrightarrow[\substack{(1) \text{ H}_2\text{SO}_4 \\ (2) \text{ HCOOH} \\ (3) \text{ H}_2\text{O}}]{} \Bigg\uparrow 90\%
$$

In general, the yields of the derivatives are higher if adamantanols are used as starting materials. They also have an advantage in the preparation of disubstituted adamantanes because silver sulfate is not required to generate the adamantyl carbonium ion intermediate. Bridgehead monosubstituted aminoadamantanes aree asily prepared by the alkaline hydrolysis of the corresponding 1-acylaminoadamantane. Disubstituted aminoadamantanes (39), however, are more easily prepared by the acid hydrolysis of 1,3-diformamidoadamantane (eq. 12).

$$
\begin{array}{c}
\text{OH} \\
| \\
\text{H}_3\text{C—Ad—OH} \\
| \\
\text{CH}_3
\end{array}
+ 2\,\text{NaC}\equiv\text{N}
\xrightarrow[\substack{(2) \text{ H}_2\text{O}}]{(1) \text{ H}_2\text{SO}_4}
\begin{array}{c}
\text{NHCHO} \\
| \\
\text{H}_3\text{C—Ad—NHCHO} \\
| \\
\text{CH}_3 \\
80\%
\end{array}
\xrightarrow{\text{H}_2\text{SO}_4}
\begin{array}{c}
\text{NH}_2 \\
| \\
\text{H}_3\text{C—Ad—NH}_2 \\
| \\
\text{CH}_3 \\
90\%
\end{array}
\quad (12)
$$

Further examples of the reactivity of both 1-bromo- and 1-hydroxyadamantanes are shown in the following reactions:

$$
\begin{array}{c}
\text{Br} \\
| \\
\text{Ad—CH}_3 \\
| \\
\text{CH}_3
\end{array}
+ \text{C}_6\text{H}_6
\xrightarrow[80°\text{C}]{\text{FeCl}_3}
\begin{array}{c}
\text{C}_6\text{H}_5 \\
| \\
\text{Ad—CH}_3 \\
| \\
\text{CH}_3 \\
80\%
\end{array}
\quad (13)
$$

$$
\begin{array}{c}
\text{Br} \\
| \\
\text{H}_3\text{C—Ad—Br} \\
| \\
\text{CH}_3
\end{array}
+ \text{C}_6\text{H}_5\text{OH} \atop (\text{excess})
\xrightarrow[\Delta]{180°\text{C}}
\begin{array}{c}
\text{C}_6\text{H}_4\text{OH } (p) \\
| \\
\text{H}_3\text{C—Ad—C}_6\text{H}_4\text{OH } (p) \\
| \\
\text{CH}_3 \\
90\% \\
\text{“DMA bisphenol”}
\end{array}
\quad (14)
$$

$$
\begin{array}{c}
\text{OH} \\
| \\
\text{Ad—CH}_3 \\
| \\
\text{CH}_3
\end{array}
+ \text{NaX}
\xrightarrow{\text{H}_2\text{SO}_4}
\begin{array}{c}
\text{X} \\
| \\
\text{Ad—CH}_3 \\
| \\
\text{CH}_3 \\
95\%
\end{array}
\quad (15)
$$

$$\underset{\underset{\overset{|}{CH_3}}{|}}{\overset{\overset{OH}{|}}{H_3C-Ad-OH}} + NaX \xrightarrow{H_2SO_4} \underset{\underset{\overset{|}{CH_3}}{|}}{\overset{\overset{X}{|}}{H_3C-Ad-X}} \tag{15a}$$
$$95\%$$

where X = Cl, Br.

Adamantane and its homologs react with olefins, or olefinic precursors, in H_2SO_4 solution, resulting in alkyl substitution (40), as shown in the following examples:

$$1,3\text{-}(CH_3)_2\text{-}Ad + CH_3CHOHCH_3 \xrightarrow{H_2SO_4} 1\text{-}CH_3CH_2CH_2\text{-}3,5\text{-}(CH_3)_2\text{-}Ad + H_2O$$

The 2-propanol dehydrates to propylene which then alkylates to give the *n*-propyl adamantane derivative.

$$1,3\text{-}(CH_3)_2\text{-}Ad + H_2C=CHCH_2CH_2CH_2CH_3 \xrightarrow{H_2SO_4} 1\text{-}C_6H_{13}\text{-}3,5\text{-}(CH_3)_2\text{-}Ad$$

1-Hexene reacts to give several isomers, owing to various rearrangements.

Alkyladamantanes can be dealkylated quite readily, however, by passing over a catalyst composed of 37% Ni on Al_2O_3 at 250–450°C (41). Ethyl-substituted adamantanes can also be dehydrogenated to form vinyladamantanes (42), which are also prepared by dehydrohalogenating the appropriate adamantylbromoethane (37). Thus, reaction of 1-bromo-3,5-dimethyladamantane with ethylene in the presence of $AlBr_3$ gives 1-(2-bromoethyl)-3,5-dimethyladamantane, which, on refluxing for 4 hr in diethylene glycol and KOH, gives 1-vinyl-3,5-dimethyladamantane (43).

$$\underset{\underset{\overset{|}{CH_3}}{|}}{\overset{\overset{Br}{|}}{Ad-CH_3}} \xrightarrow[AlBr_4]{C_2H_4} \underset{\underset{\overset{|}{CH_3}}{|}}{\overset{\overset{CH_2CH_2Br}{|}}{Ad-CH_3}} \xrightarrow[\substack{diethylene \\ glycol}]{KOH,} \underset{\underset{\overset{|}{CH_3}}{|}}{\overset{\overset{CH=CH_2}{|}}{Ad-CH_3}} \tag{16}$$

Adamantylacetic acid (44) and adamantylchloroacetic acid (45) are prepared by similar reactions.

$$Ad-Br + CH_2=CCl_2 \xrightarrow[(2)\ H_2O]{(1)\ H_2SO_4} Ad-CH_2COOH$$

$$Ad-Br + CHCl=CCl_2 \xrightarrow[(2)\ H_2O]{(1)\ H_2SO_4} Ad-CHClCOOH$$

2-Substituted Derivatives. The 2-position of adamantane is considerably less reactive in carbonium-ion processes than the bridgehead position, and direct substitution at the 2-position occurs with far less facility. Adamantanone can be synthesized in 70–75% yield, however, from 1-adamantanol or adamantane (46) by treatment with concentrated sulfuric acid (eq. 17). The ketone is formed by an intermolecular hy-

$$72\% \tag{17}$$

dride-transfer reaction of 2-hydroxyadamantane, and also by subsequent oxidation of the adamantane formed in the reaction. The simplicity and high yield of this reaction makes it possible to obtain secondary substituted adamantane derivatives.

A lower yield of ketonic product is obtained from alkyladamantanols (24) due to a more favorable side reaction in which an alkyl group takes part. Thus, 3,5-dimethyl-1-adamantanol can lead to a dimer. From 3-ethyl-5,7-dimethyl-1-adamantanol, for example, only about 5% of ketonic products is obtained, the remainder being various hydrocarbons resulting from dimerization and transalkylation. Similar results are obtained from 5,7-dimethyl-3-*n*-propyl-1-adamantanol.

As in the formation of adamantane from 1-adamantanol, these products are the result of an intermolecular hydride-transfer reaction by the adamantyl cation. Energetically this would be expected to be unfavorable but similar abstractions have been found (24) in the reaction of 3,5-dimethyl-1-adamantanol with *n*-hexane, where the −OH group is replaced by hexyl (65% yield).

A specific example of the ability of the adamantyl cation to dehydrogenate alicyclic compounds is the synthesis of Δ9(11)-estrone (47) from estrone (eq. 18).

$$(18)$$

Although the adamantane nucleus maintains its structural stability in most reactions, under certain conditions the ring undergoes fragmentation and rearrangement; for example, methyl *N*(3-bromo-1-adamantyl)urethan fragmentates, as shown in eq. 19, to give a bicyclononane derivative (48).

$$(19)$$

A similar result is obtained when 5,7-dimethyl-1,3-adamantanediol is passed over a packed bed (36) of sand, alumina, or glass wool at 200–500°C (eq. 20).

$$(20)$$

When 1-hydroxymethyladamantane is carboxylated by the method of Koch-Haaf (49), it undergoes a ring expansion to form homoadamantane-1-carboxylic acid (eq. 21).

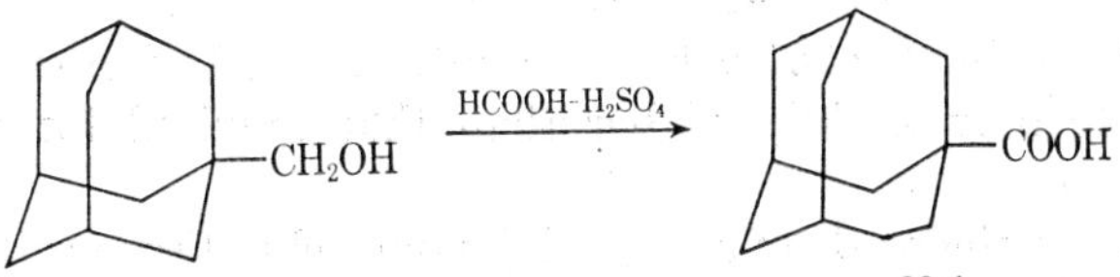

$$\text{—CH}_2\text{OH} \xrightarrow{\text{HCOOH·H}_2\text{SO}_4} \text{—COOH} \tag{21}$$

89%

Also, simple ring homologation of adamantanone with diazomethane gives 4-homoadamantanone (50), as shown in eq. 22.

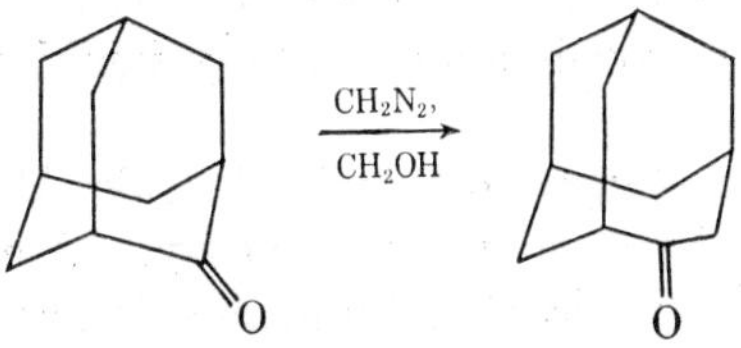

$$\xrightarrow[\text{CH}_2\text{OH}]{\text{CH}_2\text{N}_2,} \tag{22}$$

85%

Another unusual rearrangement is the formation of 2,4-dehydroadamantane (51) by the pyrolysis of the lithium salt of the *p*-tosylhydrazone of adamantanone (eq. 23).

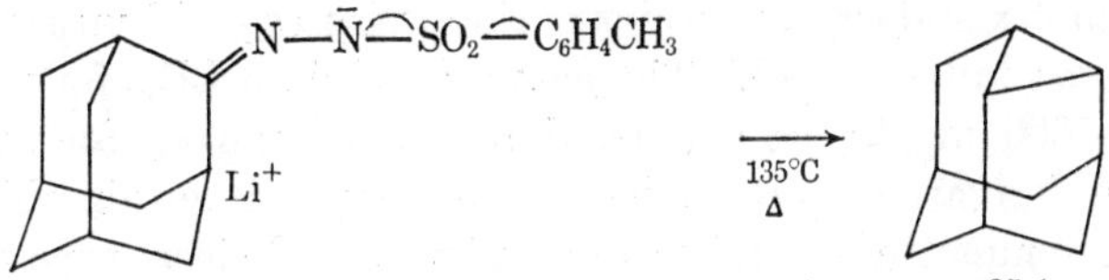

$$\text{N—}\bar{\text{N}}\!\frown\!\text{SO}_2\!\frown\!\text{C}_6\text{H}_4\text{CH}_3 \xrightarrow[\Delta]{135°C} \tag{23}$$

Li$^+$

65%

Other dehydroadamantanes have also been prepared. One of the dehydro-adamantanones is a precursor to protoadamantane (eq. 24) (52).

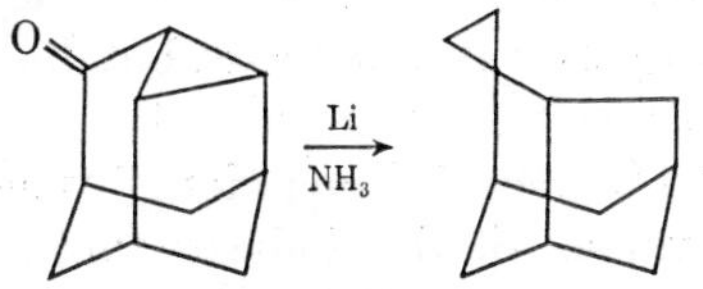

$$\xrightarrow[\text{NH}_3]{\text{Li}} \tag{24}$$

Applications

The compact, highly symmetrical structure of the adamantane molecule imparts unusual characteristics to compounds which contain this unique hydrocarbon moiety. These characteristics lead to possible utility in a number of diverse areas, including drugs, polymers, synthetic lubricants, and solvent-resistant resins. The alkylada-mantane hydrocarbons themselves have physical properties suitable for transmission lubricants.

Pharmaceuticals. The pronounced lipophilic nature associated with the compact structure of adamantane led investigators to study the biological activity of its derivatives.

The one derivative which has attracted the most attention is Symmetrel (E. I. du Pont de Nemours & Co., Inc.) (1-aminoadamantane hydrochloride, amantadine hydrochloride). In 1966, after extensive clinical studies (53–55), Symmetrel was given clearance by the Food and Drug Administration. It was to be used for the prevention of respiratory illness due to susceptible influenza A2 viruses by prophylactic treatment of patients. This generated a great deal of controversy in the medical field and a report by Sabin (56) was highly critical of the safety and efficacy of Symmetrel because of possible side effects, such as nervousness and disorientation, which can occur at a dosage only slightly higher than that required for the treatment of influenza.

Investigations of the mode of action of Symmetrel in tissue-culture systems have indicated that it does not kill the viruses, but does block penetration of the virus into the cell (57). In addition to its protective effect against A2 influenza infections of man, Symmetrel is effective against equine influenza in horses (58). It also shows some inhibition of Rous sarcoma virus and chicken leukosis viruses (59). In relatively resistant chicks, tumor production is almost totally inhibited and small tumors even regress occasionally.

In addition to 1-aminoadamantane hydrochloride, Du Pont's rimantidine, Ad—$CH_2NH(CH_3) \cdot HCl$ (α-methyl-1-adamantanemethylamine hydrochloride, 1-(1-adamantyl) ethylamine) is particularly effective against influenza A2 (60).

Functional groups other than NH_2 can be added without loss of antiviral activity. In fact, in certain cases they have activity against a much broader spectrum of viruses than Symmetrel with much lower acute oral toxicity. For example, 3-ethyl-5,7-dimethyl-1-adamantanol (61) and 1-methoxy-3,5-dimethyladamantane (62) are active against herpes simplex and certain strains of rhino viruses (cold viruses) in addition to being active against influenza A2. The acute lethal dose LD_{50} for mice of these two derivatives is >5000 mg/kg as compared to ~1000 mg/kg for Symmetrel. The activity of these derivatives toward herpes simplex and certain rhino viruses is in sharp contrast to Symmetrel which has no activity against either type of virus (63).

Virus chemotherapy is a relatively recent development. See Viral infections, chemotherapy. This has been due, in part, to the success of vaccines for the control of the viral diseases smallpox, yellow fever, and polio. For these diseases the vaccine approach has been the most practical and effective method. However, influenza vaccines have been available for over twenty years, but due to the antigenic drift of the virus, the disease is far from being controlled (64). Such drifts occurred in 1957 ("Asian" type influenza) and in 1968 ("Hong Kong" type influenza), and the older vaccines were of little or no value. Studies indicate that the efficacy of antiviral compounds is not affected by these antigenic shifts of influenza viruses and thus chemotherapy offers an alternative method of coping with such diseases. Herpes simplex is another virus which is not amenable to control by vaccines since it causes disease even in the presence of circulating antibodies. Here again chemotherapy may offer an alternative method of coping with the disease. In any event, the control of viruses by chemotherapy looks quite promising for the future, and it appears that adamantyl derivatives will play a role.

Several N-arenesulfonyl-N'-adamantyl ureas were evaluated as hypoglycemic agents. Enhanced activity, associated with low toxicity, was found for some of these. For example, N-p-toluenesulfonyl-N'-(1-adamantyl)urea, Ad—$NHCONHSO_2C_6H_4$-CH_3, possesses about five times the potency of tolbutamide (3-(p-tolyl-4-sulfonyl)-1-butylurea) (28). Its activity is rapid in onset with a tentative duration of 4–6 hr, indicating that the drug is rapidly absorbed and utilized by the body. Minor changes, however, in either the adamantyl or phenyl moieties result in lowered potency.

For example, the introduction of a single methyl substituent on the adamantane moiety reduces the potency drastically. Two methyl substituents virtually abolish activity.

Nortestosterone 17-β-(1-adamantoate) produces a profound and unique effect on anabolic potency as compared with other esters (65). It possesses significant duration of anabolic action with minimal androgenic activity. The adamantoate esters, apparently, not only serve to prolong or intensify the intrinsic activity of nortestosterone, but also effect a favorable separation of the nitrogen-retaining capacity from the undesirable hormonal activity.

Here again, the biological activity is reduced with seemingly minor structural changes in the adamantane moiety. The anabolic activity of nortestosterone 17-β-(1-adamantoate) is reduced by 80–90% in the 3-methyl-1-adamantoate; the 3,5,-dimethyl and 3,5,7-trimethyl analogs possess even less activity.

Several adamantane derivatives display choleretic activity, ie stimulate the flow of bile. One of these is 3-(1-adamantyloxy)propionic acid, Ad—OCH_2CH_2COOH (66). The other adamantyl choleretic agents have similar structures.

Still other adamantyl derivatives are active toward malaria (67) and Parkinson's disease (68). Finally, the adamantyl ester (4) is more potent and longer-acting as an analgesic than demerol hydrochloride (N-methyl-4-phenyl-4-carbethoxypiperidine hydrochloride) (69).

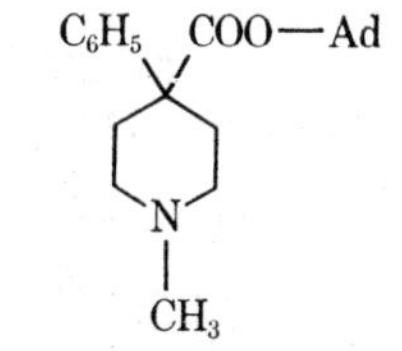

$$C_6H_5 \quad COO—Ad$$

(1-adamantyl) 1-methyl-4-phenyl-4-piperidenecarboxylate (4)

Polymers

The unique physical properties of 1,3-dimethyladamantane (DMA) are reflected in the physical properties of its polymers (37). For example, its geometric bulk results in rigidity, high thermal stability, high glass-transition temperatures, low crystallinity, high heat-distortion temperatures, and good hydrolytic stability. The absence of labile hydrogen atoms results in good oxidative stability. The following adamantyl polymers are illustrative:

Poly(3,5-dimethyl-1-adamantyl acrylate) has a glass-transition temperature of 106°C, while poly(3,5-dimethyl-1-adamantyl methacrylate) has a glass-transition temperature of 196°C (37). These are thought to be the highest glass-transition temperatures ever reported for acrylates and methacrylates, respectively. They have excellent optical properties and low mold shrinkage. They copolymerize readily under free-radical conditions with a variety of comonomers to yield interesting materials.

Polyamides prepared from DMA dicarboxylic acid and aliphatic diamines possess high flexural strength, high heat-distortion temperatures, good hydrolytic stability, low moisture absorption, good impact strength, and optical clarity (37). High-molecular-weight polyamides are also prepared by the reaction of DMA diol with dinitriles via the Ritter reaction (37).

An unsaturated polyester prepared from DMA diol, maleic anhydride, and propylene glycol, upon curing with styrene, has a high heat distortion, good hydrolytic stability, and excellent solvent resistance (37). Its resistance to chloroform and acetone is greater than that of any resin of its type, including chemically resistant types such as the fumarate of "bisphenol A" (see Vol. 1, p. 912).

Polycarbonates from DMA bisphenol, 1,3-bis(4-hydroxyphenyl)-5,7-dimethyladamantane (see p. 000) have exceptionally high glass-transition temperatures, good optical properties, and excellent flexibility. The ease of the synthesis of DMA bisphenol, combined with the outstanding properties of its polycarbonate, make this an especially attractive polymer.

Synthetic lubricants prepared from 3,5-dimethyl-1-adamantanol and linear aliphatic diacids or 5,7-dimethyl-1-1, 3-adamantol and linear monoacids are characterized by unusually high viscosities in a given molecular-weight range. These oils show excellent thermal and oxidative stability and good low-temperature-viscosity properties (70).

Bibliography

1. S. Landa and V. Machacek, *Coll. Czech. Chem. Comm.* **5**, 1 (1933).
2. H. Stetter, *Angew. Chem.* **66**, 217 (1954).
3. A. Fredga, *Svensk Kem. Tidskr.* **72**, 151 (1960); *Chem. Abstr.* **54**, 16464a (1960).
4. S. Landa, *Acta Chim. Acad. Sci. Hung.* **31**, 123 (1962); *Chem. Abstr.* **58**, 3326 (1963).
5. H. Stetter, *Angew. Chem.* **74**, 361 (1962).
6. R. C. Fort, Jr., and P. v. R. Schleyer, *Chem. Rev.* **64**, 277 (1964).
7. S. Landa, *Neftekhimiya* **7**, 476 (1967); *Chem. Abstr.* **67**, 108274q (1967).
8. O. Böttger, *Chem. Ber.* **70**, 314 (1937).
9. V. Prelog and R. Seiwerth, *Chem. Ber.* **74**, 1644 (1941).
10. H. Stetter, O. Bander, and W. Neumann, *Chem. Ber.* **89**, 1922 (1956).
11. P. v. R. Schleyer, *J. Am. Chem. Soc.* **79**, 3292 (1957).
12. H. Koch and J. Franken, *Brennstoff-Chem.* **42**, 90 (1961).
13. P. Schleyer and R. D. Nicholas, *Tetrahedron Letters* **1961**, 305.
14. A. Schneider, R. W. Warren, and E. J. Janoski, *J. Org. Chem.* **31**, 1617 (1966).
15. U.S. Pat. 3,275,000 (Sept. 27, 1966), E. J. Janoski and R. E. Moore (to Sun Oil Co.).
16. H. W. Whitlock, Jr., and M. W. Siefken, *J. Am. Chem. Soc.* **90**, 4929 (1968).
17. W. Nowacki, *Helv. Chim. Acta.* **28**, 1233 (1945).
18. S. Landa, S. Kriebel, and E. Knobloch, *Chem. Listy* **48**, 61 (1954).
19. H. Stetter and C. Wulff, *Chem. Ber.* **93**, 1366 (1960).
20. C. Wulff, PhD. Thesis, Technische Hochschule Aachen, 1961.
21. Brit. Pat. 819,240 (1959), W. Webber and P. Harthoorn (to Shell Oil Co.); *Chem. Abstr.* **54**, 15272 (1960).
22. V. A. Nekrasova and I. I. Shuikin, *Bull. Acad. Sci. USSR Chem. Sci. (English Transl.)* **3**, 649 (1969).
23. H. Stetter, M. Krause, and W. Last, *Chem. Ber.* **102**, 3357 (1969).
24. R. E. Moore, unpublished results,
25. F. W. Evans, D. M. Fairbrother, and H. Skinner, *Trans. Faraday Soc.* **55**, 399 (1959).
26. S. Landa, J. Vais, and J. Burkhard, *Z. Chem.* **7**, 233 (1967); *Chem. Abstr.* **67**, 81842j (1967).
27. U.S. Pat. 3,383,423 (May 14, 1968), R. E. Moore (to Sun Oil Co.).
28. K. Gerzon, E. V. Krumkalns, R. L. Brindle, F. J. Marshall, and M. A. Root, *J. Med. Chem.* **6**, 760 (1963).
29. M. Finklestein, Ph.D. Thesis, Yale University, 1955.
30. U.S. Pat. 3,356,740 (Dec. 5, 1967), A. Schneider (to Sun Oil Co.).
31. U.S. Pat. 3,356,741 (Dec. 5, 1967), A. Schneider (to Sun Oil Co.).
32. U.S. Pat. 3,356,739 (Dec. 5, 1967), A. Schneider (to Sun Oil Co.).
33. G. W. Smith and H. D. Williams, *J. Org. Chem.* **26**, 2207 (1961).

34. U.S. Pat. 3,258,498 (June 28, 1966), A. Schneider (to Sun Oil Co.).

35. P. v. R. Schleyer and R. D. Nicholas, *J. Am. Chem. Soc.* **83**, 2700 (1961).

36. F. N. Stepanov and V. F. Baklan, *J. Gen. Chem. USSR* **34**, 580 (1964).

37. *1,3-Dimethyladamantane, A New Research Chemical*, Sun Oil Technical Bulletin, 1969.

38. U.S. Pat. 3,250,805 (May 10, 1966), A. A. Lamola (to E. I. du Pont de Nemours & Co., Inc.).

39. U.S. Pat. 3,419,611 (Dec. 31, 1968), R. E. Moore (to Sun Oil Co.).

40. U.S. Pat. 3,382,288 (May 5, 1968), A. Schneider (to Sun Oil Co.).

41. U.S. Pat. 3,418,387 (Dec. 24, 1968), S. Landa and Z. Weidenhoffer (to Czechoslovakia Academy of Science).

42. U.S. Pat. 3,255,268 (June 7, 1966), G. Suld and R. E. Moore (to Sun Oil Co.).

43. H. Stetter and P. Goebel, *Chem. Ber.* **95**, 1093 (1962).

44. K. Bott and H. Hellman, *Angew. Chem.* **78**, 932 (1966).

45. K. Bott, *Angew. Chem.* **79**, 943 (1967).

46. H. W. Geluk and J. L. M. A. Schlatmann, *Tetrahedron* **24**, 5361 (1968).

47. W. H. W. Lunn and E. Farkas, *Tetrahedron* **24**, 6773 (1968); *Chem. Abstr.* **70**, 29167r (1968).

48. H. Stetter and P. Tacke, *Angew. Chem.* **73**, 354 (1962).

49. H. Stetter and E. Rauscher, *Chem. Ber.* **93**, 1161 (1960).

50. P. v. R. Schleyer, E. Funke, and S. Liggero, *J. Am. Chem. Soc.* **91**, 3965 (1969).

51. A. C. Udding, J. Strating, and H. Wynberg, *Chem. Comm.* **1966**, 657.

52. J. E. Baldwin and W. D. Foglesong, *Tetrahedron Letters* **1966**, 4089.

53. E. Stanley, R. Muldoon, L. Akers, and G. Jackson, *Ann. N. Y. Acad. Sci.* **130**, 44 (1965).

54. J. Quilligan, Jr., M. Hirayama, and H. Baernstein, Jr., *J. Pediat.* **69**, 572 (1966).

55. J. Finklea, A. Hennessy, and F. Davenport, *Am. J. Epidemiol.* **85**, 403 (1967).

56. A. B. Sabin, *J. Am. Med. Assoc.* **200**, 943 (1967).

57. C. Hoffman, E. Neumayer, R. Haff, and R. Goldsby, *J. Bacteriol.* **90**, 623 (1965).

58. J. Bryans, W. Zent, R. Gunert, and D. Boughton, *Nature* **212**, 1542 (1966).

59. N. Oker-Blom and L. Anderson, *Ann. Med. Exp. Biol. Fenniae (Helsinki)* **45**, 186 (1967); *Chem. Abstr.* **67**, 52471g (1967).

60. A. Dawkins, T. Callager, and Y. Togo, *J. Am Med. Assoc.* **203**, 1095 (1968).

61. U.S. Pat. 3,450,775 (June 17, 1969), A. Schneider (to Sun Oil Co.).

62. U.S. Pat. 3,383,423 (May 14, 1968), R. E. Moore (to Sun Oil Co.).

63. J. S. Oxford and G. C. Schild, *Arch. Ges. Virusforsch.* **17**, 313 (1965); *Chem. Abstr.* **64**, 5469f (1965).

64. C. E. Hoffmann, *Ann. Rept. Med. Chem.* **1967**, 116.

65. R. Rapala, R. Kraay, and K. Gerzon, *J. Med. Chem.* **8**, 580 (1965).

66. Belg. Pat. 615,267 (Sept. 19, 1962), to Rhône-Poulenc S. A.; *Chem. Abstr.* **58**, 11241a (1963).

67. L. Fieser, Z. Musa, S. Nazer, D. Berberian, and R. Slighter, *J. Med. Chem.* **10**, 517 (1967).

68. U.S. Pat. 3,320,249 (May 16, 1967), J. Bernstein (to Olin Mathieson Chemical Corp.).

69. A. Voldeng, C. Bradley, R. Kee, E. King, and F. Melder, *J. Pharm. Sci.* **57**, 1053 (1968).

70. U.S. Pat. 3,398,165 (Aug. 20, 1968), I. N. Duling and A. Schneider (to Sun Oil Co.).

Robert E. Moore
Sun Oil Company

ADHESION

Though adhesive-bonding technology has a rather long and varied history, the science of adhesion is relatively new. Many opposing viewpoints have been formulated to account for the large body of experimental data. The merit of any theory is to account for this existing body of data and, hopefully, to provide insight to guide the scientist to perform new experiments, leading to further understanding. This article attempts to present a discussion of adhesion science with particular emphasis on the formation of practical adhesive joints.

As one examines the science of adhesion, it soon becomes apparent that a wide variety of disciplines in both physics and chemistry is needed and that no one discipline is sufficient to enable the investigator to draw conclusions about the operations of a particular system. Surface chemistry, surface physics, polymer physics, rheology, fracture mechanics, etc, are but a few of the important fields of scientific endeavor with which the investigator should be familiar before beginning an excursion into the science of adhesion.

Theories of Adhesion

A proper exposition of the surface properties of polymers with respect to adhesion and adhesive joint strength should begin by defining these terms. *Adhesion*, as used in this article, refers only to the attractive forces exerted between a solid surface and a second phase (either liquid or solid). Adhesion is concerned with the phenomenon of making an adhesive joint (ie wettability, relative surface energetics of both phases, and kinetics of wetting) (1,2). These are purely surface considerations. *Adhesive joint strength* is the breaking strength of a bonded assembly (3). Once an adhesive joint has been formed, interfacial forces are no longer of primary concern, since interfacial separation probably never occurs under ordinary failure conditions, except at points where molecular contact did not exist prior to breaking the adhesive joint. What is of prime importance is the mechanical response of the composite to an applied stress. Probably a more realistic description of the breaking strength of an adhesive joint would be based on a mechanical deformation theory of adhesive joint strength.

The Electrical Theory. Voyutskii published a review paper (4) in which he discussed the merits and shortcomings of the then existing adsorption theory and the diffusion and electrostatic theories of adhesion. This paper (4) will be used as the basis for analysis. Voyutskii describes in an orderly fashion Deryagin's criticisms of the adsorption theory. Deryagin states (5):

(*1*) "That the work of peeling an adhesive film may be as great as 10^4–10^6 erg/cm², whereas the work required to overcome the molecular forces is only 10^2–10^3 erg/cm². It is claimed that this shows the actual work of adhesion to be orders of magnitude higher than could be expected to result from molecular forces."

It would seem that Deryagin has not realized that a peeling experiment gives no direct measure of interfacial molecular forces, and that the overwhelming proportion of work which Deryagin measures is expended in deforming the material prior to the break (3).

(*2*) "That the work of adhesion depends on the rate of separation of the adhesive film, whereas the work expended on overcoming the molecular forces should not depend on the rate at which the molecules separate."

Again, interfacial forces are not being measured; rather, the rheological properties of the adhesive film are being measured and there is, in general, a dependence on rate. So far, the first two points of criticism have been dispensed with without reference to any adsorption theory or, indeed, any theory of adhesion.

(3) "That the adsorption theory cannot explain the adhesion between nonpolar high polymers nor the adhesion between such nonpolar polymers as polyisobutylene, natural rubber and gutta-percha, and a number of substrates."

It has been pointed out repeatedly, that the forces involved in cohesion and adhesion of the same kind; that the existence of universal dispersion forces means that all the materials exert an attractive force (adhesion) for all other materials, ie "everything should stick to everything;" that the matter of polarity or nonpolarity is of minor significance in practical adhesive joining.

These three items, in addition to the observation that rupture can lead to electrification of the rupture surfaces produced and sometimes even to electrical discharge and electron emission during the process of separation, led Deryagin to propose the electrical theory of adhesion (5). This theory, in essence, treats the adhesive–adherend system as a capacitor which is charged due to the contact of two different substances. Separation of the parts of the capacitor, as during breaking of the joint, leads to separation of charge and to development of a potential difference which increases until a discharge occurs. Adhesion is presumed due to the existence of the electrical double layer. Voyutskii says (4): "Although the electrical theory is an advance on the adsorption theory, a number of factors limit its application to the mutual adhesion of high polymers." He then proceeds to enumerate five distinct general systems to which Deryagin's theory is not applicable.

Further serious fundamental criticisms of the electrical theory of adhesion will now be made. The electrical phenomena, on whose existence the theory is based, are phenomena which manifest themselves only when the adhesive–adherend system is broken, and there is no a priori reason to believe that phenomena resulting from the breaking of an adhesive–adherend system have any connection whatsoever with the phenomenon of adhesion which is involved in the making of an adhesive–adherend joint. Furthermore, there seems no reason to believe that the two electrically charged surfaces obtained when rupture of an adhesive–adherend system is made to occur are identically the same two electrically neutral surfaces which were placed in contact with each other initially to form the system.

The Diffusion Theory. The diffusion theory of Voyutskii (6–8), which has been applied previously only to the adhesion of polymeric materials to themselves and to other polymers, states that adhesion is due to mutual diffusion of surface layers of polymer molecules, each into the other, to form an interwoven network. That such mutual diffusion of certain combinations of polymeric systems does occur cannot be denied; that it occurs prior to wetting of one polymer by the other is seriously open to question, since this would imply that diffusion can occur prior to or without contact. The notion that diffusion is the prime cause of adhesion is, in our view, incorrect; that it is the result of adhesion is a far more reasonable point of view.

Voyutskii's arguments for the diffusion theory of adhesion are all based on measurements of the breaking strength of adhesive joints. He measures these strengths as a function of time of contact between polymers, temperature, polymer type, molecular weight, viscosity, etc, and points out that the functional dependence of strength on some of these parameters is similar to that expected for a diffusion process; therefore, adhesion is a result of diffusion. This concept carries with it the consequence that there does not exist an interface where the two polymer surfaces join, but a region of variable composition.

Voyutskii also says (4): "It is obvious that the diffusion of molecules of one high-polymer into another is nothing less than solution. The importance of mutual solubility in the adhesion of high polymers was first indicated by the present author, who suggested that the adhesion of high polymers to another should be used as a criterion of their compatibility. Subsequently Deryagin, who also emphasized the connection between compatibility and adhesion, suggested the use of compatibility to assess adhesion.

"The importance of the mutual solubility of components for adhesion, this being mainly determined by the relationship between the polarities of the high polymers, is in complete accordance with the empirical law of de Bruyne (9), according to which strong adhesion is possible only when both high-polymers are either polar or nonpolar and hindered when one is polar and the other nonpolar."

The de Bruyne rule (9) has been shown, in part, to be incorrect. Further evidence for violation of the de Bruyne rule is given below (see p. 21). The fact that crosslinking of the surface region of nonpolar polymers can take place without affecting their wettabilities shows that strong adhesive joints can be formed with conventional polar adhesives.

The diffusion theory cannot explain the joining of polymeric materials to metals, glass, or other hard solids, since it is difficult to see how adhesion to these materials can result from diffusion of the polymer into such materials.

It would be instructive to take each of Voyutskii's points in support of his diffusion theory of adhesion, and to show how they are much more reasonably treated, in a consistent manner, in terms of adhesion as a surface phenomenon, and adhesive joint strength as a rheological phenomenon. It must suffice to say that the effects of time, temperature, viscosity, molecular weight, polymer type, etc, on adhesive joint strength can be understood even if adhesion is treated strictly as a surface phenomenon.

The Adsorption Theory. Although this article is concerned primarily with the formation of an interface between two polymer adherends, the same guidelines are applicable when considering metals and metal oxides. We shall assume that no weak boundary layers exist before or after formation of the interface. In the next section we shall consider a possible mode of their generation and an apparently general method to eliminate weak boundary layers in polymers.

Formation of Interface (Wettability). Two materials probably adhere, at least initially, because of van der Waals attractive forces acting between the atoms in the two surfaces. Interfacial strengths, based on van der Waals forces alone, far exceed the real strengths of one or other of the adhering materials. This means that interfacial separation probably never occurs to any sensible extent when mechanical forces are used to separate a pair of materials which have achieved complete interfacial contact (probably a highly unlikely situation), or a number of separate regions of interfacial contact. It follows, then, that breaking the joint mechanically, in general, tells nothing directly about interfacial forces.

Van der Waals forces are operative over very small distances. Hence, in order that materials adhere, the atoms in the two surfaces must be brought close enough together for these forces to become operative. If we had a piece of A (solid) and B (solid) and each had an absolutely clean, smooth (on an atomic scale), planar surface

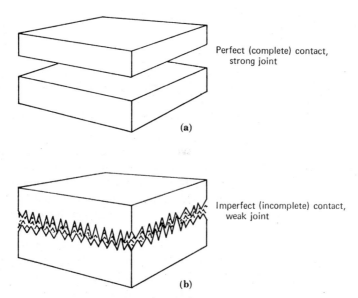

Perfect (complete) contact, strong joint

(a)

Imperfect (incomplete) contact, weak joint

(b)

Fig. 1. (**a**) Ideal surfaces: clean, atomically smooth, planar; (**b**) real surfaces: dirty, rough, non-planar.

and if these surfaces were brought together in a perfect vacuum, all attempts to separate them would result in failure in either A or B (Fig. 1a).   But real surfaces differ from these ideal surfaces in that they are rough and contaminated, and both of these imperfections contribute to a greatly decreased real area of contact between the surfaces of A and B (Fig. 1b).   In general, however, where they have achieved contact—that is, where they have been brought close enough for van der Waals forces to become operative—they have adhered, and when they are separated mechanically a little of A remains on B, and B on A, depending on the geometry in the neighborhood of each area of contact and the cohesive strength of each.   The general assumption based on visual examination is that either the solids did not adhere, or the failure was in adhesion.   The first statement, however, is incorrect, because surely some areas of A and B achieved interfacial contact, and the second is incorrect because where the surfaces were not in contact there was no adhesion and it makes no sense to talk about the failure of something that did not exist.

This point of view leads to the conclusion that to get A and B to make a stronger joint we need to increase their real area of contact.   This means that one or both of the materials must be made to conform better to the surface roughness of the other. This implies, in a practical sense, that one of the materials should be fluid when placed in contact with the other.   However, that one of the materials be fluid is a necessary, but may not be a sufficient condition, for if a high-viscosity fluid makes a sizeable contact angle with the solid, its tendency to create a large interfacial area of contact may be relatively poor.   The result is that it may do a great deal of bridging, trap a great deal of air, and achieve little penetration into the surface roughness of the solid, and stress concentrations due to the large contact angle become important.   However, if the fluid member spontaneously spreads on the solid, the interfacial area of contact increases, because the fluid can now flow more completely into the micro or submicro pores and crevices in the surface of the solid and can displace gas pockets and other contamination. In addition, the zero contact angle tends to minimize stress concentrations. The effect of creating a spontaneous spreading situation, then, is twofold, ie the real area of contact is increased and stress concentration is minimized (10).

Specifically, only van der Waals forces have been mentioned in connection with the preceding treatment. This is not to be construed as meaning that other molecular forces may be excluded from participation in adhesion. In the initial process involving the establishment of interfacial contact, all the molecular forces involved in wetting phenomena can be considered to be important. Chemisorption is not excluded, but if it is to occur, molecular contact must have already been established, ie van der Waals forces must already be operative. Therefore any such chemical reaction as does occur, occurs after adhesion has taken place. Furthermore, since interfacial separation apparently does not occur under mechanical influences even when only van der Waals forces are operative, it follows that chemisorption may not have any positive influence on the mechanical strength of an adhesive joint. It may have a negative influence on strength if weak boundary layers (12,13) are formed. However, it is possible that chemisorption may increase the permanence of an adhesive joint by retarding or preventing destruction of the interfacial region as by moisture, low surface tension liquids, etc. The author and his associates have demonstrated (14–16) how strong adhesive joints could be obtained in the epoxy adhesive–polyethylene system and the epoxy adhesive–chlorotrifluoroethylene homopolymer system. Their results clearly demonstrate the importance of the surface tension of the adhesive and the glass-transition temperature and the surface roughness of the substrate.

Rheological Theory of Adhesion. *Weak Boundary Layers.* The effect of wettability of epoxy adhesives on thermoplastics and the wetting of cured epoxy adhesives by molten thermoplastics have been demonstrated (10,14–16). Although the wettability of both chlorotrifluoroethylene homopolymer and polyethylene are similar, strong joints can be made to the former but not to the latter at temperatures well below their respective melting temperature. Polyethylene and probably many other melt-crystallized polymers seem to have associated with them a weak boundary layer which precludes the formation of strong adhesive joints even though extensive interfacial contact occurs between the polymer film and the epoxy adhesive (17,18).

Apparently, at the solid–liquid interface (S–L, cured epoxy adhesive–molten polyethylene) on solidification of the polyethylene upon cooling, a region of high cohesive strength is generated by preferential adsorption and subsequent nucleation of the high-molecular-weight species. During crystallization from the melt the low-molecular-weight species are rejected from the interface into the bulk.

A different process occurs at the liquid–air interface (polyethylene–air) or at the solid–liquid interface when the solid no longer acts as a nucleating site. Here low-molecular-weight species are rejected to the interface during the crystallization process, thereby resulting in a surface region of low mechanical strength, existing in an apparently amorphous configuration. Since many polymers are molded against non-nucleating surfaces (eg mold-release agents), thereby generating surface regions of low mechanical strength, we must be concerned with the removal of these weak boundary layers.

Surface Treatment of Polymers (Adhesive Joint Strength)

Surface Crosslinking (CASING Technique). Conventional techniques for treating polyethylene surfaces in order to obtain strong adhesive joints, such as surface oxidation by corona discharge (19) or flame treatment (20), are commonly believed to be effective because they create wettable polar surfaces on which the adhesive may spread spontaneously and thus provide extensive interfacial contact. However, as pointed out previously, extensive interfacial contact is a necessary, but not sufficient, condition for forming strong joints. It is here suggested that the primary function of surface-oxidation techniques is to remove the weak boundary layer. In fact, if surface oxidation alone occurred without removal of the weak boundary layer, only weak adhesive joints would be obtained.

The low mechanical strength of the weak boundary layer, which prevents the formation of strong adhesive joints, can be increased rapidly and dramatically by allowing electronically excited species of rare gases to impinge upon the surface of a large number of polymers. As these metastable and ionic gases come into contact with polyethylene, for example, they cause abstraction of hydrogen atoms. The polymer radicals formed by this process interact to form crosslinks and unsaturated groups without appreciable scission of the polymer chain. The cohesive strength of the surface region is increased markedly by the formation of a dense gel matrix and the wettability of the surface is relatively unaffected. This surface-treatment technique is called CASING (Crosslinking by Activated Species of INert Gases) (17,18). CASING allows us to form strong adhesive joints to a variety of polymers with conventional adhesives.

Contact time of activated gas with the polymer film of as little as one second under relatively mild conditions resulted in greatly improved adhesive joint strength for an epoxy adhesive on polyethylene. Longer contact times were required for polymers such as polytetrafluoroethylene. Helium, argon, krypton, neon, and xenon, and even hydrogen and nitrogen, were all effective crosslinking agents although nitrogen markedly changed the wettability of the surface.

A tenfold or greater increase in lap-shear joint strength was produced by bombardment with activated research-grade helium, although no change in wettability of the polymer was observed. Infrared examination of polyethylene film which had been held at a pressure of 0.05 mm for several hours, then bombarded for one hour with activated research-grade helium at 1 mm pressure, and finally kept at a pressure of 0.05 mm for 16 hr at room temperature to permit dissipation of radicals formed during bombardment (21), showed only the formation of trans ethylenic unsaturation at the surface by attenuated total reflectance techniques. Transmission spectra of treated and untreated films were identical, with no peak attributable to carbonyl or hydroxyl groups, indicating that unsaturation, as was the case for crosslinking, occurs only at or near the surface of the polymer during bombardment. Apparently the improvement in adhesive joint strength achieved by CASING is primarily due to increasing the mechanical strength of the polymer in the surface region through formation of a densely crosslinked matrix.

Some years ago Bikerman showed (22) that, when bonding polyethylene to aluminum, if the surface of the polyethylene were first solvent-extracted, the joint strength increased, although this extraction did not affect the wettability. On the other hand, we have found that when bonding polychlorotrifluoroethylene no surface pretreatment is necessary although the polychlorotrifluoroethylene has essentially the same wettability as polyethylene. Such differences need explanation. An examination was made of the effect of various surface treatments of high-density polyethylene on the lap-shear strengths of composite joints of the form aluminum–epoxy adhesive–

polyethylene film–epoxy adhesive–aluminum. (These joints were made at temperatures below the melting point of the polyethylene so that there is no question of the latter acting as an adhesive.)

The lowest results (tensile strength 200 psi) were with commercial polyethylene. Secondly, single crystals were prepared from a narrow molecular-weight fraction and, as this only removed some of the surface weakness, little improvement was apparent. Further improvement (to 800 psi) was observed after solvent extraction, but it was found that where the polyethylene was very soluble, it swelled during treatment and subsequent removal of the solvent brought the weak material back to the surface. After irradiating the polyethylene in a Van der Graaff machine the weak boundary layer was removed and the joint was consequently stronger (1000 psi). The bulk material, however, suffered degradation and consequently it was expected that no further improvement in adhesive joint strength was possible. When treated with a glass-cleaning solution, such as that conventionally used to process polar groups on

Fig. 2. Transcrystalline growth of polyethylene adjacent to the polymer metal interface.

the surface of polyethylene, a further increase in joint strenth to 2000 psi was apparent. However, similar strength joints were found after exposing the polyethylene to a glow discharge for about 10 sec. Furthermore, this process did not change the wettability of the polyethylene surface, its critical surface tension being the same before and after irradiation. This suggests that the wettability of the adherend surface is not the sole criterion for forming strong adhesive joints. (The above quoted strengths were obtained when the joint was made at 25°C; stronger joints were obtained at higher temperatures.)

In the process of preparing films of these melt-crystallized polymers, some morphological forms are driven to the interface and are too weak to support a strong adhesive joint. As a result it is necessary to knit the surface together in some fashion to increase its cohesive strength and thus to produce a strong boundary layer. Wettability may be important, but there can be a spontaneous spreading situation, with zero contact angle, and still not be able to make a strong adhesive joint because of the presence of a weak boundary layer.   The weakness in the surface region must be removed.

It has been shown that by treating the surface of materials like polyethylene with activated rare gases, an increase in wettability is not necessary in order to make a strong adhesive joint.   In fact, if the surface treatment is carried out in elemental fluorine (no excitation), a strong joint can be made even though the surface wettability has been decreased, provided the weakness in the surface region is removed.

Previously it had been postulated by de Bruyne (9) that an oxygenated or polar polymer surface was necessary to make a strong adhesive joint with polar adhesives. This is true but for reasons quite apart from those associated with wettability.   If polyethylene is subjected to a corona discharge in the presence of air or treated with a glass-cleaning solution, the wettability of the surface is increased but this is not the reason why it is possible to join it adequately.   What is most important is the removal of the weakness in the surface region, extending to a depth of between several hundred and 1000 Å.

Heterogeneous Nucleation of Polymer Melts on Surfaces.   The question arises why the melting of a polymer onto a high-energy surface (ie metal, metal oxide) generates a strong joint, provided the polymer has wet the substrate, while the free polymer film prepared by conventional techniques requires a surface treatment prior to joining.   Apparently, the substrate has a profound effect on the ultimate mechanical properties in the interfacial region of the polymer.

Surface studies on crystallizable polymers (eg polyethylene) have ignored, in general, the nature of the nucleating phase (ie vapor, solid, or liquid) used to generate the solid polymer.   There has been a neglect concerning the details of formation of the polymer melt–nucleating phase interface which, on solidification by cooling, results in a polymer solid–nucleating phase interface.

Extensive heterogeneous nucleation of polyethylene melts on high-energy surfaces results in generation of transcrystallinity in the interfacial region [(S–L) → (S–S)] (see Fig. 2).   It has been observed that there is a variation in the extent of supercooling which may depend upon surface energy and interatomic spacing in the substrate (23).   Effective nucleating agents allow for only small supercooling.   Others have concluded that stresses set up at the interface during cooling from the melt are important in determining the subsequent morphology (23).   Vapor phases are apparently ineffective nucleating agents.

When polymers are solidified in contact with a vapor phase, nucleation is precluded at the liquid–vapor interface and is apparently initiated in the bulk.   Sufficient supercooling has not occurred at the liquid–vapor interface to nucleate the interfacial region before nucleation occurs in the bulk.   Apparently, this is the reason for the lack of a well-defined transcrystalline region when polyethylene is nucleated in contact with a vapor phase.   As crystallization proceeds in the bulk, polymer molecules which cannot be accommodated into the crystal lattice during crystallization are rejected to the interface.

Employing high-energy surfaces for the nucleation of a polymer melt is effective only if sufficient time is allowed for the polymer melt to achieve extensive and intimate contact with the substrate.   This is a kinetic requirement.   If sufficient time has not been allowed, considerable interfacial voids result (see Fig. 3a) and nucleation generally occurs in the bulk.   If sufficient time is allowed for spreading to occur, a situation results which is illustrated in Figure 3b, where interfacial voids are pre-

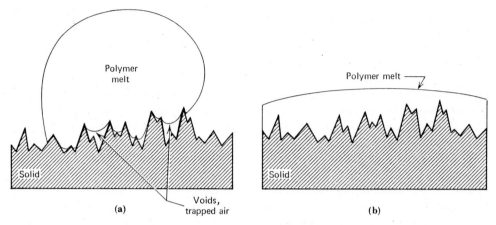

Fig. 3. (a) Poorly wetted surface; note real area of interfacial contact; (b) extensive intermolecular contact; note lack of voids from trapped air in pores and crevices.

cluded and nucleation occurs predominantly at the S–L interface. The mere presence of a high-energy surface in itself does not ensure that extensive and intimate contact occurs and a highly nucleated surface region results upon solidification of the polymer melt.

At the high-energy solid-polymer melt interface a region of substantial mechanical strength is generated by extensive wetting and subsequent nucleation and crystallization of the polymer. During crystallization from the melt, species contributing to

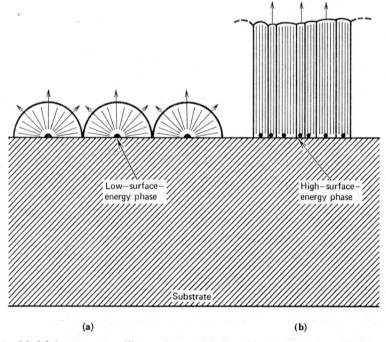

Fig. 4. Model for transcrystalline region; (a) bulk nucleation and crystallization, no transcrystalline region generated at the interface; (b) nucleation and crystallization of polymer melt at solid–liquid interface resulting in transcrystalline region.

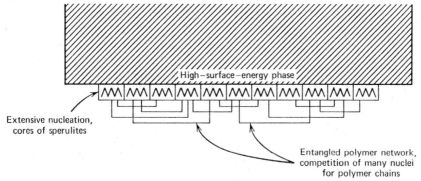

Fig. 5. Entanglements resulting from extensive nucleation and crystallization of polymer melt at solid–liquid interface.

the generation of weak boundary layers are rejected from the interface into the bulk. The resulting interfacial zone of high mechanical strength is illustrated in Figure 2 for the polyethylene–aluminum (chemically etched) system. Here a transcrystalline region is generated in the polymer surface region. Apparently, at the surface of the metal oxide, numerous crystallization nuclei are formed (see Fig. 4b); the spherulites which grow from the nuclei now can propagate in only one principal direction, since growth in the lateral directions is inhibited by neighboring spherulites. In this way, only very narrowly divergent spherulite sectors develop, which give an overall appearance of a rodlike buildup. The thickness of this transcrystalline region is estimated to be about 25–50μ. Transcrystalline growth of the polyethylene surface is not observed when generated against a low-energy phase (see Fig. 4a). As described earlier, poor nucleating phases generally contribute to the generation of weak boundary layers.

Since strong adhesive joints can be formed by melting onto a high-energy surface, we can inquire whether the surface generated at the high-energy solid-polymer melt interface is amenable to conventional adhesive bonding when the metal is removed. This is indeed the case. It is important to remove the metal by dissolution rather than by peeling which disrupts the surface region of interest. This can be seen by examining the bondability of both the polymer and foil surfaces after peeling the foil from the polymer. In both cases the joint strengths are low. When foil is peeled, cohesive failure occurs in the polymer, exposing two new surfaces which are not amenable to adhesive bonding.

From the above analysis we can conclude that the weakness in the surface region of many polymers, particularly polyethylene, is not an intrinsic property of the polymer but is dependent on the manner in which the surface region is formed from the melt. If care is taken in the preparation of the polymer sheet (ie nucleated in contact with a high-energy substrate), to prevent any mechanical work upon removal of the polymer from the substrate, then it is possible to prepare this polymer for adhesive bonding without resorting to crosslinking of the surface region. Solvent extraction (eg xylene) of the transcrystalline region showed no evidence of a gel fraction. Apparently the increase in the mechanical strength of the surface region, as a result of the extensive nucleation, is due to considerable entanglement of the polymer chains. There is a strong competition for these chains since so many nuclei are formed. Effectively, each entanglement may be considered to be a crosslink, as shown in Figure 5.

Generally, to facilitate removal from molds, polymers have been prepared for wettability studies by pressing or solidifying them in contact with low-surface-energy solids (eg polytetrafluoroethylene), or with high-energy surfaces for short times at low temperatures (ie just above the melting point of the polymer). Experience has shown that if longer periods of time are used at relatively high temperatures on high-energy surfaces, it is difficult to remove the polymer from the metal surface without damaging the surface layer of the polymer. Longer dwell times of the polymer melt on the surface of the metal results in the formation of a strong adhesive joint, provided the metal does not have a weakly adherent oxide layer. If a mechanically weak oxide layer were present, it is conceivable that this could be transferred to the polymer, thereby affecting the wettability results.

Studies of the kinetics of wetting of polymer melts on surfaces (24–26) have shown that the ability of a polymer melt to attain an equilibrium contact angle with a solid substrate is proportional to the surface tension of the polymer melt (γ_{LV}) and inversely proportional to the melt viscosity (η). Since the viscosity varies strongly with temperature, to preclude interfacial voids at low temperatures in the polymer melt–high-energy surface (ie metal, metal oxide) system, it is important to allow sufficient time to ensure complete mating of the surfaces. Figure 3a indicates a poorly wetted situation. Although the thermodynamic requirements for spreading are fulfilled (ie $\gamma_{SV} \geq \gamma_{LV} + \gamma_{SL}$), thermodynamic spreading of the polymer may not take place because of the kinetic requirements. Enhancement of wetting is rather easy to accomplish by employing higher temperatures and longer times. Since viscosity decreases markedly with increasing temperature, relatively short times are required at higher temperatures to achieve extensive mating of the liquid and high-energy solid (see Fig. 3b).

Conclusion

Wettability and the weak boundary layer concept have been shown to complement each other in a practical approach to joining materials with conventional adhesives. A study of the wetting phenomenon leads quite naturally to a study of surface properties of polymers in both the solid and liquid state. Although the temperature dependence of wettability has not been examined here in detail, this important subject is not to be ignored in any comprehensive guide to adhesive bonding.

The weak boundary layer reveals the importance, in a rheological sense, of the surface structure of the adherends and the interphase of the polymers. Even though wetting has been accomplished, strong joints may not be realized unless the mechanical strengths of the interphases are sufficient to support a large stress.

The simplified approach to adhesive joining presented in this article should help in joining a large number of adherends successfully with a large variety of materials. Perhaps more importantly, new materials can be employed, and their performance (mechanically) in a composite structure understood by a careful examination of their surface and bulk properties.

Bibliography

1. E. R. Houwink and G. Salomon, eds., *Adhesion and Adhesives*, Vol. 1, Elsevier Publishing Co., New York, 1965.
2. G. Salomon, in reference 1, pp. 1–28.
3. *Ibid.*, pp. 29–52.
4. S. S. Voyutskii, *Adhesives Age* **5**, 30 (1962).
5. B. V. Deryagin and N. A. Krotova, *Dokl. Akad. Nauk. SSSR* **61**, 849 (1948).

6. S. S. Voyutskii and Yu. L. Margolina, *Usp. Khim.* **18,** 449 (1949); *Rubber Chem. Technol.* **30,** 531 (1957).

7. S. S. Voyutskii and V. M. Zamazii, *Kolloidn. Zh.* **15,** 407 (1953); *Rubber Chem. Technol.* **30,** 544 (1957).

8. S. S. Voyutskii and B. V. Shtarkh, *Kolloidn. Zh.* **16,** 3 (1954); *Rubber Chem. Technol.* **30,** 548 (1957).

9. N. A. de Bruyne, *Aircraft Engr.* **18,** 53 (Nov. 1939).

10. L. H. Sharpe and H. Schonhorn, *Advan. Chem. Ser.* **43,** 189 (1964).

11. D. D. Eley, ed., *Adhesion,* Oxford University Press, London, 1961, Chaps. 8 and 11.

12. J. J. Bikerman, *The Science of Adhesive Joints,* Academic Press, Inc., New York, 1961.

13. *Ibid.,* pp. 1–2.

14. H. Schonhorn and L. H. Sharpe, *J. Polymer Sci.* **B2,** 719 (1964).

15. *Ibid.,* **A3,** 3087 (1965).

16. L. H. Sharpe, H. Schonhorn, and C. J. Lynch, *Intern. Sci. Technol.* **1964** (April), 26.

17. R. H. Hansen and H. Schonhorn, *J. Polymer Sci.* **B4,** 203 (1966).

18. H. Schonhorn and R. H. Hansen, *J. Appl. Polymer Sci.* **11,** 1461 (1967).

19. H. E. Wechsberg and J. B. Webber, *Mod. Plastics* **36,** 101 (1959).

20. J. A. Boxler, S. P. Foster, and E. E. Lewis, *132nd Meeting Amer. Chem. Soc., New York, Sept., 1957,* Vol. 17, No. 2, p. 58.

21. L. A. Wall and R. B. Ingalls, *J. Polymer Sci.* **62,** 56 (1962); *J. Chem. Phys.* **35,** 370 (1961).

22. Reference 12, pp. 164–176.

23. A. Sharples, *Polymer Crystallization,* St. Martin's Press, New York, 1966, pp. 21–22.

24. H. Schonhorn, H. L. Frisch, and T. K. Kwei, *J. Appl. Phys.* **37,** 4967 (1966).

25. S. Newman, *J. Colloid Interface Sci.* **26,** 209 (1968).

26. B. W. Cherry and C. M. Holmes, *J. Colloid Interface Sci.* **29,** 174 (1969).

Harold Schonhorn
Bell Telephone Laboratories

ALKYLPHENOLS

There is a great and increasing demand for antioxidants, for such diverse organic materials as gasoline, oils and greases, plastics, and food. The best antioxidants are sterically hindered phenols, that is to say, phenols substituted on the 2-, or 2- and 6-positions, with branched alkyl groups. Alkylation of phenols can be performed with a variety of acidic catalysts, but the tendency is to occupy the para and meta positions to form the thermodynamically more stable compounds. Unfortunately these para- and meta-substituted phenols, unlike their ortho isomers, do not perform well as antioxidants. See also Cresylic acids, synthetic, in this volume.

One way to overcome this difficulty is to use phenols in which the introduction of a branched alkyl group into the para position is blocked. A good example is *p*-cresol which can readily be alkylated in the two ortho positions; when the entering alkyl groups are *tert*-butyl groups, 2,6-di-*t*-butyl-*p*-cresol (BHT), a large-volume, general-purpose antioxidant is produced. 2,4-Xylenol (2,4,dimethylphenol) is another example; it has only one free ortho position which can readily be alkylated. The 6-*t*-butyl derivative is a liquid antioxidant used mostly in gasoline. Even a methyl group in the meta position, as in *m*-cresol, provides sufficient hindrance to the introduction of a *t*-alkyl group into the para position (and even more to the ortho position between the methyl and hydroxyl groups) to make the 6-*t*-alkyl derivative the more stable one. Thus, *t*-butylation of *m*-cresol yields 6-*t*-butyl-*m*-cresol almost exclusively under a variety of conditions which would normally yield predominantly para-substitution where this position is unhindered, eg, with phenol or *o*-cresol (1,2).

The desirable precursors for antioxidants, p-cresol, m,-cresol, and 2,4-xylenol, are found in tar acids (see Vol. 19, p. 671) and in the cresols from petroleum refining (see Vol. 6, p. 436) but they occur mixed with isomers from which they are difficult to separate. The use for p-cresol-derived antioxidants has grown so much that it has been necessary to develop routes to give p-cresol isomer-free.

An alternative approach to the 2- and 2,6-alkylphenols required for antioxidants is to develop a method of alkylation that is selective for the ortho position. This not only allows the use of the much cheaper phenol or the isomer-free o-cresol, as starting material, but would also permit such alkylated compounds to be modified in the para position to impart various desirable properties into the molecule. As a result of selective ortho-alkylation, such desirable antioxidant structures as

and

are now possible.

Selective Alkylation of Phenols

Much effort has been expended in the past to make the alkylation of phenols ortho-selective. Both Bronsted and Lewis acids have been adapted to achieve this selectivity. This was accomplished both by modifying the reaction conditions and the nature of the acid catalyst. It has been known that ortho-alkylation took place readily but the resultant products rearranged under normal reaction conditions to the more stable isomers. In order to suppress isomerization, usually the mildest possible conditions necessary to perform the alkylation are used. Such attenuation of conditions usually takes the form of low temperatures, short reaction times, or low catalyst concentrations (3). Conversely, high reaction temperatures to increase the rate of alkylation, especially in the ortho-position, coupled with short reaction times, to limit the allowable time for isomerization, have also proved beneficial (4,5). Incremental addition of the catalyst has also been claimed to give more selective ortho-alkylation (6).

The acids which have been used traditionally for alkylation of phenol have been replaced. For example, methanesulfonic acid and other sulfonic acids have been claimed to give better ortho-alkylation selectivity than sulfuric acid (7,8). Small quantities of phosphorus oxychloride have yielded predominantly ortho-alkylated products, where aluminum chloride would give the para isomer almost exclusively (9).

Metal Aryloxide Catalysts. In 1956 and 1957, a very elegant method of selectively introducing secondary and tertiary alkyl groups into the ortho positions of phenols became a reality.   A group headed by Kolka and Ecke (10,11) in the U.S. and another composed of Stroh, Seydel, and Hahn (12,13) in Germany, found that certain metal salts of phenols catalyzed the alkylation of phenols with olefins in such a way that selective ortho-substitution took place over a wider range of conditions than was heretofore possible.   Both research teams worked predominantly with aluminum aryloxides.   However, the American group also claimed the magnesium salts of phenols and, in addition, described the use of the zinc salt.   The German group claimed all metals capable of forming salts with phenols, and listed specifically aluminum, magnesium, zinc, iron, calcium, sodium, and lithium.   However, only the first four metals were used in the examples of their patent.   The phenoxide is usually the one derived from the phenol to be alkylated although different ones may be used.

Various methods have been used to make the catalysts:

(1) $Al + ArOH \rightarrow Al(OAr)_3 + H_2 \uparrow$

(2) $AlCl_3 + ArOH \rightleftharpoons Al(OAr)_3 + HCl$

(3) $Al(OR)_3 + ArOH \rightleftharpoons Al(OAr)_3 + ROH$

(4) $AlR_3 + ArOH \rightarrow Al(OAr)_3 + RH \uparrow$

Method (1) consists of the reaction of metallic aluminum with a phenol to form the aluminum salt and hydrogen.   With phenol itself in excess and a clean surface on the aluminum, the reaction will take place at about 150°C.   Catalysts such as $AlCl_3$ or $HgCl_2$ may be used.   The displacement reaction may also be performed in an autoclave to attain temperatures higher than the normal boiling point of the phenol.   The hydrogen may then be vented prior to the introduction of the olefin.

Method (2) is an equilibrium reaction wherein the equilibrium is to the left. However the fact that one of the products, hydrogen chloride, can be removed readily by distillation drives the reaction to the right.   Replacement gets progressively more difficult, ie, the first chlorine is most readily removed, the second with greater difficulty, and the third with still greater difficulty.

Method (3) is conveniently carried out with aluminum alkoxides.   It is also an equilibrium reaction which should be to the right.   It can be forced to completion by distilling the alcohol.   In Method (4), commercially available aluminum alkyls react readily with phenols yielding the aryloxides and the saturated hydrocarbon corresponding to the alkyl group.

The aluminum aryloxide catalysts are usually soluble in the parent phenol; thus the reaction is one of homogeneous catalysis.   The salts are sensitive to moisture and will hydrolyze readily.   This may present a problem since most phenols are very hygroscopic.

It is believed that the actual catalyst is of the type $H[Al(OAr)_4]$, similar to $H(AlCl_4)$ from $AlCl_3$ and HCl.   In 1929, Meerwein and Bersin (14) showed that aluminum alkoxides coordinate with one molecule of alcohol to form acid solutions which may be titrated with alcoholic sodium alkoxides to the thymolphthalein endpoint with the formation of the corresponding salts.   Stroh and coworkers found that a 1% aluminum phenoxide solution in phenol gave a value of 1.0 on a pH meter, compared with 4.4–4.6 for the phenol itself.   Salts of the expected $HAl(OC_6H_5)_4$ such as $NaAl(OC_6H_5)_4$ did not function as alkylation catalysts.

The usual aluminum phenoxide catalyst concentrations are 1–2% of the metal based on the phenol.   Such catalyst systems are less active than such commonly-used catalysts as sulfuric acid or aluminum chloride.   For example, whereas small concentrations of sulfuric acid on the order of 0.2–1% cause phenol itself to react with isobutylene at atmospheric pressure and room temperature, aluminum phenoxide-catalyzed reactions usually require elevated temperatures and pressures. t-Butylation of phenol itself takes place at as low as 65°C but is usually performed at 100°C to give a high conversion to 2-t-butylphenol or 2,6-di-t-butylphenol.   However, a recent patent claims that aluminum o-t-butylphenoxide causes t-butylation of o-t-butylphenol almost at room temperature (15).   Under the mildest condition for phenol t-butylation, 65°C, the alkylation yields 12 mole % phenyl t-butyl ether along with o-t-butylphenol.   At 300°C, para-substitution is predominant in a pressure reaction, while at 150–190°C and atmospheric pressure p-t-butylphenol is the only product.   Under optimum conditions of 100°C, a reaction product comprising 3% phenol, 9% 2-t-butylphenol, 74% 2,6-di-t-butylphenol, and 9% 2,4,6-tri-t-butylphenol can be obtained with excess olefin.   At a 1:1 molar ratio, 2-t-butylphenol becomes the major product (70%).   More drastic conditions have to be applied with normal olefins.   For example, the isopropylation of phenol is performed at 220–240°C.   Ethylene reacts at 280–320°C.

The fundamental catalyst system has been modified in a variety of ways by different researchers.   For example, aluminum phenoxide has been replaced by the thiophenoxide (16).   The addition of 1–1.5 mole of p-toluenesulfonic acid to aluminum phenoxide still retained the ortho-selectivity of the original catalyst, while raising the hydrolytic stability of the catalyst system (17).   Similar advantages were encountered when aluminum salts of o-phenolsulfonic acids were used (18).   These are readily prepared by sulfonating such phenols as p-cresol, 2,4-xylenol, or p-t-butylphenol.

Phenoxides of other metals were also applicable to ortho-alkylation.   Titanium tetraphenoxide is a poor alkylation catalyst but the derivative from 1,2-benzenediol (catechol), $Ti(O_2C_6H_4)_2$, gave good ortho-alkylation, especially monosubstitution (19). The addition of toluenesulfonic acid to titanium phenoxide, up to about one mole per mole of the salt, gave good alkylation and ortho-selectivity (20).   Still other metal phenoxides have proved useful without modification.   Thus, the aryloxide salts of zirconium, niobium, hafnium, and tantalum can be employed (21).   Phenyl borates have also been claimed for ortho-alkylation (22).

Uncatalyzed Alkylations.   Although the original patents dealing with the use of metal aryloxides as phenol ortho-alkylation catalysts also claimed magnesium phenoxides, the conditions necessary for this catalyst to function, ie, 325°C and 500 psi to give 9% conversion to o-t-butylphenol (11), are virtually the same as those which have been used for the uncatalyzed reaction.   For example, a group at California Research Corp. (23) reported the t-butylation of phenol with isobutylene at temperatures as low as 260°C and pressures of about 600 psig, although the more common conditions were 320–330°C and 1200 psig.   Secondary alkylation in the presence of magnesium phenoxide required even more drastic conditions than t-alkylation.   Similar but uncatalyzed secondary alkylations were performed by Skraup as early as 1927 (24).

Thus, magnesium phenoxide and other metal phenoxides which require such drastic conditions can hardly be regarded as catalysts for this reaction.

Solid Catalysts in the Liquid Phase.   In the late 1960s solid, insoluble, metal oxides were claimed as catalysts for the ortho-alkylation of phenols.   Thus, 5% of γ-alumina catalyzes the isopropylation of phenol at 280°C and 15–80 atm.   A 67% conversion to 2-isopropylphenol was reached in three hours (25,26).   Vanadia-silica, zirconia-silica, tungsten oxide-silica, and iron oxide-silica were also found to be selective ortho-alkylation catalysts (27).

Solid Catalysts in the Vapor Phase. The use of solid catalysts in the vapor phase alkylation has also been known for a number of years (28). Under the mildest conditions necessary to effect a given alkylation with olefin, alcohol, alkyl halide, or ether, ortho-substitution usually predominates (29).

Bibliography

1. H. Hart and E. A. Haglund, *J. Org. Chem.* **15,** 396 (1950).
2. D. R. Stevens, *J. Org. Chem.* **20,** 1232 (1955).
3. J. I. DeJong, *Rec. trav. chim.* **83,** 469 (1964).
4. U.S. Pat. 2,836,627 (1958), M. B. Neuworth et al. (to Pittsburgh Consolidation Coal Co.).
5. U.S. Pat. 2,923,745 (1960), V. W. Buls et al. (to Shell Development Co.).
6. U.S. Pat. 3,408,410 (1968), R. J. Laufer and M. D. Kulik (to Consolidation Coal Co.).
7. U.S. Pat. 3,116,336 (1963), J. L. Van Winkle (to Shell Oil Co.).
8. U.S. Pat. 3,177,259 (1965), J. L. Van Winkle (to Shell Oil Co.).
9. U.S. Pat. 2,655,547 (1953), F. Bryner (to The Dow Chemical Co.).
10. A. J. Kolka et al., *J. Org. Chem.* **22,** 642 (1957).
11. U.S. Pat. 2,831,898 (1958), G. G. Ecke and A. J. Kolka (to Ethyl Corp.).
12. R. Stroh et al., *Angew. Chem.* **69,** 699 (1957).
13. Ger. Pat. 944,014 (1956), R. Stroh and R. Seydel (to Farbenfabriken Bayer A.-G.).
14. H. Meerwein and T. Bersin, *Ann.* **476,** 113 (1929).
15. Can. Pat. 754,580 (1967), T. H. Coffield et al. (to Ethyl Corp.).
16. U.S. Pat. 3,032,595 (1962), M. B. Neuworth et al. (to Consolidation Coal Co.).
17. U.S. Pat. 3,267,154 (1966), T. Hokama (to Koppers Co.).
18. U.S. Pat. 3,267,153 (1966), G. Leston (to Koppers Co.).
19. U.S. Pat. 3,267,155 (1966), G. Leston (to Koppers Co.).
20. U.S. Pat. 3,267,152 (1966), T. Hokama (to Koppers Co.).
21. U.S. Pat. 3,331,879 (1967), G. Leston (to Koppers Co.).
22. Brit. Pat. 1,008,592 (1965), (to Monsanto Chemicals, Ltd.).
23. E. A. Goldsmith et al., *J. Org. Chem.* **23,** 1871 (1958).
24. S. Skraup and W. Beifuss, *Ber.* **60B,** 1070 (1927).
25. U.S. Pat. 3,290,389 (1966), W. Hahn (to Farbenfabriken Bayer A.-G.).
26. U.S. Pat. 3,367,981 (1968), J. P. Napolitano (to Ethyl Corp.).
27. Ger. Pat. 1,159,960 (1963), W. Hahn (to Farbenfabriken Bayer A.-G.).
28. N. Olita, *J. Chem. Soc. Japan, Ind. Chem. Sect.* **51,** 141–143 (1948); *Chem. Abstr.* **44,** 9226 (1950).
29. Y. Ogata et al., *Kogyo Kagaku Zasshi* **72,** 1102 (1969).

Gerd Leston
Koppers Company

AMINE OXIDES

Amine oxides were discovered by a number of investigators within a few short years of each other during the last decade of the nineteenth century.   Merling (1) and Wernick and Wolffenstein (2) oxidized N-alkylpiperidines, Bamberger and Tschirner (3) worked with dimethylaniline, while Dunstan and Goulding (4) prepared trimethylamine oxide from hydroxylamine and methyl iodide and, subsequently, from trimethylamine and hydrogen peroxide (5).

These products were initially called oxamines, but later amine oxides and treated as derivatives of amines rather than functional compounds in their own right.   Others have considered these compounds to be derivatives of the tautomeric form of hydroxylamine (6).

Amine oxides did not arouse any large interest until the 1940s and, consequently, there are few review articles about these compounds.   Culvenor (7) offers a comprehensive review and additional references (8) should also be considered.   Several textbooks (9) cover the structure, properties, and preparative methods in some depth.   The du Pont Company has published a literature and a patent survey (10) with over seven hundred references.   Interest in amine oxides as commercial chemicals is extremely high.   The surface activity of long-chain aliphatic amine oxides has invoked large-scale investigation and led to their use in detergent and shampoo formulations.   Pharmacological research on heterocyclic amine oxides resulted in the commercialization of tranquilizers and antibacterials.

Physical and Chemical Properties

Amine oxides are perhaps best described as nonionic compounds possessing a strongly dipolar nitrogen–oxygen bond.   This is supported by the higher electron density (11) on the oxygen atom, as well as other physical properties, such as solubilities and dipole moment.   This structure has been depicted as follows:

$$R_3N \rightarrow \ddot{O}:$$

The nonplanar character of these compounds was shown by Meisenheimer (12) in 1908 when he resolved ethylmethylaniline oxide into enantiomorphic forms.   He suggests that the configuration around the nitrogen atom is tetrahedral, and stereochemically similar to quaternary ammonium cations.   This has been verified by electron-diffraction studies of trimethylamine oxide (13).

Amine oxides are, for the most part, hygroscopic solids.   They form essentially un-ionized hydrates in solution existing as very weak substituted ammonium bases $(R_3NOH)^+OH^-$ (11).   This position is supported by the work of Stewart (16) who

Table 1. pH Values of Trimethylamine Oxide and Fraction Present as $(CH_3)_3N^+OH^-$

Molar concentration	pH	Fraction present
0.01	8.32	2.11×10^{-4}
0.005	8.17	2.99×10^{-4}
0.001	7.83	6.88×10^{-4}
0.0005	7.68	9.45×10^{-4}
0.0001	7.32	2.11×10^{-3}

has shown that the alkoxy derivatives $(R_3NOR)^+OH^-$ are strong bases readily ionizable in water. The pH of the solution and the fraction present as N-hydroxyammonium hydroxide may be calculated using classical equilibrium data. Values for trimethylamine oxide (pK$_A$ of $(CH_3)_3N^+OH^-$ taken as 4.65) are shown in Table 1.

Amine oxides exhibit nonionic or cationic character in aqueous solution, depending upon the pH. Above pH 7 the nonionic form predominates, although there is still a finite, but small amount, of the protonated molecule present, as shown in Table 1. At pH 3 the cationic form predominates.

Amine oxides, like most surfactants in aqueous systems, exhibit an abrupt change in physical properties over a narrow range in concentration. The concentration at which this phenomenon is observed is called the critical micelle concentration (CMC). This rapid change in physical properties is attributed to an orientation of aggregates or micelles (see Vol. 19, p. 573). The surface activity of amine oxides is due to the monomeric molecule and the micelle acts as a supplier of the unassociated surfactant.

At the critical micelle concentration of a surfactant, detergency and foaming are often at their highest, although this has not been specifically demonstrated for amine oxides. Another physical property associated with CMC for surfactants in general is that there is no decrease in surface tension with increasing concentration beyond the CMC. It has also been observed that the ability of surfactant solutions to dissolve or solubilize water-insoluble materials starts with the CMC value and increases with increase in concentration.

Tokiwa and Ohki (14) have shown that dimethyldodecylamine oxide, in solution, acts as a simple basic molecule below the critical micelle concentration. The titration behavior of the micelle, however, is different from that of the monomer. The micelle is dependent upon the degree of protonation, whereas the monomer is independent.

Dimethyldodecylamine oxide reacts with an anionic surfactant, such as sodium dodecylbenzenesulfonate, in dilute aqueous solution in several ways, depending upon whether these reactants are above or below the CMC (15). Below the CMC the protonated amine oxide precipitates metathetically with the anionic surfactant and this is accompanied by an increase in pH resulting from protonation of additional unreacted amine oxide. The reaction can be shown as follows:

$$R_3NO + H_2O \rightleftharpoons R_3N^+OH + OH^-$$

$$R_3N^+OH + R'C_6H_5SO_3^- \rightleftharpoons R_3NO^+H . R'C_6H_4SO_3^-$$

At the CMC, a mixed micelle is found containing the oxide and sulfonate in a 2:3 ratio. The value of this CMC is 7×10^{-4} moles/liter and is lower than the CMC values for either of the two reactants. Tokiwa and Ohki also found that only mixed micelles are present in this system and that micellular solubilization of the precipitate occurs above the CMC.

The oxides of aromatic amines are slightly weaker bases than the parent amine. The oxides of aliphatic amines, however, are much weaker bases. The pK$_A$ constants of several protonated amine oxides have been determined by Nylén (18) and are compared with the parent amine in Table 2. The pK$_A$ is raised when ethyl groups replace the methyl groups and lowered by phenyl groups.

The N—O distance in $(CH_3)_3N$—O was determined to be 1.36° ± 0.3 A° (13), somewhat shorter than that of a normal carbon–carbon single bond. Strong dipole moments have been found in amine oxides and for trimethylamine oxide they were found

Table 2. pK$_A$ Constants of Protonated *N*-Amine Oxides and Parent Amines

Parent amine	pK$_A$	
	Amine	Oxide
$(CH_3)_3N$	9.74	4.65
$(C_2H_5)_3N$	10.76	5.13
$C_6H_5N(CH_3)_2$	5.06	4.21
$C_6H_5N(C_2H_5)_2$	6.56	4.53
$o\text{-}CH_3C_6H_4N(CH_3)_2$	5.86	4.78
$p\text{-}CH_3C_6H_4N(CH_3)_2$	5.50	4.32

to be 5.04 D in benzene and 4.85 D for dimethylaniline oxide (17). The dipole moment for the nitrogen–oxygen bond is larger than those of phosphorus–oxygen, phosphorus–sulfur, or sulfur–oxygen.

The physical properties of aromatic amine oxides have been treated in depth by Ochiai (9).

The amine oxides of major commercial interest are of two types, alkylbis(2-hydroxyethyl)amine oxide and alkyldimethylamine oxide. The alkyl radical may vary from 8 to 20 carbon atoms. Unfortunately, physical data for the pure compounds are rare and information on the commercial offerings is in the form of industrial specifications for the most part.

A greater amount of physical data is available for dimethyldodecylamine oxide, DMDO. Lutton (19) has found that the system of DMDO–water is very complex,

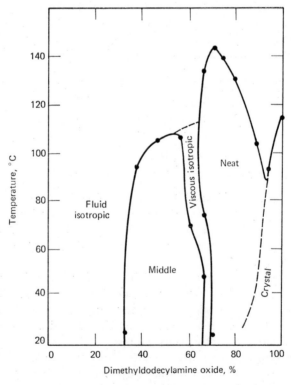

Fig. 1. Aqueous system of dimethyldodecylamine oxide.

with stable phases similar to those of anionic detergent systems such as sodium palmitate. In the phase diagram shown in Figure 1 (19) five distinct phases are found, namely, crystal, neat, viscous isotropic, middle, and fluid isotropic or nigre (niger).

The terminology assigned to these phases is somewhat arbitrary and should not be confused with similar terminology used for soaps. The crystal phase contains 70–80% DMDO and is anisotropic, that is, the physical properties vary with the direction in the sample in which they are observed. The neat phase is much more fluid but more opaque than the middle phase. The viscous isotropic phase (the physical properties observed are independent of the direction of observation) contains 65–70% DMDO and is clear but tends to be brittle and not very plastic. The middle phase, 35–65% DMDO, is transparent, anisotropic, plastic, and stringy. The fluid isotropic or nigre (niger) phase contains 0–35% DMDO. Phase diagrams and chain mobility in various mesomorphic phases have been determined by NMR studies (20). (See Vol. 18, pp. 419 and 420.)

Thermodynamic data for micelle formation at 25°C have also been calculated (21) and are listed in Table 3.

Table 3. Thermodynamic Data for Micellization of Amine Oxides at 25°C, kcal/mole

Amine oxide	$\Delta F°_m$	ΔH_m	$T\Delta S_m$
dimethyloctyl	−3.5	4.0	7.5
dimethylnonyl	−4.1	4.4	8.5
dimethyldecyl	−4.8	2.7	7.5
dimethyldodecyl	−6.1	2.6	8.7

Herrmann (22) has determined micellar properties and the effect of added salt for the nonionic and cationic forms of dimethyldodecylamine oxide, as shown in Table 4. The effect of temperature on micelle formation is shown in Table 5.

Table 4. Micellar Properties of Dimethyldodecylamine Oxide

Form	Added Cl−, M	CMC, g/100 ml	Micelle, mol wt × 10^3	Monomers/ micelle
nonionic	0	0.048	17.3	76
nonionic	0.2	0.034	17.8	78
cationic[a]	0.001	0.190	20.4	89
cationic[a]	0.010	0.180	20.7	90
cationic[a]	0.1	0.048	26.0	114
cationic[a]	0.2	0.034	31.0	136

[a] All of the values of the cationic species have been corrected by the factor nonionic mol wt/ cationic mol wt in order to compare the micelle properties of both forms more easily.

Table 5. Variation of the Micellar Properties of Dimethyldodecylamine Oxide with Temperature

Temperature, °C	CMC, moles/liter	Micelle, mol wt × 10^3
1.0	0.00284	17.7
27.0	0.00210	17.3
40.0	0.00183	17.9
50.0	0.00175	16.6

Table 6. Surfactant Properties of Amine Oxides at 25°C

$$\text{(a)} \quad R\!-\!\overset{\displaystyle CH_3}{\underset{\displaystyle CH_3}{\overset{|}{\underset{|}{N}}}}\!\rightarrow O$$

R	Concen- tration, %	Surface tension, dyn/cm	Wetting time,[a] sec	Foam height,[b] mm	Interfacial tension,[c] dyn/cm
nonyl	0.1	31.0	35	negligible	
undecyl	0.10	27.0	12		
	1.00			50	
dodecyl[d]	0.05		32.7		
	0.10		13.5		
	0.50		immediate	190 (20)[e]	
tridecyl	0.05	27.0	10.0		
	0.10	25.0	4.0		
	0.50	28.0		38	
	1.00	26.0			
tetradecyl[d]	0.05		53.1		
	0.10		18.2		
	0.50		3.9	175 (20)[e]	
pentadecyl	0.05	30.0	10.0		
	0.10	28.5	5.0		
	0.50	28.5			
	1.00	28.5		30	
hexadecyl[f]	0.10	31.6			3.3
heptadecyl	0.10	30.5	15	50	
	0.25	29.3	5		
	0.50	29.3			
	1.00	29.0			
octadecyl[d]	0.05	32.5[f]	150		
	0.10		250		5.5[f]
	0.50		72.7	45 (27.5)[e]	

$$\text{(b)} \quad R\!-\!\overset{\displaystyle CH_2CH_2OH}{\underset{\displaystyle CH_2CH_2OH}{\overset{|}{\underset{|}{N}}}}\!\rightarrow O$$

R	Concen- tration, %	Surface tension, dyn/cm	Wetting time,[a] sec	Foam height,[b] mm	Interfacial tension,[c] dyn/cm
dodecyl[f]	0.01			75 (62)[g]	
hexadecyl[f]	0.01			24 (20)[g]	
octadecyl[f]	0.10	39.0	900[h]		2.9
dodecyl- hexadecyl, 1:1	0.01		30[h]	100 (90)[g]	

[a] Draves test, see reference 23a, p. 40.
[b] Ross-Miles test, see reference 23b.
[c] Taken with paraffinic mineral oil.
[d] Reference 23c.
[e] Figure in parentheses refers to foam height after 5 min.
[f] From unpublished data, Armour Industrial Chemical Company, Chicago, Ill.
[g] Figure in parentheses refers to foam height after 10 min.
[h] Canvas disc method, Canvas Mount Vernon #6; see reference 23a, p. 41.

Some general surfactant properties of odd-numbered carbon chain dimethylamine oxides have been reported (23). These values are compared with data from miscellaneous sources on even-chained homologs as shown in Table 6. Although the data for comparison are meager, the major difference between odd- and even-chain homologs is the much quicker wetting time found for the former. Some data on alkylbis(2-hydroxyethyl)amine oxides are also reported.

Tests have been made of the biodegradability of foam stabilizers (92). Sterile two-liter Erlenmeyer flasks containing one liter of medium (a dilute solution of yeast extract and inorganic nutrients) and 30 ppm of foam stabilizer were inoculated with 10 ml of activated sludge. When the surface tension of the test solution reaches that of the control, it is assumed that the foam stabilizer has been completely biodegraded. It can be seen from Table 7 that lauryldimethylamine oxide is biodegradable, even though more slowly so than the other foam stabilizers. ("Lauryl" refers to a radical obtained from lauryl alcohol, a commercial product consisting mainly of dodecyl alcohol.)

Table 7. Biodegradation of Foam Stabilizers in Shake Culture Test as Followed by Surface-Tension Change, dyn/cm

Stabilizer	Hours				
	0	24	48	72	144
lauryldimethylamine oxide	47	47	48	50	72
N-isopropyllauramide	40	61	72		
N,N-bis(2-hydroxyethyl)lauramide	51	51	72		
control (medium only)	58	62	72		

Matson (93) compared foam stability and detergency of oxides with alkylarene sulfonates. He found the dimethyldodecyl- through the dimethyloctadecylamine oxides to be better detergents than sodium dodecylbenzenesulfonate. He also reported that as foam stabilizers they are more effective at lower use levels than N-isopropyllauramide or N,N-bis(2-hydroxyethyl)lauramide. Other investigators (94) have supported the prior work and have extended it to include alkylbis(2-hydroxyethyl)amine

Table 8. Relative Textile-Softening Efficiency

Compound	Relative softening efficiency[a]
bis(2-hydroxyethyl)"coco"amine[b] oxide	13
bis(2-hydroxyethyl) "tallow"amine[b] oxide	49
dimethyl"coco"amine oxide	21
methyl(dihydrogenated"tallow")amine oxide	49
1-(2-hydroxyethyl)-2-octadecylimidazoline oxide	75
1-(2-octadecylamidoethyl)-2-octadecylimidazoline oxide	49
1-(2-octadecylamidoethyl)-2-octadecylimidazolinium methyl sulfate	100

[a] Terry cloth swatches treated with agents ranked by feel by a panel of experts against a swatch treated with a standard quaternary textile softener arbitrarily rated as 100.

[b] See Amines, fatty.

One of the added benefits claimed for amine oxides is reduced irritancy of detergents (95) when amine oxides are incorporated. This work was based on amine oxides combined with alkylarenesulfonates. The same behavior was not observed with amine oxides and sodium lauryl sulfate.

oxides, as well as alkylmorpholine oxides, $RNCH_2CH_2OCH_2CH_2$. They have also shown that a measurable increase in softness can be obtained by rinsing fabrics with amine oxides, as shown in Table 8.

Thermal Stability of Amine Oxides. In the absence of solvents, most amine oxides decompose between 100 and 200°C. Two main reactions occur when amine oxides are subjected to thermal breakdown. These are *rearrangement*, sometimes called the Meisenheimer rearrangement, and *elimination*, at times referred to as the Cope elimination.

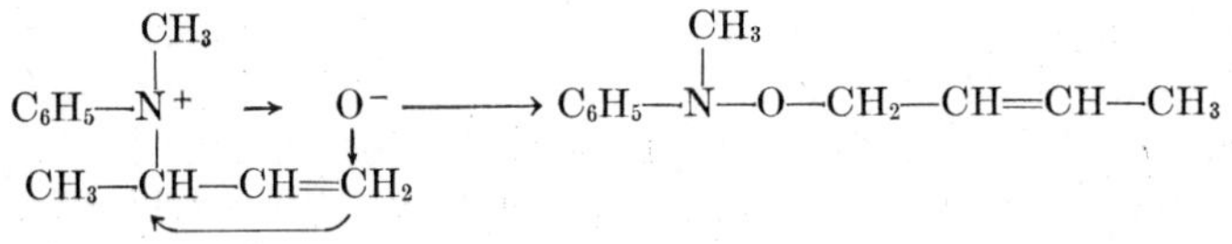

$$
\begin{array}{ccc}
CH_3 & & CH_3 \\
| & & | \\
C_6H_5-N^+ & \rightarrow \quad O^- & \longrightarrow \quad C_6H_5-N-O-CH_2-CH=CH-CH_3 \\
| & \downarrow & \\
CH_3-CH-CH=CH_2 & &
\end{array}
$$

If a benzylic or allylic group is present, or if there are no β hydrogen atoms, migration from nitrogen to oxygen takes place (25,26), as shown below.

The Meisenheimer rearrangement seems to proceed via cleavage to benzyl, allyl, and nitroxide radicals, followed by recombination (24,24a). This rearrangement is frequently carried out in the presence of a strong base, and the reaction is considered to be intramolecular (27). It has been established that the reaction rate is independent of the added alkali. The allylic shift observed is analogous to other allylic migrations. Dialkylallylamine oxides are stable in aqueous systems even in the presence of alkali due to hydration but, if freed of water, rearrange upon heating (25).

Elimination, leading to a disubstituted hydroxylamine, occurs in the absence of benzylic or allylic groups on the nitrogen atom and if there is at least one β hydrogen atom. This reaction, the Cope elimination (28), has been demonstrated to occur at room temperature in dimethyl sulfoxide or dimethylformamide (29).

$$
\begin{array}{c}
(CH_3)_2\,NCH_2CHR_2 \longrightarrow (CH_3)_2NOH + CH_2=CR_2 \\
\downarrow \\
O
\end{array}
$$

The Hofmann degradation of quaternary ammonium hydroxide leads to an olefin, a tertiary amine, and water. The elimination reaction of amine oxides may be viewed as an intramolecular Hofmann reaction and has been found useful for the preparation of olefins and dialkylhydroxylamines. The value of this reaction for the preparation of olefins is in the stability of the new double bond during pyrolysis. It does not usually migrate and conjugate with other unsaturation within the molecule (30), although specific instances of migration are recorded (28).

Aqueous solutions of aliphatic amine oxides are found to be very unstable in the presence of mild steel. It has been shown that ferrous salts are initiators for the decomposition of amine oxides to secondary amines and an aldehyde (31). The reaction has been shown to proceed by a free-radical mechanism. Trapping experiments with butadiene have demonstrated the presence of an amminium radical, $R_2\ddot{N}-\dot{C}HR$, as shown below. Tertiary amines are also obtained.

$$
\begin{array}{c}
O \\
\uparrow \\
R_2NCH_2R \xrightarrow[\;H^+\;]{Fe(II)} R_2\overset{+}{N}.CH_2R + H_2O + Fe(III)
\end{array}
$$

$$
R_2\overset{+}{N}.CH_2R \longrightarrow R_2\ddot{N}-\dot{C}HR + H^+
$$

$$R_2\ddot{N}\text{—CHR} \xrightarrow{\text{Fe(III)}} R_2\overset{+}{N}\text{=CHR} + \text{Fe(II)}$$

$$R_2\overset{+}{N}\text{=CHR} \xrightarrow{\text{H}_2\text{O}} R_2\overset{+}{N}\text{H}_2 + \text{RCHO}$$

In some instances it has been observed that both elimination and rearrangement take place (32). Thermal decomposition of amine oxide salts of strong acids leads to secondary amines and an aldehyde (4,33). In general, aromatic N-oxides demonstrate greater stability than aliphatic N-oxides.

Reduction or Deoxygenation. Amine oxides can be reduced to tertiary amines by a variety of reagents. Catalytic reducing agents include Raney nickel (34,34a,34b,35), Urushibara nickel (36), nickel formate (34a), and palladium (37). Electrolytic reduction of aliphatic and alkylarylamine oxides has also been reported (38).

Other reagents include powdered iron and acetic acid (39), tin and hydrochloric acid, sodium arsenite (40), phosphorus trichloride (41), and lead and ferrous oxalate (42). Ochiai (43) and his co-workers have also found that zinc in acid or alkaline medium, stannous chloride, ammonium sulfide, sodium thiosulfate, and sodium nitrite can be used as reducing agents. He also states (9) that sulfurous acid reduced aliphatic amine oxides at room temperature.

Phosphorus trichloride appears to be the most frequently used reagent; dioxane or dimethylformamide is sometimes used in place of chloroform as solvent.

$$R_3NO + PCl_3 \xrightarrow{\text{CHCl}_3} R_3N + POCl_3$$

Titanium trichloride has also been used as reducing agent, especially in an analytical procedure for both aromatic and aliphatic amine oxides (44).

$$R_3NO + 2\,Ti^{3+} + 2\,H^+ \longrightarrow R_3N + H_2O + 2\,Ti^{4+}$$

Alkylation. Methyl iodide reacts in the cold with trimethylamine oxide to form trimethylmethoxyammonium iodide (4). The same product is obtained by the reaction of trimethylhydroxylamine and methyl iodide (45). This shows the close relationship between the amine oxides and hydroxylamines.

$$(CH_3)_3NO + CH_3I \longrightarrow ((CH_3)_3NOCH_3)^+I^- \longleftarrow CH_3I + (CH_3)_2NOCH_3$$

Acylation (Polonvski Reaction). Aliphatic amine oxides react exothermically with acetic anhydride or acetyl chloride to yield N,N-dialkylacetamide and also an aldehyde (46a).

$$R_2(CH_3)NO + (CH_3CO)_2O \longrightarrow CH_3CONR_2 + CH_2O + CH_3CO_2H$$

The Polonovski reaction or transformation is also brought about by treatment with ferric ion (46) but the mechanism is uncertain. The expected reactions are shown below.

$$(CH_3)_3NO \xrightarrow{\text{Fe}^{3+}} (CH_3)_2NH + H_2CO$$

$$(CH_3)_3NO + H_2CO \longrightarrow (CH_3)_3N + HCO_2H$$

Reactions with SO₂ and SO₃, and Other Adducts. Lecher and Hardy (47) have isolated a reaction product of SO_2 with trimethylamine oxide and identified it as CH_3-$\overset{+}{N}OSO_2^-$ when the reaction is carried out in organic solvents. In the presence of water they found that SO_2 decomposed over 50% of the oxide to yield dimethylamine and formaldehyde. However, with triethylamine oxide in benzene, SO_2 produces triethylamine.

$$(C_2H_5)_3NO + SO_2 \longrightarrow (C_2H_5)_3NSO_3$$

$$(C_2H_5)_3NO + (C_2H_5)_3NSO_3 \longrightarrow (C_2H_5)_3NOSO_3 + (C_2H_5)_3N$$

Although the triethylamine oxide is a weak base in water, it can remove the SO_3 from the strongly basic triethylamine. This appears to show the powerful electron-donor characteristics of amine oxides, but the interpretation is clouded by the fact that precipitation occurs. Therefore one does not know whether, in fact, the amine or the oxide would be a stronger base toward SO_3 in solution. The action of SO_2 on aqueous amine oxides has been proposed as a method for preparing secondary amines.

With boron trifluoride, silicon tetrafluoride, and phosphorus trichloride in chloroform stable adducts with anhydrous trimethylamine oxide have been isolated (48).

Preparative Methods

The important reactions for preparing amine oxides include exhaustive alkylation of hydroxylamines (4,5), the reaction of tertiary amines with hydrogen peroxide, and the reaction of tertiary amines with ozone (49).

Laboratory Methods. *Ozonization.*

$$R_3N + O_3 \longrightarrow R_3N: \leftarrow O{=}O \overset{\overset{O^-}{|}}{{}^+} \longrightarrow [R_3\overset{+}{N}{-}O{-}O{-}O^-] \longrightarrow R_3N \rightarrow O + O_2$$

Ozone is passed through a dilute solution of tertiary amine in an appropriate solvent until the reaction is completed. Yields in excess of 50% of the desired amine oxide have been obtained.

Exhaustive Alkylation. Hydroxylamine is reacted with an excess of a short-chain alkyl iodide in an appropriate solvent. The *N*-dialkylhydroxylamine is isolated and further reacted with additional excess alkyl iodide. The resultant salt is treated with alkali to complete the conversion to amine oxides.

$$2\ RI + NH_2OH \longrightarrow [R_2NHOH]^+I^- + HI$$

$$R_2NOH + RI \longrightarrow [R_3NOH]^+I^- \xrightarrow{\text{alkali}} R_3N \rightarrow O + HI$$

Hydrogen Peroxide Oxidatian of Tertiary Amines (50). A tertiary amine in a solvent or mixed solvent, such as water or aqueous isopropyl alcohol, is reacted with an excess aqueous hydrogen peroxide at 60–70°C. The excess peroxide is destroyed when the reaction is complete. Amine oxides have been obtained by this procedure in yields better than 90%.

$$R_3N + H_2O_2 \longrightarrow R_3N \rightarrow O + H_2O$$

COMMERCIAL PRODUCTION PROCEDURES

Amine oxides of industrial importance are derived from several types of tertiary amines, including dimethylalkylamines and bis(2-hydroxyethyl)alkylamines. The alkyl chain varies from 8 to 20 carbon atoms and may or may not contain unsaturation. Most frequently the commercial amines are mixtures of these homologs.

The introduction of inexpensive α olefins and synthetic fatty alcohols (see Vol. 2, pp. 560–563), as well as improved procedures for reductive alkylation of long-chain amines, has made the commercialization of the oxides of these amines possible.

The classical procedure for obtaining dimethyl tertiary amines from primary amines was based on the Leuckart reaction (51) and was later modified by Eschweiler and Clark (52). This procedure, except for special needs, is not practical for the large-scale manufacture of tertiary amines.

$$RNH_2 + 2\ CH_2O + 2\ HCO_2H \longrightarrow RN(CH_3)_2 + 2\ CO_2 + 2\ H_2O$$

Reductive alkylation of primary amines with formaldehyde produces a variety of saturated and unsaturated dimethyl tertiary amines and methyldialkylamines (53).

$$RNH_2 + 2\ CH_2O \xrightarrow[\text{catalyst}]{H_2} RN(CH_3)_2 + 2\ H_2O$$

Another industrial procedure uses either alkyl chlorides or bromides and dimethylamine to produce the desired amine (54).

$$RX + (CH_3)_2NH + NaOH \longrightarrow RN(CH_3)_2 + NaX + H_2O$$

The alkyl halide may be obtained by the reaction of an alcohol with zinc chloride and hydrogen chloride or $SOCl_2$, PCl_5, or PCl_3.

The α olefins can be converted to normal terminal bromides via anti-Markownikoff addition with HBr. The by-product sodium bromide must be reconverted to HBr to make this procedure economically attractive.

The bis(2-hydroxyethyl)alkyl tertiary amines can be obtained from primary amines and ethylene oxide (without catalyst) or from bis(2-hydroxyethyl)amine (see Alkanolamines) and alkyl halides.

$$RNH_2 + \underset{\underset{O}{\diagdown\diagup}}{CH_2CH_2} \longrightarrow RN(CH_2CH_2OH)_2$$

$$RX + HN(CH_2CH_2OH)_2 + NaOH \longrightarrow RN(CH_2CH_2OH)_2 + NaX + H_2O$$

The second procedure is limited commercially to saturated alkyl derivatives.

Amination of alcohols with dimethylamine takes place at 250–300°C, at 200–300 atm, using a copper–chromite catalyst.

$$ROH + HN(CH_3)_2 \xrightarrow[\text{catalyst}]{H_2} RN(CH_3)_2 + H_2O$$

Dodecyl alcohol and dimethylamine are reported to give dimethyldodecylamine at 2000 psi and 400°C in 94% yield over a dehydration catalyst (55).

$$C_{12}H_{25}OH + HN(CH_3)_2 \xrightarrow{Al_2O_3} C_{12}H_{25}(CH_3)_2 + H_2O$$

Amination of long-chain alcohols with dimethylamine, although at one time practiced on an industrial scale, is now no longer used. One of the problems with this process, aside from high pressure and temperature, is the excessive loss of dimethylamine by disproportionation to mono- and trimethylamine.

A sodium alkyl sulfate reacts with dimethylamine in the presence of a strong aqueous base at temperatures up to 200°C to produce tertiary amines (55a).

$$ROSO_3Na + (CH_3)_2NH + NaOH \longrightarrow RN(CH_3)_2 + Na_2SO_4 + H_2O$$

The commercial process for the production of amine oxides uses hydrogen peroxide (35, 50, or 75%) as the oxidant. Less hazard is created by 35% hydrogen peroxide than by the higher concentrations, although they have also been used successfully.

Lake (56) and his co-workers have demonstrated that in aqueous systems 35% hydrogen peroxide gives a faster and more complete reaction than 70%. Hoh (57) states that the preferred procedure for oxidizing dimethyldodecylamine is to produce the amine oxide at 30–40% concentration in water. He further cautions to keep the water content as low as possible during the reaction, adding only sufficient water to keep the system fluid. Aqueous systems tend to gel during the course of the reaction.

Because hydrogen peroxide is sensitive to heavy metals and because the finished amine oxide decomposes rapidly in the presence of iron or iron salts, sequestering (chelating) agents are often added to minimize the problems of this type of contamination during industrial production. Copper, nickel, Monel, mild steel, etc, must be avoided for processing.

The following metal ions are listed in their order of importance in promoting the decomposition of hydrogen peroxide: $Cr > Mn > Ni > Cu > Fe$. It has been reported that many metals, such as iron, copper, or manganese, in concentrations as low as parts per billion, have shown a marked adverse effect on the stability of hydrogen peroxide (58).

The preferred materials of construction for piping, valves, and storage of hydrogen peroxide are certain aluminum alloys as first choice, and 316 stainless steel as second choice (59). The preferred materials of construction for reactors and storage tanks for amine oxide production are 316 stainless steel or glass (60). The reactor must be equipped with a means for providing good mixing, heating, and cooling. For good manufacturing practice open reactors are preferred.

A typical industrial preparation is as follows:

Charge	Pounds
dimethyltetradecylamine 98.4%, 6.0 moles	1475
hydrogen peroxide 35%, 6.6 moles	640
trisodium ethylenediaminetetraacetate	1.5
water	3225

The amine, water, and chelating agent are heated to 55–65°C with mixing. The hydrogen peroxide is then added over a period of 45–75 min while maintaining the same temperature range. After all the peroxide has been added, the temperature may be permitted to rise to 70–75°C and the mixture is digested at this temperature until the reaction is complete. The product is then cooled and removed from the reactor.

Economic Aspects

McCutcheon's (61) and *Chemical Week* (63) show fourteen manufacturers of amine oxides of which only one is a manufacturer of aromatic amine oxides. The largest manufacturer of amine oxides, Procter and Gamble, is not included in this listing as this company's production is for captive use only. There is no doubt that Procter and Gamble manufactures more amine oxides than all the remaining producers combined. It has been estimated that they probably produce over 80% of the total production in the United States.

It is very difficult to obtain accurate figures for the total domestic production of either the vendors or captive producers of these chemicals. In 1966 (62) it was reported that Procter and Gamble's annual production of amine oxides was about 20 million lb of 100% active material. In 1969 it has been estimated that the total market for both captive needs and merchant sales approached 30 million lb annually (on a 100% active basis). The aromatic amine oxides in this total are probably less than one percent.

The aromatic amine oxides sell for $2 to $10/lb at 98% purity. The bis(2-hydroxy-ethyl)alkylamine oxides sell for $0.65 to $1.25/lb in bulk based on 100% activity. The dimethylalkylamine oxides on the same basis sell for $0.70 to $1.10/lb.

Analysis and Specifications

Amine oxides can be determined by thin-layer chromatography (120), potentio-metric titrations (121), and gas chromatography (122). Of particular interest are analytical procedures for determining amine oxides in detergent formulations (123).

An analytical procedure used frequently for industrial aliphatic amine oxides was developed by Metcalfe (121). It requires a double titration with hydrochloric acid. The first analysis determines the total amine oxide and unreacted tertiary amine. In another sample the unreacted amine is then quaternized with an excess of CH_3I; titra-tion of this sample gives the amine oxide directly and the unreacted amine by difference.

Commercially available aliphatic amine oxides are of the following types: di-methylalkylamine oxides; bis(2-hydroxyethyl)alkylamine oxides; N-alkylmorpholine oxides, $RNCH_2CH_2OCH_2CH_2$; and N'-acyl-N,N-dimethyl-1,3-diaminopropane oxide,

$(CH_3)_2NCH_2CH_2CH_2NHCOR$.
$\downarrow$
O

The alkyl radicals include decyl, dodecyl, tetradecyl, hexadecyl, octadecyl, and oleyl, as well as mixtures derived from fatty acids from coconut oil and tallow.

The commercial aromatic amine oxides available are derivatives of pyridine, picolines (methylpyridines), 4-cyanopyridine, and 2,6-lutidine (2,6-dimethylpyridine).

Industrial specifications for these products vary from 20 to 100% active. Un-reactive amine in these products may be as high as 5% but, on the average, is less than 2% and with less than 0.5% free hydrogen peroxide. Solvent systems for these chem-icals are either water or aqueous 2-propanol, although some oxides are offered in non-polar solvents.

Health and Safety Factors

Aliphatic amine oxides, such as dimethylalkyl oxide and bis(2-hydroxyethyl)-alkylamine oxide, have been found to be practically nontoxic to slightly toxic (63a). LD_{50}'s are reported to range from 1.77 g/kg to 6.50 g/kg. The commercial concen-trated products are primary skin irritants, but only mildly irritating to the eye. At concentrations of 2% these products can be considered to be nonirritating to the skin or eye.

Uses

AROMATIC AMINE OXIDES

Although the aromatic amine oxides probably represent far less than 1% of the total product sold today, they have widely varying interesting potential uses, particu-larly in the pharmaceutical field. They have been reported to be useful as analgesics (64), antihistaminics (65), antitussives (66), diuretics (67), drug potentiators (68), sedatives and tranquilizers (69), and soporifics (70). Aromatic tertiary amine oxides have also proved to be biologically active, as shown by their potential use as anthelminthics (71), filaricides (72), fungicides (73), antiparasitics (74), antipathogenics (75), and amoebicides (76).

This class of compounds may also have some potential as anticancer agents (78) and is effective in the reduction of radioactive mortalities (77). Certain amine oxides probably function by reducing the number of enteric organisms causing the usual irradiation bacteremia (77a). Aromatic amine oxides have been suggested for control of agricultural pests, specifically as bactericides (79), fungicides (80), insecticides (81), nematocides (82), and disinfectants (83). The patent literature describes many other potential industrial uses.

Natural alkaloid amine oxides, which have not attained wide use, possess all the therapeutic and physiological values of the parent amine, but are much less toxic (84). In the treatment of Yoshida sarcoma the amine oxide of nitrogen mustards, $RN(CH_2-CH_2Cl)_2$, is only one-tenth as toxic as the parent amine (85).

Other examples of the less toxic effects of amine oxides have appeared in the patent literature. The N-oxide of sulfapyridazine has been found to be more soluble than the parent sulfur drug and, therefore, can be used with less danger of crystalluria (86). Certain piperazine oxides useful as filaricides are less toxic than the parent base (87). The N-oxides of a number of amines are reported as more effective and less toxic diuretics than the parent amines (88). It is also of interest to note that some inventors claim that the oxides of some tertiary aromatic amines give enhanced therapeutic value as analgesics, antihistaminics, and antitussive agents, as compared to the free amine (89).

ALIPHATIC AMINE OXIDES

In the late 1930s the surface activity of the long-chain aliphatic amine oxides (84) was observed, but appreciable commercial production was not developed until the late 1950s. However, these oxides have special functions that make them particularly attractive for many uses. The high dipole moment makes these compounds readily soluble in water and alcohol and only slightly soluble in nonpolar organic solvents, such as kerosene and mineral oil. A listing of some of the functions of amine oxides would include anti-irritancy in detergent formulations, antistatic activity, foam and foam stabilization, detergency, emolliency, viscosity builders, biodegradability, cloud-point depressants, lime-soap dispersants, and pigment dispersants.

Markets for the amine oxides have been found in detergent applications, specialty cleaning, cosmetics-finishing agents, paper coating and glazing, lubricating oils and greases, protective coatings, metal treating, electroplating, rubber products, and cellulosic man-made fibers. The major market for these amine oxides, probably over 95%, is in detergents and special cleaning preparations. The cosmetic market is probably the next largest outlet.

Detergents. Although amine oxides are reported to be biodegradable detergents, foam stabilizers, wetting agents, biocides, and anti-irritancy agents compatible with anionics, nearly twenty odd years elapsed after the disclosures by du Pont and I. G. Farben (90) before any attention was paid to these chemicals for household-detergent use. In the early 1960s a number of patents issued, dominated by Procter and Gamble (91,91a–c), covering the use of amine oxides in heavy- and light-duty liquid detergents, and for personal use as well.

Amine oxides are desirable in liquid lotions for personal use because they are claimed to combine the advantage of the synthetic detergents in not forming soap-curd-like precipitates in hard water, and that of soap by producing thick, dense lather. A further advantage claimed is that they leave the skin feeling lubricious, or smooth, but not oily (91a).

Liquid detergents have become the preferred detergent for household use. The difficulty in formulating a heavy-duty liquid product has been the problem of producing a homogeneous solution with sufficient detergent and builder to provide satisfactory performance. A builder, such as potassium pyrophosphate, complexes the ions of hard water which increases the level of detergency obtainable with surfactant. A standard formulation for incorporating enough of the constituents to make a homogeneous liquid includes one or more suds-builders, a hydrotrope, and a solvent. The use of amine oxides provides the means of preparing liquid detergents of reduced complexity by eliminating the suds-builder, solvent, and, in some cases, hydrotropes.

A heavy-duty liquid detergent formulation of this type is as follows (91b):

Ingredient	Percent by wt
dimethyldodecylamine oxide	19.0
tetrapotassium ethylenediaminetetraacetate	9.9
sodium silicate (SiO_2/Na_2O = 1.6)	5.0
water	66.1

One of the major advantages of amine oxides in dishwashing detergents is that they stabilize the foam in the presence of soil. A typical dishwashing liquid-detergent formulation is the following (91c):

Ingredient	Percent by wt
ammonium dodecylbenzenesulfonate	17.14
ammonium salt of sulfated nonylphenol condensed with 4 moles of ethylene oxide	11.87
bis(2-hydroxyethyl)dodecylamine oxide	6.00
ethyl alcohol	12.00
perfume	0.20
water and miscellaneous ingredients	52.90

Cosmetics. The detergent, foaming, antistatic, and antiseptic properties of amine oxides make these compounds of interest in cosmetics, particularly in shampoos and other hair-care products. Adsorption of surfactants by proteins has been noted as being a key property in the application of cosmetics to skin and hair (96). Surfactants adsorbed in the hair give body to fine hair, soften coarse hair, act as lubricants, and reduce static (106), thereby increasing manageability. Adsorption of these agents on the skin becomes important for formulation of barrier creams and detergent products in contact with the skin (97).

Amine oxides are effective in reduction of contact angle on the skin at approximately 10^{-4} molar concentration. This measurement is a rough indirect estimate of the substantivity of the surfactant on the substrate or, in other words, a measure of the tenacity with which the surfactant is held by the skin (98). Evidence of the recognition of these properties can be seen from the patents issued for these uses. Improved hair manageability in shampoos containing amine oxides has been reported (99).

Amine oxides have been used to improve dyeing of hair (100) as they are compatible with cationic dyes and do not react with them, but give a more intense color than when anionic agents are used. Formulations using amine oxides in shampoos, detergents, bubble baths, and shave creams have been published (23c, 101). Dimethyldodecylamine oxide and bis(2-hydroxyethyl)dodecylamine oxide are reported to be active ingredients in a cosmetic formulation for controlling dermal fungi and bacteria, such as *Clostridium perfringens*, *Streptococcus anaerobius*, and *Aspergillus niger* (110). A dentifrice preparation using amine oxides has also been disclosed (117).

Miscellaneous Applications. The unique character of aliphatic amine oxides has led to many other uses. The action of amine oxides as rust inhibitors and anti-icing gasoline additives has been patented and is used (102). Amine oxides are effective agents in the production of rayon by facilitating the drawing of the filament (103). The effect of adding the amine oxide to the viscose solution is to ease the problem of filtration and markedly reduce the surface tension, thereby increasing the filament-drawing capacity. Additional benefits found were lack of encrustation of the spinnerets and reduction of impurities in the precipitation bath. Dimethylcocoamine oxide has been shown to be effective for retarding dyeing of polyacrylonitrile fibers of the Orlon 42 type (104). In the drilling of oil and gas wells, amine oxides have been used as a foaming agent for the removal of drill cuttings (105).

Amine oxides are described as being useful in the polymerization of α olefins (107), esters of acrylic and methacrylic acid (108), and in ethylene–propylene polymerization (109), and as a polymerization inhibitor for styrene (111). They are used as gelling agents with clays for organic liquids (112), as a thixotropic agent for bituminous grout (113), and as a coagulant for silica in rubber (114). Several other uses of interest include amine oxides as the cationic emulsifier for bituminous-slurry seal (115), metal extractants by selective salt formation with the desired metallic anion (116), rocket-propulsion-fuel additives to promote smoother burning (118), and as an agent in electroplating baths (119).

New uses continue to be disclosed as more investigators become aware of the properties of amine oxides.

Bibliography

1. G. Merling, *Chem. Ber.* **25**, 3123 (1892).
2. W. Wernick and R. Wolffenstein, *Chem. Ber.* **31**, 1553 (1898).
3. E. Bamberger and F. Tschirner, *Chem. Ber.* **32**, 1882 (1899).
4. W. R. Dunstan and E. Goulding, *Trans. Chem. Soc.* **75**, 792 (1899).
5. W. R. Dunstan and E. Goulding, *J. Chem. Soc.* **75**, 1004 (1899).
6. N. V. Sidgewick, *The Organic Chemistry of Nitrogen*, 3rd ed., Clarenden Press, Oxford, 1966, p. 304.
7. C. C. J. Culvenor, *Rev. Pure Appl. Chem. (Australia)* **3**, 83 (1953).
8. E. Ochiai and M. Ikehara, *J. Pharm. Soc. Japan* **73**, 666 (1953); *Chem. Abstr.* **48**, 7014 (1954). O. Fernandez, *Farm. Nueva (Madrid)* **20**, 437–442, 487–496, 545–554, 603–608 (1955); *Chem. Abstr.* **50**, 4776 (1956). A. R. Katritsky, *Quart. Rev. (London)* **10**, 395 (1956). E. Hayashi et al., *Shizuoka Yakka Daigaku Kaigaku 5-Shunen Kinen Rombunshu* **1958**, 24–39: *Chem. Abstr.* **53**, 2243 (1959). M. Colonna, *Atti Accad. Nazl. Lincei, Rend Classe Sci. Fis. Mat. Nat.* **26**, 39–42 (1959); *Chem. Abstr.* **53**, 21929 (1959). D. V. Joffe and L. S. Efros, *Usp. Khim.* **30**, 1325–1351 (1961); *Chem. Abstr.* **57**, 11175 (1959). T. Kobuta, *Bunko Kenkyu* **10**, 83–106 (1962); *Chem. Abstr.* **57**, 16009 (1962).
9. P. A. A. Smith, *The Chemistry of Open-Chain Organic Nitrogen Compounds*, Vol. II, W. A. Benjamin, Inc., New York, 1966, pp. 21–28. E. Ochiai, *Aromatic Amine Oxides*, Elsevier Publishing Co., New York, 1967.

10. *Amine Oxides*, a bibliography, and *Amine Oxides*, a literature survey, Electrochemicals Dept., E. I. du Pont de Nemours & Co., Inc., Wilmington, Delaware, 1962 and 1963, resp.
11. H. S. French and C. M. Gens, *J. Am. Chem. Soc.* **59**, 2600 (1937).
12. J. Meisenheimer, *Chem. Ber.* **41**, 3966 (1908).
13. M. W. Lister and I. E. Sutton, *Trans. Faraday Soc.* **35**, 495 (1939).
14. F. Tokiwa and K. Ohki, *J. Phys. Chem.* **70**, 3437 (1966).
15. D. H. Kolp, R. G. Laughlin, F. P. Krause, and R. E. Zimmer, *J. Phys. Chem.* **67**, 51 (1963).
16. T. D. Stewart and S. Maeser, *J. Am. Chem. Soc.* **46**, 2583 (1924).
17. E. P. Linton, *J. Am. Chem. Soc.* **62**, 1945 (1940).
18. Paul Nylén, *Tidskr, Kjemi, Bergvesen Met.* **18**, 48 (1938); *Chem. Abstr.* **32**, 8888⁹ (1938).
19. E. S. Lutton, *J. Am. Oil Chemists' Soc.* **43**, 28 (1966).
20. K. D. Lawson and J. T. Flautt, *J. Phys. Chem.* **69**, 3204 (1965); *Ibid.*, **72**, 2066 (1968). K. D. Lawson, A. J. Mabis, and T. J. Flautt, *J. Phys. Chem.* **72**, 2058 (1968).
21. L. Benjamin, *J. Phys. Chem.* **68**, 3575 (1964).
22. K. W. Herrmann, *J. Phys. Chem.* **66**, 295 (1962).
23. B. H. Babu, P. K. S. Amma, and S. V. Rao, *Indian J. Technol.* **5**, 262 (1967).
23a. J. C. Harris, *Detergency Evaluation and Testing*, Interscience Publishers, Inc., New York, 1954.
23b. J. Ross and G. D. Miles, *Oil Soap* **18**, 99 (1941).
23c. *Ammonyx Tertiary Amine Oxides*, Onyx Chemical Co., Jersey City, N. J., 1967.
24. U. Schoellkopf and H. Schaeffer, *Ann. Chem.* 683, 42 (1965). J. P. Lorand, R. W. Brant, P. A. Samuel, E. O'Connell, and J. Zaro, *Tetrahedron Letters* **1969**, 4987.
24a. R. A. W. Johnstone, *Mechanisms of Molecular Migrations*, Vol. 2, Interscience Publishers, a div. of John Wiley & Sons, Inc., New York, 1969, p. 249.
25. J. Meisenheimer, *Chem. Ber.* 52, 413 (1919).
26. A. C. Cope and P. H. Towle, *J. Am. Chem. Soc.* **71**, 3423 (1949).
27. A. H. Wragg, T. S. Stevens, and D. M. Ostle, *J. Chem. Soc.* **1958**, 4057.
28. A. C. Cope, E. Ciganek, C. F. Howell, and E. E. Schweizer, *J. Am. Chem. Soc.* **82**, 4633 (1960).
29. A. C. Cope and E. R. Trumbull, in A. C. Cope, ed., *Organic Reactions*, Vol. 11, Interscience Publishers, a div. of John Wiley & Sons, Inc., New York, 1962, Chap. 5.
29. D. J. Cram and M. R. V. Sahyun, *J. Am. Chem. Soc.* **85**, 1263 (1963).
30. A. C. Cope and C. L. Bumgardner, *J. Am. Chem. Soc.* **79**, 960 (1957).
31. J. P. Ferris, R. D. Gerwe, and G. R. Gapski, *J. Am. Chem. Soc.* **89**, 5270 (1967).
32. A. C. Cope, T. T. Foster, and P. H. Towle, *J. Am. Chem. Soc.* **71**, 3929 (1949).
33. Ya. Ya. Dodonov, *J. Gen. Chem. USSR (Eng. Transl.)* **14**, 960–964 (1944); *Chem. Abstr.* **39**, 4612² (1945). J. Meisenheimer, *Chem. Ber.* **52**, 1667 (1919).
34. T. Ishii, *J. Pharm. Soc. Japan* **72**, 1315 (1952); *Chem. Abstr.* **47**, 12386d (1953).
34a. *Ibid.*, 1317 (1952); *Chem. Abstr.* **47**, 12386f (1953).
34b. E. Eisaku and H. Yamanaka, *Chem. Pharm. Bull. (Tokyo)* **6**, 323 (1958); *Chem. Abstr.* **53**, 375i (1959).
35. E. Hayashi, H. Yamanaka and K. Shimizu, *Chem. Pharm. Bull (Tokyo)* **6**, 323 (1958). II. Yamanaka, *Chem. Pharm. Bull. (Tokyo)* **7**, 158 (1959); *Ibid.*, **7**, 505 (1959).
36. E. Hayashi, H. Yamanaka, and Ch. Iijime, *J. Pharm. Soc. Japan* **80**, 839 (1960).
37. K. Bodendorf and B. Blinder, *Arch. Pharm.* **287**, 326 (1954).
38. Y. Date and H. Yamamoto, *Nippon Kagaku Zasshi* **86**, 674 (1965).
39. H. J. den Hertog and J. Overhoff, *Rec. Trav. Chim.* **69**, 468 (1950).
40. A. Guttman, *Chem. Ber.* **55**, 3011 (1922).
41. E. Ochiai, *J. Org. Chem.* **18**, 550 (1953).
42. R. A. Abramovitch and K. A. H. Adams, *Can. J. Chem.* **39**, 2134 (1961).
43. E. Ochiai and M. Katada, *J. Pharm. Soc. Japan* **63**, 186 (1943); *Ibid.*, **64**, 206 (1944). E. Ochiai and I. Suzuki, *J. Pharm. Soc. Japan* **67**, 141 (1947).
44. R. T. Brooks and P. D. Sternglanz, *Anal. Chem.* **31**, 561 (1959).
45. L. W. Jones and R. T. Major, *J. Am. Chem. Soc.* **50**, 2742 (1928).
46. J. Cymerman-Craig, F. P. Dower, A. N. Glazer, and E. C. Hornung, *J. Am. Chem. Soc.* **83**, 1871 (1961).
46a. M. Polonovski and M. Polonovski, *Bull. Soc. Chim. (France)* **39**, 1147 (1926).
47. H. Z. Lecher and W. B. Hardy, *J. Am. Chem. Soc.* **70**, 3789 (1948).
48. A. B. Burg and J. H. Bickerton, *J. Am. Chem. Soc.* **67**, 2261 (1945).

49. L. Horner, H. Schaefer, and W. Ludwig, *Chem. Ber.* **91**, 75 (1958).   U.S. Pat. 3,332,999 (July 25, 1967), L. C. Mitchell and T. H. Coffield (to Ethyl Corp.).   A. Maggiolo and S. Niegowski, "Ozone Chemistry and Technology," *Advan. Chem. Ser.* **21**, 202 (1959).

50. A. C. Cope and P. H. Towle, *J. Am. Chem. Soc.* **71**, 3423 (1949).

51. R. Leuckart, *Chem. Ber.* **18**, 2341 (1885).   R. Leuckart and E. Bach, *Chem. Ber.* **19**, 2128 (1886); *Ibid.,* **20**, 107 (1887).   R. Leuckart and H. Janssen, *Chem. Ber.* **22**, 1409 (1889).

52. W. Eschweiler, *Chem. Ber.* **38**, 880 (1905).   H. T. Clarke, H. B. Gillespie, and S. Z. Weisshauss, *J. Am. Chem. Soc.* **55**, 4571 (1933).

53. U.S. Pat. 3,136,819 (June 1964), S. H. Shapiro and F. Pilch (to Armour and Co.).

54. J. von Braun and R. Klas, *Chem. Ber.* **B73**, 1417 (1940).

55. U.S. Pat. 2,043,965 (June 1936), K. Smeykal (to I. G. Farben).

55a. U.S. Pat. 3,378,588 (April 1968), S. H. Shapiro (to Armour and Co.).

56. D. B. Lake and G. L. K. Hoh, *J. Am. Oil Chemists' Soc.* **40**, 628 (1963).

57. G. L. K. Hoh, D. O. Barlow, A. F. Chadwick, D. B. Lake, and S. R. Sheeran, *J. Am. Oil Chemists' Soc.* **40**, 268 (1963).

58. J. S. Reichert, *Paper, Comm. Chemical Assoc. Meeting*, Niagara Falls, N. Y., June 24, 1949.

59. *Concentrated Hydrogen Peroxide Properties, Uses, Storage and Handling*, SC:58–16, Shell Chemical Corporation, New York, 1958.   *Hydrogen Peroxide*, Manual SD-53, Manufacturing Chemists' Assoc., Inc., New York, 1969.

60. *Hydrogen Peroxide*, Becco Chemical Company, FMC Corporation, 1955.

61. *McCutcheon's Detergents and Emulsifiers*, John W. McCutcheon, Inc., Morristown, N. J., 1969.

62. *Oil, Paint Drug Reptr.* **195** (21), 32 (May 23, 1966).

63. "1970 Buyers Guide Issue, Chemicals," Part 2, *Chem. Week* **105** (Oct. 1969).

63a. *Toxicity Data for Aromox Amine Oxides*, Bulletin 68–7, Armour Industrial Chemical Co., Chicago, Ill., 1968.

64. U.S. Pats. 2,785,168 (March 12, 1957), and 2,862,968 (Dec. 2. 1958), B. D. Tiffany (to The Upjohn Co.).

65. U.S. Pat. 3,085,094 (April 9, 1963), C. F. Huebner (to Ciba Corp.).   U.S. Pat. 2,785,170 (March 12, 1957), F. Kagan (to The Upjohn Co.).   U.S. Pat. 2,785,171 (March 12, 1957), R. D. Birkenmeyer (to The Upjohn Co.).

66. U.S. Pat. 3,021,361 (Feb. 13, 1962), A. Pohland (to Eli Lilly Co.).   U.S. Pat. 3,065,261 (Nov. 20, 1962), V. C. Stephens (to Eli Lilly Co.).   U.S. Pat. 2,813,098 (Nov. 12, 1957), B. D. Tiffany (to The Upjohn Co.).

67. U.S. Pat. 2,868,785 (Jan. 13, 1959), D. A. Shepherd (to The Upjohn Co.).   U.S. Pat. 2,944,055 (July 5, 1960), W. C. Anthony (to The Upjohn Co.).

68. U.S. Pat. 2,966,487 (Dec. 27, 1960), James Jiu and G. P. Mueller (to G. D. Searle and Co.).   Brit. Pat. 793,227 (April 9, 1958) (to The Upjohn Co.).

69. U.S. Pat. 2,893,992 (July 7, 1962), L. H. Sternbach (to Hoffman-La Roche, Inc.).   U.S. Pat. 2,933,496 (April 19, 1960), R. V. Heinzelman, R. B. Moffett, and B. D. Aspergren (to The Upjohn Co.).   U.S. Pat. 2,789,113 (April 16, 1957), William I. Taylor (to Ciba Pharmaceutical Prod., Inc.).

70. U.S. Pat. 3,085,932 (April 16, 1963), S. H. Rubin and G. Zbinden (to Hoffmann-La Roche, Inc.).

71. U.S. Pats. 2,891,062 and 2,890,981 (June 16, 1959), J. J. Ursprung (to Chas. Pfizer and Co.).

72. U.S. Pat. 2,578,053 (Dec. 11, 1951), J. J. Denton and H. W. Stewart (to American Cyanamid Co.).

73. U.S. Pat. 2,742,393 (April 17, 1956), J. Bernstein, W. A. Lott, and K. A. Losee (to Olin Mathieson Chemical Corp.).   U.S. Pat. 2,742,476 (April 17, 1956), J. Bernstein and K. A. Losee (to Olin Matheson Chemical Corp.).   U.S. Pat. 2,921,073 (Jan. 12, 1960), L. H. Conover, A. R. English, and C. E. Larrabee (to Chas. Pfizer and Co.).   U.S. Pat. 2,995,562 (Aug. 8, 1961), D. E. Ames and T. F. Grey (to Parke Davis & Co.).

74. Brit. Pat. 829,728 (March 9, 1960), E. F. Elslager and F. H. Tendick (to Parke Davis & Co.).

75. U.S. Pat. 3,056,798 (Oct. 2, 1962), C. E. Maxwell, III, and P. N. Gordon (to Chas. Pfizer and Co.).

76. U.S. Pat. 2,644,000 (June 30, 1953), J. K. Landquist (to Imperial Chemical Ind.).

77. T. J. Haley, A. M. Flesher, and L. Mavis, *Nature* **192**, 1309 (1961); *Ibid.,* **195**, 1012 (1962).

77a. T. J. Haley, A. M. Flesher, R. Veomett, and J. Vincent, *Proc. Soc. Exptl. Biol. Med.* **96**, 579 (1957).

78. T. Itai and S. Natsume, *Chem. Pharm. Bull. (Tokyo)* **11,** 83, 342 (1963).

79. U.S. Pat. 2,809,971 (Oct. 15, 1957), J. Bernstein and K. A. Losee (to Olin Mathieson Chemical Corp.).

80. U.S. Pats. 2,922,790 (Jan. 26, 1960) and 2,940,978 (June 14, 1960), J. Rockett and B. B. Brown (to Olin Mathieson Chemical Corp.).

81. U.S. Pat. 2,814,636 (Nov. 26, 1957), M. A. Stahmann, T. C. Allen, J. E. Casida, and R. H. Chapman (to Wisconsin Alumni Research Foundation).

82. U.S. Pat. 2,986,493 (May 30, 1961), J. C. Overeem and J. D. Bijloo (to North American Philips).

83. U.S. Pat. 3,022,216 (1962), A. K. Sijpesteijn.

84. M. Polonovski, *Bull. Soc. Chim. Belges* **39,** 1 (1930).

85. I. Aiko, S. Owari, and M. Torigoe, *J. Pharm. Soc. Japan* **72,** 1297 (1962).

86. U.S. Pat. 2,881,166 (April 7, 1959), John V. Scudi, S. J. Childress, and D. B. Reisner (to Wallace and Tiernan, Inc.). Brit. Pat. 900,133 (1962), to American Cyanamid Co.

87. U.S. Pat. 2,578,053 (Dec. 11, 1951), J. J. Denton and H. W. Stewart (to American Cyanamid Co.).

88. U.S. Pat. 2,868,785 (Jan. 13, 1959), D. A. Shepherd (to The Upjohn Co.). U.S. Pat. 2,944,055 (July 5, 1960), W. C. Anthony (to The Upjohn Co.).

89. U.S. Pats, 2,813,097 and 2,813,098 (Nov. 12, 1957), B. D. Tiffany (to The Upjohn Co.). U.S. Pat. 2,820,034 (Jan. 14, 1958), F. Kagan (to The Upjohn Co.).

90. U.S. Pat. 2,159,967 (May 30, 1939), M. Engelmann (to E. I. du Pont de Nemours & Co., Inc.). U.S. Pat. 2,169,976 (Aug. 15, 1939), F. Guenther and K. Saftien (to I. G. Farbenind.).

91. So. African Pat. Appl. 5076 (Nov. 30, 1960), H. F. Drew and J. G. Voss (to The Procter and Gamble Co.). U.S. Pat. 3,085,982 (April 16, 1963), D. C. Steer and N. R. Smith (to The Procter and Gamble Co.).

91a. U.S. Pat. 2,999,068 (Sept. 5, 1961), W. Pilcher and S. L. Eaton (to The Procter and Gamble Co.).

91b. U.S. Pat. 3,001,945 (Sept. 26, 1961), H. F. Drew and R. E. Zimmer (to The Procter and Gamble Co.).

91c. Belg. Pat. 603,337 (May 21, 1962), H. M. Priestley and J. H. Wilson (to Unilever, Ltd.) (U.S. Pat. 3,387,430).

92. R. L. Huddleston and E. A. Setzkorn, *Soap Chem. Specialties* **41,** 63 (March 1965).

93. T. P. Matson, *J. Am. Oil Chemist's Soc.* **40,** 640 (1963).

94. E. Jungermann and M. E. Ginn, *Soap Chem. Specialties* **40,** 59 (Sept. 1964).

95. Can. Pat. 639,398 (April 3, 1962), H. F. Drew and J. G. Voss (to The Procter and Gamble Co.).

96. P. A. Lincoln, *J. Soc. Cosmetic Chemists* **8** (4), 222 (1957).

97. M. E. Ginn, C. M. Noyes, and E. Jungermann, *J. Colloid Interface Sci.* **26,** 146 (1968).

98. M. E. Ginn, *Cationic Surfactants*, Marcel Decker, New York, 1970, pp. 377–385.

99. U.S. Pat. 3,313,734 (April 11, 1967), E. W. Lang and H. W. McCune (to The Procter and Gamble Co.). Brit. Pat. 942,870 (Nov. 27, 1963), to The Procter and Gamble Co.

100. Ger. Pat. 1,229,249 (Nov. 24, 1966), R. Dohr and W. J. Kaiser (to Thera-Chemi, Chemisch-Therapeutisch).

101. *Aromox Amine Oxides*, Armour Industrial Chemical Co., Chicago, Ill., 1968.

102. U.S. Pat. 3,387,953 (June 11, 1968), R. A. Bouffard (to Esso Research & Engineering Co.). *Oil, Paint Drug Reptr.* **195** (19), 7 (May 12, 1969).

103. U.S. Pat. 3,114,592 (Dec. 17, 1963), E. Barthell, H. D. Schmidt-Neuhaus, and F. Hilgers (to Chemisch Fabrik Stockhausen & Cie).

104. S. Cohen and A. S. Endler, *Am. Dyestuff Reptr.* **47,** 325 (1958).

105. U.S. Pat. 3,303,896 (Feb. 14, 1967), C. C. Tillotson and K. E. James (to The Procter and Gamble Co.).

106. Philip Alexander, *Mfg. Chemist Aerosol News* **36** (6), 58 (June 1965).

107. U.S. Pat. 3,288,773 (Nov. 29, 1966), A. A. Harban and C. W. Moberly (to Phillips Petroleum Co.).

108. Brit. Pat. 787,693 (Dec. 11, 1957), to Rohm and Haas.

109. U.S. Pat. 3,405,107 (Dec. 11, 1968), D. N. Matthews and R. J. Kelly (to Uniroyal, Inc.).

110. Fr. Pat. M4264 (Aug. 8, 1964), to Soc. de Prod. Chim. et de Synthese.

111. Belg. Pat. 633,341 (Nov. 4, 1963), T. E. Deger and H. A. Albert (to Pennsalt Chemical Corp.).

112. U.S. Pat. 3,290,243 (Dec. 6, 1966), E. W. Sawyer (to Minerals and Chemicals Corp.).

113. Fr. Pat. 1,436,737 (April 29, 1966), to Soc. de Produits Chimiques d'Auby.

114. U.S. Pat. 2,663,650 (Dec. 22, 1953), R. K. Iler (to E. I. du Pont de Nemours & Co., Inc.).

115. Fr. Pat. 1,449,776 (Aug. 19, 1966), to Establissements Lassailly et Bichebois.

116. J. Kennedy and R. Perkins, *J. Inorg. Nucl. Chem.* **26** (9) 1601 (1964). D. F. Pepard, *Advan. Inorg. Chem. Radiochem.* **9,** 1 (1966).

117. Neth. Pat. 6,413,447 (June 21, 1965), to Colgate-Palmolive Co.

118. U.S. Pat. 3,196,607 (July 27, 1965), T. F. Doumani and C. S. Coe (to Union Oil Co.).

119. U.S. Pat. 3,296,105 (Jan. 3, 1967), J. D. Rushmore (to E. I. du Pont de Nemours & Co., Inc.).

120. J. R. Pelka and L. D. Metcalfe, *Anal. Chem.* **37** (4), 603 (1965).

121. L. D. Metcalfe, *Anal. Chem.* **34,** 1849 (1962).

122. T. H. Liddicoet and L. H. Smithson, *J. Am. Oil Chemists' Soc.* **42** (12), 1097 (1965).

123. H. Y. Lew, *J. Am. Oil Chemists' Soc.* **41** (4) 297 (1964). S. Tanimori, K. Abe, and H. Onzuka, *Kogyo Kagaku Zasshi* **69** (3), 464 (1966); *Chem. Abstr.* **65,** 15678f (1966). M. E. Turney and D. W. Cannel, *J. Am. Oil Chemists' Soc.* **42** (6), 544 (1965).

S. H. Shapiro
Armour Industrial Chemical Co.

AUTOMOBILE EXHAUST CONTROL

The recent concern about both direct and photochemical air pollution has hastened governmental and industrial efforts to combat this environmental problem. The early work in this area has been described by W. B. Innes and K. Tso (34) in the second edition of this encyclopedia.

This article summarizes the latest advances in the art of internal-engine design for minimal emissions, describes "add-on" control devices for internal-combustion engines (ICE), and reviews possible alternative solutions involving non-ICE power plants. It does not attempt to cover the present and proposed governmental regulations on automotive emission standards.

This article is divided into four parts: photochemical smog; the nature of automotive emissions; control methods for internal combustion engines; and unconventional power plants.

Photochemical Smog

Some effects of photochemical smog are eye irritation, respiratory discomfort, visibility reduction, atmospheric coloration, plant damage, and rubber cracking. Haagen-Smit (1) in 1952 first demonstrated that these characteristics could be simulated in fumigation chambers by irradiation of mixtures of hydrocarbons, HC, and nitrogen dioxide, NO_2, although at much higher concentrations than prevalent in the atmosphere of the city of Los Angeles. Subsequent studies established that the smog was associated with products of the reactions of hydrocarbons and nitrogen oxides with atmospheric oxygen under the action of sunlight. Hydrocarbons and nitric oxide, NO, are present in vehicular exhaust; carbon monoxide, which is also present in exhaust, has not been shown to play a role in photochemical smog (16). Haagen-Smit's findings stimulated numerous studies of laboratory-generated smog (2–15). Some of the important reaction products were shown to be nitrogen dioxide NO_2, ozone O_3, aldehydes, and peroxyacyl nitrates (PAN). Irradiation of diluted automobile exhaust also gives effects that simulate smog (11–13).

The mechanism by which hydrocarbons and NO produce secondary pollutants has been the subject of extensive research. Some general mechanistic features have been

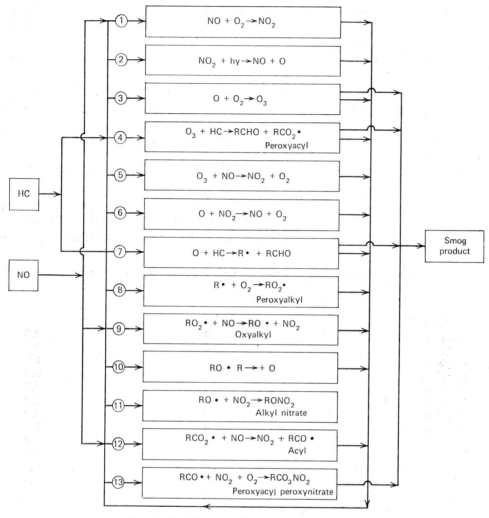

Fig. 1. Possible photochemical smog reactions.

determined, but a major portion of the reaction scheme is not understood (17). If a mixture of air and NO_x ($NO + NO_2$) is irradiated in the absence of hydrocarbons, the reactions are as follows:

$$NO_2 + light \rightarrow NO + O$$

$$O + O_2 \rightarrow O_3$$

$$O_3 + NO \rightarrow NO_2 + O_2$$

NO_2 is dissociated by light absorption into NO and atomic oxygen (O). In air, the predominant fate of O is to combine with oxygen, O_2, to form ozone, O_3, which rapidly oxidizes NO to NO_2. A photostationary state is achieved in which the O_3 concentration is determined by the ratio of the NO_2 and NO concentrations:

$$(O_3) = K(NO_2)/(NO)$$

The constant, K, is a function of light intensity and temperature. At equal concentration of NO_2 and NO, the O_3 concentration would be about 0.02 ppm (75°F and noon Los Angeles sunlight intensity) (18).

Addition of hydrocarbons to the above system causes NO-to-NO_2 conversion with consequent increase of the O_3 concentration. It has been suggested that hydrocarbons form radical intermediates by reaction with O or O_3 (17). The radicals oxidize NO to NO_2, and produce aldehydes, PAN, nitrates, and other products through a complex series of reactions. The scheme presented in Figure 1 includes some of the important reactions. Extensive reviews have been published detailing the current knowledge of the photochemical mechanisms of smog (18–23).

A number of conclusions pertinent to the control of automotive emissions have been drawn from these smog-chamber experiments. Various hydrocarbon species differ markedly in the extent to which they are effective in producing smog characteristics (23–27). Reactivity scales have been established to take account of these differences. Two such scales are shown in Table 1 (24–27). Both scales were constructed by mea-

Table 1. Relative Hydrocarbon Reactivity Scales Based on Eye Irritation

Hydrocarbon	EPA	GM[b]
C_1-C_5 paraffins	0	0
C_{6+} paraffins	0	0.5
acetylene	0	0
ethylene	5	1
propylene	6	3.9
1-olefins	6	2.5
internal olefins	6	1.8
diolefins	10	6.9
benzene	0	1
monalkylbenzenes	4	3.3[c]
(polyalkyl)benzenes	6	2.7
aromatic olefins	10[c]	8.3
aliphatic aldehydes	5[c]	2.0[c]
aromatic aldehydes	8[c]	8[c]

[a] A. P. Altshuller, *J. Air Pollution Control Assoc.* **16** (5), 257 (1966).
[b] General Motors data; J. M. Heuss and W. A. Glasson, *Environ. Sci. Technol.* **2** (12), 1109 (1968).
[c] Estimated (13).

suring eye-irritation threshold times when the particular hydrocarbon, mixed with NO_x and air, was photolyzed in a smog chamber. Similar scales have been obtained measuring olefin-photooxidation rates, NO-to-NO_2 conversion rates, ozone-production rates, oxidant production, PAN production, plant damage, and rubber cracking. The different criteria sometimes yield significant differences in reactivity scales.

Earlier smog-chamber experiments established formaldehyde, acrolein, and PAN as the major eye irritants (18). More recently, peroxybenzoyl nitrate (PBzN) (25) has been shown to be 200 times more potent as a lacrimator than formaldehyde. This discovery has elevated the index for aromatic compounds in the reactivity scales.

One conclusion from smog-chamber studies has been particularly relevant to the philosophy of exhaust-emission control. It is the concept that the most efficient route to smog alleviation may be a reduction of reactive hydrocarbon emission and that a reduction of NO might actually increase smog (26). In view of the importance of this

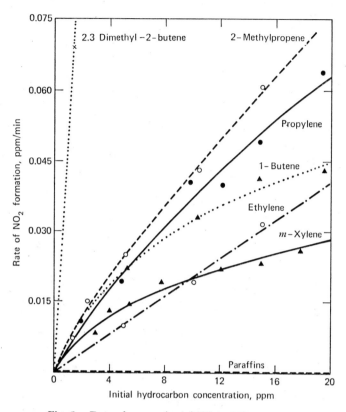

Fig. 2.   Rate of conversion of NO to NO₂.

idea, several of the studies that have been cited to argue its validity, and also some against it, will be discussed.   Compare Figure 2, in which the rate of conversion of NO to NO₂ was shown by Glasson and Tuesday (9) to exhibit a monotonic decrease as the initial HC concentration is decreased, with Figure 3, in which the rate of disappearance of olefin goes through a maximum as the initial NO is decreased.   Similar differences in behavior between hydrocarbons and NO were observed for production of ozone, aldehyde, and PAN (9).   This apparent inhibitory effect of NO has been independently confirmed by Altshuller et al., both for the static conditions used in the above experiments and for dynamic irradiations (10).   The same effect was also obtained in the EPA (Environmental Protection Agency) laboratories, using complex hydrocarbon mixtures from automotive exhaust in place of the simple mixtures which are discussed above (11–12).

Atmospheric measurements have also been interpreted as showing the NO inhibition effect.   Schuck, Pitts, and Wan have correlated the frequency of smoggy days with early morning concentrations of hydrocarbons and NO$_x$ and obtained the contour diagram presented in Figure 4 (28).   This confirms, in general, the laboratory studies of EPA but differs quantitatively in two important respects: (1) Schuck et al. use percent of days resulting in smog as the measure of severity while the EPA analysis uses eye irritation, and (2) the concentration range of the atmospheric data is below the lowest values studied in the laboratory experiments.   From their analysis, Schuck et al. conclude that a 50% reduction in hydrocarbons would result in a 50% reduction

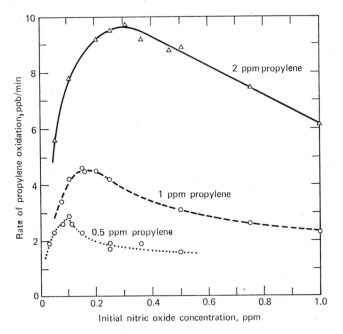

Fig. 3. Rate of disappearance of olefin.

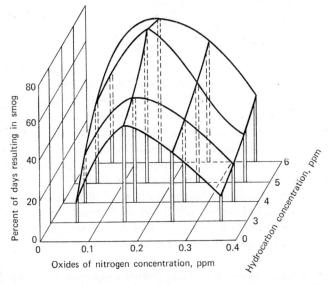

Fig. 4. The frequency of smoggy days correlated with early-morning concentrations of hydrocarbons.

in the number of "smoggy" days, while a 50% reduction in oxides of nitrogen would have no effect.

Hamming and Dickinson (29) have come to the opposite conclusion based on an analysis of a number of studies of eye irritation in a smog chamber. They concluded that a slight to moderate reduction of automotive hydrocarbon emissions may lead to worsened smog conditions while reduction in emission of oxides of nitrogen can only improve the situation.   A point of departure in Hamming and Dickinson's analysis is that they argue that there are two eye irritation maxima, one occurring early in the irradiation, associated with the NO_2 maximum, and the other at a later stage of the irradiation, associated with the accumulation of products such as ozone.   They feel that the early maximum is a more important index of smog in downtown Los Angeles than the more commonly used index based on product accumulation.   Nicksic et al. (31) have analyzed the same data as Hamming and Dickinson and concluded that there was no reason to change the State of California's abatement policy of that time of controlling only hydrocarbons.   Thus, there is a basis for disagreement about the control of nitrogen oxides.   The majority view remains that moderate control of NO_x does not alleviate smog symptoms and that extreme NO control is necessary to have a beneficial effect.

In spite of a large body of laboratory data that has been collected with respect to photochemical smog, a number of important questions about the applicability of the laboratory studies to the atmosphere have not yet been resolved.   One important problem has been that the levels of known eye irritants needed to produce a response in chamber studies is always much higher than observed in atmospheric eye irritation. The discovery of PBzN suggests that this compound, as well as possibly others, although present in the atmosphere in nonmeasurable amounts, may be more important than the measurable irritants, formaldehyde, acrolein, and PAN.   Another serious question has been the poor mass balance obtained for NO_x in practically all of the work; as much as 70% of the NO_x has sometimes been unaccounted for among the products. Recently Gay and Bufalini (32) have reported that nearly all of the NO can be deposited on the reactor walls as nitrate (possibly nitric acid), by irradiation of ethylene–NO mixtures.   The removal of a substantial fraction of the NO_x from this system should have a serious effect both on the chemistry and on the location of the NO_x maximum. In addition, Los Angeles atmospheric aerosols have been revealed by recent analyses to differ chemically from the aerosols of other cities (33).   Most urban aerosols are composed primarily of inorganic sulfates, but Los Angeles aerosols contain about as much nitrate as sulfate.   This important nitrogen-containing atmospheric product would be completely missed in laboratory experiments because the walls of smog chambers tend to prevent significant aerosol formation.   Perhaps the most perplexing question is why a noticeable smog alleviation has not been observed in Los Angeles.   According to the 1969 Los Angeles County Air Pollution Control District Profile, emission controls have reduced total hydrocarbons from motor vehicle sources to the 1955 level (30). Furthermore, controls applied to stationary sources have effectively reduced total hydrocarbon emissions into the Los Angeles basin even further.   Also, on the basis of the NO inhibition argument, an additional smog reduction would have been expected, since the ambient NO_x levels have been increased about twofold over the 1955 level. Yet, no significant smog alleviation has been observed.   Thus, the experience in Los Angeles seems to run counter to the view that a decrease in hydrocarbons and an increase in NO_x would be the most effective means of smog abatement.

Implementation of projected Federal standards from automobiles (hydrocarbons 0.5 g/mile and NO_x 0.9 g/mile in 1975) would result in an emission reduction of 95% for hydrocarbons and 80% for NO_x, compared to precontrol vehicles.   This should produce rapid and substantial smog abatement, whichever side of the preceding controversy is correct, provided that stationary sources are controlled to a similar degree. This simultaneous tightening of both NO_x and hydrocarbon standards, however, greatly complicates the technical problems involved in the reduction of automotive emissions, since the conditions required for control of nitrogen oxides could increase hydrocarbons and vice versa.

Nature of Automotive Emissions

The general composition of automobile pollutants has been outlined earlier (34). However, additional and more comprehensive studies have further defined and quantified these pollutants while proposing mechanisms for their formation. Since essentially complete control of crankcase emissions has been reported (34), it will not be discussed again. Evaporative and exhaust emissions have been reduced significantly, but additional control is required based on recent legislative action.

Evaporative Losses. The photochemical potential of evaporative loss is almost completely dependent on the volatility of the fuel and its light olefin composition, as shown in Table 2 (35), and as determined experimentally by many investigators (35–41).

Table 2. Effect of Fuel Composition on Photochemical Reactivity of Evaporative Emission (38)

RVP,[a] psi	Fuel classification	Evaporative reactivity[b]
13.0	higher volatility	20.9
10.0	commercial reference	13.7
7.9	reduced volatility	6.7
5.3	low volatility	2.6
10.3	no C_3-C_5 olefins	5.9
10.4	no C_3-C_7 olefins	6.0

[a] Reid vapor pressure (ASTM D 323).
[b] Formation rate of NO.

The overall effects of the fuel changes may be summarized as follows: (*1*) Reduced fuel volatility, while maintaining acceptable driveability (36), will reduce evaporative photochemical potential by from 50 to 80% (35–39, 41–42) and will increase exhaust HC reactivity from 5 to 11% (35,38–39,41); (*2*) replacement of light olefins by paraffins will reduce evaporative reactivity by from 35 to 85% (35,37–39,41) and will reduce exhaust hydrocarbon reactivity by from 10 to 20% (35, 38–39); and (*3*) control of evaporative emission reactivity by fuel changes could cost the average motorist from $1.60 to 11.00 a year, depending on the type and amount of fuel changes made (43,44).

Exhaust Emissions. Probably the majority of exhaust-emission formation and composition studies have dealt with the hydrocarbons (15,26,45,48–50,53–57). The hydrocarbon emissions attributable to wall quenching, low-speed operation, deceleration conditions, faulty ignition, and exhaust-valve leakage have already been stated (34). However, many other aspects of hydrocarbon formation have been studied.

Early work dealing with the effects of air-fuel ratio and spark timing on hydrocarbon emission employed both nondispersive infrared (NDIR) and flame ionization detector (FID) hydrocarbon analysis (45). The NDIR analysis compares the infrared absorbtion characteristics of the exhaust sample to a reference sample of normal hexane by means of the differential pressure in a detector cell which is dependent on the amount of infrared radiation passing through the sample and reference cells (47). Therefore,

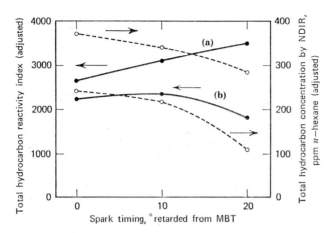

Fig. 5. Effect of spark timing (single-cylinder engine) on reactivity index and concentration measured by infrared analyzer at (**a**) a lean ratio of air:fuel = 16.0:1; and (**b**) a rich ratio of air:fuel = 13.0:1.

NDIR hydrocarbon analysis measures those hydrocarbons which have IR absorption spectra similar to that of normal hexane, or more specifically, the paraffins. On the other hand, the flame ionization detector burns the exhaust sample in a hydrogen–nitrogen–air flame and electronically measures the carbon ions formed from all C—H bonds (48). When the instrument is optimized according to the recommendations of the manufacturer, it registers total carbon. Thus, the ratio total hydrocarbon to NDIR hydrocarbon is greater than one. The standards stated in the Federal Register assume that this ratio is 1.8 for all cases, so that total hydrocarbon emissions equal NDIR hydrocarbon × 1.8. However, as more data have been generated, it has been shown that the FID/NDIR ratio is dependent on fuel type, spark timing, and A/F (air to fuel) ratio (46). This ratio becomes important when applying the present emission standards derived with NDIR to future emission testing with FID.

Retarding the spark timing from MBT (minimum spark advance for best torque) has been known and used to reduce hydrocarbon emissions for many years (46). However, experiments on single-cylinder engines (50) have shown that while NDIR hydrocarbon emissions are reduced by retarding spark timing, the photochemical reactivity of the exhaust hydrocarbons (at a 13:1 A/F ratio) is increased (Fig. 5). At an A/F ratio of 16:1, more typical of today's vehicles, the NDIR hydrocarbon is reduced drastically while the reactivity remains almost unchanged (Fig. 5). An increase in mass flow also accompanies retarded spark.

The hydrocarbon wall-quenching theory (34) has been further documented by a series of tests with varying surface-to-volume ratios (49). It has been found that an important factor is the volume of the "crevice" that exists in and around the top piston ring. As the crevice volume is reduced, hydrocarbon emissions are also reduced. This effect is compounded by a decrease in exhaust hydrocarbon accompanying an increase in blow-by (leakage of the gases in the combustion past the piston ring). It is believed that unburned hydrocarbons may be trapped in the piston-bore-ring area and that both gap location and blow-by flow-rate control the amount of the unburned hydrocarbon exhausted.

Carbon monoxide formation is only a function of equivalence ratio. See Figure 6 (51). The use of a large, heated fuel-air mixing chamber (vapor tank) on a multi-

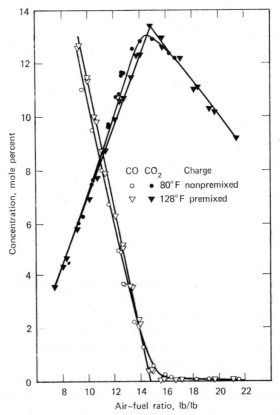

Fig. 6. CO and CO₂ concentration vs air:fuel ratio for premixed and nonpremixed charges (51).

cylinder engine to obtain a completely homogeneous charge approaches the theoretical composition of CO and CO₂ exhaust. However, the use of a conventional carburetor–manifold system and its inherent maldistribution does not approach theoretical CO and CO₂ since each cylinder is operating at a different equivalence ratio and also at leaner than stoichiometric conditions. With perfect distribution from a vapor tank, the CO never exceeds 0.5 mole %. The conventional carbureted engine, with also leaner than stoichiometry, acceleration pump, power valve, and A/F maldistribution, seldom has CO as low as 0.5 mole %.

Formation of oxides of nitrogen is a much more complicated mechanism than that for either hydrocarbon or CO. Historically, it has been postulated that the NO concentration in engine exhaust was the equilibrium value at the peak combustion temperature. Present thinking is that NO is primarily formed in postflame gases (57). This debate and still unresolved issues may be emphasized by comparing the conclusions drawn in 1966 (52) and 1969 (57) concerning the formation of NO$_x$.

1966 Conclusions:

1. NO is formed in appreciable quantity only in a flame front.

2. A limited amount of NO decomposition occurs in the postflame period; this decomposition is stopped, presumably due to recombination of radicals.

3. The observed concentration of NO in engine exhaust is an average of the combustion-chamber concentrations, which vary with respect to both time and position.

1969 Conclusions:

1. Both the formation and decomposition of NO in the postflame gases are rate limited at the conditions under which engines normally operate.

2. At least in the lean case, the NO formed in the flame front is negligible.

3. The state of the burned gas is not uniform; a substantial temperature gradient, and hence a gradient of NO concentration, exists behind the flame front.

About the only point of agreement of these two studies is that NO_x concentration in the combustion chamber is not uniform. Another point of agreement, although not mentioned specifically in both studies, is that methods used to reduce peak temperature, flame speed, and/or duration of the postflame front, such as exhaust-gas recirculation (EGR), spark retard, extreme richness or leanness, and addition of other inert material, will reduce NO_x emissions.

Effect of Lead Additives on Operation and Emissions. Early studies were conducted to determine the effect of tetraethyllead (TEL) on fuel antiknock quality and to determine the nature of particulate emissions which may be attributed to TEL (58). However, since about 1965, a new question has arisen: What is the effect of stabilized leaded engine deposits on exhaust hydrocarbon emissions? It has been found that the exhaust hydrocarbons are greater with stabilized leaded engine deposits than with unleaded deposits (59,60,62). Generally, this difference is reported to be significant, although one investigator questions its significance (59).

The effect of mileage-accumulation rate on the TEL hydrocarbon effect has been declared to be important by one investigator (63) although another (62) considers it to have no bearing.

The aromatic content of the fuel and its effects on deposits have also been shown to increase exhaust hydrocarbons after a mild duty deposit schedule (61).

Control Methods for Exhaust Emissions

INTERNAL CONTROLS ON ICE

Most modern vehicles (1969–1970) have been modified to control emissions within the engine itself. These modifications include the following: leaner carburetion for more complete combustion (64–69), redesigned chokes for less enrichment at the start-up, tighter idle-adjustment tolerance, and retarded spark timing (65). Combustion chambers have been redesigned for lower-quench areas (70,72) and intake manifold design has emphasized F/A distributional quality (70,72). Reductions in nitric oxide emission can be made with retarded spark timing if emissions are the only criteria (51). On the other hand, retarding the spark timing lessens the fuel economy and worsens the driveability.

Another method (not presently being used) to control nitric oxide formation in the combustion chamber is to dilute the intake charge with inert material. The effect is twofold; it reduces both the peak combustion temperature and the flame speed. The reduction of peak combustion temperature is attributed to both the addition of a heat sink (the inert material) and the effect of reduced flame speed.

The use of exhaust gas as a diluent has been briefly described in Vol. 2 under Automobile exhaust control. Theoretical studies have shown a potential control of 95% NO_x at 1.1 A/F equivalence ratio by recycle of 30% of the exhaust (76). Actual vehicle studies (74,75) have shown that equivalent NO control is possible. To date, the use of EGR (exhaust gas recirculation) on a vehicle requires valves to turn off

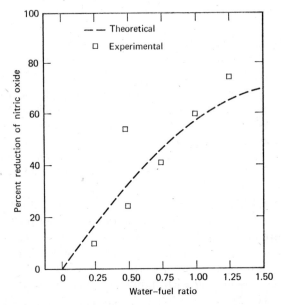

Fig. 7. Experimental and theoretical reduction of nitric oxide with water injection; fuel-air equivalence ratio = 1.0 (71).

EGR at idle, at wide open throttle, and under choke conditions to maintain satisfactory vehicle performance. The effects of EGR on engine and lubricant life are presently being evaluated.

Both theoretical and experimental studies have indicated the potential benefit of injection of water into the inlet manifold to control NO_x formation (Fig. 7) (73). The maximum benefit is occuring at approximately 1.5 lb of water per pound of fuel. This necessitates a large supply of water and the associated problems of antifreeze compounds, mixing, and metering. In general, it is felt that water injection is not a practical solution to the NO_x problem.

Operating with a large amount of excess air (approximately 1.3 A/F equivalence ratio) also reduced the NO_x formation substantially. This technique avoids the metering problems associated with EGR and water addition. The major problem associated with this lean-burn approach is the narrow tolerance between unsatisfactory NO_x emissions and the lean combustability limit.

EXTERNAL CONTROLS ON ICE

Devices which control pollutants after they leave the combustion chamber are discussed in this section, specifically, the limited application of air-injection systems on production vehicles, the potential of future large-volume thermal manifolds, and the present state of the art in catalytic development for exhaust control.

THERMAL REACTORS

One of the first attempts to control the emission exhaust of hydrocarbon and CO from vehicles used a positive displacement air pump to inject secondary air into each exhaust port (80). This system added air in conjunction with carburetion richer than stoichiometric. It also had a retarded spark timing for greater heat rejection and was

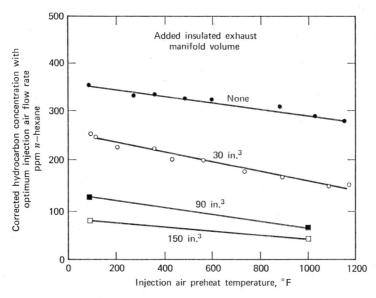

Fig. 8. Effect of injection-air preheating on hydrocarbon concentration (77).

quite effective for the control of hydrocarbon and CO. This system was used on some vehicles in California in 1966. The design problems inherent with this approach include: the need for closer carburetor and ignition tolerances, for an antibackfire valve, and for a check valve to protect the air pump from exhaust-gas backflow during high-speed operation. For these and other reasons, this system has been replaced by the internal-engine modification system whenever possible. As technology begins to solve these associated problems, air injection with larger-volume exhaust systems may become more feasible. There has been much activity in the design and development of exhaust manifold reactors in recent years (77–81,98). Most studies have utilized rich carburetion, A/F = 11–13:1(lb/lb), with secondary air. Early attempts evaluated the effect of manifold volume, insulation, and secondary air temperature on emission performance (Fig. 8) (77). Computers have been used to predict the thermal behavior of reactors with a series of radiation shields surrounding the inner core (78). These studies have led to shielded exhaust manifold reactors, such as the radiation shield shown in Figure 9 (79). Typical operation temperatures of an efficient thermal reactor during a Federal Emission Test are shown in Figure 10 (79). Considering the normal operating temperature of 1650–1800°F for efficient hydrocarbon and CO control, excursions into temperature regions beyond the physical limits of the reactor materials are of prime concern. Present studies are using secondary air shut-off as a means to regulate reactor-core temperatures during high-speed or high-power modes. A problem yet to be solved is localized combustion which may take place within the reactor during engine-misfire conditions.

Conservation of thermal energy of the exhaust is an important factor in building an efficient reactor. Radiation shielding, insulation, and preheated secondary air have been used to improve reactor performance. Another method is the addition of exhaust port liners to conserve sensible heat. Port liners, either solid or with a matrix of secondary air holes (transpiration-cooling principle), have proved to be effective in further reduction of CO emissions (79).

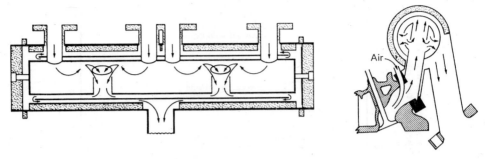

Fig. 9. Shielded exhaust manifold reactor (79).

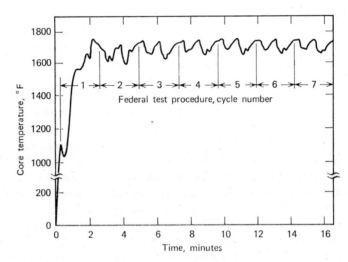

Fig. 10. Reactor-core temperature during Federal test procedure (79).

CATALYTIC TREATMENT

A review of the possible catalytic reactions and a summary of possible catalyst have been reported earlier (34). Catalytic processes comprise a number of consecutive elementary acts involving both breaking and formation of reactant molecule bonds and electron transfers between the reactant molecules and the catalyst. Consequently, the catalytic process is dependent on the electronic properties of the catalytic surface (87). The stability of the valence state of the active catalytic material in automotive exhaust gas thus becomes an important criterion. Before continuing the discussion on catalyst development, a review of present catalyst converters is in order.

Catalyst Converter Design. A large number of early converter designs have been studied and reported (83). In recent years, a more selective assortment of converters has been chosen as possible solution.

The radial-flow converter (Fig. 11) has a fairly large inlet cross-sectional area with an expanding cross section as the gas flows through the bed. This design has minimal back-pressure due to the large cross section and thin catalyst bed even though the entry- and exitflow pattern is not optimum for low pressure drops. Physical design of the converter and varying thermal expansion rates of the components are problem areas with this design.

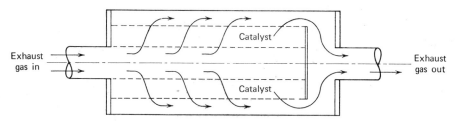

Fig. 11.   Radial-flow catalyst converter.

The downflow converter (Fig. 12) normally has a sloped bed with a large and constant cross-sectional area. The back pressure, which is usually low, depends on the bed depth, cross-sectional area, and entrance and exit design.

The axialflow converter (Fig. 13) is the outgrowth of a computer simulation of catalytic performance during warm-up testing, developed in an attempt to optimize efficiency. The simplicity of the design and good performance are two merits of this converter (96,97).

Ceramic honeycombs and coated metal mesh have also been developed for use as a support material in an axialflow-type converter system.

Hydrocarbon and CO Oxidation Catalysts. The effects of surface area, space velocity, catalyst temperature, and catalyst material have been discussed previously (34). The most recent programs have been conducted to evaluate and improve catalyst life with both leaded and unleaded fuel (83–85,88).

In the early days of emission control (1955–1959), the reduction of exhaust hydrocarbons was the prime requirement. The early catalysts studied (eg vanadium pentoxide) were specifically chosen for their selectivity for hydrocarbon oxidation over CO. This mitigated a potential overtemperature condition inherent with oxidation of large quantities of CO. Later the control of CO was also deemed necessary by governmental agencies. Development of catalysts continued and many good oxidation catalysts were evaluated. The present regulatory task is to control hydrocarbon, CO, and NO_x and the present engineering goal is a catalyst to control hydrocarbon, CO, and NO_x simultaneously. The recent move to unleaded fuel makes catalysts far more attractive.

The effect of the TEL content of a fuel on the durability of a vanadium, copper, and paladium catalyst has been investigated (85). Radial-flow converters were installed on near-production vehicles which were driven for 18,000 miles with four levels of fuel TEL content. Catalyst hydrocarbon efficiency was affected by both mileage and fuel TEL content as shown in Figures 14 and 15. It is believed that catalysts operating at higher temperatures with low fuel TEL contents account for the decrease in hydrocarbon efficiency as shown in Figure 15. Carbon monoxide conversion efficiency was almost independent of fuel TEL content (Fig. 16). This study also revealed that the oxidation selectivity for photochemically reactive compounds was destroyed by leaded fuel in 12,000 miles and remained almost constant for the unleaded fuel.

A spherical precious-metal catalyst has been evaluated in a downflow converter for a 50,000-mile stretch of light-duty operation followed by a 18,000-mile high-speed, rough-road test (84). This mileage-accumulation and emission testing was taken on nonleaded fuel except for one erroneous addition of leaded fuel at 38,500 miles. A tetraethyllead analysis taken after this fill showed an average content of 0.5 ml/gal

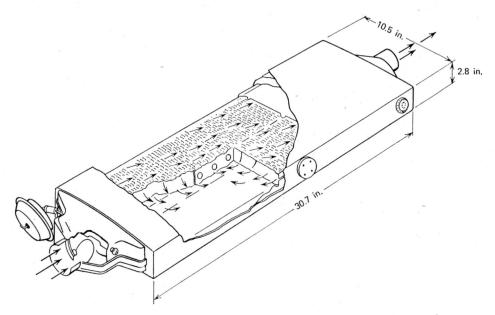

Fig. 12. Cutaway view of a downflow catalyst converter (34).

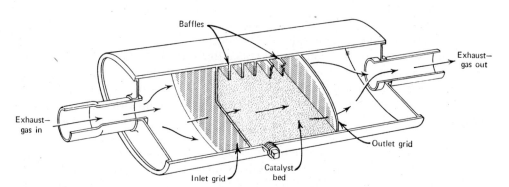

Fig. 13. Axialflow catalyst converter.

of fuel in the tank. The hot-cycle emission efficiencies show almost no depreciation of CO control over the 68,000 total miles accumulated (Fig. 17).

In an attempt to understand catalytic reactions better, transport equations have been used to predict temperatures within a catalyst pellet (88). These studies have shown that the maximum temperature within a catalyst pellet may be higher than the adiabatic flame temperature during transient conditions. This estimation is based on both the sensible heat input and the kinetic heat released at the site in question.

The development of an alumina-coated steel mesh to be used as a catalyst support (89) opened to door for "unitized" catalyst packages. A series of screening tests showed that copper chromite on this support was most active, but that vanadium was more resistant to lead poisoning. For a given catalyst volume, the alumina-coated mesh was better than the more typical spherical alumina support, as shown in Table 3.

Catalysts for NO$_x$ Control. Recent NO$_x$ catalyst studies have attempted to define the mechanisms leading to control of nitric oxide emissions from high-temperature com-

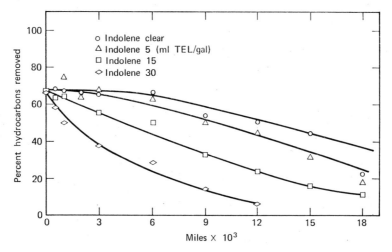

Fig. 14. Catalyst efficiency: cold start and NDIR hydrocarbon data, average of two vehicles.

Table 3. Comparison of Cartridges with Spheroidal Catalysts (89)[a]

Catalyst	Support	Hydrocarbon removal at 510°C, %		Wt change: gain (+), loss(−), g
		Initial	17 hr	
V_2O_5	Al_2O_3 on mesh	65	40	6
V_2O_5	spheroidal Al_2O_3	21	9	−2
$CuO.CuCr_2O_4$	Al_2O_3 on mesh	70	24	6
$CuO.CuCr_2O_4$	spheroidal Al_2O_3	45		−32

[a] Volume of catalyst, 310 cc.

bustion sources. Chemisorption of the NO molecule is a preliminary step in its catalytic conversion. Seven types of bonds have been proposed during NO chemisorption. Although a detailed discussion of this subject will not be presented here, two points are worthy of mention: (1) bonding of the NO molecule to an active site does not weaken the N—O bond in most cases, and (2) the bonding is usually through the nitrogen end of the molecule.

The heterogeneous decomposition of NO has been postulated as a possible control mechanism (34). However, many investigations of the catalytic decomposition of nitric oxide, as reported by Shelef (90), gave reaction-rate orders ranging from 0 to 2. It must be remembered that the majority of these investigators did not allow for interference in the surface reactions due to the transport phenomenon. There has been much debate relating to the practicality of NO decomposition. In an attempt to clarify this, Shelef has screened a large number of decomposition catalysts and concluded that: (1) the rate constants of all catalysts tested with one exception are unity; (2) the rate constant for a commercial noble-metal catalyst is 0.5; and (3) all catalysts tested have specific NO decomposition ratios far too low to be of practical use (91).

The catalytic reduction of nitric oxide has been studied intensively, due largely to the unpromising results of the decomposition studies and also to the variety and amount of reducing agents available in automobile-exhaust gas. The majority of these studies used a stoichiometric excess of reducing agents with respect to the NO and O_2

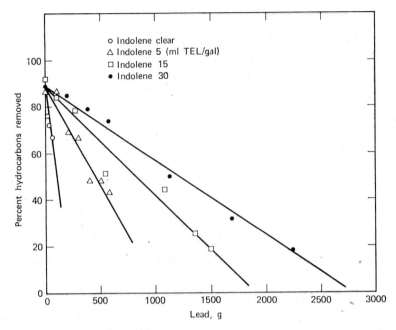

Fig. 15. Effect of lead consumed on catalyst efficiency; cruise 30, for fuels with varying TEL content, FID data (85).

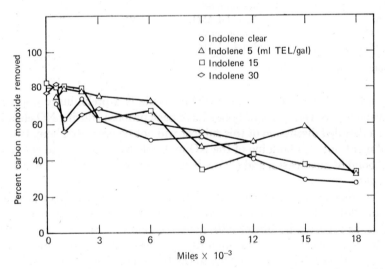

Fig. 16. Catalyst efficiency: cold start and carbon monoxide data, average of two vehicles (85).

present in the exhaust stream. Since this tends to maintain the metal-oxide catalyst in
a low oxidation state, the chemisorption of NO is increased by perhaps several orders of
magnitude. Five reducing agents have been used successfully to catalytically control
nitric oxide: C, CO, H_2, HC, and NH_3. Carbon monoxide, hydrogen, and hydrocarbons are all available in automobile effluents. Ammonia has been added to the exhaust stream and carbon has been tried as a catalytic agent, although carbon is consumed in the reaction and therefore is not a true catalyst.

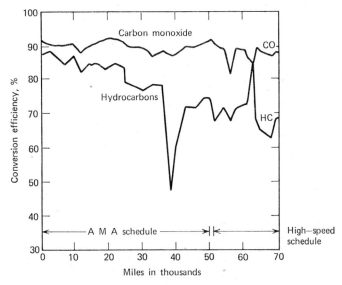

Fig. 17. Catalyst efficiency: hot-cycle NIDR hydrocarbon and carbon monoxide data.

Experiments tend to support the theory that N_2O is an intermediate in the reactions shown below:

$$2 NO + CO \rightarrow N_2O + CO_2$$
$$N_2O + CO \rightarrow N_2 + CO_2$$

Water, which comprises 10–14% of the exhaust, may hasten the reduction of NO by promoting a water–gas shift (86).

the water–gas equilibrium	$CO_2 + H_2 \leftrightharpoons CO + H_2O$
becomes	$CO + H_2O \rightarrow CO_2 + H_2$
and is followed by	$2 NO + 2 H_2 \rightarrow N_2 + 2 H_2O$

Ammonia has been shown to be a very effective reducing agent for either homogeneous or heterogeneous NO_x control. It is believed that the high efficiency is due to the presence of two nitrogen-containing molecules at any given site.

$$NO + NH_3 \rightarrow N_2 + H_2O + H$$

The catalytical control of NO_x is not fully understood. The complexity and number of possible reactions taking place have made it difficult to investigate.

Only recently have investigators found that ammonia is a potential product of catalytic NO_x control. However, Maquerian et al. have formulated a catalyst which selectively reduces NO without producing ammonia (99).

An excellent summary of ICE emission-control systems and their relationship to fuel economy has been published by Campau (100).

Unconventional Power Plants

This discussion will attempt to summarize technology as reported in 1967 (92) and 1969 (93).

Among the external-combustion power plants, the Rankine cycle seems to offer the greatest promise of being competitive for general urban automotive application,

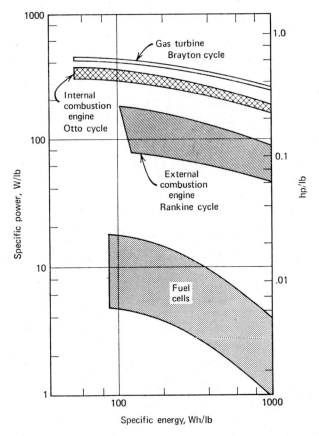

Fig. 18. Vehicle requirements and motive power-source requirements. Assumes 2000-lb vehicle, 500-lb motive power source, and steady driving. Power and energy taken at output of conversion device.

although the Brayton cycle is in competition. The other unconventional systems projected are to be "too big, too heavy, and too expensive to be competitive" (93). Some of the alternatives are compared on Figure 18 (92), in terms of vehicle requirements and power-plant potential. See also a similar diagram under Cells, electric, in this volume. Neglecting costs and other nonefficiency factors, the Brayton cycle (gas turbine), the Otto cycle (gasoline and diesel ICE), and the Rankine cycle (steam) seem most attractive.

Brayton Cycle. The majority of prototype automotive gas-turbine engines are equipped with regenerators to increase the efficiency to an acceptable level. An inherent problem associated with regenerative units is their bulk and weight. The addition of a regenerator increases the specific weight (lb/hp) from 0.6–1.0 to 3.2–4.5 (93). Emission testing indicates the gas turbine to be very good when compared to today's engine in terms of CO and HC; nitric oxide emission tends to be higher, although some investigators have reported that the turbine has a slight advantage in NO_x emission over ICE-power plants (94). It is not known whether this difference is real, or if it may be attributed to instrumentation errors.

Rankine Cycle. In recent years, four working prototypes of automotive steam engines have been constructed and reported. The emission performances of these vehicles vary by an order of magnitude. In general, hydrocarbon and CO are low. On the other hand, NO_x emissions range from 40 to 100 ppm (93), not corrected for the large increase in mass flow. These correction factors for increased mass flow, said to range from 1.5 to 2.0, are due to differences in operating efficiency and the numerically higher air–fuel ratio of the external combustion.

Stirling Cycle. At present, only two versions of automotive Stirling engines have been described in the literature. These engines seem to have an acceptable automotive performance but may be too heavy and costly for automotive applications. The emissions of both of these engines show very good hydrocarbon and CO control, but nitric oxide emissions are above mid-1970s standards. A more practical approach might be to combine the Stirling engine into a hybrid system. The Stirling engine would be used only for lower-power-output modes (deceleration, idleness).

Electric Vehicles. Today's commercial batteries are not capable of producing the power or range required to offer electric motors as a replacement for the internal combustion engine. The only potential for the use of conventional batteries is in limited-production vehicles designed for specific use in closed buildings. Researchers agree that a breakthrough in electrical storage units, or in fuel cells, is needed before electric vehicles are feasible. It is also generally agreed that today's technology in electric-motor design is adequate but that electrical-control mechanisms may be a stumbling block.

It is estimated that at least 10 years of research are required before any new battery systems could be feasible for production considerations. The major problems are range, power, ease of recharging, thermal containment, and the possibility of producing pollutants potentially more dangerous than those of today's ICE engine. There is also the problem of a shortage of electrical power in many parts of the country. In any event, a thorough study of the engine-vehicle package is required to utilize electric propulsion. It has been shown that the range of a compact-size electric car can be increased by 125% with proper design of the entire vehicle package (95). See Fuel cells in this volume.

Bibliography

NOTE: *SAE preprints* and *Techn. Progr. Ser.* (*TP*) can be obtained from the Soc. of Automotive Engrs., New York; *API preprints* can be obtained from the Am. Petrol. Inst., New York.

1. A. J. Haagen-Smit, *Ind. Eng. Chem.* **44,** 1342 (1952).
2. A. J. Haagen-Smit, C. E. Bradley, and M. M. Fox, *Ind. Eng. Chem.* **45,** 2086 (1953).
3. A. J. Haagen-Smit and M. M. Fox, *SAE Trans.* **63,** 575 (1958).
4. A. J. Haagen-Smit and M. M. Fox, *Ind. Eng. Chem.* **48,** 1484 (1956).
5. E. A. Schuck, G. S. Doyle, and N. Endow, *Report No. 31,* Air Pollution Foundation, San Marino, Calif., Dec. 1960.
6. *Intern Symp. on Chemical Reactions in the Lower and Upper Atmosphere, Stanford Research Inst., San Francisco, Calif., April 1960.*
6a. C. S. Tuesday, in reference 6, p. 15.
7. E. R. Stephens, in reference 6, p. 51.
8. L. G. Wayne and J. C. Romanovsky, in reference 6, p. 71.
9. W. A. Glasson and C. S. Tuesday, *Environ. Sci. Technol.* **4,** 37 (1970).
10. A. P. Altshuller, S. L. Kopczynski, W. A. Lonneman, T. C. Becker, and R. Slater, *Environ. Sci. Technol.* **1,** 899 (1967).
11. M. W. Korth, A. H. Rose, Jr., and R. C. Stahman, *J. Air Pollution Control Assoc.* **14,** 168 (1964).
12. P. W. Leach, L. J. Leng, T. A. Bellar, J. E. Sigsby, Jr., and A. P. Altshuller, *J. Air Pollution Control Assoc.* **14,** 176 (1964).

13. B. Dimitriades, *J. Air Pollution Control Assoc.* **17**, 460 (1967).
14. W. E. Wilson and A. Levy, "A Study of Sulfur Dioxide in Photochemical Smog," *First Annual Progress Report, Project S-11*, Am. Petrol. Inst., New York, August 1968.
15. L. A. McReynolds, H. E. Alquist, and D. B. Wimmer, *SAE reprint 650525, May 1965*.
16. "Air Quality Criteria For Carbon Monoxide," *AP-62*, Natl. Air Pollution Assoc. (NAPCA), Washington, D.C., March 1970.
17. E. R. Stephens, *J. Air Pollution Control Assoc.* **19**, 181 (1969).
18. P. A. Leighton, *Photochemistry of Air Pollution*, Academic Press, Inc., New York, 1961.
19. A. P. Altshuller and J. J. Bufalini, *Photochem. Photobiol.* **4**, 97 (1965).
20. E. A. Schuck and E. R. Stephens, *Advan. Environ. Technol.* **1**, 73 (1970).
21. A. C. Stern, ed., *Air Pollution*, (3 Vols.), Academic Press, Inc., New York, 1968.
22. "Air Quality Criteria for Photochemical Oxidants," *AP-63*, NAPCA, March 1970.
23. "Air Quality Criteria for Hydrocarbons," *AP-64*, NAPCA, March 1970.
24. J. M. Heuss and W. A. Glasson, *Environ. Sci. Technol.* **2**, 1109 (1968).
25. W. A. Glasson and C. S. Tuesday, *J. Air Pollution Control Assoc.* **20**, 239 (1970).
26. J. D. Caplan, *SAE preprint No. 650641, Aug. 1965*.
27. A. P. Altshuller, *Air Water Pollution Intern. J.* **10**, 713 (1966).
28. E. A. Schuck, J. M. Pitts, Jr., and J. K. S. Wan, *Air Water Pollution Intern. J.* **10**, 689 (1966).
29. W. J. Hamming and J. E. Dickinson, *Air Water Pollution Intern. J.* **10**, 637 (1966).
30. L. Fuller, "Profile of Air Pollution Control in Los Angeles County," *Ann. Publication of the Los Angeles Air Pollution Control District*, Los Angeles, January 1969.
31. S. W. Nicksic, J. Harkins, and L. J. Painter, *Air Water Pollution Intern. J.* **10**, 15, 637, 638 (1966).
32. B. W. Gay and J. J. Bufalini, *Paper No. WATR 034, 158th National Meeting Am. Chem. Soc., New York, Sept. 1969*.
33. H. J. R. Stevenson, D. E. Sanderson, and A. P. Altshuller, *Air Water Pollut. Intern. J.* **9**, 367 (1965).
34. W. B. Innes and K. Tsu, "Automobile Exhaust Control," in A. Standen, ed., *Encyclopedia of Chemical Technology*, Vol. 2, Interscience Publishers, a div. of John Wiley & Sons, Inc., New York, 1963, pp. 814–839.
35. R. K. Stone and B. H. Eccleston, "Vehicle Emissions vs. Fuel Composition," *API preprint 43-68*, Am. Petrol. Inst., New York, May 16, 1968.
36. E. E. Nelson, "General Motors Corporation Interim Report, GM Low Volatility Gasoline Program," *Paper presented to Western Oil and Gas Association Committee on Air and Water Conservation*, June 6, 1968.
37. F. Bonamassa, "Progress Report, Joint Projects to Evaluate the Potential of Gasoline Modification as an Air Pollution Control Measure in Los Angeles County," *Ann. Publication of the Los Angeles Air Pollution Control District*, Los Angeles, February 1969.
38. R. K. Stone and B. H. Eccleston, "Vehicle Emissions vs. Fuel Composition, Part II," *API preprint 41-69*, May 13, 1969.
39. G. D. Ebersole and L. A. McReynolds, "An Evaluation of Automobile Total Hydrocarbon Emissions," *SAE preprint 660408, June 1966*.
40. G. D. Ebersole, "Hydrocarbon Reactivities of Motor Fuel Evaporation Losses," *SAE preprint 690089, January 1969*.
41. H. G. Lassen, "Discussion of SAE preprint 690089," *SAE Ann. Meeting, Detroit, Mich., January 1969*.
42. M. W. Jackson and R. L. Everett, "Effect of Fuel Composition on Amount and Reactivity of Evaporative Emissions," *SAE preprint 690088, January 1969*.
43. D. H. Clewell, "Commentary on Engine Fuels Papers," *Paper presented at the 33rd Midyear API Meeting, Philadelphia, Pa., May 16, 1968*.
44. S. D. Lawson, et al., "Economics of Changing Volatility and Reducing Light Olefins, U.S. Motor Gasoline, A Report by the Lead/Volatility Economics Task Force," *API preprint 41-68*, May 16, 1968.
45. M. W. Jackson, W. M. Wiese, and J. T. Wentworth, "The Influence of Air-Fuel Ratio, Spark Timing and Combustion Chamber Deposits on Exhaust Hydrocarbon Emissions," *SAE preprint 486A, March 1-16, 1962*.
46. M. W. Jackson, "Analysis for Exhaust Gas Hydrocarbons-Nondispensive Infrared Versus Flame-Ionization," *J. Air Pollution Control Assoc.* **16** (12), 697 (Dec. 1966).

47. *Continuous Infrared Analyzers, Bulletin 1R-4055-C*, Beckman Instrument, Inc., Scientific and Process Instruments Division, Fullerton, Calif.

48. *108A and 109A Hydrocarbon Analyzers, Bulletin 1306-A*, Beckman Instruments, Inc., Scientific and Process Instruments Division, Fullerton, Calif.

49. C. E. Scheffler, "Combustion Chamber Surface Area, A Key to Exhaust Hydrocarbons," *SAE preprint 660111, January 10–14, 1966.*

50. M. W. Jackson, "Effects of Some Engine Variables and Control Systems on Composition and Reactivity of Exhaust Hydrocarbons," *SAE preprint 660404, June 6–10, 1966.*

51. T. A. Huls, P. S. Myers, and, O. A. Uyehara "Spark Ignition Engine Operation and Design for Minimum Exhaust Emission," *SAE preprint 660405, June 6–10, 1966.*

52. M. Alperstein and R. L. Bradow, "Exhaust Emissions Related to Engine Combustion Reactions," *SAE preprint 660781, November 1–3, 1966.*

53. W. A. Daniel, "Engine Variables Effects on Exhaust Hydrocarbon Composition (A Single Cylinder Engine Study with Propane as the Fuel)," *SAE preprint 670124, January 9–13, 1967.*

54. J. H. Jones and J. C. Gagliardi, "Vehicle Exhaust Emission Experiments using a Pre-Mixed and Pre-Heated Air Fuel Charge," *SAE preprint 670485, May 15–19, 1967.*

55. J. T. Wentworth, "Piston and Ring Variables Affect Exhaust Hydrocarbon Emissions," *SAE preprint 680109, January 8–12, 1968.*

56. J. S. Ninomiya and A. Golovoy, "Effects of Air-Fuel Ratio on Composition of Hydrocarbon Exhaust from Isooctane, Diisobutylene, Toluene, and Toluene and Heptane Mixture," *SAE preprint 690504, May 19–23, 1969.*

57. G. A. Lavoie, J. B. Heywood, and J. C. Keck, "Experimental and Theoretical Study of Nitric Oxide Formation in Internal Combustion Engines," *Papers, Fluid Mechanics Laboratory, Mass. Institute of Technology, November 1969.*

58. D. A. Hirschler et al., "Particulate Lead Compounds in Automotive Exhaust Gas," *Ind. Eng. Chem.* **49**, (7) July 1967.

59. A. J. Pahnke and E. C. Squire, "Lead in Gasoline," *Oil Gas J.* **64**, 50 (Dec. 12, 1966).

60. J. C. Gagliardi, "The Effect of Fuel Anti-Knock Compounds and Deposits on Exhaust Emissions," *SAE preprint 670128, January 9–13, 1967.*

61. D. A. Hirschler et al., "Particulate Lead Compounds in Automotive Exhaust Gas," *Ind. Eng. Chem.* **49** (7) (July 1957).

62. J. C. Gagliardi and F. E. Ghannam, "Effects of Tetraethyl Lead Concentration on Exhaust Emissions in Customer Type Vehicle Operation," *SAE preprint 690015, January 13–17, 1969.*

63. A. J. Pahnke and J. F. Corte, "Effect of Combustion Chamber Deposits and Driving Conditions on Vehicle Exhaust Emissions," *SAE preprint 690017, January 13–17, 1969.*

64. E. Barthlomew, "Potentialities of Emission Reduction by Design of Induction Systems," *SAE TP-12, 1968.*

65. E. W. Beckman, W. S. Fagley, Jr., and J. O. Sarto, "Exhuast Emission Control by Chrysler—The Cleaner Air Package," *SAE preprint 660107, January 1966.*

66. J. M. Chandler, et al., "The Ford Approach to Exhaust Emission Control," *SAE preprint 660163, January 10–14, 1966.*

67. H. H. Dietrich, "Automotive Exhaust Hydrocarbon Reduction During Deceleration by Induction System Devices," *SAE TP-6, 1964.*

68. L. Eltinge et al., "Potentialities of Future Emissions Reductions by Engine Modifications," *SAE preprint 680123, January 1968.*

69. D. F. Hagen and G. W. Holiday, "The Effects of Engine Operating and Design Variables on Exhaust Emissions," *SAE TP-6 1964.*

70. D. L. Hittler and L. R. Hamkins, "Emission Control by Engine Design and Development," *SAE preprint 680110, January 8–12, 1968.*

71. G. J. Nebel, "Automobile Exhaust Gas Treatment, An Industry Report," *SAE TP-6, 1964.*

72. A. F. Martin, "A New Luxury Car V-8 Engine by Ford," *SAE preprint 680020, January 8–12, 1968.*

73. J. E. Nicholls et al., "Inlet Manifold Water Injection for Control of Nitrogen Oxides," *SAE preprint 690018, January, 1969.*

74. J. D. Benson, "Reduction of Nitrogen Oxides in Automotive Exhaust," *SAE preprint 690019, January, 1969.*

75. W. F. Deeter, et al., "An Approach for Controlling Vehicle Emissions," *SAE preprint 680400, 1968.*

76. H. L. Newhall, "Control of Nitrogen Oxides by Exhaust Gas Recirculation—A Preliminary Theoretical Study," *SAE preprint 670495, May 17, 1967*.

77. D. A. Brownson and R. F. Stebar, "Factors Influencing the Effectiveness of Air Injection in Reducing Exhaust Emissions," *SAE TP-12, 1968*.

78. E. N. Cantwell and A. J. Pahnke, "Design Factors Affecting the Performance of Exhaust Manifold Reactors," *SAE TP-12, 1968*.

79. E. N. Cantwell et al., "A Progress Report on the Development of Exhaust Manifold Reactors," *SAE preprint 690139, January, 1969*.

80. J. M. Chandler et al., "Development of Non Flame Exhaust Gas Reactors," *SAE preprint 486M, March 1962*.

81. W. K. Steinhagen et al., "Design and Development of the General Motors Air Injection Reactor System," *SAE TP-12, 1968*.

82. R. A. Baker and R. C. Doerr, "Catalytic Reduction of Nitrogen Oxides in Automobile Exhaust," *J. Air Pollution Control Assoc.* **14** (10) (Oct. 1964).

83. H. Schaldenbrand and J. H. Struck, "Development and Evaluation of Automobile Exhaust Catalytic Converter Systems," *SAE TP-6, 1964*.

84. H. Schwochert, "Performance of a Catalytic Converter on Non-Leaded Fuel," *SAE preprint 690503, May 19-28, 1969*.

85. E. E. Weaver, "Effects of Tetraethyllead on Catalyst Life and Efficiency in Customer Type Vehicle Operation," *SAE preprint 690016, January 1969*.

86. "Method of Treating Exhaust Gases of Internal Combustion Engines," U.S. Pat. 3,370,914 (Feb. 27, 1968), G. P. Grose et al. (to Esso Research and Engineering Co.).

87. L. Y. Margolis, "Catalytic Oxidation of Hydrocarbons," *Advan. Catalysis* **14**, IP 429 (1963).

88. J. Wei, "On the Maximum Temperature Inside a Porous Catalyst," *Chem. Eng. Sci.* **21** 1171 (1966).

89. R. J. Leak et al., "Use of Alumina-Coated Filaments in Catalytic Mufflers—Testing with Single Cylinder Engine," *Environ Sci. Technol.* **2** (10), (Oct. 1968).

90. M. Shelef and J. T. Kummer, "Important Chemical Reactions in Air Pollution Control, Part II—The Behavior of Nitric Oxide in Heterogeneous Catalytic Reactions," *62nd Annual Meeting of AIChE, Washington, D.C., Nov. 16-20, 1969*.

91. M. Shelef, K. Otto, and H. Gandhi, "The Heterogeneous Decomposition of Nitric Oxide on Supported Catalysts," *Atmospheric Environ.*, **3**, 107 (1969).

92. "The Automobile and Air Pollution, Part II," *Report of the Panel on Electrically Powered Vehicles, U.S. Department of Commerce, Dec. 1967*.

93. J. A. Hoess and R. C. Stahman, "Unconventional Thermal, Mechanical and Nuclear Low Pollution Potential Power Sources for Urban Vehicles," *SAE preprint 690231, January 13-17, 1969*.

94. M. W. Korth and A. H. Rose, "Emissions from a Gas Turbine Automobile," *SAE preprint 690402, May 20-24, 1968*.

95. D. M. Tenniswood and H. A. Graetzal, "Minimum Road Load for Electric Cars," *SAE preprint 670177, January 9-13, 1967*.

96. R. E. Taylor and R. M. Campau, "The IIEC (Inter-Industry Emission Control)—A Cooperative Research Program for Automotive Emission Control," *API preprint 17-69, May 12, 1969*.

97. J. C. W. Kuo, C. R. Morgan, and H. G. Lassen, "Mathematical Modeling of CO and HC Catalytic Converter Systems," *SAE preprint 710289, January 1971*.

98. A. Jaimee, D. E. Schneider, A. I. Ruzaranith, and J. W. Sjoberg, "Thermal Reactor—Design, Development, and Performance," *SAE preprint 710293, January 1971*.

99. G. H. Mequerian and C. R. Lang, "NO_x Reduction Catalyst for Vehicle Emission Control," *SAE preprint 71029, January 1971*.

100. R. M. Campau, "Low Emission Concept Vehicles," *SAE preprint 710294, January 1971*.

Harry G. Lassen
Ford Motor Co.
E. Daby, N. Hiki, and
B. Weinstock (Photochemical smog)
Ford Motor Co.

B

BERYLLIDES

Beryllium forms intermetallic compounds with the majority of the metals, the resulting large family of compounds being collectively referred to as the beryllides. These intermediate phases in binary beryllium–metal systems have attracted considerable research attention as materials which exhibit exceptional oxidation resistance and mechanical strength at high temperatures.

The structural types of beryllides most frequently found are shown in Table 1. A

Table 1. Beryllide Types

Formula	Structure	Metals
MBe	cubic	Ti(?), Co, Ni, Cu, Pd, Au
MBe_2	face-centered cubic	Ti, Cu, Nb, Ag, Ta
	hexagonal	V, Cr, Mn, Fe, Zr, Mo, Hf, W, Re
MBe_5	face-centered cubic	Fe, Co(?), Pd
	cubic	Au
	hexagonal	Zr, Hf
M_2Be_{17}	rhombohedral	Ti, Zr, Nb, Hf, Ta
MBe_{12}	body-centered tetragonal	Ti, V, Cr, Mn, Fe, Co, Nb, Mo, Pd, Ag, Ta, W, Pt
MBe_{13}	face-centered cubic	Mg, Ca, Sc, Sr, Y, Zr, La, Ce, Pr, Nd, Pm, Sm, Eu, Gd, Tb, Dy, Ho, Er, Tm, Yb, Lu, Hf, Th, U, Np, Pu, Am
MBe_{22}	face-centered cubic	Mo, Tc, W, Re

number of other intermediate phases may be encountered in a given system, particularly on the beryllium-deficient side of the equilibrium diagram which was not considered in the preparation of this table. The detailed structures and original references to these compounds may be found in Pearson (1). In some instances the structure and stoichiometry of the phase have not been fully resolved; eg, $FeBe_{12}$ with the tetragonal $ThMn_{12}$-type of structure has been identified, but $FeBe_{11}$ with a hexagonal structure is consistently encountered as an impurity phase in commercial beryllium and is the usual result of attempts to prepare a single-phase beryllide in this composition region. The M_2Be_{17} compounds of Ti, Nb, and Hf exhibit the rhombohedral structure in the α modification and a hexagonal structure in the β form.

The combination of properties exhibited by some members of the beryllide family includes excellent oxidation resistance, high strength at elevated temperature, good thermal conductivity, and low densities, as compared to refractory metals and many ceramics. The beryllides which are the more promising members of the family in this regard are listed in Table 2 with their melting points, densities, and crystallographic structures (2,2a). The compounds with the highest melting points in this series are

73

Table 2. High-Temperature Oxidation-Resistant Beryllides

Beryllide system	Compound	Be, wt %	Melting point, °F	X-ray density, g/cm³	Structure
Nb–Be	$NbBe_{12}$	53.8	3070	2.92	body-centered tetragonal
	Nb_2Be_{17}	45.2	3100	3.28	rhombohedral
Ta–Be	$TaBe_{12}$	37.4	3360	4.18	body-centered tetragonal
	$TaBe_{17}$	29.8	3610	5.05	rhombohedral
Mo–Be	$MoBe_{12}$	53.2	~3100	3.03	body-centered tetragonal
Ti–Be	$TiBe_{12}$	69.3	2900	2.26	hexagonal
	Ti_2Be_{17}	61.5	2970	2.46	rhombohedral
Zr–Be	$ZrBe_{13}$	56.2	3500	2.72	face-centered cubic
	Zr_2Be_{17}	45.7	3600	3.08	rhombohedral
Hg–Be	$HfBe_{13}$	39.7	2900	3.93	face-centered cubic
	Hf_2Be_{17}	30.0	<3180	4.78	rhombohedral

found in the Ta–Be, Zr–Be, and possibly the Hf–Be systems. The densities range from a low of 2.26 g/cm³ for $TiBe_{12}$ to 5.05 g/cm³ for Ta_2Be_{17}. The exact range of composition possible while maintaining the base structure has not been examined thoroughly, but the materials discussed here are essentially "line" compounds, that is, significant variation from the indicated stoichiometry results in the appearance of second phases in the materials.

Mechanical Properties

The beryllides, like intermetallic compounds in general, are hard, strong materials which exhibit very little, if any, ductility at low temperatures. The hardness at room temperature of several beryllides is given in Table 3, as measured by the Vickers hard-

Table 3. Room-temperature Hardness of the Beryllides

Compound	Vhn, 2.5 kg load
Nb_2Be_{17}	1000
$NbBe_{12}$	500
Ta_2Be_{17}	1120
$TaBe_{12}$	720
Zr_2Be_{17}	1130
$ZrBe_{13}$	1000
$MoBe_{12}$	950

ness (Vhn) test with a 2.5 kg load. (See Hardness.) On this scale aluminum is about 40, tungsten about 400, beryllium oxide about 1300, and titanium carbide 3200. The beryllides are, therefore, much harder than common metals, but are not among the extremely hard materials.

The modulus of rupture (flexural strength) of Ta_2Be_{17} as a function of temperature is shown in Figure 1. The shape of this curve is quite typical of the beryllide family in that a gradual increase in strength with temperature is noted until the region of about 1600°F is reached, after which a sharp increase in strength occurs, peaking in the region of 2300°F. In this particular case, the effect of minor variations in composition was examined, and it was found that slight variations on either side of the stoichiometric

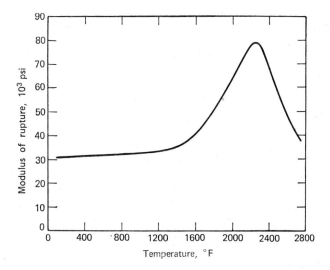

Fig. 1. Modulus of rupture of Ta_2Be_{17}.

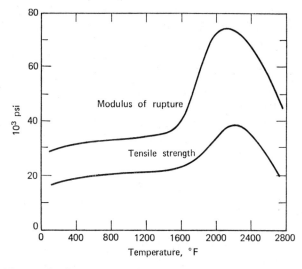

Fig. 2. Tensile strength and modulus of rupture of Nb_2Be_{17}.

29.8% Be had little effect on the modulus of rupture or that the effect was masked by the scatter band of the recorded values. Typical values of modulus of rupture for other beryllides are listed in Table 4.

Table 4. Modulus of Rupture of Some Niobium, Tantalum, and Zirconium Beryllides, psi

Compound	Room temp	2300°F	2500°F	2750°F
Nb_2Be_{17}	31,000	70,000	63,000	36,000
$NbBe_{12}$	22,000	45,000	40,000	22,000
Ta_2Be_{17}	30,000	78,000	56,000	35,000
$TaBe_{12}$	31,000	53,000	43,000	26,000
Zr_2Be_{17}	25,000	40,000	40,000	35,000
$ZrBe_{13}$	25,000	40,000	37,000	25,000

Tensile tests on Nb_2Be_{17} at elevated temperature are shown in Figure 2 along with the modulus of rupture of this particular lot of material. As is normally expected, the tensile values range from 50 to 60% of the modulus-of-rupture values. The tensile testing at elevated temperature was performed by using stainless-steel grips on extended specimens with induction heating (3).

Static Young's modulus data show little variation between members of the family, the values being $43-47 \times 10^6$ psi at room temperature, 40×10^6 psi at 1600°F, and $20-25 \times 10^6$ psi at 2500°F for the M_2Be_{17} and MBe_{12} or MBe_{13} compounds of niobium, tantalum, and zirconium. Dynamic measurements of Young's modulus have indicated anomalies in the behavior of the niobium compounds in that a minimum was recorded at about 1400°F, followed by a rapid rise to a peak value at 2400°F. Recorded values for Nb_2Be_{17} were 43×10^6 psi at room temperature, 41×10^6 psi at 1400°F, 47×10^6 psi at 2000°F, 53×10^6 psi at 2300°F, and 46×10^6 psi at 2500°F (3,4). The compressive strengths of $NbBe_{12}$ and $ZrBe_{13}$ have been measured at 190,000–200,000 psi at room temperature, 130,000–150,000 psi at 1600°F, and 70,000–80,000 psi at 2500°F (2,2a).

Little capacity for plastic strain is exhibited by the beryllides under discussion between room temperature and 2000°F, but significant plastic deformation has been recorded at higher temperatures. Calculations from the deflection of the modulus-of-rupture bars indicate that a maximum of about 0.1% tensile elongation occurs in the outermost fibers of such bars at room temperature prior to fracture. At 2500°F elongations between 1 and 2.6% may be calculated for the niobium and the tantalum compounds, but the zirconium materials remain at about 0.1%. Ta_2Be_{17} and Nb_2Be_{17} indicate calculated values of about 5 and 7% elongation, respectively, at 2750°F, while Zr_2Be_{17} shows only 0.1% and $ZrBe_{13}$ only 0.6% at this temperature. Tensile elongations for Nb_2Be_{17}, as measured in actual tensile tests, showed a maximum of 2%. Lewis reported some evidence of slip in $NbBe_{12}$ at $-196°C$ during determination of microhardness (5).

Oxidation Resistance

One of the most important characteristics of the beryllide family is their oxidation resistance at elevated temperature. A number of the compounds have been surveyed for this characteristic. On the basis of performance in air at 2300°F and higher, Paine (6) listed beryllides which exhibited excellent oxidation resistance along with some members of the family which exhibited relatively poor resistance, as summarized in Table 5. The degree of oxidation resistance of several of the beryllides is illustrated in Table 6 (7).

Booker studied the oxidation and vapor pressure of several of the beryllides (8). He found that oxidation proceeded in a step-wise fashion so that the products of oxidation of $ZrBe_{13}$ were Zr_2Be_{17} and BeO. Oxidation proceeds in this manner from a higher beryllide to the next lower beryllide and BeO until only the refractory metal remains; this in turn also oxidizes. While consistent rate-law relations were not obtained for $TaBe_{12}$, Ta_2Be_{17}, $ZrBe_{13}$, and Zr_2Be_{17} in the temperature range of 2300 to 2750°F, the power of the observed rate law was always greater than two.

Like some other intermetallic compounds, most notably $MoSi_2$, certain beryllides exhibit an anomalous oxidation behavior in that oxidation resistance is excellent at high temperature, but little or no oxidation resistance is shown in some lower tempera-

Table 5. Relative Performance of Beryllides in Air at 2300°F

Beryllides with good oxidation resistance

$TiBe_2$	$NbBe_{12}$
$TiBe_{12}$	$MoBe_{12}$
$CrBe_2$	Hf_2Be_{17}
$CrBe_{12}$	$TaBe_3$
Zr_2Be_{17}	Ta_2Be_{17}
$ZrBe_{13}$	$TaBe_{12}$
Nb_2Be_{17}	WBe_{22}

Beryllides with poor oxidation resistance

$ZrBe_5$	$GdBe_{13}$
$NbBe_3$	$TaBe_2$
$MoBe_2$	WBe_2
$LaBe_{13}$	WBe_{12}
$CeBe_{13}$	$ThBe_{13}$
	UBe_{13}

Table 6. Oxidation Resistance of Beryllides in Air at High Temperatures, calcd penetration mils

Compound	After 100 hr, °F					After 10 hr, °F	
	2300	2500	2700	2800	2900	2900	3000
$TiBe_{12}$	0.4	1.1	5.0				
Zr_2Be_{17}	1.0	0.5	1.2				
$ZrBe_{13}$	1.0	0.5	1.3	1.4	3.2		
Nb_2Be_{17}	0.3	0.6	1.9				
$NbBe_{12}$	0.2	0.9	2.0				
Ta_2Be_{17}	0.2	0.3	0.8	3.2		1.2	3.3
$TaBe_{12}$	0.4	0.5	0.9	1.1	9.4	1.6	3.7
$MoBe_{12}$	0.2	0.3	0.6	5.6			

ture ranges. Paine surveyed the beryllides for the occurrence of these phenomena and found no anomalous behavior with $TaBe_{12}$, Ta_2Be_{17}, $MoBe_{12}$, $TiBe_{12}$, or WBe_{12}, but such behavior was observed with Nb_2Be_{12}, $NbBe_{12}$, Zr_2Be_{17}, and $ZrBe_{13}$ (9). Exposure of the zirconium beryllides to air in the 1300–1600°F temperature range resulted in complete disintegration to a powder within 24 hr despite a penetration of less than 2 mils per side in 100 hr in the 2300–2750°F temperature range. In the case of the niobium compounds, Paine found that the problem manifests itself in the formation of heavy oxide layers at 1700 and 1800°F, although weight gains of only about 5 mg/cm² were recorded for these compounds in 100 hr at 2500°F. The addition of aluminum either as the metal or as NiAl solved this problem through a mechanism postulated as the relief of stresses by free aluminum at the grain boundaries in either case (NiAl decomposing at fabrication temperature with the nickel going into solid solution).

Thermal Properties

Thermal-expansion coefficients of several of the beryllides are shown in Table 7 (2,2a). These coefficients are of the same order of magnitude as those exhibited by metals and are higher than the thermal-expansion coefficients of refractory oxides. Only small differences are noted between the expansion of individual beryllides, the difference between Zr_2Be_{17} and $ZrBe_{13}$ being greater than between any other two compounds in this group.

Table 7. Mean Linear Thermal-Expansion Coefficients ($\times 10^{-6}$) for Several Beryllides, at °F

Compound	80–600	80–1200	80–1800	80–2400	80–2700
Nb_2Be_{17}	6.3	7.3	7.9	8.5	8.8
$NbBe_{12}$	6.7	7.5	8.3	9.0	9.3
Ta_2Be_{17}	6.2	7.1	7.8	8.4	8.7
$TaBe_{12}$	5.8	6.9	7.6	8.1	8.4
Zr_2Be_{17}	5.6	7.0	7.5	8.1	8.4
$ZrBe_{13}$	6.5	7.7	8.6	9.4	9.8
$MoBe_{12}$	6.7	7.8	8.4	9.0	9.3

The thermal conductivities of beryllides of niobium, zirconium, and tantalum are given in Table 8 (2) and specific heat values are shown in Table 9 (2,2a). The con-

Table 8. Thermal Conductivity of Several Beryllides, Btu/(hr) (ft²) (°F/ft)

Compound	\multicolumn{5}{Temperature, °F}
	1200	1600	2000	2400	2600
Nb_2Be_{17}	18.1	18.5	18.9	19.3	19.5
$NbBe_{12}$	17.7	17.9	18.2	18.5	18.6
Ta_2Be_{17}	16.9	17.5	18.2	18.9	18.2
$TaBe_{12}$	16.7	18.3	19.5	21.0	22.3
$ZrBe_{13}$	23.1	22.0	21.0	20.0	19.5

Table 9. Specific Heat of Beryllides, Btu/(lb) (°F)

Compound	\multicolumn{5}{Temperature, °F}
	1000	1500	2000	2500	2800
$NbBe_{12}$	0.385	0.400	0.414	0.429	0.437
Ta_2Be_{17}	0.213	0.227	0.240	0.253	0.261
$TaBe_{12}$	0.271	0.280	0.288	0.297	0.302
$MoBe_{12}$	0.381	0.402	0.423	0.444	0.457
$ZrBe_{13}$	0.381	0.406	0.431	0.456	0.471

ductivity of BeO at 2500°F is about 9.7 Btu/(hr) (ft²) (°F/ft). These beryllides, therefore, have a thermal conductivity at elevated temperature of about twice that of the highest conductivity refractory oxide. Specific-heat values are quite high as a result of the large percentage of beryllium in these materials.

Electrical Properties

The electrical conductivity of $NbBe_{12}$, $ZrBe_{13}$, $MoBe_{12}$, and $TaBe_{12}$ as a function of temperature is given in Figure 3. By comparison, the electrical conductivities of some metals are as follows: Cu, 598×10^3 ohm^{-1}cm^{-1}; Be, 250×10^3 ohm^{-1}cm^{-1}; Mo, 193×10^3 ohm^{-1}cm^{-1}; Nb, 76×10^3 ohm^{-1}cm^{-1}; Ta, 74×10^3 ohm^{-1}cm^{-1}; Zr, 24×10^3 ohm^{-1}cm^{-1}.

Bucher and Palmy (10) have reported that the MBe_{22} compounds (where M = Mo, W, Tc, and Re) are superconducting with the following transition temperatures: $MoBe_{22}$, 2.51°K; WBe_{22}, 4.12°K; $TcBe_{22}$, 5.21°K; $ReBe_{22}$, 9.65°K. Wolcott and

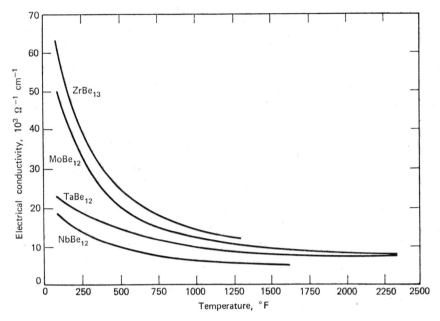

Fig. 3. Electrical conductivity of beryllides as a function of temperature.

Falge (11) reported that Nb_2Be_{17}, $NbBe_{12}$, Ta_2Be_{17}, $TaBe_{12}$, $MnBe_{12}$, UBe_{13}, $MoBe_{12}$, $ZrBe_{13}$, and $CaBe_{13}$ were not superconducting above $1.4°K$. They found $CrBe_{12}$ to be ferromagnetic at low temperatures.

Preparation and Fabrication

In the preparation and fabrication of beryllides powder-metallurgy techniques are used for the most part. The principal reason for this is the problem of maintenance of the desired composition since beryllium has a very substantial vapor pressure at the temperatures required to melt the constituents. This was well illustrated in the preparation of arc-cast specimens of $ZrBe_{13}$ and $NbBe_{12}$ for the U.S. Atomic Energy Commission (12). The powder-metallurgy route also obviates a great deal of the difficulty of high-temperature casting, but does leave something to be desired with respect to grain-boundary cleanliness.

The preparation of the compounds is normally carried out by solid-state reaction of the blended powder constituents in suitable nonreactive containers (MgO, BeO, etc) at a temperature in the region of 2300°F (13). After reaction a variety of techniques may be used to consolidate the reacted powder. The most convenient method is vacuum hot-pressing using graphite molds with a pressure on the order of 2000 psi in the temperature range of 2460 to 3000°F. Alternative procedures for consolidation, such as cold pressing (axial or isostatic) and sintering, have produced materials with properties equivalent to the hot-pressed properties (3). Due to the hardness of the beryllides, it is normally necessary to use diamond tooling for machining operations. Ultrasonic machining, electrochemical machining, and electrochemical grinding (see Electrolytic machining) are alternative procedures which might be used advantageously.

Applications

The original interest in beryllides was as high-temperature components for airborne nuclear-power plants. Considerable emphasis was placed on the combination of low density and high strength in the 2300–2500°F temperature range, coupled with favorable nuclear characteristics. This application was not carried to full development primarily because of the cancellation of development efforts on such nuclear-power plants.

The beryllides continue to be of interest because of their oxidation resistance, low density, and high strength, primarily for turbine engine applications. To date, however, the limited plastic deformation capability of the materials, particularly at low temperatures, has prevented their utilization in this type of application.

Bibliography

1. W. B. Pearson, *Handbook of Lattice Spacings and Structures of Metals and Alloys*, Vols. 1 and 2, Pergamon Press, Inc., New York, 1958 and 1960.
2. J. T. Weber et al., eds., *Compounds of Interest in Nuclear Reactor Technology*, American Institute of Mining, Metallurgical and Petroleum Engineers, Inc., New York, 1964.
2a. A. J. Stonehouse, R. M. Paine, and W. W. Beaver, *Physical and Mechanical Properties of Beryllides*, in reference 2, pp. 445–455.
3. R. S. Truesdale, B. B. Lympany, C. A. Bielawski, E. M. Grala, and W. W. Beaver, *Investigation of the Effects of Processing Variables and Fabrication Techniques Upon the Properties of Intermetallic Compounds*, ASD-TDR-62-476, Metals Laboratory, U. S. Air Force, Wright-Patterson Air Force Base, Ohio, Sept. 1961.
4. A. J. Stonehouse, R. M. Paine, and W. W. Beaver, "Mechanical Properties of Some Transition Element Beryllides," in J. H. Westbrook, ed., *Mechanical Properties of Intermetallic Compounds*, John Wiley & Sons, Inc., New York, 1960, Chap. 13.
5. J. R. Lewis, "Further Evaluation of the Beryllides," *J. of Metals* **13** (11), (1961).
6. R. M. Paine, A. J. Stonehouse, and W. W. Beaver, "High Temperature Oxidation Resistance of the Beryllides," *Corrosion* **20** (10), 307t–313t (1964).
7. W. W. Beaver, A. J. Stonehouse, and R. M. Paine, "Development of Intermetallic Compounds for Aerospace Applications," in F. Benesovsky, ed., *Plansee Proceedings 1964—Metals for the Space Age*, Metallwerk Plansee AG., Reutte, Austria, 1965.
8. J. Booker, R. M. Paine, and A. J. Stonehouse, *Studies on the Vapor Pressure and Oxidation of Certain Beryllides*, in reference 2, pp. 477–493.
9. R. M. Paine, A. J. Stonehouse, and W. W. Beaver, *Oxidation of the Beryllides at Intermediate Temperatures—Anomalous Behavior and a Solution*, in reference 2, pp. 495–509.
10. E. Bucher and C. Palmy, "Superconductivity and Isotope Effect in $Be_{22}X$ Compounds and Molybdenum," *Phys. Letters* **24A** (7), 340–341 (1967).
11. N. M. Wolcott and R. L. Falge, Jr., "Ferromagnetism of $CrBe_{12}$," *Phys. Rev.* **171** (2), 591–595 (1968).
12. P. Stark, "Intermetallic Compounds and Their Mechanical Behavior," *J. Metals* **16**, 152–157 (1964).
13. U.S. Pat. 3,150,975 (Sept. 29, 1964), W. W. Beaver, R. M. Paine, and A. J. Stonehouse (to the Brush Beryllium Company).

A. James Stonehouse
The Brush Beryllium Company

C

CANCER CHEMOTHERAPY

Although cancer has been identified in ancient civilizations, it is still one of the unconquered diseases of mankind. Only as recently as the 19th and early 20th centuries has the surgical approach been utilized and, subsequently, irradiation procedures. Technique has so improved these conventional methods that they are now considered the standard treatment of choice for all cancers.

In the past 25 years research into the biokinetics of cell growth has clarified concepts of carcinogenesis: the roles of viruses and immunology; the biochemical development of the cancer cell. This interest has resulted in a host of chemical entities designed to kill the cancer cell either directly or by inhibition of its essential growth elements.

Chemical treatment of cancer is a new but rapidly developing mode of therapy. The first development based on knowledge of the effects of castration in prostatic cancer occurred about 30 years ago. Disseminated cancer of the prostate was treated with female sex hormones. In the 1940s, knowledge of the efficacy of nitrogen mustard against certain cancers grew from military research into poison gas. In 1947 Dr. Sidney Farber in Boston observed the cancer-inhibiting effects of antifolic acid antagonists, aminopterin, and later methotrexate, in leukemic children.

These were the early chemical developments. Now a whole new host of chemical agents have been discovered by research chemists and their continued efforts offer hope that eventually a truly *curative* drug will be found.

Anticancer agents can be classified according to their general pharmacologic activity as follows:

(1) Alkylating Agents
(2) Antimetabolites
(3) Antibiotics

(4) Vinca Alkaloids
(5) Hormones
(6) Miscellaneous

These agents are not specific for their effects on tumor cells; their action is directed at normal cells as well. Therapeutic usefulness is obtained by careful balancing of dosage so that maximum cytotoxic activity is obtained against the proliferating cancer cells with minimum effect against the healthy, normal, dividing body cells.

The *alkylating agents* destroy tumor cells by linking to the guanine in the nucleotide of DNA. They act during all portions of the mitotic cycle of the cell, disrupting the hydrogen bonds of DNA. The *antimetabolites*, however, compete with normal metabolites thus replacing these elements and interfering with the synthesis of DNA.

Antibiotics are compounds produced by lower life forms, eg, yeast, molds, or bacteria, and are antagonistic to other life cell forms. They act by inhibiting protein synthesis or by inhibiting RNA or DNA synthesis.

The *vinca alkaloids*, derivatives of the periwinkle plants, interfere with cellular division and maturation by arresting mitosis in metaphase or by producing aberrations of the nuclei of cells.

Chemical poisons such as arsenic or the radioactive isotopes, eg, ^{32}P, ^{131}I, are cytotoxic and are occasionally used in cancer chemotherapy. The radionucleotides have a mechanism of action similar to irradiation.

The *hormonal agents*, including estrogens, progesterones, and corticosteroids, are employed to manipulate the hormonal environment in endocrine-dependent cancers such as those of the breast, ovary, or prostate. These agents employed in cancer chemotherapy are not specific oncolytic agents and are not included in this summary.

Alkylating Agents

The nitrogen mustards are all analogues of the parent compound, sulfur mustard. Administration of alkylating agents results biochemically in a substitution of an alkyl group for a hydrogen in the nucleic acids of cell DNA. Chemically the nitrogen mustards are tertiary amines which undergo cyclization in vivo to a cyclic quaternary ammonium ion. The active moiety is an ethyleneimonium intermediate which reacts with organic amino or sulfide groups in cell DNA. This alkylation disrupts or destroys the function of the organic material resulting in cell death.

Mechlorethamine hydrochloride.

$$CH_3-N \begin{cases} CH_2-CH_2-Cl \\ CH_2-CH_2-Cl \end{cases}$$

2,2'-dichloro-*N*-methyldiethylamine hydrochloride (nitrogen mustard, HN$_2$)

DOSE: Available in 10-mg vials for parenteral use (IV), 0.3–0.4 mg/kg single dose; intrapleurally or intraperitoneally 0.1–0.2 mg/kg.

DISEASE: Hodgkin's disease; lymphomas; lymphosarcoma; giant follicular lymphoma; ovarian and mammary carcinoma; bronchogenic small-cell or oat-cell carcinoma; neoplastic effusion.

SIDE EFFECTS: Bone marrow depression; vesicant; anorexia; nausea; diarrhea.

Triethylenemelamine.

2,4,6-tris(1-aziridinyl)-s-triazine (TEM)

DOSE: Available only in 2.5-mg tablets for oral use, 1–5 mg/day (rarely, 10 mg).

DISEASE: Lymphomas; ovarian and mammary cancer; chronic leukemias; polycythemia vera.

SIDE EFFECTS: Leukopenia; thrombocytopenia; no vesicant action on skin or mucous membranes.

Thiotepa Triethylenethiophosphoramide.

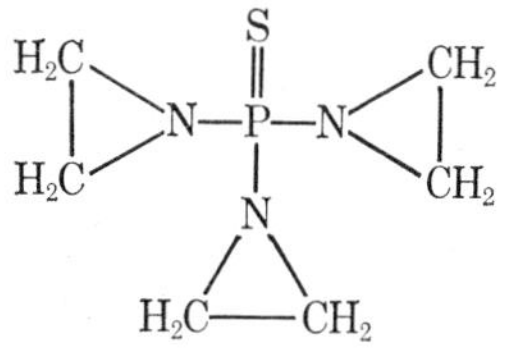

$$H_2C \diagdown \atop H_2C \diagup N-\underset{\underset{N}{\overset{\overset{S}{\|}}{P}}}{}-N \diagup CH_2 \atop \diagdown CH_2$$

$$\underset{H_2C——CH_2}{}$$

DOSE: Available in 15-mg vials. Usually given IV or IM, intrapleural, intrapericardial, intraperitoneal. IV or IM: 15–30 mg/week initially; intracavitary: 45–60 mg/week initially or 0.6–0.8 mg/kg once a week.

DISEASE: Adrenocarcinoma of the breast and ovary; lymphoma and sarcoma. Some response for bronchopulmonary, gastrointestinal, genitourinary, and central nervous system carcinomas.

SIDE EFFECTS: Hematopoietic suppression; no vesicant action.

Bulsulfan.

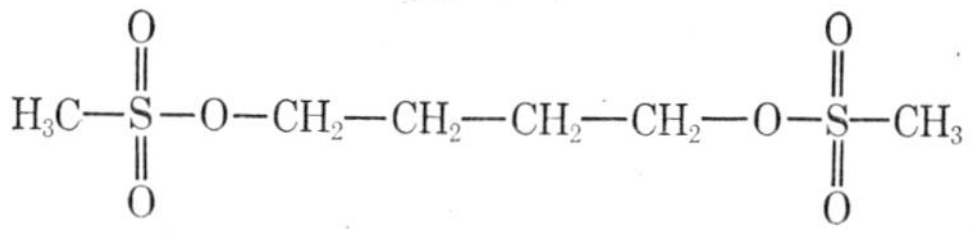

$$H_3C-\underset{\underset{O}{\overset{\overset{O}{\|}}{S}}}{}-O-CH_2-CH_2-CH_2-CH_2-O-\underset{\underset{O}{\overset{\overset{O}{\|}}{S}}}{}-CH_3$$

1,4-bis(methanesulfonoxy)butane

DOSE: Available in 2-mg tablets; 2–10 mg/day initially, 1–4 mg/day maintenance.

DISEASE: Chronic granulocytic leukemia.

SIDE EFFECTS: Bone marrow depression; skin pigmentation; interstitial pulmonary fibrosis; amenorrhea.

Chlorambucil.

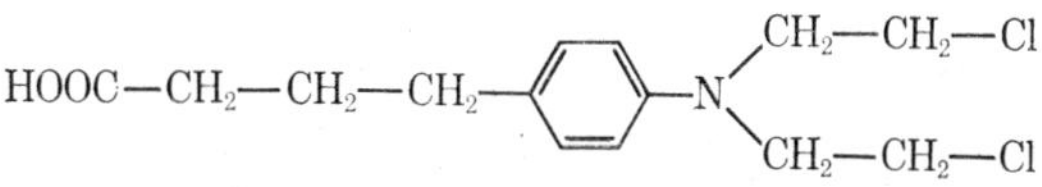

$$HOOC-CH_2-CH_2-CH_2-\bigcirc-N \diagup CH_2-CH_2-Cl \atop \diagdown CH_2-CH_2-Cl$$

4-{p-[bis(2-chloroethyl)amino]phenyl}butyric acid

DOSE: Available in 2-mg tablets; 0.1–0.2 mg/kg body weight per day.

DISEASE: Chronic lymphocytic leukemia; lymphosarcoma; Hodgkin's disease; ovarian and mammary carcinoma.

SIDE EFFECTS: Bone marrow depression; anorexia; nausea and vomiting.

Cyclophosphamide.

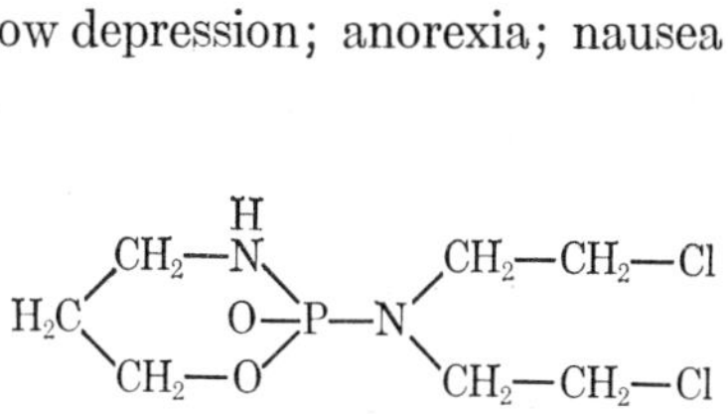

$$H_2C \diagup{}^{CH_2-\overset{H}{N}} \diagdown \atop \diagdown CH_2-O \diagup{}^{O-P-N} \diagdown{}^{CH_2-CH_2-Cl} \atop {}^{CH_2-CH_2-Cl}$$

1-bis(2-chloroethyl)-amino-1-oxo-2-aza-5-oxaphosphoridin

DOSE: Available in 100-, 200-, and 500-mg ampuls and in 50-mg tablets. Oral or IV: 150–200 mg/day.

DISEASE: Ovarian and mammary carcinoma; bronchogenic carcinoma; neuroblastoma; rhabdomyosarcoma; acute lymphocytic leukemia; chronic leukemias; lymphosarcomas; multiple myeloma; epidermoid or oat-cell carcinoma of lung; retinoblastoma; mycosis fungoides; Burkitt's lymphoma.

SIDE EFFECTS: Anorexia; nausea; vomiting; bone marrow depression; alopecia; occasional hemorrhagic urinary cystitis.

Melphalan.

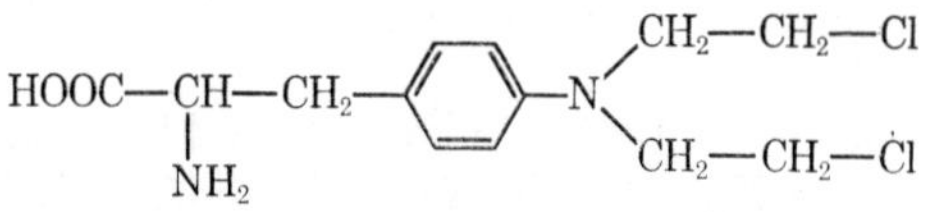

$$HOOC-CH-CH_2 \quad N \diagup CH_2-CH_2-Cl \diagdown CH_2-CH_2-\dot{C}l$$
$$\underset{NH_2}{|}$$

p-(di-2-chloroethylamino)phenylalanine (phenylalanine mustard)

DOSE: Available in 2-mg tablets; 6 mg daily for 2–3 weeks.

DISEASE: Multiple myeloma; plasmacytic myeloma; macroglobulinemia; cystadenocarcinoma of the ovary.

SIDE EFFECTS: Anorexia; nausea; vomiting; leukopenia, thrombocytopenia; agranulocytosis.

BCNU (bischloroethyl nitrosourea) (experimental).

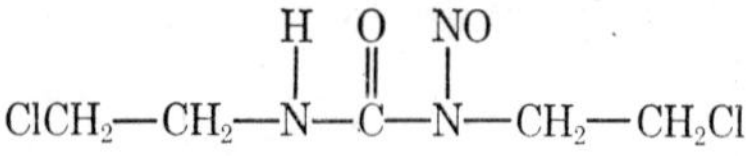

$$ClCH_2-CH_2-\overset{H}{\underset{}{N}}-\overset{O}{\underset{}{C}}-\overset{NO}{\underset{}{N}}-CH_2-CH_2Cl$$

1,3-bis(2-chloroethyl)-1-nitrosourea

DOSE: 1–2 mg/kg/month.

DISEASE: Hodgkin's disease; possibly some sarcomas and bronchogenic carcinoma.

SIDE EFFECTS: Bone marrow depression (sometimes delayed).

Antimetabolites

The antimetabolite competes with, and displaces the substrate of enzymes essential in DNA synthesis. Combination of the antimetabolite with the enzyme results in interference with nucleic acid synthesis of cell DNA and inhibition of cell reproduction. The antimetabolites may be classified according to specific inhibitory action of each:

(1) Purine Antagonists
(2) Glutamine Antagonists
(3) Folic Acid Antagonists
(4) Pyrimidine Antagonists
(5) Deoxycytidylic Acid Antagonists

6-Mercaptopurine (purine metabolism antagonist).

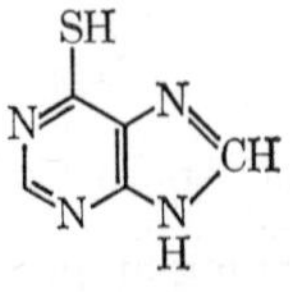

6-purinethiol (6-MP)

DOSE: Available in 50-mg tablets; 2.5–5 mg/kg/day.

DISEASE: Acute leukemia (children); acute leukemia (adults); chronic myelogenous leukemia.

SIDE EFFECTS: Leukopenia; thrombocytopenia; anemia; hepatic necrosis; ulceration of gastrointestinal tract; nausea; vomiting; anorexia; cumulative bone marrow depression.

DON and azaserine (glutamine antagonists).

$$N_2CH-\overset{\overset{O}{\|}}{C}-CH_2-CH_2-\underset{\underset{NH_2}{|}}{CH}-COOH \qquad N_2CH-\overset{\overset{O}{\|}}{C}-O-CH_2-\underset{\underset{NH_2}{|}}{CH}-COOH$$

6-diazo-5-oxo-L-norleucine. o-diazoacetyl-L-serine.

DISEASE: Acute leukemia. Antitumor activity is limited in man but DON has been somewhat effective in treatment of choriocarcinoma.

SIDE EFFECTS: Hepatotoxicity (azaserine); ulcerations of buccal mucosa and tongue; glossitis; superficial ulcerations of GI tract.

Methotrexate (folic acid antagonist).

4-amino-N^{10}-methyl-pteroylglutamic acid

DOSE: Available in 2.5-mg tablets; parenteral: 5- and 50-mg vials; intrathecal: 0.15–0.25 mg/kg every 2–5 days until symptoms clear or until systemic toxicity; oral: 1.25–5 mg/day or 30 mg/m^2/twice weekly or 5–10 mg daily; divided daily dose: 1.25 mg ($^1/_2$ tablet) every 6 hours or 0.62 mg 4 times a day; intra-arterial: 50 mg/day plus IM citrovorum factor 6 mg every 4 hours.

DISEASE: Uterine choriocarcinoma; chorioma, chorioadenoma destruens, and hydatidiform mole; acute and subacute leukemias and leukemic meningitis; neuroblastomas; other fields of interest include: lymphosarcoma; tumors of head, neck, and pelvis; and in mycosis fungoides.

SIDE EFFECTS: Generalized erythematous rash; occasional alopecia; stomatitis; gingivitis; enteritis; oral and GI ulceration, occasionally with hemorrhage; nausea; vomiting; diarrhea; hematologic depression with occasional hemorrhage and/or septicemia; hepatotoxicity (acute liver atrophy, necrosis, fatty degeneration).

5-fluorouracil (pyrimidine metabolism antagonist).

DOSE: Available in 500-mg vials; 15 mg/kg daily for 5 days.

DISEASE: Advanced cancer of the breast and GI tract; adenocarcinoma colon; adenocarcinoma rectum; adenocarcinoma breast; lower response rate for: stomach, esophagus, pancreas, genitourinary tract, lungs (even lower).

SIDE EFFECTS: Diarrhea; mouth ulcers; pancytopenia; mucositis; various skin reactions; GI ulcers resulting in hemorrhagic enteritis; alopecia.

Cytarabine (deoxycytidylic acid antagonist).

1-β-D-arabinofuranosylcytosine (cytosine arabinoside)

DOSE: 3 mg/kg for induction 6 to 20 days; maintenance therapy twice weekly.

DISEASE: Acute and chronic lymphocytic leukemia in children; acute myeloblastic leukemia in adults; Hodgkin's disease.

SIDE EFFECTS: Acute—occasional nausea and vomiting; headaches; fever and localized dermatitis; Cumulative—bone marrow depression; liver damage.

Antibiotics

The biochemical activity of certain antibiotics against bacterial cells can also be applied to tumor cells. The mechanisms of action for the antibiotics are similar to the well known bactericidal and bacteriostatic effects against bacterial cells. The antibiotics used in cancer chemotherapy may exert their action by inhibiting synthesis of protein, RNA, or DNA in rapidly dividing cells.

Actinomycin D dactinomycin (inhibits RNA synthesis).

DOSE: Parenteral: 0.5-mg vials;   (1) 15 μg/kg × 5, repeat every 2 weeks;   (2) 3–6 μg/kg for total of 125 μg/kg, then 7.5 μg/kg weekly.

DISEASE: Trophoblastic tumors; testicular cancer; neuorblastoma; Wilm's tumor; hepatoma; rhabdomyosarcoma; melanoma.

SIDE EFFECTS: Hypoplasia of bone marrow; hepatic and renal toxicity; anorexia; nausea; vomiting; alopecia.

Other antibiotics for which little information is available include:

Mithramycin (experimental). Japanese; a chromomycin (inhibits RNA synthesis).

This is an experimental drug still under investigation. A standard dosage has not been determined. Preliminary evidence indicates efficacy in testicular cancer; neuroblastoma. Clinical experiments have shown the following toxicity: hypocalcemia; hemorrhagic phenomenon; hypoplasia of bone marrow; hepatic and renal toxicity.

Daunomycin (experimental). An anthracycline (inhibits RNA synthesis).

This is an experimental drug still under investigation.

DOSE: IV: 0.8–1 mg/kg/day for 3–6 days.

DISEASE: Induction acute lymphocytic leukemia in children; acute leukemia in adults.

Mitomycin C (experimental). Japanese (inhibits DNA synthesis).

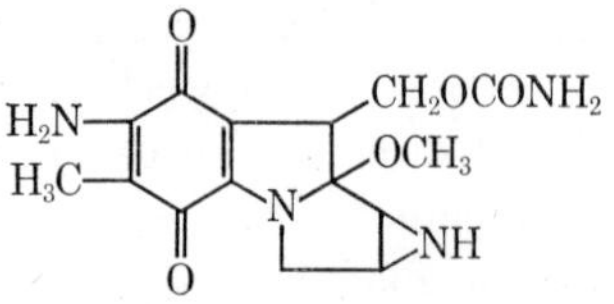

This is an experimental drug still under investigation. A standard dosage has not been determined. Preliminary evidence indicates efficacy in carcinoma of colon; rectal carcinoma; carcinoma of the stomach; carcinoma of pancreas.

Vinca Alkaloids

These alkaloids, extracts of the plant *Vinca rosea* Linn., act biologically to interfere with cell mitosis by producing metaphase arrest. Other cytologic changes including abnormal nuclear cleavages, multinucleated cells, and condensed nuclei are also produced. These biologic cytotoxic effects result in tumor cell death during replication.

Vinblastine sulfate.

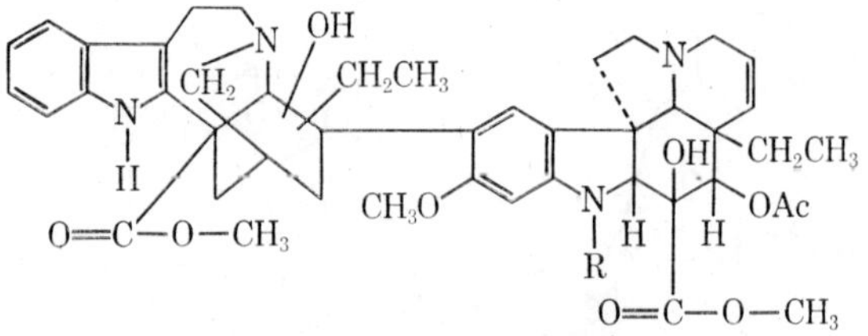

Vinblastine ($R = CH_3$)

DOSE: Parenteral: 10 mg/vial. Start with 0.1–0.15 mg/kg with weekly increments in dose of 0.05 mg/kg depending on hematological picture; then weekly optimum maintenance dose.

DISEASE: Hodgkin's disease; choriocarcinoma; lymphosarcoma; mycosis fungoides; acute and chronic leukemias; occasional response in a wide variety of other tumors.

SIDE EFFECTS: Leukopenia; neurological manifestations, including mental depression, paresthesias, loss of deep tendon reflexes, headache, convulsions; dysfunction of autonomic nervous system, including ileus; urinary retention; GI disturbances of nausea, vomiting, diarrhea, and anorexia; rare dermatitis and alopecia; phlebitis at site of injection.

Vincristine sulfate.

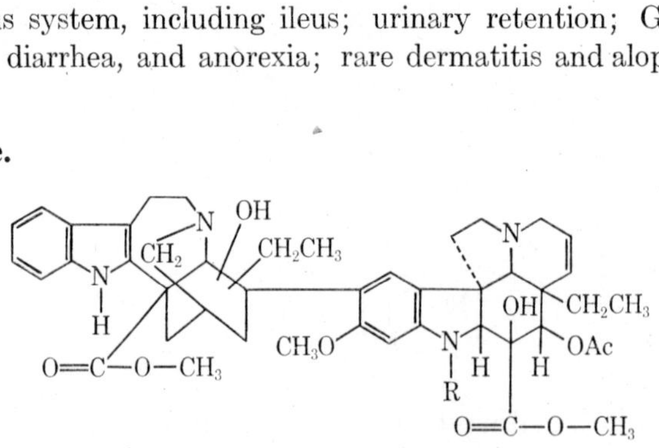

Vincristine ($R = O—C—H$)

DOSE: Parenteral: 1 or 5 mg/vial. Start with 0.01 mg/kg with weekly increments of 0.01 mg/kg to response or toxicity; then weekly maintenance at optimum dose.

DISEASE: Acute leukemia in children; Hodgkin's disease and related lymphomas.

SIDE EFFECTS: Neurological including paresthesias, foot drop, double vision; autonomic nervous system dysfunction; alopecia; hematological suppression; hyperuricemia.

Miscellaneous

1-Asparaginase. 1-Asparaginase is a complex enzyme of unknown structure (amino acid inhibitor).

The enzyme 1-asparaginase when injected catalyzes the destruction of the amino acid, 1-asparagine, converting it to 1-aspartate and ammonia. The nutrient, asparagine, is more essential to the malignant leukemic cell than to the normal lymphocyte. 1-Asparaginase activity, therefore, *denies* the amino acid to the tumor cell.

DOSE: 50–2000 IU/kg daily for 3 weeks.

DISEASE: Acute and chronic leukemia; lymphomas.

SIDE EFFECTS: Nausea; anorexia; vomiting; fever; hypersensitivity; anemia; clotting abnormalities; liver dysfunction; axotemia; pancreatitis; central nervous system toxicity (adults only).

Hydroxyurea.

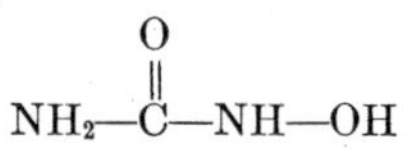

$$NH_2-\overset{\overset{\textstyle O}{\|}}{C}-NH-OH$$

Interferes with DNA synthesis, probably at a late stage. It appears to alter the conversion of ribonucleotide to deoxyribonucleotide. This latter nucleotide is a significant source of deoxyribose essential to the synthesis of DNA.

DOSE: Oral: 20–40 mg/kg/day.

DISEASE: Chronic granulocytic leukemia; melanomas.

SIDE EFFECTS: Bone marrow depression.

Procarbazine.

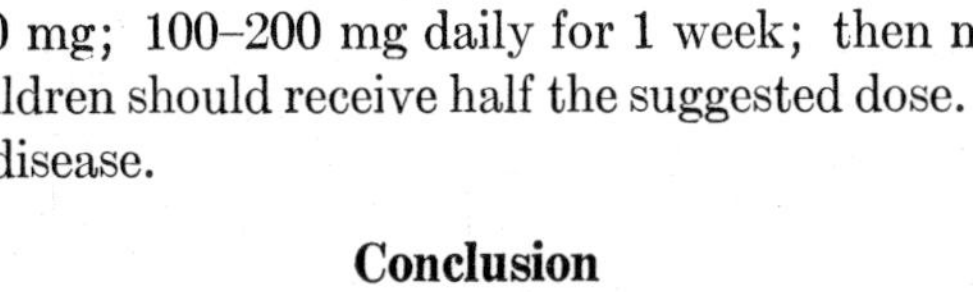

$$\underset{\underset{\textstyle CH_3}{|}}{\overset{\overset{\textstyle CH_3}{|}}{HC}}-\overset{\overset{\textstyle H}{|}}{N}-\overset{\overset{\textstyle O}{\|}}{C}-\bigcirc-CH_2-\overset{\overset{\textstyle H}{|}}{N}-\overset{\overset{\textstyle H}{|}}{N}-CH_3 \cdot HCl$$

N-isopropyl-α-(2-methylhydrazino)-p-toluamide monohydrochloride.

Probably acts by inhibition of RNA and DNA synthesis, but the exact manner of action has not been defined.

DOSE: Capsules of 50 mg; 100–200 mg daily for 1 week; then maintained at 100 mg daily to toxicity. Children should receive half the suggested dose.

DISEASE: Hodgkin's disease.

Conclusion

At this time no chemotherapy is considered curative with the rare exception of that for choriocarcinoma and Burkitt's lymphoma. However, palliative benefits are definitely attainable and include prolongation of useful survival as well as subjective and objective remission of physical and emotional disability. Objectively, decreases in tumor mass and metastatic involvement occur with chemotherapy alone. It has proved to be, moreover, a valuable adjunct to surgical and irradiation procedures.

In addition to the discovery of new experimental compounds, chemotherapy research has been directed toward alteration in dosimetry and employment of various drug combinations to enhance tumoricidal effects, decrease toxicity and prolong survival.

Bibliography

1. A. Goldin, et al., "Experimental Screening Procedures and Clinical Predictability Value." *Cancer Chemother. Rep.* **50,** 173 (1966).
2. J. D. Watson, *The Molecular Biology of the Gene.* 1st ed., W. A. Benjaman & Co., New York 1965.
3. C. G. Zubrod, et al., "Chemotherapy Program of National Cancer Institute,". *Cancer Chemotherapy Rep.* **50,** 349 (1966).
4. V. T. Oliverio and C. G. Zubrod, "Clinical Pharmacology of the Effective Antitumor Drugs," *Ann. Rev. Pharmacol.* **5,** 335–356 (1965).
5. J. K. Luce, G. P. Bodey Sr., and E. Frei, III, "The Systemic Approach to Cancer Therapy," *Hosp. Prac.* **2,** (10); 42–55 (1967).
6. E. Frei, III "The Effect of Cancer Chemotherapeutic Agents on Normal Tissues in Man," *Fed. Proc.* **26,** 918–924, (1967).
7. E. Frei, III and T. L. Loo, "Pharmacologic Basis for the Chemotherapy of Leukemia," *Pharmacol. for Physicians* **1** (1), 4 (1967).
8. E. Frei, III and E. J. Freireich, "Progress and Perspectives in the Chemotherapy of Acute Leukemia," *Advances Chemother.* **2,** 269–298 (1965).
9. O. S. Selawry, et al., "New Treatment Schedule with Improved Survival in Childhood Leukemia," *J.A.M.A.* **194,** 75–81 (1965).
10. S. A. Schwartz and S. Perry, "Patient Protection in Cancer Chemotherapy," *J.A.M.A.* **197,** 623–627 (1966).
11. R. S. Schwartz, "Immuno-Suppressive Drugs," *Progr. Allerg.* **9,** 246 (1965).
12. E. M. Hersh and E. J. Freireich, "Host Defense Mechanisms and Their Modification by Cancer Chemotherapy," *Meth. Cancer. Res. IV* (in press).
13. B. Hattlor and B. Amos, "The Immunobiology of Cancer," *Monogr. Surg. Sci.* **3,** 1 (1966).
14. J. K. Luce, G. P. Bodey, and E. Frei, III, "The Systemic Approach to Cancer Therapy," *Hosp. Prac.* **2** (10) (October, 1967).
15. U.S. Department of Health, Education, & Welfare, "Progress Against Cancer Report," U.S. Gov't. Printing Office, Washington, D.C., 1969, pp. 1–77.

CHARLES J. MASUR, M.D.
Lederle Laboratories

CARBON BLACK

Since 1960 the domestic consumption of carbon black, already a billion-pound-per-year commodity chemical product in 1950, has increased considerably more than expected. In the two decades, 1950–1970, growth was at the compound rate of 4.9% annually, but during the decade 1960–1970, the annual rate jumped to 7.2%. Why? In the United States tire consumption has exceeded predictions, truck-tire consumption has grown faster than that of passenger tires, and the loading of carbon has increased due to greatly improved synthetic elastomers and correspondingly improved carbons.

The growth figures for the Free World outside the United States are 10.3 and 9.8% for 1950–1970 and 1960–1970, respectively.

Looking ahead, the U.S. growth rate is expected to drop to 4.6% annually in the year 1975 and to about 7% for the rest of the free world. By the end of the century it is likely that the U.S. annual growth rate will not exceed about 2–3%. The cause of the decline will be a saturation of the transportation market for automobiles as other forms of transportation inevitably take over a larger fraction of total miles traveled.

Nevertheless, carbon black consumption in the Free World will reach the staggering total of at least approx 16 billion lb by the year 2000 of which the U.S. share of consumption will be about 40%, dropping from 50% in 1970. These trends are depicted in Figures 1 and 2. The only published source of detailed statistics on carbon black manufacture and its raw materials in the United States is the Minerals Yearbook of the U.S. Bureau of Mines (1).

The U.S. world dominance in carbon black production and technology has been an almost unique case in the chemical and allied products industry. Since 1950, the dominance in production facilities has been diminishing at an accelerating rate, but

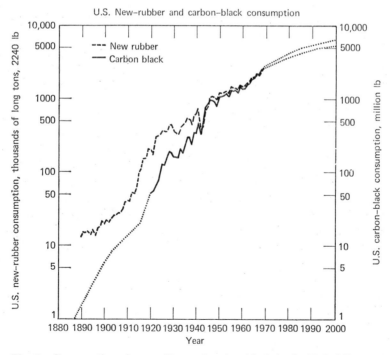

Fig. 1. Consumption of new rubber and carbon black in the United States.

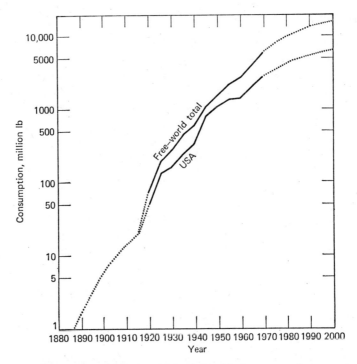

Fig. 2. Worldwide growth in carbon black consumption.

the technology is still almost exclusively in American hands as is a large portion of the ownership of carbon plants outside the United States.

Except for the partial ownership of one large carbon black facility in Europe by a group of tire companies, the carbon black business has remained essentially noncaptive.

An important trend of the last two decades has been the worldwide dispersion of carbon black plants. Instead of building mammoth plants as in other petrochemical product lines, the carbon black industry has chosen, for logistic and competitive reasons, to build small, expandable plants in nearly every consumer country of five to ten million or greater population. In countries of about 30 million or more population, often there are three or more producers. Japan has the amazing total of twelve. This fragmentation of capacity is shown in Table 1. From these data it is seen that the average capacity of plants outside the United States is about 60 million lb/yr, there being only two cases (Germany and Japan) in which a single producer has interest in more than one plant in a given country. By contrast, the United States has ten producers, of which two have almost negligible capacity, making special-purpose carbons only. The total U.S. capacity is on the order of 3.5 billion lb, giving an average capacity per important producer of about 400 million lb with an average per plant of over 100 million lb, about twice the average outside the United States. The largest U.S. plants have capacities up to about 400 million lb.

To make a pound of carbon black requires roughly two pounds of oil. Carbon black is shipped as beads or powder in bags, cartons, or in bulk (beads only) at a bulk density of 25–30 lb/ft³. Shipment is largely in rail cars and trucks. The raw-material oil is shipped in barges or tankers and has a bulk density of about 65 lb/ft³. Because of the inherently lower shipping costs for oil in large-volume movements it is cheaper

Table 1. Distribution of World Carbon Black Capacity[a]

Country	Number of plants	Estimated annual capacity, million lb
North America		
Canada	2	270
Mexico	1	90
total	3	360
South America		
Argentina	1	70
Brazil	2	130
Colombia	2	50
Venezuela	1	30
total	6	280
Europe		
Belgium	1	20
England	5	630
France	4	350
West Germany	6	550
Holland	2	260
Italy	3	280
Spain	3	140
Sweden	1	50
Yugoslavia	1	30
total	26	2310
Australia, S.E. Asia		
Australia	3	160
India	2	90
Japan	12	550
Korea	1	30
Philippines	1	30
total	19	860
Africa	2	90
Israel	1	30
total free world excluding U.S.	57	3930
United States	37	4000
remainder of the world[b]		1000
grand total		9000

[a] Including expansions through 1971.

[b] Estimated capacity.

in most cases to move 2 lb of oil than 1 lb of carbon black.   For this reason and because service with respect to supply and technical assistance are important, the small local plant apparently has, up until now, made good business sense in this highly competitive industry.

In the next ten years this trend of small-plant proliferation will level off particularly if the industry retains its noncaptive status, thus avoiding a rash of new small plants sited at each major tire plant.   For purely economic reasons, there will be a tendency to consolidate at present sites, building such plants up in size and economic efficiency.   Sites with deep-water transportation will be strongly preferred so that raw materials can come from any part of the world.

Data are not available on carbon black production outside the Free World. These countries have imported large quantities from the West over the past decade; decline of imports to the USSR and other eastern European countries indicates a fairly rapid buildup of their carbon black facilities. From data on tire production and on production of synthetic rubber, as well as natural-rubber import trends, it is possible to make a good estimate of non-Free World carbon consumption. By the end of 1971, the total consumption for this group of countries, including Communist China, should fall in the range of 1 to 2 billion lb/yr with the lower figure more probable. By 1976, the range should be 2–3.5 billion with a most probable range of 2.5–3.0 billion. The corresponding figures for Communist China alone are 100–300 million lb, for 1971, and 500–700 million lb, for 1976. The lower end of the range is more probable. In substantiation of such predictions, the USSR alone has published intentions of increasing from two fully integrated polyisoprene rubber plants in operation in 1970 to ten such plants in the next five to ten years.

Process Technology and Economics

The process descriptions under Carbon black (see Carbon) generally depict the basic principles of various processes used to make carbon black. Any changes in the process flow sheets will be evident from the following discussion.

The channel-black process has persisted in use well beyond most expectations, but now is finally almost obsolete, accounting for only about 4% of U.S. carbon black consumption in 1970. No new plants have been built in over two decades. There are left in the United States only three plants, one in Germany, and one or two very small ones in Japan. Most rely heavily on enrichment of natural or coke-oven gas with liquid hydrocarbons. A large portion of the output, which probably does not exceed a world total of about 150 million lb, is used for pigmentary and other special purposes, but rubber users still cling to the rest. In ten years or sooner the channel process will have disappeared; besides being obsolete, it also entails the smoke-pollution problem.

Progress in the furnace process, while evolutionary rather than revolutionary, has been of considerable economic significance and has kept the United States firmly entrenched in its world leadership in this industry. Furnace black now accounts for about 85% of all U.S. carbon black, contrasted to about 68% in 1950 and 79% in 1960. Outside the United States the proportion of furnace black is even higher.

As described in detail in Vol. 4, the process consists essentially of injecting, usually in horizontal cylindrical reactors, an atomized heavy aromatic oil into a swirling mass of combustion products of an auxiliary fuel burned with air introduced at ambient temperature or preheated to 1000–1400°F. In the last decade the main process change in the reactors has been a relatively large variation in turbulence by increased reactor velocities (2,3) and/or by use of refractory restrictor rings (4). The high-turbulence processes are used for the finer particle size, more reinforcing carbons for tire treads.

In an opposite trend to lower and more precisely controlled turbulence, the efficiency and versatility of the furnace black process for the coarser carbons have been increased by introduction of mammoth vertical cylindrical furnaces by at least one producer (5–7). Detailed information on processes carried out in the reactors is proprietary. The reader is referred to the patent literature for details available to the public.

Another process innovation of considerable significance is the use of alkali metal salts as oil additives to control the properties of the product (8,9). This technique is used to make major quality changes, the so-called low-modulus or low-structure carbons, and to achieve "trim" control of carbon structure and modulus properties.

Yields per gallon of oil have been increased somewhat by increasing both reactor size and throughput relative to size. The latter trend has been due largely to the use of preheated air. Another factor indirectly affecting yield is the discovery of process conditions that improve road-wear quality at a given particle-size level throughout the tread grades of carbon. This permits achieving a given road-wear level with slightly coarser, higher-yield carbons with a bonus of lower heat buildup as well.

First cost of plants per annual pound of capacity has been kept under reasonable control at around 15¢/(lb/yr) (for grass roots expandable plants at 50 million lb/yr initial capacity) by engineering improvements. Several of these improvements are the result of greater use of atmospheric and forced-circulation air-cooling to replace part of the direct water coolant. The reduction in volume of flue gases assists collection. Formerly, plants used electrostatic agglomerators followed by two to four cyclones and a bag filter or wet scrubber. Modern plants use one cyclone agglomerator and a high-capacity, high-pressure-drop bag filter. Bag filters have been improved tremendously not only because a wide range of temperature-resistant glass-fiber filter media have been perfected but also due to mechanical improvements in many important respects. The combustible waste gases are used to an increasing extent for steam generation and for drying the carbon beads. Increased use of preheated air obtained in flue-gas heat exchangers has raised the heating value of the wet stack gases from 33 to a level of about 45 Btu/ft^3 wet basis. Moisture content has been reduced from 55 to 45% by volume. Since sulfur in the carbon feed stock converts largely to H_2S, the trend is to burn all waste gas, using higher and higher stacks to dissipate sulfur as SO_2. Improvements in stack burners also allow burning traces of carbon. Because the oils used as raw materials are substantially ash free, a modern carbon plant has negligible emission of solids from the stack.

Beading equipment has been increased in power and throughput per unit; bead quality has improved at the same time.

Raw materials for furnace black are largely from petroleum refineries, highly recycled catalytically cracked heavy gas oils, extracts from such catalytic cycle stock, and still a certain amount of tar from thermal cracking of catalytic cycle stocks or straight-run gas oils. Relatively little heavy aromatic oil from petrochemical plants finds its way into carbon black as yet. Anthracene oil from coal-tar distillation is still used extensively in Europe where this practice originated. It is also used in Japan.

Most producers prefer to operate with auxiliary gaseous fuels although operation with oil as auxiliary fuel is practiced successfully. The preferred auxiliary fuels are natural and refinery gas, but coke oven gas is used to some extent.

All of these changes, coupled with vastly improved and compact layouts, instrumentation and general engineering, have made the modern carbon plant like its many clean, colorful counterparts in the chemical process industry. Such modern carbon plants are cleaner than even a modern power plant burning residual fuel oil. One of the latest U.S. plants put on stream in 1969 is shown in Figure 3. This layout places all controls at the furnace end by folding the plant back on itself instead of stringing it out in a single line as in former practice. The flow sheet (Fig. 4) which depicts a modern furnace plant design, is to be compared with the flow sheets shown in the article in Vol. 4.

Looking ahead in furnace black technology, it is clear that this method will eventually account for all carbon black production with the exception of thermal carbons and possibly acetylene black. Lamp blacks already need no longer be discussed sepa-

Fig. 3. Two-unit furnace carbon plant of modern design (plant on stream in 1969). Courtesy Columbian Division, Cities Service Company.

rately. The small amount of lamp black still is made by variants on the continuous furnace-black process method. Except for the high cost of already developed high-temperature heat treatments, furnace black could, through such posttreatment, replace acetylene black now. As by-product acetylene from off-specification calcium carbide becomes less available and/or more costly, replacement of acetylene black may occur within ten years or less.

We can expect certain definite trends in furnace black technology (as opposed to product trends which are discussed separately):

1. Larger individual furnaces or reactors coupled with larger plants. (Larger reactors improve economics and simplify controls; larger plants greatly improve economics.)

2. Increased emphasis on indirect cooling with economic benefits in collection equipment capacity, in sensible heat recovery (supplying preheated air for the process), and in increased heating value of waste gases.

3. Closed-loop control, awaiting only the development of automatic on-stream sensing methods for the properties of the product or satisfactory correlation of already continuously measurable indirect output variables with carbon properties. The potential economic gain from this step is very large.

4. Limited use of oxygen enrichment in special cases in which oxygen is relatively cheap and the nitrogenfree waste gas can be used for synthesis involving carbon monoxide and hydrogen. This type of operation would also eliminate the need for an outside refinery or natural gas. As the heating value of the off-gas is raised, it becomes usable as the auxiliary gas for the process.

5. A gradual increase in the pressure in the reactor and in the collection system as process trends to get improved qualities require greater energy input at each step. In addition to quality reasons, higher pressure drops can give more economical collection systems and make possible easier recovery of the stock gases for chemical synthesis. There is no fundamental reason why pressures of several atmospheres could not be used, ie pressure levels at least equivalent to one stage of compression when, for

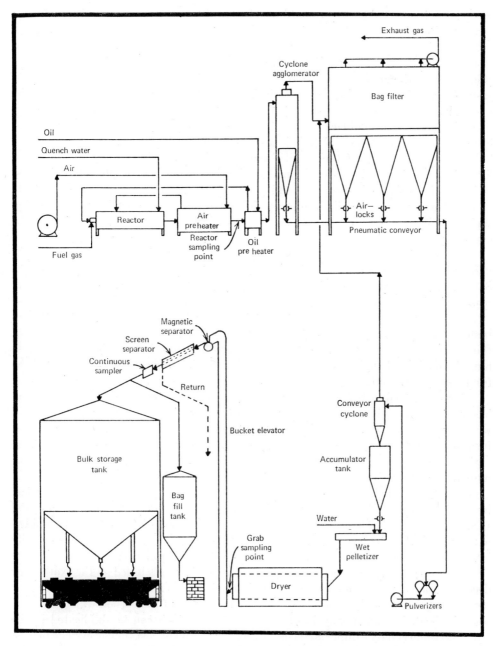

Fig. 4. Flowsheet of a modern furnace carbon plant showing greatly improved design and preheating arrangements.   Courtesy American Chemical Society

example, recovery of synthesis gas and reuse become important, at which time total replacement of air with oxygen could come into use.

6.   Limited direct or indirect integration of raw-material production with other petrochemical operations needing olefins and light aromatics as feed stocks.   The carbon operation requires fuels at the extremes of the normal petrochemical require-

ments, ie light gas and heavy aromatics. There will be a concurrent trend to use more heavy feed stocks (gas oils) in ethylene production which will produce a relatively large amount of heavy aromatics (C_{11} and higher) compared with the present naphtha feed stocks. These heavy aromatics will be used to an increasing extent as carbon feed stocks. With the gradual decline in the relative importance of catalytic cracking for gasoline manufacture and an increase in hydrocracking, carbon feed stock from the by-products of ethylene manufacture will be needed to fill the gap in feed stock supply.

The thermal carbon black process, a cyclical process based usually on natural gas, has not changed in essential detail since the early 1960s in the U.S. However, there has been an emergence of the all-oil thermal black process in Britain after years of limited operation. If European thermal black prices, which are supported by the need to import from the United States, hold at 1970 levels, there will be additional plants built in Europe using the all-oil process. The all-oil process produces carbons having slightly different properties so that complete interchangeability with gas-based thermal carbons is not always possible.

In the U.S., progress is being made in the manufacture of thermal black by enriching the low-carbon natural-gas feed to increase the carbon output per unit investment. So far, mainly liquified petroleum gas (qv) (LPG) has been used, but there is no reason why heavier natural-gas liquids and light petroleum oils could not be used. Use of still heavier enriching oils leads to inhomogeneity of cracking as the dissociation temperature for heavy oils is far below that for methane. As the molecular weight of the enriching oil increases, a point is reached at which a switch to the all-oil process must be made, although gas can still be used in the heating cycle to supplement heat from carbon burn out.

Use of thermal carbons as a percentage of the total U.S. carbon black consumption has grown from 5% in 1952 to over 11% in 1970. Thermal carbon use will grow somewhat faster than all carbon black over the next decade. However, the highly efficient furnace processes used for coarser blacks will be adapted to make carbons that compete with thermal carbons, the prices of which have risen much faster than the prices of more reinforcing carbons in recent years.

By the end of the century the cyclical thermal process will become a much less important factor, probably reaching a peak at no more than about 15% of the total U.S. output in another five to ten years. After this, decline will be increasingly rapid as natural-gas value increases for pipe-line distribution, forcing thermal blacks finally into direct price competition with the ever more versatile furnace blacks.

The acetylene black process is a modified thermal process based on the exothermic decomposition of acetylene carried out continuously and in absence of air. The process persists only because of the peculiar electrical properties of the carbon which have not been duplicated commercially in other carbons but which can be duplicated in the laboratory and could be duplicated commercially at a higher cost than acetylene blacks. If acetylene black remains as important in dry cells as in the past, the eventual size of this market will induce the development of economical heat-treating processes for furnace carbons to convert them into equal or superior raw materials for dry cells. Acetylene, even that from off-specification calcium carbide, costs more as feed stock than many furnace blacks sell for today.

Pollution, health, and safety factors have not been critical problems in the industry for a decade except in cases of limited air pollution around older plants in which bag, filter installations were uneconomic. Dust explosions are unknown. No evidence exists that carbon is a health hazard over and beyond that of any powdered or dusty material. Clearly, the growing concern over carbon monoxide as an air pollutant will mean that all stack gases (containing about 12% CO on a dry basis) will have to be burned before discharge. Looking ahead, all technology needed to keep this industry from health and pollution difficulties is already known and merely needs to be applied.

Products and Applications

Since about 1962 product development of carbon black has had a new surge of activity and a large number of new rubber and special-purpose carbons have been introduced.

In the rubber field the most notable developments have been oil-based furnace carbons of very low structure and also of high and very high structure. In the field of specialty blacks the important developments are replacements for channel black, ranging from low-color blacks similar to rubber grades up through highly successful long-flow-ink blacks with superior dispersion properties and a desirable blue tone. However, no really satisfactory substitutes for the high-color channel blacks have been marketed on a significant scale.

Partly because of the increase in the number of carbons and partly because of the need to standardize tire construction and performance to meet government regulations, ASTM standards have finally penetrated the for a long time mysterious art of carbon black. There are ASTM standards for some 42 grades of furnace, thermal, and channel process carbons for rubber (10). In addition, ASTM has gone to a numerical designation which displaces the long-used letter designations; for example, SAF is now N/110. It is interesting that ASTM standards were established even for the rapidly vanishing channel black. Detailed procedures for analyzing and characterizing blacks have now been published for the first time (11). This new source, which is a milestone in the carbon black literature, gives sufficient information for almost any need a consumer or producer would have in characterizing carbons.

The improved carbons with carefully balanced combinations of structure, particle size, and surface area, which have been developed over the last ten years, have added about the same increment of road wear to tires made from synthetic rubber as was added to synthetic rubber of the older type in the 1940–1950 period by the introduction of oil-furnace blacks replacing channel and reinforcing gas-furnace blacks. The emphasis now is on carbon changes to make other tire improvements, such as decreased heat generation, improved skid resistance, improved cord adhesion, and improved tire reliability in general. The expected future trends in product qualities for rubber have been reviewed by Burgess and Lyon (12). Of course, improvements in the rubbers have added greatly to road wear and the improvements due to carbon and also to rubber, are at least partially additive.

Looking ahead, it is highly likely that improvements of rubber carbons will be made through modifications in carbon surface chemistry. This is the approach needed to produce a "synthetic channel black." Such a product can be expected on the market, as there is a definite small residual demand for this type of carbon in compounding rubber and no really satisfactory substitute has been marketed for certain critical uses.

In applications technology a significant breakthrough in rubber processing is the so-called hydrosolution masterbatching (HSMB) process introduced in the early 1960s (13,14). This process borrows, from older technology used in the color pigment industry, the technique of flushing or transferring pigment from an aqueous dispersion to an organic phase that wets the pigment better than water. In the HSMB process, carbon is dispersed in water without surfactants; a solution of rubber (usually the rubber directly from polymerizers) is similarly dispersed in water and the extender oil is dispersed in water also. These three streams are combined, mixed well, and then the rubber–carbon–oil mixture is recovered as coagulum by injecting the mixture into hot water which completely removes the solvent. The resultant masterbatch, after mechanical dewatering and extrusion drying, can be produced to yield a dispersion of carbon as good as is made by banbury mixing. It can be used directly by adding curatives in a roll mill followed by extrusion. Two large commercial units have been on stream in the U.S. for several years and several other commercial units are under consideration.

In a modification of the HSMB process, rubber in latex form is co-masterbatched with rubber in solution form (15). This process is also being used commercially and is a great convenience since common practice calls for blending SBR (styrene-butadiene rubber) and polybutadiene solution rubber to achieve the right overall balance in tire-tread properties.

For reasons that seem hard to analyze, these new processes have not assumed the importance that process economics would indicate. However, in the next decade, when the carbon plants will be larger and closer to the rubber plants, the use of these techniques for the large-volume tread-rubber compounds could increase markedly.

Surprisingly enough, there have been no basically new grades of thermal carbon introduced in the U.S. in 30 years or more. New grades can be expected as this older process is revised by enriching with oil to increase throughput. Thus, the all-oil thermal blacks made in England can be considered a definite quality variant to the U.S. gas thermal blacks.

A wide range of carbons for nonrubber applications has been developed based on direct process and chemically treated furnace blacks. While the older treated channel carbons are still used, they can all be replaced when necessary by carbons of furnace origin made from oils. The most notable development along these lines has been a chemically treated long-flow lithographic ink black which surpasses the older channel carbon on a price performance basis (16). The properties of these newer treated and untreated carbons have been carefully reviewed in relation to the older oxidized channel carbons by Venuto and Hess (17).

The largest single nonrubber use of carbon is for newspaper ink. World consumption for this use is on the order of 100 million lb/yr; practically all news ink is now made from furnace black, whereas 20 years ago it was practically all made from channel black.

The use of newer synthetic-resin vehicles in protective coatings has made the older and very expensive oxidized high-color channel blacks less necessary. Furthermore, it is increasingly possible to make good substitutes starting with furnace carbons which are then chemically oxidized, eg with nitric acid.

One of the few new uses for carbon black has been in dry toners for electrostatic copy machines. If this technique is finally successfully adapted to general printing there would be a large increase in demand for special carbons in dry printing toners. To some extent this would replace carbon now used in fluid inks.

In the plastics field there has been a large increase in the use of thermal carbons in highly-loaded crosslinked polyethylene. This trend will continue as the product has greatly improved weathering, ultraviolet resistance, and mechanical properties.

Research

Ever since the remarkable effects of carbon black on properties of vulcanized rubber were discovered in the 1910–1920 period, research workers have vied with each other to explain the mysterious thing called "reinforcement." For years, there were two schools of thought: physical reinforcement vs reinforcement by the chemical interaction between carbon and vulcanized rubber. In the last ten years, some of the mysteries and erudite controversies have been cleared up. The word "reinforcement," as a generality, is used less often; specific phenomena influencing reinforcement are discussed instead. Today, we can measure and observe carbon–rubber interactions by countless practical, highly precise end-use tests and by use of ever more sophisticated routine laboratory testing devices and research instruments.

It is known that carbons increase the wear of tires made from all types of rubber, in varying degrees. We can now predict the relative wear enhancement in different rubbers, based on the properties of the particular carbon used. We cannot always explain the absolute wear levels for different tire compounds nor can we relate absolute wear levels uniquely to the carbon as there are many factors of tire engineering that greatly influence wear.

New highly useful prediction tools have been described by Micek, Lyon, and Hess (18) in the form of equations relating properties easily measured in the laboratory to the road wear of commercial tires. The properties measured relate to variations in carbon surface area, particle size, and structure.

From a large sampling of results (183 commercial and experimental blacks of different types), it was shown that over 80% of the treadwear variations could be explained on the basis of carbon-black particle size (electron-microscope surface area) and structure (dibutyl phthalate (DBP) or oil absorption). Less interpretive, but equally significant results were achieved by substituting the simpler colloidal properties of tinting strength and iodine number for the electron-microscope (EM) determinations. The latter observations were confirmed by the subsequent studies of Snow (19).

In a subsequent paper (20), Micek et al. developed significant response equations for the prediction of other vulcanizate properties, dealing with natural and synthetic rubber systems. More recently, Hess, McDonald, and Whitlock (21) showed significant correlations of vulcanizate properties (eg modulus, tensile strength, resilience, and treadwear) based solely on electron-microscope measurements of carbon-black particle size and structure (aggregate size and shape). The EM measurements are based on new, automated image-analysis techniques (22) using a Quantimet image-analyzing computer (23). Similar direct electron-microscope measurements on carbon black primary aggregates were also carried out by Medalia and Heckman (24,25). These direct measurements provide more specific information on the physical characteristics of carbon black in terms of the size and shape of the primary units. In this respect they are superior to the nondefinitive DBP and oil-absorption tests which can only broadly classify different carbon blacks on the basis of their structure.

From a more fundamental viewpoint, the carbon–rubber interaction may be viewed in terms of adhesion bonding which, in turn, can be measured and relates well to road wear and other vulcanizate properties. Bonding differences have been measured and correlated with specific differences in the carbons by Hess, Lyon, and Burgess (26). The bonding phenomenon shown as pigment–polymer separation under stress was noted in motion films of carbon-loaded rubber vulcanizates taken under the electron microscope using supported ultramicrotoned sections.

Others who have related pigment–polymer interaction to an adhesion phenomenon are Pickett (27) and Voyutskii et al. (28), the latter having described elastomer reinforcement in terms of the sum of an enormous number of separate, small, bonded structures.

Finer particle size, higher structure, and greater surface activity all improve the adhesion of the black particles to the rubber matrix. However, the particle size and structure effects appear to be closer related to stress distribution than the improved

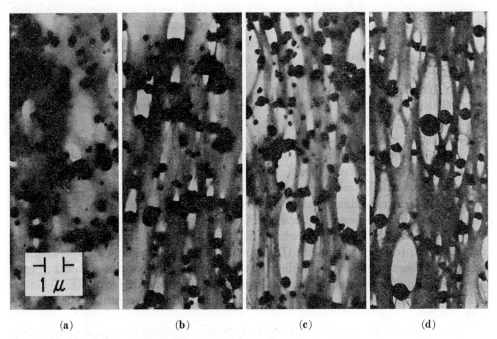

(a)   (b)   (c)   (d)

Fig. 5. Carbon black–rubber adhesion as demonstrated by stretched carbon reinforced rubber sections at varied strains: (a) 100%; (b) 200%; (c) 300%; and (d) 500%.

bonding of the black surface to the rubber. In a classic paper, Andrews and Walsh (29) demonstrated that the strength characteristics of a filled vulcanizate are closely related to the diverting of the path of rupture as it passes from one high-stress region to another at or near the filler surface. Hence, it is likely that small-particle-size carbon blacks are more difficult to separate from the vulcanizate matrix simply because they distribute the stress more uniformly over a higher surface area.

Increased surface activity has been achieved by deoxygenation of the carbon black surface. Such treatments have resulted in increased modulus and abrasion resistance in synthetic rubber systems such as SBR and BR. Adhesion is adversely affected in both of these systems by air or chemical oxidation of the black surface, as well as by partial graphitization of the black at high temperatures. For butyl rubber systems, however, the work of Gessler (30,31) has indicated higher surface activity for oxidized carbon blacks when they are compounded under special conditions (eg high-temperature heat treatments using a chemical promoter, prior to vulcanization).

The remarkable demonstration of the adhesion phenomenon and its excellent correlation with road wear are illustrated by Figure 5, showing a stretched film of vulcanized rubber, and Figure 6, showing the road wear–adhesion index relationship.

These results and those in a subsequent paper by Hess, Burgess, Lyon, and Chirico (32) have indicated that carbon black–polymer interaction is largely physical in nature, and that most of the vulcanizate performance differences associated with commercial types of black can be explained on the basis of the physical parameters of particle size and structure. This view is substantiated by the recent work described earlier (18,21)

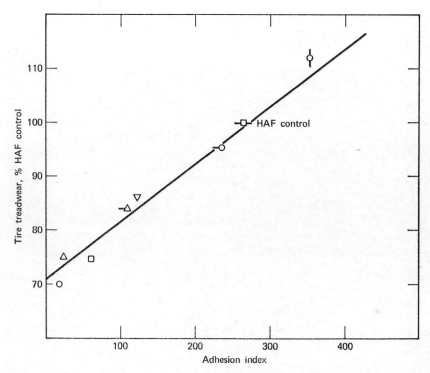

Fig. 6. Correlation of carbon black–rubber adhesion index with actual tire wear. Legend: control, □, high-abrasion furnace black, HAF; △, low-structure HAF, chemically oxidized; ○: graphitized HAF; □, high-structure HAF, graphitized; △, HAF attrited, ball milled; ▽, low-structure HAF; ○, HAF deoxidized, devolatilized; and ◊, high-structure HAF.

and also by studies of Harwood, Payne, and Smith (33), who studied filler reinforcement of elastomers in terms of hysteresis measurements at different strain rates and temperatures. They have concluded that the presence of small filler particles in a rubber increases the hysteresis in at least two ways: (1) hydrodynamically, and (2) viscoelastically.

The two contributions are additive, the first remaining essentially constant with temperature and strain rate, and the second increasing with decreasing temperature. The viscoelastic contribution may be attributed to a region of immobile rubber chains (eg bound rubber) close to the surface of the filler particles. This layer would have the effect of changing the viscoelastic response of the rubber network and accounts reasonably well for the observation that the strength behavior of a filled rubber at one temperature is similar to that of an unfilled rubber at a lower temperature.

The many possibilities for carbon-elastomer interaction have been reviewed by Stickney and Falb (34). It is clear that carbon black can react with polymers by radical capture and a variety of other mechanisms. It is now questionable, however, that chemical interaction is necessary to achieve a high level of reinforcement (eg the high modulus and abrasion resistance that is imparted to modern tire-tread compounds through the use of high-structure, small-particle-size carbons). The inherent surface heterogeneity of carbon black, in terms of out-of-phase stacking of the surface graphite layers and layer plane bending, basal dislocations, etc (35,36), appears adequate to

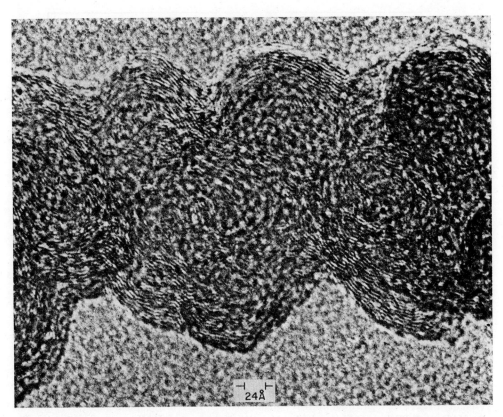

Fig. 7. Paracrystalline orientation of graphite layers in fibrous carbon black primary aggregate (HAF-H).

restrict the mobility of elastomer molecules at the black surface on the basis of physical adsorption.

The great advances made in carbon black research in the 1960s are, in large measure, due to the development of greatly improved techniques and instruments for high-resolution electron microscopy (diffracted-beam and phase-contrast imaging). Work with these instruments and methods on carbon black has been extensively reported by Hess and co-workers (37–40) and has led to a more detailed elucidation of the internal structure of the carbon particle, as well as of the interparticle chaining (structure); the latter phenomenon had not been adequately explained before, only observed qualitatively or measured in a more definitive manner by absorption methods.

It has been shown that the carbon particle is somewhat more ordered in its crystalline arrangement than was formerly supposed. Hess and Ban now call the particle "paracrystalline" instead of the description used earlier as "groupings of small, discrete crystallites." This type of orientation was previously suggested by Ergun (41), based on x-ray diffraction studies. The possibility for such a configuration based on high-resolution, phase-contrast electron microscopy was first suggested by Hess, and Ban (42). A structural model for carbon black along these lines has been proposed by Harling and Heckman (43).

By definition, a "paracrystal" exhibits a degree of order somewhere between the truly crystalline and the amorphous states. In the case of carbon black primary aggregates, there appears to be a continuous network of distorted graphite layers. These show the same general interlayer spacing as graphite without showing any discrete crystalline units. This type of orientation is illustrated in Figure 7 for a segment of a primary aggregate of an ISAF-H-type carbon black. The graphite layers appear as alternate light and dark lines on these images with a period of about 3.6 Å. The layers form a continuous network between the "particles" in the primary aggregates and show a tendency to orient about the various growth centers of formation. The layers also show considerable bending and general distortion. Frequently, one layer can be seen wedged between two others, this always being accompanied by bending. This wedged pattern is similar to the nonbasal edge dislocations that are found in graphites. It now appears that the graphite layers in carbon black particles are largely strung together in this fashion. Examples of nonbasal edge dislocations are shown in Figure 8, both for a standard carbon black (ISAF-H) and a highly graphitized sample. The dislocation areas are much clearer in the graphitized sample because of the larger layers.

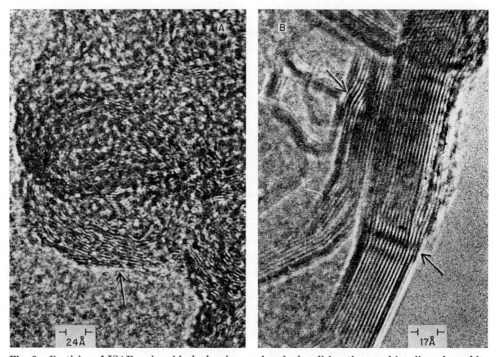

Fig. 8. Particles of ISAF carbon black showing nonbasal edge dislocations and bending of graphite lattice ($d \simeq 3.6$ A).

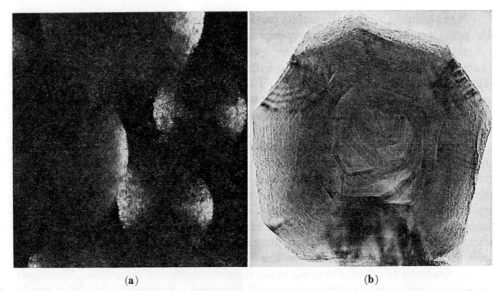

(a)   (b)

Fig. 9. (a) A (002) diffracted-beam electron micrograph of thermal black particles. The white spots represent highly ordered segments of the graphite layer network. The wedge-shaped zones indicate concentric orientation of surface parallel layers. The lack of detail in the centers of the particles indicates higher porosity and/or lower crystalline order internally. (b) Further evidence of high internal porosity is presented in this phase-contrast micrograph of a partially graphitized thermal black particle. Here, a more continuous network of graphite layers now encapsules the entire particle. The outer band represents an image cross-section of the shell, and the 3.4 Å (002) d-spacing is visible in many areas. The fact that the imaging of the graphite layer structure does not continue into the center indicates that the particle is hollow.

Other studies of carbon black particle morphology are illustrated in Figure 9. This figure shows that the graphite layers are oriented around an essentially "hollow" particle center. In nonheat-treated carbon black the hollow center is not necessarily to be regarded as truly hollow, but as an area of less dense, more amorphous character. It represents the less carbonized soft center of the original highly condensed (poly-merized) droplet of hydrocarbon material which forms the original particle in the carbon black formation process. During heating at elevated temperatures, the graph-ite layers tend to straighten and become larger. Orientation proceeds in an outward manner away from the center which then does become more hollow in the true sense of the word.

With the introduction of *cis*-polybutadiene elastomer (BR) in the early 1960s, the use in tire treads of blends of synthetic rubbers, and of blends of natural and synthetic rubber, became established practice. The phase-contrast light microscope studies of Walters and Keyte (44) showed that few if any elastomers can be blended to a level of homogeneity approaching a molecular scale. Subsequent electron microscope studies (45—47) also showed that carbon blacks compounded into such blends do not always distribute statistically between separate polymers. Furthermore, differences in carbon distribution have been related to significant variations in the end-use performance of tire-tread compounds. For example, Hess et al. (47) studied the effects of black distri-bution (ISAF type) in 50/50 natural rubber/*cis*-polybutadiene blends. The carbon loading was maintained constant at 40 phr, and all masterbatches were prepared by solution mixing to minimize polymer breakdown in the NR phase. The total mechanical work on each compound was also equated and all black dispersions (based on optical measurements) were at an excellent level. The carbon black distribution was varied by the blending of separate masterbatches (eg 20, 40, 60, 80 phr of black in each polymer). The actual distributions (ranging from 7 to 95% black in the BR phase) were determined from measurements on electron micrographs. Testing of the final compounds showed that abrasion resistance (road wear) and tensile strength were highest with most of the carbon black in the polybutadiene. Hysteresis and tear strength were optimized with about 60–65% of the black in the polybutadiene.

Looking ahead in carbon black research activity in the 1970s it will become possible to characterize carbon blacks for obtaining optimum results in almost any rubber and any end use. This ability to characterize precisely the carbon needed will finally be related to rapid on-stream analytical methods so that process units may be put on some kind of closed-loop control, something absolutely out of the question today. This control objective probably offers as much potential reward as any other single research objective now visible.

Overall Perspective. Carbon black will remain one of the most important single petrochemical products. As a functional pigment and filler, it is outranked in dollar value only by one other finely divided material, titanium dioxide, which is roughly twice as large in value.

While great advances in the use of treated and untreated silica fillers are to be expected, it is unlikely that carbon blacks for rubber reinforcement will be challenged seriously on a price-performance basis in the next decade and well beyond. A possible exception would be competition at the coarse-particle-size, low-price end of the quality scale brought about by the use of ground carbons of various kinds. Carbon black as a permanent-type black colorant will continue in use indefinitely.

Bibliography

1. "Metals, Minerals, and Fuels," *Minerals Yearbook, 1967*, Vols. 1 and 2, U.S. Bureau of Mines, Washington, D.C., 1968, pp. 263–272.
2. Can. Pat. 822,024 (Sept. 2, 1969), George L. Heller (to Columbian Carbon Co.).
3. U.S. Pat. 3,353,915 (Nov. 21, 1967), B. F. Latham, Jr., et al. (to Continental Carbon Co.).
4. U.S. Pat. 2,865,717 (Dec. 23, 1958), J. C. Krejci (to Phillips Petroleum Co.).
5. U.S. Pat. 3,003,855 (Oct. 10, 1961), G. L. Heller et al. (to Columbian Carbon Co.).
6. U.S. Pat. 3,253,890 (May 31, 1966), C. L. de Land et al. (to Columbian Carbon Co.).
7. U.S. Pat. 3,301,639 (Jan. 31, 1967), C. L. de Land (to Columbian Carbon Co.).
8. U.S. Pat. 3,010,794 (Nov. 28, 1961), George F. Friauf and Brian Thorley (to Cabot Corporation).
9. U.S. Pat. 3,010,795 (Nov. 28, 1961), George F. Friauf and Brian Thorley (to Cabot Corporation).
10. "Carbon Black Used in Rubber Products," *ASTM Standards D-1765-68*, Am. Soc. for Testing and Materials, Philadelphia, Pa., 1968, pp. 857–861.
11. B. Schubert, F. T. Ford, and F. Lyon, "Carbon Black," in F. D. Snell and L. S. Ettre, eds., *Encyclopedia of Industrial Chemical Analysis*, Vol. 8, Interscience Publishers, a div. of John Wiley & Sons, Inc., New York, 1969, pp. 179–243.
12. K. A. Burgess and F. Lyon, "The Technical Future of Carbon Blacks," *Rubber J.* **150,** 26–28 (1968).
13. Can. Pat. 685,017 (April 21, 1964), Nicholas Halkias, J. Lewandowski, and Stanley M. Hirchfield (to Columbian Carbon Co.).
14. U.S. Pat. 3,449,284 (June 10, 1969), Lyle W. Pollock (to Phillips Petroleum Co.).
15. Can. Pat. 702,841 (Jan. 26, 1965), Paul N. Hare, Lynn Parker, and George L. Decuir (to Columbian Carbon Co.).

16. U.S. Pat. 3,245,820 (April 12, 1966), Paul J. Melore and Frank J. Eckert (to Columbian Carbon Co.).
17. L. J. Venuto and W. M. Hess, "A New Look at Carbon Black," *Am. Ink Maker*, **45**, 1–19 (1967).
18. E. Micek, F. Lyon, and W. M. Hess, "SBR and BR Tread Performance as a Function of Carbon Black Properties," *Rubber Chem. Technol.* **41** (5), 1271–1284 (1968).
19. C. W. Snow, *Rubber Chem. Technol.* **41** (5), 1386 (1968).
20. E. Micek, F. Lyon, and W. M. Hess, *Rubber J.* **150** (7), 42–44 (1968).
21. W. M. Hess, G. C. McDonald, and W. Whitlock, "Morphological Classification of Carbon Black by Computer-Programmed E.M. Image Analysis," *Proc. Intern. Rubber Conf. of the French Rubber Inst., Paris, June 1–5, 1970.*
22. W. M. Hess, L. L. Ban, and G. C. McDonald, *Rubber Chem. Technol.* **42** (4), 1209 (1969).
23. C. Fisher and M. Cole, *The Microscope* **16** (2), 81 (1968).
24. A. I. Medalia and F. A. Heckman, *Paper presented at the 8th Biennial Conf. on Carbon, Buffalo, N.Y., June 1967.*
25. A. I. Medalia, F. A. Heckman, and D. F. Harling, *Proc. Natural Rubber Conf., Kuala Lampur, Malaysia, Aug. 1968.*
26. W. M. Hess, F. Lyon, and K. A. Burgess, "The Influence of Carbon Black-Elastomer Adhesion upon Vulcanizate Properties," *Kautschuk Gummi Kunstoffe* **20**, 135 (1967).
27. A. J. Pickett, *Rubber Plastics Age* **45** (10), 1175 (1964).
28. S. S. Voyutskii, V. G. Raevskii, and S. M. Yagnatinskaya, *Rubber Age* **95** (5), 729 (1964).
29. E. H. Andrews and A. J. Walsh, *J. Polymer Sci.* **33**, 250 (1962).
30. A. M. Gessler, *Rubber Chem. Technol.* **37**, 1013 (1964).
31. *Ibid.*, 1034.
32. W. M. Hess, K. A. Burgess, F. Lyon, and V. Chirico, *Kautschuk Gummi Kunstoffe* **21** (12), 689 (1968).
33. J. A. C. Harwood, A. R. Payne, and J. F. Smith, *Rubber Chem. Technol.* **43** (4), 687 (1970).
34. P. B. Stickney and R. D. Falb, *Rubber Chem. Technol.* **37** (5), 1299 (1964).
35. E. M. Dannenberg, *Rubber Age* **98** (9), 82 (1966); **98** (10), 81 (1966).
36. L. L. Ban and W. M. Hess, "Orientation of Graphite Layers in Standard and Heat-Treated Carbon Blacks," *Paper presented at 9th Biennial Conf. on Carbon, Boston, June 1969.*
37. W. M. Hess and F. P. Ford, "Microscopy of Pigment–Elastomer Systems," *Rubber Chem. Technol.*, **36** (5), 1175–1229 (1963).
38. W. M. Hess and L. L. Ban, "High Resolution Dark Field Microscopy of Carbon Black," *Paper presented at the 6th Intern. Congr. for Electron Microscopy, Kyoto, Japan, Aug. 28–Sept. 6, 1966.*
39. W. M. Hess, L. L. Ban, F. J. Eckert, and V. Chirico, "Microstructural Variations in Commercial Carbon Blacks," *Rubber Chem. Technol.* **41** (2), 356–372 (1968).
40. W. M. Hess, L. L. Ban, and G. C. McDonald, *Rubber Chem. Technol.* **42** (4), 1209 (1969).
41. S. Ergun, in P. L. Walker, Jr., ed., *Chemistry and Physics of Carbon*, Vol. 3, Marcel Dekker Inc., New York, 1968, p. 211.
42. L. L. Ban and W. M. Hess, "Microstructure of Quasi-Graphitic Carbons," in C. J. Arceneaux, ed., *Proc. 26th Ann. Meet. EMSA (Electron Microscopy Society of America), New Orleans, 1968,* Clator's Publishing Div., Baton Rouge, La., 1968, p. 256.
43. D. F. Harling and F. A. Heckman, *Paper presented at Intern. Plastics and Elastomers Conf., Milan, Italy, October 1968.*
44. M. H. Walters and D. N. Keyte, *Trans. Inst. Rubber Ind.* **38**, 40 (1962).
45. J. E. Callan, B. Topcik, and F. P. Ford, *Rubber World* **151**, 60 (1965).
46. W. M. Hess, C. E. Scott, and J. E. Callan, *Rubber Chem. Technol.* **40** (2), 341–384 (1967).
47. J. E. Callan, W. M. Hess, and C. E. Scott, "Elastomer Blends: Compatibility and Relative Response to Fillers," *Paper presented at Rubber Division of Am. Chem. Soc., Los Angeles, April 1969.*

C. A. Stokes
Consultant

CARBON FIBERS

This article deals with carbon fibers having very high elastic-modulus values. These fibers have been developed in recent years as reinforcing elements for strong, stiff, lightweight composite structural materials (1). Such fibers are to be distinguished from other carbon fibers having relatively low elastic-modulus values which are not dealt with here. Low-elastic-modulus fibers are also used with organic resins to form fibrous composites, but their usefulness is based on their excellent thermal stability, and particularly their ablative characteristics, rather than on their structural efficiency. Both types of carbon fibers are produced by the pyrolysis of precursor textile fibers. The unwanted chemical constituents of the precursor textile fiber are driven off by thermal treatment and, as in the case of high-elastic-modulus fibers, the remaining carbon is left in the form of imperfect graphitic crystallites preferentially aligned with the axis of the fiber.

During the last few years attention has been focused on stiff, lightweight ceramic materials in the form of strong fibers as potential load-bearing elements in composite structural materials for aerospace use. The graphite crystal is much superior to other materials in terms of its elastic-modulus-to-density ratio, and the anisotropy of the crystal is of no fundamental disadvantage, providing the high-elastic-modulus direction of the crystal can be caused to lie along the longitudinal axis of the fiber. Young's modulus values in excess of 100 million psi have been observed (2), approaching the fundamental limit of the graphite crystal, and this is an improvement of an order of magnitude over glass-reinforcing fibers in use today.

The importance of the new composite materials lies in their much-enhanced structural efficiency compared with orthodox structural metals. Depending on the mode of stressing, structural efficiency can be measured either by the elastic modulus divided by the density or by the elastic modulus divided by the square of the density. Unidirectionally reinforced carbon-fiber–synthetic-resin composites are about five times better than orthodox metal alloys on the basis of the first criterion and ten times better on the second. Because of relatively high initial production costs engineering applications of the material are, at this stage, primarily of importance in the aircraft industry. For such applications it is worth about $100 to save one pound of structure weight and it has been established that the use of carbon-fiber composites would permit a reduction of aircraft-structure weight by about 30%. The material is already under development for use as fan blades in large aircraft gas turbines.

The theoretical strength of an elastic crystalline solid has received considerable attention in recent years (3), and tensile strengths corresponding to an elastic strain of about 10% can be expected theoretically. Very strong solids are found experimentally to show elastic strains of a few percent and it is now accepted that the strength is reduced below the theoretical ultimate because of the presence of stress-concentrating flaws. Flaws can be of various types but are usually associated with sharp-cornered foreign particles, voids, or surface irregularities. Elastic strains in excess of 2% have been observed with carbon fibers, and stress-concentrating flaws are found similar to those observed in the case of other strong ceramic solids, but other types of failure processes have been identified which are linked with the fiber microstructure.

The primary requirement of the polymer precursor is that it should go through a conversion process during which the polymer structure is converted to an essentially graphitic form without the morphology of the fiber being destroyed. Moreover, for any convenient continuous-production process it is highly desirable that the fibers should retain a significant tensile strength during all stages of the conversion process. Carbon fibers have been formed from a variety of precursors, such as rayon, polyacrylonitrile (PAN), poly(vinyl alcohol), polybenzimidazole, and certain types of pitches and asphalts (4).

Two issues are of primary importance in the preparation of high-strength, high-stiffness carbon fibers from textile precursors. Firstly, the polymer structure has to be converted into a crystal structure basically graphitic in form, even though crystalline perfection is not achieved. Secondly, because of the highly anisotropic nature of the graphite crystal, the basal planes of the graphitic crystallites need to be oriented preferentially with the axis of the fiber if a high longitudinal elastic modulus is to be obtained. This orientation can be achieved by longitudinal deformation of the fiber in the textile form, during pyrolysis, or at high temperatures when the fiber consists essentially of carbon.

Currently the most important precursor fibers are polyacrylonitrile and cellulose. The pyrolysis of cellulose-based textile fibers has been described by Bacon and Tang (5,6) and also by Ruland (7-9). The process proceeds by various stages, the first extending to a temperature of 150°C and being concerned with the loss of physically absorbed water. The second stage occurs between 150 and 240°C with the elimination of OH groups and the formation of C=O and C=C bonds within the cellulose structure. Cellulose retains its crystalline structure up to about 245°C, above which it breaks down, becoming amorphous just above 300°C. Complete breakdown of the cellulose ring occurs between 350 and 400°C. Between 400 and 700°C condensation of this material into graphite-like rings occurs with the evolution of some hydrogen and methane, and x-ray diffraction studies show the presence of graphite-like structures beginning at 400°C with some degree of preferred orientation of the graphite-layer planes along the fiber axis beginning at 1000°C. Despite the intermediate amorphous stage a preferred orientation of the carbon structure develops in fibers heat-treated to high temperature; this orientation is indirectly correlated with the degree of orientation of the molecular structure of the precursor cellulose fiber.

An extensive study of the pyrolysis of polyacrylonitrile to produce carbon fibers has been made by Shindo (10) and the preparation of high-elastic-modulus carbon fibers from PAN precursors has been reported by Watt, Phillips, and Johnson (11), and by Standage and Prescott (12). The repeat unit of polyacrylonitrile is —CH_2-CHCN— and this can be thought of, stoichiometrically, as $3C + NH_3$, carbon plus ammonia. The polymer chains are aligned preferentially with the axis of the fiber. The pendent nitrile groups are highly polar and reactive, and their arrangement along the polymer chain is atactic. This gives a noncrystalline fiber but with an x-ray diffraction pattern corresponding to the alignment of the molecular chains. Watt and Johnson (13) have summarized various transformation processes through which PAN can be converted by pyrolysis into a structure having graphitic characteristics. The x-ray diffraction data on carbon fibers, heat-treated to a very high temperature, indicate an absence of three-dimensional order and this has been ascribed by Johnson and Watt (14) as being due to random orientation of basal planes about the c axis. Such a structure is known as turbostratic (see Vol. 4, p. 306). Because of the lack of order the layer-spacing is appreciably greater than that found with natural graphite and Badami, Joiner, and Jones (15) obtain a value of 3.39 Å compared with 3.35 Å for natural graphite. On heating the polymer fiber, chemical reactions occur which can be intra- or intermolecular depending on the approach distances of the reacting groups. Many crosslinking reactions are possible and will proceed independently, all leading to the production of a six-membered ring structure lying parallel to the direction of the molecular chains.

Shindo (10) observed from x-ray diffraction studies of heat-treated polyacrylo-nitrile fiber that diffraction arcs corresponding to the (002) planes of a graphite crystal are detectable at about 300°C, in the case of fibers which have been given a previous heat treatment in an oxidizing atmosphere. The (002) planes are also developed with heat treatment in fibers which have not been preoxidized but this occurs at a rather higher temperature. The gaseous by-products generated during pyrolysis are primarily ammonia and hydrogen cyanide.

As produced, PAN fibers are formed from a number of small elements or fibrils. These are formed from approximately parallel bundles of polymer chains and are

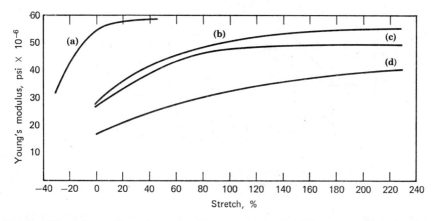

Fig. 1. Effect of stretching of some textile precursors on the Young's modulus of carbon fibers produced by subsequent heat treatment: (**a**), 1½-den PAN fibers stretched during preoxidation at 220°C (13); (**b,c,d**), 9-den PAN fibers stretched at 100°C (16). Negative stretch refers to fibers which are allowed to contract under internal stresses developed by chemical action during processing.

branched so that the fibrils are linked together by bundles of polymer chains passing between them. There is, therefore, a high degree of orientation of the fibrils with the axis of the fiber. The dimensions of the fibrils, which can very well be a few hundred Å in diameter, seem to control the dimensions of the turbostratic graphitic crystallites, produced by pyrolysis, when the appropriate lateral shrinkage factor (of about 0.6) is taken into consideration.

Effect of Stretching on Fiber Elastic Modulus. The elastic modulus of the fibers is primarily dependent on the degree of alignment of the graphitic crystallites with the fiber axis. Alignment can be enhanced by stretching carbon fibers at very high temperatures and this process is currently used in the manufacture of high-elastic-modulus carbon fibers from cellulose precursors. In the case of PAN precursors, present manufacturing techniques depend on the development of a well-aligned polymer structure while the material is still in the textile form. This preferred alignment is then maintained through the conversion process to the final carbon form. The elastic modulus of carbon fibers based on PAN increases with increased heat-treatment temperature and can also be increased by tensile deformation at high temperatures in a manner similar to those of cellulose-based carbon fibers.

In the case of PAN precursors the extent of the alignment of the molecular chains with the fiber axis depends on the details of the manufacturing process. Where the alignment is relatively poor it can be improved by stretching at temperatures of around 100°C. The effect is illustrated in Figure 1 and for the particular material shown the elastic modulus of the carbon fibers (obtained after heat treatment to 2500°C) approaches a limiting value for a deformation of 200% in the polymer stage. High rates of heating tend to disrupt the chemical structure of the material during

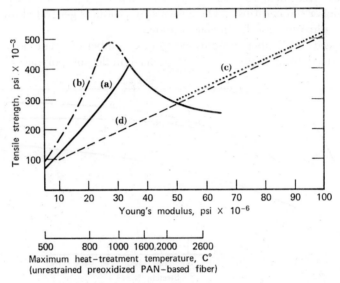

Fig. 2. Average tensile strengths of PAN- and rayon-based fibers: (a) PAN-based fibers pre-oxidized and unrestrained during further heat treatment; (b) as (a) but with subsequent surface etching; (c) as (a) but subjected to subsequent longitudinal deformation at high temperature; (d) rayon-based carbon fibers.

processing, with a consequent reduction in the elastic modulus of the carbon fibers produced. Heat treatment in the presence of oxygen during the early stages of the conversion process for PAN fibers has the effect of increasing the chemical stability of the material, allowing higher rates of processing to be achieved. Examples of both these phenomena are given in Figure 1 (13,16).

Unless a tensile stress is applied sufficient to prevent the contraction of PAN fibers during oxidation the preferential alignment of the molecular structure is reduced with a consequent reduction in the elastic modulus of the carbon fibers produced for a given heat-treatment temperature. This effect is illustrated in Figure 1 (13).

After oxidation the PAN precursor is sufficiently stable to permit further heat treatment without the necessity for further mechanical restraint. The elastic modulus increases rapidly with further heat treatment to a temperature of about 1000°C when an elastic modulus of about 30×10^6 psi is obtained. The elastic modulus continues to increase for further increases in heat-treatment temperature but at a lower rate, a temperature of about 2500°C being required to produce a fiber-elastic-modulus of 55×10^6 psi. Much higher elastic moduli for PAN-based precursor fibers are obtainable following tensile deformation of the carbon fibers at high temperatures, as shown in Figure 2 (17).

Similar increases in elastic modulus following tensile deformation at high temperature have been reported by Bacon and Schalamon (18) and by Gibson and Langlois (19) for carbon fibers produced from rayon (cellulose) precursors. This is the most important parameter influencing the elastic modulus of the carbon fibers manufactured from rayon. A linear relationship exists between the elongation and the Young's modulus developed in the fiber, an elastic modulus of 60×10^6 psi being produced for a fiber elongation of 50%.

Factors Affecting the Tensile Strength of Carbon Fibers. The observed tensile strengths of carbon fibers are about an order of magnitude less than the theoretical ultimate strength of single-crystal graphite, and fiber failure is associated with stress-raising discontinuities of various types. Flaws have been identified unambiguously as causing failure of relatively low-elastic-modulus PAN-based carbon fibers formed by heat treatment up to about 1000°C. PAN and cellulose-based carbon fibers subjected to deformation at high temperatures possess similar strengths and elastic moduli (Fig. 2). For such fibers the tensile strength increases with increasing Young's modulus. PAN-based fibers heat-treated without longitudinal restraint behave very differently. For processing temperatures above about 1200°C the tensile strength decreases with increasing heat-treatment temperature while the elastic modulus is increasing (Fig. 2). There is some uncertainty about the details of the failure mechanism operating in the case of high-elastic-modulus carbon fibers.

Low- and medium-elastic-modulus PAN-based carbon fibers show fracture faces similar to those of a homogeneous brittle solid such as glass. This enables the source of fiber fracture to be identified from the morphology of the fracture surface. It is known that such fibers fail in tension from the presence of stress-concentrating flaws associated with voids, foreign particles, and surface irregularities in the precursor textile fiber (20). The voids are elongated cavities sometimes containing a foreign particle or particles, which can be organic or inorganic in origin. Both the voids and the fiber-surface irregularities are preserved through all stages of thermal treatment and failure of the carbon fiber can be identified with these discontinuities. The frequency of occurrence of voids and particles in acrylic precursor fibers is of major importance in controlling the strength of carbon fibers made from them (21). Increases in tensile strength for low- and medium-modulus PAN-based carbon fibers are observed when the surface of the fiber is etched by heating in oxygen. This reduces the effect of surface stress-concentrating flaws associated with the surface irregularity of the material (Fig. 2) (20).

PAN-based fibers heat-treated to temperatures above about 1250°C have strengths which are unaffected by surface etching. This indicates a fracture process associated with the increased ordering of the crystal structure of the fibers and distributed relatively uniformly throughout the body of the material. Small-angle x-ray-scattering data indicate that the graphite-layer planes are quite extensive but are crinkled, the layers of crystalline material between successive bends being aligned approximately with the fiber axis (22–24). This is very similar to the structure observed in cellulose-based high-modulus carbon fibers (9). There is an absence of three-dimensional order and x-ray data indicate the presence of planar voids lying between the graphite-layer planes. The distances between successive bends can be regarded, to some extent, as indicating a crystallite size and these dimensions increase with increasing fiber-elastic modulus.   It has been suggested (25) that, under an applied stress, dislocations are generated in the crystallites and are driven toward the crystallite boundaries.   The pile-up of such dislocations produces an increasing stress at the boundary until the critical crack-nucleation stress is reached and the fiber fails.

Use of Carbon Fibers in Advanced Fibrous Composite Materials

Structural composite materials utilizing carbon fibers as reinforcing members can be very much lighter, stronger, and stiffer than the equivalent metal component.   The maximum advantage is gained when the component is stressed primarily in only one direction since this permits the fibers to be unidirectionally aligned to withstand the applied stress.   When a tensile stress is applied to a composite consisting of continuous fibers embedded in a suitable matrix both matrix and fibers elongate by the same amount.   The fibers therefore contribute to the longitudinal stiffness of the material in proportion to their intrinsic stiffness characteristics and the proportion of the cross-sectional area of the composite which they occupy.   This simple "rule of mixtures" calculation enables the longitudinal stiffness of the composite to be computed with reasonable accuracy.   For more precise calculations it is necessary to take into account the various elastic constants of the two materials (26,27).

The fibers can occupy up to something like 70% of the cross-sectional area of the composite so that, for the unidirectional case, the intrinsic properties of the fibers are translated fairly efficiently into the characteristics of the composite.   It is in this context that the very high values of specific stiffness (longitudinal elastic modulus divided by density) for carbon fibers is of major importance.   Unidirectional composites based on commercially-available carbon fibers have specific stiffness values five times superior to those of orthodox structural metals.

Fiber-reinforced composites do not have such attractive specific stiffness values compared with those of metals when stresses are applied in more than one direction. For example when a stress is applied perpendicularly to the unidirectionally aligned fibers the composite stiffness characteristics are largely determined by those of the matrix and not those of the fibers (28).   In these circumstances a polymer matrix which has a relatively low stiffness value is at a severe disadvantage.   A laminated structure in which the fibers in the different laminations are oriented in different directions is better in this respect.   Sheets formed in such a fashion can have relatively uniform tensile-stiffness characteristics but these are now reduced to something like a third of the value of the unidirectional case so that much of the specific stiffness advantage of the composite is lost.   At present by far the most widely used matrix materials are polymers, since such materials are light in weight and convenient to fabricate; but, in the longer term, it is possible that metals and ceramics will have potential commercial applications as matrix materials used in conjunction with carbon fibers.

There is a complex relationship between strength and toughness characteristics of fibrous composites and the properties of the fibers, matrix, and interfaces from which they are formed.   The tensile strength of a unidirectional composite can be estimated only approximately from the average strengths of the fibers composing it.

In general the fiber strengths are very variable and the fibers contain numerous severe flaws (20).   If there is negligible coupling between the fibers and the matrix the composite approximates to a fiber bundle with the fibers behaving independently of each other. If the dimensions of such a composite are appreciable there is a likelihood of a severe flaw occurring in most of the fibers so that the composite strength will be governed by this factor and will be very low. As the bond strength between the fibers and the matrix is improved, stress can be transferred between fibers so that when a fiber has failed, its unbroken portions can still contribute to the strength of the composite. Since the fibers first fail at the most severe flaws, the strengths of the portions left unbroken are greater and can be utilized more effectively as the fiber–matrix bond strength increases. Unfortunately, as the effective coupling between adjacent fibers through the matrix increases, the fibers no longer fail independently of each other and the failure of one fiber can initiate failure of its neighbors. In a similar manner, as the coupling between fibers and the matrix increases, stress concentrators, associated with surface damage or other discontinuities in the composite body, will tend to propagate as cracks. There is, therefore, a preferred level of fiber–matrix bond strength. For bond strengths less than this value the fibers fail more and more independently of each other, and the unbroken portions are used less and less effectively to reinforce the composite. For bond strengths above the optimum value the composite tends to fail in a progressively more brittle fashion, the tensile strength is more erratic in value, and progressively less energy is absorbed during the failure process.

Energy is primarily absorbed when the fibers are pulled out of the matrix. For high values of work of fracture by this process, fibers have to fail at fairly widely separated points with appreciable lengths of fibers being pulled out of the matrix on either side of the failed region of the composite. This is dependent on the flaw distribution in the fibers and on the strength in shear of the fiber–matrix interface. It should be noted that it is necessary for flaws to be distributed along the lengths of the fibers if energy is to be absorbed by fiber pull-out during tensile failure. Where the fibers have perfectly uniform strength characteristics they tend to fail in tension in a single plane through the composite, with little or no tendency for fiber failure some distance away from the failed region and subsequent energy absorption by fiber pull-out. Other things being equal, the energy absorbed by fiber pull-out tends to increase as the fiber–matrix bond strength is reduced. The characteristics of the matrix itself are also of significance in influencing the strength and the energy absorbed during failure of fiber composites.

The issue is further complicated when other types of failure process are considered. When a tensile stress is applied perpendicularly to the direction of the fibers, in a weakly-bonded unidirectional fiber composite, the stress is carried primarily by the matrix (29). The maximum stresses are generated in the narrow bridges of matrix separating the fibers. As the volume fraction of fibers increases the bridges get narrower and the composite strength is reduced. This is a general characteristic of fibrous composites, since the fiber–matrix bond strength cannot be set too high because of the incidence of brittle failure.

In the case of applied longitudinal shear stresses the material tends to fail in shear at the interface, if this is weakly bonded, because the shear stress has a maximum value at the interface (30). For high transverse tensile strengths and high longitudinal shear strengths, therefore, appreciable values of the fiber–matrix bond are required and this is in conflict with the requirements for crack deflection and fiber pull-out demanded for high toughness values under a longitudinal tensile stress. Many of the commercial manufacturers of carbon fibers offer fibers with particular surface treatments designed to optimize the bond strength with polymer matrix materials to meet the various characteristics required of the composites.

Engineering Application of Carbon Fibers

Carbon fibers are ideally suited for use in lightweight composite structures designed to resist loads which are applied predominantly in one direction. A typical example is a fan blade used in a gas turbine. A component of this type is subjected primarily to a large centrifugal tensile load with relatively small lateral and torsional loads which are generated from aerodynamic forces. The complex aerodynamic shape of a fan blade can be fabricated conveniently from a number of thin laminates placed one on top of the other.

Fabrication is carried out by hot pressing using a mold having the dimensions of the component (31). The shape of the individual laminates and their positions relative to each other control the dimensions of the finished part. The laminates are pre-impregnated with a controlled quantity of matrix resin and for such forms of construction it is necessary for the resin to have a controllable degree of tackiness after solvent release. This is necessary in order that the individual laminates can be stacked together to produce a composite preform without danger of loss of register of the various elements during the molding operation. Adequate stability during storage together with rapid curing is also demanded of the resin system used for such application.

This form of construction enables the fiber orientation to be controlled in different parts of the composite and this is a feature of considerable importance in designing a composite to withstand combined stresses. For example, torsional stress can be withstood by arranging a small number of laminates to be aligned at some angle to the longitudinal axis of the blade. The bulk of the fibers remain oriented along the length of the blade in order to withstand the very high centrifugal loads.

More complex composites consisting of sheet metal reinforced with carbon-fiber–polymer-matrix composite members can be fabricated. Aircraft applications are again important and one particular example of interest is that of a metal sheet which has to be reinforced to withstand buckling under compressive forces applied in the plane of the sheet. In such applications carbon-fiber reinforced-plastic replaces metal reinforcing members and the characteristics of low density and high stiffness of the material show to advantage. Weight savings of around 30% compared with those of orthodox panels reinforced with metal elements are obtainable (32). This type of application has the advantage that the metal sheets can be joined to the rest of the structure by orthodox techniques.

Carbon-fiber–resin composites have other engineering applications in the form of filament-wound structures. In this form of construction a continuous carbon-fiber bundle, again usually preimpregnated with resin, is wound continuously on a mandrel. The fiber direction is again chosen to optimize resistance against the loads which will eventually be applied to the component. Typical applications are in pressure-vessel construction in which case some of the fibers are aligned to withstand the hoop stresses and others to withstand longitudinal forces. Generally speaking, surfaces of revolution are very conveniently fabricated by these techniques.

Manufacturing Processes for Carbon Fibers

In the high-temperature deformation process used to manufacture high-elastic-modulus carbon fibers from cellulose precursors the material is produced in the form of a continuous carbon-fiber bundle (yarn) (19). Although continuous processes are now used to manufacture carbon fibers from PAN precursors, batch and semibatch processes can be conveniently used with this material and initial production was based on such techniques.

The material can be manufactured by simply winding PAN precursor fiber onto a frame so that the fibers are prevented from contracting longitudinally during oxidation as a result of the tensile stress developed in the fibers during this stage of the process (33). Oxidation is then carried out in a suitable oven having adequate air circulation and, since the oxidation step is exothermic, it is necessary to arrange for the fibers to be suitably distributed so as to prevent the build-up of excessive temperatures. After oxidation the fibers can be removed from the frame and processed to higher temperatures in appropriate inert-atmosphere furnaces.

Perhaps the most important outlet for carbon fibers is in the form of a pre-impregnated fiber laminate. A sheet of material of this type contains a resin which is usually partly cured. The fibers are aligned in one direction and the sheet thickness and the relative proportions of fiber and resin are held to very close tolerances. A typical sheet thickness when molded into a composite is 5×10^{-3} in. Resin-impregnated unidirectional fiber sheet can be prepared from bundles of carbon fibers but this step is much more conveniently carried out when continuous fibers are available. Sheet manufacture can be carried out with continuous fibers in the precursor textile form or when the fibers are available as a continuous carbon-fiber bundle after processing. By winding a continuous parallel bundle (tow) of PAN-textile fibers uniformly on a frame a unidirectional fiber sheet can be produced (33). Although the fibers in such a bundle are nominally unidirectional there is inevitably some degree of mis-alignment and this limits the width to which a bundle can be spread conveniently to give a uniform sheet. The larger the number of fibers in the bundle the greater will be the thickness of the sheet which can be conveniently produced. The problem is eased, to some extent, if the sheet is prepared in the textile form because of the greater tolerance of the textile fibers to deformation compared with that of fully processed carbon fibers. A textile sheet of this form can be held together during subsequent processing after removal from the oxidation frame by a limited amount of cross-stitching. In this way a unidirectional carbon-fiber sheet is produced and this can then be impregnated uniformly with a controlled quantity of suitable resin. The size of the pre-impregnated sheet produced by this semibatch process is, therefore, mainly controlled by the size of the initial oxidation frames.

The process can be made into a continuous one by preparing the textile sheet in the required thickness from a suitable number of parallel textile tows and then passing the continuous textile sheet through the various stages of heat treatment, maintaining the sheet structure through the complete process. Impregnation with a suitable resin is then carried out as a final step (33). Special seals are required where the fiber sheet enters and leaves the various processing stages in order to exclude oxygen and also prevent the escape of the products of pyrolysis during processing (Fig. 3).

Since the carbon fibers are electrically conducting at high temperatures it is possible to facilitate high-temperature treatment by passing electrical power through the fibers themselves. This technique can be combined with a high-temperature continuous-deformation process when the highest values of longitudinal Young's modulus for the fiber are required and is applicable, therefore, to production processes based on both PAN and cellulose precursors.

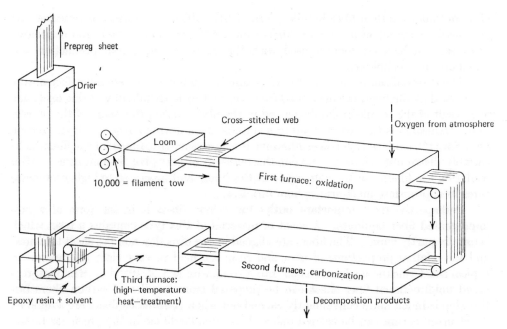

Fig. 3. Continuous-production process for resin-impregnated carbon-fiber sheet (33).

Where continuous carbon-fiber bundles, yarns, or tows are available they can be used to manufacture preimpregnated fiber sheet by a filament-winding process. A continuous-fiber bundle, having the desired number of fibers in it, is impregnated with a suitable resin and wound continuously onto a cylinder to form a sheet of controlled thickness. The sheets can then be removed from the cylinder, the size of the sheets being limited to the size of the drum used.

Table 1. Selected List of World Producers of High-Elastic-Modulus Carbon Fibers and Their Trade Names

Country and location	Producer	Fiber trade name
France		
Paris	Le Carbone-Lorraine	Rigilor
West Germany		
Meitingen bei Augsburg	Sigri Electrographit, GmbH	
Japan		
Tokyo	Toray Industries Inc.	
United Kingdom		
Coventry	Courtaulds Ltd.	Grafil
London	Morganite Research and Development Ltd.	Modmor
Derby	Rolls Royce	Hyfil
United States		
New York	Great Lakes Carbon Corp.	Fortafil
New York	Union Carbide Corp.	Thornel
Costa Mesa, Calif.	Whittaker-Morgan Inc.	
Summit, N. J.	Celanese Corp.	Celion™
Gardenia, Calif.	Hitco Materials Div.	Hitron

Availability of Carbon Fibers

Carbon fibers having elastic moduli greater than 25×10^6 psi are being manufactured, or are about to be manufactured, by the organizations listed in Table 1.

High-modulus carbon fibers are produced in various grades with elastic moduli mainly in the range of 25×10^6 to 55×10^6 psi. Most of the fibers produced have individual diameters of about 0.3×10^{-3} in. but the number of fibers contained in a single yarn or tow vary widely among the different manufacturers. In many cases fibers with special surface treatments are available which are designed to optimize the bond strength of the fiber–polymer-matrix interface. Preimpregnated fiber-resin tape and sheet are available from some manufacturers and various proprietary brands of epoxy resins are generally used with this form of material. Prices vary considerably according to fiber type, quantity, and form of product, but are generally in the range of $40 to $400/lb. In the long term it is estimated that fiber costs will fall to a level of about $10/lb.

Bibliography

1. L. Holliday, ed., *Composite Materials*, Elsevier, Amsterdam, 1966. L. J. Broutman and R. H. Krock, eds., *Modern Composite Materials*, Addison-Wesley Publishing Co., Inc., New York, 1967. G. S. Holister and C. Thomas, *Fiber Reinforced Materials*, Elsevier, Amsterdam, 1966. J. E. Gordon, *The New Science of Strong Materials*, Penguin Books, Ltd., Harmondsworth, England, 1968.
2. D. Peters, *Engr.* **229** (5938), 37 (1969).
3. A. Kelly, *Strong Solids*, Clarendon Press Ltd., Oxford, 1966.
4. J. Preston, ed., "High Temperature Resistant Fibers from Organic Polymers," *Appl. Polymer Symp.* **1969** (9).
4a. R. Bacon, *An Introduction to Carbon/Graphite Fibers*, p. 213; Akio Shindo, Yoichiro Nakanishi, and Isao Soma, *Highly Crystallite Oriented Carbon Fibers from Polymeric Fibers*, p. 305; S. Otani, A. Yokoyama, and A. Nukui, *Effects of Heat Treatment Under Stress on MP Carbon Fiber*, p. 325; Herbert M. Ezekiel, *Graphite Fibers from an Aromatic Polyamide Yarn*, p. 315; all in reference 3.
5. M. M. Tang and R. Bacon, *Carbon* **2**, 211 (1964).
6. R. Bacon and M. M. Tang, *Carbon* **2**, 221 (1964).
7. W. Ruland, *J. Appl. Phys.* **38**, 3585 (1967).
8. W. Ruland, *J. Poly. Sci.* **C28**, 143 (1969).
9. W. Ruland et al., *Compt. Rend.* **C269**, 1597 (1969).
10. A. Shindo, *Studies on Graphite Fiber*, Report No. 317, Government Industrial Research Institute, Osaka, Japan, 1961.
11. W. Watt, L. N. Phillips, and W. Johnson, *Engr.* **221**, 815 (1966).
12. A. E. Standage and R. Prescott, *Nature* **211** (5045), 169 (1966).
13. W. Watt and W. Johnson, *The Effect of Length Changes during the Oxidation of Polyacrylonitrile Fibers on the Young's Modulus of Carbon Fibers*, in reference 4, p. 215.
14. W. Johnson and W. Watt, *Nature* **215**, 384 (1967).
15. D. V. Badami, J. C. Joiner, and G. A. Jones, *Nature* **215**, 386 (1967).
16. R. Prescott, *Carbon Fiber Development Programme to December 1966*, Rolls-Royce Research Report No. RR(OH) 276, private communication to author.
17. J. W. Johnson, J. R. Marjoram, and P. G. Rose, *Nature* **221** (5187), 357 (1969).
18. R. Bacon and W. A. Schalamon, *Physical Properties of High Modulus Graphite Fibers made from a Rayon Precursor*, in reference 4, p. 285.
19. D. W. Gibson and G. B. Langlois, *A. C. S. Preprints*, **9**(2), 1376 (1968).
20. J. W. Johnson, *Factors Affecting the Tensile Strength of Carbon Graphite Fibers*, in reference 4, p. 229.
21. D. J. Thorne, *J. Appl. Polymer Sci.* **14**, 103–113 (1970).
22. D. J. Johnson and C. N. Tyson, *Brit. J. Appl. Phys. Ser. 2* **2**, 787 (1969).

23. S. Allen, G. A. Cooper, D. J. Johnson, and R. M. Mayer, "Carbon Fibers of High Modulus," *J. Appl. Chem.* to be published.
24. *I.M.S. Report 7*, National Physical Laboratory, Division of Inorganic and Metallic Structure, Teddington, Middlesex, England. November 1969.
25. G. A. Cooper and R. M. Mayer, *J. Mater. Sci.* **6**, 60–67 (1971).
26. R. Hill, *J. Mech. Phys. Solids* **12**, 199 (1964); *ibid.* **12**, 213.
27. Z. Hashin and B. W. Rosen, *J. Appl. Mech.* **31**, 223 (1964).
28. D. F. Adams and D. R. Doner, *J. Composite Mater.* **1**(2), 152 (1967).
29. G. A. Cooper and A. Kelly, "Role of the Interface in the Fracture of Fiber-Composite Materials," *ASTM S.T.P. 452*, American Society for Testing and Materials, Philadelphia, 1969, p. 90.
30. D. F. Adams and D. R. Doner, *J. Composite Mater.* **1**(1), 4 (1967).
31. H. E. Gresham and C. G. Hannah, *J. Roy. Aeron. Soc.* **71**, 355 (1967).
32. A. C. Ham, *Phys. Bull.* **20**, 474 (1969).
33. W. T. Gunston, "Carbon Fibers," *Sci. J.* **5**(2), 39 (1969).

S. G. Morley
University of Nottingham, Wolfson Institute

CELLS, HIGH TEMPERATURE

A variety of devices, including primary thermal cells, some secondary (electrically rechargeable) cells, fuel cells, and thermally regenerative cells could, in a broad sense, be categorized as high-temperature cells. This article is limited to a discussion of those high-temperature cells that are considered to show the most promise of future development into high-performance, compact, rechargeable batteries which are needed for new, highly demanding practical applications. Such applications include long-lived power sources for spacecraft, military communications, artificial heart pumps, propulsion of civilian and military vehicles, and off-peak energy storage for central power stations. Although several new types of batteries have become available commercially since about 1960, none can deliver the required power per unit weight or the required energy per unit weight to satisfy the needs of most of these applications. Commonly quoted performance requirements for these purposes are a specific power of 220 W/kg and a specific energy of 220 Wh/kg. It appears that these performance goals can be achieved only through the development of electrochemical cells that operate at elevated temperatures (eg above 200°C).

In order to maximize the specific power of an electrochemical cell, the internal electronic and electrolytic resistances of the cell must be minimized. This is accomplished by using low-resistance materials and by designing the cell to minimize the lengths of the conduction paths and the interelectrode distance. Because the largest component of the internal resistance in a cell usually is found in the electrolyte, a material of as high conductivity as possible should be selected as the electrolyte. Molten-salt electrolytes have far higher conductivities than those using aqueous or organic solvents. Molten-salt electrolytes, however, have the disadvantage that they must be operated at a temperature above the melting point of the salt, which ordinarily ranges from about 200 to as high as 650°C, depending upon the composition of the salt. Ionically conducting solid electrolytes, eg β alumina ($Na_2O \cdot 11Al_2O_3$), are used in some high-temperature cells. Solid electrolytes also require a minimum operating temperature in the vicinity of 300°C to provide the necessary mobility of the cations. The high operating temperatures of molten-salt or solid electrolytes nevertheless offer the

Table 1. Characteristics of High-Performance Electrochemical Cells

| Characteristic | Reactant | | Electrolyte |
	Anode	Cathode	
electronegativity	low	high	
equivalent weight	low	low	low
conductivity	high	high	high
exchange-current density[a]	high	high	high
solubility in electrolyte	low	low	

[a] Electrochemical reaction rate.

bonuses of increasing the exchange-current density (rates of the electrode reactions), and permitting the use of liquid–metal electrodes. Exchange-current densities of several A/cm^2 of electrode area can be obtained with liquid–metal electrodes, compared with 10^{-3} and 10^{-9} A/cm^2 for hydrogen and oxygen electrodes, respectively, at room temperature. Apparently the number of sites per unit area, at which the reaction can proceed with low overvoltage, is much greater for liquid metals than for solids or adsorbed gases.

Several high-temperature electrochemical cell systems, which have been under investigation at various laboratories, show promise of attaining high specific energy, as well as high specific power. Although these systems are still in the research and development stages, laboratory performance data, together with conceptual design studies, have indicated that they should be able to achieve specific energies above 220 Wh/kg in practical battery configurations.

The most important characteristics to be considered in selecting a high-performance electrochemical cell system are listed in Table 1. A cell of high specific energy depends upon a large difference in the electronegativities of the anode and cathode reactants. The elements possessing the lowest electronegativities are those of groups IA and IIA of the periodic table, ie the alkali and alkaline-earth metals. These metals are most suitable for use as anode materials because of the relative ease with which they give up electrons to form positive ions. Conversely, elements of high electronegativity are most suitable as cathode materials because of their strong affinity for electrons. These elements (the chalcogens and halogens) fall in groups VIB and VIIB. The large differences in electronegativity between these anode and cathode materials result in relatively large emf's of about 2 to 4 V. In order to maximize the specific energy of the cell, the anode and cathode reactants, as well as the electrolyte, should have low equivalent weights. (The equivalent weight of a reactant is its atomic weight divided by the number of electrons involved in its electrochemical oxidation or reduction.) Consequently, the elements used in these components are usually selected from the upper rows of the periodic table.

The specific power of a cell depends upon the rates of the transport processes associated with the electrochemical reaction. Within the anode and cathode, the electronic conductivity must be high enough to permit the flow of adequate current to the electrochemical reaction sites. If the anode or cathode material itself has too low a conductivity, this problem may be overcome by inserting a current collector which usually consists of an open-structured or porous, highly conducting material, such as a metal mesh. The necessity for an electrolyte of high ionic conductivity was discussed earlier. A cell of high specific power must have high exchange-current densities, which

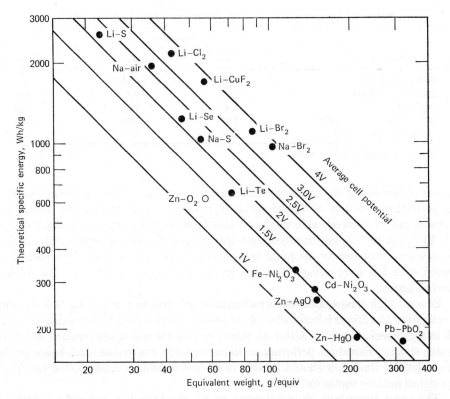

Fig. 1. Effect of the difference of electronegativity between anode and cathode (as reflected by the cell voltage) and of the equivalent weight (of anode plus cathode materials) on the maximum theoretical specific energy of various electrochemical cells.

reflect the rates of the electrochemical reactions within the cell. These reactions usually proceed at relatively high rates because of the high operating temperatures of cells of this type. As indicated in Table 1, the anode and cathode reactants should have a low solubility in the electrolyte to prevent their direct chemical reaction, which would decrease the amount of electrical work that can be performed by the cell.

The mass-transport rates of materials within a cell have a strong influence upon its electrical performance, particularly at high-current densities. High operating temperatures are beneficial in this respect because they enhance the rates of diffusion, convection, and ionic transport through liquid and solid electrolytes, with the result that the overvoltages associated with these processes are low. In the cell design, it is desirable to use an open-structured current collector that promotes the diffusion and convection of the reaction products within the bulk cathode material. This need, however, tends to conflict with the requirement for a more closely structured current collector in poorly conducting cathode materials, such as sulfur. Mass-transport rates are likely to be the limiting factor on power density in cells that employ viscous, poorly conducting cathode reactants.

Figure 1 illustrates the effects of difference in electronegativity (as reflected by the cell voltage) and equivalent weight of the anode plus cathode material upon the maximum theoretical specific energy for various cell systems of interest. Some conventional systems, such as $Pb-PbO_2$ (lead–acid) and $Cd-Ni_2O_3$, are included for comparison.

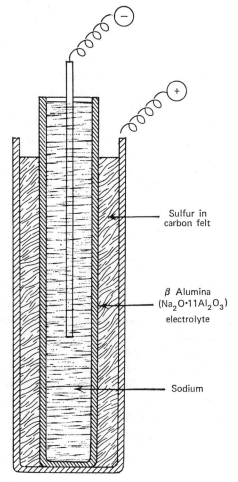

Fig. 2. Diagram of a sodium–sulfur cell.

It is apparent that the alkali metal–halogen and alkali metal–chalcogen cells have the highest theoretical specific energies, generally 1000 Wh/kg or more. In theory, lithium–fluorine cells should have a very high specific energy of about 5300 Wh/kg and develop an emf of 5.2 V. However, alkali metal–fluorine cells are not shown because no work has been reported on them, probably because they would have to be operated at undesirably high temperatures (850–1000°C) and because of the difficulties and hazards associated with handling elemental fluorine. The specific energies in Figure 1 were calculated from the weights of the anode and cathode reactants only, with no allowance for the weights of the electrolyte, cell housings, terminals, and other hardware required for a practical battery. When these additional items are taken into account, the values of the specific energy are decreased by a factor of about 5 or 6, depending on the battery design. Thus, those systems in Figure 1 that have theoretical specific energies greater than about 1000 Wh/kg may reasonably be expected to meet the practical goal of 220 Wh/kg. All of these systems have been investigated to some extent, with the major emphasis on the Li–S, Na–S, Li–Cl₂, and Li–Se systems. All of these cells operate at elevated temperatures (above 300°C) and all except one

(Na–S) have molten-salt electrolytes. A solid, β alumina electrolyte is used in the Na–S cell. With a reasonable battery design, all of these cell systems should approach or exceed a specific power of 220 W/kg and a specific energy of 220 Wh/kg.

High-temperature batteries are currently in various stages of development at different laboratories; none has yet reached the stage of practical application. The potential advantages of batteries using these cells are high-power density, high-energy density, rapid recharge rates, and long shelf-life. The main disadvantage is the high operating temperature, which requires efficient thermal insulation and methods of temperature control. Factors that have not yet been evaluated fully include cycle life (number of charge-discharge cycles before failure), cost, and safety, although preliminary studies have indicated no severe fundamental limitations in these areas. The strong points and problems associated with a number of high-temperature cells are discussed below.

The Sodium–Sulfur Cell

Among the cells discussed in this article, the sodium–sulfur cell (1–3) is the only one that employs a solid ion conductor instead of a molten salt as the electrolyte. A diagram of a laboratory version of the sodium–sulfur cell is shown in Figure 2. The anode consists of liquid sodium, which is contained in a ceramic tube of β alumina $(Na_2O \cdot 11Al_2O_3)$. The β alumina conducts sodium ions to the liquid sulfur, which surrounds the solid electrolyte. Because sulfur has a low electronic conductivity, a carbon-felt current collector is held in intimate contact with the electrolyte. Carbon felt is a product consisting of matted carbon fibers. It functions both as an electronic conductor and as a wick which holds the sulfur in place by capillary action. This cell is operated at a temperature of about 300°C.

In the sodium–sulfur cell the overall reaction that determines the emf is as follows:

$$2\,Na + (x-1)\,Na_2S_x \rightarrow x\,Na_2S_{(x-1)} \tag{1}$$

where $x = 3, 4, 5$ (1). In the anode the following reaction occurs at the sodium–electrolyte interface:

$$2\,Na \rightarrow 2\,Na^+ + 2\,e^- \tag{2}$$

In the cathode, only sodium ions are transferred at the electrolyte–sulfide interface. At the sulfide–carbon interface the reaction is the following:

$$(x-1)\,S_x^{2-} + 2\,e^- \rightarrow x\,S_{(x-1)}^{2-} \tag{3}$$

At the sulfide–sulfur interface a purely chemical transfer of sulfur atoms takes place:

$$Na_2S_{(x-1)} + S \rightarrow Na_2S_x \tag{4}$$

An advantage of this cell is that the reactants, being liquid, are regenerated in the same physical form on repeated charge–discharge cycling (dendrite formation is avoided, for example). In addition, the solid electrolyte prevents self-discharge of the cell resulting from solubility of the cell reactants in the electrolyte.

The β alumina electrolyte has been the subject of considerable study and development work. β Alumina is a general term that includes various compositions of the system $Na_2O-MgO-Al_2O_3$, which forms hexagonal layer structures that permit unusually high cationic mobility within the structure. A study of single-crystal $Na_2O \cdot 11Al_2O_3$ has shown that high sodium-ion conductivity occurs only in directions per-

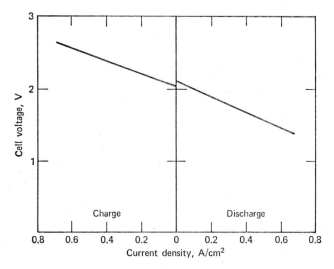

Fig. 3. Typical voltage–current-density curves for a sodium–sulfur cell (Na–Na$_2$O·11Al$_2$O$_3$–S); cell temperature = 300°C, interelectrode distance = 0.07 cm.

pendicular to the c axis of the crystal, with a resistivity of about 3.5 Ω-cm at 300°C (2). It has been reported that the addition of MgO improves the sodium-ion conductivity (4). One such form of β alumina (called β'') has been identified as Na$_{1.67}$Mg$_{0.67}$-Al$_{10.33}$O$_{17}$ (5).

β Alumina tubes for use in cells have normally been made by sintering a tube formed from a finely divided powder. This method tends to produce a material having less than the theoretical density. A novel zone-sintering method has been developed which produces high-density tubes. This method employs a rapid heating and short uniform firing procedure which yields tubes impervious to helium at 25°C (4).

Cells constructed from modified β alumina tubes, as shown in Figure 2, yielded the voltage–current-density curves presented in Figure 3 (1a). The fact that these curves are essentially straight lines may be taken as evidence that no significant overvoltages caused by electrochemical reactions or slow mass transport occur at current densities up to 0.68 A/cm². Similar results are reported by other authors (3,3a,4). Voltage–capacity-density curves for the same type of cell are shown in Figure 4. This cell had a cathode composed of a layer (0.3 cm thick) of sulfur-filled graphite felt; the electrolyte was a β alumina tube (0.5 cm OD), having an active zone about 10 cm long and a wall thickness of 0.08 cm. A power density of 0.6 W/cm² (at 1.9 V) can be estimated from the data in Figure 4, but this type of cell is claimed to have delivered up to 1.3 W/cm² (1). Newer data (3a) show a power density of 0.4 W/cm² at 1.5 V.

It is necessary to use a highly expanded current collector in the sulfur cathode because an insulating layer of sulfur is formed when the cell is charged and solid Na$_2$S$_2$ is deposited on the electrode surface during discharge. Both of these materials are slow to dissolve in the bulk of the melt. As a result, the maximum true current density on the carbon surface is limited to about 10 mA/cm² (1).

Materials of construction present some problems when sulfur and sodium are used at 300°C. The electrolyte, β alumina, is said not to be attacked by sodium or sulfur (1a,2) and there is almost no chance for a significant rate of self-discharge by diffusion of reactants through the electrolyte. However, the ceramic materials are sensitive to mechanical shock and sometimes to thermal shock and thermal cycling. In terms of mechanical strength, zone-sintered β alumina tubes (1.45 cm OD, 1.15 cm ID, and 40 cm in length, with a porosity ranging from 3 to 5%) have been found to fracture at a bending moment of 48 newton-m (4) which roughly corresponds to a tensile strength of 13,000 psi. Stainless steels have been used as materials of construction for laboratory cells (6) and aluminum has been found to be stable toward sulfur and polysulfide at 300°C (2,3a). However, aluminum is stable only as long as it is not in contact with the graphite electrode.

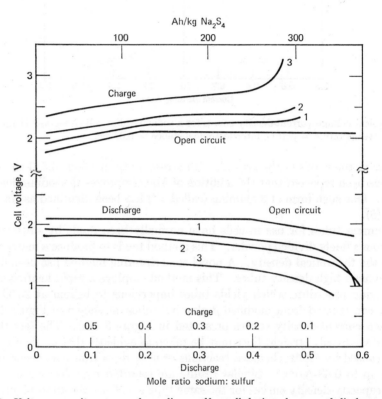

Fig. 4. Voltage-capacity curves of a sodium–sulfur cell during charge and discharge; note the two abscissa scales for discharge and charge. LEGEND: 1, 0.17 A/cm² for 120 min; 2, 0.34 A/cm² for 60 min; 3, 0.68 A/cm² for 30 min.

The Lithium–Chlorine Cell

Two types of lithium–chlorine cells are being actively studied. One of these, shown schematically in Figure 5, consists of a porous, stainless-steel, fiber-metal wick designed to contain and transport liquid lithium (by capillary action), a molten LiCl electrolyte (mp, 609°C), and a porous carbon cathode at which the chlorine reacts (7). The reactions at the anode and the cathode are shown in equations 5 and 6, respectively.

$$Li \rightarrow Li^+ + e^- \tag{5}$$

$$\tfrac{1}{2} Cl_2 + e^- \rightarrow Cl^- \tag{6}$$

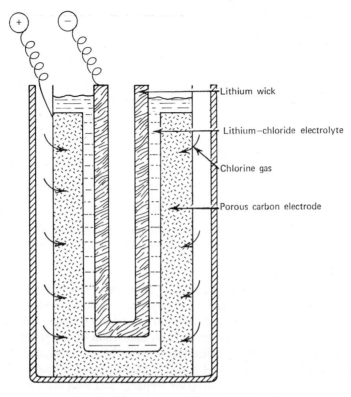

Fig. 5. Diagram of a lithium–chlorine cell.

The product is LiCl, which serves as the electrolyte. The lithium reactant and the LiCl reaction product are stored within the cell, whereas the chlorine is fed to the cell from external storage. The resistivity of the electrolyte is 0.17 Ω-cm and it represents one major source of resistance in this cell, the other being the carbon cathode. The electrode reaction at the chlorine cathode is not as fast as that at the lithium anode (8); the exchange-current density is about 0.2 A/cm². This corresponds to a voltage loss of about 0.2 V, attributable to the cathode reaction, at current densities near 3 A/cm². The most bothersome source of voltage loss in this cell is that caused by the accumulation of inert impurities from the chlorine in the pores of the cathode. These impurities (for example, CO_2 and N_2) present a diffusion barrier to the incoming chlorine that is the source of a limiting current density. The magnitude of the limiting current density is a function of the purity of the chlorine and the structure of the porous carbon electrode (9). Even in the absence of impurities, the current density is limited by the transport of chlorine through the porous carbon and its diffusion through the melt to the melt–graphite interface. This type of electrode differs from the usual gas electrodes used in fuel cells in that the carbon is not wetted by the molten salt. With cathodes having the optimum pore size (av diam 0.6 μ) and a thickness of 0.1 cm, a limiting current density of about 10 A/cm² can be achieved at a chlorine pressure of 3 atm (10). It proved to be helpful to "sweep out" the cathode with an excess flow of chlorine (5 or 10%) to minimize the accumulation of impurities.

Even with the limitations just discussed, a maximum power density of 40 W/cm² has been achieved for periods of 20 min when the cell design has been optimized for

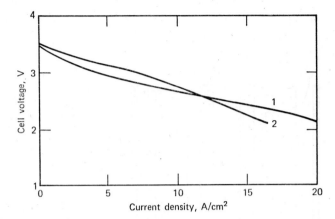

Fig. 6. Typical voltage–current-density curves for a lithium–chlorine cell (Li–LiCl–Cl_2); cell temperature = 680°C; interelectrode distance = 0.1 cm. LEGEND: chlorine pressure, 1 at 1.5 atm; 2 at 3 atm.

discharge operation only (10). This probably represents the highest power density ever reported for an electrochemical power source. Two typical voltage–current-density curves for a Li–Cl_2 primary cell are shown in Figure 6 (10). The modest deviation from linearity shown by these curves is an indication of the small voltage losses due to diffusion or to slow electrochemical reactions in the current-density range shown.

The high performance of the Li–Cl_2 cell is accompanied by some disadvantages associated with the difficulty of providing for recharge and long life. During recharge, the electrolysis products (liquid lithium and gaseous chlorine) must be liberated in such a manner that they are easily separated and stored. This can be accomplished at some cost of performance (as a result of increased internal resistance) by the use of special electrodes which have porous, electronically insulating layers on the sides facing the electrolyte; these layers are wetted by the electrolyte and they form a seal that prevents the escape of electrolysis products from the porous electrodes which are not wetted by the electrolyte. This type of structure, called a valve electrode, has been tested in the Li–Cl_2 cell with limited success (11).

The stability of the materials of construction, especially insulators, toward lithium, chlorine, and LiCl, is the main factor which determines the life of this cell which, in the high-power-density configuration, is limited to less than one hour. Molten lithium attacks almost all known insulators. Beryllium oxide has been used successfully but only for about an hour; the binding agent used in sintering the beryllium oxide is attacked, causing the insulators to disintegrate (12). It may be possible to use lithium aluminate, $LiAlO_2$, as an insulator (12). It is necessary to keep the lithium away from the carbon cathode (an interlamellar attack takes place) and the chlorine away from the stainless-steel cell parts. The high temperature and elevated chlorine pressure promote self-discharge by diffusion of reactants (particularly lithium) through the electrolyte.

Considerable effort has been devoted to design calculations and performance estimations for fully engineered Li–Cl_2 batteries. For short-discharge applications in the primary mode (no electrical recharge), these batteries are expected to deliver about 1000 W/kg and 400 Wh/kg of system (including reactant storage). For longer-term operation, it may be more desirable to operate at somewhat lower specific power (600

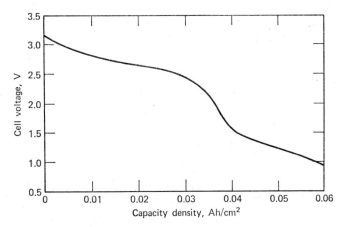

Fig. 7. Typical voltage–capacity-density curves for a lithium (aluminum)–chlorine (graphite) cell; electrode size (cm) = 15 × 25 × 0.8; area = 725 cm²; discharge = 0.04 A/cm².

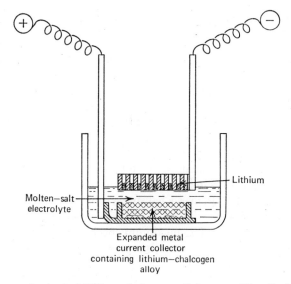

Fig. 8. Diagram of a typical lithium–chalcogen cell for use with a liquid electrolyte.

W/kg), which permits the use of lower-purity chlorine and is conducive to longer cell life. Some laboratory cells have performed well at reduced power densities and with large interelectrode distances for longer than 1000 hr (13).

The Lithium (Aluminum)–Chlorine (Carbon) Cell

A second version of the lithium–chlorine cell stores the chlorine within the cell by adsorption on the carbon cathode, which has a high specific area (about 1000 m²/g). The lithium is stored in the form of a solid lithium–aluminum alloy (14,15,15a). The electrolyte is molten LiCl–KCl eutectic (mp, 352°C) held in a separator of undisclosed composition.

An open-circuit voltage of 3.35 V, and a maximum current density of 2 A/cm² (based on the aluminum–lithium alloy surface) have been reported for this cell (16).

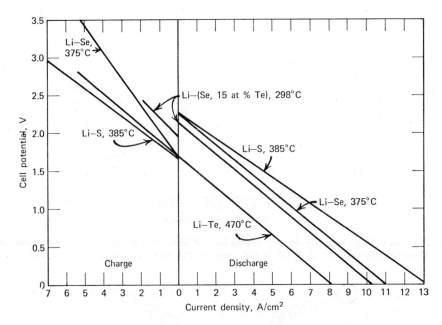

Fig. 9. Voltage–current-density curves for lithium–chalcogen cells with a liquid electrolyte, LiF–LiCl–LiI (mp = 341°C). The data for these curves were taken a few seconds after closing the circuit; therefore concentration overvoltages had not yet built up.

The voltage–capacity-density curve does not represent steady-state performance because of slow diffusion of lithium in the lithium–aluminum alloy and because the chlorine electrode exhibits a potential which is a strong function of its state of charge. This is made clear by Figure 7. Redox additives to the carbon electrode have been of some help in creating voltage plateaus in the voltage–capacity-density curves (1b).

Large (15 cm × 25 cm × 1 cm) sealed single cells have been constructed and subjected to life tests at 450–500°C. The best of these cells can deliver about 2000 cycles over a period of three months. The maximum specific energy demonstrated by these cells has been about 85 Wh/kg. These cells represent the most advanced design of any high-temperature cells.

Lithium–Chalcogen Cells

Lithium–chalcogen cells with molten-salt (lithium halide) electrolytes, which use tellurium (17), selenium (18), and sulfur (19) as the cathode materials, have been reported. The electrode reactions at the anode and cathode are shown in equations 7 and 8, respectively,

$$Li \rightarrow Li^+ + e^- \tag{7}$$

$$Y + 2\,e^- \rightarrow Y^{2-} \tag{8}$$

where Y represents the chalcogen. The final product, which forms in the cathode, is Li_2Y. Since the electronegativity increases in the order Te, Se, S, the cell voltages increase in the same order. Typical open-circuit voltages for these cells in the charged condition are 1.75, 2.2, and 2.3 V, respectively. The specific powers of these cells do not necessarily follow the same order because the electronic resistivities of the chal-

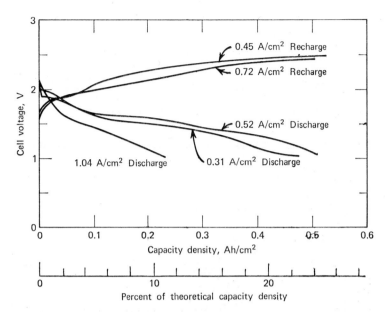

Fig. 10. Voltage–capacity-density curves for a lithium–sulfur cell with a liquid electrolyte, LiCl–KCl eutectic (mp = 352°C); cathode area = 0.96 cm²: temperature = 375°C.

cogens and their mixtures with lithium increase in the order Te, Se, S. This causes the current collection (or electron distribution) at the cathode to become more difficult in the order Te, Se, S. The melting points of the chalcogens are as follows: tellurium, 449.8°C; selenium, 220°C; sulfur, 118°C; thus, cell-operating temperatures of at least these values are required.

A typical lithium–chalcogen laboratory cell for use with a liquid electrolyte is shown schematically in Figure 8. Some short-time voltage–current-density curves for this type of cell operating at 375–475°C with various chalcogens as cathode material are presented in Figure 9. The average interelectrode distance for these cells was 0.4 cm; the active electrode area varied from 0.7 to 10 cm². The maximum power densities achieved with these cells were 7.5, 6.0, and 3.5 W/cm² for S, Se, and Te cells, respectively. The discharge curves are for fully charged cells and the charge curves are for discharged cells. The linear characteristics of these curves indicate that no significant concentration or activation overvoltages were present in the short run. The slopes of the curves correspond to the internal cell resistances which were primarily composed of electrolyte resistances.

Current-collection from selenium and sulfur-based cathodes is a problem because of the low electronic conductance of these chalcogens, especially sulfur. In the cells described above, current collection was accomplished by designing the current collector to maximize the area of contact between the molten cathode reactant and the current collector. In the lithium–tellurium cell (17) iron fins were provided in the cathode compartment, whereas several layers of expanded metal mesh were placed in the cathode cup of the lithium–selenium cells (18). For the lithium–sulfur cells (19) the current collector for the sulfur electrode was a sintered metal felt or a porous graphite. The voltage–capacity-density curves for a lithium–sulfur cell are shown in Figure 10.

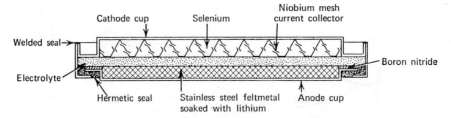

Fig. 11. A lithium–selenium cell (diam = 7.5 cm) with a paste electrolyte.

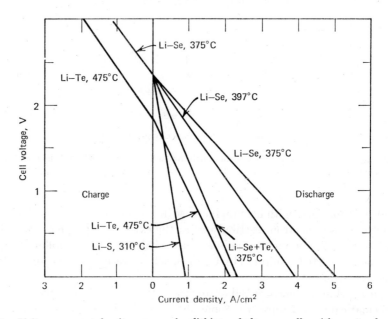

Fig. 12. Voltage–current-density curves for lithium–chalcogen cells with paste electrolytes.

The use of lithium–aluminum alloy instead of lithium in lithium–sulfur cells has been investigated (20). The anode was a solid 50 at.% lithium–50 at.% aluminum alloy that was prepared by allowing electrochemically deposited lithium to diffuse into a pure aluminum disk. Replacement of the lithium by lithium–aluminum alloy resulted in a reduction of the cell voltage by about 0.3 V at the operating temperature. In general, lithium–sulfur cells having a lithium–aluminum alloy anode showed somewhat lower performance than those with the liquid lithium anode. Although the lithium–aluminum alloy anode may be useful for special experimental purposes or in cells where it is necessary to immobilize the anode material, it is not being used at present in the development work on lithium–chalcogen cells.

The three-liquid cell of Figure 8 is not practical for some mobile applications. It is desirable to immobilize at least one of the liquid phases to make the cell position-insensitive. The fused-salt electrolyte was immobilized in the form of a stiff paste by mixing it with a finely divided (0.1 μ in diam) powder, such as lithium aluminate, in a 1:1 weight ratio (21). The paste electrolyte has a continuous molten-salt phase and the strength of the paste is due to the surface tension of the electrolyte in the fine-pore network formed by the inert ceramic powder.

A typical lithium–selenium cell (7.5-cm diam) with a paste electrolyte is shown in Figure 11 (24).   Some voltage–current-density curves for paste-electrolyte cells are given in Figure 12.   The data were taken with scaled-up lithium–selenium cells of 7.5 or 2.5-cm diam.   The thickness of the paste electrolyte for these cells was 0.3 cm.   A voltage–capacity-density curve for a lithium–selenium cell of 7.5-cm diam is presented in Figure 13.

The energy-storage capacity of lithium–chalcogen cells is determined by the amounts of lithium and chalcogen in the cells.   It is necessary to maximize the ratio of lithium to chalcogen in order to maximize the specific energy, but this ratio cannot exceed the value corresponding to the solidification of the cathode material at com-

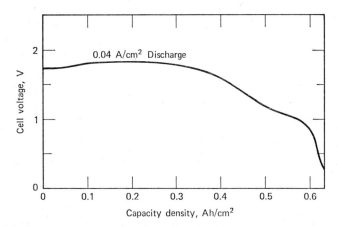

Fig. 13.   A voltage–capacity-density curve for a lithium–selenium cell with a paste electrolyte (60 wt% LiF–LiCl–LiI eutectic + 40 wt% LiAlO$_2$); electrode area = 31.6 cm²: temperature = 375°C.

plete discharge.   The solidification composition approaches that of the Li$_2$Y compound (where Y represents a chalcogen) so that 60 at.% lithium may be regarded as a practical upper limit for the lithium content of the cathode.

The lithium–chalcogen secondary cells have power densities second only to those of the lithium–chlorine primary cell.   They operate at temperatures near those of the sodium–sulfur cells and the problems concerning the materials of construction are less serious than those of the lithium–chlorine cell.   The cycle life of lithium–chalcogen cells is not yet sufficient for practical applications, the life being measured in tens of cycles (and hundreds of hours) compared to a common requirement of hundreds of cycles (and thousands to tens of thousands of hours).

Other Cells

Two other types of high-temperature cells which are no longer under active development, but which deserve brief mention, are the sodium–air cell (23) and the aluminum–chlorine cell (24).   The sodium–air cell involves two cell reactions, which may be represented as shown in equations 9 and 10.

$$2\,\text{Na} + 2x\,\text{Hg} \rightarrow 2\,\text{NaHg}_x \tag{9}$$

The sodium is transported through the liquid amalgam by diffusion and convection to a 50 wt% NaOH solution where the second cell reaction occurs.

$$2\,\text{NaHg}_x + \tfrac{1}{2}\,\text{O}_2\ (\text{air}) + \text{H}_2\text{O} \rightarrow 2\,\text{NaOH(aq)} + 2x\,\text{Hg} \tag{10}$$

Thus, the amalgam electrode functions as the cathode of the first electrochemical reaction and as the anode of the second one. The calculated value of the reversible emf for the overall cell reaction ($Na + \frac{1}{4} O_2 + \frac{1}{2} H_2O \rightarrow NaOH$) for a 50 wt% NaOH solution at 130°C is 2.72 V.

When the cell is recharged, the NaOH solution is electrolyzed, resulting in the deposition of sodium on the amalgam and evolution of oxygen at the air electrode. The sodium migrates across the amalgam electrode, and is transported back through the molten-salt electrolyte to the sodium electrode. The concentration of the NaOH electrolyte is kept constant by evaporating water at the required rate as the NaOH is electrolyzed.

Electrical performance tests were taken on sodium–air cells in which the molten-salt electrolyte was contained in a porous ceramic material and the air electrode was a gold-coated nickel screen backed with porous polytetrafluoroethylene and loaded with 10 mg/cm² of platinum. The active electrode area was 8 cm². The open-circuit voltage was 2.60 V and upon discharge the current densities ranged from 0.02 to 0.07 A/cm² with corresponding power densities of 0.048–0.154 W/cm². On the basis of these data, the estimated energy and power densities for a complete battery ranged from about 350 to 660 Wh/kg and 65 to 120 W/kg, respectively (23).

The aluminum–chlorine cell consists of a solid aluminum anode, a molten NaCl–KCl–AlCl₃ electrolyte, and a porous carbon–chlorine cathode (24). The electrode reactions at the anode and cathode are shown in equations 11 and 12, respectively:

$$Al \rightarrow Al^{3+} + 3\ e^- \tag{11}$$

$$\tfrac{3}{2} Cl_2 + 3\ e^- \rightarrow 3\ Cl^- \tag{12}$$

A brief feasibility test of the aluminum–chlorine cell was performed with an operating temperature of 150°C and a chlorine pressure of about 10 psig at the cathode. The molten-salt electrolyte (mp, 70°C) was 20 mole% NaCl–14 mole% KCl–66 mole% AlCl₃. The results of the electrical test indicated that a current density of 0.02 A/cm² can be achieved at a cell potential above 1.8 V. However, no data were reported on the capacity or energy density. The aluminum–chlorine cell is in a very early state of development, and several problems, such as dendrite formation at the anode and disintegration of the carbon electrode, remain to be solved.

Possible Applications

If some of the high-temperature secondary cells discussed above are developed into batteries with specific energies in the range of 220 Wh/kg, specific powers above 220 W/kg, and with cycle lives of hundreds to thousands, then a number of applications could be considered. Some of these, and the required power levels, are listed below.

Energy storage for spacecraft (W to kW); implantable power sources for biomedical applications, such as artificial heart-pumps (tens of W) (22), or military communications and emergency power (kW); materials-handling vehicles (kW), military vehicles (tens to hundreds of kW), boats and submarines (tens to hundreds of kW), remote locations (kW to tens of kW), electric buses, trucks, and autos (tens to hundreds of kW); and decentralized storage of off-peak power from central stations (tens of kW to M W). Broadly speaking, the above applications are arranged in the order of decreasing promise; both technical and economic difficulties increase toward the end of the list.

In applications which require a very high specific energy and have a high ratio of peak power to average power demand, a hybrid combination of a relatively small

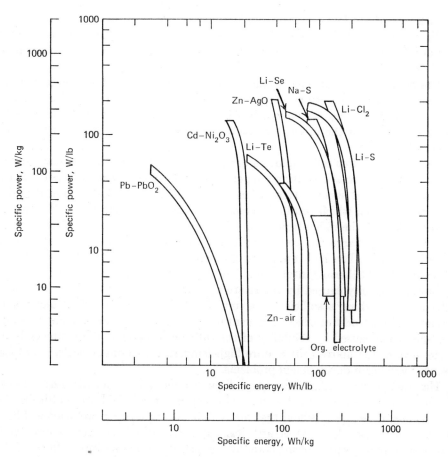

Fig. 14. Estimated specific-power–specific-energy curves for high-temperature batteries, compared to those for conventional batteries.

primary energy source, such as a fuel cell or an engine generator with a high-temperature secondary battery to provide peak power, weighs less than either a battery or a primary source alone. Some possible applications for hybrid systems are electric vehicles, boats, and submarines. For details of hybrid systems, see reference 25. See also Automobile exhaust control and Fuel cells in this volume. For applications which involve low power levels and only occasional use, high-temperature cells are probably unsuitable because of the inconvenience of startup and shutdown.

In order to compare the projected capabilities of high-temperature batteries to the demonstrated capabilities of commercially available batteries, the specific, power vs specific, energy relationships for a number of batteries are shown in Figure 14. The curves for the high-temperature batteries are estimates for multi-kW batteries based on the laboratory results presented above and on specific battery designs. The estimates for sodium–sulfur cells were made by Weber and Kummer (2), for lithium–chlorine by Hietbrink et al. (10), and for lithium–chalcogen by the authors. The organic-electrolyte batteries in Figure 14 have a lithium anode, a nickel halide cathode, and an organic electrolyte, such as propylene carbonate or dimethylformamide (26). These batteries operate at room temperature, but are not capable of high power densities because of the low electrical conductivity of the electrolyte. Figure 14 shows that the projected capabilities of high-temperature cells are far superior to the current capabilities of the other cells shown; therefore, a considerable incentive for their continued development exists.

Outlook. Many problems remain to be solved for each of the high-temperature cell systems. The practicality of the solutions to these problems will undoubtedly have a considerable influence on which of the high-temperature batteries find application in preference to the others. Some of the problems which remain to be solved are as follows:

The sodium–sulfur cell employs a ceramic electrolyte which has a relatively high resistivity (5–35 Ω-cm at operating temperature) and in some forms is sensitive to thermal and mechanical shock. It also has the problem of metallic sodium deposition within the ceramic, which results in cracking of the solid electrolyte. The lithium–chlorine cells pose the difficult problem of capturing and storing the chlorine that is evolved during recharge and returning it to the cathode at the appropriate pressure during discharge. The high operating temperature (ca 650°C) presents difficulties with materials and thermal insulation. The Li(Al)–Cl$_2$(C) cell suffers from a low energy-storage capacity caused by the relatively low capability of the high-area carbon electrode in adsorbing a sufficient amount of chlorine per unit weight and volume. Lithium–chalcogen cells also have stringent materials requirements and may be subject to self-discharge caused by solubility of the cathode reactant in the molten-salt electrolyte. All of the above cells require high-temperature hermetic seals, which have presented significant development problems.

High-temperature cells of the types discussed here are in an early stage of development and only a very limited amount of experience is available on multicelled batteries. Thus, it can be expected that many difficult engineering problems will be encountered in the development of practical batteries. Problems such as maintaining the operating temperature during standby periods, startup procedures, effects of thermal cycling, and safety must be considered. Although many of these problems are difficult and a major investment of effort is required to achieve a practical battery, the results to date have been encouraging. The potential advantages of high-temperature batteries are sufficient to warrant spending a concerted effort on their development.

Bibliography

1. R. P. Tischer, Ford Motor Co., private communication, 1970.
1a. J. T. Kummer and N. Weber, *SAE Automotive Eng. Congr., Detroit, Mich., Jan. 9–13, 1967*, paper No. 670179.
2. N. Weber and J. T. Kummer, *Proc. 21st Ann. Power Sources Conf.* **21,** 37 (1967).
3. *Intern. Power Sources Symp., Brighton, England, Sept. 15–17, 1970.*
3a. J. L. Sudworth and M. D. Hames, in reference 3, preprint No. 13.
4. L. J. Miles and I. Wynn Jones, in reference 3, preprint No. 14.
5. N. Weber and A. F. Venero, *Paper 76th Ann. Meet. Amer. Ceram. Soc., Philadelphia, May 1970.* M. Bettman and C. R. Peters, *J. Phys. Chem.* **73,** 1774 (1969).
6. S. Hattori, Yuasa Battery Co., Ltd., private communication, 1970.
7. D. A. J. Swinkels, *J. Electrochem. Soc.* **113,** 6 (1966).
8. D. A. J. Swinkels, *IEEE Spectrum* **5,** 71 (May, 1968).
9. D. A. J. Swinkels, *J. Electrochem. Soc.* **114,** 812 (1967).
10. E. H. Hietbrink, J. J. Petrarts, D. A. J. Swinkels, and G. M. Craig, *Technical Report to Air Force Aero Propulsion Lab TR-67-89*, General Motors Co., Detroit, Mich., 1967.

11. D. A. J. Swinkels, *Electrochem. Technol.* **5**, 396 (1967).

12. E. J. Cairns, C. E. Crouthamel, A. K. Fischer, M. S. Foster, J. C. Hesson, C. E. Johnson, H. Shimotake, and A. D. Tevebaugh, *ANL-7316*, Argonne Natl. Lab., Argonne, Ill., 1967.

13. T. G. Bradley, *Research Laboratory Report No. GMR-795*, General Motors, Detroit, Mich., Aug. 1968.

14. R. A. Rightmire and A. L. Jones, *Proc. 21st Ann. Power Sources Conf.* **21**, 42 (1967).

15. *SAE Intern. Automotive Eng. Congr., Detroit, Mich., Jan. 13–17, 1969.*

15a. E. J. Dowgiallo, D. H. Bomkamp, R. A. Rightmire, and J. W. Sprague, in reference 15, paper No. 690207; R. A. Rightmire, J. W. Sprague, W. N. Sorensen, T. H. Hacha, and J. E. Metcalfe, in reference 15, paper No. 690206.

16. J. L. Benak, *Paper Washington, D.C., Sect. Electrochem. Soc., Dec. 4, 1969* (Standard Oil Co., Ohio, Electrokinetics Div., Project 6892, preprint 3893); see also J. L. Benak, J. E. Metcalfe, and J. W. Sprague, *Contr. DAAKO2-68-C-0253 (USAMERDC), Final Rept. AD835881.*

17. H. Shimotake, G. L. Rogers, and E. J. Cairns, *Paper Electrochem. Soc. Meet., Chicago, Oct. 1967;* see also *Extended Abstr. Battery Div.* **12**, 42 (1967).

18. H. Shimotake and E. J. Cairns, *Paper Intern. Comm. Electrochem. Thermodyn. Kinet. Meeting, Detroit, Mich., Sept. 1968; Extended Abstr.*, p. 254.

19. H. Shimotake and E. J. Cairns, *Paper Electrochem. Soc. Meet., New York, May 1969.*

20. N. P. Yao, L. A. Herédy, and R. C. Saunders, *Paper No. 60, Electrochem. Soc. Meet., Atlantic City, Oct. 4–8, 1970.*

21. H. Shimotake, G. L. Rogers, and E. J. Cairns, *Ind. Eng. Chem. Process Design Develop.* **8**, 51 (1969).

22. H. Shimotake, A. A. Chilenskas, R. K. Steunenberg, and E. J. Cairns, *Proc. 5th IECEC, Intersociety Energy Conversion Engineering Conference,* Am. Nuclear Soc., Los. Vegas, Nev., Sept. *20–25, 1970.*

23. L. A. Herédy, H. L. Recht, and D. E. McKenzie, *Power Systems for Electric Vehicles,* U.S. Dept. of Health, Education, and Welfare, Washington, D.C., 1967, p. 245.

24. J. Giner and G. L. Holleck, *Tyco Laboratories Technical Report to NASA, NASA-CR-1541,* March 1970. (Available through the Clearinghouse for Federal Scientific and Technical Information (CFSTI), U.S. Dept. of Commerce, Springfield, Va.).

25. E. J. Cairns and H. Shimotake, "Fuel Cell Systems II," *Advan. Chem. Ser.* **90**, 392 (1969).

26. R. Jasinski, *High-Energy Batteries,* Plenum Press, New York, 1967.

E. J. CAIRNS, R. K. STEUNENBERG,
AND H. SHIMOTAKE
Argonne National Laboratory

CERAMIC COMPOSITE ARMOR

This article deals with protective materials, used largely, but not exclusively, in military applications, and consisting at least in part of a ceramic. Ceramic armor is usually a composite, consisting of a hard ceramic front face backed with a glass reinforced plastic (GRP) layer.

Fabrication

The adhesive layer is important in that good adhesion will hold the broken ceramic pieces in place. This offers a surface which is stiff in compression, and friction makes it difficult to move the material to the sides (3). This implies that there must be no dry spots or areas of no adhesion. On the other hand, an excessively thick adhesive layer would allow the ceramic to flex and thus fail in tension on the back surface. (See under Adhesives.)

One of the first applications for ceramic armor involved the seats for helicopter pilots and copilots. This involved flat ceramic plates and flat backups. It was relatively easy to maintain flatness of the two components and, therefore, achieve a thin uniform adhesive layer. But this became more difficult when personnel armor with complex curvatures was needed. The difficulties arose due to the high (18–20%) shrinkage of alumina in the firing kiln. Because of this shrinkage, no twoface plates are exactly the same. Boron carbide and silicon carbide shrink less and, therefore, pose less of a problem; but again, perfect uniformity from piece to piece is difficult to obtain.

In order to get the desired fit between the components, the ceramic is often used as the mold to form the mating backup; thus, the two components are parts of a matching pair until final assembly.

The back surface of the ceramic is sprayed or painted with a mold-release agent, such as a solution of poly(vinyl alcohol) or fluorocarbon. The solvent is allowed to evaporate so that a film of the release agent is retained on the surface of the ceramic. Then a layer of the glass-woven roving is laid on the coated ceramic, resin applied, and smoothed out. Alternate layers of reinforcement and resin are applied until the required thickness of the backup is achieved. An airtight poly(vinyl alcohol) bag is placed around the assembly, a vacuum is drawn on the bag to compact the assembly, and the bag is sealed. Then the assembly, with the vacuum maintained in the bag, is placed in an autoclave, where pressure and heat (from steam-jacketed walls of the autoclave) are applied. This causes the excess resin to flow and then brings about crosslinking to form an insoluble, infusible mass.

The item is removed and the two components are separated. The ceramic portion is cleaned with solvent (usually acetone) to remove the release agent and any contamination. The fiber-glass component is sanded to provide a roughened surface and then the solvent is washed. Adhesive is applied to both surfaces. Assembly may be directly thereafter, or the adhesive may be allowed to become tacky or gelled prior to assembly. After assembly, the parts are held together by spring-loaded clamps, and the adhesive is cured. The cure may be at elevated or room temperature.

The edges of the backup, which extend beyond the edges of the ceramic, are then trimmed with a band saw. This procedure is obviously in need of improvement. A one-step or primary bonding technique would lower costs by eliminating the need for applying the release agent, the surface preparation steps, and the rebonding step.

With the adhesives most commonly used, primary bonding efforts resulted in weak bonding and lack of multiple-hit capability. It is believed that the polyurethans or polysulfides had an inhibiting effect upon the cure of the polyester resin used.

A fairly good adhesive system was developed which resulted in good ballistics combined with good ceramic retention. This is further described in the section on Adhesives.

Plastic

During World War II, there was no effective armor against rifle projectiles at a weight which was tolerable for personnel or aircraft. However, protective vests were utilized against fragments from bursting munitions. One type of material used in these vests was a glass-reinforced polyester resin laminate. These were extensively used by the Marine Corps in amphibious landings. They later saved many lives during the Korean conflict.

With the development of ceramic composite armor, it was only logical to use this type of material as a backup material since impact of an armor-piercing projectile on the ceramic results in fragments of both the projectile and the ceramic face plate.

Extensive testing in the period 1944-1945 indicated that the most effective reinforcement for the backup plate was the glass fabric, made from E glass (see Vol. 10, p. 572) and known in the glass-fiber trade as 143 cloth. This is a unidirectional glass fabric with the strength in the warp direction about ten times the strength in the fill direction. It is approximately 0.009 in. thick and weighs 9 oz/yd². In the process of forming the fabric a starch-oil coating is applied to the individual filaments to prevent the abrasion of one fiber by another. For many applications, the starch-oil weaving aid is removed by heat and another coupling agent is applied that is more effective in reinforcing the bond to the matrix. However, ballistic results showed that the greige state (retention of the starch-oil) was better for this specific application.

The glass fabric described above was crossplied (the warp direction in each layer was at 90° to the adjacent layers) and molded into a solid sheet with 25% by weight of a thermosetting unsaturated polyester resin. This product is described in Military Specification MIL-I-17368B, Insert Body Armor (22 Aug. 1967). Much of the armor procured during the early 1960s used this material as a backup for the ceramic armor. However, efforts to improve the backup were continued.

MECHANISM

The mechanics of ballistic resistance are not well defined or understood, although much effort has gone into studies in this area. In many cases, the observations precede the theories. For example, both aluminum and glass-reinforced plastics are effective backups for ceramic-faced armor. It has been proposed that these two materials with significantly different "static" properties defeat projectiles by different mechanisms (1–4).

It is an accepted fact that ceramics are much more likely to fail in tension than in compression. When a projectile impacts one surface of a ceramic plate, that surface is subjected to compressive forces; the opposite surface is subjected to tensile forces.

This is similar to any flexural test. It has been stated that the effectiveness of aluminum as a backup material is dependent upon its stiffness as indicated by its modulus, 10×10^6 psi. In the absence of adequate support, the ceramic fails easily in tension at the surface opposite to the support of the projectile. The importance of rigidity in the backup has been demonstrated by an experiment in which specimens were similar in all respects except that in one case the backup was a single $\frac{1}{4}$-in. plate of aluminum; and in the other, it was made of $2\frac{1}{8}$-in. thick plates. Since rigidity is a function of thickness, it was expected that the single plate would offer higher ballistic protection. The expectation was verified by the ballistic limits obtained.

With glass-reinforced plastic backup, the defeat of the projectile is attributed to the large deflections attained. In arriving at a possible explanation for the seeming contradiction (ie, rigidity in the case of aluminum and ability to deflect in the case of the plastic), similar tests as described above were conducted. The effect of multiple layers was much less for the plastic than for the aluminum. Another experiment was conducted in which ring mounts of 2- and 4-in diam supported the specimens. The smaller opening would, of course, limit the backup deflection more than would the 4-in. ring mount. With the aluminum backup, the ballistic results were essentially equal; but with the plastic backup, the greater deflection allowed by the larger mount resulted in better penetration resistance (1).

At one time, it was thought that interlaminar shear was a major factor in absorbing energy from the projectile. The single vs multiple-layer experiment tended to indicate the effect to be relatively minor. Also, when woven roving was substituted for the thinner 143 cloth, the available number of surfaces for interlaminar shear was reduced by two-thirds. Had interlaminar shear been of primary importance, the ballistic results would have been much poorer. Instead, a benefit was gained.

The above observations still did not explain why two materials with significantly different static properties should behave in such a similar fashion. An insight to this behavior is given by a study of dynamic load-deflection measurements. These were obtained from a fast-moving ram used to impact the backup plate. Both the displacement of the ram and the load exerted on the ram were recorded. The curves obtained showed that the maximum dynamic load at failure is the same for 0.25 in. plates of woven roving and for the aluminum. The glass-fiber-reinforced plastic reached this maximum load at a larger deflection.

The mechanisms of projectile defeat can be summarized by saying that an effective backup must support the fracture conoid formed by the impact from the beginning. The breakup of the ceramic is thus delayed. As the conoid is completely broken and the load transmitted to a smaller area, the backup must deflect in order to avoid high shear stresses.

The importance of ductility is also shown by the equation:

$$\frac{P_t}{P_i} = \frac{2d_2C_2}{d_1C_1} + d_2C_2 = \frac{2(d_2E_2)^{\frac{1}{2}}}{(d_1E)^{\frac{1}{2}}} + (d_2E_2)^{\frac{1}{2}}$$

where $\dfrac{P_t}{P_i} = \dfrac{\text{transmitted pressure}}{\text{incident pressure}} = $ impedance/mismatch pressure ratio,

d = density,
C = longitudinal acoustical or elastic wave velocity,
E = elastic modulus;
subscript 1 refers to facing and subscript 2 refers to backup.

Table 1. Moduli and Specific Gravities of Various Glasses

Description	YM31A	S	E	D
modulus $\times 10^6$, psi	15.5	12.6	10.5	7.5
specific gravity	2.88	2.48	2.54	2.16

It can be seen that a low density and a low modulus in the backup results in a low numerical impedance/mismatch ratio or, in other terms, lower transmitted stresses to the backup. As could be expected, this means better ballistics (5).

REINFORCEMENTS

Although the armor backup using 143 cloth was able to stop armor-piercing and ball projectiles, it could not be assumed that the reinforcement was optimized for a backup material. In addition, reinforcements unavailable in 1945 were commercially available in 1965. Although nearly 99% of the glass fibers available were made in the electrical or E-glass formulation, also available as specialty items were high-strength S glass, dielectric D glass, and high-modulus YM31A glass. Ballistic testing indicated that the YM31A glass was drastically inferior to the E glass. The S glass was only slightly better than the E glass and was less cost effective since it cost approximately 15 times as much as the E glass. The D glass appeared to offer significantly better ballistic resistance. When the properties of the glass fibers of the various compositions were studied to see if a clue could be obtained as to why one glass was better than another, the greatest differences among the glasses appeared to be the modulus of elasticity. The moduli and specific gravities are shown in Table 1.

This observation was strengthened by uniaxial tension tests conducted at a rate sufficient to fracture the specimen in 0.005–0.010 sec (6). When "good" and "bad" backup materials were tested at slow and high rates, the "good" materials exhibited: (1) A modulus that remained unaffected or was slightly lower at high rates than at low rates, and (2) a minimum elongation of approximately 5%. Within the range of materials tested, the tensile strength did not appear significant; although there is probably a threshold of lower strength limit.

Based on the above considerations, it was believed that a fiber of still lower modulus might be beneficial. Since 75–80% of the weight of the glass-reinforced plastic is the reinforcement itself, a reinforcement with a lower density should also be of value in lowering the weight required for a specified ballistic requirement. An industrial contract was then initiated with the following stated aims:

1. Modulus of elasticity, 5,000,000 psi ± 10%.
2. Tensile strength, 150,000 psi minimum.
3. Emphasis to be placed on lowering the density below 2.54 g/cm³.
4. "Nascent" fibers (ie, immediately after fiberizing) to lose no more than 50% strength after 24 hr exposure to 100% rh at room temperature.

In order to hold the variables associated with the fiber and fabric formation to the minimum for every test on glasses of other composition, E glass was processed in the same manner (as far as possible). Many compositions were fiberized and characterized. The composition of the most promising glass is compared to that of E glass in Table 2. This composition became known as low-modulus or LM glass (7).

The property comparison with E glass is made in Table 3.

Table 2. Composition of E Glass Compared to LM Glass

Component	E	LM
silicon dioxide	54	52.8
calcium oxide	17.5	
aluminum oxide	14	5.7
boron oxide	10	28.8
sodium and potassium oxide	0–1	6.8
magnesium oxide	4.5	
lead oxide		4.8
fluorine		.4

This LM glass was not in production in 1970 and, as could be expected, pilot-lot batches are not as reproducible as material from a continuous operation would be. However, as a backup material against the 0.30-caliber armor-piercing (AP) M2 projectile, it is approximately 8% better ballistically than is E glass at the same weight. Without the ceramic facing, when tested with the 0.22-caliber 17-grain fragment simulator, the LM glass is close to 30% better. This material is being tested with other types of projectiles to establish its merit against a variety of ballistic threats.

Another approach to increasing the effectiveness of the reinforcement has been to change the weave. The continuous filaments formed by the fiber bushing can be made into yarns (ie, the individual filaments are twisted) or rovings (untwisted bundles). Normally, the yarns are woven into a tighter construction with resulting crimps in the yarns. Woven roving, on the other hand, is a much looser weave; and the crimping of the bundle is less severe. It was reasoned that both the twisting operation and the crimps resulted in lowered strength in the fabric. Additionally, the loose open weave of the woven roving should allow more excursion of the fibers in the area of impact and, thus, a greater energy absorption. The substitution of a 23.5 oz/yd² woven roving for the 9 oz/yd² 143 cloth was attempted. The resulting increase in ballistic resistance was marginal, only a 5–10% increase in V_{50} (see page 149). However, substantial cost reductions resulted from the material change. Woven rovings, as a class, cost only one-third as much as the finer fabrics. The laying up of the multiple plies required to make a suitable thickness is a hand operation. Since the woven rovings are nearly three times as thick as the 143 cloth, only one-third the number of layers is required to achieve the same thickness and the labor cost is thus drastically reduced. In spite of the fact that the anticipated ballistic improvement was not achieved, no Army armor has been made with a reinforcement other than the woven roving since 1965.

Other factors in connection with glass reinforcements have been investigated. The standard woven roving is described as 5 × 4 weave, indicating five rovings per inch in the warp direction and four rovings per inch in the fill direction. No one weave is optimum for all ballistic threats. The effect of better and worse balanced weaves

Table 3. Property Comparison of E Glass and LM Glass

Property	E	LM
modulus × 10⁶, psi	10.5	5.4
tensile strength × 10³, psi	500	260
wet-strength retention	98	70
density, g/cm³	2.54	2.24

on the ballistic resistance has been shown not to be of great significance. Likewise, the thickness of the woven roving as indicated by the weight per square yard (8, 16, 24, 35 oz/yd^2) has not had a significant effect.

Contrary to what was established with the 143 cloth, whether the reinforcement is crossplied or laid up parallel is not as critical with the woven roving since it is a much more balanced weave. Not all woven rovings are equal either in ballistics or in variability. The optimum woven roving has some relationship to the process used, ie, whether the laminate is made by autoclaving or pressing. This has not been thoroughly investigated.

As might be expected, materials with densities below that of glass have been investigated in an effort to lower the total weight of the armor. This led to an examination of organic fibers which, in general, are less than half as dense as E glass. Unfortunately, no organic fiber tested to date has a weight–efficiency ratio comparable to that of glass against the heavier fragments moving at the higher velocities.

Nylon fabric (MIL-C-12369) and nylon felt are efficient fragment armors at the lower areal densities (weight in lb/ft^2 of coverage regardless of thickness or density), but it was found that the nylon fabric was approximately 10% less effective than glass and the nylon felt was inferior to the fabric. A linear polyester-fiber fabric and glass mats were drastically inferior ballistically. For the mats, it is believed that lack of sufficient resistance to splitting allows a sharp-nosed projectile to separate the fibers rather easily; whereas, in a fabric, the two axes in the plane of impact are restrained from splitting.

It may be possible to upgrade the performance of organic fibers by certain techniques. In some plastic films, it was demonstrated many years ago that the presence of a low-molecular-weight fraction is more detrimental when the load is applied multiaxially than it is when a uniaxial load is applied. Since a ballistic impact is applied in a multiaxial fashion, a low-molecular-weight fraction may be present and the presence would not be detected by uniaxial tensile tests on the fibers. Later on, a "slip-stick" theory will be discussed as a possible mechanism of ballistic defeat. It is possible that materials such as polypropylene, which has a high-energy absorption at high strain rates, would behave more favorably if the surface lubricity could be reduced.

Carbon fibers are often thought of as high-modulus (25–100 $\times$ 10^6 psi) carbon or graphite fibers. (See Carbon fibers in this volume.) However, there are available carbon fibers which have moduli in the 3–6 $\times$ 10^6 psi range. These have lower densities than glass, acceptably high strengths, and moduli comparable to the LM glass. However, they have not performed well to date. It is believed that much work would be needed upon both the physical and the chemical nature of the surface of these carbon fibers before performance could be improved to an acceptable level.

In the work which led to the development of LM glass, the glasses with lower moduli often had a lower density also. Efforts currently are underway to establish whether improved ballistics result from the lower modulus, the lower density, or a combination of these properties. In order to establish another datum point on the modulus/density vs ballistics chart, woven quartz fibers were evaluated. Quartz has a lower density than glass but is essentially equal in modulus and strength to E glass. The quartz was inferior against the 17-grain fragment simulator and 0.30-caliber AP projectile by 16 and 8%, respectively.

Attempts to lower weight by using hollow glass fibers were also disappointing.

The failure in this case was ascribed to the higher section modulus which resulted from the hollow fibers.

In many of the cases described above, decisions were based on results obtained from small samples. The need for better armor was so urgent that if a material did not look promising in the initial attempts that material was discarded.

SURFACE FINISHES ON REINFORCEMENTS

As mentioned, the 143 cloth utilized in body armor seemed to be most effective when the fibers were finished with a starch-oil size. In addition, this lowered the cost because it eliminated the need for heat cleaning to remove the starch-oil and the subsequent application of a coupling agent.

It was assumed that the woven roving would also be more effective if it were treated with a starch-oil size rather than a silane or chrome complex coupling agent. However, it was not a practice in the glass industry to furnish rovings with a starch-oil size. Due to their nontwisted nature, rovings with starch-oil size would "slump" on the spool and cause severe problems for the weaver. Continued efforts to modify the starch-oil formulation resulted in the ability to provide the weavers with rovings that were usable. (It should be noted that the so-called "starch-oil" size may contain as many as 14 or 15 different ingredients, each incorporated for a specific function.) This resulted in a moderate increase in ballistics. The effect of the surface finish is believed to lie in the adhesion between the reinforcement and the resin matrix. Experiments have been conducted in which the surfaces were either heat treated or deliberately coated with a nonadhering (eg, silicone grease) substance. The poor ballistics were attributed to the fact that the reinforcing fibers were allowed to slide through the matrix without friction. On the other hand, a very strong bond between the reinforcement and the resin allows no movement of the fibers and the fibers break with the absorption of very little energy. An intermediate degree of bonding appears to allow a "slip-stick" mechanism to become effective. It should be noted that the slipping and sticking at the rates of ballistic impact are those that control. Since there is no evidence that static absolute values, or even relative rankings, are of value in predicting response at ballistic rates of loading, much of the testing has been empirical.

It has been postulated that energy absorption can be influenced by the frictional forces generated by the fiber being pulled through the resin matrix. If the force is too great, the fiber will snap with very little movement and little energy absorption. The experimental results which show that an epoxy resin with an epoxy-compatible finish is not ballistically resistant would tend to support this view since it is presumed that a strong bond results from this combination. The "slip-stick" theory is also consistent with other known phenomena (8).

Since it was believed that unidirectional, static shear tests were not indicative of performance under multiaxial high rate of loading conditions, a length of woven roving was heat-cleaned, and then selected additives were applied to portions of the fabric. Ballistic testing was then conducted on laminates made from these materials. These additives consisted of starch-oil at various loading levels, saturated and unsaturated polyesters, polyoxyethylene stearate, and poly(vinyl acetate) with and without added silane coupling agent.

Of the additives tested, the starch-oil gave the best ballistic results, although the optimum amount was not rigidly defined. In this series, the type of additive could influence the ballistic results by nearly 20%. The amount of additive had a lesser, though still significant, effect. Adding a coupling agent to the poly(vinyl acetate) did not increase the ballistic resistance. The heat-cleaned glass was used as a control without any additive. This did not provide effective armor. Although it has been reported that heat cleaning can lower the tensile strength of glass fibers by 10%, it is suspected that the poor resin-to-reinforcement bond is a larger factor than is the reduced strength.

RESINS

Much work was done during the period 1944–1945 to establish the optimum resin to be used as the matrix material. Of the resins then available, the unsaturated polyesters appeared to be the best. With the renewed interest displayed in armor in the 1960s, it was natural that the polyesters again be used.

It is obvious from the previous discussion that a relationship between reinforcement, finish, and matrix must exist. However, it has been the feeling of most people in the field that the resin is the least important. Also, there has been little incentive for work since the polyesters are quite cheap. In order to be cost-effective, most of the newer, more expensive, resins would have to increase ballistic limits by a large factor.

As mentioned before, epoxies are generally not suitable, presumably because too strong a bond is formed between the resin and the reinforcement. However, there is some evidence that epoxies might be effective in some cases (9).

Although it could be reasoned that a more rubbery type of resin would be more effective ballistically, mixtures of brittle and rubbery polyesters were not as effective as the 100% brittle polyesters. A 100% rubbery type of polyester was quite inferior. Rather surprisingly, the brittle polyester and a rubbery polyurethan were essentially equal in performance; but resins of intermediate stiffness were inferior to either. However, no polyurethan matrix has gone into production of armor because of the higher costs that this would require.

When a wet layup is used, the polyesters are normally crosslinked with styrene. However, if the backup is made from preimpregnated woven roving, the prepregging process requires that diallyl phthalate, DAP, or other crosslinkers less volatile than styrene be used as the crosslinker. There is no difference in the ballistic response of these two systems for a single ballistic impact. However, the DAP-containing resin delaminates more readily and is less useful for multiple-shot applications.

Currently, little is being done to investigate better resins for glass reinforcements. However, a stretched plastic film is being investigated as a backup. Too little has been done to date (1971) to permit making firm statements, but these films appear to offer some promise.

MAKEUP

The effectiveness of glass-reinforced plastic as either a backup material for a ceramic facing or unfaced for fragment protection can be influenced by such factors as percent resin content, the ratio of the weight of the facing to the backup (where applicable), and others.

On the subject of resin content, statistical analyses indicated that for pressed unfaced panels tested with a 17-grain fragment simulator, a variation of from 16 to 20% loss on ignition (LOI) is not significant. However, if the LOI increases to 26% (at an areal density of 4 lb/ft^2), the results are 18% lower than at 20% LOI. If the LOI indicates a 30% resin content, the results are 25% lower than at 20%.

On the other hand, autoclaved panels at 30% resin content are equivalent to the pressed panels at 20% resin content. This is probably related to resin distribution in and around the fiber bundles under the two different fabrication conditions. The autoclave technique applies isostatic pressure, and this could lead to more uniform resin distribution within the fiber bundles. Since the two techniques yield essentially different materials, data on autoclaved panels should not be included with pressed-panel data in performing a regression analysis. Equations are available which indicate the optimum areal density and percent resin within a system and within the limits of the areal densities and LOI's utilized in the multiple-regression-analysis. However, extrapolation should not be employed. These equations show that ballistic performance decreases as the molding pressure increases. It is believed that the added pressure can result in fiber breakage or damage. It can also result in weave distortion.

It should not be assumed that the slope of the curve plotting V_{50} against areal density is a linear function. Fragment simulator data show at least two slopes. The slope of the curve is very steep up to 1 lb/ft² and then significantly less from 1.5 to 3 lb/ft² (11).

It would appear that straight continuous parallel fibers would be best since the lack of crimp would avoid fiber damage and stress concentrations. On the other hand, this construction is poor at spreading the load to other filaments. Woven fabrics, on the other hand, are good at spreading the load. The best geometry in many ways would be layers of crossed filaments thoroughly bonded at the crossings. Obtaining a strong bond at the crossings has not yet been achieved and designing a textile structure to permit the maximum distribution of energy would be a promising approach (10).

Within the total weight allowed for ceramic armor by the application, the proportion of the weight which is used for the ceramic can have an effect upon the ballistics. The optimum proportion will vary with the projectile used and the total weight allowed. For instance, for some ceramic–plastic combinations, if a total weight of 6 lb/ft² is all that is allowed, a three-to-one ratio of ceramic to backup plate is most effective. If the total areal density allowed is 10 lb/ft², a two-to-one ratio is more effective against the 0.30-in. armor-piercing projectile.

On the other hand, if a 14.5-mm projectile is the threat, weight ratios of 2.1:1 and 4.3:1 are equivalent in ballistic protection; but 3.2:1 is more effective than either.

A general rule of thumb often used as a starting point to determine optimum ceramic facing thickness for steel armor-piercing projectiles is that the thickness should approximately equal the projectile diameter.

Ceramic

Requirements. The particular ceramic-armor system depends on the level of protection desired and the object to be protected. Personnel armor is worn as a vest and, thus, is required to be lighter than vehicular armor. Alumina (Al_2O_3) has been used as the front plate in most ceramic personnel armor giving protection against a 30-in. caliber projectile. But since B_4C has become available, it is considered more desirable due to its lighter weight. Personnel armor for 0.50 caliber protection is not currently used, but it is feasible if the total required weight of the armor system would not interfere with the combatant's performance and if the impulse transfer from the projectile to the combatant could be negated or minimized to a passive or nonlethal level. For aircraft use, most ceramic armor for both 0.30 and 0.50 caliber protection is Al_2O_3, but, for minimum-weight requirements, B_4C and B_4C-based materials are used.

Table 4. Comparison of Ceramic-Armor Materials

Material	ρ, g/cm³	$E \cdot 10^{-1}$, psi	H_{Knoop}, kg/mm²	$E_{Sp} \cdot 10^{-6}$, in.	F, lb/in.
B₄C	2.48	63.6	2790	712	2830
KT-SiC[a]	3.10	50.0	2700[b]	448	1720
TiB₂[c]	4.52	~65	~3000	400	1708
BeO (99%)	2.85	60	1200	585	998
Al₂O₃ (85%)	3.42	33.0	1800	268	685
MgAl₂O₄[c]	3.6	43	1300	332	614
MgO[c]	3.6	45	800	348	396

[a] See p. 150.

[b] Dependent on area tested since KT-SiC has free silicon dispersed throughout.

[c] Theoretical density and related properties.

For ground and naval vehicles, aluminum and steel armor are used except when weight is critical, then some Al₂O₃ front plates are used for both 0.30 and 0.50 caliber protection. Armor plate for 0.50 caliber protection is thicker than for 0.30 caliber protection, but it should not be inferred that any level of protection can be obtained simply by making the armor plate thicker. The thickness of an armor plate influences the time to failure and the distribution of the impulsive load on the plastic-backup layer. The thickness also determines the areal density of the armor system and, thus, is a design variable which in most cases is required to be a minimum for a specified level of protection having a minimum-weight requirement. The ballistic performance is also dependent on the physical properties of the ceramic plate. Table 4 compares various ceramic-armor materials according to their bulk physical properties of density, ρ, elastic modulus, E, and hardness, H. The ratio of elastic modulus to density, called the *specific modulus* and defined in equation 1, is sometimes used to compare different materials for small-caliber protection. The specific modulus is proportional to the square of the shock-wave velocity in a material.

$$E_{Sp} = \frac{E}{\rho} \tag{1}$$

Another ratio that is used is the *figure of merit*, F, defined in equation 2 as the product of the specific modulus and the Knoop microhardness number.

$$F = E_{Sp} H_{Knoop} \tag{2}$$

The figure of merit gives a good ranking of materials when compared to actual ballistic performance using small-caliber projectiles, but it still does not give the proper order or level of performance in every case. Relative ballistic performance of such armor materials as Al₂O₃ and MgAl₂O₄, as well as BeO and B₄C is still uncertain. Studies on B₄C and Al₂O₃ show that they undergo brittle failure, whereas BeO appears to yield plastically under ballistic conditions. Plastic deformation may also be the reason for the poor performance of MgAl₂O₄ although this has not yet been determined.

TERMINAL BALLISTICS

The mechanisms of projectile-armor impact and interaction, commonly referred to as terminal ballistics, have been studied using computer techniques in conjunction with experimental ballistic tests. Assuming normal incidence, the sequence of events,

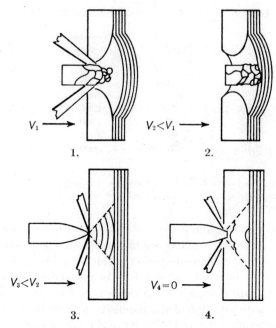

Fig. 1. Schematic of projectile, armor impact and interaction. The projectile leaves with velocity V; at $V_4 = 0$ the projectile has been defeated.

shown schematically in Figure 1, which occur in less than 50 microsec after the initial projectile–ceramic-armor contact, are:

1. A spherical shock-wave front is induced by compression in the ceramic plate and the projectile. The tip of the projectile is shattered.

2. Compressive shock-waves propagate through the ceramic plate and projectile and reflect from any free surface. The reflected waves are tensile-shock waves which fracture the ceramic at or near the surface opposite to that of impact but on the line-of-flight of the projectile. The ceramic in the vicinity of the projectile fractures within a volume whose boundary forms a conoid and the ceramic particles near the free surface spall.

3. The projectile continues to penetrate the fractured ceramic causing deformation of the plastic backup layer. At some point the projectile fractures.

4. The plastic backup layer deforms until the projectile and ceramic particles are stopped. If the momentum of the projectile is greater than the designed limit of the armor system, pieces of the projectile and ceramic will completely penetrate the plastic backup layer.

Besides providing a descriptive analysis of the armor-penetration mechanisms, the terminal ballistic studies have confirmed the basic design of ceramic-armor systems. The studies have also pointed to ways of improving ballistic performance and to design approaches which should not be used. In order to improve the ballistic performance over standard armor systems, the tensile strength of the ceramic plate and the time required to fracture the ceramic should be increased; both approaches would increase the energy absorbed by the ceramic plate. In addition, armor-plate designs of ceramic laminates have been shown to have a lower ballistic limit than a single ceramic layer of the same total thickness, due primarily to shorter fracture times.

Table 5. Estimated Costs and Established Suppliers of Armor Materials

Material	Cost, $	Supplier
Al_2O_3	2.00	Coors Porcelain Co.
KT-SiC	20.00	Carborundum Co.
B_4C	20.00	Norton Co.
BeO	50.00	National Beryllia Corp.
modified B_4C	25.00	Carborundum Co.
TiB_2		Norton Co. or Avco Corp.

Definitions and Terms. The following list explains the more important definitions and terms commonly used in ceramic-armor technology:

Fair Impact. An impact in a ballistic test made by an unyawed projectile (ie, one that is not traveling in such a way that its own axis differs from the line of flight) normal to the ceramic surface and separated from any other impact, edge of the plate, hole, crack, or spalled area by a distance sufficient to form a crack free 4-in.-diameter area, the center of which would be the impact point.

V_{50} *Protection Ballistic Limit.* For a specific projectile, the average of six fair-impact velocities comprising the three lowest velocities resulting in complete penetration and the three highest velocities resulting in partial penetration, with a maximum velocity spread of 150 ft/sec. A V_{50} protection ballistic limit determination usually requires 12–15 actual ballistic tests.

Partial Penetration. Any fair impact that is not a complete penetration.

Complete Penetration. A fair impact that causes any projectile or plate fragments to pass beyond the limits of the backup plate with sufficient energy to penetrate a 0.020-in. aluminum witness plate 6 in. behind the sample.

Velocity Merit Rating. The ratio of the V_{50} protection ballistic limit of the candidate experimental armor to the V_{50} protection ballistic limit of homogeneous standard-steel armor having the same areal density.

Weight Merit Rating. The ratio of the areal density of homogeneous steel armor to the areal density of the experimental armor, both armor systems having the same V_{50} protection ballistic limit.

A U.S. Department of Defense Security Classification must be determined by a qualified agency before such information on either of these merit ratings can be released. However, it may be said that velocity merit ratings on the order on 2–3 can be obtained.

OPAQUE ARMOR

The materials currently used for opaque ceramic-armor plate are few. The reason for this is that so many materials are either too scarce, too expensive, or too difficult to fabricate. Ballistic performance for a particular material is increased as the fabricated ceramic density is increased, which, in turn, provides improved mechanical and structural material properties. Fully dense ceramics normally require high-temperature fabrication methods which are usually expensive. As a result, when the best ballistic protection for a particular ceramic-armor material is required, the cost of producing such material is high. However, a chosen level of protection or utilization of the armor plate allows cost–performance analyses to determine a particular material in most cases. In addition, there is a wide range of costs between different ceramic-

Table 6. Physical and Mechanical Properties of Opaque Armor

Property	B_4C	Al_2O_3, 85%	KT-SiC	BeO, 99%
density, g/cm^3	2.48	3.42	3.10	2.85
flexural strength, 10^3 psi	40	46	24	30
modulus of elasticity, 10^6 psi	64	33	50	60
Knoop microhardness, kg/mm^2	2790	1800	2700[a]	1200

[a] Maximum value. Measured value depends on the specific area tested.

armor materials. Table 5 lists the established suppliers and the estimated costs of different armor materials fabricated in a 6 × 6 × ¼ in. slab.

Boron Carbide. See Vol. 3, p. 670. Since it is prepared by reduction of boron oxide with carbon, it usually contains some residual free carbon. The material is ground to a low-micron particle size, screened, blended with a binder, and cold pressed to form a "green" preform prior to hot pressing. Use of a preform precludes the necessity of extensive sizing and finishing of the tiles after hot pressing. Hot pressing is performed in a conventional manner, using graphite molds, a reducing atmosphere, temperatures around 2000°C, and pressures on the order of 2000 psi. The actual processing conditions, including time, depend on the furnace size, mold shape, graphite grade, and the size and shape of the boron carbide armor plate being fabricated. Temperature is the most critical and most difficult parameter to determine; at the high temperatures required, only optical pyrometric methods are satisfactory. Quality-control procedures are used throughout the processing steps and the fabricated articles are inspected using conventional nondestructive techniques, such as dye penetration, x radiography, and sonic velocity. Table 6 lists the physical and mechanical properties of boron carbide armor plate.

Aluminum Oxide. High-purity aluminum oxide is made from aluminum hydroxide which was obtained from raw bauxite ore. See Sintered Aluminas, vol. 2, p. 55. Aluminum oxide ceramics have various percentages of aluminum oxide actually present in the final fabricated shape. Typical aluminum oxide armor plate has 85% aluminum oxide with intentional additives of primarily silicon oxide, magnesium oxide, and calcium oxide. Higher aluminum oxide contents do not substantially affect the ballistic protection. Aluminum oxide armor plate is produced primarily by two different methods: cold pressing and isostatic forming. For both processes, the mixed oxide grain is suspended in a slurry, ball milled, blended, and dried. For cold pressing, the dried powders fill the die cavity and are pressed. For isostatic pressing, the dried powders fill a rubber sack or rubber mold which is then sealed and subjected to hydrostatic pressure. In cold pressing, the uniformity of shape, size, and density of the aluminum oxide part are limited by the pressure available. In isostatic forming, the aluminum oxide part is uniform throughout, can be fabricated in large or small sizes, and can be formed with irregular or curved shapes.

After either pressing operation, the aluminum oxide article is subjected to a high-temperature sintering cycle for further densification. Up to 20% shrinkage is usually experienced during this sintering stage. If close dimensional tolerances are required, then grinding with diamond is usually necessary. The standard 6 in. × 6 in. armor plate can be produced by cold pressing and sintering while curved plates or complex parts can be formed by isostatic pressing and sintering. Quality-control procedures are established for each stage of the processing, and nondestructive tests are used for checking the fabricated articles. Typical properties of 85% aluminum oxide armor plate are presented in Table 6.

Silicon Carbide. See Vol. 4, p. 114. Silicon carbide articles are produced most economically by a cold-pressed reaction-sintered method. Such silicon carbide has been designated as KT silicon carbide by the Carborundum Company, who developed the production method. For armor plate, silicon carbide, carbon, and a binder are blended and formed into the desired shape by cold pressing or slip casting. The green shape is then fired at low temperature to volatilize the binder and increase the green strength. Then the green body is fired in a silicon-rich environment at temperatures in the range of 2100–2300°C for periods around one-half hour, depending upon the shape and thickness of the body. The initial firing step can be eliminated once the

Table 7. Properties of Oxide Ceramics of Interest for Transparent Armor

Material	Crystal symmetry	Refractive indexes
α BeO	hexagonal	1.719[a]
		1.739[b]
α Al$_2$O$_3$	hexagonal	1.760[a]
		1.768[b]
MgAl$_2$O$_4$	cubic	1.728
MgO	cubic	1.736

[a] c axis.
[b] a axis.

amount of residual carbon from the organic binder is determined. All of the free carbon is converted to silicon carbide during the reaction sintering step which results in a body containing free silicon as the major impurity with a density, based on pure silicon carbide, of greater than 95% of theoretical. No shrinkage occurs in the reaction-sintering stage with the result that close tolerances from the green state to the final product can be achieved. Quality-control procedures and nondestructive inspection techniques are utilized both during and subsequent to the armor-plate production. Properties of KT silicon carbide are listed in Table 6.

Beryllium Oxide. See Beryllium compounds. Beryllium oxide armor plate generally is at least 99% pure and is fabricated by conventional techniques, such as cold pressing and sintering, slip casting and sintering, and hot pressing. The techniques are similar to those already described. Other pertinent items are: shrinkage during sintering varies from 15 to 18%; hot-pressing temperature range is 1450–1800°C; and curved shapes are produced by the slip casting and sintering method. In using any beryllium oxide products, the factor of toxicity is always of concern. However, the U.S. Surgeon General's Office now considers beryllium-containing armor plate to be safe, provided the fabricated article has been heat-treated above 1600°C. Selected properties of 99% beryllium oxide plates are listed in Table 6.

Titanium Diboride. See Vol. 3, pp. 673–676; Vol. 20, p. 418. Titanium diboride is of interest because it is superior to the other materials listed in Table 6 against projectiles of higher caliber. Titanium diboride is fabricated as flat plates using conventional hot-pressing techniques at nominally 4000 psi and 2000 °C for around 240 min. Plate sizes of 6 in. × 6 in.^{2} with different thicknesses ranging from $\frac{1}{8}$ in. to $\frac{1}{2}$ in. can be fabricated.

TRANSPARENT ARMOR

In order to be transparent, a material must approach theoretical density and have the following characteristics:

1. A band gap between the valence states and the next higher allowed states which is greater than the photon energy of visible light;

2. A cubic (isotropic) symmetry, or, for birefringent materials, alignment of the optic axis as in a single crystal, or a polycrystalline grain size smaller than that of the wavelength of light to eliminate reflections at the grain boundaries;

3. No dissolved impurities which have energy levels in the band-gap region of the matrix material; and

4. No second phases which are opaque or which have refractive indexes different from the matrix material.

With these conditions, only certain ceramics, primarily in the oxide class, are suitable for transparent ceramic armor. Table 7 lists the oxides of interest and their properties related to transparency.

Most transparent ceramic armor requires a good ceramographic polish to eliminate surface roughness and the translucent ground-glass effect remaining after consolidation. Light transmittance through such highly polished materials is decreased by nominally 14% due to the loss of light intensity as a result of reflection from the polished surfaces. If necessary, this loss can be greatly reduced by applying a coating having a thickness of an odd number of quarter wavelengths of light (usually chosen as one wavelength in the middle of the visible spectrum, 500–600 nm) and composed of a material having a refractive index equal to the square root of the refractive index of the ceramic material. Effective coatings can be made of MgF_2 ($n = 1.38$) or $3NaF \cdot AlF_3$ ($n = 1.36$) and applied by vapor deposition. In addition, durable coatings, such as MgF_2, can protect the transparent ceramic from environmental attack if it is detrimental to transparency.

Beryllium Oxide. Based on the specific-modulus or figure-of-merit values in Table 4, beryllium oxide is the best choice for transparent armor. However, the stable phase at room temperature, α beryllium oxide, has hexagonal crystal symmetry and, therefore, is optically birefringent. For transparency and undistorted sight, beryllium oxide would have to be produced in single-crystal form. Beryllium oxide single crystals large enough for transparent armor are probable not due to an α-β solid-state phase transformation at $2050 \pm 32°C$ which results in a volume change approaching 10% which, on cooling, would induce stresses and subsequent cracking of the crystals.

Aluminum Oxide. Aluminum oxide has hexagonal crystal symmetry and, therefore, is optically birefringent. As with beryllium oxide, single-crystalline material i required for transparent armor applications. Techniques for growing single-crystal aluminum oxide, that is, sapphire, have been developed to support the laser-crystal needs. The Czochralski technique (see Vol. 17, p. 864) gives the best-quality sapphire-crystal rods and has been modified to produce square plates for transparent armor. This technique is a crystal-pulling method whereby an oriented seed crystal is inserted into a melt and withdrawn vertically at a programmed rate, usually in the range of ⅛–½ in./hr. Sapphire grows more rapidly along the a axis; therefore, the seed crystal is oriented to pull the crystal in the a-axis direction. Plates 4 in. × 4 in. × ½ in. have been made by the Union Carbide Corp. and techniques for plates up to 6 in. × 6 in. × ½ in. are being studied.

Magnesium Aluminate Spinel, MgAl$_2$O$_4$. For transparent armor, magnesium–aluminate spinel has the greatest potential for use, but has received little attention due primarily to its high melting point and a certain variability in composition. Spinel has cubic crystal symmetry and would be transparent in polycrystalline, as well as single-crystalline form; thus, single-crystal spinel is not necessary for transparent armor applications. Polycrystalline spinel has been made in small specimen sizes having better transparency than either beryllium oxide or aluminum oxide single crystals. Larger sizes, about 3 in. in diameter by $\frac{1}{2}$ in. thick, prepared by hot pressing, lack transparency due to less than theoretical density and nonhomogeneous microstructures. The problems of technique development for producing suitable sizes of transparent spinel appear to be difficult, but it is reasonable to expect profitable returns for success.

Magnesium Oxide. Magnesium oxide has cubic crystal symmetry and is transparent in polycrystalline form. Plates up to 11 in. in diameter by $\frac{3}{16}$ in. thick have been produced by the Avco Corporation using vacuum hot pressing with a pressure of 5000 psi, temperature up to 1100°C, and time at temperature up to 180 min. As a sintering aid, 0.3 wt% lithium fluoride is added to the magnesium oxide powder. After consolidation, the plates are annealed in a hydrogen atmosphere at nominally 1000°C for 60 hr to volatilize the lithium fluoride. However, as shown in Table 4, opaque magnesium oxide is inferior in properties to other opaque materials, and the comparison is the same among transparent materials. In addition, magnesium oxide requires a coating for protection against humid environments to inhibit the formation of opaque magnesium hydroxide on the polished surfaces.

INVESTIGATIONS OF ARMOR MATERIALS

Many other materials and/or combinations of materials for ceramic armor plate are currently being studied. A ceramic material called "modified B$_4$C," developed by the Carborundum Company, has shown promise as an armor material which could be more economical to produce than standard B$_4$C. The Norton Company is investigating materials such as AlB$_{12}$, mixtures of B$_4$C + B, B$_4$C + SiC, B$_4$C + AlB$_{12}$, and B$_4$C + TiB$_2$. Battelle Memorial Institute has investigated fusion casting of quasi-binary eutectic compositions of B$_4$C–SiC and B$_4$C–TiB$_2$. The Franklin Institute Research Laboratories is investigating metal-wire-reinforced alumina and magnesium–aluminate spinel. The Air Force Materials Laboratory is conducting research on a series of boron suboxides ranging from B$_4$O to B$_{12}$O. Many other potential materials exist in the carbide, boride, silicide, and nitride classes but most are laboratory curiosities and may never be available on a scale large enough for consideration as armor materials. Research and development of transparent ceramics will continue. Current investigations on MgAl$_2$O$_4$ include cold press and sintering small particles and hot pressing MgO + Al$_2$O$_3$ powder mixtures; other techniques of interest are fusion casting and vapor-diffusion reactions. Work on sapphire plates will be continued and methods to produce transparent polycrystalline Al$_2$O$_3$ will be investigated.

Adhesives

The two main components of ceramic armor are discussed elsewhere (see p. 139 and p. 146). However, the ceramic and the backup material are normally joined together with an adhesive. It was originally thought that a rubbery type of adhesive was needed. It was reasoned that such a material would result in a greater impedance/ mismatch pressure (1) which would transfer less stress to the backup component. In addition, the ceramic and the glass-reinforced plastic backup have different thermal expansion coefficients. It was believed that a rubbery material could accommodate the resulting dimensional changes more readily.

More recent experience has shown that the nature of the adhesive is not as critical as once thought. However, since the two types of adhesives originally chosen have performed well and because the techniques of application and cure have become routine, their use has been continued. These two types of adhesives are polysulfides (see Polymers containing sulfur) and polyurethans (see Urethan polymers). To prove that these adhesives would function as intended, ceramic and glass-reinforced plastics were joined with these adhesives and the assemblies were subjected to severe environments. Such environments have consisted of weather, vibration, temperature cycling, and temperature shock, immersion in water and in jet fuel, high temperatures and high humidities, and mechanical shock. Both adhesives have shown negligible effects from these exposures. Of course, the same attention to surface preparation and cleanliness essential to any adhesive bonding is required in order to get these results.

As mentioned under Plastic the thickness of the adhesive layer has a bearing upon the ceramic retention. A two-component polyurethan was cured at room temperature and also at elevated temperatures (160°F). The former resulted in an adhesive thickness of 0.011–0.015 in., and the latter gave a thickness of 0.003–0.004 in. The thicker layers resulted in better ceramic retention. In one known case, a thickness of 0.300 in. resulted from failure to have the backup conform to the ceramic. This allowed the rear surface of the ceramic to break in tension because the rubbery nature of the adhesive failed to lend any support.

It should be noted that the polyurethan used was of the polyether type rather than the polyester. The latter is known to revert under conditions of high humidity.

Work reported by Goodyear Aerospace Corporation (2) indicated that neither type of adhesive contributed to better ballistics. On the basis of ceramic retention, the polysulfide performed better against the 7.62 mm (AP or ball) projectile; but the polyurethan was better when impacted by the 0.30-in. caliber AP projectile.

Although both of the above systems are relatively expensive, as compared with other available adhesives, the amounts used are quite small and manufacturers have been reluctant to change to other cheaper adhesives which might not be as durable. In addition, the adhesive cost is so minor compared to the cost of the other components that there has been a natural reluctance to risk a rejection of a lot of armor and the ensuing monetary loss.

Some work has indicated that the nature of the bonding material used is insignificant (3) from the viewpoint of V_{50} or other calculations based on single impacts. It was not even necessary that the bonding material adhere to either the ceramic or the backup plate. This was established by curing the adhesive with plastic films between it and the target material. It was also shown that molybdenum disulfide could be used between the ceramic and the plastic without degradation of the ballistic properties. It was reasoned that the adhesive had instead an effect upon the ceramic surface. The small irregularities in the rear surface of the ceramic allow the surface to be stressed in tension. It is believed that the bonding material fills in the voids of this irregular surface. This hypothesis was checked by very carefully grinding the surface of a ceramic to achieve an extremely smooth surface. The ballistic values for bonded and unbonded smooth-surfaced ceramics were the same and also equal to those for bonded nonground ceramics.

The above discussion is limited to the effects of bonding in the case of single impacts. It does not follow that the adhesive is unimportant. The adhesive will affect the ceramic retention, and this becomes important from the viewpoint of the amount of ceramic remaining to defeat subsequent projectiles. It is also of concern in connection with the emission of frontal spall. When a brittle material, such as a ceramic, is impacted by a projectile, fragments of the ceramic can be ejected to the front and sides. In some cases, these ceramic particles can cause casualties to personnel adjacent to the armor wearer (4). An effective adhesive will reduce the number of these secondary particles emitted.

The two-step assembly of the ceramic and the backup was described under Plastic. The application of the release agent, the separation of the components, the surface preparations, and the rebonding obviously took an appreciable amount of time and, therefore, added to the cost of the armor procured. It appeared that a primary or one-step bonding technique would be desirable.

Previous efforts to prepare finished body armor by means of a primary-bonding technique had been only moderately successful. Ceramic retention after the first ballistic impact was not as good as wished. It was believed that the adhesive and the polyester resin used in the backup were partly incompatible and that the cure was not complete.

It had been observed that the two-step polyurethan adhesive bonded well to the ceramic, but the bond to the plastic backup was not as good. Epoxy-film adhesives, on the other hand, bonded better to the plastic than to the ceramic.

It appeared logical to combine the two adhesive systems. However, the elevated temperature cure of the polyurethan adhesive required much more time than did the cure of the epoxy. The increased oven time was undesirable. Oven time was decreased by applying the polyurethan to the ceramic and allowing it to cure at room temperature. The epoxy-film adhesive was then placed on top of the cured polyurethan, and one dry ply of a woven roving with an epoxy-compatible coupling agent was placed on the epoxy. The remaining plies of woven roving were then alternated with polyester resin until the desired backup thickness was obtained. The complete assembly was then cured in an autoclave. Qualitative ballistic evaluations of these composites indicated a significant increase in ceramic retention.

The epoxy film contained a nylon-scrim fabric and a small percentage of an inert filler material. Neither of these components added to the bond strength. In addition, the film adhesive is quite expensive and must be stored under refrigeration. It was decided to try a liquid epoxy adhesive. Ceramic retention when this substitution was made was even better.

Composites were then made using two thixotropic epoxy adhesives, one polysulfide/epoxy adhesive and one polyamide modified epoxy. Qualitative ballistic tests indicated that all four systems exhibited better ceramic retention than the secondary bonding method utilizing only the polyurethan or the primary bonding using a combination of polyurethan and epoxy film adhesive.

Quantitative ballistic data were then obtained to ensure that the ballistics had not been degraded by the changed adhesives. The values obtained indicated no degradation on flat panels.

The next step was to prepare specimens with extreme curvature to ensure that the shape would not cause adhesive drain-off. Thigh armor was chosen as a shape to be tested. Again, ceramic retention was good and ballistics were not lowered.

The final proof was to fabricate complete armor panels with ballistic nylon frontal spall shields to see if the better adhesion did reduce the spall, as had been anticipated. Spall was reduced, and the 4–9% decrease in ballistics that had previously been associated with spall covers did not appear. It was also noted that the failure mode of the ceramic was altered by the improved adhesion. It appeared to fail in planar shear with the ceramic remaining bonded to the backup in the impact area. All the ceramic ejected as spall was sheared from the outermost surface of the ceramic (5).

More work is needed to verify some of the prior conclusions and to explain some of the mechanisms involved; but, as of early 1971, there is substantial evidence that the nature of the adhesive does not significantly affect the first-shot ballistic resistance. However, the presence of an interlayer is helpful even if it is of a lubricating nature rather than of an adhesive nature. An adhesive can perform a useful function in reducing the ejection of frontal spall and in retaining the ceramic for subsequent ballistic impacts.

Bibliography

Fabrication and Plastics

1. M. Wilkens, *Third Progress Report of Light Armor Program*, UCRL 50460, University of California, Livermore, July 1968.
2. M. Wilkens, C. Honodel, and D. Sawle, *An Approach to the Study of Light Armor*, UCRL 50284, University of California, Livermore, June 1967.
3. M. Wilkens, *Second Progress Report of Light Armor Program*, UCRL 50349 (classified), University of California, Livermore, Nov. 1967.
4. M. Wilkens, C. F. Cline, and C. Honodel, *Fourth Progress Report of Light Armor Program*, UCRL 50694, University of California, Livermore, 1969.
5. C. Semple, *Projectile and Lightweight Ceramic Composite Armor Interactions* (Special Report), Army Materials and Mechanics Research Center, Watertown, Mass., 1968.
6. E. McAbee and M. Chmura, *Correlation of Tensile Properties and Ballistic Performance of Reinforced Plastics, Picatinny Arsenal Tech. Report 3195*, Dept. of the Army, Picatinny Arsenal, Dover, N. J., March 1965.
7. T. J. Whang, *Low Modulus Glass Fibers, Final Report on Contract DAAA21-67-C-0193*, Ferro Corp., Cleveland, Ohio, March 1968.
8. E. P. Plueddemann, *Adhesion through Silane Coupling Agents, Proc. 25th Conf. Reinforced Plastics/Composites Div. Soc. Plastics Ind., Washington, D.C. February 1970.*
9. E. McAbee and W. Bechtold, *Tensile and Ballistic Performance of Glass Reinforced Epoxy Laminates, Picatinny Arsenal Tech Memorandum 1912*, Dept. of the Army, Picatinny Arsenal, Dover, N. J., July 1970.
10. W. Sheehan, *Report on Personnel Armor Materials*, National Academy of Sciences, Washington, D.C., Sept. 1968.

Ceramic

1. W. D. Kingery, *Introduction to Ceramics*, John Wiley & Sons, Inc., New York, 1960.
2. J. F. Lynch, C. G. Ruderer, and W. H. Duckworth, "Engineering Properties of Ceramics," *Am. Cer. Soc. Bull.* (1966).
3. Richard M. Fulrath and Joseph A. Pask, eds., *Ceramic Microstructures, Their Analysis, Significance, and Production*, John Wiley & Sons, Inc., New York, 1968.
4. J. G. Dunleavy and W. H. Duckworth, eds., "Ceramic-Armor Technology," *Symposium Proceedings, Defense Ceramic Information Center, Columbus, Ohio, DCIC Report 69-1, Part I, May 1969.*

5. Eleanor R. Smith in reference 4, Bibliography, Part III, (Total of 270 references listed).

6. W. H. Rhodes, D. J. Sellers, A. H. Heuer, and T. Vasilos, "Development and Evaluation of Transparent Aluminum Oxide," *U.S. Naval Weapons Laboratory Contract N178-8986, June 1967*.

7. Leonid V. Azaroff, *Introduction to Solids*, McGraw-Hill Book Company, Inc., New York, 1960.

8. Jacob J. Stiglich, Jr., "A Survey of Potential Ceramic Armor Materials," *Army Materials and Mechanics Research Center, AMMRC MS 68-04*, Watertown, Mass., March 1968.

Adhesives

1. C. Semple, *Projectile and Lightweight Ceramic Armor Interactions* (Special Report), Army Materials and Mechanics Research Center, Watertown, Mass., 1968.

2. R. Kalorik, *Composite Aircraft Armor Materials Research and Development, Report 67-37-CM* (Classified), Goodyear Aerospace Corp., Akron, Ohio (Feb. 1967).

3. M. Wilkens, *Third Progress Report of Light Armor Program*, UCRL 50460, University of California, Livermore, July 1968.

4. J. Gulbierz and C. Yearwood, *Evaluation of Systems for Containing Frontal Spall Ejected from Hard-Faced Composites on Impact by Small Arms Fire, Picatinny Arsenal Tech Report 3751* (Classified), Dept. of the Army, Picatinny Arsenal, Dover, N. J., Dec. 1968.

5. C. Yearwood, *An Improved Adhesive System for Primary Bonding Ceramic to Glass Reinforced Plastics in Composite Lightweight Armor, Picatinny Arsenal Letter Report to U.S. Army Materials and Mechanics Research Center*, Dept. of the Army, Nov. 1969.

GEORGE RUGGER
(Fabrication
and plastics)
Dept. of the Army
JOHN R. FENTER
(Ceramic and
adhesives)
Dept. of the Air Force

CHEMICAL CLEANING

Chemical cleaning may be defined as the removal of inorganic and organic foulants from process systems or process equipment by chemical or more specifically, physicochemical methods. Chemical cleaning, then, as the term is popularly used and as it will be described in this article, refers to the cleaning of complete processing systems such as commercial air conditioners, as well as individual units such as boilers, heat exchangers, cracking towers, piping, and storage tanks. The cleaning agents usually employed include acids, bases, chelants, organic solvents, and surfactants. Often mechanical scale-fracturing equipment is used to aid the action of these chemical solvents. This type of cleaning is usually employed *after* process equipment has been fabricated (see also Metal surface treatment; and Pickling in this volume).

Chemical cleaning may be divided into two major categories: preoperational cleaning and maintenance cleaning. Preoperational cleaning refers to the cleaning of process equipment after fabrication and/or installation, but prior to actual first use. The purpose of this type of cleaning is to remove preserving oils, varnishes, mill scale, weld scale, and construction debris before startup. This cleaning may be performed by the fabricator or plant engineer but is usually handled by contract chemical cleaning service firms.

Maintenance cleaning is necessary since process equipment and storage vessels inevitably become fouled with time and use. A plant or maintenance engineer has three options at his disposal. In the first instance, he may carefully control input chemicals, water, and other raw materials so that they do not damage his equipment too severely (1–2). He might, for example, employ elaborate water control techniques or he might use certain corrosion inhibitors in his processing towers to prevent the metal attack by the aggressive chemicals being handled. This is in the realm of preventive maintenance, but is nevertheless mentioned since it may prevent, or at least delay shutdown cleaning. Secondly, a plant engineer may decide to take his equipment off stream and clean it using his own crews and chemicals. As a third possibility, a plant engineer may employ the services of a contract chemical cleaning firm.

The types of equipment generally cleaned or maintained by chemical techniques include boilers (low pressure, high pressure, and supercritical), heat exchangers, barge tanks, storage tanks, hydraulic lines, reactors, condensers, piping (liquid, gas, or compressed gas), refinery towers, cracking units, fractionating towers, water cooling towers, and compressor as well as reactor jackets. The industries most commonly employing chemical cleaning include the following: steel, petroleum, paper and pulp, electric generating, shipbuilding, missile, chemical, food processing, food handling, and petrochemical.

The most common chemical cleaning systems used are listed below:

1. Inorganic acids—hydrochloric, sulfuric, phosphoric, nitric, amidosulfuric acid (see Sulfamic acid), and sodium bisulfate.

2. Organic acids—citric, malic, gluconic, oxalic, acetic, hydroxyacetic-formic, and tartaric.

3. Chelating and complexing agents—ethylenediaminetetraacetic acid, nitrilotriacetic acid, sodium diethanolglycine, triethanolamine, ammonia, and ethylenediamine.

4. Alkaline cleaners—sodium hydroxide, sodium carbonate, trisodium phosphate, and sodium silicates.

5. Surfactants—alkyl sulfates and alkylbenzenesulfonates (anionic), fatty amines and quaternaries (cationic), ethoxylated alkylphenols (nonionic), and fatty betaines (amphoteric).

6. Organic solvents—aliphatic and aromatic hydrocarbons and halogenated hydrocarbons, alcohols, ketones, esters, and ethers.

7. Specialty additives—bromates, peroxysulfates, thioureas and proprietary complexors for copper systems, ammonium bifluoride for silicates, and stannous chloride for high ferric ion concentrations.

8. Mechanical and physico-chemical combinations—vapor phase, emulsion, foam, gel, steam jet, and mechanical slug cleaning systems.

Although no reliable estimate is available on the dollars spent for preventive maintenance cleaning or for inplant cleaning, the sales volume for contract chemical cleaning in the U.S. exceeds $30 million per year. The major contract chemical cleaning firms in the U.S. are Dow Industrial Service, Richardson Chemical Cleaning Service, Halliburton Industrial Cleaning Services, and Cesco. Contract chemical cleaning as it is known in the U.S. is not as well established in Europe or other parts of the world; but this is rapidly changing.

Acid chemical cleaning is one of the most widely used methods of cleaning process equipment today and began the turn of the century.

In 1916, H. H. Raymond of Buffalo, New York, obtained a patent on a *Method of Cleaning Pipes* using a mixture of hydrochloric and sulfuric acids that were circulated inside piping systems (3). Although no corrosion inhibitors were used, this method was a great improvement over the prior art which then suggested dismantling the system to be cleaned and immersing the individual parts in acid baths, a technique that resulted in severe corrosion of the unscaled outer surfaces. During the twenties, work carried out at Massachusetts Institute of Technology resulted in the development of corrosion inhibitors for the acid pickling of steels (4). This inhibitor technology was directly carried over into acid chemical cleaning. By 1926, Silvio Garbarino of Genoa, Italy was issued a patent for a *Composition and Method of Cleaning Condensers and the Like* (5). This cleaning composition consisted of an aqueous solution of 12% hydrochloric acid, 1% copper sulfate, and 0.1% sodium sulfate. Corrosion inhibitors were not mentioned. The first documented acid chemical cleaning operation was mentioned by Spellar, Chappel, and Russell in 1927. Inhibited hydrochloric acid was used to clean the rusted piping systems of the Bankers Trust Building in New York City (6). By 1940, The Dow Chemical Company had the first national contract chemical cleaning service. Growth from this point was quite rapid. Some of the more recent important acid chemical cleaning patents include: Inhibited Hydrochloric Acid Cleaning Process (7), Copper Removal with Oxidizing Agents (8), Organic Acid Cleaning (9), Copper Removal Using Thiourea (10–11), Citric-Formic Acid Cleaning Systems (12), Citric Acid Cleaning Methods (13), Aluminum Cleaning with Nitric Acid (14), Phosphoric Acid Esters for Cleaning Process Equipment (15), Chelating Agents (16).

With the advent of more complex processing equipment, fabricated with newly developed materials, greater demands are being made for safe, effective, and economical chemical cleaning solvents. This is particularly true of nuclear submarines, supercritical boilers, and space-age hardware. Many research efforts are now being directed toward the solution of these problems together with the problem of disposal of the spent fluids.

Foulants

Foulants may be defined as unwanted scales and soils that accumulate in process equipment during fabrication or through use. Their removal is the major concern of chemical cleaning. These foulants range from metal oxides to organic sludges and debris. Some of the more common foulants are listed along with several generally used techniques for their removal.

Metal oxides may be dissolved with inhibited inorganic acids, organic acids, or chelants. The preoperational cleaning of steel equipment usually involves the removal of mill scale, weld scale, and rust. Common iron oxides encountered include FeO, Fe_2O_3, Fe_3O_4. Copper oxides (Cu_2O, red and CuO, black) are most conveniently removed with inhibited acids, if ferrous metals such as carbon steels are not part of the system to be cleaned. If steels are included in the system along with copper alloys, copper beads and sheets are often found before and/or after acid cleaning. Copper beads are usually the size of small peas. Copper sheets vary in thickness from 1 to 60 mils and in area from a few in.^{2} in boiler tubes to several ft^2 in boiler mud drums. This metallic copper may be removed with oxidizing agents such as bromates ($NaBrO_3$, $KBrO_3$, NH_4BrO_3), and peroxysulfates such as $(NH_4)_2S_2O_8$. Other cleaning techniques for steel–copper systems involve the use of chelants, organic acids, or copper complexors, such as thiourea. Aluminum oxides are usually removed with trisodium phosphate or alkaline solutions with silicate inhibitors. Surfactants are often included. If deposited

MnO_2 is to be removed with HCl, chlorine gas is evolved, so this is not a recommended procedure. Oxalic acid is generally used in this case as a reducing agent.

Sulfides are generally difficult to handle. Ferrous sulfide may be dissolved by acids, but toxic hydrogen sulfide is evolved and must be scrubbed with a caustic solution. Other sulfides such as FeS_2, CuS, and Cu_2S are extremely difficult to dissolve. "Sour crude" petroleum often leads to the formation of FeS_2 in refinery reformer units; this is usually removed by treatment with CrO_3 or by steam–air sparging followed by acid treatment.

Carbon or coke foulants are also hard to handle chemically. There are no known solvents for carbon. Mechanical or hydraulic fracturing techniques are usually used.

Silicates may be decomposed with caustic soda. The more difficultly soluble silicates are treated with inhibited inorganic acid–ammonium bifluoride solutions.

Phosphates such as hydroxylapatite $[Ca_3(PO_4)_2]_3 . Ca(OH)_2$ can be dissolved by acids or chelants (17).

Calcium sulfate is very difficult to dissolve, but sequestering agents are sometimes useful here. Gypsum, $CaSO_4 . 2H_2O$, can be solubilized in hot dilute HCl. In general, $CaSO_4$ varies in ease of removal depending on porosity and hydration factors.

Carbonates are usually readily dissolved by acids.

Hardwater soaps, sludges, and other organic foulants are most often removed with emulsion cleaners, or solvents, or by jetting techniques. Loose debris such as sticks, stones, and pieces of metal are usually removed by mechanical methods (18).

Mud, clay, sand, and silt are often found along with common scales. These may be flocculated with polyelectrolytes such as acrylamide polymers (19) to form dispersed slurries, which are then pumped out.

There are also microbiological foulants; algae, often in the form of slimes; fungi, and bacteria. Anaerobic desulfovibrio bacteria are particularly damaging, since they are sulfate reducers, and lead to the formation of sulfides. These bacteria leave characteristic circular deposits on metal surfaces. Any corrosion taking place beneath these deposits is particularly damaging. Preventative methods, by suitable biocides, are strongly recommended against these microbiologically formed foulants; but if they do form, conventional chemical cleaning methods such as acid cleaning can be employed for their removal.

While the removal of foulants from process equipment is the major concern of chemical cleaning, this removal must not proceed at the expense of short or long range damage to the equipment. A maintenance engineer must balance the speed and thoroughness of a chemical cleaning process with the protection of his equipment. Whenever possible, the type of foulant(s) to be removed and the fabrication material to be cleaned should be pretested on a small scale with the cleaning process contemplated. If the cleaning is adequate and the corrosion rates acceptable, then the equipment may be cleaned with assurance (20–21). Pretesting is often very difficult because of the inaccessibility of foulants as they have been deposited in the actual equipment. If a piece of scaled metal is removed to be test-cleaned it may be costly to replace later. Further, if a large piece of equipment is to be cleaned, foulants may vary in composition, thickness, and order of deposit from section to section. Monitoring the effect of chemical cleaning solutions during the actual cleaning operation is very important. Representative test coupons, corrosion rate meters (22–23), or chemical analyses (24) are helpful as part of a testing program during cleaning. In addition to knowing the corrosion rate, the type of corrosion is important. For example, although a mild steel corrosion rate of 50 mpy (mils penetration per year) or 0.0056 lb/(ft²) (day) may seem low enough, if this is due to pitting or crevice corrosion, premature equipment failure may occur. On the other hand a corrosion rate of 100–500 mpy *may* be acceptable if this corrosion is *uniform*. The possibility of bimetallic corrosion should also be considered. In addition, the corrosion products from one type of corrosion or from the foulants in solution may accelerate other types of corrosion. See Corrosion. A list of references for corrosion inhibitors used in acid cleaning is included (25–42).

Some of the precautions in cleaning typical fabrication materials are listed.

Cast iron is not very tough, mechanically. Inorganic acids should be used with caution even though inhibited, since corrosion rates are generally high.

Low-carbon steels may be cleaned with inhibited inorganic acid, organic acids, chelants, alkalis, or organic solvents. High Fe^{3+} concentrations can cause pitting.

Stainless steels are resistant to many aggressive environments encountered in use; however, these steels, particularly the 400 and 300 series, have certain vulnerabilities. These include weld sensitizations, stress corrosion cracking (300 series) in chloride solutions, pitting in chloride solutions, and deterioration when stressed mechanically in certain nonoxygenated solutions. Stainless steels are usually cleaned with inhibited, sulfuric or phosphoric acids, organic acids, or chelants.

Copper and copper alloys are damaged by amines, ammonia, and oxidizing acids but can be cleaned with inhibited HCl, H_2SO_4, organic acids, chelants, or alkaline solutions.

Aluminum is attacked by strong alkalis and halogen acids. Inhibited trisodium phosphate solutions have been used with success, as have acetic acid and phosphoric acid inhibited with chromic acid.

Concrete is attacked rapidly by HCl but not nearly so quickly by H_2SO_4. Glass is attacked by strong alkalis. Most polymers are attacked by the more powerful organic solvents such as dimethylformamide, dimethyl sulfoxide, tetrahydrofuran etc. Gaskets, and packings made of fluorocarbon polymers or polyolefins, are generally resistant to most inorganics and many organics.

Cleaning Methods

Inorganic Acids. Inorganic acids are the solutions most often used in contract chemical cleaning at this time. They are effective, fast, and relatively inexpensive, and they can be used in most types of processing equipment. They do, however, have some drawbacks. They require corrosion inhibitors, they are often too aggressive for sensitive metals, and they require special handling techniques. By far, the most used acid is inhibited HCl. Hydrochloric acid is used in concentration ranges of 3–30% (wt). Temperatures and contact times are determined by the type of metal and scale. Some of the important additives used with HCl include:

corrosion inhibitors	0.1–0.4% (vol)
surfactants	0.1–0.5% (vol)
NH_4F_2H (for silicate scales)	0.2–1.0% (wt)
copper complexors (for complexing copper)	0.5–2.0% (wt)
oxalic acid (for MnO_2, separate step)	by estimate of MnO_2
$SnCl_2$, for high Fe^{3+} conc (43–46)	0.1–0.5% (wt)

Hydrochloric acid is used to clean mild steel boilers, heat exchangers, storage tanks, reactors, and piping. A typical nine-step cleaning procedure for a mild steel low-pres-

Table 1. Chemical Cleaning Solutions (49)

Materials of construction	Inorganic nonoxidizing acids, ie inhibited HCl, H₂SO₄, amidosulfuric, H₃PO₄	HNO₃	Organic acids (inhibited)	Strong alkalis	Solvents for copper-ammonia amines	Organic solvents
ferrous alloys	check recommendations for each acid inhibitor	no	yes	yes	yes	yes
low-carbon steels	temperature limits generally 170°F	no	yes	yes	yes	yes
cast iron	temperature limit usually not over 120°F	no	yes	yes	yes	yes
chromium steel up to 12% Cr	may be less resistant than mild steels; watch temperature limitations	no	yes	yes	yes	yes
400 series S.S.	watch for 12% chrome valve trim or alloy parts that have been exposed to sulfur compounds	no	yes	yes	yes	yes
300 series S.S.	avoid use of HCl. For other solvents, use chloride free water	yes use Cl⁻ free water	yes	yes	yes	avoid prolonged exposure of chlorinated solvents to moisture
copper alloys copper brasses bronzes Cu–Ni	corrosion rates are low in absence of oxidants, added or formed as reaction products, for example Fe³⁺	no	yes	yes	no perhaps in special cases on Cu–Ni (Monel)	yes
aluminum	no, except H₃PO₄ plus CrO₃	perhaps	perhaps	special formulations only	yes	yes
tin-lead	yes	no	yes	yes	yes	yes
galvanized iron	no	no	no	very mild alkalis only	perhaps	yes

sure boiler is shown below. During the descaling step, solution concentrations, temperature, corrosion rates, and dissolved scales are continuously checked.

(1) Pressure test for leaks in circuitry; (2) degrease with alkaline solutions and surfactants; (3) flush system thoroughly with warm water; (4) descale with 4–7% HCl with 0.1–0.3% inhibitor; usually a 6 hr soak cycle at 140–170°F is used; (5) flush using pH control; (6) passivate by adding 1% (wt) NaNO₂ with pH control (8–9), temperature 130–140°F; (7) flush to remove passivator; (8) drain; (9) inspect.

Sulfuric and nitric acids are generally used to clean stainless steels. Amidosulfuric acid, phosphoric acid, and sodium bisulfate are typically used by maintenance engineers for small inplant maintenance cleaning (47–49). Table 1 indicates the typical chemical cleaning solutions employed and their effects on common metals used in fabricating process equipment.

Organic Acids. Organic acids as a group have much to offer in the way of safety, cleaning specificity, and ease of disposal. Although they cost more than the inorganic

Table 2. Comparison of Organic Acids used in Chemical Cleaning

Property	Hydrochloric	Formic	Hydroxyacetic (Glycolic)	Malic
pK_a (25°C) 1		3.75	2.83	3.40
2				5.11
3				
pH (0.1N–25°C)	1.1 (1N=0.1)	2.3		2.2
1.00% solution[a] equivalent	1.00	1.26	2.08	1.84

Property	Citric	Tartaric	Oxalic
pK_a (25°C) 1	3.08	2.93	1.23
2	4.74	4.23	4.19
3	5.40		
pH (0.1N–25°C)	2.2	2.2	1.6
1.00% solution[a] equivalent	1.75	2.06	1.23

[a] Wt % solutions equivalent in total ionizable hydrogen to a 1.00% solution of HCl.

acids, other factors, such as easier handling, lower toxicity, and lower corrosion rates, can often swing the choice of cleaning acid from inorganic to organic, particularly for cleaning supercritical steam generators, nuclear power systems, and austenitic steel parts. However, these acids usually require higher temperatures (up to 200°F), longer contact times (up to 12 hr), and sometimes circulation in order to descale process equipment properly (50). Table 2 compares some properties of the organic acids with those of HCl.

Citric acid is a widely used organic acid for descaling ferrous metals. It is generally used at 1–5% concentrations with corrosion inhibitors. If heavy copper oxide scales are to be removed along with iron oxides, a pretreatment with bromates may be necessary. If light to medium copper and/or copper oxide deposits are to be removed, a simplified process can be employed using ammoniated citric acid (13,51–52), which chelates Fe^{2+} and Cu^{2+} so that copper replating is minimized if not eliminated. Citric acid, as well as ammoniated citric acid, has been used to remove soils and aluminum oxides from aluminum and aluminum alloys. Stainless steels have also been effectively cleaned with citric acid.

Hydroxyacetic-formic acid mixtures have been used for the preoperational cleaning of stainless steel boilers (53) as well as other sensitive steel equipment. This mixture has been found to be much more effective than either acid alone and is therefore very often specified.

Oxalic acid has been used as a rust remover; however, it is toxic and many of the reaction products formed are insoluble.

Malic, tartaric, gluconic and lactic acids have been used to some extent as descaling acids, but are not as popular as the above mentioned acids. Little work has been done in exploring the uses of other organic acids such as fatty acids and sulfonic acids.

Chelants. Chelants or chelating agents (see Complexing agents) are a rather recent innovation in chemical cleaning. They can be used where inorganic or even organic acids might damage sensitive equipment. Although chelating agents are more expensive than inorganic acids and they generally require longer contact times as well as higher temperatures to descale process equipment, they often are the *only* chemicals that can be used to remove certain scales safely. Some of the chelating agents that have been used for chemical cleaning include citric acid, gluconic acid, ethylenediaminetetraacetic acid (EDTA), and nitrilotriacetic acid (16,54–56,64). For example, ethylenediaminetetraacetic acid sequesters calcium, forming $CaEDTA^{2-}$; thus, it can be used to remove calcium carbonate scale without the use of a corrosive acid, and it may also be used to remove other calcium scales. Since chelants are relatively new in this area, they should be tested prior to actual use in unknown process systems as added assurance against possible unsuspected corrosive attack.

An interesting technique of cleaning boiler scale with hydrazine has recently been published (65). Apparently the hydrazine interacts with the iron oxides causing decomposition. This technique has possibilities for indirect as well as direct cleaning.

Alkaline Cleaners. Alkaline rinses are used to neutralize residual acids on cleaned metal surfaces in a caustic boil-out step that follows acid cleaning. This step also passivates the metal surface to minimize rerusting prior to startup. Further, this step supposedly drives out residual hydrogen absorbed by the metal during the cleaning process.

Caustic soda, sodium silicates, soda ash, and sodium phosphates can be used to remove preserving varnishes and oils from the process equipment. These alkaline agents are often used with surfactants that emulsify oils, sludges and tars (see Metal surface treatments). Sometimes a combination of alkaline and oxidizing agents is used to decompose resistant organic coatings. Combinations of caustic soda and sodium gluconate are often used to clean aluminum surfaces (57). Caustic soda—gluconic acid in combination with phosphates and surfactants are useful bottle-washing formulations that eliminate bottle haze and rust spots as well as prevent scale deposits on washing equipment. This combination decomposes and emulsifies protein soils as well as chelates metal ions.

Solvent and Emulsion Cleaners. Organic solvents are used to remove preserving greases, oils, and varnishes as well as foulant tars and sludges. Typical solvents include kerosene, Stoddard solvent (see Vol. 7, p. 314), diesel oils, carbon tetrachloride, perchloroethylene, trichloroethylene, aromatic solvents, and dimethylformamide. Most types of processing equipment and piping can be cleaned safely with these solvents. Often vapor degreasing units (58) are employed.

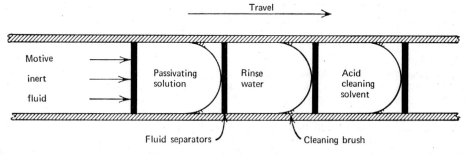

Figure 1. Schematic of mechanical pigs used in chemical cleaning.

Sometimes these solvents are emulsified in water using emulsifying agents. These *emulsion cleaners* can be used with spray equipment or in immersion applications. Rust inhibitors (see Corrosion inhibitors) may be added along with other specific cleaning agents. In a typical process, storage tanks and barges can be cleaned with emulsion cleaners. These emulsion cleaners and emulsified sludges are then pumped into holding tanks where the emulsion is broken into organic and aqueous phases with salts and/or acids. The aqueous phase may be neutralized and disposed of while the now concentrated sludge phase may be hauled away or burned. Foam cleaning is sometimes used, for example, when overhead piping would not support the weight of cleaning solvents (59).

Vapor phase cleaning (noncondensed phase cleaning) is a technique in which volatile cleaning agents such as formic or nitric acids are pushed through equipment with uncondensed fluids such as steam. The dissolved foulants are then simply flushed out with a rinse step. Several cleaning steps may be used employing minimum amounts of cleaning agents (60–62).

Mechanical Techniques. Numerous mechanical cleaning methods may be used prior to or in conjunction with chemical cleaning solvents. Hydraulic line moles are frequently used to remove scale deposits from inaccessible underground piping. A line mole consists of a jetting head that sprays water at high pressures as it is passed through piping circuits. The head is attached to a small diameter line, driven by a hydraulic drive unit. Line moles will easily traverse bends, turns, and elbows that are not too contorted. Water jetting (63) or steam jetting equipment is useful for cleaning the tube bundles of heat exchangers. If long sections of piping are to be cleaned with solvents, large amounts of cleaning fluids are generally required. For example, a 6 in. pipe a mile long will require over 7500 gal of fluid for each cleaning step. One method which might be employed to clean such a section of pipe economically is to use mechanical *pigs* as shown in Fig 1. A train of these pigs can be used with successive compartments containing different cleaning fluids (18).

Bibliography

1. *Betz Handbook of Water Conditioning*, 6th ed., Betz Laboratories, Philadelpia 1962.
2. E. S. Troscinsk and R. G. Watson, *Chem. Eng.*, Mar. 9, 1970, p. 125.
3. U.S. Pat. 1,194,542 (Aug. 1916) and, H. H. Raymond (to Clifton Mfg. Co.).
4. E. L. Chappell, B. E. Roetheli, and B. Y. McCarthy, *Ind. Eng. Chem.* **20** (6), 582 (1928).
5. U.S. Pat. 1,582,974 (May 1926), S. Garbarino (to Carlo Benegri and M. Grannoni).
6. F. N. Speller, E. L. Chappell, and R. P. Russell, *Trans Am. Inst. Chem. Enyrs.* **19,** 1953 (1927).
7. U.S. Pat. 2,524,754 (Oct. 10, 1950), M. E. Brines (to Dow Chemical Co).

8. U.S. Pat. 2,567,835 (Sept. 11, 1951), F. N. Alquist et al. (to Dow Chemical Co.).
9. U.S. Pat. 2,817,606 (Dec. 24, 1957), R. B. Barrett (to Klenzade Prod. Inc.).
10. U.S. Pat. 2,959,555 (Nov. 8, 1960), R. D. Martin and W. T. Abel (to Dow Chemical Co.).
11. U.S. Pat. 3,458,354 (July 29, 1969), C. F. Reich (to Dow Chemical Co.).
12. U.S. Pat. 3,003,898 (Oct. 10, 1961), C. F. Reich (to Dow Chemical Co.).
13. U.S. Pat. 3,072,502 (Jan. 8, 1963), S. Alfano (to Charles Pfizer & Co.).
14. U.S. Pat. 3,106,499 (Oct. 8, 1963), E. W. Kendall (to Rohr Corp.).
15. U.S. Pat. 3,281,268 (Oct. 25, 1966), R. C. Martin (to Dow Chemical Co.).
16. U.S. Pat. 3,447,965 (June 3, 1969), N. Teumac (to Dow Chemical Co.).
17. U.S. Pat. 3,360,399 (Dec. 26, 1967), J. A. Knox and W. E. Billings (to Haliburton Co.).
18. C. M. Loucks, *Chem. Eng.* **69**, 103 (1962).
19. Ger. Pat. 1,717,008 (Sept. 18, 1969), W. E. Zimmie and F. W. Bloecher (to American Cyanamid Co.).
20. R. D. Merrick, *Materials Protection*, May 1962, pp. 107–117.
21. A. S. Krisher, *Materials Protection*, Oct. 1965, pp. 8–12.
22. G. A. Marsh and E. Schaschl, *Proc. Am. Petrol. Inst.* **44**, 166–171 (1964).
23. R. R. Annand, "An Investigation of the Utility of Instantaneous Corrosion Rate Measurements for Inhibitor Studies," a paper presented at the 21st Annual Conference of the NACE, St. Louis, Mo., March 19, 1965.
24. ASTM D-2790-69T, *ASTM Book of Standards*, Tentative Methods of the Analysis of Solvent Systems Used for the Removal of Water-Formed Deposits, Part 23, p. 911, Philadelphia, Pa., Nov. 1969.
25. U.S. Pat. 2,564,758 (Aug. 21, 1951), H. A. Haggard (to Hercules Powder Co.).
26. U.S. Pat. 2,564,759 (Aug. 21, 1951), H. A. Haggard (to Hercules Powder Co.).
27. U.S. Pat. 2,758,970 (Aug. 14, 1956), A. J. Saukaitis (to Amchem Prod. Inc.).
28. U.S. Pat. 3,047,510 (July 31, 1962), A. Cizek (to Armour and Co.).
29. U.S. Pat. 3,107,221 (Oct. 15, 1963), H. T. Harrison et al. (to Dow Chemical Co.).
30. U.S. Pat. 3,147,244 (April 5, 1961), B. E. Marsh et al. (to Armour and Co.).
31. Brit. Pat. 897,762 (Sept. 14, 1960), A. J. Saukaitis et al. (to Amchem Prod. Inc.).
32. U.S. Pat. 2,564,757 (Aug. 21, 1951), A. L. Glasebrook (to Hercules Powder Co.).
33. N. Hackerman, *Corrosion* **18**, 37t (1962).
34. J. Bregman, *Corrosion Inhibitors*, Crowell, Collier & Co., Macmillan, N.Y. 1963.
35. J. N. Putliova, S. A. Balezin, and V. P. Barannik, *Metallic Corrosion Inhibitors*, Pergamon Press, N.Y., 1960.
36. G. L. Foster, B. D. Oakes, and C. H. Kucera, *Ind. Eng. Chem.* **51**, 825–828 (1959).
37. J. G. Funkhouser, *Corrosion* **17**, 283t–287t (1961).
38. R. J. Tedeschi, P. W. Natali, and H. C. McMahon, "The Role of the Triple Bond in Acid Corrosion Inhibition," NACE Conference Preprint, The National Association of Corrosion Engineers, Houston, Texas, 1969.
39. R. M. Hudson, C. J. Warning, *Metal Finishing*, **64**, 58–62 (1966).
40. W. E. Billings, D. Morris, *Corrosion* **17**, 200t (1961).
41. L. T. Overstreet, *Materials Protection*, August 1963, pp. 48–51 Vol. 2 No. 8.
42. E. D. Junkin, Jr., and D. R. Fincher, *Materials Protection*, August 1963, pp. 18–23 Vol. 2 No. 8.
43. I. P. Anoshchenko, *Zhur. Priklad. Khim.* **33**, 1319–1324 (1960).
44. U.S. Pat. 3,077,453 (Feb. 12, 1963), B. D. Oakes (to Dow Chemical Co.).
45. T. P. Hoar and S. Saior, *Sheet Metal Ind.* **14**, 947–948 (1960).
46. I. P. Anoshchenko, *Zhur. Priklad. Khim.* **33**, 1421–1422 (1960).
47. U.S. Pat. 3,124,534 (Mar. 10, 1964), J. K. O'Brien et al. (to Maco Inc.).
48. C. T. Gallinger, *Materials Protection*, **5**, 39–42 (1966).
49. C. M. Loucks, *Chemical Cleaning Manual*, Richardson Chemical Cleaning Service, Inc., Melrose Park, Ill., 1968.
50. C. M. Loucks, E. B. Morris, and E. A. Pirsh, "Organics Acid for Cleaning Power Plant Equipment," a paper presented at 1958 Annual ASME Meeting.
51. S. Alfano and W. E. Bell, "Chemical Removal of Magnetite and Copper," a paper presented at the International Water Conference, Engineers Society of Western Pennsylvania, 22nd Annual Meeting, Oct. 23, 1961.
52. W. E. Bell, *Combustion* **35** (10), 23 (1964).

53. H. A. Klein and K. L. Atwood "Chemical Cleaning of Utility Boilers," a paper presented at the American Power Conf., Chicago, April 14–16, 1964.
54. W. E. Bell, *Materials Protection*, Feb. 1965, p. 79.
55. C. M. Loucks, *Power*, Vol. **105**, p. 186 Dec. 1961.
56. F. J. Prescott, J. K. Shaw, and J. Lilker, *Metal Finishing*, Vol. 51, p. 65 Oct. 1953.
57. T. A. Downey and J. J. McCallion, *Soap and Chemical Specialties*, Vol. 35, p. 45 Oct. 1959.
58. A. Pollack and P. Westphal, *An Introduction to Metal Degreasing and Cleaning*, Robert Draper Ltd., Teddington, 1963.
59. D. B. Carroll, C. L. Eddington, and J. P. Engle, "Chemical Cleaning with Foamed Solvents," a paper presented at the 22nd Annual Water Conference of the Engineers Society of Western Pennsylvania, Oct. 1961.
60. C. M. Loucks, *Power Engineering* **65,** 58 (1961).
61. U.S. Pat. 3,084,076 (April 2, 1963), C. M. Loucks (to Dow Chemical Co.).
62. U.S. Pat. 3,297,481 (Jan. 10, 1967), K. W. Newman (to Purex Corp.).
63. U.S. Pat. 3,225,777 (Dec. 28, 1965), R. Shelton, F. C. Pittman, and R. G. Love (to Haliburton Co.).
64. Brit. Pat. 863,117 (March 15, 1961), R. E. Shaw.
65. N. N. Mankina, *National Engineer*, **72,** 11 (Feb. 1968).

T. M. Muzyczko
The Richardson Co.

CHLORINE

For the past six decades, which are those for which adequate statistical data are available for the United States, the growth of chlorine production and consumption in this country has averaged nearly three times that of sodium hydroxide plus sodium carbonate. This has led to the gradual replacement of lime–soda caustic by electrolytic caustic which has chlorine as its coproduct. This substitution is substantially complete in 1970 and we are in the midst of a rapid burgeoning of oxychlorination and oxy-hydrochlorination processes which, for many organic uses, are capable of reducing the chlorine requirement by 50%. These processes slowed the growth of the chlorine industry temporarily but are inadequate to meet the long-range problem of the increasing demand for chlorine. It is now feasible to make chlorine as a coproduct of the ammonia–soda process instead of calcium chloride which has a very limited market. The new processes for oxidizing hydrogen chloride directly to chlorine and the probable effect of this development on the chemical industry are the subject of this article.

Chlorine is one of the elements first prepared by the great Swedish chemist, Karl Wilhelm Scheele. He made chlorine by the oxidation of hydrogen chloride and, calling it "dephlogisticated marine acid air," considered it to be an oxygen compound. Thirty-six years later Sir Humphry Davy made chlorine by electrolysis and recognized it to be an element. These two researchers foreshadowed every successful process for making chlorine which has so far been discovered.

Chlorine occurs in nature only in combination with other elements. Its most abundant source is sodium chloride, of which there is on earth the equivalent of about six million cubic miles. When we realize that all the sodium chloride mankind has ever used has not taken us very far into the first cubic mile, it it evident that this is a truly inexhaustible resource. Lesser, but still enormous amounts of the chlorides of potassium, magnesium, and calcium occur in nature, and ammonium chloride is or can be a by-product of the ammonia–soda process. Any important process for making chlorine must be based upon one or more of these five chlorides.

The first processes for obtaining chlorine on a large scale involved the oxidation of hydrogen chloride. Manganese dioxide was first employed but later the Deacon-Hurter process replaced it, using air and a copper catalyst.

$$2\,CuCl_2 \rightleftarrows 2\,CuCl + Cl_2$$
$$2\,CuCl + \tfrac{1}{2}O_2 \rightarrow Cu_2OCl_2$$
$$Cu_2OCl_2 + 2\,HCl \rightarrow 2\,CuCl_2 + H_2O$$
$$2\,HCl + \tfrac{1}{2}O_2 \rightleftarrows Cl_2 + H_2O$$

The hydrogen chloride was obtained as a product of the action of sulfuric acid upon sodium chloride.

$$NaCl + H_2SO_4 \rightarrow NaHSO_4 + HCl$$
$$NaCl + NaHSO_4 \rightarrow Na_2SO_4 + HCl$$

Originally the sodium sulfate was made as the first step of the Le Blanc soda process which is now obsolete. (It is now made mostly for kraft paper pulping and the glass industry.)

A closely related process was invented by Hargreaves which avoids the need of a sulfuric acid plant.

$$2\,NaCl + SO_2 + \tfrac{1}{2}O_2\,(air) + H_2O \rightarrow Na_2SO_4 + 2\,HCl$$

This is operated in one plant in Louisiana near some of the kraft pulping plants.

The Deacon-Hurter process provided a stream of chlorine gas diluted by nitrogen, unreacted oxygen, and hydrogen chloride which, when treated with lime, gave bleaching powder, required by England's textile industry.

The next important development was an American one. Because of the genius of Thomas A. Edison and his associates, who built upon earlier discoveries by Faraday, Ampere, Volta, Ohm, and many other Europeans, electric current became cheap toward the end of the nineteenth century and this gave a strong incentive to the development of electrochemistry. The aluminum process of Hall in America and Héroult in France, Acheson's carborundum, and synthetic graphite, electric-furnace phosphorus, and electrolytic chlorine all came along in a relatively brief time.

Present Status. The commercial production of chlorine is carried out at present mostly by electrolysis of sodium chloride brine, although potassium chloride can be used with small changes. In the United States about 80% of the chlorine is made in cells of the diaphragm type using graphite anodes, asbestos diaphragms, and steel cathodes. The recent introduction of metallic anodes, made of titanium with a coating of noble metal, which do not change dimensions in use, threatens a major change in this picture, however.

Most of Europe's and 28% of the U.S. chlorine is made in cells using graphite anodes, no diaphragms, and mercury cathodes. This use of mercury cells in the United States is increasing relative to diaphragm cells. In both types of cells the products are Cl_2, NaOH, and H_2. Mercury cells give a purer grade of caustic which is essentially chloridefree.

To the extent that metallic sodium is required, chlorine is also produced by electrolysis of fused sodium chloride. The electrolysis of magnesium chloride at present (1970) makes no net contribution to chlorine supply because it is recycled to convert magnesium oxide to the anhydrous magnesium chloride. This will change in the near future as richer brines are used which make the direct isolation of anhydrous magnesium chloride practical. See Great Salt Lake chemicals in this volume.

Use Pattern. The pattern of uses for chlorine which has developed is very different from that of a century ago. Textile bleaching, which provided the original incentive for developing chlorine manufacture, now requires only about 0.5% of the chlorine. Pulp and paper take about 16%, water and sewage treatment about 3%, inorganic chemicals about 7%, and the remainder, well over 70%, goes into the manufacture of organic chemicals. These are plastics, solvents, antiknock ingredients for gasoline, pesticides, refrigerants, and a host of others. This is not only the largest category of uses for chlorine, but also the one with the highest rate of growth. This is where almost three fourths of our annual production of 9.43 million tons of chlorine (1969) is going. This is over 90 lb of chlorine per capita per annum.

In most of these organic uses a mole of hydrogen chloride is returned for each mole of chlorine which reacts. This can be illustrated by the equations for the manufacture of vinyl chloride from ethylene:

$$C_2H_4 + Cl_2 \rightarrow CH_2ClCH_2Cl$$

$$CH_2ClCH_2Cl \xrightarrow{500°C} CH_2{=}CHCl + HCl$$

Oxychlorination and Oxyhydrochlorination. Chemists have not succeeded in discovering markets for hydrogen chloride at a sufficient rate to keep pace with its production from organic chlorinations. Large quantities of hydrochloric acid are neutralized with lime and the resulting calcium chloride dumped into our streams, which increases the hardness of their water.

This situation has been the incentive for the development of oxychlorination and oxyhydrochlorination processes. Strictly speaking, a reaction such as

$$C_6H_6 + \tfrac{1}{2}Cl_2 + \tfrac{1}{4}O_2 \rightarrow C_6H_5Cl + \tfrac{1}{2}H_2O$$

in which chlorine, oxygen, and a material to be chlorinated are the reactants, is an oxychlorination, while one such as

$$C_6H_6 + HCl + \tfrac{1}{2}O_2 \rightarrow C_6H_5Cl + H_2O$$

in which hydrogen chloride, oxygen, and a material to be chlorinated are the reactants, is an oxyhydrochlorination. Generally, the term oxychlorination is used for either or both.

The first commercially successful example of oxyhydrochlorination is the Raschig phenol process which can be summarized in the following equations:

$$C_6H_6 + HCl + \tfrac{1}{2}O_2 \text{ (air)} \rightarrow C_6H_5Cl + H_2O$$
$$C_6H_5Cl + H_2O \rightarrow C_6H_5OH + HCl$$
$$C_6H_6 + \tfrac{1}{2}O_2 \rightarrow C_6H_5OH$$

Since benzene is resistant to oxidation but easily chlorinated it is relatively easy to find conditions for its oxyhydrochlorination. A copper chloride catalyst suspended on an inert support does the trick nicely at 290°C. The hydrolysis of chlorobenzene is more difficult. The catalyst is hydroxyl-apatite or silica and a temperature of 420°C is required. The process went into operation 36 years ago. The main difficulty was in finding materials of construction which had a reasonable life expectancy in the presence of hot steam, chlorine, and hydrogen chloride. That this problem was solved is a credit to the ability and determination of W. H. Prahl and his associates, who used such exotic devices as porcelain valves. (See under Raschig-Hooker process, Vol. 15, p. 150.) The cumene–phenol process, however, is being used in almost all of the new phenol plants.

The next major discovery in this field was the development of suitable processes for the manufacture of vinyl chloride from ethylene. The equations are as follows:

$$C_2H_4 + 2\,CuCl_2 \rightarrow CH_2ClCH_2Cl + 2\,CuCl$$
$$CH_2ClCH_2Cl \rightarrow CH_2{=}CHCl + HCl$$
$$2\,CuCl + 2\,HCl + \tfrac{1}{2}O_2 \rightarrow 2\,CuCl_2 + H_2O$$
$$C_2H_4 + HCl + \tfrac{1}{2}O_2 \rightarrow CH_2{=}CHCl + H_2O$$

This process has resulted in the price of vinyl chloride dropping to about 5¢/lb, so that recently no more very large plants are being built to make it from acetylene by the following reaction:

$$C_2H_2 + HCl \rightarrow CH_2 = CHCl$$

If the vinyl chloride plant is in a location where chlorine is more readily available than HCl the decision will be to make some of the dichloroethane by direct addition of chlorine, as shown in a previous equation. The HCl obtained by pyrolysis of dichloroethane can then be used for the oxyhydrochlorination reaction.

Figure 1 shows the growth of vinyl chloride which, in terms of annual tonnage, is the second largest organic chlorine compound. Its precursor, dichloroethane, which has a higher molecular weight and is also added to antiknock fluid to scavenge the lead, is in first place. Vinyl chloride can be purchased on long-term contract for 4–5¢/lb and at this price its polymers and copolymers are growing at a rate of about 10% per year.

Oxychlorinations for saturated hydrocarbons, such as methane, are more difficult and, while the idea was patented many years ago, it has been slow to develop. The presence of a hydrocarbon upsets the Deacon equilibrium in a favorable way as follows:

$$4\,HCl + O_2 \rightleftharpoons 2\,Cl_2 + 2\,H_2O$$
$$CH_4 + Cl_2 \rightarrow CH_3Cl + HCl$$

Unfortunately, it has not proved feasible to avoid reaction between hydrocarbon and oxygen to produce CO, CO_2, and H_2O. In the case of methane the economics are not injured by burning up, for example, 40% of the organic starting material, but other hydrocarbons are more expensive and, in any case, the large heats of combustion of hydrocarbons must be dissipated and their effects controlled. This takes some doing.

Alternative Routes to Chlorine. The original Deacon-Hurter process was discontinued shortly after World War I; it could not compete with the electrolysis of brine. After oxygen became cheap, as methods for liquefying and distilling air were improved, other attempts were made to oxidize hydrogen chloride, but they were beset with corrosion problems and the plants were scrapped. Shell built a modern Deacon plant at Pernis, Holland, using an improved copper catalyst which is more active and less volatile than its predecessors. Two European companies are building and promoting plants to electrolyze hydrochloric acid to chlorine and hydrogen and thus dispose of the ubiquitous HCl. An American plant was built by Allied at Hopewell, Virginia, to make sodium nitrate by the action of nitric acid upon salt; chlorine was a coproduct. The plant made chlorine for years without making alkali, but operation was discontinued largely because sodium nitrate is a lean source of plant food and has trouble competing with ammonium nitrate, urea, and ammonia which are much more concentrated sources of available nitrogen.

A plant making KNO_3 from nitric acid and potassium chloride has recently gone into successful operation at Vicksburg, Miss. The economics are tied principally to the value of potassium nitrate as fertilizer. Both ions of KNO₃ are needed by plants and its use avoids contaminating the soil with chloride ions from KCl which, in arid regions, are deleterious to plants. Tobacco growers must avoid the use of fertilizers containing chloride ions because their presence lowers the melting point of the ash and interferes with the combustion of the tobacco. See also Fertilizers in this volume.

The manufacture of chlorine by air oxidation of NOCl was patented by Datta in 1919 (2) and a Hercules patent by Stow in 1964 (3) describes the use of nitrogen dioxide

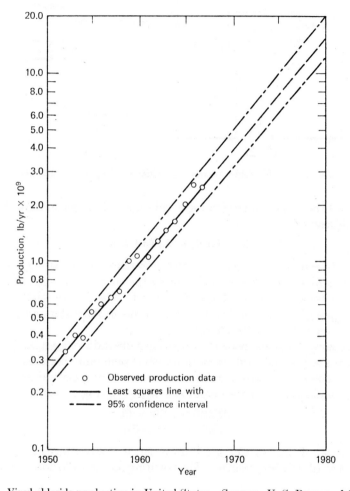

Fig. 1. Vinyl chloride production in United States. Source: U. S. Bureau of Census.

as a homogeneous catalyst for the oxidation of hydrogen chloride. It is believed, however, that neither of these processes has proved successful on a commercial scale.

In 1969 the M. W. Kellogg Co. announced the Kel-Chlor process (5) for the oxidation of hydrogen chloride. This newer approach is to combine a very active gaseous catalyst with a powerful dehydrating agent which reduces the activity of the steam to a negligible value and thus allows the reaction to proceed to completion. The process can be understood by considering the separate steps as shown in a diagram in Figure 2. In step one a solution of nitrosyl sulfuric acid in dilute sulfuric acid is treated

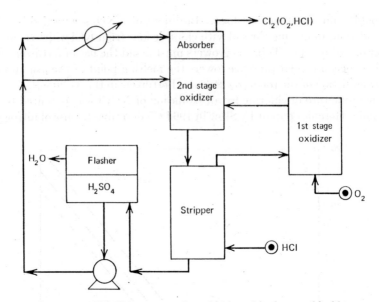

Fig. 2. The Kel-Chlor process for oxidation of hydrogen chloride.

countercurrently with a stream of hydrogen chloride and oxygen in the stripping tower. The reversible reaction

$$HCl + NOHSO_4 \rightleftharpoons NOCl + H_2SO_4$$

goes virtually to completion because of the countercurrent contacting. Traces of HCl in the sulfuric acid are removed by introducing the necessary oxygen at a point in the stripping tower below where the HCl is introduced. The sulfuric acid leaving the bottom of the stripping tower is flashed to remove some of the water and to cool it and is recycled to the top of the absorber tower.

We have now a gaseous mixture of hydrogen chloride, oxygen, and nitrosyl chloride. This goes to the first oxidizer stage which is preferably backmixed for temperature control. The temperature is raised sufficiently to dissociate nitrosyl chloride and the oxygen present reacts with the nitric oxide to form nitrogen dioxide.

$$2\,NOCl \rightleftharpoons 2\,NO + Cl_2$$
$$2\,NO + O_2 \rightleftharpoons 2\,NO_2$$

Since the kinetics of this reaction are third order, it is advantageous to carry out the entire process at 10–15 atm pressure. The resulting nitrogen dioxide oxidizes hydrogen chloride.

$$NO_2 + 2\,HCl \rightarrow NO + Cl_2 + H_2O$$

In this way the nitrogenous compounds present function as a catalyst in an oxidation–reduction cycle.

The gases leaving the first-stage oxidizer are then passed to a second-stage oxidizer wherein they are contacted with liquid which is obtained from the flashing zone previously mentioned. A substantial amount of conversion of HCl takes place in the second-stage oxidation zone. Several reactions occur simultaneously in the second-stage oxidizer, one of which is the reverse of that occurring in the stripper.

$$NOCl + H_2SO_4 \rightleftharpoons NOHSO_4 + HCl$$

Again, it goes nearly to completion because of the countercurrent contacting. The HCl released is largely oxidized to chlorine in this stage. The gases from the second-stage oxidizer are passed to an absorption zone and sulfuric acid introduced therein also removes steam from the reaction products. This steam has been generated, as shown previously, by the oxidation of hydrogen chloride.

The chlorine leaving the absorber tower contains a little hydrogen chloride and may contain traces of nitrogen compounds. It is suitable as such for many of the uses of chlorine and, of course, may be liquefied and further purified in ways known to the industry. Chlorine made by this process can easily be brought to a higher purity than ordinary commercial chlorine prepared by electrolysis. It has been tested for various uses within a large chemical company and been found perfectly suitable for them.

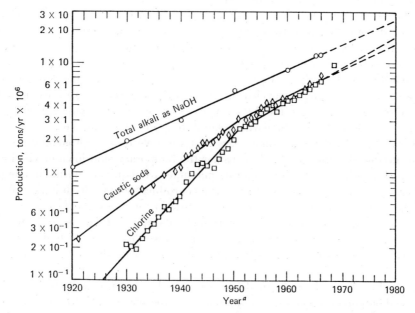

Fig. 3. Chlor-Alkali production in United States. Legend: ○ Total alkali as NaOH (from Alkali and chlorine industries, in Vol. 2); ◇ Caustic soda (Chemical Economics Handbook); □ Chlorine (Chemical Economics Handbook).

The concentration of nitrogen compounds can easily be held below 500 ppm without special purification. If desired, the nitrogen content can be decreased below the limit of analytical detection.

Any corrosion problems from the process fluids, which resemble aqua regia, are minimized by proper selection of materials. It is believed that these problems are solved and that the cost of oxidizing hydrogen chloride in a very large plant will be about $10 per ton, increasing to $17 per ton in a smaller plant.

Projected Effect on the Chemical Industry. It is therefore appropriate at this point to consider the probable effect of such a process on the chemical industry. It is the intention of M. W. Kellogg to license the process widely to companies which find a place for it in their present or future operations.

Figure 3 shows the historical growth and projections of chlorine production and that of sodium hydroxide and of total alkali in the United States. The most important point is that chlorine production has always grown much faster than that of sodium hydroxide or total alkali. In the electrolysis of brine there is a fixed ratio of 1.13 tons of sodium hydroxide for each ton of chlorine produced. Up to 1970, the industry has accommodated the faster growth of chlorine by the gradual abandonment of the production of sodium hydroxide by the causticization of sodium carbonate by calcium hydroxide. As is evident from the curve, the production of chlorine seems likely to exceed t hat of caustic for the first time. This possibility arises from four facts: (*1*) virtually al the sodium hydroxide is made electrolytically; (*2*) appreciable amounts of chlorine are made by electrolysis of fused sodium chloride, which produces no caustic, in one plant at Freeport, Tex.; (*3*) the electrolysis of brine is operated to produce sodium carbonate rather than sodium hydroxide; and, (*4*) potassium chloride is being converted to chlorine and potassium nitrate at Vicksburg, Miss.

The electrolysis of aqueous hydrochloric acid to give hydrogen and chlorine is practiced to some extent in Europe but it is not yet an important factor in the United States. It may have a place in small installations, but for large ones it is believed that it cannot compete with direct oxidation. It should be mentioned that the production of magnesium by electrolysis of magnesium chloride is not now a net producer of chlorine because the chlorine is recycled to convert magnesium oxide to the chloride. The future production of magnesium by electrolysis of rich magnesium chloride brines will produce chlorine, but this source will be small compared to the market.

It has been evident for some years that we have been approaching a crisis. If anyone doubts this fact he should consider the temporary shutdown of vinyl chloride plants in Japan in 1969. Vinyl chloride manufacture requires chlorine in one form or another and there was no place to put the coproduct, sodium hydroxide. When the chemical industry proposed dumping the caustic in the ocean the Japanese fishermen reacted in a predictable manner, ie they brought about political action to stop it.

It is therefore appropriate to consider the possible sources of hydrogen chloride which could be oxidized to chlorine without concurrent production of sodium hydroxide.

1. In Israel they have learned how to make hydrogen chloride by the action of nitric acid on potassium chloride and a plant has recently gone into commercial operation. At Vicksburg, as already mentioned, these same reactants are used to give chlorine as a coproduct of the potassium nitrate.

2. Magnesium chloride can be hydrolyzed by very hot steam to give magnesium oxide and hydrochloric acid. This is also an Israeli process using magnesium chloride from carnallite from Dead Sea brines. The MgO is of a purity in excess of 99% and is finding use as a refractory.

3. Ammonium chloride, a by-product of the Solvay process, can be dissociated to ammonia and hydrogen chloride and the two separated by various methods described in the chemical literature. The ammonia could be recycled through the Solvay plant and the hydrogen chloride used as a source of chlorine. The change is illustrated by the two following equations (the first one representing the ammonia-soda process):

$$2\,NaCl + CaCO_3 \rightarrow Na_2CO_3 + CaCl_2$$

$$2\,NaCl + CO_2 + \tfrac{1}{2}O_2 \rightarrow Na_2CO_3 + Cl_2$$

This more than doubles the value of the products of the process, assuming present prices. Chlorine can be a coproduct of sodium carbonate just as it is now a coproduct of sodium hydroxide. An incidental benefit of the newer modification is that sodium chloride can be completely utilized while, at present, about 30% of it is wasted in the effluent calcium chloride brine.

4. The action of sulfuric acid on sodium chloride has been for many years a source of hydrogen chloride.

5. Fertilizers of which both anion and cationr ae utilized by plants are much less apt to cause plasmolysis of the plants than those which are not completely absorbed, such as potassium chloride. Thus, there is an incentive to convert potassium chloride to such products as potassium phosphate, as well as the nitrate. The by-product could be hydrogen chloride. Ammonium chloride and phosphoric acid could similarly serve as a source of hydrogen chloride.

6. Work is under way in the industry to recover hydrochloric acid from calcium chloride, a by-product of the Solvay process. This would have the effect noted under 3. of greatly improving the economics of the process.

7. By far the largest source of hydrogen chloride at present is the chlorination of organic compounds. Of these, the largest single one is dichloroethane which is pyrolysed to vinyl chloride. With a plant available for the direct oxidation of chlorine it might be more economical to start with ethane, where available, which costs about one third as much as ethylene, and recycle the hydrogen chloride by oxidizing it to chlorine.

$$C_2H_6 + 2\,Cl_2 \rightarrow CH_2{=}CHCl + 3\,HCl$$

Although in many organic chlorinations one half of the chlorine returns as hydrogen chloride this is not always true, as is shown by the production of hexachlorocyclopentadiene from pentane and/or isopentane. This is an intermediate for chlorendic acid (see Halogenated fire retardants in this volume), Hetron (Hooker Chemical Corp.) resins (chlorendic acid condensed with ethylene glycol) and many chlorinated insecticides.

$$C_5H_{12} + 9\,Cl_2 \rightarrow C_5Cl_6 + 12\,HCl$$

Here two thirds of the chlorine returns as hydrogen chloride.

The reactions which start with methane and produce dichlorodifluoromethane, a widely used refrigerant, are the following:

$$CH_4 + 4\,Cl_2 \rightarrow CCl_4 + 4\,HCl$$
$$CCl_4 + 2\,HF \rightarrow CCl_2F_2 + 2\,HCl.$$

In this case 6 moles of HCl are produced for each mole of dichlorodifluoromethane and only one fourth of the chlorine ends up in organic combination. For this synthesis the oxidation process would reduce the chlorine requirement to one fourth its present value.

The most extreme case is the synthesis of a fluorocarbon, such as polytetrafluoroethylene, shown in the following equations:

$$CH_4 + 3\,Cl_2 \rightarrow CHCl_3 + 3\,HCl$$
$$CHCl_3 + 2\,HF \rightarrow CHClF_2 + 2\,HCl$$
$$2\,CHClF_2 \rightarrow CF_2{=}CF_2 + 2\,HCl$$
$$CF_2{=}CF_2 \rightarrow polymer$$

Here all the chlorine is converted to HCl and none remains in organic combination.

Some of the interesting possibilities for application of the direct-oxidation process involve chlorination, followed by dehydrochlorination and recycling the hydrogen chloride to chlorine. Thus, during World War II a study was made of the production of butadiene by adding chlorine to butenes followed by pyrolysis.

$$C_4H_8 + Cl_2 \rightarrow C_4H_8Cl_2$$
$$C_4H_8Cl_2 \rightarrow C_4H_6 + 2\,HCl$$

No one knew what to do with the hydrogen chloride so that process was abandoned in favor of other which did not produce such a troublesome by-product. Now it must be looked at again.

In a similar way isoprene could be made from isopentane or isopentenes, chloroprene could be made from butane or n-butenes, and styrene could be made from ethane and benzene via ethyl chloride and ethylbenzene. The gas-phase chlorination of ethylbenzene gives principally 1-chloro-1-phenylethane, which is particularly easy to dehydrochlorinate.

Recently the use of molecular sieves has made pure, normal alkanes of six to twenty carbon atoms more readily available than ever before. The prediction has been made that the chemistry of these products will be subjected to intense study in the years immediately before us. One possible reaction is monochlorination followed by dehydrochlorination to give pure normal alkenes with a random position of the double bond. These compounds are subject to the reactions of monoolefins which have proved so productive with the lower homologs. The hydrogen chloride would, of course, be recycled to direct oxidation. In a similar way cyclohexene can be made from cyclohexane in high selectivity.

The economics of the oxidation process improve as the plant size increases. Capital requirements go up approximately with the 0.6 power of the capacity. This contrasts with an electrolytic chlorine plant whose capital requirements follow a 0.9-power rule. It seems likely that this fact will tend to create large chlorination complexes built around a Kel-Chlor plant and a large source of chlorine and/or hydrogen chloride. The by-product hydrogen chloride from a whole series of chlorinations could thus be combined to provide feed for the direct-oxidation unit.

For example, the production of 1,2-dichloropropane, a by-product of both the chlorohydrin and the electrolytic processes of making propylene oxide, has always exceeded the market requirement and much of it is simply burned to dispose of it and to recover the HCl as aqueous hydrochloric acid. It will now be feasible to subject all of it to chlorinolysis.

$$C_3H_6Cl_2 + 8\,Cl_2 \rightarrow 3\,CCl_4 + 6\,HCl$$

The ratio of carbon tetrachloride to perchloroethylene can be adjusted to the market requirement by recycling the undesired chlorocarbon using the reversible reaction.

$$2\,CCl_4 \rightarrow C_2Cl_4 + 2\,Cl_2$$

Hexachlorobenzene, which is also formed in the reaction, is easily hydrolyzed to pentachlorophenol, a timber preservative.

Chlorinated paraffin wax, chlorinated naphthalene, chlorinated biphenyls, chlorinated polyethylenes, chlorinated poly(vinyl chlorides), and 1,1,1-trichloroethane will all become less expensive relative to their competitors.

The economics of chlorinations will be considerably improved, which should tend to promote the use of chlorine compounds. For example, glass is used very widely for food containers but, unfortunately, it is fragile. Recently we have seen glass-clear tough copolymers of propylene and vinyl chloride begin to replace glass bottles for certain uses such as containers for alcoholic beverages. Lowering the cost of vinyl chloride should help promote such uses, as well as for pipes, siding for houses, bathrooms, and many others.

There is another probable effect of the direct oxidation of hydrogen chloride, namely, the buried processes which never saw the light of day because they were not quite economical. For example, the chlorination of certain types of coal (4) followed by a short steaming gives an excellent grade of adsorptive carbon in high yield. It was never quite economical before but it must be looked at again, now that the chlorine, which mostly ends up as hydrogen chloride in the process, can be recycled.

In summary, it would seem that this process for the direct oxidation of hydrogen chloride to chlorine is destined to have a profound effect upon the chlor-alkali industry and upon the whole field of organic chlorinations.

Bibliography

1. Belg. Pat. 599,241 (1961).
2. U.S. Pat. 1,310,943 (July 22, 1919), R. Datta.
3. U.S. Pat. 3,131,028 (April 28, 1964) F. S. Stow (to Hercules Powder Co.).
4. S. Boyk and H. B. Hass, *Ind. Eng. Chem.* **38**, 745–748 (1946).
5. A. G. Oblad, *Ind. Eng. Chem.* **61** (7), 23 (1969).

HENRY B. HASS
Chemical Consultant

COAL

In the English speaking countries, in the industries dealing with fossil fuels, progress towards the use of Standard International units has been very slow. The first two sections of this article make use of a wide variety of nonmetric units. Some conversion factors are listed below:

To convert from	To	Multiply by
ft^3	m^3	0.028317
gal(US)[a]	liters	3.7854
gal(Imp)[a]	liters	4.5461
bbl[b] (barrel, 42 gal(US))	m^3	0.1588
lb	kg	0.45359
ton[a] (short, 2000 lb)	kg	907.18
ton[a] (long, 2240 lb)	kg	1016.05
Btu[c]	joule	1054.35
Btu[c]	kcal	0.2520
Btu/ft^3[c]	kcal/m^3	8.8993
hp	kW	0.746
psi (lb/in^2)	kg/cm^2	0.07031
psi	newton/m^2	6894.76

[a] In the United States and in this article, the gallon quoted is usually the gal(US), and the ton is usually the short ton.

[b] Quantities of petroleum products are customarily given in this volumetric unit. In order to convert to a weight unit, it is necessary to know the gravity, which is usually expressed in °API. See Vol. 14, p. 835.

[c] There are slight differences, depending on the exact definition of Btu. See also Units in this volume.

SYNTHETIC CRUDE OIL FROM COAL

Consideration of coal as a source of synthetic crude oil has increased since the mid-1960s. This interest is the coincidence of several important happenings. The first was the substantial increase of Government support for coal research. The second was the decline in the finding of new crude reserves in this country, together with an ever increasing demand for petroleum products.

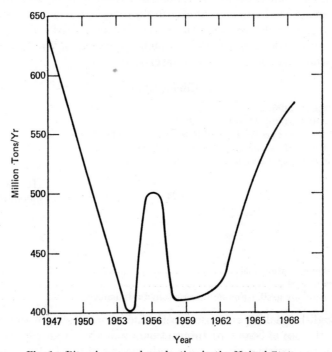

Fig. 1. Bituminous coal production in the United States.

As noted in Figure 1, production of coal in the United States shrank from 638 million tons in 1947 to 433 million tons in 1959 (1). (The marked rise in the period of 1954–1958 resulted from increased exports of coal and from increased U.S. coke production. Both of these markets fell off again in 1958.) Growth since 1959 has been exclusively in the utility-fuel market. Great concern was expressed by the United States Congress at the shrinking coal economy and the resultant increase in unemployment in the coal-producing areas. Accordingly, the 86th Congress established the Office of Coal Research (OCR) on July 7, 1960. This Congressional Act was "to encourage and stimulate the production and conservation of coal in the United States through research and development by authorizing the Secretary of the Interior to contract for coal research, and for other purposes." Under this Act, the OCR could utilize the various disciplines and the scientific and engineering staffs of American industry and universities. The first contracts with the OCR were signed in 1961.

The demand for petroleum products in the United States is growing at about 3.5% per year. From a level of 13 million barrels per day (bbl/day) in 1970, the demand for crude petroleum is expected to reach 18 million bbl/day by 1980. Since 1950, when the ratio of proven reserves to annual consumption for crude petroleum was 11 years, this ratio has steadily fallen to 8 in 1965, and is expected to be about 7 years in 1970.

During this same time, the ratio of proven reserves to annual consumption for natural gas has about halved to 13.5, as expected for 1970. To keep up with the projected growth, the petroleum industry has found it necessary to search for oil at greater depths, and to recover oil from off-shore areas and from Alaska.

However, to satisfy the increasing market, new sources of crude oil must also be found. Included in these is the development of an industry for the conversion of coal to synthetic crude oil. In the late 1960s many of the major petroleum companies in

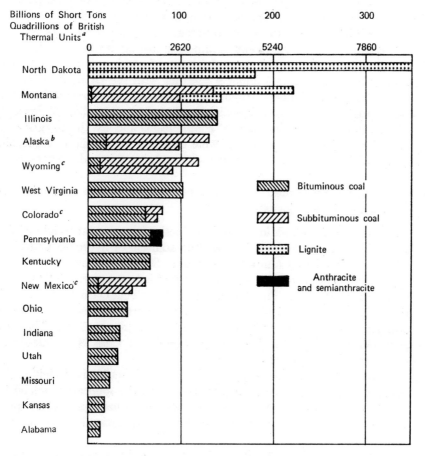

Fig. 2.   Coal reserves of sixteen states (1a).

[a] Anthracite, 12,700 Btu/lb; bituminous, 13,100 Btu/lb; subbituminous, 9,500 Btu/lb.
[b] Small resources of lignite included with subbituminous.
[c] Includes very small quantities of anthracite.

the U.S. have acquired large holdings of coal reserves or have acquired operating coal companies. In addition, they have also acquired holdings in tar sands (qv) and oil shale (see Shale).

Thus, there is a resurgence of interest in coal as a source of synthetic crude oil. The research and development effort of the OCR is aimed at creating a larger market for coal. The growing petroleum market has increased the necessity to find alternate sources of crude oil. Both have contributed to the likelihood of an industry being established to produce synthetic crude oil, referred to as "syncrude" from coal in the 1970s. Compare Coal gasification, in this volume.

Coal Reserves for Synthetic Crude Oil. There is an abundance of coal located geographically near the nation's principal energy-consuming centers. The distribution of coal in the U.S. is shown in Vol. 5, p. 614. Approximately 75% of the known U.S. recoverable energy resources are found in the coal reserves of sixteen states. These reserves are shown in Figure 2 (1a). The major interest of the petroleum companies is in the subbituminous and bituminous coals of the Rocky Mountain area, and of Illinois, Indiana, and western Kentucky. Here large blocks of reserves exist, and in many instances thick seams with low overburden lead to a low mining cost. This is particularly true in certain of the Rocky Mountain states, eg, Wyoming and Montana.

The optimal characteristics of the coal for manufacturing synthetic crude oil are not completely known. Working under a contract with the OCR, Penn State University (2) has made a preliminary attempt to predict oil yield from the knowledge of the coal types used in a process. Oil yields are affected by the carbon–hydrogen ratio, the volatile-matter content, the maceral composition, and by the oxygen content. Nitrogen, sulfur, and oxygen are undesirable elements for synthetic crude oil. In addition, high moisture content of coal is undesirable, as this adds to the processing cost.

Coal-Conversion Processes. Methods for converting coal to synthetic crude oil can be grouped into three major categories:

1. Direct Conversion. This involves the reduction in molecular weight of the coal to form distillable products through the addition of hydrogen under the application of moderate temperatures (about 800°F) and high pressure. Two basic approaches have been taken. The first is based on catalytic hydrogenation of the whole coal. The second is based on solvent extraction of a portion of the coal, followed by hydrogenation of the extracted fraction. The first is exemplified by the Bergius (3,4) and the H–Coal (5) processes. The second is exemplified by Pott-Broche (6,7), Consolidation Coal (8), Uhde-Pfirrmann (9,10), and the Pamco (11) processes.

2. Partial Conversion. This involves the reduction in molecular weight of the coal to distillable products by cracking the coal under the application of moderate to high temperatures (less than 1600°F) usually at or near atmospheric pressure. The COED process (12) developed by FMC Corporation is an example of this approach.

3. Indirect Conversion. This involves complete gasification of the coal to carbon monoxide and hydrogen, which are subsequently catalytically reacted via the Fischer-Tropsch synthesis to give a variety of paraffinic and/or oxygenated products. South African Coal, Oil and Gas Co., Ltd. (SASOL) is producing large quantities of liquid fuels from coal using this process in the Republic of South Africa.

The first two of the above mentioned major categories are described in further detail here.

Direct Conversion

Bergius Process. The earliest work leading to development of this route was initiated by Bergius (3,4), who studied the high-pressure catalytic hydrogenation of brown coal. This process involved feeding a slurry of finely divided coal in an equal many instances thick seams with low overburden lead to a low mining cost. This is amount of heavy recycle oil, including a few % of a titaniferous iron ore, to a series of reactors operating at about 480°C and under a hydrogen pressure of about 200 atm. Contact time of the coal was about 2 hr. Yields obtained, based on coal fed (moisture- and ashfree, maf), are as follows:

Component	Wt percent
oil	40–45
gas	20
residue	40–35

The oil was of poor quality, high in oxygen, nitrogen and sulfur, and practically non-distillable. No improvement was made by further hydrogenation, probably because, with the poor catalysts used, the hydrogenation rate was not high enough to suppress the polymerization of the primary products of the thermal dissociation of coal. No further progress was made with this process until I.G. Farbenindustrie A.G. succeeded in developing catalysts of greatly increased activity. They started large-scale development of the process in Germany in 1926. By 1938, German production of motor fuel from coal and coal tars had reached 1.5 million tons. Concurrently, similar development went on in England. German productive capacity was further increased to almost 5 million tons annually because of wartime economics. Changing economic and political conditions in Europe, between the middle 1930s and the late 1940s, resulted in eliminating the need for coal as a source of liquid fuels. Consequently, nearly all of the coal-hydrogenation plants in western Europe by 1958 were either shut down or converted to other uses.

No up-to-data economics are available on the Bergius process for production of liquid fuels. It does appear, however, that significant process improvements would be needed to bring that process to a minimum level of attractiveness under today's market conditions. One step toward improving this process is made by the H–Coal process described below.

H–Coal Process. This process was developed by Hydrocarbon Research, Inc., under a contract with the OCR (5). The major improvements of this process over the Bergius process, described in the section above, result from the use of an ebullating bed rather than a plugflow hydrogenation reactor. Catalyst can thereby be retained in the reactor and continuously separated from the coal solids. This permits a much reduced catalyst usage (as low as 0.05 wt % on coal feed, as compared with up to 10 wt % for the Bergius process). Further, because of the back-mixed nature of an ebullating bed, the reactor operates essentially isothermally. This simplifies temperature control by cooling the circulating reactor contents to remove the heat of hydrogenation of the coal. In the Bergius-type plugflow reactor, the reactor tends to run adiabatically and control of the temperature between reasonably narrow limits is somewhat more difficult. It can be done by a multiplicity of extra-cold hydrogen bleeds and/or internal cooling surfaces. Also, since the ebullating-bed reactor operates isothermally, cold feed can be pumped in directly using part of the heat of hydrogenation to bring it up to reaction temperature. This is not possible in the Bergius process and hence feed preheating is needed, resulting, as noted before, in operating problems especially when handling bituminous coal.

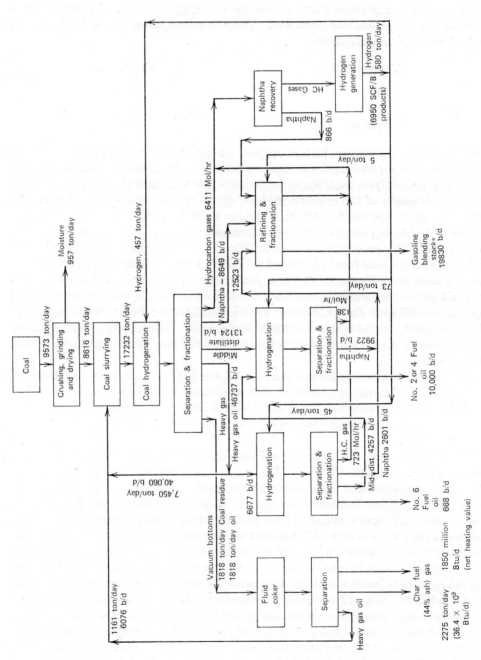

Fig. 3. H–Coal process flow sheet for 30,000 bbl/day liquid fuels from Illinois No. 6 Coal.

Figure 3 shows a schematic flow diagram for the H–Coal process, converting 9573 tons of Illinois No. 6 coal to 30,498 (bbl/day) of liquid fuels. This flow sheet was developed by A. L. Conn et al. of the American Oil Co. (13), from data obtained

Table 1. Operating Conditions and Product Distribution
For H-Coal Process (Illinois No. 6 Coal)

	Pilot plant, 8 in. ID	Bench unit, 0.8 in. ID	Plant design
catalyst "age," lb coal/lb catalyst	<520	<1935	2000
coal feed, lb/(hr)(ft³)	29.3	31.1	28
reactor temperature, °F	827	848	850
products, wt% dry coal			
C_1–C_3 gas	7.4	9.2	9.0
C_4-400°F naphtha	23.5	16.2	16.0[a]
400–650°F distillate fuel oil[b]	12.0	15.2	24.7[a]
650–975°F gas oil[b]	13.6	6.8	11.2[a]
975°F residual fuel oil[b]	14.6	19.6	10.9
unreacted coal	9.3	12.8	9.5
ash	11.3	11.5	11.6
H_2O + NH_3 + CO_2	10.0	10.9	10.2
H_2S	2.9	2.5	2.2
total (100 + H_2 reacted)	104.6	104.7	105.3
C_4^+ liquids, net production			
wt % dry coal	63.7	57.8	62.8
bbl/ton dry coal	3.90	3.42	3.80

[a] Boiling ranges of these cuts are: naphtha, C_4–375°F; distillate, 375–675°F; gas oil, 675–975°F.

[b] See Vol. 14, p. 836.

Table 2. Economics of H-Coal Process

Economics	30,000-bbl/day plant, $ million	100,000 bbl/day plant, $ million
plant investment	135.9	363.1
working capital	10.1	33.7
total investment	146.0	396.8
annual operating costs		
coal ($3.61/ton, dry)	10.2	34.0
catalysts and chemicals	7.9	26.3
utilities	4.6	15.3
conversion costs	12.6	27.8
total operating costs	35.3	103.4
annual capital charges[a]	24.3	64.7
total cost of products	59.6	168.1
by-product credits		
net costs	4.7	15.7
required annual revenue		
on products	54.9	152.4
motor fuel[b]	39.3	110.5
furnace oil[c]	15.6	41.9

[a] At 18% of investment.

[b] At 14.3 and 12.1¢/gal for the 30,000- and 100,000-bbl/day plant, respectively.

[c] At 11.3 and 9.1¢/gal for the 30,000- and 100,000-bbl/day plant, respectively.

by Hydrocarbon Research, Inc., in bench-scale units and in a 3 tons of coal per day pilot plant. Coal is slurried in a heavy gas-oil recycle stream, and fed to a reactor containing an ebbulating bed of a hydrogenation catalyst. About 90% of the coal is converted to liquids by addition of hydrogen to the coal and by removal of the major portion of the original oxygen, nitrogen, and sulfur of the coal as water, hydrogen, sulfide, and ammonia, respectively. The coal-derived liquids are processed to recover end products using petroleum refining technology. In the course of so doing, various light hydrocarbon gases are recovered in sufficient quantity to be steam reformed and shifted to generate the necessary hydrogen for the overall process (see Vol. 11, pp. 347–350), as shown in Figure 3. A summary of operating conditions, requirements, and performance is shown in Table 1 for Illinois No. 6 coal.

Economics of the H–Coal process were independently evaluated by Hydrocarbon Research and by American Oil. A summary of their average findings is given in Table 2 (13), based on 1967 costs, operation with Illinois No. 6 or similar coal, and the process as developed to that date. These estimates show that gasoline made by this process could be sold for about $0.14/gal from a 30,000 bbl/day plant, or for about $0.12/gal from a 100,000 bbl/day plant.

EXTRACTION PROCESSES

The basic approach in these processes is to avoid hydrogenation of the refractory portions of the coal by extracting the higher hydrogen fractions of the coal, cracking the refractory residue to lower-molecular-weight materials by pyrolysis, and hydrogenating these two fractions. The overall yield of synthetic crude is lower than is obtained by complete the hydrogenation of the whole coal, but it is claimed (8) that this is offset by eliminating the expense of direct hydrogenation of the hydrogen-poor refractory fractions of the coal.

Pott-Broche Process. This is the earliest development based on coal extraction (6,7). A 125 ton per day plant was operated on this process in Welheim, Germany, from 1938 to 1944. Extraction of ground, dried coal was conducted at 415–430°C and 100–150 atm with a contact time of about 1 hr. A variety of different solvents were used. The first solvent used was an 80:20 mixture of tetrahydronaphthalene and cresol. This was replaced in commercial operation by the middle distillate from the hydrogenation of coal-tar pitch. Various hydrogenated petroleum fractions have been studied as hydrogen donors in the extraction operation. A good coal-extraction solvent operates through hydrogen transfer from the solvent to the coal. Thus, tetrahydronaphthalene, in hydrogenating the coal, is converted to naphthalene. Various petroleum fractions containing polycyclic aromatics have been hydrogenated to give satisfactory coal extraction solvents. The spent, dehydrogenated extraction oil was recovered from the extract by distillation, rehydrogenated, and recycled. Extract yield (based on total coal) averaged about 68%; liquefaction yield (based on maf) was 78–84%. The extract solution is filtered at 150°C and 3–4 atm at a rate of about 0.2 gal/(min)(ft²). The residue contains upwards of five times as much ash as in the original coal. It can be used as a fuel for process heat, or, as in the Consolidation Coal Co.'s version of the extraction process (8), it can be carbonized to give a distillate tar fraction which can be combined with the coal extract for hydrogenation to synthetic crude oil or gasoline. The filtrate is vacuum distilled to recover the spent solvent for rehydrogenation and possible recycle and the product is extracted.

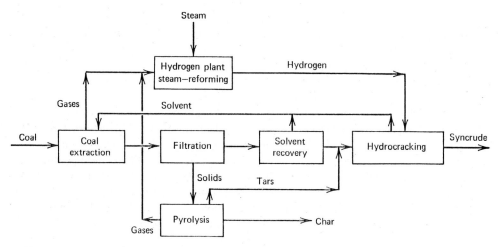

Fig. 4. Schematic flow diagram of the CSF process.

For a short time, the extract from the Welheim plant was hydrogenated at 700 atm to gasoline and fuel oil. However, because of difficulties in hydrogenating this material, this practice was discontinued and the coal extract was then used for making carbon electrodes. Hydrogenation of the extract was about as difficult as the hydrogenation of the parent coal from which it was derived. This drawback was overcome by the later developments of the Consolidation Coal Company.

Consolidation Coal Process. Work on this process by Consolidation Coal Company was started in 1949 (8). Some of the initial work was done with the Standard Oil Company of Ohio. In 1963, research and development was greatly accelerated by influx of additional funds from the Office of Coal Research. Pilot phase of the develop-

Table 3. Economics of CSF Process

Economics	46,000 $ million		250,000 $ million	
	Appalachia	Western	Appalachia	Western
fixed investment	189	189	783	783
working capital	24	24	70	70
total investment	213	213	853	853
operating costs/yr				
coal	23.6[a]	7.9[b]	128.2[a]	42.9[b]
other raw materials, chemicals, and catalysts	8.3	8.3	36.8	36.8
utilities				
other direct and indirect	1.6	1.6	8.4	8.4
conversion costs	29.2	29.2	112.3	112.3
total plant-level costs	62.7	47.0	285.7	200.4
by-products	10.5	5.8	57.0	31.5
net costs	51.8	41.2	228.7	168.9
profit and income taxes	25.7	25.7	99.5	99.5
required sales of crude oil	77.5	66.9	328.2	268.4
at $/bbl crude	5.14	4.44	3.98	3.25

[a] Coal at $3.75/ton.

[b] Coal at $1.25/ton.

ment was started in 1966 when a 24 ton/day pilot was completed. This process is an extension and improvement over the Pott-Broche process. It differs mainly in the hydrogenation feedstock, and that it uses a more efficient hydrogenation catalyst. The feedstock is essentially the same coal extract fraction plus additional liquids from low-temperature pyrolysis of the residue. The improvements in catalysts are the result of continued research in this field since World War II.

A flow sheet of the Consolidation Synthetic Fuel (CSF) process is given in Figure 4. Economics of the CSF process were developed by the Ralph M. Parsons Co. based on process data obtained in the laboratory and in a small pilot plant. (Reliable data from the pilot plant at Cresap, W. Va., were not available.) Their findings are summarized in Table 3 for plants having a capacity of 46,000 and 250,000 bbl/day of 33.4° API crude oil. This indicates a required selling price of the crude of $5.14/bl at the plant for the smaller plant in the Appalachia region, and $3.25 for the larger plant in the Intermountain region of the U.S. Parsons assessed the value of the oil at about the latter figure.

Uhde-Pfirrmann Process. This process differs from the Pott-Broche process by the use of hydrogen during the extraction step, thereby conducting in situ hydrogenation of the solvent and reducing the solvent usage. This process was patented by Uhde and Pfirrmann (9,10). It operated at about 410°C and up to 300 atm with a contact time of about 30 min. The extract was more hydrogenated than that from the Pott-Broche process, and contained about 25% more H and 25% less O, N, and S than the original coal. Data on the economics of this process are not available. However, because of its similarity to the CSF and the Pott-Broche processes, it may be safe to conclude that the economics of the Uhde-Pfirrmann process should be in the same general area as that of the others.

Pamco Process. This process was developed by the Spencer Chemical Company under a contract with the OCR starting in 1962 (11). Work on this project is continuing under the Pittsburg and Midway Coal Mining Company (P&M), a part of Spencer, now a division of Gulf Oil Corporation. This process is essentially the same as the Uhde-Pfirrmann process. It represents some improvement over Uhde, such as lower extraction pressure (100 vs 300 atm). Economics for this process are in the same range as for the CSF process.

Partial Conversion

COED Process. Partial conversion of coal to synthetic crude oil is typified by the COED process now being developed by the FMC Corporation under a contract with the OCR (12). It is basically a multistage fluidized-bed pyrolysis of high-volatile coals of various ranks. Coal tars and product gases are distilled off leaving a char residue. The coal tars are separated from the product gases and catalytically hydrogenated to a synthetic crude oil, using hydrogen recovered from the process gases. A block-flow diagram of this process is shown in Figure 5.

The key to this process is the use of coals which give high liquid yields, compared to the other coals, under conditions which avoid agglomeration of the coal. This is done by controlling the pyrolysis temperature in each fluidized-bed stage at a temperature short of the agglomeration point of coal. It was found that by doing this, the agglomeration temperature of the solids residue is increased, thereby permitting increasing the temperature of the solids further and obtaining additional yields of liquid products and gases. A typical high-volatile bituminous B coal, such as Illinois No. 6 or Utah

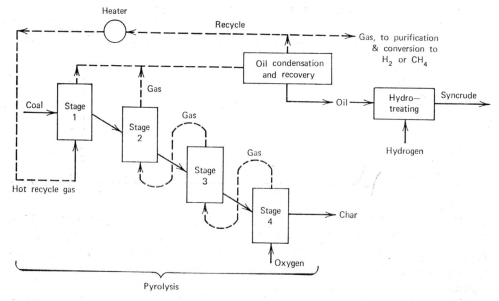

Fig. 5. Schematic flow sheet for COED process.

A-seam, can be pyrolyzed by heating the solids successively at temperatures of 600°F in the first stage, 850°F in the second, 1000°F in the third, and finally 1600°F in the last. Heat for the process is generated in the last stage by combustion of a portion of the solid (char) residue with oxygen. The hot gases from this stage proceed counter-currently with respect to the solids, thereby heating and fluidizing the solids in each stage. Additional process heat to each stage can be provided by recycle of hot char from a subsequent stage. Thus, if added heat is needed in the second stage, hotter char from the third or fourth stage can be recycled to it.

This process has been successfully operated in a continuous 100 lb/hr four-stage process-development unit on a wide range of coals. Typical pyrolysis conditions and yields for some of the coals tested are summarized in Table 4. A 36 ton per day pilot plant was completed at FMC Corporation's R&D Center in Princeton, N.J. in 1970.

Table 4. Typical COED Operations

	Coal	
Operation	Utah	Illinois
pyrolysis temperatures, °F		
first-stage	600	600
second-stage	850	830
third-stage	1000	990
fourth-stage	1600	1575
yields/ton dry coal		
char, lb	1050	1175
syncrude oil, bbl	1.4	1.15
hydrogen, scf$\times 10^3$	4.8	5.3
oil hydrogenation		
pressure, psi	3000	3000
temperature, °F	800	800

Table 5. Typical Gas Analysis from COED Process

Component	Mole %[a]
hydrogen	40.3
carbon monoxide	22.0
carbon dioxide	9.3
hydrogen sulfide	3.2
methane	11.1
ethylene	0.3
ethane	7.5
propylene	1.6
propane	1.6
butanes	3.1

[a] Dry basis.

Tars recovered from the pyrolysis are filtered to remove entrained solids and hydrogenated at about 3000 psig and 800°F using commercially available sulfided Ni-Mo catalysts (eg, American Cyanamid Corporation's HDS-3A catalyst). Hydrogen consumption is about 3000 scf per barrel of product. The resulting synthetic crude oil is described later.

The product gases can be marketed as a low-Btu fuel gas or upgraded olefins etc, technology to more valuable products, such as hydrogen, methane, L PG , by known The choice of which way to handle the gases will basically depend on the local markets. Typical analyses of the gases from the pyrolysis operation are given in Table 5.

The product char could be marketed as a boiler fuel for a utility plant, or could be upgraded, for example, to synthesis gas ($CO + H_2$) which can be converted to other valuable products.

Typical economics of the COED process are summarized in Table 6. These indicate that the process is potentially economic and hence could be a future supplemental source of crude oil in the United States.

Table 6. COED Process Economics for 10,000 Tons/Day of Coal

Economics	$ million
fixed capital	44.7
working capital	3.1
total investment	47.8
manufacturing costs	
coal, approx $3.00/ton	10.5
other variable costs	4.1
conversion and indirect costs	6.8
total manufacturing costs	21.4
sales	
char, approx $2.75/ton	3.3
oil, approx $4.00/bbl	18.8
hydrogen, approx $0.25/scf×10³	11.7
total sales	33.8
selling costs	1.7
net sales	32.1
profit before taxes	11.7
profit after taxes	5.9
return on investment, %	12.4
discounted cash flow, %	17.0

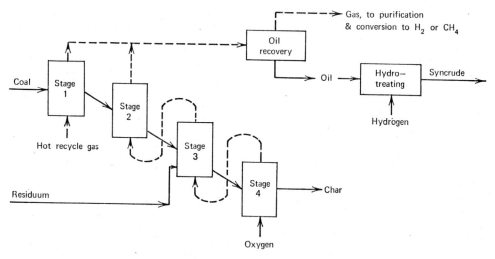

Fig. 6. Schematic flow sheet for Seacoke process.

Seacoke Process. This process is based on the copyrolysis of coal and petroleum residual oil, using multistage fluidized beds in the same manner as in the COED process. It was developed by the Atlantic Richfield Co. with the assistance of the FMC Corporation, under contract with the OCR (14). A schematic description of the process is given in Figure 6. The oils produced from this process are discussed later. Product char and gases can be handled in the same way as discussed above for the COED process.

Indirect Conversion

This process is operated by SASOL in South Africa on a commercial scale because of a combination of very cheap coal and lack of petroleum reserves in that country. See Carbon monoxide–hydrogen reactions. It is generally agreed that the process, as practiced by SASOL, would not be commercially attractive in the United States.

Syncrude Oil

Although the coal-conversion processes differ substantially, the principal end product is intended to be a petroleum-refinery feedstock. In general, the raw oils from coal are low in hydrogen content, viscous, and contain the heteroatoms oxygen, sulfur, and nitrogen in prohibitive amounts. Hydrogen is the leveling agent; it removes the heteroatoms, lowers the viscosity, and raises the API gravity (see Vol. 14, p. 835) by reducing the carbon: hydrogen ratio.

The COED and Seacoke processes are similar in that both are based on thermal cracking of coal. In the Seacoke process, petroleum residuum is pyrolyzed with coal. The resultant raw oil is a combination of coal-derived oil and cracked residuum (14). The COED process does not involve residuum. Both oils are subsequently hydrotreated to produce a syncrude oil. Distillation curves for two COED oils and a Seacoke oil are presented in Figure 7. Included too is a curve for a West Texas Permian crude (petroleum) oil. Whereas the petroleum crude is characterized by nearly a straight line over the boiling range, the COED oils are concentrated in the middle

Table 7. Properties of COED Synthetic Crude Oil[a]

Properties	Value
°API	28.2
pour point, °F	−40
elemental analysis, wt %	
C	87.8
H	12.0
O	0.16
N	0.05
S	0.02

[a] Pyrolysis product of Illinois No. 6-seam coal.

Table 8a. Properties of COED Synthetic Crude Oil[a]

	Fraction				
Properties	Naphtha, C_6-435°F	Furnace oil, 435–665°F	Gas oil, 667–715°F	Residue, 715°F +	Total syncrude
wt %	11.6	64.8	10.3	13.3	
vol %	12.2	66.5	10.1	11.2	
°API	38.7	30.1	24.5		28.9
pour point, °F		30			80
caustic extract, wt %	<0.1	<0.1			
elemental analysis, wt %					
C	86.7	87.0	87.3	87.5	87.1
H	13.1	12.8	12.4	12.3	12.7
O	0.06	0.2	0.3	0.1	0.13
N	0.1	0.06	0.05	0.06	0.05
S				0.3	<0.005

[a] Pyrolysis product of Utah A-seam coal.

Table 8b. Hydrocarbon Composition of COED Synthetic Crude Oil[a]

	Fraction			
Hydrocarbon	Naphtha,[b] C_6-435°F	Furnace oil,[b] 435–665°F	Gas oil,[c] 667–715°F	Residue,[c] 715°F+
paraffins				
straight and branched	18.1	25	27.4	18.5
monocyclo	39.2	⎫	16.7	19.9
dicyclo	24.2	⎬ 39	⎫ 21.5	⎫ 20.5
tricyclo	1.2	⎭	⎭	⎭
alkylbenzenes	12.4	8	⎫	⎫
indans and tetrahydronaphthalenes	4.8	13	⎬ 26.5	⎬ 26.6
indenes		6	⎭	⎭
naphthalenes	0.1	3	⎫	⎫
acenaphthenes		2	⎬ 5.3	⎬ 6.9
acenaphthylenes		2	⎭	⎭
tricyclic aromatics		2		
benzanthracene and pentacyclics			1.0	2.4
other tetracyclics			1.1	3.0

[a] Pyrolysis product of Utah A-seam coal.
[b] Vol %.
[c] Wt %.

range, 400–800°F for the Utah oil, and 300–700°F for the Illinois oil. The influence of the coal-derived portion on the distillation curve for the Seacoke oil is obvious.

The Properties of two COED oils is presented in Tables 7 and 8(a,b); for Seacoke oil, in Table 9(a,b) (14); for a typical West-Texas Permian petroleum crude, in Table 10. A comparison of three COED oils and of a Seacoke oil is shown in Figure 8. The Seacoke oil and the one COED oil were produced from Illinois No. 6-seam coal; the second COED oil, from Utah A-seam coal; and the third, from W. Va. Pittsburgh-

Table 9a. Properties of Seacoke Synthetic Crude Oil[a]

	Fraction						
Properties	Naphtha, C_5-330°F	Total naphtha, C_5-420°F	Jet Fuel, 330–500°F	Furnace oil, 420–650°F	Hydro-cracker feed, 420–777°F	Gas oil, 650–1000°F	Total syn-crude
yield range, vol %	3.5–18.7	3.5–25.9	18.7–34.2	25.9–57.2	25.9–76.9	57.2–96.8	
wt %	12.7	19.7	15.2	31.9	52.9	42.2	
vol %	15.2	22.4	15.5	31.3	51.0	39.2	
°API	58.3	49.5	30.9	24.5	21.6	17.0	27.6
smoke point, °F			12				
pour point, °F			−78	−20		90	−20
elemental analysis, wt %							
C	85.8	86.4				88.9	87.8
H	14.1	13.4				10.9	12.0
O	0.096	0.14				0.05	0.18
N	0.006	0.009			0.0340	0.09	0.04
S	0.0002	0.0007		0.0026		0.03	0.05

[a] Pyrolysis product of short residuum and Illinois No. 6-seam coal.

Table 9b. Hydrocarbon Composition of Seacoke Synthetic Crude Oil[a]

	Fraction					
Hydrocarbon	Naphtha,[b] C_5-330°F	Total naphtha,[b] C_5-420°F	Jet fuel,[b] 330–500°F	Furnace oil,[c] 420–650°F	Hydro-cracker feed,[c] 420–777°F	Gas oil,[c] 650–1000°F
paraffins						
straight-chain and branched	23.5	18.6	6.1	5.0	5.1	4.0
monocyclo	67.9	57.0	} 53.8	} 37.3	} 35.8	17.5
polycyclo	3.3	13.0				16.0
alkylbenzenes	5.0	7.0	11.5	10.8	10.2	
indans and tetra-hydronaphthalene	0.3	3.6	23.0	20.5	13.8	} 52.0
indenes		0.8		13.0	14.7	
naphthalenes			1.2	5.0	7.1	} 5.1
acenaphthylenes			3.9	1.4	3.5	
tricyclic aromatics				3.0	4.7	5.4[d]

[a] Pyrolysis product of short residuum and Illinois No. 6-seam coal.
[b] Vol %.
[c] Wt %.
[d] Of which 1.2 are tetracyclic and 2.0 pentacyclic aromatics.

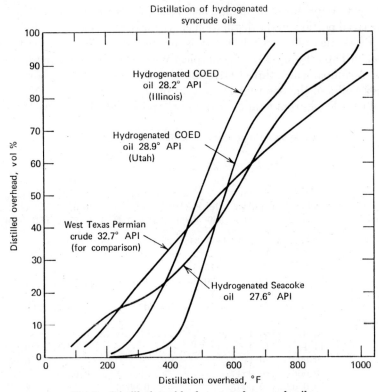

Fig. 7. Distillation of hydrogenated syncrude oils.

seam coal. A comparison of the Seacoke oil with the petroleum crude is shown in Figure 9. These analyses and the hydrotreating of the COED oils were performed by Atlantic Richfield Co.

Table 10. Hydrocarbon Composition of West-Texas Permian Crude[a] wt %

	Fraction			
Hydrocarbon	Naphtha,[b] C_5-330°F	Jet fuel,[b] 330–500°F	Kerosene,[b] 330–580°F	Gas oil,[b] 650–1000°F
paraffins				
straight-chain and branched	48.8	⎫	⎫ 37	25
monocyclo	34.0	⎬ 80.0	⎬ 30	21
polycyclo	2.0	⎭	⎭	11
alkyl benzenes	14.6			
indans and tetra- hydronaphthalene	0.6	⎫ 16.1	10 6	⎫ 27
indenes		⎬	4	⎬
naphthalenes		⎭	8	⎭
acenaphthenes		⎫ 3.9	4	⎫ 8.9
acenaphthylenes		⎬	0	⎬
tricyclic aromatics		⎭	1	7.1[c]

[a] Atlantic Richfield Co.
[b] The fractions have the following °API: naphtha, 58.4; jet fuel, 43; kerosene, 36.8; gas oil, 26.7.
[c] Of which 2.2 are tetracyclic and 0.5 pentacyclic aromatics.

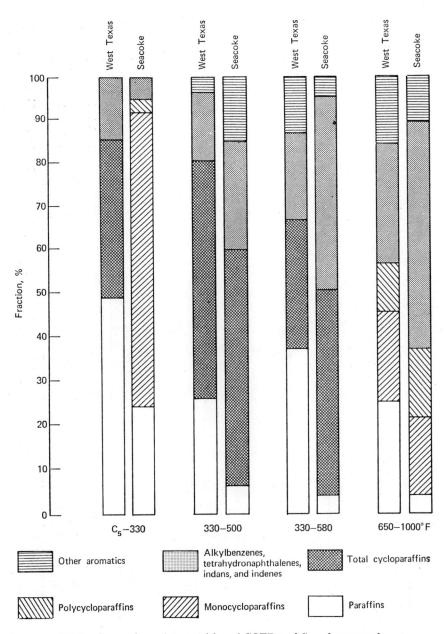

Fig. 8. Comparison of composition of COED and Seacoke syncrude.

The Rocky Mountain coals produce synthetic crude oils higher in paraffins than coals in the mid-West or in the Appalachian area by the COED process. In turn, the Eastern and mid-Western coals produce oils higher in aromatic compounds than do the Western coals. These comparisons are made in Figure 8 with the three COED oils. Also shown in this figure for comparison is Seacoke oil produced from residuum and the Illinois No. 6-seam coal. The middle fraction of Seacoke oil is higher in aromatics than that for the comparable COED oil from Illinois coal. However, this is reversed in the heavier gas-oil fraction.   The aromatic content of all the oils increased with the temperature range.

The Seacoke oil is lower in paraffins than the West-Texas Permian petroleum crude, as shown in Figure 9.   Except for the light naphtha fraction, the Seacoke oil is

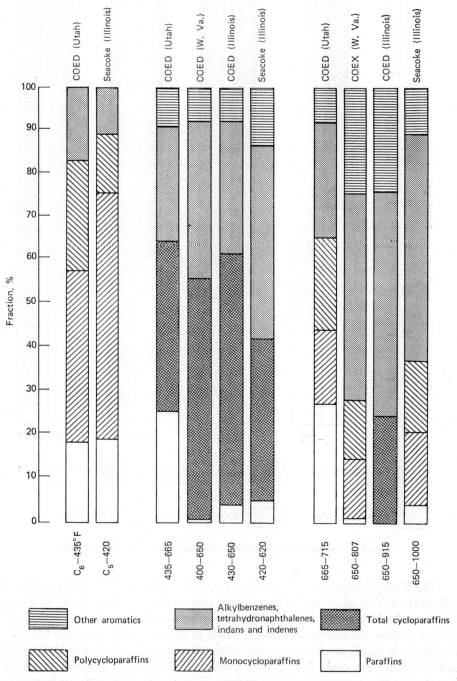

Fig. 9. Comparison of petroleum crude and seacoke syncrude

higher in aromatics than the petroleum crude. The naphthenic content of the Seacoke oil is higher in all but the heavy gas-oil fraction.

Referring to Tables 7, 8, and 9, the syncrudes from COED and Seacoke would be classified as low-gravity, low-sulfur naphthenic crudes. The Seacoke oil would also be classified as a low-pour crude. The pour point for the COED Utah oil is substantially higher, reflecting the higher paraffin content of this oil. By contrast, the pour point for the COED oil from Illinois is minus 40°F, as shown in Table 7. About one-fourth of the raw Utah coal-derived oil is collected as a separate waxy fraction, lighter than water. This is not the case with Illinois coal. The naphtha fractions from the Seacoke or COED oils would be normally charged to a catalytic reforming unit. The extremly high naphthene content would produce a 100-octane gasoline readily with only a small-yield loss. The 0.14% oxygen content of the Seacoke oil may require hydrogen pretreatment prior to reforming.

The jet-fuel and kerosene fractions of the Seacoke oil would require additional hydrogenation. This could be done in the conventional-type hydrogenation units present in many refineries. The smoke points of 12 and 11 are well below specifications because of the high aromatic content. Jet fuel has a minimum smoke-point specification of 20, which would require the hydrogenation of about 23% aromatics to cycloparaffins. The need for low aromatic content in kerosene is even more stringent, and it is doubtful that kerosene could be produced economically from this syncrude.

The furnace-oil fractions of the COED and Seacoke oils have a higher aromatic content than conventional home-heating oils. If used as a home-heating oil, the low sulfur level would be well below any probable sulfur restriction for air-pollution control.

The fraction analyzed as the potential hydrocracker feedstock constitutes 51% of the Seacoke syncrude, and has a nitrogen content of 340 ppm. The high aromatic and naphthene content of this fraction (94.9 wt % total cyclics) makes this an excellent hydrocracker feed. The fraction boiling up to 850°F could be included in the hydrocracker feed, which would add an additional 6.4% yield. The quantity and composition of the potential hydrocracker feed means that hydrocracking probably would be the main refinery process used for this syncrude. This is also true for the COED oils

The gas-oil fraction of the Seacoke oil is a good-quality catalytic cracking feedstock. Its high cycloparaffinic and monoaromatic content indicate that it would crack readily under relatively mild cracking conditions. The cracking yields obtained in the laboratory cracking tests of this fraction are shown in Table 11(a,b). Also shown are yields obtained in similar tests on a petroleum gas oil and a COED gas oil from the pyrolysis of Illinois No. 6-seam coal. The high monoaromatic content (52.0%) of the Seacoke gas oil indicates that the gasoline product from catalytic cracking would have a high-octane level. The low sulfur level (0.03%) indicates that the furnace oil produced by catalytic cracking would not have to be hydrotreated. It would also be suitable feed for a hydrocracker. The volume percent conversion for the COED oil is lower than that of the Seacoke oil, primarily because of the higher nitrogen content, 0.38%, for the COED oil. The higher content of the dicyclic and tricyclic aromatics also contributes to the lower volume percent conversion. As noted in Table 7, subsequent work done by ARCO produced an oil from Illinois No. 6-seam coal with a substantially lower nitrogen content, 0.05%. Although the analyses are not available, it would be expected that the content of dicyclic and tricyclic aromatics would also be lower for this COED gas oil.

Table 11a. Properties of Gas Oils Used in Catalytic Cracking Tests

Properties	Gas oil		
	Seacoke	Hydrogenated[a]	Av petroleum
boiling range, °F	650–1000	650–915	600–1000
°API	17.0	13.5	23.4
elemental analysis, wt %			
C	88.9	88.1	
H	10.9	10.7	
O	0.05	0.78	
N	0.09	0.38	0.24
S	0.03	0.03	1.19
hydrocarbons, wt %			
paraffins			
straight-chain and branched	4.0		16.0
cyclo	33.5	24.1	35.0
aromatics			
monocyclic	52.0	52.2	25.5
dicyclic	5.1	15.1	13.6
tricyclic	2.2	4.7	6.4
tetracyclic and heavier	3.2	3.9	3.5

[a] Obtained from Illinois No. 6-seam coal via COED process.

Table 11b. Comparative Catalytic Cracking Tests of Gas Oils[a]

Cracking test	Gas oil		
	Seacoke	Hydrogenated	Av petroleum
lb catalyst/lb oil	3.5	3.4	2.7
wt space velocity, lb oil/(hr) (lb catalyst)	1.4	1.5	1.9
temperature, °F	900	900	900
vol % conversion at approx 430°F	72.5	58.1	56.4
yields			
C_2's and lighter, wt %	2.8	2.6	2.0
C_3's, wt %	4.9	3.1	3.6
C_4's, vol %	15.0	8.9	10.6
C_5–430°F naphtha, vol %	55.2	43.9	46.4
430°F cycle stock, vol %	27.5	41.9	43.6
coke	9.7	8.6	4.6
relative coke producing			
factor at constant conversion	0.9	1.7	1.0

[a] Clean, steam-deactivated, zeolitic cracking catalyst, 84 activity, and 0.3 carbon-producing factor.

Table 12. Properties of Consolidation Coal Co.'s Synthetic Crude Oil[a]

Properties	Value
°API	21.0
S, wt %	0.0925
N, wt %	0.17
bromine no. (mg Br_2/g oil)	7
fluorescent indicator analysis (FIA)	
aromatics	75.3
olefins	0.9
paraffins and naphthenes	23.8

[a] Extraction product of Pittsburgh-seam coal.

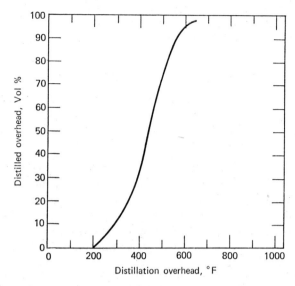

Fig. 10. Distillation of hydrogenated Consolidation Coal Co. syncrude oil.

The low yield of 1000°F-plus residuum for the Seacoke and COED oils makes these syncrudes more valuable than crude oils of similar gravity. For instance, a 27.5% API Middle-East crude has a 35% yield of 1000°F-plus residuum.

Less information is available on other coal-derived syncrude oils. The chemical composition of the syncrude oil produced by Consolidation Coal Co. under its OCR sponsored work is presented in Table 12 (8). This oil was produced by hydrogenation of the liquid extraction product from a Pittsburgh-seam coal. The distillation curve for this oil is shown in Figure 10. This crude has no heavy ends because it is a distillate product, the heavy ends being recycled as the extraction medium.

Bibliography

1. *Bituminous Coal Data*, 1968 ed., National Coal Assoc., Washington, D. C., p. 10.
1a. P. Averitt, 'Coal Resources of the United States, January 1, 1969," *U.S. Geol. Surv. Bull*, **1275**, 20 (1969).
2. Office of Coal Research, OCR, *Annual Report 1969*, Dept. of Interior, Washington, D.C., Jan. 15, 1969, p. 52.
3. Ger. Pat. 301,231 (1913), F. Bergius and J. Bilwiller.
4. F. Bergius, Z. *Ver. Deut. Ingr.* **69**, 1313–1320, 1359–1362 (1925).
5. Hydrocarbon Research, Inc., Project H-Coal Report on Process Development, Rept. PB 173765, Clearinghouse Fed. Sci. Tech. Inform., Springfield, Va.
6. C. Kröger, *Erdoel Kohle* **9**, 441–446, 516–520, 620–624, 839–843 (1956).
7. H. Broche and W. Reinmerth, "Kohlenextraktion," in *Ullmann's Encyclopädie der Technischen Chemie*," Vol. 10, 3rd ed., Urban und Schwarzenberg, Munich, 1958, pp. 570–575.
8. Consolidation Coal Co., *Project Gasoline Pre-Pilot Plant Phase 1, Research on CSF Process*, Vol. II, R&D Rept. No. 39, OCR, Washington, D.C., 1968.
9. Fr. Pat. 800,920 (1936), F. Uhde.
10. U.S. Pat. 2,167,250 (1939), T. W. Pfirrmann.
11. Spencer Chemical Div., *Solvent Processing of Coal to a De-Ashed Product Aug. 1962–Feb. 1965*, R&D Rept. No. 9, OCR, Washington, D.C.
12. J. F. Jones et al., *Char-Oil-Energy Development*, R&D Rept. No. 11, OCR, Washington, D.C., Jan. 1967.

13. A. L. Conn et al., "Evaluation of Project 'H-Coal'," Rept. PB 177068, Clearinghouse Fed. Sci. Tech. Inform., Springfield, Va., Dec. 1967.
14. Atlantic Richfield Co., *Project Seacoke—Final Report*, Vol. I, R&D Rept. No. 29, OCR, Washington, D.C., Aug. 1964–June 1969.

L. Seglin and
R. T. Eddinger
FMC Corporation

GASIFICATION OF COAL

Recent developments in coal gasification have been concerned largely with the production of high heating value gas of pipeline quality. Pipeline-quality gas generally contains 90% or more of methane, is practically free of carbon monoxide and sulfur compounds, and has a heating value of over 900 Btu per standard ft³. This shift in interest from the production of town gas (approx 500 Btu per standard ft³) and synthesis gases from coal, to the production of synthetic pipeline gas is due to:

1. The rapidly increasing use of natural gas throughout the world, which has resulted in widespread conversion to a nominal 1000 Btu per standard ft³ heating-value basis.
2. The ready availability of either low-cost natural gas or low-cost petroleum naphtha in most parts of the world, which has resulted in the replacement of coal as a source of synthesis gases for the manufacture of ammonia, methanol, etc, by these more desirable raw materials.

The conversion to natural gas as a source of fuel and synthesis gases has proceeded furthest in the U.S., where the replacement of coal and petroleum oils as raw materials for gasification has been essentially complete since the 1950s. Consequently, beginning in the 1960s, natural gas has provided approximately one-third of the primary energy and petrochemical raw material requirements in the U.S. The Soviet Union is also rapidly converting to a natural-gas basis and even in Western Europe, where large discoveries of natural gas are of relatively recent origin, it is expected that over 10% of primary energy requirement will be met with natural gas by 1975.

Further impetus to the trend toward standardizing on fuel gas of high methane content, 1000 Btu per standard ft³, throughout the world has been given by the new developments in ocean transport of natural gas in liquefied form. As a result of these developments, liquefied natural gas (LNG) is being exported from such areas of over-supply as North Africa, Borneo, and Alaska to markets for gas in western Europe and Japan. In 1970, projects for shipping LNG from North Africa and Venezuela to the eastern seaboard of the U.S. were also under development and many other projects were in the planning stage. See Gas, natural, in this volume.

Shortage of Natural Gas in the U.S. The change in the energy-supply picture, which has the greatest impact on the new developments in coal-gasification technology, is, however, the growing shortage of natural gas in the U.S. For example, as of 1969, the U.S. had only 18% of the world's 1550 trillion ft³ (1 trillion = 10^{12}) of proved natural-gas reserves, while still producing well over half of the world's natural gas. From 1953 through 1969, the discovery rate of natural gas in the U.S. did not increase, averaging 18 trillion ft³ per year, while requirements rose rapidly to over 21 trillion ft, (1). Consequently, in 1968 and 1969, the U.S., for the first time since World War II³ withdrew from the wells more gas than was added to the proved reserves. Gas requirements, by the year 2000, are expected to more than double to over 45 trillion ft^3 annually so that, even with substantial imports, a total of nearly 1000 trillion ft^3 would have to be produced from domestic sources during the rest of the century (2). After allowing for sufficient proved reserves to maintain a minimum reserve-to-production ratio of 10 years, this would necessitate roughly doubling the historical rate of gas discoveries. Such an increase is not considered to be attainable in the foreseeable future.

Sources of Supplemental Gas. The U.S. is in a unique position in so far as production of supplemental gases from coal is concerned. In contrast with most other highly developed countries, bituminous coal and lignite are relatively cheap in the U.S. compared to petroleum feedstocks suitable for gasification. For example, because of import controls and the large demand for motor fuels, there has been none of the abundant supply of low-cost naphtha so typical of Western Europe. In the U.S., residual and distillate petroleum feedstocks suitable for gas production cost from 30 cents to $1 per million Btu, whereas typical mine-mouth costs of bituminous coals and lignite during the 1960s ranged from 10 to 20 cents per million Btu. Although coal prices in some areas were expected to increase sharply in 1970 because of new mine-safety regulations, coal should maintain its competitive position as a source of base-load synthetic pipeline-quality gas in much of the country.

Similarly, importation of LNG from South America, North Africa, and Nigeria could not provide a competitive source of supplemental base-load gas, except near the east-coast delivery points. Estimates of dockside prices of LNG from these sources, made in 1969, ranged from 40 to 64 cents per million Btu (3), whereas comparable price estimates for synthetic pipeline gas from bituminous coals and lignite produced in large, mine-mouth plants ranged from 35 to 55 cents per million Btu. Naturally, continuing escalation in the price of these supplemental gases must be expected under inflationary pressures.

However, price rises of natural gas during the 1970s will be due not only to inflationary forces. There will be the added impact of the supply shortage which will result in increasing reliance on more costly off-shore and deep horizon gas and on importation of even costlier pipeline natural gas from remote regions of Canada and possibly even Alaska. This creates a favorable situation for early introduction of synthetic pipeline gas from coal in the U.S., especially in such areas as western North Dakota, eastern Montana, northeastern and southern Wyoming, central and western Colorado, eastern Utah, northwestern New Mexico, and central and southern Illinois, where large supplies of relatively low-cost uncommitted coal are available. Additional promising areas exist in West Virginia and western Pennsylvania, although less low-cost uncommitted coal is available there. Many of these coal reserves are traversed by large interstate pipeline systems connected to underground storage reservoirs and are reasonably near the major eastern seaboard, midwestern, and west-coast markets for gas.

Coal Resources. The most important factor favoring coal-based processes for providing a significant portion of long-range supply of pipeline-quality gas in the U.S. is the tremendous available supply of coal. As shown in Table 1, the most recent estimate of remaining U.S. coal resources, determined from mapping and exploration and located under less than 3000 ft of overburden, is 780 billion (1 billion = 10^9) tons. This assumes a 50% recovery to account for mining losses and corresponds to nearly 16,000 quadrillion (1 quadrillion = 10^{15}) Btu of primary energy supply. At 70%

Table 1. U.S. Fossil-Fuel Reserves (January 1, 1969)

Reserve	Measured or proved		Estimated remaining recoverable	
	Billions of units	Quadrillion (10^{15}) Btu	Billions of units	Quadrillion (10^{15}) Btu
natural gas, 1000 ft³[i]	287[a]	297[b]	1514[c]	1560[b]
natural gas liquids, bbl	8.6[a]	36[d]	45[e]	190[d]
crude oil, bbl	30.7[a]	178[f]	463[g]	2690[f]
shale oil, bbl[h]	80	464[i]	1140	6610[i]
coal, ton[k]	54	1080	780	15,650
			(1436)	(28,810)

[a] Reference 4.

[b] Natural gas heating value = 1032 Btu/ft³.

[c] Based on Potential Gas Committee estimate of potential supply of 1227 trillion ft³ (5) plus 287 trillion ft³ of proved reserves (4), both as of December 31, 1968.

[d] Natural-gas-liquids heating value = 4,200,000 Btu/bbl.

[e] Estimated to be the same ratio to future natural gas recoveries as for proved reserves.

[f] Crude-oil heating value = 5,800,000 Btu/bbl.

[g] Based on estimate by T. A. Hendricks (6) of 400 billion bbl of crude oil economically recoverable from the 1600 billion bbl originally in place, revised to 550 billion bbl by U.S. Geological Survey in 1968 (including Alaska and continental shelves to a water depth of 660 feet) (7), less 86.8 billion bbl total production through December 31, 1968 (4).

[h] Reference 8.

[i] Standard ft³ at 14.73 psia and 60°F (scf).

[j] Crude shale-oil heating value = 5,800,000 Btu/bbl.

[k] Reference 9; values in parentheses include 656 billion tons probably recoverable in unexplored and unmapped areas to a depth of 3000 ft.

conversion efficiency, it would be equivalent to 11,000 trillion ft³ of natural gas, or seven times the most recent estimate of remaining recoverable natural-gas resources shown in Table 1 (5). This estimate by the Potential Gas Committee includes over 400 trillion ft³ of inferred supply in Alaska which may or may not become available to continental U.S. markets. The recoverable coal resources also dwarf those of natural gas liquids, crude oil, and even of shale oil which is recoverable from the abundant and relatively rich oil shale deposits in the United States.

The large recoverable coal resources, determined from mapping and exploration, are nearly doubled if probable additional resources in unmapped and unexplored areas are included. It is important to note that, according to the U.S. Geological Survey (9), of the 780 billion tons of recoverable coal determined by mapping and exploration, 89% are under 1000 ft or less of overburden. Further, 29% of this coal, or 226 billion tons, is in thick beds (more than 42 in. for bituminous coal and more than 10 ft for sub-bituminous coal and lignite) primarily under less than 1000 ft of overburden, and, therefore, recoverable at or near present costs. More than half of this coal is in beds 28 in. or more thick (more than 5 ft for subbituminous coal and lignite), again largely under less than 1000 ft of overburden and recoverable at present to $1\frac{1}{2}$ times present costs.

Long-term fuel-cost trends favor coal as a raw material for synthetic pipeline gas since the major coal market, ie thermal power plants, will come under renewed attack by nuclear energy under the impetus of increasingly stringent air-pollution-control regulations. In the late 1950s and during much of the 1960s, the threat of nuclear energy resulted in a decline, followed by stabilization, of coal prices through rapid improve-

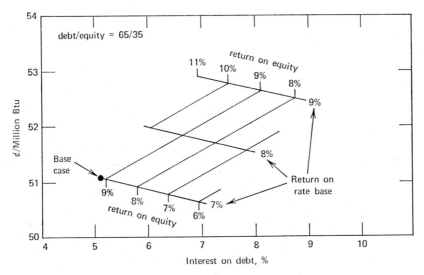

Fig. 1.   Effect of financial factors on price of pipeline gas from coal via IGT Hygas (Institute of Gas Technology) process.

ments in mining techniques, shutdown of uneconomical mines, and substantial reductions in transportation costs.   These factors should continue to counter many of the inflationary pressures in the long run, in spite of the renewed upward trend of coal prices in the late 1960s and in 1970 under the impact of rapidly expanding electric-power demands, coupled with a slowdown in nuclear-plant construction, and of new coal-mine safety legislation.

Although the recoverable oil-shale resources are capable of providing at least 4000 trillion ft^3 of natural-gas equivalent, oil-shale-based processes do not appear to have prospects that are quite as good as those of coal-based processes (10).   However, technologic progress may bring synthetic pipeline gas from shale oil into competition.

Cost Estimates for Synthetic Pipeline Gas from Coal.   The recent advances in synthetic pipeline gas technology can best be demonstrated by decreases in the price estimates for gas produced from coal.   For example, estimates made in 1960 for 90–100 million ft^3 per day plants operating at 90% load factor and utilizing $4/ton bituminous coal, ranged from $1 to $1.10 per million Btu (11,12).   Estimates made in the late 1960s, and based on 250 million ft^3 per day plants utilizing new technology were mostly in the 50 cents per million Btu range (13,14).   These synthetic gas prices are 20-yr averages.   They are computed by an accounting procedure developed by the General Accounting Committee of the American Gas Association and will be used throughout this article to maintain consistency with earlier published values.   This procedure is based on the financing of utility-gas plants at 65% debt and 35% equity.   Straight-line depreciation is assumed over a 20-yr period.   Interest charged is 5% of the outstanding debt.   A 7% return on undepreciated fixed investment is assumed.   The 20-yr average capital charge composed of federal income tax, debt, and net income amounts to about 5.8%.   State and local taxes and insurance are taken at 3% and annual depreciation at 5%.   It was felt at the time this procedure was devised that these financial arrangements best fit the needs of a regulated utility which would be engaged in this gas-manufacturing activity.

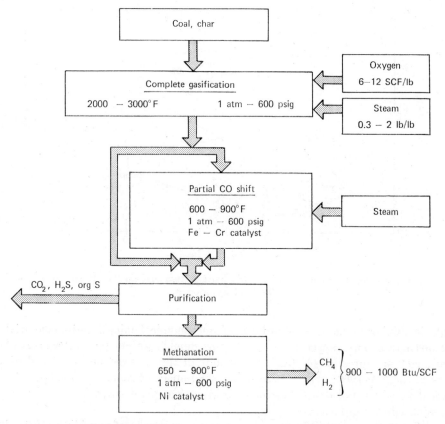

Fig. 2. Schematic diagram of conventional processes for production of pipeline gas from coal by catalytic methanation of synthesis gas.

Higher interest rates and returns on investment corresponding to the levels which prevailed in the late 1960s and in 1970 would have only a minor effect on the prices computed by this method. This is illustrated in Figure 1 with the cost estimate for the IGT Hygas process (13). It can be seen that increases to 7.5% interest on debt and to 9% return on rate base (corresponding to 10% average return on equity) would increase the gas price less than 2 cents per million Btu.

Basic Process Considerations for Synthetic Pipeline-Gas Manufacture. The conversion of coal to pipeline gas is explained most readily in terms of the composition of the raw material and the product. A typical bituminous coal contains 75% carbon, 5% hydrogen, and about 20% of undesirable constituents, mostly ash and sulfur, which must be removed or discarded in the course of processing. In contrast, natural gas or methane contains 75% carbon, 25% hydrogen, and only negligible quantities of undesirable constituents. So, to convert coal to pipeline gas, one must either add a lot of hydrogen or reject a lot of carbon. The most efficient way is to add hydrogen.

There are two basic methods for adding hydrogen to coal with many variants of each (15). In one, coal is reacted with steam to form synthesis gas, hydrogen, and carbon monoxide, which are then recombined over a nickel catalyst to produce methane. The reaction of coal and steam, typified by $C + H_2O \rightarrow H_2 + CO$, is highly endothermic and requires very high temperatures to proceed at practical rates, whereas

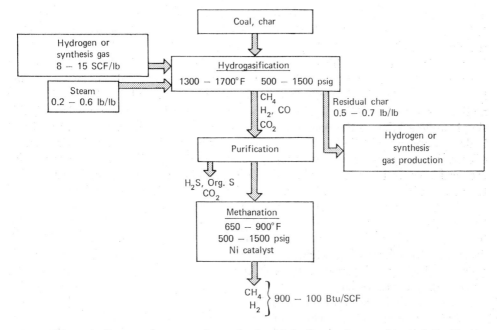

Fig. 3. Schematic diagram of processes for production of pipeline gas from coal by hydrogasification.

the synthesis reaction, typified by $CO + 3\,H_2 \rightarrow CH_4 + H_2O$, is quite exothermic and must be conducted at relatively low temperatures to obtain high methane yields. Because of this, the process is thermally quite inefficient. In a practical system such as that shown in Figure 2, the overall plant thermal efficiency is on the order of 50–55%, although ideally with maximum heat recovery, it could be 75% (15).

The first step of this process, synthesis-gas production, has been traditionally accomplished by the use of oxygen to provide the endothermic heat of reaction for steam decomposition by partial combustion of the coal. The various conventional methods are described under Gas, manufactured, Vol. 10. Oxygen rather than air must be used in synthesis-gas manufacture to avoid dilution of the product gas with nitrogen and to achieve the high temperatures required for efficient operation. Prior to methanation, part of the synthesis gas is subjected to carbon monoxide shift, $CO + H_2O \rightarrow CO_2 + H_2$, over one of the many commercial catalysts, usually of iron–chromia composition. This adjusts the hydrogen–carbon monoxide mol ratio to 3:1, the preferred composition for carrying out the methanation reaction. Any excess oxygen introduced into the overall process, both in the gasification step and the subsequent carbon monoxide shift step, is rejected as carbon dioxide. Thus, the carbon dioxide formation during the total process represents, in effect, a measure of its inefficiency.

As will be discussed below, the synthesis-gas-manufacturing step is also an integral part of other methods for pipeline-gas production. Consequently, many of the new developments in synthetic pipeline-gas technology deal with the reduction or elimination of oxygen requirements for synthesis-gas manufacture in view of the high capital costs of this mode of operation (14).

The other basic method of adding hydrogen to coal is destructive hydrogenation at pressure to form methane directly. Nearly complete conversion of lignite and bituminous coals to methane is possible at sufficiently high hydrogen partial pressures and reaction times, but this is not practical or necessary from a process standpoint (15). It is advantageous to gasify only the more reactive fractions of the coal and use the less reactive residual char for hydrogen production. This is the original concept of the *hydrogasification process*, which has an ideal thermal efficiency of about 90%, because it operates at least in part at much lower temperature levels and employs methane-forming reactions of relatively low exothermicity, compared to the synthesis-gas methanation process (15). Again, in practice, compromises must be made with this simple approach, since the reactions between the more reactive portions of coal and hydrogen are so rapid that even with their lower overall heat release they cannot be effectively moderated by indirect cooling. As in catalytic methanation, the reason for the need to control temperature in hydrogasification is thermodynamic; lower reaction temperature increases the equilibrium yield of methane, as does higher pressure (15).

As shown schematically in Figure 3, a practical way to conduct the hydrogasification step is by adding steam, as well as hydrogen, to the reactor. The steam acts as a temperature moderator in that, as the temperature rises above a level of 1500°F, it will decompose to an increasing extent, thereby absorbing heat. Of equal importance, this generates hydrogen internally, thereby reducing external hydrogen requirements. Since hydrogen generation represents a substantial portion of the process costs, this constitutes a significant improvement (14).

Another practical modification of the simple hydrogasification concept has been the substitution of raw synthesis gas for relatively pure hydrogen because of the high cost of purifying synthesis gas, both in terms of chemical processing and the thermal inefficiencies involved. The resulting cost benefits outweigh the higher costs caused by the corresponding decrease in hydrogen partial pressure. With the addition of steam to the hydrogasification step, carbon oxides, as well as methane, are formed. The use of synthesis gas as the source of hydrogen further adds to the carbon oxide content of product gas. Thus, the modified hydrogasification process no longer produces pipeline-quality gas directly, but a mixture of methane, carbon oxides, and unreacted hydrogen. Therefore, it resembles the classic synthesis-gas methanation process in that it requires a catalytic methanation step to produce pipeline-quality gas. It differs primarily in the amount of methane formed by catalytic methanation, normally only one-third of the total, the remainder being formed directly by reaction of hydrogen and coal. Even with this hybrid mode of operation, the hydrogasification process, employing one of the several practical schemes for hydrogen-rich gas production from residual char, has an overall plant thermal efficiency of 65–70%, compared to 50–55% for the traditional synthesis-gas methanation process.

In all of the processes for production of synthetic pipeline gas from coal, the raw gas contains not only carbon dioxide as an undesirable constituent, but also substantial amounts of hydrogen sulfide, ammonia, and benzene, and lesser amounts of organic sulfur compounds, such as carbon oxysulfide and carbon disulfide. The sulfur compounds must be reduced to extremely low concentrations prior to methanation since they poison the very active nickel catalysts used in this step (17). It is also convenient to remove carbon dioxide prior to methanation since most commercial gas-purification processes remove the "acid gas," ie carbon dioxide and hydrogen sulfide, simultaneously (18,19). A typical purification scheme would comprise hot potassium carbonate scrubbing for carbon dioxide and hydrogen sulfide removal, followed by passage through fixed beds of hot alkalized iron or hot zinc oxide to remove any remaining hydrogen sulfide and a portion of the organic sulfur compounds, water scrubbing for

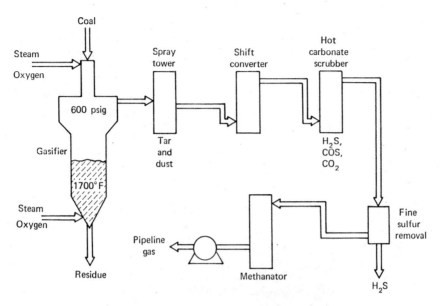

Fig. 4. Bureau of Mines gasification-methanation process.

removal of ammonia and, finally, passage through activated carbon to remove any remaining traces of organic sulfur and benzene. Elemental sulfur can be recovered from the acid gas stream by the Claus process. Since, in all synthetic pipeline-gas processes, most of the sulfur in the coal is converted to hydrogen sulfide, its recovery in elemental form will result in a substantial by-product credit (20).

Process Requirements and Economics. Synthesis gas methanation is the older of the two classical synthetic pipeline-gas processes. It has been demonstrated on a pilot-plant scale in the U.S. by the Institute of Gas Technology under sponsorship of the American Gas Association (17) and by the Bureau of Mines (21), as well as in Great Britain by the former Gas Research Board (22). Many components of this process have been used commercially in the closely related manufacture of synthetic liquid fuels. Unfortunately, most recent economic evaluations of this process in its traditional form (ie, production of synthesis gas in one of the conventional fixed-bed or suspension-phase processes, followed by carbon monoxide shift, purification, and synthesis gas methanation over fixed- or fluid-bed nickel catalyst), have shown that gas prices based on the accounting procedure described above would be about $1 per million Btu for a 90–100 million ft³ per day base-load plant using bituminous coal that costs $4 per ton (11,12). Investment costs for such relatively small plants would be on the order of $100 million, roughly the same as for 250 million ft³ per day hydrogasification plants (13,14). The reasons for these high costs have been primarily the conventional methods of synthesis-gas manufacture. With the suspension gasification process, for example, about 4500 tons of oxygen per day would be required for a 90–100 million ft³ per day synthetic pipeline-gas plant because all of the coal is first gasified to carbon oxides and hydrogen without any attempt to produce methane directly. With fixed-bed Lurgi-type gasifiers only about 2300 tons of oxygen per day would be needed because of the countercurrent contact between hot, hydrogen-rich synthesis gas and coal. As a result, some of the coal is gasified directly to methane by simple destructive distillation (coking) and destructive hydrogenation (hydrogasification). There is also

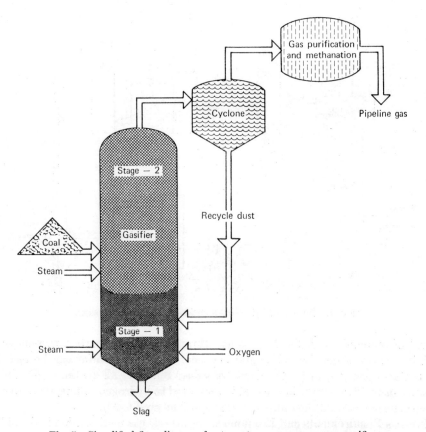

Fig. 5. Simplified flow diagram for two-stage super-pressure gasifier.

some recovery of sensible heat from the hot product gases before they leave the reactor. However, the gains resulting from lower oxygen consumption and higher thermal efficiency are offset by higher investment costs due to the limited capacity, and the complex coal-feeding and ash-removal systems, typical of fixed-bed gasifiers. Further, in such fixed-bed gasifiers, most U.S. coals will tend to cake so that a costly and thermally inefficient pretreatment step would be required.

It is for these reasons that the new approaches to synthesis-gas methanation attempt to minimize oxygen consumption and increase thermal efficiency, while avoiding costly pretreatment, as well as the need for a large number of small gasifiers. The Bureau of Mines, for example, is developing a combination free-fall, fluid-bed gasification step operating at pressures up to 600 psig and at a relatively low maximum temperature of 1700°F (Fig. 4) (23,24). At these conditions, oxygen consumption is reduced, reportedly 5000 tons per day for a 250 million ft³ per day plant, and about half of the total methane needed for pipeline gas manufacture is produced in the gasification step.

Another embodiment of the synthesis-gas methanation approach, the *Two-stage Super-pressure process*, is being developed by Bituminous Coal Research, Inc., with support from the Office of Coal Research (OCR) of the U.S. Department of the Interior (25,26). Again, the principal feature of this process is the direct production of methane from coal at pressures of 1000 psig or higher in substantially higher yields than achiev-

Table 2. Costs of Synthetic Pipeline Gas From Coal (13) (90% Plant Operating Factor)

Operating conditions and costs	Hydrogasification (Raw synthesis gas, Texaco-type steam–oxygen gasification)	CO₂ Acceptor (Internal)	Fuel Gas Assoc. (Steam-iron process)	Electrothermal gasification	Hygas
Process:					
Hydrogen source:					
product gas					
million ft³/day	270	250	266	275	523
heating value, Btu/scf	955	948	941	937	954
pressure, psig	1,000	1,000	1,000	1,000	1,000
purchased raw materials and utilities					
bituminous coal ($4/ton), ton/day	17,790[a]	26,760[b]	17,790[a]	17,790[a]	55,640[c]
lignite ($1.50/ton), ton/day		592			
dolomite ($5.27/ton), ton/day					
iron ore ($20/ton), ton/day			20.5		
electric power (3 mill/kWh), kW	118,900	5,120[d]		355,600	
generated-on-site raw materials and utilities					
oxygen, ton/day	4,280				
electric power, kW		250,900	46,200	63,400	873,000[e]
shaft power, hp			180,000		
by-products					
char(at fuel value), ton/day	2,540			4,160	
oil (25¢/million Btu), bbl/day					10,000
benzol (15¢/gal), bbl/day					2,230
low Btu gas (10¢/million Btu), billion Btu/day			81		
electric power (3 mill/kWh), kW				126,600	
total credits[f], ¢/million Btu product gas	6.5	83.4	5.8	8.3	7.9
total capital investment, $ million	106.7		105.3	93.2	235.2
pipeline-gas price, 20-yr av, ¢/million Btu	50	41[g]	48	51	37

[a] 4.4% sulfur; 12,390 Btu/lb.
[b] 6,613 Btu/lb.
[c] 7,345 Btu/lb.
[d] 4.5 mill/kWh.
[e] On-site electric-power production by MHD generator.
[f] Including char fines at fuel value and sulfur at $20/long ton less recovery costs.
[g] Published value of 39.7¢/million Btu (30) corrected from 95 to 90% operating factor and for omission of interest during construction (14).

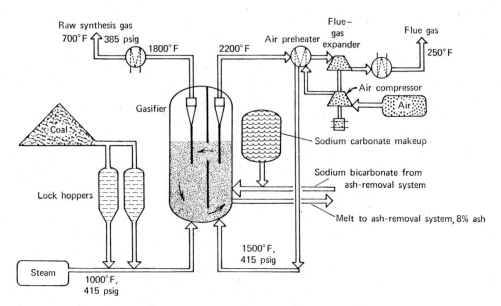

Fig. 6. Simplified flow sheet for the Kellogg gasification process.

able in conventional steam–oxygen gasifiers. As shown in Figure 5, this is accomplished by introducing coal and steam directly into a rising column of hot synthesis gas produced in the lower section of a gasifier by the slagging gasification of recycle char with oxygen and steam at temperatures of 2500°F or higher. In the upper section (stage 2) of the gasifier, the volatile portion of the fresh coal is converted directly to methane at temperatures of 1700–1800°F; the unconverted coal is swept out of the gasifier in the product-gas stream into a cyclone where it is separated for recycling to the lower section (stage 1). The raw gases leaving the cyclone are subsequently purified and subjected to methanation.

A preliminary cost estimate for the Two-stage Super-pressure process using the standardized procedure described above, and based on a 250 million ft³ per day plant with a 90% operating factor gave a gas price of 56 cents per million Btu with a $4 per ton (14.8 cents per million Btu) bituminous coal (14). This would increase to 58 cents if the cost of the coal were 16.1 cents per million Btu, similar to that used as the basis for the cost estimates of other processes summarized in Table 2. Coal requirements for this case were 11,420 ton per day and oxygen requirements a relatively low 5020 ton per day. The total capital investment for such a plant, including oxygen generation, was estimated at $142 million.

Another new process for synthesis gas production which has been under development with funds provided by the OCR is the *Kellogg gasification (molten salt) process* (27–29). The development work, dormant in the late 1960s because of lack of funds, was resumed under private sponsorship in 1970. In this process, shown in Figure 6 finely ground coal feed enters one of two lock hoppers (one discharges while the other fills) where it is pressurized with an inert gas or compressed synthesis gas. Coal is withdrawn continuously into steam (1000°F, 415 psig) and the stream injected into the gasifier. Molten salt (sodium carbonate) provides the heat for production of synthesis gas, and possibly catalyzes the reaction. In the gasifier configuration shown, a vertical partition perforated below the liquid level separates the synthesis-gas section from the

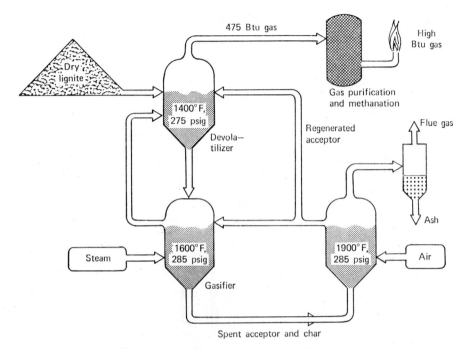

Fig. 7. Flow diagram for the Consolidation Coal Co., CO_2-acceptor process.

heating section. A difference in degree of aeration causes the molten salt to circulate between the two sections. In the heating section, flue gas, formed by combustion of unreacted coal with air, reheats the salt directly. The flue gas leaves the molten salt at about 2200°F and 390 psig and, after separation of entrained molten salt, flows in series through the air preheater and an expander which provides most of the power needed for air compression. Synthesis gas, leaving the gasifier at 1800°F and 385 psig, flows through a heat exchanger and is then available for further processing by methanation into pipeline gas.

Another process which eliminates the need for oxygen in the production of synthesis gas and which provides for contacting of raw coal and hydrogen-rich synthesis gas to form a substantial portion of the methane directly is Consolidation Coal Company's *CO_2 acceptor process* (30–32). In 1969, ground was broken for a large pilot plant for commercial development of this process which will have a capacity of 1 ton/hr (moisture and ashfree basis) of Dakota lignite. This development program is again supported by the OCR. A flow diagram of the process is shown in Figure 7.

In this process, the heat source for the steam–coal reaction is hot, calcined dolomite or limestone (the acceptor). The acceptor also releases additional heat when the calcium oxide constituting its active component forms calcium carbonate by combining with the carbon dioxide evolved in the steam–carbon and carbon monoxide shift reactions taking place in the gasifier. The spent acceptor is continuously regenerated by reconverting the calcium carbonate to calcium oxide and carbon dioxide, utilizing residual carbon from the gasification step to supply the necessary heat by combustion with air. The driving force for regeneration is provided by the higher temperature and lower carbon dioxide partial pressure in the regenerator. Dolomite is preferred to limestone as an acceptor because of its superior ability to withstand physical decrepita-

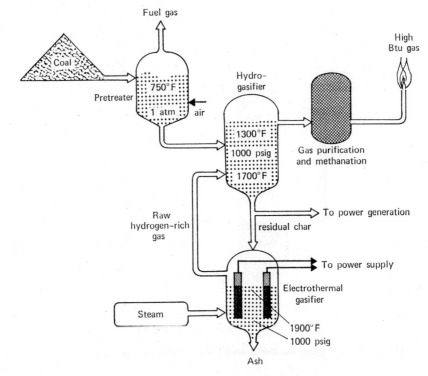

Fig. 8. Flow diagram for the IGT Hygas process.

tion and chemical deactivation in cycling through the process. The CO_2 acceptor process is designed primarily for lignite, which is much more reactive than bituminous coal and, in the U.S., costs approx one-third less per unit of heat energy content. It is also applicable to the more reactive subbituminous coals which are in abundant supply in the western parts of the U.S. In Table 2, the economics and material and utility requirements of the CO_2 acceptor process are compared with several of the hydrogasification processes discussed below (13).

It is of interest to note that in the Kellogg molten salt process and the CO_2 acceptor process the heat source materials will react with the hydrogen sulfide formed from the sulfur content of the coal in the course of gasification. This requires that the regeneration conditions for these two processes must be designed to allow for sulfur removal from the heat-source materials.

The hydrogasification process also has undergone a long period of development, beginning with Dent's first fixed-bed experiments in Great Britain in 1937–1938 (33,34). Since then, this work was carried on, with several interruptions, by the British Gas Research Board and Ths Gas Council until its final termination in 1967–1968 (35). A major pilot-plant program was conducted by the Commonwealth Scientific and Industrial Research Organization on fluid-bed hydrogasification of Australian coals, but was terminated in 1968 (36). In the U.S., the Bureau of Mines has maintained a continuous effort on a laboratory scale since the 1950s (37). The largest effort has been carried forward by the Institute of Gas Technology, first under sole sponsorship of the American Gas Association and, since 1964, under joint sponsorship with the OCR (11,12,38–40).

As a result, the most advanced version of the hydrogasification process is the *Hygas process* of the Institute of Gas Technology (41,42). Construction of a pilot plant capable of producing 1.5 million ft³ per day of synthetic pipeline gas from bituminous coal was completed in 1970. The nominal coal-feed rate is 3 ton/hr. As shown in Figure 8, in this process, pulverized and pretreated bituminous coal is reacted at 1300–1700°F and a typical pressure of 1000 psig with hot, raw hydrogen-rich gas containing a substantial amount of steam. Pretreatment is deemed necessary for most bituminous coals because they tend to agglomerate during hydrogasification. It consists of mild surface oxidation of the pulverized coal with air in a fluid-bed reactor at about 750°F and atmospheric pressure. Although under these conditions most of the valuable reactive portion ("volatile matter") of the coal is preserved, the pretreatment step still generates a substantial volume of a low heating value (on the order of 50 Btu per standard ft³) fuel gas, containing as much as 25% of the sulfur content of the coal in the form of sulfur dioxide. Small amounts of tar and light oil are also formed. Lignite normally does not require pretreatment. Efforts are under way to eliminate this step, even with agglomerating bituminous coals, to avoid the resulting losses in thermal efficiency of the process. Specially designed contacting methods between raw coal and hot, hydrogen-rich gas are being investigated for this purpose.

The hydrogasification reactor of the Hygas-process pilot plant has three separate stages: a fluidized preheat stage in which the unreacted residual char gives up its heat to the incoming reaction gas; a fluidized-bed gasification stage in which a portion of the less reactive coal constituents is converted to methane and carbon oxides by hydrogen and steam reactions; and a dilute-phase stage in which the most reactive coal constituents are converted to methane by hydrogenolysis reactions.

Approximately half of the pretreated coal is converted in the hydrogasifier to form about 65% of the methane, with the remainder being formed in a fixed-bed catalytic methanation step. To produce the hydrogen-rich gas, part of the residual char from the hydrogasification reactor is gasified at process pressure with superheated steam in a fluidized bed heated to approximately 1900°F by passing an electric current through it. In a commercial plant, the remaining residual char would probably go to power generation.

Resistance heating of fluidized beds in so-called electrothermal or electrofluid reactors has recently been investigated for a variety of potential uses in chemical manufacturing and metallurgical processes (43). Such a reactor has been used commercially for production of hydrocyanic acid in a coke bed fluidized with ammonia and a hydrocarbon gas. In the application to the Hygas process (44), concentric electrodes are used, with the center electrode preferably constructed from stainless steel. The reactor wall serves as the outer electrode. Nominal current density at the center electrode is 3A/in². and power consumption is on the order of 30 kWh per thousand ft³ of hydrogen plus carbon monoxide produced. Direct current allows better control than alternating current.

Material and utility requirements and process economics for the Hygas process are summarized in Table 2 for a typical operation with bituminous coal and lignite and employing electrothermal gasification as the hydrogen source. The sensitivity of the gas price to power cost is about 3 cents per million Btu for every 1 mill per kWh, so that this hydrogen source will be favored when low-cost power is available. Oxygen-based hydrogen sources are one alternative. For example, also shown in Table 2 are data for hydrogasification of bituminous coal when raw synthesis gas from a Texaco-

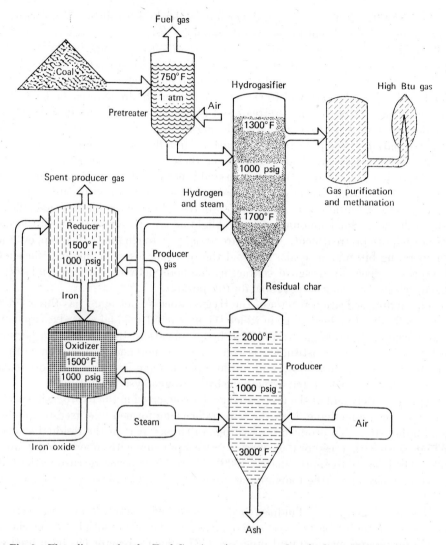

Fuel gas

Coal

Pretreater
750°F
1 atm
Air

Hydrogasifier

High Btu gas

1300°F

1000 psig

Gas purification
and methanation

Spent producer gas

Hydrogen
and steam

Reducer
1500°F
1000 psig

1700°F

Producer
gas

Iron

Residual char

Oxidizer
1500°F
1000 psig

2000°F

Producer

1000 psig

Steam

Air

Iron oxide

3000°F

Ash

Fig. 9. Flow diagram for the Fuel Gas Associates steam- iron hydrogasification process.

type steam–oxygen suspension gasifier (see Gas, manufactured) is used as the hydro-gen-rich gas (45).   The gas price is equivalent to the electrothermal gasification case with 3 mill power since the oxygen requirements are quite low compared to conventional gasification–methanation schemes which lack a hydrogasification stage in which the major portion of the methane is formed directly.   Efforts are also under way to replace the high-temperature (2500–3000°F), suspension-phase Texaco-type gasifier, with a dense-phase, fluid-bed gasifier operating at 1900°F or less and at the nominal 1000-psig gasification pressure.   Under these conditions, oxygen requirements should drop sharply, in part due to the formation of substantial amounts of methane, although the required reactor volume would increase considerably (46).

Finally, another version of the hydrogasification process has been under development by a group of industrial firms identified as Fuel Gas Associates (FAG).   This process, known as the *steam-iron hydrogasification process*, is shown in Figure 9 and

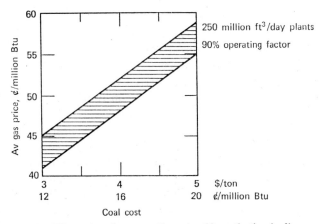

Fig. 10. Effect of coal cost on the price of synthetic pipeline gas.

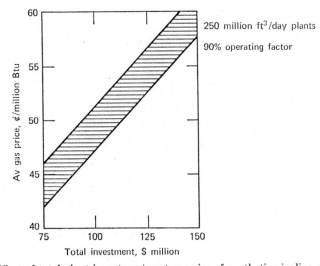

Fig. 11. Effect of total plant investment cost on price of synthetic pipeline gas from coal.

utilizes a hot hydrogen–steam mixture produced in a continuous, high-pressure steam–iron reactor (47,48).   In this improvement over the conventional steam–iron process for hydrogen production (49,50), a stream of iron ore is first partially reduced with producer gas and then partially reoxidized by decomposition of steam.   The resulting hydrogen and unreacted steam provide the feed gas to the hydrogasifier.   The reducing gas is generated by a high-pressure producer from residual char from the hydrogasifier. Typical operating conditions for the steam–iron portion of the process are:

1400–1500°F,
1000–1200 psig,
50% steam decomposition, and
60% producer gas utilization.

The spent producer gas contains about 15% of the heating value of the coal feed to the process, as well as a large amount of mechanical energy which must be recovered in expansion turbines to make the process economical.

The steam-iron process has apparently been developed further to eliminate the need for the separate hydrogasification and producer-gas stages shown in Figure 9 (51). In the modified process, coal is fed directly into the oxidizer where the steam decomposition and hydrogasification reactions occur simultaneously. The mixture of oxidized iron solids and residual char is then transferred to the reducer where generation of producer gas from char and air occurs simultaneously with the reduction of the iron oxides. In addition to reducing the number of reactor vessels required, the patented modified process is also credited with several other advantages which contribute to its higher thermal efficiency. These are the following: elimination of the need for coal pretreatment by virtue of the diluent effect of the circulating iron solids; utilization of the exothermicity of the iron-oxidation and coal-hydrogasification reactions in the oxidizer to support the endothermic steam–carbon reaction; decrease in the quantity of spent producer gas because the char in the reducer converts some of the carbon dioxide formed back into carbon monoxide.

In summary, at 90% operating factor and with $4 per ton bituminous coal, 250 million ft³ per day capacity plants embodying the various versions of the hydrogasification process shown in Table 2 could all produce synthetic pipeline gas at a 20-yr average price of about 50 cents per million Btu on the basis of cost estimates made in the late 1960s. Other process schemes, such as those employing gasification with steam and oxygen without a step that maximizes direct formation of methane via coal hydrogenolysis reactions, generally yield gas-price estimates on the order of 5 to 10 cents per million Btu higher (14). This is also true of hydrogasification schemes in which the raw hydrogen-rich (synthesis) gas is first processed into a relatively high-purity hydrogen stream. With lignite, because of its much lower cost, both the CO_2 acceptor and the hydrogasification processes give synthetic gas prices on the order of 40 cents per million Btu.

The price sensitivity of most synthetic-pipeline-gas processes to coal and investment costs is shown in Figures 10 and 11. Generally, an increase in costs of $1 per ton of bituminoug coal is reflected in an increase of 7 cents per million Btu in gas price. Similarly, an increase of $10 million in total investment is reflected in an increase of 2 cents per million Btu.

Several other new developments in coal gasification are summarized in references 25, 35, and 52.

Bibliography

1. "Report on Natural Gas Reserves and Production," *Am. Gas. Assoc. Montly 52* (5), 4–7 (1970).
2. H. R. Linden, "Current Trends in U.S. Gas Demand and Supply," *Public Utilities Fortnightly* **86** (3), 27–38 (1970).
3. "LNG: A Sulfur-Free Fuel for Power Generation," *Institute of Gas Technology, Final Report, PHS Contract No. PH 22-68-58*, National Center for Air Pollution Control, Public Health Service, Washington, D.C., 1969; available as *PB 184,353*, Clearinghouse Fed. Sci. Tech. Inform., Springfield, Va. 1969.
4. *Reserves of Crude Oil, Natural Gas Liquids, and Natural Gas in the United States and Canada as of December 31, 1968*, Vol. 23, Published jointly by American Gas Association, Inc., American Petroleum Institute, and Canadian Petroleum Association, 1969.
5. "Potential Supply of Natural Gas in the United States (as of December 31, 1968)." Prepared by Potential Gas Committee. Sponsored by Potential Gas Agency, Mineral Resources Institute, Colorado School of Mines Foundation, Inc., Golden, Colorado, October 1969.
6. T. A. Hendricks, "Resources of Oil, Gas, and Natural Gas Liquids in the United States and the World," *U.S. Geol. Surv. Circ.* **522** (1965).

7. S. P. Schweinfurth, Branch of Organic Fuel and Chemical Resources, U.S. Geological Survey, private communication, October 24, 1969.
8. D. C. Duncan and V. E. Swanson "Organic Rich Shale of the United States and the World Land Areas," *U.S. Geol. Surv. Circ.* **523** (1965).
9. P. Averitt, "Coal Resources of the United States, January 1, 1967," *U.S. Geol. Survey Bull.* **1275** (1969).
10. H. F. Feldmann, W. G. Bair, H. L. Feldkirchner, C. L. Tsaros, E. B. Shultz, Jr., J. Huebler, and H. R. Linden, "Production of Pipeline Gas by Hydrogasification of Oil Shale," *Inst. Gas Technol. Res. Bull.* **36** 1966.
11. H. R. Linden, "Pipeline Gas from Coal: Status and Future Prospects," *Coal Age* **71** (1), 64–71 (1966).
12. H. R. Linden, "Coal Gasification. . . And Natural Gas," *Am. Gas J.* **194** (5), 19–25 (1967).
13. H. R. Linden, "Coal Gasification and the Coal Mining Industry," *Trans. AIME* **244** (4), 417–426 (1969).
14. C. L. Tsaros and T. J. Joyce, "Comparative Economics of Pipeline Gas from Coal Processes," *Proc. 2nd Synthetic Pipeline Gas Symp., Pittsburgh, Pa., November 22, 1968*, Am. Gas Association, New York, 1969, pp. 131–148.
15. H. R. Linden, "Conversion of Solid Fossil Fuels to High-Heating-Value Pipeline Gas," *Chem. Eng. Progr. Symp. Ser.* **61** (54), 75–102 (1965).
16. M. A. Elliott and H. R. Linden, "Gas, manufactured," in A. Standen, ed., *Encyclopedia of Chemical Technology*, 2nd ed., Vol. 10, Interscience Publishers, a div. of John Wiley & Sons, Inc., New York, 1966, pp. 353–442.
17. H. A. Dirksen and H. R. Linden, "Pipeline Gas from Coal by Methanation of Synthesis Gas," *Inst. Gas Technol. Res. Bull.* **31** (1963).
18. G. Nonhebel, ed., *Gas Purification Processes*, George Newnes Ltd., London, 1964.
19. A. L. Kohl and F. C. Riesenfeld, *Gas Purification*, McGraw-Hill Book Co., Inc., New York, 1960.
20. C. L. Tsaros, J. L. Arora, and W. Bodle, "Sulfur Recovery in the Manufacture of Pipeline Gas from Coal," *Am. Chem. Soc. Div., Fuel. Chem. Preprints* **13** (4), 252–269 (1969).
21. J. H. Field, A. J. Forney, and R. J. Demski, "Pilot Plant Development of the Hot-Gas-Recycle Process for the Synthesis of High-Btu Gas," *U.S. Bur. Mines, Rept. Invest.* **5811** (1961).
22. F. J. Dent and D. Hebden, *Catalytic Synthesis of Methane. Experimental Work at the Fuel Research Station*, Commun. GRB 21/11, Gas Research Board London, 1948.
23. A. J. Forney, R. F. Kenny, and J. H. Field, "Gasification of Caking Coal in a Free-Fall, Fluid-Bed Reactor," *Am. Chem. Soc. Div. Fuel Chem. Preprints* **11** (4), 322–328 (1967); "Fluid-Bed Gasification of Pittsburgh Seam Coal with Oxygen and with Air," *ibid.*, **12** (3), 32–42 (1968).
24. A. J. Forney, Sidney Katell, and William L. Crentz, "High-Btu Gas from Coal via Gasification and Catalytic Methanation." Unpublished manuscript, Bureau of Mines, U.S. Department of the Interior, Washington, D.C., 1970. Summarized as *Tech. Progr. Rept.* **24** (April 1970).
25. "Gas Generator Research and Development, Survey and Evaluation," *Bituminous Coal Res. Rept. No. L-156*, to Office of Coal Research, *RD Rept. No. 20*, U.S. Govt. Print. Office, Washington, D.C., 1965.
26. R. A. Glenn and R. J. Grace, "An Internally-Fired Process Development Unit for Gasification of Coal Under Conditions Simulating Stage Two of the BCR Two-Stage Super-Pressure Process," *Proc. 2nd Synthetic Pipeline Gas Symp., Pittsburgh, Pa., November 22, 1968*, American Gas Association, New York, 1969, pp. 21–39.
27. G. T. Skaperdas, "The Kellogg Coal Gasification Process," *Proc. 1st Synthetic Pipeline Gas Symp., Pittsburgh, Pa., November 15, 1966*, American Gas Association, New York, 1966, pp. 95–103.
28. P. A. Lefrancois, K. M. Barclay, and G. T. Skaperdas, "Bench-Scale Studies of the Kellogg Coal Gasification Process," *Advan. Chem. Ser.* **69**, 64–80 (1967).
29. "Commercial Potential for the Kellogg Coal Gasification Process," The M. W. Kellogg Co., Final Report to Office of Coal Research, R & D Rept. No. 38, Washington, D.C., 1967; available as *PB-180,358*, Clearinghouse Fed. Sci. Tech. Inform., Springfield, Va., 1967.
30. *Pipeline Gas from Lignite Gasification—A Feasibility Study*, Consolidation Coal Co., Res. Div. Rept. No. R-1, to Office of Coal Research, R&D Rept. No. 16, Washington, D.C., 1965; available as *PB-166,817* and *PB-166,818*, Clearinghouse Fed. Sci. Tech. Inform., Springfield, Va., 1965.

31. J. A. Phinney, "The CO₂ Acceptor Process—A Status Report," *Proc. 1st Synthetic Pipeline Gas Symp., Pittsburgh, Pa., November 15, 1966*, 35–42. American Gas Association, New York, 1966, pp. 35–42.

32. G. P. Curran, C. E. Fink, and E. Gorin, "CO₂ Acceptor Process—Studies of Acceptor Properties," *Advan. Chem. Ser.* **69**, 141–165 (1967).

33. J. W. Wood, F. J. Dent, W. H. Blackburn, A. M. Eastwood, and H. C. Millett, "41st Report of the Joint Research Committee, The Investigation of the Use of Oxygen and High Pressure in Gasification—Part II, Synthesis of Gaseous Hydrocarbons at High Pressure," *Inst. Gas. Engr. Publ. (London)* 167/56 (1937); *Trans. Inst. Gas Engrs.* **87**, 231–287 (1937–1938). *Gas J.* **220** (3886), 470, 473–475 (1937).

34. F. J. Dent, W. H. Blackburn, and H. C. Millett, "43rd Report of the Joint Research Committee, The Investigation of the Use of Oxygen and High Pressure in Gasification—Part III, Synthesis of Gaseous Hydrocarbons at High Pressure," *Inst. Gas Engr. Publ. (London)* 190/73 (1938); *Trans. Inst. Gas Engrs.* **88**, 150–217 (1938–1939); *Gas. J.* **224** (3938), 442–445 (1938).

35. "Report of the Committee on Production of Manufactured Gases," *10th International Gas Conference, Hamburg, 1967*, International Gas Union, Brussels, Belgium, 1967, pp. 18–32.

36. T. J. Birch, P. Casamento, N. C. Grave, and D. J. McCarthy, "Hydrogasification of Brown Coal Char in a 20 ft Continuous Fluidized Bed Reactor," *J. Inst. Fuel* **42** (336), 4–11 (1969).

37. P. S. Lewis, S. Friedman, and R. W. Hiteshue, "High B.t.u. Gas by the Direct Conversion of Coal," *Advan. Chem. Ser.* **69**, 50–63 (1967).

38. B. S. Lee, E. J. Pyrcioch, and F. C. Schora, Jr., "Hydrogasification of Pretreated Coal for Pipeline Gas Production," *Advan. Chem. Ser.* **69**, 104–127 (1967).

39. Frank C. Schora, Jr., "Present Status of the IGT Hydrogasification Process," *Proc. 2nd Synthetic Pipeline Gas Symp., Pittsburgh, Pa., November 22, 1968*, American Gas Association, New York, 1969, pp. 5–19.

40. F. C. Schora and B. S. Lee, "Hydrogasification Process," *AIChE Preprint No. 29b, 65th Natl. Meet., Am. Inst. Chem. Engs., Cleveland, 1969*.

41. S. J. Knabel and C. L. Tsaros, *Process Design and Cost Estimate for a 258 Billion Btu/Day Pipeline Gas Plant—Hydrogasification Using Synthesis Gas Generated by Electrothermal Gasification of Spent Char*, Office of Coal Research, R&D Rept. No. 22, Interim Rept. No. 3, Washington, D.C., 1967.

42. C. L. Tsaros, J. L. Arora, B. S. Lee, L. S. Pimentel, D. P. Olson, and F. C. Schora, *Cost Estimate of 500 Billion Btu/Day Pipeline Gas Plant Via Hydrogasification and Electrothermal Gasification of Lignite*, Office of Coal Research, R&D Rept. No. 22, Interim Rept. No. 4, Washington, D.C., 1968.

43. A. H. Pulsifer, T. M. Knowlton, and T. D. Wheelock, "Coal Char Gasification in an Electrofluid Reactor," *Ind. Eng. Chem. Process Design Develop. 8* (4), 539–545 (1969).

44. V. J. Kavlick, B. S. Lee, and F. C. Schora, "Electrothermal Coal Char Gasification," *Paper 3rd Joint Meet. Instituto de Ingenieros Quimicos de Puerto Rico and Am. Inst. Chem. Engrs. San Juan, 1970*.

45. C. L. Tsaros, S. J. Knabel, and L. A. Sheridan, *Process Design and Cost Estimate for Production of 265 Million SCF/Day of Pipeline Gas by the Hydrogasification of Bituminous Coal*, R&D Rept. No. 22, Interim Rept. No. 1, Office of Coal Research, Washington, D.C., 1965; available as *PB 176,982*, Clearinghouse Fed. Sci. Tech. Inform., Springfield, Va., 1965.

46. A. M. Squires, "Steam-Oxygen Gasification of Fine Sizes of Coal in a Fluidised Bed at Elevated Pressure; Part I. Reaction of Carbon with Hydrogen; Part II. Reaction of Carbon with Steam; Part III. Relation of Integral to Differential Rates." *Trans. Inst. Chem. Engrs. (London)* **39** (1), 3–27 (1961).

47. H. E. Benson, "Pipeline Gas from Coal by the Steam Iron Hydrogasification Route," *Proc. 1st Synthetic Pipeline Gas Symp., Pittsburgh, Pa., November 15, 1966*, American Gas Association, New York, 1966, pp. 25–34.

48. C. L. Tsaros, S. J. Knabel, and L. A. Sheridan, *Process Design and Cost Estimate for Production of 266 Million SCF/Day of Pipeline Gas by the Hydrogasification of Bituminous Coal–Hydrogen by the Steam-Iron Process*, Office of Coal Research, R&D Rept. No. 22, Interim Rept. No. 2, Washington, D.C., 1966; available as *PB 174,064*, Clearinghouse Fed. Sci. Tech. Inform., Springfield, Va., 1966.

49. U.S. Pat. 3,222,147 (December 7, 1965), Homer E. Benson (to Con-Gas Service Corp.).

50. U.S. Pat. 3,442,620 (May 6, 1969), J. Huebler, J. L. Johnson, F. C. Schora, Jr., and P. B. Tarman (to Consolidation Coal Co.).
51. U.S. Pat. 3,503,724 (March 31, 1970), Homer E. Benson (to Consolidation Coal Co.).
52. "Report of the Committee on Production of Manufactured Gases," *11th International Gas Conference, Moscow, 1970*, Inrernational Gas Union, Brussels, Belgium, pp. 17–59, 1970.

HENRY R. LINDEN
Institute of Gas Technology

POWER FROM COAL BY GASIFICATION AND MAGNETOHYDRODYNAMICS

Conventional generation of electric power involves motion of metallic conductors relative to a magnetic field. In recent years a new approach has attracted attention in which one utilizes the motion of a fluid-conducting medium in the magnetic field (1–4). This method, known as magnetohydrodynamics or MHD, was actually conceived in principle by Faraday one hundred and forty years ago (5). Faraday gave attention to liquid conductors. He made some experiments on the Waterloo Bridge over the River Thames, with immersed electrodes connected to a galvanometer. The river, flowing in the magnetic field of the earth, could conceivably produce an emf.

With a gaseous conducting medium one has first of all the problem of realizing adequate electrical conductivity at a reasonable temperature level. This matter is discussed in more detail below. A second feature related to use of a gas in the generator is that this medium may also serve as the principal working fluid of the thermal power cycle. It can be taken through a sequence of processes, for example, involving compression, heating, expansion, and cooling, as in the usual Brayton cycle. The MHD generator serves as the expander component, and corresponds to the turbine in a gas-turbine power loop. It is thus apparent that in the MHD power plant a great simplification can result; mechanical shaft work does not need to be produced as a part of the power-generation process. Only a relatively small amount of shaft work is required, namely that needed to drive the compressor.

A simplified diagram of an MHD generator is shown in Figure 1. We note that the gaseous medium flows in the x direction in the duct, that a transverse magnetic field is provided in the z direction, and that the induced electric field uB acts in the y direction. When the electrodes (in this case continuous electrodes are shown) are connected to an external load, current will be sent to the load; at the same time an electric field E is set up by the electrodes. We shall use mks units. Distances are in m, velocity u is in m/sec, magnetic induction B is in webers/m^2, or teslas, and E is in V/m. If d is the distance between electrodes the open-circuit voltage will be uBd. If σ is the electrical conductivity of the gas in ohm^{-1} m^{-1} and j is current density in A/m^2 we have the following relationship:

$$j = \sigma(uB - E) \tag{1}$$

The electric field relative to the moving gas is $(uB - E)$.

When the MHD generator is built into a power-plant system two arrangements may be considered. One is the closed system; the other is the open system. In the closed cycle, Figure 2, the gas is caused to flow continually in a closed loop. Heat would generally be supplied by a nuclear reactor. To realize good thermodynamic efficiency a recuperator is employed. In the open cycle, Figure 3, air is compressed

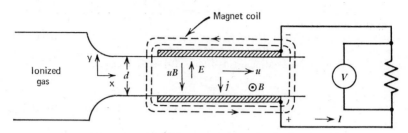

Fig. 1. Simple MHD generator. LEGEND: E = field due to electrodes; uB = induced field; V = Ed; j = current density (no Hall effect).

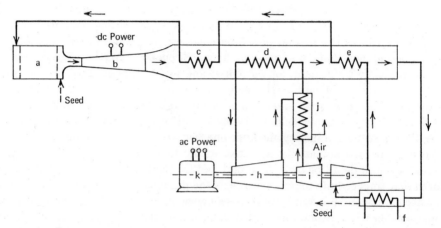

Fig. 2. Closed-cycle MHD system. LEGEND: a, nuclear reactor; b, MHD generator; c, high-temperature air heater; d, air heater; e, low-temperature heater; f, precooler; g, helium compressor; h, air turbine; i, air compressor; j, regenerator; k, ac generator.

and preheated and sent to a combustion chamber. The hot combustion products flow through the MHD generator and generate power. The hot gases then pass to the recuperator. In both the open and closed cycles it is generally advisable to recover as much of the waste heat as possible. For this purpose a "bottom plant" may be employed. Figures 2 and 3 show a hot-air turbine as bottom plant. This turbine also drives the main gas compressor. A steam-power unit can also be used as bottom plant.

Mention has been made of the necessity of achieving electrical conductivity in the working gas. This conductivity may be provided by seeding with a small percentage of an element of relatively low-ionization potential. Cesium at 3.89 eV and potassium at 4.34 eV are the elements of primary interest. In closed-cycle systems the pure element would be used for seeding; in the open cycle the alkali metal would be usually introduced in the form of the carbonate or sulfate. Special equipment must be used to recover and recycle the seed material.

Open-cycle MHD systems present less formidable problems than closed systems, since the latter require a very high temperature nuclear reactor. Engineering interest for earliest realization centers on the open system and consequently the balance of this discussion will be based on such a system. Fuel is burned to generate the working gaseous medium.

MHD power plants require use of a powerful magnet. A great step forward in recent years was realized with development of large superconducting magnets. The

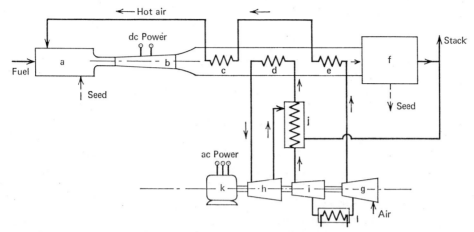

Fig. 3. Closed-cycle MHD system. LEGEND: a, combustor; b, MHD generator; c, high-temperature air heater; d, heater for air turbine; e, low-temperature air heater; f, gas cleaner; g, low-pressure air compressor; h, hot-air turbine; i, high-pressure compressor; j, regenerator; k, ac generator.

windings of such magnets preferably operate at the temperature of liquid helium. The necessary thermal insulation has been developed, and the refrigeration power requirements are a minute fraction of the total power generated.

Generator Fundamentals

The simple continuous electrode generator has been shown in Figure 1, and equation 1 gives the current density. In this case we are neglecting Hall effects in the generator. If we let $K = E/uB$ we can write as follows:

$$j = \sigma uB(1 - K) \tag{2}$$

The parameter K is called the generator coefficient, and it is a measure of the ratio of terminal voltage to open-circuit voltage, or emf, of the generator.

When current j flows at right angles to the magnetic field there is a Lorentz body force produced. This is the force that must be overcome in pushing the gas through the generator to generate power. The Lorentz force per unit volume in this case is jB, newtons/m³, and it acts in the upstream direction. From equation 1, the rate of doing work, per unit volume, against the Lorentz force can be formulated as follows:

$$juB = jE + j^2/\sigma \tag{3}$$

Therefore, the input work juB appears as electrical work jE and ohmic dissipation j^2/σ. The electrical efficiency η_e at a certain location in the generator duct is the ratio of electrical work to work done against the Lorentz forces. One notes that this efficiency is equal to K:

$$\eta_e = \frac{jE}{juB} = K \tag{4}$$

The power generated per unit volume in the generator, denoted P', is jE, or can be expressed as follows:

$$P' = \sigma u^2 B^2 K(1 - K) \tag{5}$$

We see that P' is maximum when $K = 0.5$:

$$P_{max}' = \sigma u^2 B^2 / 4 \qquad (6)$$

This simple formula will help one decide on the necessary level of electrical conductivity in an MHD generator. Thus, if we take $B = 5$ tesla (50000 gauss), $u = 800$ m/sec, $\sigma = 5$, we have $P' = 2 \times 10^7$ watts/m³. A generator of 20 MW would have 1-m³ internal volume. Though there are other factors that must be considered, this simple calculation indicates that average electrical conductivities in the gas of 5–10 ohm^{-1} m^{-1} can yield quite acceptable power densities. Fortunately, it turns out that such conductivities can be reached with gas temperatures of tolerable level, when we use modern materials and appropriate techniques of construction, and seed the gas with an alkali metal.

For a more accurate evaluation of the generator process, Hall effects must be considered (6,7). We may begin by setting down expressions for the conductivity and the electron current density in terms of electron density and charge:

$$\sigma = n_e \mu_e e \qquad (7)$$

$$\bar{j}_e = -n_e \bar{v}_e e \qquad (8)$$

Here, n_e is the number of electrons per m³, μ_e is electron mobility in m/sec per volt/m, and e is the electronic charge, 1.602×10^{-19} coulombs. Current density $\bar{j}_e$ and electron drift velocity $\bar{v}_e$ are written as vectors (barred symbols). The negative sign appears in equation 8 because current is generally regarded as a flux of positive charges while $\bar{v}_e$ is the velocity of negative (electron) charges.

The electric field relative to the moving gas is vectorially,

$$\bar{E} = \bar{E} + \bar{u}\bar{B} \qquad (9)$$

However, since the electrons move at velocity $\bar{v}_e$, we are also concerned with the field, designated $\bar{E}''$, experienced by the electrons in a reference frame moving relative to the gas at the drift velocity $\bar{v}_e$:

$$\bar{E}'' = \bar{E} + \bar{u}\bar{B} + \bar{v}_e\bar{B} \qquad (10)$$

The additional field $\bar{v}_e \times \bar{B}$ is termed the Hall field. The field $\bar{E}''$ is the field that, when multiplied by the electrical conductivity, gives the current density in the gas. In this way we obtain the electron-current equation in vector form including Hall effects:

$$\bar{j}_e = \sigma(\bar{E} + \bar{u}\bar{B} + \bar{v}_e\bar{B}) \qquad (11)$$

or

$$\bar{j}_e = \sigma(\bar{E} + \bar{u}\bar{B}) - \mu_e\bar{j}_e\bar{B} \qquad (12)$$

In a generator for which $u_x = u$, $u_y = u_z = 0$, $B_x = B_y = 0$, $B_z = B$, and $E_z = 0$, we can resolve equation 12 into the components j_{ex}, j_{ey}, and j_{ez} and obtain the following relationships:

$$\left. \begin{array}{l} j_{ex} = \dfrac{\sigma}{1 + \beta_e^2} \left\{ E_x - \beta_e(E_y - uB) \right\} \\[2mm] j_{ey} = \dfrac{\sigma}{1 + \beta_e^2} \left\{ E_y - uB + \beta_e E_x \right\} \\[2mm] j_{ez} = 0 \end{array} \right\} \qquad (13)$$

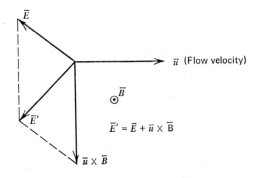

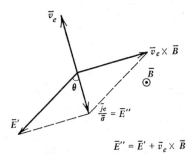

Fig. 4. Illustration of electric fields and Hall angle, θ.

The parameter β_e, termed the Hall parameter, is equal to $\mu_e B$. It is a measure of the relation of the Hall field $v_e B$ to the effective field E''. Thus, if θ is the angle between the vectors $\bar{E}'$ and $\bar{E}''$ (or $\bar{j}_e/\sigma$), as shown in Figure 4, we find that $\beta_e = \tan \theta$. Since $\tan \theta$ is obviously $\sigma v_e B/j_e$, equations 7 and 8 indicate that it is simply $\mu_e B$.

The equations 13 give the current components due to the electrons. There are also much smaller currents due to drift of ions. The mobility of the ions is designated μ_i and the ionic conductivity and current are expressed as follows (for singly charged positive ions):

$$\sigma_i = n_i \mu_i e \qquad (14)$$

$$\bar{j}_i = n_i \bar{v}_i e \qquad (15)$$

The ratio of ion mobility to electron mobility, μ_i/μ_e, is approximately the square root of the ratio of electron mass to ion mass. For cesium μ_i/μ_e is about 0.0022, for potas-

Table 1. Formulas for Field and Current Components, Power Density, and Efficiency

	(a) Continuous electrodes	(b) Segmented Faraday	(c) Hall generator
E_x	0	$-\beta_e uB(1-K)$	$-\beta_e uBK'/X$
E_y	KuB	KuB	0
K (def.)	E_y/uB	E_y/uB	$-E_x X/uB\beta_e$
j_x	$\sigma\beta_e uB(1-K)/Y$	0	$\sigma\beta_e uB(1-K')/Y$
j_y	$-\sigma XuB(1-K)/Y$	$-\sigma uB(1-K)/X$	$-\sigma uB(X^2+K'\beta_e^2)/XY$
η_e	K	K	$\beta_e^2 K'(1-K')/(X^2+K'\beta_e^2)$
P'	$\sigma u^2 B^2 XK(1-K)/Y$	$\sigma u^2 B^2 K(1-K)/X$	$\sigma u^2 B^2 \beta_e^2 K'(1-K')/XY$

sium 0.004. The resulting small drift velocity of the ions means that the ion Hall field v_iB is negligibly small in all cases of interest in MHD generators, and ionic Hall effects can be neglected. The ion current density, accordingly, is given simply by:

$$\bar{j}_i = \sigma_i(\bar{E} + \bar{u} \times \bar{B}) \tag{16}$$

The components of $\bar{j}_i$ are combined with those of $\bar{j}_e$ to give components of total current $\bar{j}$:

$$\left. \begin{aligned} j_x &= \frac{\sigma}{1 + \beta_e^2}\left\{E_x - \beta_e(E_y - uB)\right\} + \sigma\frac{\mu_i}{\mu_e}E_x \\ j_y &= \frac{\sigma}{1 + \beta_e^2}\left\{E_y - uB + \beta_eE_x\right\} + \sigma\frac{\mu_i}{\mu_e}(E_y - uB) \\ j_z &= 0 \end{aligned} \right\} \tag{17}$$

In a great many cases $\bar{j}_i$ can be neglected in comparison to $\bar{j}_e$.

We next will indicate the current, field, and power formulations for three well-known types of generators, shown in Figure 5(**a**) (**b**), and (**c**). Type (**a**) is the continuous electrode generator as discussed previously and shown also in Figure 1. Type (**b**) is a segmented electrode, or Faraday generator, wherein each pair of opposed electrodes is connected to its separate load. Type (**c**) is called the Hall generator. Opposed electrode pairs are connected together and the load is connected between upstream and downstream electrodes. With Hall effects present, type (**a**) generators have axial currents j_x that lead to dissipative losses and reduce effective transverse conductivity. Type (**b**) generators effectively block flow of axial current and give good power density. Type (**c**) generators capitalize on the axial electric field and use it to generate power.

It will be clear that in type (**a**) generators $E_x = 0$. In Type (b) we have $j_x = 0$, and type (**c**) is typified by $E_y = 0$. Table 1 gives the formulas of interest for field and current components, power density P', and efficiency η_e for the several types of generators. For brevity we let $X = 1 + \beta_e\beta_i$ and $Y = 1 + \beta_e^2$, where $\beta_i = \mu_iB$.

Careful review of the formulations in Table 1, keeping in mind that K' is defined differently for Hall generators than for Faraday generators (though it is always the ratio of electric field to open-circuit field), shows that at a given generator efficiency the power density of the Hall generator is somewhat lower than that of the Faraday generator. Nevertheless there is some interest in Hall generators because of the simplicity of the load circuit.

Hall generators tend to operate preferably not far from short-circuit conditions (small K'), while Faraday generators are best operated not too far from open-circuit conditions (large K).

There is a fourth version of the MHD generator, shown in in Figure 5 (**d**), in which the electrode pairs are connected diagonally (8). In this way, performance close to that of type (**b**) generators is realized but with much simplification of the load circuits.

One notes from Table 1 that the segmented Faraday generator has appreciably higher power density than the continuous electrode generator, unless β_e is very small. For $\beta_e = 1$ the power density of type (**a**) is only half that of type (**b**), and the difference is more pronounced at larger β_e.

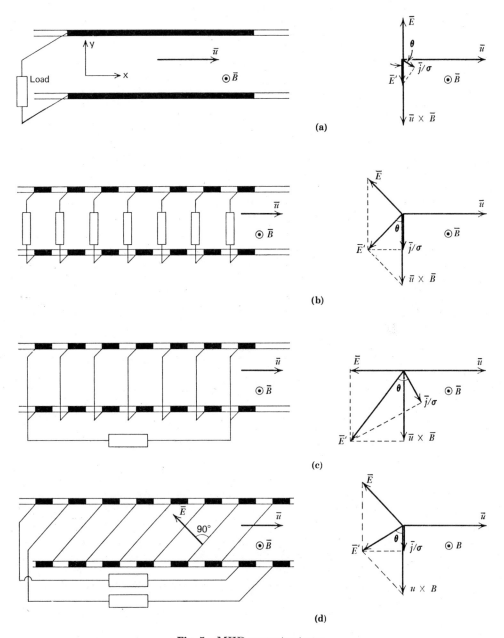

Fig. 5. MHD generator types.

At the present stage of technical development, one feels confident in designing for β_e values as large as 4. Electrode losses and other problems become serious at higher β_e. The β_e value is usually much lower near the generator duct inlet where pressure is high and μ_e is low, and the largest β_e may occur near the outlet. It is possible to keep β_e constant over a portion of the generator length by appropriate variation of B. The limits on magnetic field strength used in generator design tend to be set more by the permissible β_e than by superconducting magnet technology.

So far the discussion of generators has dealt with the local situation in the generator duct. Let us turn our attention now to the generator as a whole. The flow through the duct is accompanied by changes of pressure, temperature, density, enthalpy, entropy, conductivity, and gas composition. The velocity may or may not vary, depending on the designer's choice. For analysis of the flow in an open-cycle system, using combustion products, calculations must first of all be made of equilibrium gas compositions and properties at various temperatures and pressures. The conservation equations of momentum, energy, and mass, along with the gas law, can then be used to analyze the flow in the duct. We have also the current equation. In writing these equations below, we use j as the magnitude of the current density and B as the magnetic induction magnitude. A Faraday segmented generator is assumed and ion currents are neglected. We then have the following equations:

$$\text{current: } j = \sigma uB(1 - K) \tag{18}$$

$$\text{momentum: } \rho u \frac{du}{dx} + \frac{dp}{dx} = -jB\left(1 + \frac{f}{\xi(1 - K)}\right) \tag{19}$$

$$\text{energy: } \rho \frac{d}{dx}\left(h + \frac{u^2}{2}\right) = -jKB(1 + \lambda) \tag{20}$$

$$\text{mass: } \rho uA = m \tag{21}$$

$$\text{gas law: } \rho = \frac{pw}{RT} \tag{22}$$

where

ρ = density	f = friction factor
p = pressure	λ = heat loss ratio
h = specific enthalpy	r_h = hydraulic radius
w = molecular weight	m = mass flow rate
R = universal gas constant	A = flow area

$$\xi = \frac{2r_h\sigma B^2}{\rho u}$$

The heat-loss ratio, λ, is ratio of heat loss per unit volume to power generated per unit volume.

In equations 18–21 we are using a one-dimensional, or "hydraulic," theory in which velocity and other state quantities are treated as though they were constant over the cross section, at their average values. Friction is likewise introduced in the usual hydraulic manner. This is, of course, an approximation. We actually have boundary layers building up along the walls, from the inlet. The treatment given, however, is reasonably satisfactory for initial investigations.

To carry out the analysis of the flow it is convenient to assume a pattern of flow-speed variation in which the ratio of kinetic energy drop to isentropic enthalpy drop is constant, per unit length. We designate this ratio as follows:

$$\alpha = \rho u.du/dp \tag{23}$$

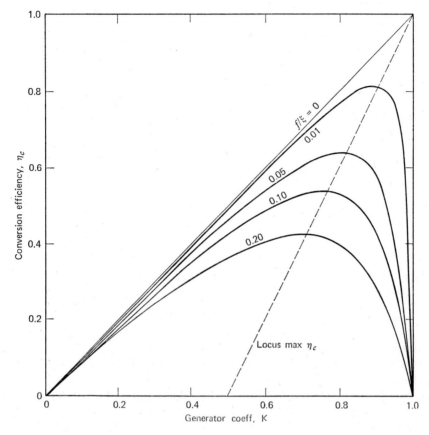

Fig. 6. Conversion efficiency for constant-velocity segmented Faraday MHD generator.

A constant-velocity design is realized by taking $\alpha = 0$. We now obtain from equations 19 and 20 the following:

$$dx = \frac{-(1 + \alpha)dp}{\sigma u B^2 (1 - K + f/\xi)} \qquad (24)$$

$$dh = \frac{dp}{\rho} \cdot \left\{ \frac{K(1 + \lambda)(1 + \alpha)}{1 + f/\xi(1 - K)} - \alpha \right\} \qquad (25)$$

Equation 24 permits calculation of generator length by integration. Equation 25 allows us to carry out a numerical (finite-difference) analysis of the generator process. With the aid of a Mollier diagram (or appropriate tables) and a conductivity chart (or tables), one can assume Δp, determine $\Delta p/\rho$ (which is enthalpy drop at constant entropy) and calculate Δh (equ. 25). The state point at the end of the incremental change is determined by the final values of h and p. Average values of σ, u, and B for the interval would be used in calculating Δx (equ. 24). In the calculations, f, K, λ, and α are assumed. It is hardly justifiable to be concerned with variation of f along the duct, in the light of the approximate manner in which friction effects are here treated. However, the f value should be conservatively chosen. Selection of λ as a design choice implies that subsequent calculation should be made to determine

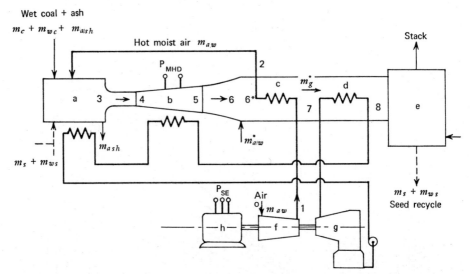

Fig. 7. MHD-Steam combined plant. Details of reheat and feed heaters not shown. LEGEND: a, gasifier and combustor; b, MHD generator; c, air heater; d, steam generator system; e, gas cleaner; f, air compressor; g, steam turbine; h, alternator. (Air and steam heaters may be re-arranged in actual plant.) P_{MHD} = MHD power; P_{SE} = steam generated power.

the wall temperatures corresponding to the assumed heat loss. The ξ value, termed the interaction parameter, can be calculated point by point as the analysis proceeds down the duct.

In some instances it is desirable to analyze the generator by starting at the outlet and working back toward the inlet.

The conversion efficiency, locally in the generator, is given, for the case $\alpha = 0$, which corresponds to a constant-velocity design:

$$\eta_c = \frac{K}{1 + f/\xi(1 - K)} \qquad (26)$$

A plot of this efficiency for various K and f/ξ is instructive and is given in Figure 6. To realize good efficiency f/ξ should be smaller than 0.05. For very large machines we usually have $f/\xi \leqq 0.01$. The efficiency goes through a maximum at any f/ξ. When K is too high the generator becomes long and frictional losses are excessive. When K is too small, the ohmic heating losses are excessive.

The total power generated in the MHD generator is given as follows:

$$P = \frac{m(h_3 - h_6)}{1 + \lambda} \qquad (27)$$

where h_3 is the inlet total enthalpy (combustion chamber) and h_6 is outlet total enthalpy. In this notation we would let h_4 be the inlet-gas enthalpy and h_5 the outlet-gas enthalpy. Numbering conforms to the open-cycle power plant diagram of Figure 7.

Electrical Conductivity

The electronic conductivity in the gas is given by equation 7. The theoretical treatment of the problem involves calculation of mobility μ_e and electron density, n_e.

A fairly satisfactory theory, widely referred to, is proposed by Frost (9) and Way (10) and it will be outlined here. The electron mobility is calculated taking account of dependence of collision frequency on electron speed, as follows:

$$\mu_e = -\frac{4\pi e}{3m_e} \int_0^\infty \left(\frac{v^3}{\nu}\right) \left(\frac{d}{dv}\right) F(v)dv \tag{28}$$

$$F(v) = \left(\frac{m_e}{2\pi kT}\right)^{3/2} \exp\left(\frac{-m_e v^2}{2kT}\right) \tag{29}$$

The collision frequency ν of the electrons with various species is a function of electron speed, the distribution of which is given by equation 29. In the equations 28 and 29 the notation is as follows:

e = electronic charge, 1.602×10^{-19} coulombs
m_e = electron mass, 9.11×10^{-31} kg
v = electron speed, m/sec
ν = collision frequency, sec^{-1}
$F(v)$ = speed distribution function
k = Boltzmann constant, 1.38×10^{-23} J/deg K
T = gas temperature, deg K

The collision frequency depends on the particular species. The electron-ion collision frequency must also be included, as shown below for s-species of nonionized particles.

$$\nu = \sum_1^s \nu_k + \nu_{ei} \tag{30}$$

The collision frequency ν_k can be expressed as

$$\nu_k = (10^3 p_k/T) \cdot f_k(U) \tag{31}$$

where p_k is pressure of the k-species in atm and U is the electron energy in eV, namely $m_e v^2/2e$. Functions $f_k(U)$ depend on experimental observation and data have been summarized for a number of species of importance by Frost.

The electron density is calculated taking account not only of the electrons released by ionization of the alkali atoms, but also of the electrons lost by attachment to certain species to form negative ions. There may be several types of negative ions, but the positive ions are assumed to consist solely of K^+ or Cs^+, depending on the seed material used. Suppose we consider two types of negative ions, which, for the moment, we simply designate as the α-group and the β-group, the α-group being typified by electron affinity $E_{A\alpha}$ and the β-group by electron affinity $E_{A\beta}$. Since the gas is electrically neutral (in any domain of dimensions larger than the Debye length) we will have the following charge-balance equation (particles per m^3):

$$n_e + n_\alpha^- + n_\beta^- = n_A^+ \tag{32}$$

Here η_A^+ signifies the number of alkali-metal ions per unit volume. In terms of partial pressures in atmospheres:

$$[\epsilon] + [\alpha^-] + [\beta^-] = [A^+]$$

This pressure equation leads to an expression for $[\epsilon]^2$ as follows:

$$[\epsilon]^2 = \frac{[A^+][\epsilon]}{1 + \dfrac{[\alpha^-]}{[\epsilon]} + \dfrac{[\beta^-]}{[\epsilon]}} \tag{33}$$

The ionization-reaction equations and the equilibrium constants are as follows:

$$
\begin{aligned}
A &\rightleftharpoons A^+ + \epsilon^- & K_e &= [A^+][\epsilon]/[A] \\
\alpha^- &\rightleftharpoons \alpha + \epsilon^- & K_\alpha &= [\alpha][\epsilon]/[\alpha^-] \\
\beta^- &\rightleftharpoons \beta + \epsilon^- & K_\beta &= [\beta][\epsilon]/[\beta^-]
\end{aligned}
\tag{34}
$$

where A represents K or Cs. Equation 33 then gives

$$[\epsilon]^2 = \frac{[A]K_e}{1 + \dfrac{[\alpha]}{K_\alpha} + \dfrac{[\beta]}{K_\beta}} \tag{35}$$

Now, if one knows the equilibrium constants, and the partial pressures of species A, α, and β, one can determine the electron partial pressure and hence η_e. In equation 34 the partial pressures represent the values which remain after partial ionization, rather than partial pressures calculated without regard to ionization reactions. In general this distinction is trivial, but in some cases it is important.

The equilibrium constants (from consideration of the appropriate Saha equations) are given below:

$$\log_{10}K_e = \tfrac{5}{2}\log_{10}T + \log_{10}\left(\frac{2g_i}{g_o}\right)_A - 6.48 - \frac{5040}{T}V_i$$

$$\log_{10}K_\alpha = \tfrac{5}{2}\log_{10}T + \log_{10}\left(\frac{2g_i}{g_o}\right)_\alpha - 6.48 - \frac{5040}{T}E_{A\alpha} \tag{36}$$

$$\log_{10}K_\beta = \tfrac{5}{2}\log_{10}T + \log_{10}\left(\frac{2g_i}{g_o}\right)_\beta - 6.48 - \frac{5040}{T}E_{A\beta}$$

where g_i/g_o is the ratio of statistical weight of the ion ground state to that of the neutral particle ground state. The several partial pressures are calculated from equations 35 and 36. Number densities are then found from

$$n_\alpha = \frac{n}{p}[\alpha]; \qquad n_\beta = \frac{n}{p}[\beta]; \qquad n_A = \frac{n}{p}[A] \tag{37}$$

where p is the total pressure in atmospheres and n is the total particle density:

$$n = 0.7339 \times 10^{28}p/T \tag{38}$$

A word must now be said concerning the negative ion species α and β. The most prominent negative ion will be OH^-. The electron affinity of OH^- is taken at 1.83 eV. There will be two other species, namely O and C_3, which might be included in the α-group. The α-group thus includes OH and also O and C_3 which are regarded as playing roles somewhat similar to OH. However, we do not include in $[\alpha]$ the full partial pressure of all three species, but rather weigh them with numbers proportional to their relative statistical weights. We thus write $[\alpha]$ as:

$$[\alpha] = [OH] + \tfrac{3}{8}[O] + \tfrac{1}{4}[C_3] \qquad (39)$$

The β-group is assumed to include CN, NO_2, and C_2, with typical electron affinity 3.6 eV. Since statistical weight ratios g_i/g_o are all alike (at $\tfrac{1}{2}$) for these species, we have:

$$[\beta] = [CN] + [NO_2] + [C_2] \qquad (40)$$

The inclusion of both α and β groups of negative ions was proposed by Frost after his original publication (9); the matter is also discussed in reference 10.

More exact theoretical treatments of conductivity may be developed in the future, but the theory outlined here has been found to agree fairly well with experimental determinations (11,12). In particular, it would be desirable to have available improved values of certain equilibrium constants and attachment potentials.

One can use the theory given above to calculate electrical conductivity and electron mobility. One must know, first of all, the equilibrium chemical composition. This can be obtained by standard calculation procedures (10).

Applications in Coal or Char-Burning Power Plants

In the MHD process of power generation a hot electrically conducting gas is caused to flow through a duct at high speed in the presence of a transverse magnetic field. Electromotive forces are induced in the gas and, with appropriately disposed electrodes, current can be extracted and delivered to an external-load circuit. Seeding of the gas with a low concentration of a substance such as potassium or cesium, which has low ionization potential, assures adequate electrical conductivity at temperatures within an attainable range. MHD generators generally require inlet total temperatures in the neighborhood of 2700°K and electrical conductivities of 5–10 ohm^{-1}m^{-1}. Electron densities around 10^{14}/cm^3 are appropriate.

Although there is a possibility of developing MHD power plants involving a closed Brayton cycle, with heat supplied by a nuclear reactor, it appears that plants using combustion products offer a prospect of earlier realization and lower power cost. In view of the tremendous coal resources on the North American continent, there is a great incentive to perfect power systems based on the use of this fuel. The MHD system offers the prospect of (1) an easing of air and thermal pollution problems; (2) highly efficient power generation with moderate power cost; (3) utilization of our very extensive coal resources to meet our growing power needs; and (4) conservation of these fuel resources through highly efficient conversion. The general arrangement of typical fossil-fuel MHD power plants is represented in simplified manner in Figure 3 and Figure 7. For improved efficiency an air preheater, taking its heat from the exhaust gases, should be employed. Also a bottom plant of gas-turbine or steam-turbine type is desirable to effectively use the available energy of the exhaust stream. An indication of the attainable efficiency is obtained if we let η_1 be the fraction of the original fuel energy converted to electric power (after deducting air-compression work) in the MHD generator, and η_2 the efficiency of conversion of the residual energy, inclusive of stack losses, in the bottom plant. Then the efficiency of the combined plant is approximately as follows:

$$\eta = \eta_1 + \eta_2(1 - \eta_1)$$

It is considered possible to realize η_1 values of 0.20–0.40, while η_2 may be 0.30–0.40. Thus, overall efficiencies of 50 to over 60% may be anticipated. The attractiveness of the MHD process rests to a large extent on the fact that the hot-gas system involves stationary, lowly stressed parts at moderate pressures, and thus quite high temperatures can be used and higher values of η_1 are realized than in other types of topping cycles.

The MHD power plant requires preheating the air to a high temperature and good durability of the duct wall and electrodes. The size of the generator and magnet are reduced if electrical conductivity can be improved, and plant cost is lower if

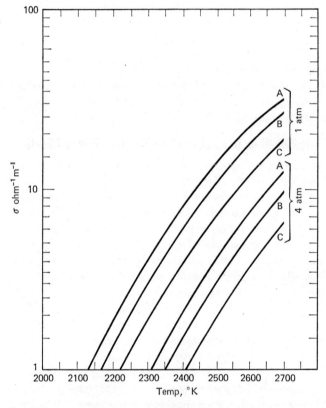

Fig. 8. Conductivity of combustion products; 0.35 wt % cesium seeding by dry carbonate; $\phi = 1$. LEGEND: A, char and moist air, H:C = 0.182 in fuel; B, wet coal and moist air, H:C = 0.724 in fuel; C, natural gas and moist air, H:C = 3.899 in fuel.

operating temperatures are not excessive. Consequently, it is important to examine various fuels and their combustion products, as well as the conditions of operation, to realize lower operating temperatures, better conductivity, and the best conversion efficiency (13–15).

Studies have shown that since the density of free electrons in the gas is diminished to some extent by attachment to chemical species, such as OH, to form negative ions, it is desirable to use fuels of low H/C ratio. Another reason for doing this is to reduce formation of potassium (or cesium) hydroxide, which robs the gas of free alkali atoms available for ionization. Electrical conductivities as a function of the H:C ratio are in-

Table 2. Fuel Analyses

Typical Coal Assumed, %		Typical Char Assumed, %	
vol	26.5	vol	3.6
FC[a]	65.6	FC	87.1
ash	7.9	ash	9.3
S	2.6	S	0.8
H	4.9	H	1.3
C	80.6	C	85.2
N	1.4	N	1.7
O	2.6	O	1.7
3% moisture assumed in coal		no moisture	
atom formula:		atom formula:	
$CH_{0172435}O_{0102421}N_{0101489}S_{0101208}$		$H_{0118177}O_{0101407}N_{0101711}S_{0100352}$	
HHV[b], 36.31×10^1 J/kg[c]		HHV[a], 33.543×10^1 J/kg	

[a] Fixed carbon, see Vol. 5, p. 653.

[b] Higher or gross heating value, including the heat released on condensation of the water formed.

[c] Dry ash free (daf).

dicated in Figure 8. One sees that coal, and especially char derived from coal, are superior fuels. Table 2 gives fuel analyses.

Another factor of considerable importance is the selection of the oxygen-equivalence ratio, ϕ, for the combustion products in the generator. Use of $\phi < 1$ (fuel rich)

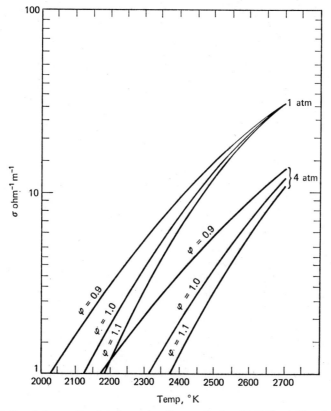

Fig. 9. Conductivity of char and moist air combustion products with 0.35 wt % cesium seed by dry carbonate. Effect of oxygen equivalence ratio.

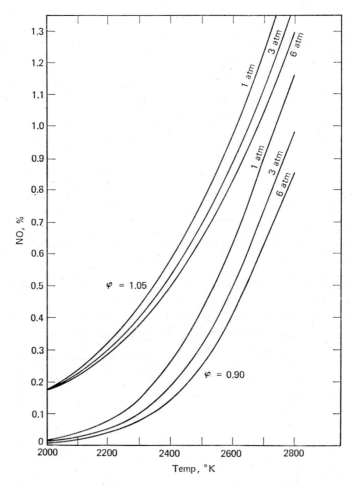

Fig. 10. Equilibrium NO concentrations (char and air).

promotes better electrical conductivity and also results in higher flame temperature for given air-preheat temperature. Influence of ϕ on electrical conductivity for char and air combustion products is shown in Figure 9. One disadvantage of a fuel-rich operation is the reduction of mass flow for a given fuel flow. A way around this difficulty is to recycle a portion of the fuel-rich exhaust products. An additional advantage of use of $\phi < 1$ is the reduction of NO formation. Equilibrium NO concentrations for various ϕ, p, and T are shown in Figure 10. Actual level of NO formed in the combustor will be less than the equilibrium value because of kinetic factors. The level of NO concentration in the exhaust stream is in any case considerably lower than that in the combustion chamber.

The conductivity of the working gas depends strongly on the type and amount of seeding. Cesium, with ionization potential 3.89 eV, is definitely superior to potassium with 4.34 eV. The comparison is shown in Figure 11 for char and air products. The high level of ionization obtainable with cesium permits the use of quite low seeding concentrations, for example, 0.35 wt % in the gas or 0.075 mole percentage. This low value is favorable in slowing reactions of the working gas with exposed surfaces; also it helps reduce the cost of cesium seed makeup material.   For the makeup feed, finely pulverized pollucite would be used, which is about 25% cesium.   In an MHD power plant using cesium seeding it is economical to employ a very efficient gas cleaner, such as an electrostatic filter of 99.8% effectiveness.   Cost of seed makeup becomes less than 3% of the fuel cost.

With the use of the several measures discussed above, MHD central stations of efficiencies in the 50–54% range are now envisaged with moderate air-preheat temperatures (1100–1200°K); no oxygen enrichment is needed.   With high-temperature air preheat, which could be more easily realized with clean, gasified fuel, efficiencies of over 58–60% are projected.

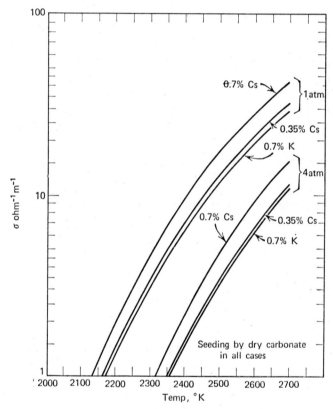

Fig. 11.   Conductivity of char and moist air combustion products at Q = 1.05 seed comparison. Seed expressed as weight percent in gas.

Problems arise which are associated with the ash carry-over during coal combustion.   These problems, whether in the generator duct, in the air heater, in the bottom plant, or in the seed-recovery system, can be minimized by arranging the fuel and combustion system so as to keep the inert ash material out of the main stream of working gas.   The problems just referred to include ash condensation in the MHD duct, slag deposits on heat-transfer surfaces, and mixing of condensed seed with condensed slag with resulting complication of seed recovery.   One important aspect of coal gasification in relation to MHD power is, therefore, the production of a clean fuel gas and clean combustion products.   A combined gasifier-combustor is of great interest for MHD.

Another aspect of the relationship of coal gasification and MHD power generation is the combination of a gas-producing plant and an MHD power plant. In this case the power plant may burn the char left over from the gasification process, and the gas might be used for general industrial or consumer needs.

MHD SYSTEMS USING GAS PRODUCED FROM COAL

In order to eliminate as far as possible the mineral matter from the stream of working gas entering the generator, one may have to take recourse to:

1. Systems involving gasification of the coal followed immediately by combustion.

2. Generation of a product fuel gas by use of recycled combustion products containing CO_2, with subsequent burning of this gas in the combustion chamber.

3. Generation of fuel gas by direct contact of the fuel and the combustion products leaving the MHD generator.

The Combined Gasification and Combustion Systems. The one method of particular interest is that using a two-stage cyclone combustor (16), as represented in Figure 12. The first stage runs with excess fuel, at about $\phi = 0.65$, and generates a gas rich in CO. The flame temperature must be kept sufficiently low ($<2200°$K) for the prevention of appreciable vaporization of ash constituents. Frozen slag will form a layer on the water-cooled wall surface, and liquid slag will collect on the fire side of the frozen slag layer and run out through a slag tap. The walls of the cyclone first-stage chamber would best be made of water-cooled metal and silicon carbide facing (17).

The second stage would receive the CO-rich fuel gas and burn it with the preheated air. This might also be a cyclone chamber, and any liquid slag droplets would be thrown out by the inertia forces. The extensive accumulated experience with cyclone furnaces for utility boilers will be helpful in design and development of the two-stage combustion chamber mentioned here. The pressure level will be approximately 6 atm and temperatures are high, so rates of reaction will be appreciably increased, and the chamber will be relatively compact. Further development work is needed, however, on this two-stage gasifying combustor.

Steps must be taken to prevent carry-over of swirl into the MHD generator inlet when a cyclone chamber is used. This could be accomplished by use of ceramic straighteners, or by use of opposed primary chambers feeding into a common secondary chamber. Swirls from the primary chambers would be of opposite direction. Such an arrangement is illustrated in Figure 13.

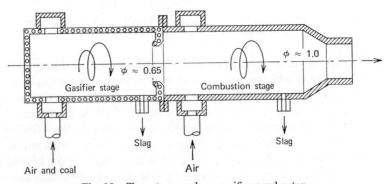

Fig. 12. Two-stage cyclone gasifier combustor.

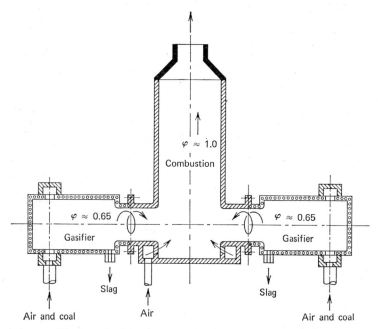

$\varphi \approx 1.0$

Combustion

$\varphi \approx 0.65$

$\varphi \approx 0.65$

Gasifier

Gasifier

Slag

Slag

Air and coal

Air

Air and coal

Fig. 13. Cyclone gasifier combustor with opposed swirl.

With combined gasification and combustion in the two-stage arrangement, it is expected that 90–95% of the mineral matter may be retained and thrown out as liquid slag. The sensible heat of this slag may be partially recovered. The combustion products will be those corresponding to near-equilibrium conditions, for the reaction of the coal and preheated air at the specified equivalence ratio, ϕ.

A schematic diagram of an arrangement with an MHD topping-unit and steam-bottom plant is shown in Figure 7. Stations are numbered at various points in the system, and Table 3 gives calculated values of state quantities and power levels for a possible plant arrangement. It is important to note that there is a tendency to degradation of the steam-bottom-plant performance in those cases when feed water is used to a considerable extent for heat absorption from hot walls or from the stack gas. (In a conventional plant, feed-water heating is accomplished mainly by the regenerative method, using bled steam.) We can minimize this degradation by designing the MHD generator with hot walls, rather than heavily water-cooled walls, and by doing what cooling is necessary with feed water at higher pressure and temperature. This applies also for combustion-chamber cooling.

As an alternative to the cyclone gasifier-combustor, a fixed-bed gasifier may be used. In this case a portion of the heated air is admitted to burn a fraction of the coal in order to generate heat for the endothermic reactions. Carbon dioxide is produced which circulates through the fuel bed and is reduced to CO by contact with the coal in the upper portion of the gasifier. The volatile matter is driven off the coal in the upper region, and the gaseous fuel products go at once to the main combustion chamber. Note that all tar substances are burned immediately and have no chance to foul the system. Velocities must be kept low enough to prevent entrainment of fine ash particles. Noncaking coals would be preferred; otherwise pretreatment must be applied.

Table 3. Results for Coal Burning MHD-Steam Plant[a,b] (Fig. 7)

$T_0 = 298.16°K$	air inlet (ambient)	$T_6 = 2243°K$	diffuser outlet
$T_3 = 2625°K$	combustor outlet	$p_6 = 1.152$ atm	diffuser outlet
$p_3 = 5.0$ atm	combustor outlet	$T_6^* = 2205°K$	afterburner outlet
$p_1 = 5.6$ atm	compressor outlet	$T_8 = 380°K$	stack
$T_1 = 505°K$	compressor outlet	$B_4 = 7$ tesla	generator inlet
$T_2 = 1122°K$	air preheat	$B_5 = 3.6$ tesla	generator outlet
$T_c = 600°K$	coal preheat	$\lambda_1 = 0.05$	combustor heat loss ratio
$T_4 = 2498°K$	generator inlet	$\lambda_2 = 0.06$	generator heat loss ratio
$p_4 = 3.375$ atm	generator inlet	$\eta_c = 0.90$	compressor efficiency
$u_4 = 750$ m/sec	generator inlet	$K = 0.81$	MHD generator coeff
$T_5 = 2142°K$	generator outlet	$\beta_{max} = 4.17$	max Hall parameter
$p_5 = 0.90$ atm	generator outlet	$\theta = 36.31 \times 10^6$ J/kg	coal heat value
$u_5 = 599.1$ m/sec	generator outlet	$m_c\theta = 2897.1$ MW	thermal input
$m_g = 1000$ kg/sec	flow in generator	$p_{MHD} = 730.6$ MW	MHD power
$m_c = 79.79$ kg/sec	daf coal	$P_c = 191.9$ MW	compressor power
$m_{aw} = 909.33$ kg/sec	moist air	$P_{SE} = 772.7$ MW	net steam power
$m_{aw}^* = 95.72$ kg/sec	afterburner air	$P = 1503.3$ MW	net plant output
$m_s = 6.065$ kg/sec	Cs_2CO_3	$\eta = 0.519$	net plant efficiency
$L = 20.5$ m	generator length	$\bar{H} = 6576$ Btu/kWh	plant heat rate

[a] Wet coal and moist air (1% wt) with seeding by Cs_2CO_3 solution (250 g/100 ml) to give 0.5% total cesium in product gas; $\phi = 0.95$ oxygen equivalence ratio; $\phi = 1.05$ after supplementary air injection; 3% moisture in coal.

[b] These figures apply for dc power output from MHD generator. For ac conversion, assuming 1.5% converter loss, net plant power becomes 1492.6 MW and efficiency becomes 0.515.

With increase of angular momentum in cyclone gasifier-combustors, it should be possible to remove 95% of the mineral matter. With 0.5 wt % seeding the ratio of seed material to carried-over ash becomes 10:1. Heat-exchanger corrosion and fouling problems thus become essentially questions of reactions dominated by the presence of alkali contaminants rather than ash contaminants. There will be some combination of the cesium or potassium with the small residue of ash to form feldspar-like materials, but only a small fraction of the seed could become involved in this manner owing to the low ash concentration in the exhaust. The nonsoluble material so formed would be recycled to the combustion chamber, thus avoiding loss of the seed. Elaborate facilities for recovery of seed from ash residues are not required.

One of the reasons for interest in coal gasification in conventional utility plants is the possibility presented for capture of the sulfur before the fuel gas is burned. In the MHD plant elaborate components associated with such sulfur recovery are not needed, thus leading to considerable simplification. The SO_2 formed from combustion reacts, finally, in the presence of $CsOH$ (or KOH) and O_2, to form Cs_2SO_4 (or K_2SO_4). This process is highly effective in capture of sulfur from the exhaust stream (19). The alkali sulfate is finally removed in the gas-cleaning system. It can then be caused to react with a synthesis gas, and the H_2S is finally removed by the Claus process (see Vol. 19, pp. 357–354, 386–387). The seed is finally recycled as oxide or carbonate. Some test results on the effectiveness of sulfur removal by this process have been reported by Feldman, Simons, Gallagher and Bienstock (18) of the U.S. Bureau of Mines, and results are given in Table 4.

Table 4. Sulfur Dioxide Removal with K_2CO_3 Seed[a]

	Run			
	1	2	3	4
coal burned, lb/hr	105	94	97	98.5
K_2CO_3 added, % of coal + seed		5.5	11.7	14.5
g mole K_2CO_3/kg coal		0.42	0.96	1.23
SO_2 in flue gas, ppm	2150	571	241	60
SO_2 removal, %		71.4	88.0	97.0

[a] Reference 18, experiment 8.

The MHD Plant with Recycled Combustion Products. With the production of a clean fuel by gasification, the problem of air preheating is simplified. Regenerative heaters with a matrix of high-purity magnesia have been found by Hals and Keefe to be satisfactory for preheating air to temperatures approaching 1900°K with direct firing with products of combustion of clean fuels (19). Such heaters were found to function satisfactorily also with seeded gases. Similar favorable results with high-purity magnesia regenerators have been reported by Kiehl (20).

With possible use of high air preheat one has the options of (1) burning with high excess air, (2) burning at close to stoichiometric ratio ($\phi = 1$) and attaining a very high flame temperature, and (3) burning close to $\phi = 1$ and diluting the products with recycled combustion products (21). The first option is unattractive because the electrical conductivity is reduced at high ϕ value. The second and third options are about equally beneficial in improving the thermal efficiency, but the third method has

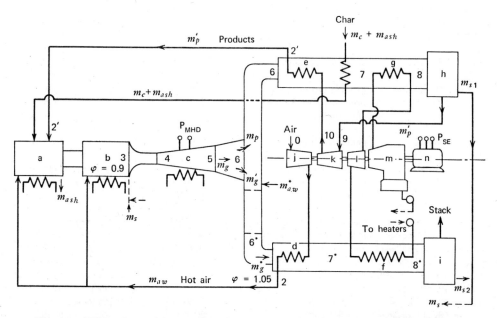

Fig. 14. MHD plant with recycled products. LEGEND: a, gas producer; b, combustor; c, MHD generator; d, air heater; e, products heater; f, steam generator; g, reheater; h, cleaner; i, cleaner; j, air compressor; k, gas compressor; l, high-pressure turbine; m, low-pressure turbine; n, alternator. Power = MHD power, P_{MHD} + steam-plant power, P_{SE}.

the advantages of lower NO formation, lower heat losses to cooling water, and less difficult containment problems.

Let a portion of the combustion products be diverted from the stream leaving the MHD generator, and then cooled, compressed, and preheated and recycled to a gas producer as shown in Figure 14. This producer would be designed to react carbon with hot carbon dioxide. The heat of the recycled gas would provide most of the heat needed for the endothermic reaction with the coal. There will, of course, be nitrogen mixed with the CO_2 recycled, at about a 3.76:1 mole ratio, and the enthalpy of the nitrogen would also be available to support the endothermic reaction. It is expected that a small amount of the preheated air would also be fed to the gas producer to augment the oxygen/carbon ratio and increase the velocity of the reaction. The gas producer might be of fixed-bed, vortex, or fluidized-bed type. In any case hot CO and N_2 are generated with some admixture of CO_2, H_2, and volatile constituents. This fuel-gas mixture would be sent directly to the main combustion chamber where it would burn with highly preheated air. Alkali seed would not be present in the gasifier; it would be introduced near the exit of the combustor, with adequate allowance for mixing prior to entering the generator duct.

Table 5. Results for Products Recycle MHD-Steam Plant[a] (Fig. 14)

$T_0 = 298.16°K$	air in (ambient)	$p_5 = 0.90$ atm	generator outlet
$T_3 = 2680°K$	combustor outlet	$u_5 = 542.8$ m/sec	generator outlet
$p_3 = 6.0$ atm	combustor outlet	$K_4 = 0.79$	generator coeff at inlet
$p_1 = 6.6$ atm	compressor outlet	$K_5 = 0.75$	generator coeff at outlet
$T_1 = 523°K$	compressor outlet	$T_6 = 2225°K$	diffuser outlet
$T_2 = 1890°K$	air preheater outlet	$p_6 = 1.11$ atm	diffuser outlet
$T_2' = 1890°K$	prod. preheater out	$T_6^* = 2202°K$	afterburner outlet
$T_9 = 310°K$	prod. compressor, in	$T_8 = 380°K$	boiler outlet temp (m_p)
$p_9 = 1.0$ atm	prod. compressor, in	$T_8^* = 380°K$	boiler outlet temp (m_g^*)
$T_{10} = 541°K$	prod. compressor, out	$B_4 = 7.0$ tesla	generator inlet
$p_{10} = 6.6$ atm	prod. compressor, out	$B_5 = 2.98$ tesla	generator outlet
$T_c = 800°K$	char preheat temp	$\lambda_1 = 0.05$	combustor heat loss ratio
$T_4 = 2556°K$	generator inlet	$\lambda_2 = 0.05$	generator heat loss ratio
$p_4 = 4.15$ atm	generator inlet	$\eta_c = 0.90$	compressor efficiency
$u_4 = 725$ m/sec	generator inlet	$\beta_{max} = 4.00$	max Hall coeff
$T_5 = 2130°K$	generator outlet	$\theta = 33.543 \times 10^6$ j/kg	char heat value
$m_g = 1000$ kg/sec	flow in generator	$m_c\theta = 1777$ MW	thermal input
$m_c = 52.977$ kg/sec	ashfree char	$P_{MHD} = 802.56$ MW	MHD power (dc)
$m_{aw} = 541.37$ kg/sec	moist air	$P_c = 217.37$ MW	compressor power
$m_{aw}^* = 90.23$ kg/sec	supplementary air	$P_{SE} = 251.04$ MW	net steam power
$m_g' = 596.90$ kg/sec	exhausted	$P = 1053.6$ MW	net plant power
$m_p = 403.10$ kg/sec	recycled	$\eta = 0.592$	net plant efficiency
$m_p' = 401.37$ kg/sec	after seed removal	$H = 5760$ BTU/kWh	plant heat rate
$m_g^* = 687.13$ kg/sec	$m_g' + m_{aw}^*$	$L = 20.6$ m	generator length
$m_s = 4.29$ kg/sec	recycled Cs_2CO_3		

[a] Char and moist (1% wt) air with seeding by dry Cs_2CO_3 to give 0.35% total cesium in product gas; $\phi \approx 0.90$ oxygen equivalence ratio; $\phi = 1.05$ after supplementary air injection.

The thermodynamic analysis of an MHD power plant of the scheme of Figure 14, with recycled products, can use much of the information (such as properties of combustion products gas) obtained in analysis of systems without recycling. A system with recycled products, high air, preheat temperature, char fuel, and cesium seeding, was analyzed with results given in Table 5.

The efficiency of 59% attained in the system of Figure 14 is quite attractive. It is of some interest that development of the several components of a plant of this type does not appear (as of 1971) to present insurmountable difficulties; indeed small experiments have verified possible attainment of many of the component performance goals. One point of interest in this arrangement is the relatively small fraction of the total power generated in the bottom plant, a fact which is very beneficial in reducing the plant capital cost. In this case we have 251-MW steam power and 803-MW MHD power.

It will be noted that the seeding concentration is only 0.35% cesium by weight (0.08% mole fraction). With 99.7% electrostatic filter cleanup efficiency, the cost of cesium makeup in the form of pollucite ore is only 0.037 mils per kWh generated.

The thermal discharge to the condenser cooling water in the power station here considered would be 0.53 kW per electrical kW of generated power kW(e). This compares with 2.12 kW per kW(e) for a present-day nuclear plant or 1.26 kW per kW(e) for a 39% efficient conventional fossil-fuel steam-power plant. If a gas turbine were used in the bottom plant for the system of Figure 14, there would be only negligible thermal discharge to cooling water.

Production of Fuel Gas Which Uses the Generator Exhaust. It is possible, in principle, to generate the fuel gas directly in a gas producer supplied with the hot exhaust products from the MHD generator. Here again, the fuel reacts with the hot carbon dioxide and water vapor to form a producer gas. This gas would then be cooled, compressed, and reheated for introduction into the combustion chamber where it is burned with preheated air. This process employs what has been termed chemical regeneration. Studies of such systems have been made by several investigators (22,23).

In the system pictured in Figure 15, half the char would be gasified. The remaining half would be fired into the first stage of a two-stage cyclone chamber where it would be burned with limited air to form additional gaseous fuel. Any seed material entrained in the char fuel supplied to the first stage would be vaporized. In the second stage the gaseous fuel previously generated would be burned, consuming the excess air, and bringing the final equivalence ratio, ϕ, to a value close to unity.

The arrangement mentioned here involves partial gasification in the unit located at the generator exit. A great advantage presented is the recovery of energy of the exhaust stream in chemical form, rather than as sensible heat in the preheated air. This permits either use of lower air-preheat temperature for given flame temperature T_3, or use of an unusually large proportion of recycled gas.

The system of Figure 15 is of advanced and unusual type, but mention is made of it here in anticipation of further theoretical and possibly experimental studies of such systems.

Results of cycle calculations for a chemical-regeneration MHD plant are given in Table 6. Here, again, the seeding ratio is assumed to be 0.35% Cs. Top temperature is 2680°K and preheat temperature is 1897°K, a value which is realized in regenerative MgO, direct-fired heater units when the ash is virtually eliminated from the combustion products. The efficiency may be over 60%, as indicated in Table 6, with the 52% gas recycling shown.

The bottom plant may have a rather high conversion efficiency when we use high-temperature compressed water for structural cooling, with judicious utilization of heat from the stack gas. (A waste-heat ammonia boiler could be used with an ammonia turbine.)

In this plant as well as the plants of 1 and 2 (see p. 234), the compressors would be driven by steam turbines (or possibly ammonia turbines). This is important from an economic standpoint, to minimize capital investment.

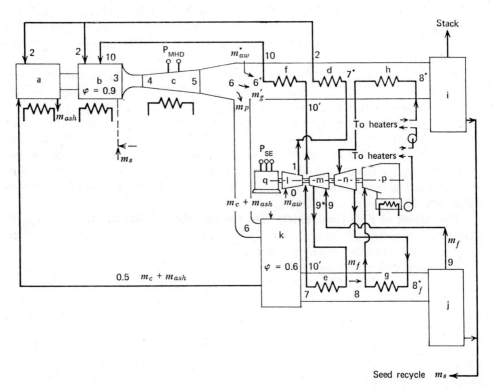

Fig. 15. MHD plant with chemical regeneration. LEGEND: a, gas producer; b, combustor; c, MHD; generator; d, air heater; e, low temperature gas heater; f, high temperature gas heater; g, steam reheater; h, steam generator; i, stack gas cleaner; j, fuel gas scrubber; k, gasifier; l, air compressor; m, fuel gas compressor; n, high-pressure turbine; p, low-pressure turbine; q, alternator. Power $= P_{MHD} + P_{SE}$. Char input $= m_c + m_{ash}$.

The development of the gasifier-combustor for the coal-burning plant described on p. 234 requires only adaptation and extension of present technologies of cyclone-combustion chambers. There may be some problems associated with operation of the first stage on the fuel-rich side, but use of silicon carbide refractory coatings in high temperature reducing atmospheres is expected to be beneficial.

The gasifiers in concepts 2 and 3 (see p. 235) are distinguished by the requirement for reacting coal or char with hot combustion products containing appreciable CO_2. Owing to the presence of a large concentration of nitrogen the reaction rates will be slowed. On the other hand, the temperature is higher than usually is the case in gas

Table 6. Results of Chemical Regeneration MHD-Steam Plant[a] (Fig. 15)

$T_0 = 298.16°K$	air inlet (ambient)	$p_5 = 0.90$ atm	generator outlet
$T_3 = 2680°K$	combustor outlet	$u_5 = 542.8$ m/sec	generator out
$p_3 = 6.0$ atm	combustor out	$K_4 = 0.79$	generator coeff inlet
$p_1 = 6.6$ atm	air compr. out	$K_5 = 0.75$	generator coeff out
$T_1 = 523°K$	air compr. out	$T_6 = 2225°K$	diffuser outlet
$T_2 = 1897°K$	air preheat	$p_6 = 1.11$ atm	diffuser outlet
$T_{10} = 1725°K$	fuel gas preheat	$T_6{}^* = 2202°K$	afterburner out
$T_9 = 310°K$	gas compr. inlet	$T_8{}^* = 380°K$	in $m_g{}^*$ leaving boiler
$p_9 = 1.00$ atm	gas compr. inlet	$T_{8f}{}^* = 380°K$	in m_f leaving boiler
$T_9{}^* = 549°K$	gas compr. out	$B_4 = 7.0$ tesla	inlet
$p_9{}^* = 6.6$ atm	gas compr. out	$B_5 = 2.98$ tesla	outlet
$T_4 = 2556°K$	generator inlet	$T_7 = 1725°K$	fuel gas from regenerator
$p_4 = 4.15$ atm	generator inlet	$\lambda_1 = 0.05$	combustor heat-loss ratio
$u_4 = 725$ m/sec	generator inlet	$\lambda_2 = 0.05$	generator heat-loss ratio
$T_5 = 2130°K$	generator out	$\eta_c = 0.90$	compressor efficiency
$m_g = 1000$ kg/sec	gas flow in generator	$L = 20.6$ m	generator length
$m_c = 44.376$ kg/sec	char (ashfree)	$m_c\theta = 1488.5$ MW	thermal input
$m_p = 500$ kg/sec	to regenerator	$P_{MHD} = 802.56$ MW	MHD power (dc)
$m_g' = 500$ kg/sec	exhaust	$P_c = 233.45$ MW	compressor power
$m_{aw}{}^* = 75.58$ kg/sec	supplementary air	$s_{SE} = 119.8$ MW	net bottom plant power
$m_{aw} = 453.47$ kg/sec	moist air rate	$P = 922.4$ MW	net plant power
$m_f = 520.04$ kg/sec	fuel gas rate	$\eta = 0.620$	net plant efficiency
$m_g{}^* = 575.58$ kg/sec	$m_g' + m_{aw}{}^*$	$H = 5505$ Btu/kWh	plant heat rate
$m_s = 4.29$ kg/sec	cesium carbonate		

[a] Char and moist (1% wt) air. Seeding by dry Cs_2CO_3 to give 0.35% total cesium in product gas; $\phi = 0.90$ oxygen equivalence ratio in MHD generator; $\phi = 0.6$ in gasifier; $\phi = 1.05$ after supplementary air addition.

producers, and this speeds the reaction. The development problem here will be centered on the achievement of sufficiently high reaction velocities.

COMBINATION OF MHD POWER PLANTS WITH GASEOUS FUEL PRODUCTION PLANTS FOR PRODUCTION OF METHANE AND LIQUID FUELS

With the growing need for gaseous and liquid fuels coupled with limited supply, it is understandable that attention should be given to producing these fuels from coal.

One process, under development by the Office of Coal Research, is entitled COED, which stands for Char Oil Energy Development (24). See p. 242. In this process a typical Illinois No. 6 coal could be heated in a series of fluid beds to produce about 50 gal of crude liquid product per ton of coal, along with about 4000 scf of high Btu pipeline-quality gas, and 880 lb of char. See Figure 16.

The char produced in this process is similar to that considered in the power plant analyses in Table 2 above, approximately carbon 85.2%, hydrogen 1.3%, nitrogen 1.7%, sulfur 0.1%, oxygen 1.7%, and ash 10%. This char is an excellent MHD fuel. Ash content would be higher for coals of high initial ash content.

The utilization of coal for production of needed gaseous and liquid fuels thus yields a highly desirable MHD power-plant fuel of low cost, and an MHD plant could be

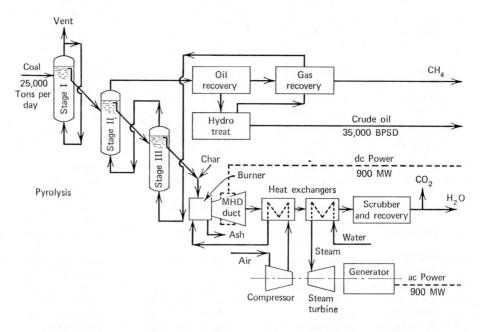

Fig. 16. Combined methane, crude oil, and MHD power system.

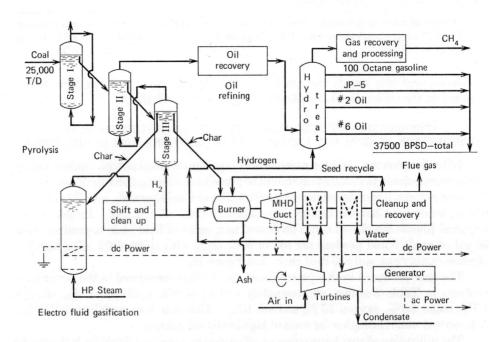

Fig. 17. Combined methane, liquid fuel, and MHD power system.

combined with the fuel-synthesis plant. A plant consuming 1000 tons of coal per hour yields about 222 lb/sec of char (on an ashfree basis), or 100 kg/sec. The heat input with such a fuel would be at a rate of 3354 MW. For a station of 55% efficiency, the generated power would be 1846 MW.

Another version is obtained by using the Hygas process in which some of the char is diverted to an electrogasifier where it is mixed with high-pressure steam and allowed to react. The gas produced, which is rich in hydrogen, is fed to the hydro-gasifier unit (24,25).

Figures 16 and 17 show in simplified version, arrangements for a gas plus liquid fuel plant and the electrogasification plant, respectively.

In the electrogasification unit, dc electric power is supplied and passes directly through the char bed. This provides the endothermic heat of reaction for the steam and carbon. The process is carried out at about 1800–1900°F and 1000 psi pressure. The gas is further mixed with steam to enter the hydrogasifier.

It is possible to balance the flows so that the residual char from the electrothermal gasifier is just sufficient to produce the dc power needed for electrogasification. Since the exhaust gases from the MHD generator contain additional heat, a bottom-steam or gas-turbine plant may be used to produce additional power for external distribution. Various combinations are possible leading to options of (*1*) on-site consumption of all char and power, (*2*) generation of extra power, and (*3*) supply of char for the market, if such exists.

A development program for the Hygas plant is in progress. As a second phase of this program, a 2000-kW electrothermal gasifier would be installed. Power for this unit could be purchased in the initial stages, but there is no reason why it might not be provided by a small experimental MHD generator (26).

The sulfur content of the char, 0.1%, as indicated above, is lower than that actually assumed in the char considered in Table 2 of this article. In the Hygas process, most of the sulfur in the coal is converted to H_2S in the hydrogasifier, and it must be removed to protect the nickel catalyst in the methanation unit. The elemental sulfur resulting from H_2S removal and subsequent treatment can be sold as a by-product.

METALLURGICAL COKE PRODUCTION

In the production of metallurgical coke, gases are evolved which may be burned advantageously in an on-site MHD power plant. The advisability of fuel utilization in this manner depends to some extent on the general fuel situation in the country. For example, if low-sulfur coal is scarce and coke is in great demand for steel making, it may be advisable in certain regions to consider use of the coke-oven gas for power generation to partially relieve the demands for coal. Such measures have been considered in Germany, for example (27).

The coke-oven gas is not the best fuel for MHD power, by any means, because of its appreciable hydrogen content. Nevertheless, it may be used quite satisfactorily, especially with cesium seeding. The cleanliness of the fuel makes it amenable to direct firing of high-temperature air preheaters.

The question may be raised as to why MHD generation should be preferred to gas turbines in this instance. This is a matter of economics. Twice as much electric power can be produced from a given amount of fuel in a 50% efficient MHD plant, as in a 25% efficient open-cycle gas-turbine plant, and economic studies may well indicate that the added capital cost is more than compensated by the reduced fuel cost.

A typical composition for the coke-oven gas is as follows:

Component	Mole %
N_2	2.1
CO	3.6
CO_2	0.8
H_2	59.4
CH_4	21.7
C_2H_6	0.8
H_2O	7.2
higher hydrocarbon	4.3

The higher heating value is about 46.5×10^6 J/kg. Unfortunately, the high H_2 content is not conducive to good electrical conductivity.

Assessment of MHD Power Generation

MHD development programs in several countries in the past decade have been expansions of interest, but extensive reductions of activity have taken place in some nations, owing to the local fossil-fuel situations and interest in nuclear power.

If a nation finds it necessary or desirable to use fossil fuels extensively for power generation, an assessment of the future potential of MHD may be quite favorable. Examples are U.S.A., Canada, Germany, Poland, U.S.S.R., and Japan.

Attractive features of the MHD process include (1) plant simplification; (2) attainment of lower heat rates; (3) reduction of air and thermal pollution; (4) ease of combination with gas plants; and (5) direct production of dc power, where needed.

The simplification of the power plant results principally from the unification of the processes of energy conversion from chemical to electrical form. The fuel is burned at high pressure, products are accelerated in a nozzle, and enthalpy is converted to electrical energy in the MHD generator; thus, processes of evaporation, superheating, steam-turbine mechanical-energy production, reheating, and final mechanical-to-electrical conversion in the alternator are largely eliminated. In the MHD steam combined plant, the steam power components would be one-third the size of those in a conventional plant of the same output rating.

As has been indicated, MHD plants with air preheat to around 1150°K can yield efficiencies of over 50%. In one char-burning plant analyzed, an efficiency of 54% was estimated with this nominal air-preheat temperature. With more thorough fuel preparation through gasification, regenerative air heaters can be used, and efficiencies in the 58–60% range would be anticipated. For a fuel cost of 30 cents per million Btu, a reduction of heat rate from 8530 Btu/kWh to 6200 Btu/kWh (55% efficient MHD plant compared to 40% conventional plant) the savings on the fuel bill amount to 0.70 mills/kWh, or, for a 1000 MW plant operating 7000 hours per year, an annual savings of 4.9 million dollars. Additional capital of $36/kW could be justified in the light of the potential fuel savings alone. Economic studies have indicated, however, that virtually no increase in plant-capital cost is necessary by following the MHD route, though, admittedly, initial plants would be more expensive (28).

The environmental aspects of MHD generation are particularly interesting. A very troublesome and expensive problem with conventional coal-burning plants is the elimination of SO_2 emissions. Changeover to low-sulfur fuels is usually very costly. In the MHD process, a built-in feature exists for sulfur removal as explained above.

Particulate emissions are very low in the MHD plant, especially with cesium seeding; it then becomes economical to use a highly efficient electrostatic cleaning system. With 0.35% by weight cesium seeding in the gas, and carry-over of 5% of the ash in the coal, the dust loading ahead of the cleaner would be 0.0051 kg per kg of gas. After 99.75% efficient cleaning the dust loading is 12.8×10^{-6} kg per kg gas, or about 15.5 mg per m^3.

As regards thermal discharge, one may compare power plants of various heat rates. For example, a nuclear plant of 10,700 Btu/kWh heat rate has a heat input of 10,000 Btu for each kWh output; since 1 kWh = 3413 Btu, it follows that the plant discharges to the environment 10,700 − 3413 or approximately 7300 Btu per kWh generated.

A good conventional plant of 8500 heat rate would discharge about 5100 Btu/kWh to the surroundings. On the other hand, an MHD plant of 6200 heat rate would discharge only 2800 Btu/kWh. The actual amount of thermal discharge to the condenser cooling water in fossil-fuel plants is about 1.2 times the turbine power. This would lead to values for heat discharged per total-plant kWh to the circulating water for the three plants just mentioned as follows: 7300 nuclear, 4100 for conventional fossil-fuel plant, and 2050 Btu for the MHD plant. The latter figure is lower not only because of the lower heat rate but also because only about half of the total power appears as turbine power. (Note that the steam turbines would also be called upon to run the air compressors, so turbine power is 30–35% larger than the ac power from the alternators.)

The possible combination of MHD power plants and gas-producing plants is an attractive feature. The MHD plant can burn char very advantageously. The char fuel makes the MHD plant more economical because of the higher conductivity afforded. Another matching area is that the cryogenic systems of the MHD plant, having to do with magnet cooling, may complement raw-oxygen requirements of certain types of gasification facilities. In fact, in some cases, the MHD plant could be fired with oxygen rather than air, thus eliminating completely NO formation.

There are a number of applications where dc power may be wanted. Electrothermal gasification has been mentioned. Another application is in aluminum smelting and in other electrolytic operations. Voltages available from large MHD machines could range from 2000 to 60,000 Vs in a single generator, depending on the type of electrode connections used. By using two generator ducts, one could achieve ±60,000 Vs, or 120 kV overall. Still another dc application may be in electric-arc heating devices which might be used either for gas heating or melting of scrap metal.

MHD power generation is also not without its problems. Most of the earlier experimental studies of MHD power generation were carried out with oxygen rather than air, and consisted generally of rather short time runs. Also, clean fuels have generally been used. It is very important to conduct experimental investigations with air rather than oxygen, with full cognizance and appreciation of the problems of high-temperature air preheating. Long-time operation must be demonstrated to a much more extensive degree, particularly with fuels such as coal that will produce vaporized (or condensing) ash constituents. The duct and heat-exchanger parts must be capable of accommodating such materials, or combustion and gasification systems must be developed which virtually eliminate carry-over of ash constituents. In short, the MHD system as a whole must be investigated to a greater degree with long-term operation and with the cheapest and most intractable fuels.

Table 7. Summary of Results for MHD Plants with Gasification[a]

Plant type	Air-preheat temp	Top temp	Efficiency, %	Heat rate, Btu/kWh
Figure-7 plant,[a] burning coal, with 0.5 wt % cesium seeding and gasifying cyclone combustor	1122°K (1560°F)	2625°K (4265°F)	51.9	6576
Figure-14 plant,[b] burning char, with 0.35 wt % cesium seeding and recycled products with gas producer	1890°K (2942°F)	2680°K (4364°F)	59.2	5760
Figure-15 plant,[b] burning char, with 0.35 wt % cesium seeding and chemical regeneration gasification of half the fuel	1897°K (2955°F)	2680°K (4364°F)	62.0	5505

[a] Plant uses recuperative air heater.
[b] Plants would use regenerative heaters.

Perhaps the most pressing problem in the MHD system is that of long-time operation of the electrodes. Although cold electrodes and side walls may be used, and actually have been used, there are thermodynamic disadvantages as well as great plumbing and insulation complications of such constructions, and therefore, it is very desirable to develop and demonstrate systems with hot walls and electrodes. Recent studies indicate the possibility of reaching 2000°C (29).

There may be problems from the alkali-metal salt (eg, sulfate) accumulation in heat-exchange systems, and new blowdown techniques may have to be employed. Until actual tests are made, the full extent of the problems cannot be ascertained.

One of the most important areas for investigation in connection with MHD power generation is certainly that of fuel gasification and combustion (see Table 7). The gains that may be realized eventually by complete combustion of coal while rejecting all the ash constituents are so great that all future serious studies of coal-fired MHD power generation should include consideration of this matter of ash rejection. An initial start may consist of the use of a good cyclone chamber of several stages.

A word may be said concerning some of the practical attainments in MHD power generation. We mention first the pioneering work of Karlovitz in the period 1938–1945 (1). Karlovitz' experiments showed the possibility of MHD generation from combustion products and demonstrated the principles of the Hall generator. Power level, however, was very low owing to the poor electrical conductivity realized and the low magnetic field. In the ensuing years considerable progress was made in the development of high-temperature materials and in knowledge of plasma physics. New investigations in MHD generation began in 1959–1960, both noble gas (30) and combustion product (31) generators being studied. Levels of power reached in these early experiments was 5–10 kW. MHD activity then accelerated and sizable programs were supported in the USA and other nations. Among the attainments were the self-excited 22 MW Mark V generator (32) and the Lorho generator (33) of 18 MW. In Japan, the Mark II generator (34) was developed at the Electrotechnical Laboratory. In the USSR a very large program on open-cycle MHD is supported (35) with both fundamental work and studies with such generator facilities as the U-02 and the ENIN-2. A sizable project was set up (3 MW thermal) at Swierk, Poland (36). Basic and important studies of generator problems have been carried out at Stanford University (37) and at the University of Tennessee Space Institute (38), while at the Westinghouse Laboratories numerous cycle analyses and feasibility studies (28) were made, in addition to experimental investigations of seeding problems, and the previously mentioned work of Frost and co-workers on electrical conductivity and electron-scattering cross sections. At the U.S. Bureau of Mines studies have been made of deposits and corrosion of metal tubular structures, such as might be used in the air preheater, with products of combustion of coal (39). This program has also contributed to understanding of the coal-combustion problems. The very sizable program that existed on MHD in England from 1961 to 1967 lead to many valuable and interesting results (40) but unfortunately the program has been terminated.

Good summaries of the status of MHD from year to year are provided by the reports of the International Liaison Committee on MHD (41).

A most interesting development at the present time is the U-25 project in the USSR (42). The plant under construction will provide 25 MW power from the MHD generator and an additional 50 MW from an appended steam plant. Natural gas will be used as fuel. As an initial venture the plant is rather conservatively designed. It will employ some oxygen enrichment of the combustion air, and indirectly fired heaters will be employed.

Bibliography

1. B. Karlovitz, "History of the K and H Generator and Conclusions Drawn from the Experimental Results," *Third Symposium on Engineering Aspects of MHD*, Am. Soc. Mech. Engrs. Rochester, *1962;* U.S. Pat. 2,210,918 (Aug. 13, 1940).

2. P. Sporn and A. Kantrowitz, "Magnetohydrodynamics—Future Power Process," *Power,* **103,** 62–65 (1959).

3. S. Way and R. L. Hundstad, "Direct Generation of Power from a Combustion Gas Stream," *Eighth International Symposium on Combustion, Pasadena, Calif., 1960.*

4. R. Rosa, *Magnetohydrodynamic Energy Conversion*, McGraw-Hill Book Co., New York, 1968.

5. M. Faraday, *Experimental Researches in Electricity, Series I*, Quaritch, London, 1839; Bakerian Lecture Series, *Phil. Trans. Roy. Soc.* **15** (Jan. 12, 1832).

6. L. P. Harris, J. D. Cobine, "The Significance of the Hall Effect for Three MHD Generator Configurations," *J. Eng. Power, Ser. A* **83** (4), 392–396 (1961).

7. S. Way, "Investigations in Magnetohydrodynamics," *Proc. Eleventh Intern. Congress on Applied Mechanics, Munich, August, 1964.*

8. A. de Montardy, "MHD Generator with Series Connected Electrodes," *Paper 19, First Intern. Symp. on MHD Electric Power Generation, Newcastle on Tyne, 1962.*

9. L. S. Frost, "Conductivity of Seeded Atmospheric Pressure Plasma," *J. Appl. Phys.* **32,** 2029–2036 (1961).

10. S. Way, "Chemical Aspects of MHD Power Generation," *Proc. AIChE Symposium, London (Inst. of Chemical Engineers), June, 1965.*

11. P. E. English and T. D. Rantell, "The Determination of the Electrical Conductivity of the Gases in a Pilot-Scale Coal Fired MHD Combustor," *Brit. J. Appl. Phys. Ser. 2,* **2,** 1215–1224 (1969).

12. A. Sumida, T. Ito, T. Morikawa, Y. Murai, and S. Matsubara, "An Experimental Study on Physical Properties of Combustion Gas," *Third International Symposium on MHD Electrical Power Generation, Salzburg, 1966.*

13. S. Way, "New Directions in Power Generation," *North American Fuel Technology Conference, Am. Soc. Mech. Engrs., Ottawa, May 31, 1970.*

14. S. Way, W. E. Young, "MHD Power Generation, Status and Prospects in Connection with Central Power Stations," *Purdue University Symposium on Power Systems, Lafayette, Ind., May, 1970.*

15. J. B. Dicks, T. R. Brogan, S. Way, and M. S. Jones, Jr., "Current Status and Recent Attainment in MHD Power Generation," *Am. Soc. Mech. Engrs. Winter Annual Meeting, New York, 1968, paper 68-WA/ENER-17.*

16. S. Way, W. E. Young, and T. C. Tsu, "Combustion Systems," *Progress Report No. 3, April 1965, comprising Appendix 8 of Vol. II "Feasibility Study of Coal Burning MHD Generation," Final Report on Office of Coal Research Contract 14-01-001-476,* Westinghouse Research Laboratories, Pittsburgh, Pa.; U. S. Pat. 3,358,624, S. Way, Dec. 19, 1967.

17. N. Seidl, "Development and Practice of Cyclone Firing in Germany," *Proceedings of Joint Symposium on Combustion, London 1955, p. 48. Institution of Mechanical Engineers;* "The Horizontal Cyclone as a Coal Burner," *Eleventh Coal Science Lecture, Gazette 46, British Coal Utilization Research Assoc., October 1962.*

18. H. F. Feldman, W. H. Simons, J. J. Gallagher, and D. Bienstock, "Kinetics of Recovering Sulfur from the Spent Seed in a MHD Power Plant," *Environmental Sci. Technol.,* **4** (6), 496–502 (June 1970); Also see Bienstock discussion of paper in ref. 13.

19. F. Hals and L. Keefe, "A High Temperature Regenerative Air Preheater for MHD Power Plants," *Paper 63, Third Intern. Symp. on MHD Electrical Power Generation, Salzburg, 1966.*

20. J. P. Kiehl, "Study of Refractory Materials for Temperatures up to 1900°C in a Storage Type Heater," *Paper 74, Fourth Intern. Symp. on MHD Electrical Power Generation, Warsaw, 1968.*

21. S. Way, "Char Burning MHD Systems," *Am. Soc. Mech. Engrs. paper WA-69-ENER-13, Annual Meeting, Los Angeles, Nov. 1969.*

22. J. Carrasse, "Chemical Recovery of Energy in a Combined MHD-Steam Central Station Power Plant," *Third Internat. Sympos. on MHD Electrical Power Generation, Salzburg, 1966.*

23. A. E. Scheindlin, B. Y. Shumyatsky, and A. G. Sokolsky, "Thermal Efficiency of Commercial MHD Power Plants in Terms of Different Methods of Obtaining High Temperature," *Tenth Symp. on Engineering Aspects of MHD, Cambridge, Mass., 1969.*

24. W. E. Young, T. C. Tsu, D. Q. Hoover, S. Way, and N. P. Cochran, "Recent Studies of Advanced Coal Burning Power Plants," *Intersociety Energy Conversion Engineering Conf., Am. Soc. Mech. Engrs., Miami, Florida, 1967.*

25. B. S. Lee, "Synthetic Pipeline Gas from Coal by the HYGAS Process," *Am. Power Conference, Illinois Inst. Technol. Chicago, April, 1970.*

26. S. Way, "Design of a Small MHD Pilot Plant," *Fourth Intern. Symp. on MHD Electrical Power Generation, Warsaw, 1968.*

27. W. Peters, "Entwicklungsstand des Bergbau-Forschung-Verfahrens zur Kontinuierlichen Formkoksherstellung," *Glückauf,* **103** (25) 1273–1279 (1967).

28. D. Q. Hoover et al., "Feasibility Study of Coal Burning MHD Power Generation," *Final Report, U.S. Dept. of Interior, Office of Coal Research, Contract 14-01-0001-476* Westinghouse Research Laboratories, Pittsburgh, Pa., 1966.

29. J. Millet, Discussion of Ivanov Paper, *Proc. Fourth Intern. Symp. on MHD Electrical Power Generation, Warsaw, 1968.*

30. M. Camac and G. S. Janes, "Applied Magnetohydrodynamics at the AVCO-Everett Research Laboratories," *Dynamics of Conduction Gases,* Northwestern Univ. Press, Chicago, Ill., 1960, pp. 112–125.

31. S. Way, S. M. DeCorso, R. L. Hundstad, G. A. Kemeny, W. A. Stewart, and W. E. Young, "Experiments with MHD Power Generation," *J. Eng. Power* **83,** 397–408 (1961).

32. A. C. J. Mattsson, E. L. Ducharme, E. M. Govani, J. B. Morrow, Jr., and T. R. Brogan, "Performance of a Self Excited MHD Generator," *AVCO-Everett Research Lab, Res. Rept. 238, Contract AF 33(615)-1862, Oct. 1965,* Air Force System Command, Wright-Patterson A.F. Base.

33. J. Teno, S. W. Petty, T. R. Brogan, and E. M. Govani, "Performance Evaluation Studies with 20 MW Hall Configuration MHD Generator;" O. K. Sonju, J. Teno, and T. R. Brogan, "Comparison of Experimental and Analytical Results for a 20 MW Combustion Driven Hall Configuration MHD Generator," *IEEE Winter Power Meeting, New York, January 1970.*

34. F. Mori, K. Fushimi, and S. Ikeda, "Experiments on MHD Generation by ETL Mark II," *Paper 30, Proc. Fourth Intern. Symp. on MHD Elec. Power Generation, Warsaw, 1968.*

35. V. A. Kirillin and A. E. Scheindlin, *Magnetohydrodynamic Method of Electrical Power Generation,* Energia, *Moscow, 1968.*

36. W. S. Bryzozowski, "Description of the 3 MW (t) Open Cycle MHD Converter under Con-

struction at Swierk," *Paper 93, Proc. Intern. Symp. on MHD Elec. Power Generation, Warsaw, 1968.*

37. K. G. Resek, R. H. Eustis, and C. H. Kruger, "Design and Performance of the Stanford Combustion MHD Generator, *Sixth Symposium on Engineering Aspects of MHD, Pittsburgh, 1965.*

38. D. L. Denzel, et al., "Experimental Study of Diagonal Conducting Wall Generators using Solid Propellants," *AIAA, Journal* **6,** 1968, p. 1647. J. B. Dicks et al., "Continuation of Diagonal Conducting Wall Generator Research," *Tenth Symposium on Engineering Aspects of MHD, Cambridge, Mass., 1969.*

39. D. Bienstock, R. J. Demski, and R. C. Kurtzrock, High Temperature Combustion of Coal Seeded with Potassium Carbonate in the MHD Generation of Electric Power, *U.S. Bur. Mines Rep. Invest.* **7361** (March 1970).

40. J. B. Haywood and G. J. Womack, *Open Cycle MHD Power Generation,* Pergamon Press, London, 1969.

41. IAEA/ENEA Intern. Liaison Group on MHD Electrical Power Generation, *Intern. Atomic Energy Agency, Vienna, Status Report on MHD Electrical Power Generation, 1969.*

42. V. A. Kirillin, P. S. Neporozhnig, and A. E. Scheindlin, "A 25000 KW Pilot MHD Power Plant," *Ninth Symp. on Engineering Aspects of MHD, Tullahoma, Tenn., April 1968; VII World Power Conference, Moscow, March, 1969.*

STUART WAY
Westinghouse Electric Corp.

COPPER

The decade of the sixties was one of rapidly expanding technology and a high rate of economic growth which has resulted in an increase in world copper consumption from 5 million tons in 1960 to 7.5 million tons in 1969. Projections of the market through 1973 anticipate an annual growth rate of 4.5%.

As a consequence of the market demand, a shortage of copper has persisted throughout most of the period. Strikes and political unrest in foreign mining countries have aggravated the shortage, resulting in continued upward pressure on prices. These factors have fostered exploration and capital investment to expand production. A five-year forecast of non-communist production shows a growth in output from 5.8 million tons in 1969 to 7.7 million tons in 1973. The year 1970 saw a marked change in copper availability and pricing. The increased free-world output in 1970 at a time of a depressed market resulted in a surplus in copper. It is anticipated that an adequate supply of copper will be experienced for the early 1970s which will tend to control pricing during this period. Table 1 shows the distribution of copper production from the ten principal copper-producing countries in 1968 and a projection for 1973.

The other side of the economic picture is the rapid increase in operating costs for mining and processing the ore. Also, lower-grade ores and higher ratios of overburden to ore are common in the industry. These factors have compelled an acceleration in mining and metallurgical technological development. In mining, this is manifest in more massive approaches in earth moving and the more extensive leaching of very low-grade overburden in waste dumps. Leaching of waste rock will be an increasingly important economic factor in the copper industry in the coming decade. Consequently, the hydrometallurgical route of leaching and extraction of copper is a prime target for research in the industry.

Flotation and the ancient art of smelting sulfide ores have been unchallenged until recent years. The effectiveness and low cost of the flotation-smelting processes have

Table 1. Total Free-World Copper Production, Short Tons

Country	1968	1973, Projection	Increase, %
United States	1,681,000	2,217,000	31.8
Zambia	785,000	914,000	16.4
Chile	773,000	1,173,500	51.8
Canada	656,000	859,000	30.9
Congo (Kinshasa)	375,000	435,000	16.0
Peru	240,000	485,000	102.0
Republic of South Africa	140,000	140,000	
Australia	140,000		
Japan	130,000	155,000	19.0
Philippines	107,000	157,000	44.0

discouraged significant departures in the classical approaches. In flotation, the principal process-improvement efforts have centered on process instrumentation and computer control, neither of which has been notably successful. In smelting, innovations have been largely in equipment design with little attack on the basic process concepts.

For the first time the industry is seriously investigating alternative approaches to the conventional smelting of concentrates. The pressure being brought to bear by air-quality legislation and public reaction to pollution has prompted a major inquiry into chemical processing of concentrates. Also, air quality is the principal factor in most research studies on the smelting of other metals. Cyclone smelting, oxygen enrichment, and processes for treatment of low-grade SO_2 effluents from furnaces are all the outgrowth of pollution-control requirements.

Electrolytic copper refining has experienced only minor modification in the equipment. The boldest attack on this well-established art is the new British Copper Refinery plant at Manchester, England. This is a major experiment in the use of larger cells, continuously cast anodes, and plastics as materials of construction. The major area for development is in continuous and semicontinuous casting. Static- and wheel-type casting have given way to continuous and semicontinuous casting of cakes and billets. The use of "belt and wheel" casting and "dip forming" for rod has been commercially developed and seems destined to replace the long-established horizontal casting of wirebars.

The general advance in technology has brought a parallel need for improved properties of the copper. This has necessitated a better definition of the effects of trace impurity composition and the corresponding processes for their control.

Leaching Technology

Since the article on copper in Vol. 6 (1965) was prepared, increased application of leaching technology has had a very clear and important impact on copper production. In the year 1965 leaching yielded over 162,000 tons or about 12% of U.S. annual new copper production (1). But in 1969 over 200,000 tons of copper were reported to have been produced in the western United States by heap and vat leaching of ore, dump leaching of waste, and in-place leaching of caved underground workings (2). Some producers have been affected to a greater extent than others by these developments. For instance, officials of Kennecott Copper Corporation estimate that over 20% of their copper production is now coming from the leaching of copper from waste-rock and overburden. In addition to recovering copper not formerly available, this activity has influenced production technology. Production of large quantities of copper in solution has required the development of new techniques of recovery and utilization of metallic copper.

Dump Leaching. Recovery of copper by hydrometallurgical means from copper ores or waste-rock has been influenced most by increased efforts in dump leaching. Malouf (3) states that over $\frac{3}{4}$ million tons per day of mine waste are accumulating at present in areas surrounding the various open-pit copper mines of the western United States. Since accumulation at this and lesser rates has gone on for many years, very large quantities of low-grade material lie in existing dumps. Limited-scale leaching of this material commenced approximately 30 years ago. Only in the past ten years, however, has there been any really systematic effort applied to recovery of copper from waste dumps. For many years hydrometallurgical recovery of copper consisted simply in allowing normal underground flow from mines or water, which had percolated through dumps, to pass over iron scrap in simple launder systems. Recirculation of the solution from which the copper had been removed was practiced on a haphazard scale.

With the realization that waste dumps represented a potential source of millions of tons of copper if properly exploited, came study by various companies on the best method of recovering copper from waste dumps (4). Mine water containing dilute sulfuric acid (see Vol. 6, p. 169) is generally used as a leaching agent. The size of the dumps, and whether they were laid down in a haphazard manner or specifically for the purpose of copper recovery through leaching, are important considerations. Compaction and distribution of fine materials must be considered in a well-thought-out dump-leaching program. These items do much to determine solution distribution and availability of oxygen within the dump which are essential considerations for good copper recovery.

Recycling of solutions was practiced in earlier days only by those wishing to take advantage of leaching characteristics of the recycled solution. At the present time in the western United States it is imperative to recycle to conserve water and to prevent water pollution. When recycling is used, ferrous and ferric ion concentrations build up and acid must be added to prevent formation of impervious layers of hydrated ferric sulfate within the dumps. As iron concentrations increase in the leach solutions on successive cycles, progressively greater additions of sulfuric acid are required to adjust the pH; therefore, it is desirable to strip these salts from solution prior to pH adjustment and recycling. This can be accomplished by oxidation and hydrolysis in settling ponds, as shown in equations 1 and 2.

$$2\,Fe^{2+} + \tfrac{1}{2}\,O_2 + 2\,H^+ \rightarrow 2\,Fe^{3+} + H_2O \tag{1}$$

$$3\,Fe^{3+} + (n+3)H_2O + 2\,SO_4{}^{2-} \xrightarrow{\text{pH 3.5}} Fe_2(SO_4)_3 \cdot Fe(OH)_3 \cdot nH_2O + 3\,H^+ \tag{2}$$
$$\text{(variable composition)}$$

Reactions similar to reaction 2 occur for aluminum at pH 4 and above and mixed sulfates may form.

Vat Leaching, Heap Leaching. Next in importance with regard to the total production of copper are systems involving heap or vat leaching of copper ore. Recent important installations in the western United States utilizing vat leaching for the recovery of copper are at the Inspiration Consolidated property in Arizona (1), the Anaconda property at Weed Heights, Nevada (1), and the Ray Mines Division of

Kennecott Copper Corporation at Ray, Arizona (5). McKinney, Evans, and Simpson (6) presented evidence that improved recoveries from open-pit waste could be obtained by crushing and sizing, followed by flotation of an enriched fine fraction and leaching of the remaining coarse material. The coarse material would presumably be leached in heaps if the grade were suitable or transferred to dumps where freedom from fines should aid permeability and leachability.

Vat leaching is generally employed to extract copper from oxide or mixed oxide–sulfide ores containing more than 0.5% acid-soluble copper. The method is used in preference to heap leaching if the ore material is not porous, and crushing is necessary to permit adequate contact between the leach solution and the copper minerals. Advantages of vat leaching include higher copper recovery in shorter periods, reduced solution losses, and higher copper content in the effluent solution.

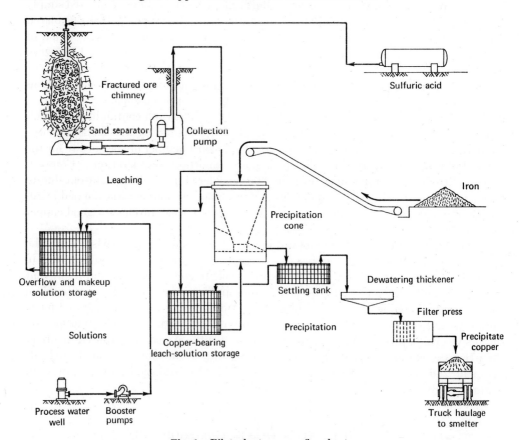

Fig. 1. Pilot-plant process flowsheet.

An important example of heap leaching is found at the Ranchers Exploration and Development Corporation's Bluebird Mine (7). The greatest difference between heap leaching and dump leaching is that, in heap leaching, ore material is leached instead of waste material. The method is not applicable to the dissolution of sulfide minerals or to ores containing large amounts of carbonate or other acid-soluble minerals. Copper content of the pregnant liquor at the Bluebird Mine is 3–7 g/liter and is used as feed to a liquid ion-exchange plant as will be discussed later.

In-place Leaching. In-place leaching involves the leaching of ore as it occurs in the ground. Current in-place leaching employs the dissolution of copper minerals contained in underground mines that had utilized block-caving methods. Because the leaching cycle is very long, almost all of the copper oxides and sulfide minerals encountered in these deposits are leachable by this method if contact of the solutions with the ore is uniform. The best example of a current in-place leaching operation is at the Miami mine of the Miami Copper Company in Arizona. A description of this operation has been given by Fletcher (8).

Nuclear Fracturing. Nuclear fracturing has been proposed as a means of breaking up underground ore deposits for subsequent leaching operations. The Sloop feasibility study, a joint effort of the Atomic Energy Commission, the U.S. Bureau of Mines, and Kennecott Copper Corporation, was undertaken as a detailed investigation of this concept (9). The study included an evaluation of a proposed test site located near Safford, Arizona. The ore body considered is of an oxidized nature and very deep and would presumably lend itself well to in-place leaching with acid solutions. Rosenbaum and McKinney (2) explored the concept of in-place leaching of nuclear-fractured, deeply buried copper sulfide deposits and concluded that a nuclear chimney of copper sulfide ore reduced to rubble may be considered as roughly analogous to a copper-mine waste dump. If this is true, acid ferric sulfate solutions, such as are conventionally used in waste-dump leaching, should be applicable for leaching as illustrated in Figure 1, the Sloop pilot-plant process flowsheet.

Problems of concern in consideration of a nuclear-fracturing approach relate to rock-breaking, safety, and contamination of the resulting extracted copper. At the present, it is believed that the only important long-lived radioisotope that would precipitate with copper from solution is ruthenium-106. Most of the small quantity of ruthenium entering the leach solutions will remain with the copper through the smelting step. All but 1–2% of that entering the leached solutions should be removed during an electrolytic refining process. Some provision in the process would have to be made to prevent excessive buildup of ^{106}Ru in the cell electrolyte and to handle the anode mud should its radioactive content become too high. Workers at the Oak Ridge National Laboratory do not anticipate any problem with residual radioactivity in the electrorefined copper.

Considerable technical and political problems are involved in a project such as Sloop and no specific action has been taken as of 1970 toward executing this program. The concept of extracting copper by in-place leaching without physically mining and transporting the ore continues to present distinct cost-saving possibilities, however, and continued active interest is envisoned.

TREATMENT OF LEACH SOLUTIONS

Cementation. The precipitation of copper from various solutions by replacement with iron, is the most commonly used method of recovering the copper values. The type of iron used is important; the most commonly used material at the present time is detinned scrap iron. Many equipment configurations have been designed for utilization of scrap in cementation operations. A recent approach to this problem is shown in Figure 2 where a so-called scrap-iron cone designed and used by Kennecott Copper Corporation is illustrated (10).

As the cost of collecting and preparing scrap increases, the cost of using detinned iron as a reagent goes up and alternative materials come under consideration. The faster copper-precipitation rates obtainable with sponge or particulate iron promise economic and processing advantages if particulate iron becomes competitive costwise with available scrap iron. A precipitation cone for utilizing various particulate iron precipitants and the use of this cone in extensive pilot-plant operations has been described by Back (11). Sponge iron for use in this precipitation cone could be produced by direct reduction of magnetite concentrates, iron ore, or pyrite cinders. See Iron in this volume. Kennecott has investigated the feasibility of producing sponge iron for copper precipitation by the reduction of the iron in copper reverberatory slag from the firm's smelter. Another precipitant which may become important in the future is shredded automobile scrap. Dean and co-workers have discussed the use of such relatively coarse scrap in the production of copper powder using drum-type precipitators (12).

Extraction. The copper in leach solutions can be extracted and concentrated by liquid ion-exchange techniques prior to its recovery by electrolytic processes. In 1965 General Mills reported the successful development of LIX-64, an α-hydroxyoxime designed for the specific extraction of copper from aqueous solutions (13). The general formula for α-hydroxyoxime extractants is $RR''C(OH)CR'NOH$ where R, R', and R'' may be any of a variety of organic hydrocarbon radicals such as aliphatic and alkylaryl radicals. R'' may also be hydrogen. It is believed that the extraction proceeds as shown in equation 3.

$$2\begin{bmatrix} \overset{\text{HO}}{\underset{\overset{|}{R''}}{\overset{|}{R-\underset{}{C}}}\overset{\text{NOH}}{\underset{}{-C-R'}} \end{bmatrix}_{\text{org}} + (Cu^{2+} + SO_4{}^{2-})_{\text{aq}} \rightleftharpoons \begin{bmatrix} & R'' & & \\ & RC\!\!-\!\!-\!\!-\!\!CR' & \\ H & O & N & O \\ | & \diagdown & Cu & \diagup & | \\ O & N & O \cdots H \\ & R'C\!\!-\!\!-\!\!-\!\!CR & \\ & R'' & \end{bmatrix}_{\text{org}} + (2H^+ + SO_4{}^{2-})_{\text{aq}} \qquad (3)$$

The extractants and complexes are characterized by having a solubility of at least 2% by weight in the hydrocarbon solvent (generally kerosene) that constitutes the organic phase and are insolube in water. In 1969 Hartlage of Ashland Chemical Company reported on Kelex-100, another solvent-extraction reagent which is presumed to function in a similar manner (14). Both companies have subsequently modified their reagents to overcome problems of limited pH range and loading.

The concept of extracting copper ions from leach liquors using an ion-selective reagent dissolved in an immiscible organic liquid has been studied on a pilot scale by a number of copper producers. In particular, work has been done by Bagdad Copper Corporation at Bagdad, Arizona, where a plant operating at 3300 gal/min went on-stream in the latter part of 1970 (15,16), and at Ranchers Exploration and Development Corporation's Bluebird Mine near Miami, Arizona, where the process has been installed on a commercial scale.

In the Bluebird operation (17) copper is recovered from the ore by heap leaching and liquid ion exchange. The copper is then extracted into an aqueous phase again by treatment of the pregnant organic solution with a solution containing 100–150 g/liter sulfuric acid. Electrowinning is then used to recover copper from the high-grade,

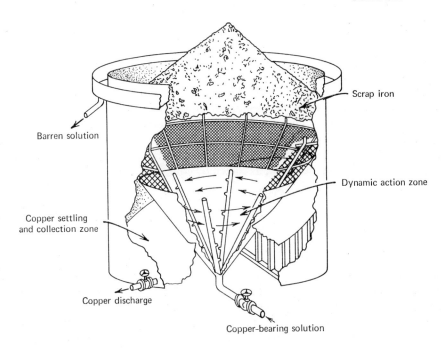

Fig. 2. Sketch of cone precipitator showing solution inflow and copper-precipitate discharge. Courtesy *Journal of Metals* and The Metallurgical Society.

purified copper liquor. Nearly 9 million lb of cathode copper were produced in the plant's first full year of operation.

Electrowinning. As has been pointed out, vat leaching can often yield solutions that are concentrated enough to allow direct electrowinning of copper. Such processes are in use presently at Inspiration Consolidated Mines and Kennecott's Ray Mines Division in Arizona. Because of the presence of relatively high concentrations of cations other than copper and relatively low copper concentrations, it is more difficult to obtain high-purity electrolytic copper by direct electrolysis of leach solutions than by electrolysis of purified solution resulting from liquid–liquid-ion exchange extraction.

TREATMENT OF PRECIPITATE COPPER

The bulk of the copper produced in the leaching operations is utilized directly as feed to existing smelters. The precipitates can be introduced either into reverberatory furnaces or converters, depending upon the balance of the particular process. Because of the relatively low level of many impurities, copper precipitates are also a useful feed for fire-refining operations.

A smaller percentage of copper precipitates is sold directly to consumers. One to 2 million lb/yr are utilized as pigment in antifouling paints. Precipitate copper is presently being used as a raw material for the production of copper hydroxide fungicide by the Kennecott Copper Corp. The ease of oxidation of precipitate copper makes it a useful material for catalyst preparation and about 2 million lb/yr go to this use.

Investigators at the U.S. Bureau of Mines have reported on the refining of cement copper by nonsmelting techniques (18). Two routes were investigated. One, making copper powder for industrial use, employed flotation for rejecting the bulk of the impurities, acid leaching to remove residual iron and aluminum, reduction sintering to eliminate oxygen, and grinding to obtain a powdered product. The other route was to sinter the floated and leached copper into the form of anodes and electrolyze these to yield refined copper cathodes. Feasibility of preparing commercial-sized anodes by sintering is still to be assessed.

Finally, considerable study has been made of the refining or purification of cement copper by chemical means. The ammine carbonate process described by Kunda, Feltman, and Evans (19) is perhaps best known. It involves the extraction of copper from copper scrap or precipitate by leaching with air at 30–50°C and atmospheric pressure in an ammonium carbonate solution, as shown by equations 4–7.

$$CuO + (NH_4)_2CO_3 + 2\,NH_3 \rightarrow Cu(NH_3)_4CO_3 + H_2O \tag{4}$$

$$2\,Cu + (NH_4)_2CO_3 + 2\,NH_3 + \tfrac{1}{2}\,O_2 \rightarrow Cu_2(NH_3)_4CO_3 + H_2O \tag{5}$$

$$Cu + Cu(NH_3)_4CO_3 \rightarrow Cu_2(NH_3)_4CO_3 \tag{6}$$

$$Cu_2(NH_3)_4CO_3 + \tfrac{1}{2}\,O_2 + (NH_4)_2CO_3 + 2\,NH_3 \rightarrow 2\,Cu(NH_3)_4CO_3 + H_2O \tag{7}$$

These reactions show that the leaching of copper oxide in an ammoniacal–ammonium carbonate solution may be carried out without an oxidizing agent. For dissolution of metallic copper, oxygen or cupric ammine carbonate is required. Leaching in the presence of air or oxygen, even at room temperature, gives cupric ammine carbonate as the final product. This solution is then treated to remove impurities and copper powder is recovered by reduction of the solution in a high-pressure autoclave at 150–200°C with a 200–500 psig hydrogen overpressure, P, as shown in equations 8 and 9.

$$Cu(NH_3)_4CO_3 + H_2 \xrightarrow[\Delta P]{\Delta T} Cu° + (NH_4)_2CO_3 + 2\,NH_3 \tag{8}$$

$$Cu_2(NH_3)_4\,CO_3 + H_2 \xrightarrow[\Delta P]{\Delta T} 2\,Cu° + (NH_4)_2CO_3 + 2\,NH_3 \tag{9}$$

The copper in the form of a fine powder is prepared for sale by washing, sintering in a hydrogen stream, pulverizing, and scrubbing. The ammonium carbonate and ammonia are recycled to the leach circuit. Recovery may also be accomplished by boiling the ammine carbonate solution at 120°C to yield copper oxides and then reducing the oxides with hydrogen. This method can be applied only to copper solutions free of Zn and Ni; in other cases the oxides must be dissolved and the copper recovered by electrolysis.

An acid process for producing high-purity copper powder, developed by Chemetals Corporation, has been installed and operated by the Bagdad Copper Corporation (20). The process starts with cement copper which is dissolved in aerated sulfuric acid solution. The solution is filtered to remove impurities, heated, and reduced with hydrogen in an autoclave at 300°F (150°C) and 400 psi. The process eliminates the use of ammonia as a reagent but is more subject to corrosion difficulties than the ammine carbonate system.

Sulfur-Control Technology

Increased public attention to air pollution in all forms has emphasized a problem long recognized by primary copper producers. Treatment of copper concentrates in reverberatory furnaces and converters involves elimination of sulfur by the oxidation of copper sulfide minerals as an essential step in producing the metal. A large portion of all primary copper produced in the world today is processed in this manner. Production of sulfurous gases is, therefore, an inherent part of presently available commercial copper smelting processes.

Sulfur dioxide emission is, of course, not confined to smelting operations. Oxides of sulfur are the leading contaminants from industry in general, and fossil-fuel power plants, which are among the worst offenders, have been under heavy fire from environmentalists. The average smelter, however, emits sulfur oxides in concentrations such that, under certain wind and weather conditions, temporarily high local concentrations are evident. Superimposing these peaks upon the endemic SO_2 level resulting from other sources often results in the total blame being placed upon the shoulders of the smelter operator.

The industry has, over the years, developed techniques to produce sulfuric acid from high-strength gases. However, gases containing lower percentages of sulfur oxides are generated in all reverberatory furnaces and these gases are not amenable to treatment by present technology. A summary of sulfur oxide generation and recovery at U.S. copper smelters in 1969 is presented in Table 2 (21). From these data one sees

Table 2. Sulfur Oxide Generation and Recovery at U.S. Smelters (1969)

Copper smelters	Sulfur equivalent, short tons/yr		Recovered, %
	Generated	Recovered	
roasters	360,100	127,100	35.3
reverberatory furnaces	391,100		
converters	1,064,700	217,100	20.4
total	1,815,900	344,200	19.0

that nearly 1.5 million tons of sulfur equivalent are emitted into the atmosphere each year from U.S. copper smelters.

Two basic approaches are being pursued by the industry in attempting to solve the problem of removing sulfur oxides from low-strength gases. The first approach involves control of SO_2 after it is produced in the smelting operation. The other, longer-term approach is to try to prevent the formation of SO_2 by radical changes in copper-processing methods.

CONTROL OF SULFUR DIOXIDE EMISSION FROM CONVENTIONAL SMELTING OPERATIONS

Control of SO_2 emissions from existing or modified facilities appears to offer more hope in the short term, and efforts in this area follow two avenues. The first approach is to modify the basic smelter flowsheet to incorporate pyrometallurgical processing equipment that will produce more high-strength SO_2 gas and less of the lean gases characteristic of reverberatory furnaces. Fluid-bed roasters (22) and flash-smelting furnaces produce gases ranging from 15% SO_2 when oxygen-enriched air is used (23,24) to 80% SO_2 when almost pure oxygen is used (25). Production of elemental sulfur, liquid sulfur dioxide, or sulfuric acid is possible with these rich gases. Converter smelting of concentrates using oxygen-enriched air is another process modification that permits concentration of SO_2 (26). Several processes are in the development stage that could reduce the generation of low-strength gases as well as allow processing advantages. Soviet as well as U.S. workers are investigating cyclone smelting processes which could produce high concentrations of SO_2 in process gases (27). Single-step or continuous-smelting processes could also eliminate the emission of low-strength gases (28,29).

Successful installation of modifications such as these will reduce the quantity of low-strength sulfur dioxide and could help to alleviate the emission problem. There would still be, however, some low-strength sulfur dioxide gas generated as long as reverberatory furnace operations are maintained. This would have to be removed from stack effluents if the pollution problem were to be solved completely.

Several major problems face the smelting industry in attempting to select processes for capturing SO_2 from gas streams containing about 4% SO_2 or less. Most new processes are tailored for exit gases from coal-fired electric generating plants. Zentgra (30) has reviewed methods being tested in Japan, the U.S., and Germany. Maurin and Jonakin (31) summarized nineteen chemical processes for removing sulfur oxides from stack gases. A list of some of the most prominent of these processes being considered for use in the United States is presented in Table 3 (32). Unfortunately, gas characteristics at smelters are quite different than those at power plants. For example, smelter gases are higher in SO_2, contain more particulates, and are not as hot as power-plant gases. As a result, many engineering evaluations and pilot-plant results cannot be applied directly to smelters.

Wet Processes. Most SO_2 processes fall into two distinct categories and serious technological problems are associated with each. About half could be classified as wet processes in which the gas is scrubbed with a solution such as aqueous sodium hydroxide to absorb the sulfur oxides chemically. A simplified flowsheet for a typical wet process is shown in Figure 3. High efficiency is claimed for this type of process in capturing sulfur compounds. The added potential advantage of reducing particulate emissions is an important consideration. The main disadvantage of this process is that the 400–500°F (200–260°C) gas must be cooled to about 100°F (38°C) ahead of the scrubbing process and then reheated after the scrubbers in order to give the gas buoyancy as it discharges from the stack. Cooling is accomplished normally with water but both the quantity and quality of available water make this a serious obstacle in the case of many smelters. Discarding the loaded absorbent is possible if a ready supply of low-cost absorbent is available and the danger of contaminating water sources and causing surface-dusting problems can be avoided. Regeneration and sulfur recovery

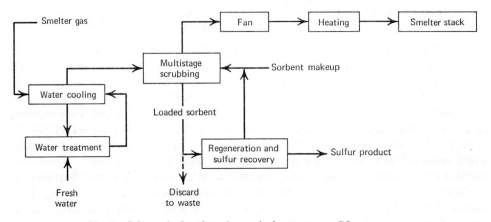

Fig. 3. Schematic flowsheet for typical wet-process SO_2 recovery.

Table 3. U.S. SO$_2$ Processes and Stages of Development (32a)[a]

Process	Developer	Salable product(s)	Remarks
molten carbonates	Atomics International, Canoga Park, Calif.	sulfur or sulfuric acid	still lab scale; ready to be tested in pilot plant on continuous basis
alkalized alumina	Bureau of Mines, Washington, D.C.	sulfur	Has not come up to expectations; attrition is the problem; work may be discontinued
limestone injection/wet scrubber	Combustion Engineering, Windsor, Conn.	none	some mechanical problems, yet producers and users are optimistic; now undergoing modifications
dry absorbent (undisclosed)	Esso Research & Engineering, Linden, N.J.; Babcock & Wilcox, New York, N.Y.	sulfur dioxide or sulfuric acid	small pilot-plant scale; may go to 25-MW size within next few months
dry limestone injection	Tennessee Valley Authority, Muscle Shoals, Ala.	none	going now to full-scale testing
potassium or sodium sulfite chamber	Wellman-Lord, Lakeland, Fla.	sulfur dioxide	successful in 50,000-cfm demonstration plant; going commercial
catalytic oxidation (vanadium pentoxide)	Tyco Laboratories, Waltham, Mass.	sulfuric acid and nitric acid	also removes nitrogen oxides; 10-cfm plant gives favorable results
	Monsanto, St. Louis, Mo.	sulfuric acid	most advanced commercially, some experts say
hydrogen sulfide (undisclosed catalyst)	Princeton Chemical Research, Princeton, N.J.	sulfur	pilot-plant stage
self-regenerative (undisclosed catalyst)	United International Research, Long Island City, N.Y.	sulfuric acid	large laboratory-scale stage; process good for intermediate or high sulfur levels
alkaline scrubbing/electrolytic cell	Stone & Webster, Boston, Mass; Ionics, Inc., Watertown, Mass.	sulfuric acid, hydrogen, oxygen	ready for 25-MW demonstration plant

[a] Courtesy *Chem. Eng. News.*

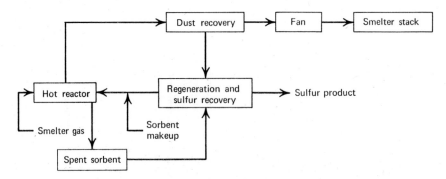

Fig. 4. Schematic flowsheet for typical dry-process SO_2 recovery.

could be accomplished chemically by crystallizing a sulfur compound, such as sodium sulfite, and heating this compound to a high temperature to release rich sulfur dioxide.

Dry Processes. As an alternative to wet gas-cleaning processes, dry processes remove sulfur oxides by absorption and/or adsorption. A schematic flowsheet typical of these processes is shown in Figure 4. Processes that fall into this category involve contacting the waste gas with a solid absorbent, such as dry limestone, in either a fixed-bed or fluid-bed reactor. The efficiency of sulfur removal is generally somewhat lower than in wet processes because efficient gas–solids contact is difficult to accomplish. The reactors in most dry processes are operated at high temperature so that gas cooling and reheating are avoided. Materials of construction, however, pose a problem, as do conveying of absorbents at high temperatures, dust-collection equipment, and attrition of absorbents.

ECONOMICS OF RECOVERY OF SULFUR FROM DILUTE GAS STREAMS

If the total sulfur equivalent presently emitted to the atmosphere were to be recovered as salable material, a considerable marketing problem would result. Ferguson (33) estimated that if this production were marketed as elemental sulfur, operators of western United States smelters would have to sell over half their production overseas and charge $4.50/long ton less than the prevailing Gulf Coast price. If marketed as sulfuric acid over half would be unsalable for geographic reasons even if sold at $1.00/ton of acid fob smelter.

Estimates (21) of the capital costs for acid plants handling dilute gas (4.5% SO_2) were more than twice those for plants handling rich gas (15.8% SO_2), both plants being scaled to handle the same quantity of SO_2. This gives yet another reason why it is important that the SO_2 in the smelter gas should be as concentrated as possible.

These considerations emphasize that SO_2 conversion costs will exceed product values unless there is a change in copper-extraction practices such as generation of undiluted converter gas or "chemical smelting."

HYDROMETALLURGICAL TREATMENT OF COPPER SULFIDE CONCENTRATES

Prevention of the emission of SO_2 in the production of copper can be accomplished by hydrometallurgical (chemical) processing techniques. As discussed under Leaching processes have been developed for oxide copper ores but the problem is more complex for sulfide ores. The main problem is that the bulk of the copper sulfide mineralization is not easily solubilized. Strong solvents, such as sulfuric acid or cyanide, are required to get even part of the copper dissolved.   Unfortunately in most such potential processes, fumes are emitted during the chemical reactions that may pose more serious problems than the SO_2 emission.

Kunda and co-workers (19) used copper sulfide concentrates calcined in air at 750°C as feed for the Sherritt-Gordon process for production of copper from the ammine copper system.   The roasting of copper concentrates under these conditions yields SO_2 and a combination of Fe_xO, $FeSO_4$, Cu_xO, and $CuSO_4$ from which the copper values could be readily leached as shown in equation 4.   They also stated that certain copper sulfide concentrates could be leached directly in an ammonium carbonate solution with encouraging extractions presumably as shown in equations 10–12.

$$Cu_2S + (NH_4)_2CO_3 + 4\,NH_3 + 2\,O_2 \rightarrow Cu_2(NH_3)_4CO_3 + 2\,NH_4^+ + SO_4^{2-} \qquad (10)$$

$$Cu_2(NH_3)_4CO_3 + \tfrac{1}{2}\,O_2 + (NH_4)_2CO_3 + 2\,NH_3 \rightarrow 2\,Cu(NH_3)_4CO_3 + H_2O \qquad (11)$$

$$CuS + (NH_4)_2CO_3 + 4\,NH_3 + 2\,O_2 \rightarrow Cu(NH_3)_4CO_3 + 2\,NH_4^+ + SO_4^{2-} \qquad (12)$$

Over-roasting of copper concentrates can yield copper ferrites ($CuFeO_2$ or $Cu\text{-}Fe_2O_4$) which would respond poorly to such treatment.

The economics of the direct leaching of concentrates would be dependent on the subsequent recovery of ammonium sulfate.   It should be pointed out that a major problem inherent in this process is that many of the minor metals in copper ores are not soluble in the ammonia used in the process and their values can not be recovered readily.

Workers at the Sherritt-Gordon Mines laboratories have devised a process in which sulfide concentrates are leached with dilute sulfuric acid to yield copper sulfate solution and sulfur.   The sulfur and some unchanged copper sulfide are separated from the tailings by flotation.   The sulfur is then separated from the concentrate by hot filtration above the melting point of sulfur, by solvent extraction, or by distillation. The concentrate is recycled to the leaching circuit.   The copper sulfate solution can be treated by any accepted copper winning method.   Recoveries of 98% for copper and 85% for sulfur are claimed (34).

Treadwell Corporation and Anaconda Company have piloted a direct reduction process wherein sulfide concentrates are treated with 90% sulfuric acid to dissolve the

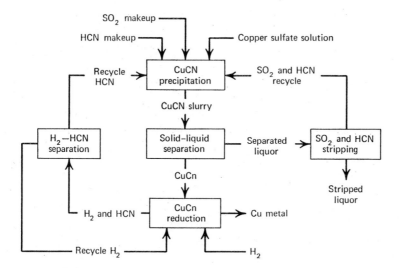

Fig. 5. Outline of cuprous cyanide method for the recovery of copper from solution (35).

copper as cupric sulfate.   In one scheme the iron and other impurities are separated by liquid ion exchange and the copper is recovered by electrolysis.   In the alternative scheme outlined in Figure 5 copper is precipitated as cuprous cyanide using hydrogen cyanide and sulfur dioxide.

$$2\,CuSO_4 + SO_2 + 2\,HCN + 2\,H_2O \rightarrow 2\,CuCN + 3\,H_2SO_4 \tag{13}$$

The cuprous cyanide is then reduced with hydrogen to yield 99.99% pure copper powder (35).   A multimillion dollar plant is now under construction (34).

A breakthrough in hydrometallurgical processing could be imminent but a proven and developed process that can be applied commercially is probably many years away. In any event, it would be unrealistic to expect every nonferrous smelter in the country to abandon existing facilities in favor of a new process which may not be applicable to all copper sulfide ores.   Therefore, prevention of SO_2 emissions by changes in copper-processing techniques can be considered only a long-term potential solution to the over-all emission problem, particularly since this approach may involve other emission or effluent problems.

Continuous Rod Production

In the production of copper wire, a copper rod $\frac{3}{8}$–$\frac{1}{2}$ in. in diameter is cold drawn through a succession of dies to yield wire of the desired gage.   Usually this rod is prepared, by hot rolling, from specially cast copper shapes called wirebars.   These wirebars come in a variety of sizes but the average is about $54 \times 4 \times 4\frac{3}{8}$ in. and weighs approximately 275 lb.   Since the operation of wiredrawing requires long periods of continuous operation, the rod from a number of wirebars must be welded, end to end.

Two processes have been developed to an operational status in recent years which promise to have an important effect upon copper-wire fabrication.   Both of these processes relate to the direct production of copper rod without going through the intermediate wirebar stage.   The dip-forming method was developed by Carreker of the General Electric Research Laboratories (36), and the belt and wheel method (37) was developed for copper in a joint effort by Western Electric Company and Southwire Company (38).   The primary goal in the development of these techniques was related to cost savings through elimination of the separate casting of wirebars, preheating the wirebars, and their breakdown into rod.   Both casting techniques have potential for improvement in quality as well as cost.   In both instances a substantially reduced number of welds results and the effects of trace impurities are lessened.   The rod resulting from the dip-forming process is in essence oxygenfree.   Both processes have been brought to the point of substantial tonnage production at several locations.

Dip Forming.   The dip-forming process was developed in the General Electric Research Laboratory in the middle 1950s and taken to production scale by the General Electric Manufacturing Development Laboratory in the early 1960s.   It consists of passing a metallic cold core (like rod or strip) through a molten bath of the same or different material so that the molten metal accretes or freezes on the core.   The amount of accretion depends on the "heat sink" of the core and the heat properties of the molten metal.   It is essentially a "cladding" process, wherein one metal is deposited on another in a continuous operation.   There is no mold, the process is not "casting" but is unique.

Various metallic combinations are possible and have been shown to be feasible: copper on copper, copper on iron or steel, aluminum on aluminum, brass on brass, brass on steel, various steels on steel, and other combinations in round rod, strip, or other forms. Only copper on copper and copper on nickel-iron have been taken to commercial production, although other combinations can be easily performed.

General Electric has operated copper on copper and copper on iron for over five years in production units, and there are copper-rod licensees in Sweden, Japan, and Yugoslavia, as well as the United States. A number of additional installations are being planned.

Only oxygenfree copper rod is produced because for the dip-forming process oxygen must be less than 20 ppm in both the input (or seed) rod and the molten copper so as to avoid attack of the input die and seal to the molten bath. For copper, the theoretical accretion ratio is $3:1$ with about $2.9:1$ being attained in practice.

Copper cathodes are fed one at a time but continuously into a preheat furnace from which they enter a large induction melting furnace. Molten copper flows through the launder to a smaller holding (or pouring) furnace and into a small chamber or crucible where it accretes or freezes around the feed rod (recycled from previously produced product) which is shaved to present a clean surface for accretion.

The dip-formed rod then passes upward in the cooling tower, over a 90° turn to a tandem rolling mill where it is reduced to its original diameter, and thence to the coiler. The input copper is in a protective atmosphere and the seed rod, from shave die to coiler, is also in such an atmosphere, so that dip-formed rod is bright and clean and ready for use. No surface or other oxides are formed and long coils of oxygenfree copper rod which can be used without shaving are produced. Iron inclusions are reduced because the rolling operation is short and it is in a protective atmosphere.

Any size rod can be produced by adjusting the input-seed rod size and the number of stands in the rolling mill. Four stands are usually sufficient for the usual commercial wire mill input size.

Speeds depend on the melting rate, input size, and output size. Any size coil can be produced.

Investment per ton is low compared to other systems because the furnaces are relatively small, only four stands are needed in the mill, there is no pickling or cleaning of output rod, and the rod entering the mill is round, requiring no edge or cleaning equipment.

Since dip-forming allows both small and larger rod users or producers to make rod near using locations, expensive transportation of rod is greatly reduced. Locating the dip-forming installation a few feet from the wire mill has great advantages.

The process is continuous and maintenance is not a major factor. Shave dies average 20–25 hr. The net output is the melting rate of the furnace (seed rod stays in the system). Many combinations of metals and shapes are possible.

Belt and Wheel Casting.   The joint venture between Western Electric Company and Southwire Company of Carrollton, Georgia, in 1962 was the first application of belt and wheel casting to the continuous casting of copper rod, although this approach had been used previously in the preparation of aluminum rod. Since this initial installation, a considerable evolution in techniques has occurred (39).

In recent installations, raw material in the form of either electrolytic cathode copper or a blend of cathode with a nominal amount of high-quality scrap is charged into a melting furnace by a skip-loading device which transports the input material from floor level to the furnace-charging door.   From the melting furnace, the molten metal is transferred to a rotating drum-type holding furnace of constant pour point design. The molten copper flows to a pour pot mounted on the casting machine from which it is transferred by a pouring spout to the grooved periphery of the 96-in. diameter casting wheel.   A steel band encompasses approximately 239° of the casting wheel's circumference and forms the casting cavity in which the molten metal solidifies.   After solidification, a cast bar, 4-in.^{2} in cross section, exists from the casting cavity.   This bar then passes through continuous milling operations, whereby it is reduced to a rod of the desired dimensions.   During its passage through the mill, the rod is protected from surface oxidation by soluble oil which also serves to quench, cool, and lubricate the rod. On coming out of the rolling mill, and prior to being coiled, the copper rod enters an in-line pickling process.   The most important advantage of the in-line pickling process is that it permits the accumulation of "jumbo" size rod coils which could not be satisfactorily pickled in the conventional "dip" pickling process due to the density of the jumbo package.

Several distinct advantages, both from the standpoint of finished rod quality and economy of operation, are claimed for the present-day belt and wheel process.   Because solidification occurs from all four sides of the bar, there is less surface oxidation than with wirebars, and the high solidification rate produces a more even distribution of oxide throughout the cast bar and better annealing characteristics.   The density of the continuous casting is higher and more uniform than is obtained with wirebars. The process results in continuous rod coils the size of which is limited only by material handling capacities.   Costs are reduced because both welding time and welding materials are eliminated.   Since welds are a major cause of wire breaks, indirect cost savings result from a reduced number of breaks during the wire-drawing stage.   This is also true with regard to inclusions and rolled defects.

The installed systems presently are rated from 10 to 30 tons per hour.   Plans for the immediate future include increasing the potential to 40 tons per hour, as well as developing smaller variations of the system capable of production rates of 6–8 tons per hour.

Presently, belt and wheel continuous rod-casting installations are operated by Western Electric's Nassau Smelting and Refining Company, at Staten Island, New York; by Westinghouse, at Buffalo, New York (being moved to Abington, Virginia); by Southwire Company, at Carrollton, Georgia; by Transvaal Copper Rod Company, at Phalaborwa, South Africa; by Inspiration Consolidated Copper Company, at Inspiration, Arizona; and by Capital Wire and Cable, at Plano, Texas.   In early 1970 Inspiration's mine-located copper-rod plant was reported to be producing 7 million lb of rod/month on a two-shift basis with the company considering adding a third shift. Several other systems are in various stages of design, construction, or installation.

Future Utilization.   The degree to which continuous rod casting will supplant the traditional wirebar method remains to be seen; however, present trends indicate that these techniques will be an important factor in the future of copper-rod fabrication. The flexibility provided by lower capital and operating costs for small production units will allow installations to be placed close to individual wire mills and should be a determining factor in the replacement of conventional techniques with these newer methods.

Impurities and the Fabrication Properties of Copper

Of the materials of commerce, electrolytic copper is one of the purest. The average copper content of electrolytic tough pitch copper, for instance, is over 99.95% and even the highest level of impurities other than oxygen are found only to the extent of 15–30 ppm. Up to 0.05% of oxygen is present in the form of cuprous oxide. Even at these low impurity levels, properties of interest to fabricators are affected in varying degree. Conductivity, fabricability, and annealability, as they are affected by impurities commonly found in electrolytic tough pitch copper, will be considered in the following sections.

Electrical Conductivity. As pointed out by Smart (40), all dissolved impurities lower the conductivity of copper. In tough pitch copper the presence of oxygen (100–500 ppm) decreases the conductivity slightly due to its volume effect, but it is of more importance in that it prevents most impurities from entering into solid solution in the metal, and, consequently, reduces their deleterious effects on conductivity. Iron, tin, and lead are thus precipitated. In the case of antimony and cadmium the rate of precipitation is relatively slow, but some effect is observed. Impurities such as silver, arsenic, nickel, selenium, tellurium, and sulfur do not form stable oxides and will affect conductivity regardless of the oxygen content. The normal tendency of selenium and tellurium to precipitate from solution is inhibited by rapid quenching and their effects are more pronounced. Figure 6 contrasts the decrease in conductivity of tough pitch copper with that for oxygenfree copper as impurity contents are increased. The importance of oxygen in modifying the effect of impurities on conductivity is illustrated clearly. Phosphorus, which is often used as a deoxidizer, has a pronounced effect in lowering electrical conductivity in oxygenfree copper but little effect in the presence of excess oxygen. The individual effects of the impurities have been found to combine arithmetically to give the total effect of all impurities present in any refined copper.

Fabricability. Impurities in electrolytic copper are of such low level as to be of no importance in hot-working and of very little importance in cold-working operations. The concentration of cuprous oxide is of more importance in cold-working methods than minor variations encountered in other impurities. Even so, tough pitch copper can be cold drawn to greater than 99% reduction in area without difficulty. Oxygenfree copper can be drawn to 95% and high purity copper, 99.999+% pure, exhibits no apparent limit to cold working. Key items of importance in determining fabricability characteristics of less pure coppers are the individual impurities, their solubilities, and tendencies to form compounds.

Soluble impurities, such as silver, gold, nickel, and arsenic, do not affect hot workability. Selenium, tellurium, sulfur, and oxygen form brittle compounds and decrease hot and cold workability as their quantities increase well beyond the ranges encountered with tough pitch copper. Sulfur contents in excess of 0.0025% can cause problems in casting in static molds. In continuous casting, however, this is not as important. Selenium and tellurium are sometimes added at the 0.5% level to give a free machining effect but there is a distinct loss in fabricating properties, especially in cold-working operations. Bismuth and lead have limited solubility in copper and tend to separate as the temperature falls during hot working of oxygenfree copper. An extremely brittle condition results. The practical limit for bismuth in oxygenfree copper is about 0.002%. Because lead separates in globular form about 0.02% can be tolerated. Tough pitch coppers can tolerate approximately twice these concentrations of

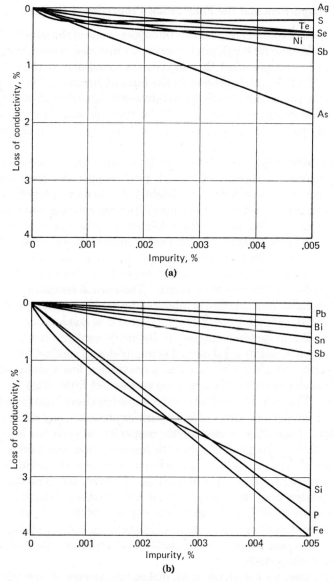

Fig. 6. Effect of impurities on conductivity of copper (40): (a) decrease of conductivity of tough pitch copper with content of impurities; (b) decrease of conductivity of oxygenfree copper with content of impurities. Courtesy Van Nostrand Reinhold Company.

bismuth and lead. Both lead and bismuth can impair cold-working properties unless the limits mentioned are maintained.

Annealability. Studies of the effect of impurities on the softening behavior of copper and the methods of measuring this property have been accelerated during the past decade. The advent of low-temperature curing films for magnet wire has necessitated the use of copper which would anneal sufficiently during the baking operation. The film-coated wire must have a minimum springback after being wound on a form.

The first reported studies of impurity effects in copper were made by Smart and Smith (41–43) in conjunction with research on the production of spectrographically pure copper. Their first study of impurity effects covered iron and nickel in the 0.7–500 ppm range, and cobalt in the 20–500 ppm range. It was concluded that in oxygen-bearing copper, ie, oxygen in the "tough pitch" range, these impurities did not change the recrystallization temperature. In subsequent studies these authors investigated the effects of silver, antimony, cadmium, tin, tellurium, phosphorus, arsenic, sulfur, and selenium. Their results showed that in tough pitch copper, phosphorus had no effect on the softening temperature up to 200 ppm because of compound formation with oxygen. Arsenic up to 5 ppm had no appreciable effect, silver showed no significant effect up to 35 ppm, and neither tin nor cadmium showed effects since they reacted with oxygen to form compounds. Antimony, sulfur, tellurium, and selenium were found to be highly effective in increasing the softening temperature of copper; however, the effects of these elements were strongly affected by the heat treatment prior to cold reduction or penultimate anneal. The effect of antimony was only studied in the range of 18–600 ppm, an appreciably higher concentration than is normally encountered in present-day electrolytic copper.

In the work of Smart and Smith, the effects of combinations of impurities were not determined. This was also the case in an investigation by Phillips and Phillips (44) of the effect of phosphorus, cadmium, silver, arsenic, and tellurium on recrystallization of copper.

Lundquist and Carlen (45) investigated the influence of arsenic, bismuth, lead, antimony, and sulfur in the concentration range of 5–26 ppm. They found that of the elements studied, bismuth had the greatest unit effect and that a decrease in the temperature of anneal prior to cold deformation led to a decrease in the measured unit effectiveness, indicating that at low temperature the bismuth is not in solid solution. It was found that lead lowered the recrystallization temperature, provided the samples were annealed at 1292°F (700°C) or lower. This effect was explained on the basis of a precipitation reaction between lead and sulfur and the work formed the basis for a patent (46).

Harper, Goreham, and Willmott (47), in studying the factors which influence the springiness of copper wire, utilized several commercial brands of copper. They found a strong relationship between the bismuth concentration in the range of 2–18 ppm and springiness. Selenium in the range of 1–5 ppm was also very effective in increasing springiness. They verified the importance of the penultimate anneal on softening behavior.

A later study of the effects of various impurities on springiness was made by Mackay and Armstrong-Smith (48). It was found that the most deleterious impurities were selenium and sulfur, and that silver, iron, nickel, cobalt, and oxygen had no effect. Bismuth, tellurium, antimony, and arsenic were harmful, but the levels encountered in most electrolytic coppers are below those which would cause significant increase in springiness. The behavior of lead was erratic in that it sometimes appeared to have a beneficial effect. The effects noted were based on the following ranges of impurities: selenium 0.2–3 ppm, sulfur 5–15 ppm, iron up to 40 ppm, silver 5–15 ppm, lead up to 20 ppm, nickel up to 45 ppm, and oxygen 120–1000 ppm.

Müller, Pawlek, and Wever (49) investigated the effects of trace quantities of silver, iron, sulfur, lead, selenium, and phosphorus on the conductivity and recrystallization behavior of copper. Their technique involved the preparation of ternary alloys

Cu–Se–Ag, Cu–S–Ag, Cu–Se–Pb, Cu–Fe–S, Cu–Pb–S, and Cu–Fe–P by powder-metal-lurgical methods. They found that a minimum recrystallization temperature occurs in the ternary systems Cu–Ag–Se and Cu–Pb–Se when the Ag–Se or Pb–Se are present in stoichiometric ratios for the formation of selenides or double selenides. They also confirmed the effect of the Pb–S interaction found by Lundquist and Carlen.

Another study of this type is that of Reese and Condra (50) who measured the annealing behavior of copper rod and wire which had been fabricated from wirebars containing various levels and combinations of tellurium, selenium, antimony, bismuth, lead, and silver at concentrations that might be expected in commercial wirebars. They found that tellurium had the greatest unit effect but that selenium, antimony, and bismuth were also effective in raising the softening temperature. Silver decreased the recrystallization temperature. The effect of lead was dependent on the thermal history of the copper, ie, under certain annealing conditions lead decreased the softening temperature. Regression equations relating impurity concentrations and annealing characteristics were developed from the data.

Effect of Thermal History. Many of the impurities present in commercial copper are in concentrations in excess of the solid solubility at low temperatures, eg 300°C. Other impurities oxidize in oxygen-bearing copper to form stable oxides at lower temperature. Hence, since the recrystallization kinetics are influenced primarily by solute atoms in the crystal lattice, the recrystallization temperature is extremely dependent on the thermal treatment prior to cold deformation.

Heating at temperatures below 600°C would have the effect of precipitating certain impurities as metallic particles and others as oxides whereas heating to about 800°C would ensure the solution of most of the impurities in copper with the exception of elements such as iron, cobalt, tin, phosphorus, calcium, and perhaps zinc. It is therefore necessary to control rolling-mill parameters in order to achieve the lowest annealing wire. The most important parameter is the finishing temperature, ie, the temperature prior to quenching. If the hot-rolled rod were allowed to cool slowly then many of the harmful impurities would be rendered ineffectual.

In many high-speed mills the finishing temperature is above 700°C which is sufficiently high to promote a significant solid solubility of detrimental elements. Since all mills do not maintain the same conditions, any test for annealability must be adjusted so that it will measure the properties of the copper in a state similar to that produced by the milling process. That is, if a particular mill finishes and quenches from 740°C then in testing the copper a solution treatment of 740°C should be made a part of the test. The time of this treatment should be adjusted to match the mill condition.

Bibliography

1. Sheffer, H. W. and L. G. Evans, "Copper Leaching Practices in the Western United States," *Information Circular 8341*, U.S. Department of Interior, Bureau of Mines, Washington, D.C., 1968.
2. Rosenbaum, J. B. and W. A. McKinney, "In Situ Recovery of Copper from Sulfide Ore Bodies Following Nuclear Fracturing," *presented at American Nuclear Society Topical Meeting on Engineering with Nuclear Explosives, Las Vegas, Nevada, January, 1970.*
3. Malouf, E. E., E. Peters, and R. S. Shoemaker, "Short Course in Bio-Extractive Mining," *presented at Annual AIME Meeting, Denver, Colorado, February, 1970.*
4. Malouf, E. E. and J. D. Prater, "New Technology of Leaching Waste Dumps," *Mining Congr. J.* **48** (1), 82–85 (1962).

5. Simpson, D. L., B. H. Ensign, and K. F. Marquardson, "Design of the Process Facilities for the Recovery of Copper from Silicate Ores at Ray Mines Division of Kennecott Copper Corporation," *presented at Operating Metallurgy Conference AIME, Chicago, Illinois, 1967.*

6. McKinney, W. A., L. G. Evans, and W. W. Simpson, "Recovery of Copper from Crushed and Sized Porphyry Mine Waste," *presented at Annual AIME Meeting, Denver, Colorado, February, 1970.*

7. Power, K. L., "Operation of the First Commercial Copper Liquid Ion Exchange and Electrowinning Plant," in R. P. Ehrlich, ed., *Copper Metallurgy, Proceedings of the Extractive Metallurgy Division Symposium on Copper Metallurgy, AIME, Denver, Colorado, February, 1970.*

8. Fletcher, 1. R., "In-Place Leaching Miami Mine," *presented at Arizona Section Meeting, Milling Division, AIME, April, 1962.*

9. *Sloop, PNE 1300, Nuclear Explosives Peaceful Applications,* Atomic Energy Commission, Washington, D.C., June, 1967.

10. Spedden, H. R., E. E. Malouf, and J. D. Prater, "Use of Cone-Type Copper Precipitators to Recover Copper from Copper Bearing Solution," *Trans. Soc. Mining Engrs.* **238,** 12–16 (1967).

11. Back, A. E., "Use of Particulate Iron in the Precipitation of Copper from Dilute Solutions," *Trans. Soc. Mining Engrs.* **238,** 12–16 (1967).

12. Dean, K. C., R. D. Groves, and S. L. May, "Copper Cementation Using Automobile Scrap in a Rotating Drum," *Rept. of Investigation 7182,* U.S. Department of Interior, Bureau of Mines, Washington, D.C., 1968.

13. Agers, D. W., J. E. House, R. R. Swanson, and J. L. Drobniek, "Copper Recovery from Acid Solutions Using Liquid Ion Exchange," *Trans. Soc. Mining Engrs.* **235,** 191–198 (1966).

14. Hartlage, 1. A., "Kelex 100—A New Reagent for Copper Solvent Extraction," *presented at SME Fall Meeting, Salt Lake City, Utah, September, 1969.*

15. McGarr, H. J., N. H. Berlin, and W. F. A. Slolk, "Cost of Copper—Solvent Extraction and Electrowinning Look Great on Paper," *Eng. Mining J.* **170,** 66–67 (1969).

16. McGarr, H. J., "Solvent Extraction Stars in Making Ultrapure Copper," *Chem. Eng.* **77,** 82–84 (1970).

17. Rawling, K. R., "Commercial Solvent Extraction Plant Recovers Copper from Leach Liquors," *World Mining* **15** (13), 30–33 (1969).

18. Groves, R. D., J. K. Winter, and S. J. Hussey, "Refining of Cement Copper by Non-Smelting Techniques," *presented at Annual AIME Meeting, Denver, Colorado, February, 1970.*

19. Kunda, W. H. Feltman, and D. J. I. Evans, "Production of Copper from the Ammine Carbonate System," in R. P. Ehrlich, ed., *Copper Metallurgy, Proceedings of the Extractive Metallurgy Division Symposium on Copper Metallurgy, AIME, Denver, Colorado, February, 1970.*

20. "Commercial Plant to Produce High Purity Copper by Chemical Process," *Chem. Eng.* **72,** 14 (1965).

21. Semrau, K. T., "Sulfur Oxides Control and Metallurgical Technology," in R. P. Ehrlich, ed., *Copper Metallurgy, Proceedings of the Extractive Metallurgy Division Symposium on Copper-Metallurgy, AIME, Denver, Colorado, February, 1970.*

22. Lanier, H., "Copper," in *Kirk-Othmer Encyclopedia of Chemical Technology,* 2nd ed., Vol. 6, Interscience Publishers, a division of John Wiley & Sons, Inc., N.Y., 1965, p. 145.

23. Bryk, P., J. Rysilin, I. Honkasalo, and R. Malmstrom, "Flash Smelting Copper Concentrates," *J. Metals* **10,** 395–400 (1958).

24. Okazoe, T., T. Kato, and K. Murao, "The Development of Flash Smelting Process at Ashio Copper Smelter, Furukawa Mining Company, Ltd.," *presented at AIME Symposium on Pyrometallurgical Processes in Non-Ferrous Metallurgy, Pittsburgh, Pennsylvania, November, 1965.*

25. Suddington, R. R., Curlook, W., and Queneau, P., "Use of Tonnage Oxygen by the International Nickel Company," *presented at AIME Operating Metallurgy Conference, Pittsburgh, Pennsylvania, 1965.*

26. Messner, M. E., and D. A. Kinneberg, "Direct Converter Smelting at Utah Using Oxygen," *J. Metals* **22,** 23–29 (1969).

27. Onaev, I. A., A. F. Krochken, A. L. Tseft, N. I. Adson, V. V. Golovko, and V. I. Krutasov, "Cyclone Smelting of Balkhashsk Copper Concentrates with an Oxygen Enriched Blast," *Vestn. Akad. Nauk Kaz. SSR* **21** (1), 27–34 (1965).

28. "Copper Smelting and Refining Featured at London Symposium," *World Mining* **3** (6), 23 (1967).

29. "Noranda Pilots Continuous Copper Smelting," *Eng. Mining J.* **169,** 85 (1968).

30. Zentfraf, K. M., "The Present State of Flue Gas Desulphurization," *Combustion* **41** (5), 6–11, (1969).

31. Maurin, P. G. and 1. 1onakin, "Removing Sulfur Oxides from Stack," *Chem. Eng.* (*Deskbook Issue*) **77** (9), 173–180 (1970).

32. "TVA Tests Dry Limestone Process for SO_2 Control," *Chem. Eng News* **48** (4), 30–31 (1970).

33. Ferguson, F. A., "Symposium on Future Sources for the Fertilizer Industry," *158th Am. Chem. Soc. National Meeting, New York, September, 1969.*

34. "29th Inventory of New Processes and Technology," *Chem. Eng.* **77** (16), 148 (1970).

35. U.S. Pat. 3,321,303 (Sept. 1966), E. S. Roberts, (to Treadwell Corp.).

36. Carreker, Jr., R. P., "Dip Forming—A Continuous Casting Process," *J. Metals* **15,** 774–780 (1963).

37. Russell, J. B. and F. R. Nichols, "Equipment and Practice for Continuous Casting and Rolling by the Properzi Process," *Inst. Metals, J.* **87,** 209 (1959).

38. Cole, 1. and H. Moss, "Nassau's Process for Continuous Casting and Rolling of Copper Rod," *Wire Wire Prod.* **44** (6), 1132–1213 (1967).

39. Kinard, K. J., "Evaluation of the Southwire Continuous Copper Rod System," *Wire* **101,** 1–4 (1969).

40. Smart, Jr., J. S., "The Effect of Impurities in Copper," in A. Butts, ed., "Copper—the Science and Technology of the Metal, Its Alloys and Compounds," *Am. Chem. Soc. Monogr. 122,* Reinhold Publishing Corp., New York, 1954, Chap. 19.

41. Smart, Jr., J. S., and A. A. Smith, Jr., "Effect of Iron, Cobalt and Nickel on Some Properties of High Purity Copper," *Trans. AIME* **147,** 48–56 (1942).

42. Smart, Jr., J. S., and A. A. Smith, Jr., "Effect of Certain Fifth Period Elements on Some Properties of High Purity Copper," *Trans. AIME* **152,** 103–116 (1943).

43. Smart, Jr., J. S., and A. A. Smith, Jr., "Effect of Phosphorus, Arsenic, Sulfur and Selenium on Some Properties of High Purity Copper," *Trans. AIME* **166,** 144–155, (1946).

44. Phillips, V. A., and A. Phillips, "The Effect of Certain Solute Elements on the Recrystallization of Copper," *J. Inst. Metals* **81,** 185–208 (1952).

45. Lundquist, S., and S. Carlen, "Die Bestimmung der Erweichungtemperatur in Einsatz für die Güterüberwachung von Sauerstoffhaltigem Drahtbarrenkupfer," *Erzmetall.* **9,** 145–154 (1956).

46. U.S. Pat. 2,897,107 (July 28, 1959), S. Carlen, and S. Lundquist (to Bolidens Gruvaktiebolag).

47. Harper, S., A. R. Goreham, and J. Willmott, "Factors Affecting the Springiness of Copper Wire," *J. Inst. Metals* **93,** 405–417 (1965).

48. Mackay, K. E., and G. Armstrong-Smith, "Quality Control of Electrolytic Tough Pitch Copper," *J. Inst. Mining Metallurgy* **75C,** 269 (1966).

49. Muller, D., F. Pawlek, and H. Wever, "The Effects of Trace Elements on the Electrical Conductivity and Recrystallization Temperature of Copper," *Z. Metallk.* **57,** 175 (1966).

50. Reese, D. A., and L. W. Condra, "The Effects of Wirebar Composition on the Annealing Properties of Copper Wire," *Wire J.* **2** (7), 42–50 (1969).

W. M. Tuddenham
Kennecott Copper Corp. and
H. Lanier
Essex International Inc.

CRESYLIC ACIDS, SYNTHETIC

The term cresylic acids covers all the methyl derivatives of phenol, from mono to penta. The monomethylphenols are called cresols; the dimethylphenols are called xylenols. The term "tar acids" is often used for the cresylic acids, referring to their traditional source, coal tar.

Coal-tar acids are a by-product of the manufacture of coke for the steel industry, and petroleum-derived acids are by-products of the "sweetening" of petroleum distillates. Gas works in Great Britain, where the major product is gas, also yield tar acids. In Great Britain, low-temperature tar, a by-product in the manufacture of smokeless fuel, is another source of tar acids. Of these four sources, only the first two are of importance in the United States. In continental Europe only coke oven tar is of importance, while in Great Britain, the gas works are closing down since natural gas has been found in the North Sea. Low-temperature tar is becoming more available since the demand for smokeless fuel is rising. However, although the supply of tar acids is not increasing, the uses for them are, thus outstripping the supply and forcing users to look at synthetically produced cresylic acids. (See also Alkylphenols in this volume.)

Uses for Tar Acids

Not only are the traditional outlets for tar acids growing (phenolic resins, phosphate plasticizers, disinfectants, wire enamel solvents, engine and metal cleaners, and antioxidants), but new uses have sprung up.

o-Cresol is a starting material for a variety of pesticides, such as DNOC (4,6-dinitro-o-cresol, see Vol. 11, p. 689) and MCPA ((2-methyl-4-chlorophenoxy)acetic acid), a post-emergence herbicide (see Weed killers). m-Cresol is the starting material for a contact insecticide introduced by Sumitomo Chemical Company of Japan as Sumithion (see Vol. 11, pp. 701, 702). 2,6-Xylenol undergoes an oxidative polymerization in the presence of oxygen and a copper–amine complex to give PPO (polyphenylene oxide) resin, see Vol. 15, p. 173.

Routes to Synthetic Cresols

Synthetic p-Cresol. Two routes have been used to prepare p-cresol. Both of them are classical phenol processes (see Phenol, Vol. 15, p. 148). The first is the sulfonation of toluene to make predominantly p-toluenesulfonic acid. Fusion of the alkali salt with caustic soda yields the salt of p-cresol from which the latter can be recovered by acidification. Pure p-cresol can be isolated by distillation.

The second route to p-cresol is via p-cymene (4-isopropyltoluene). This material can be obtained from naval stores (see Terpenes, Vol. 19, p. 816). The cymene is treated with oxygen to give the hydroperoxide. However, oxidation of the tertiary hydrogen of the isopropyl group is heavily favored. Treatment of the hydroperoxide with strong acids cleaves it to give p-cresol and acetone. Hydroperoxidation of the methyl group and subsequent cleavage would result in p-isopropylphenol, which can readily be separated from p-cresol by fractional distillation.

Vapor-Phase Methylation of Phenol. The reaction generally used is the methylation of phenol with methanol over a solid acidic catalyst. This reaction has been known since 1945 when Cullinane and Chard (1) first investigated it. Great variations in catalyst, feed, and reaction conditions are possible.   The catalyst of choice is a porous alumina or silica-alumina of various ratios of silica-to-alumina.   In general, at the lowest temperature, 200–290°C, anisole (methyl phenyl ether) constitutes one of the major products over an alumina catalyst (2).   At higher temperatures ortho-methylation is the predominant reaction, giving o-cresol and 2,6-xylenol as major products.   It has been speculated that even at these higher temperatures, anisole is the intermediate and that an isomerization takes place from the O-methylated to the C-methylated isomer.   Evidence for this is the fact that anisole, when subjected to the same conditions that lead to C-methylation starting with phenol and methanol, gives similar product distribution (1).   As the temperature is raised above 350°C, meta- and para-methylation become more pronounced leading to the formation of m,p-cresol, the various xylenols other than the 2,6-isomer, and (polymethyl)phenols. The use of the more acidic silica-alumina also causes the reaction to become less ortho-selective and increases the proportions of meta- and para-methylated phenols.   At the higher temperature, catalyst fouling due to cooking becomes a problem, which can be overcome by periodically burning off the coke.

The ratio of mono- to polymethylated products can be controlled by the ratio of methanol to phenol.   Liquid hourly space velocities (volume of feed (at room temperature) per volume of catalyst) from very low values to 2–3 will result in a high degree of methylation.   However, lower feed rates, and thus longer contact time, not only effect more complete conversion but may change the product distribution from the less stable products to the more stable ones.   Thus, longer contact times will make ortho-methylation less selective and cause the formation of more meta- and para-methylated products.   That this could be the result of isomerization can be surmised by converting ortho-methylated phenols under similar conditions (1,3–5).

The methyl group needed for the methylation of phenols may be derived from sources other than methanol.   Thus, methyl ether, methyl halides, and methylamines (6) have been investigated.   Even methyl groups already attached to phenolic rings can be transferred to phenol (transmethylation) (5).   Phenols other than phenol itself can be methylated.   They do so very readily which leads to the formation of pentamethylphenol and hexamethylbenzene via pentamethylbenzene (1,7).   A special case of methylating a methylated phenol by a similar molecule is disproportionation. Thus *o*-cresol will yield phenol and 2,6-xylenol. Usually this takes place along with isomerization, resulting in the products derived from both reactions.

Catalysts other than alumina and the more acidic silica-alumina which have been applied to the vapor-phase methylation are ceria, magnesia, thoria, zirconia, urania, titania, and aluminum fluoride (8). Titania (9) is similar to alumina in activity, but produces less 2,6-xylenol, substituting *p*-cresol and 2,4-xylenol for it. Ceria (10) requires a temperature of 450–500°C and gives *o*-cresol more selectively than alumina at the lower temperatures. Magnesia (11) is also specific for ortho-methylation at 500°C, yielding predominantly 2,6-xylenol with excess methanol. Mixed oxide catalysts have also been used (12).

The use of hydrogen chloride in the phenol methylation over alumina is claimed to give higher ortho-selectivity than is possible without the gas (13).

In 1965, Koppers Company started the first synthetic cresylic acid plant at Follansbee, West Virginia, designed to make a variety of methylphenols rather than a single compound. About one year after Koppers Company went into commercial production of synthetic cresols and xylenols, Consolidated Coal Company followed with a similar plant at Newark, New Jersey. Both Koppers and Consolidated Coal have expanded their facilities to meet the increased market demands.

***m,p*-Cresol by Sulfonation.** In Japan, Sumitomo has produced *m,p*-cresol by sulfonation-fusion. Normal sulfonation of toluene yields *p*-toluenesulfonic acid. However, isomerization of the sulfonic acid takes place at higher temperatures and in the presence of sulfuric acid to give a mixture high in the meta isomer (14). Fusion gives the corresponding cresols.

***m,p*-Cresol by Hydroperoxidation.** More recently, Japanese chemical companies have used the hydroperoxidation route, producing *m,p*-cresol from a mixture of *m*- and *p*-cymene (methylisopropylbenzene). These are derived from toluene by alkylation with propylene. This is the typical cymene-to-phenol process (Vol. 15, p. 150).

Liquid-Phase Methylation. A liquid-phase process for methylation of phenol has been patented (15). Phenol and methanol are reacted in an autoclave. The catalyst is an aqueous solution of a zinc halide, preferably the bromide, with hydrogen bromide. Typical conditions are 175–250°C, 5–60 atm pressure, 2 hr reaction time. The products are *o*-cresol, *p*-cresol, and 2,4-xylenol. A commercial unit of Union Rheinische Braunkohlen Kraftstoff A.-G. is in operation at the Wesseling works.

3,5-Xylenol from Isophorone. In 1969 it was announced that Midland-Yorkshire Tar Distillers are to start production of 3,5-xylenol at Four Ashes, near Birmingham. The process was originally developed by Shell and they will handle the sales. The route is the demethanation of isophorone (3,5,5-trimethyl-2-cyclohexene-1-one) to the xylenol (16).

The reaction is carried out in the vapor phase over alumina per se or combined with a dehydrogenation catalyst at 450-550°C. The isophorone is derived from acetone (see Vol. 1, p. 166).

Bibliography

1. N. M. Cullinane and S. J. Chard, *J. Chem. Soc.* **1945,** 821.
2. Brit. Pat. 600,837 (1948), N. M. Cullinane and W. C. Davis (to Peter Spence and Sons, Ltd.).
3. I. Pigman et al., *J. Am. Chem. Soc.* **76,** 6169 (1954).
4. Brit. Pat. 695,464 (1953), to CURA Patents, Ltd.
5. U.S. Pat. 2,777,881 (1957), M. B. Neuworth (to Consolidation Coal Co.).
6. U.S. Pat. 2,440,036 (1948), D. E. Winkler and S. A. Ballard (to Shell Development Co.).
7. P. S. Landis and W. O. Haag, *J. Org. Chem.* **28,** 585 (1963).
8. U.S. Pat. 2,551,628 (1951), to J. E. Nickels (to Koppers Co.).
9. Brit. Pat. 1,125,087 (1968), to The Coal Tar Research Association.
10. Brit. Pat. 1,124,839 (1968), to The Coal Tar Research Association.
11. Brit.Pat. 1,034,500 (1966), to General Electric Co.; and U.S. Pat. 3,446,856 (1969), S. B. Hamilton, Jr. (to General Electric Co.).
12. U.S. Pat. 3,347,936 (1967), M. Froitzheim et al. (to Rütgerswerke und Teerverwertung A.-G.).
13. U.S. Pat. 3,426,358 (1969), H. L. Schlichting et al. (to Hooker Chemical Corp.).
14. A. A. Spryskov, *Zhur. Obshch. Khim.* **30,** 2449 (1960); *Chem. Abstr.* **55,** 12337a (1961). A. A. Spryskov, *Izv. Vysshikh Uchebn. Zavedenii Khim. i Khim. Tekhnol.* **4,** 981 (1961); *Chem. Abstr.* **57,** 16464 (1962).
15. U.S. Pat. 3,349,048 (1966), E. Biller (to Union Rheinische Braunkohlen Kraftstoff A.-G.).
16. U.S. Pat. 2,344,226 (1944), S. A. Ballard and V. E. Haury (to Shell Development Co.); P. W. Sherwood, *Erdöl Kohle* **8,** 884 (1955); Brit. Pat. 588,099 (1947) D. E. Winkler and S. A. Ballard (to Shell Development Co.).

GERD LESTON
Koppers Company

D

DIAMOND

During the past few years some new developments have taken place in the areas of shock synthesis of diamond, the crystal structures of diamond, metastable growth of diamond, semiconducting diamond thermistors, and large diamond crystals.

Shock Synthesis of Diamond. Two somewhat different processes are now in use for commercial production of diamond powder by shock-wave methods. The first, which uses massive graphite as the source of carbon, was described by DeCarli and Jamieson (1,2) in 1961 (see Vol. 4, p. 303). The Allied Chemical Corporation sells diamond made by this process. The purified product is a light gray powder suitable for use in lapping and other fine abrasive applications.

The second process, used by E. I. du Pont de Nemours & Co., Inc. (3), begins with graphite as small, well-crystallized lumps in nodular cast iron. This mass is exposed to the brief, intense pressure generated by a suitable charge of high explosive. The graphite lumps are more compressible and so reach much higher temperatures than the surrounding iron at the peak pressures, which last for a few microseconds, and part of the graphite turns into diamond. The carbon is then cooled rapidly by the iron environment and the new diamond is thereby preserved. After recovery of the mass, the iron is dissolved and the diamond is separated by controlled oxidation of the graphite. The final product is a gray powder whose particles range in size up to 30 micrometers (4).

Crystal Structure of Diamond. In the course of examining diamond prepared by the direct conversion of well-crystallized graphite at pressures of about 130 kbar, Bundy and Casper (5,6) found certain unusual reflections in the x-ray-diffraction patterns. These reflections could be explained by assuming a hexagonal diamond structure (related to wurtzite) with $a = 2.52$, $c = 4.12$ Å, space group $P6_3/mmc - D_{6h}^4$ with 4 atoms per unit cell. The calculated density would be 3.51 g/cc, the same as for ordinary cubic diamond, and the distances between nearest neighbor carbon atoms would be the same in both hexagonal and cubic diamond, 1.54 Å.

Figure 1 shows the crystal structures of graphite, ordinary cubic diamond, and hexagonal diamond. The layers of carbon atoms lie in flat sheets in graphite, but in diamond the sheets are more wrinkled and lie closer together. Taken separately, the sheets in diamond all look pretty much alike, but one may stack them in various lateral positions and still have bonding between sheets. These lateral positions are called A, B, C, in the figure.

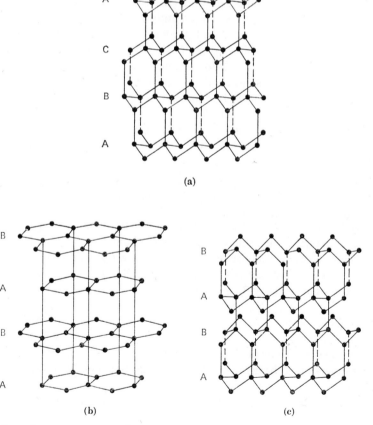

(a)

(b)   (c)

Fig. 1. Crystal structures of graphite, ordinary cubic diamond, and hexagonal diamond.

In cubic diamond the wrinkled sheets lie in the (111) or octahedral face planes of the crystal and are stacked in an ABCABC... sequence. Thus if we start at sheet A, we find that all the carbon atoms in sheet B do not lie directly above all the atoms in sheet A, and the atoms in sheet C do not all lie above the atoms in either sheet A or sheet B. However, in the third sheet above A, all the atoms again lie over those in the original sheet A. Similarly, all the atoms in B sheets lie directly above each other, etc. In real crystals this ABCABC sequence continues for hundreds or thousands of layers, but deviations from the sequence do occur. For example, a "twinned" diamond is not unusual. Here two crystals are grown face to face as mirror images. The mirror is called a "twinning plane" and the sequence of sheets crossing the mirror goes ...ABC-ABCCBACBA.... One might also imagine even more complex sequences of sheets and probably many unusual sequences exist in real crystals, but they are not always easy to study. Silicon carbide, for example, is noted for the varieties of ways in which its layer planes may be stacked.

In hexagonal diamond the wrinkled sheets are stacked in an ABABAB...sequence, as shown in the figure. If one looks down on the stack from above, one sees hexagonal holes formed by the six-membered carbon rings and the crystal has hexagonal symmetry about this axis, hence the name "hexagonal diamond." This structure is analogous to the wurtzite structure in the same way that cubic diamond is analogous to the zincblende structure.

The sequence of sheets in graphite is also ABAB... but an examination of the atomic positions shows that they are not simply related to those in either kind of diamond. Thus the simple compression of graphite should not be expected to yield diamond. However, well-crystallized graphite, in which the ABAB... sequence extends for at least hundreds of layers, tends to form hexagonal diamond more easily than cubic diamond. The experiments show that the sheets of hexagonal diamond are not parallel with the original graphite sheets but instead are roughly perpendicular to them, so that the greater the extent of the ABAB... sequence in the original graphite, the larger the sheets of the resulting hexagonal diamond may be. Poorly crystalline graphite, made up of many small sheets not stacked very high, would not be so favorable for forming hexagonal diamond crystals.

In spite of the close relationship between the two structures, some reshuffling of the atoms is necessary to complete the transformation of graphite into hexagonal diamond crystals of a size large enough to detect. The necessary atomic motions can be provided by heating to about 1200°C, much lower than the 2000–3000°C required to make cubic diamond from ordinary graphite without a catalyst. Even so, various departures from ideality make it difficult to prepare material which is entirely hexagonal diamond, even when the best graphite is used. The products obtained so far always contain some ordinary diamond and also some remnant graphite, parts of which are compressed by the nearby diamond regions. Hence many of the physical properties of hexagonal diamond are not known very well, including its stability relative to cubic diamond.

The same general kinds of effects described here for carbon have also been noted in the direct conversion of hexagonal boron nitride (see Vol. 3, p. 678) to the denser forms (7).

These laboratory findings stimulated a search for hexagonal diamond elsewhere, and it was found in the Canyon Diablo meteorite and also in the shock-made diamond from DuPont, but not in the diamond from Allied Chemical nor in regular abrasive synthetic diamond (8).   This new mineral form of natural carbon has been named Lonsdaleite.   One associates hexagonal diamond with a highly crystalline graphite precursor.   Precursor effects somewhat related to this have been observed in high-pressure carbonization experiments, where the reaction path depends on the molecular structure of the starting material (9).

Metastable Growth of Diamond.   By this is meant the growth of diamond at low pressures where graphite is thermodynamically stable.   The subject has a long and not always respectable history, but recent work in the United States and the Soviet Union indicates that diamond may form at moderate pressures during decomposition of gases such as methane.   Patents by Eversole (10) and Hibshman (11) described a process which was confirmed by the work of Angus, Will, and Stanko (12).   Batches of clean diamond powder were alternately exposed to methane at about 1050°C and 0.1 atmosphere for a few hours followed by hydrogen at 1033°C and 50 atmospheres.   The hydrogen treatment removed graphite.   After several such cycles the diamond masses gained in weight by several percent and only diamond could be found in them.

Deryagin, Fedoseev, et al. (13) report a similar process for growth of diamond whiskers on a single crystal diamond heated by radiation during observation under a microscope.   The mean growth rate was about 10 micrometers per hour, and crystals of 400 by 20 by 20 micrometers were grown.   They were identified as diamond by electron diffraction.

So far this general method of diamond growth is not used commercially.

Semiconducting Diamond Thermistors.   Wentorf and Bovenkerk (14) reported the synthesis of semiconducting diamonds by the incorporation of foreign atoms such as B, Al, or Be during the growth process, or by diffusion of boron into existing diamond crystals at high pressure and temperature.   The crystals were p-type with resistivities in the range 10^2–10^{10} ohm-cm and activation energies for conduction in the range of 0.1 to 0.3 eV.   Such crystals can be fabricated into durable, sensitive thermistors which are available from the General Electric Company.   They have a useful working range between $-200°C$ and $500°C$, with nominal resistances in the range 4000 to 40,000 ohms at 100°C (15).

Large Diamond Crystals.   Recently the General Electric Company announced that improved control of the diamond growth process has allowed the synthesis of gem quality crystals in size up to about 5 mm (1 carat or 0.2 gram).   In this method small diamonds are used as the source of carbon in a hot portion of a molten catalyst metal (Fe, Ni, etc) bath.   The bath is saturated with carbon at high pressures (55–60 kbar) and the temperature is held in the range 1400–1500°C.   Diamond crystallizes on seed crystals placed in a cooler portion of the bath and the transfer of carbon from hot to cooler diamond continues for periods up to a week in order to make the largest crystals. The process is not commercially economical, but the control of growth rates and bath compositions permits the formation of high-quality diamond crystals of various kinds for studies of their properties (16,17).

Bibliography

1. P. S. DeCarli and J. C. Jamieson, *Sci.* **133,** 1821 (1961).
2. U.S. Pat. 3,238,019 (March 11, 1966), to P. S. DeCarli (Allied Chemical Corp.).
3. U.S. Pat. 3,401,019 (Sept. 10, 1968) to G. R. Cowan, B. W. Dunnington, and A. H. Holtzman (E. I. du Pont de Nemours & Co., Inc.).
4. L. F. Treub, *J. Appl. Phys.* **39,** 4707 (1968).
5. F. P. Bundy and J. S. Casper, *J. Chem. Phys.* **46,** 3437 (1967).

6. F. P. Bundy, "Direct Phase Transformations in Carbon" in J. W. Mitchell, R. C. DeVries, R. W. Roberts, and P. Cannon, eds., *Reactivity of Solids*, John Wiley & Sons, Inc., New York, 1969, pp. 817–826.
7. F. P. Bundy and R. H. Wentorf, Jr., *J. Chem. Phys.* **38**, 1144 (1963).
8. R. E. Hanneman, H. M. Strong, and F. P. Bundy, *Sci.* **155**, 995 (1967).
9. R. H. Wentorf, Jr., *J. Phys. Chem.* **69**, 3063 (1965).
10. U.S. Pat. 3,030,187 (April 17, 1962) and 3,030,188 (April 17, 1962) to W. G. Eversole (Union Carbide Co).
11. U.S. Pat. 3,371,996 (March 5, 1968) to H. J. Hibshman.
12. J. C. Angus, H. A. Will, and W. S. Stanko, *J. Appl. Phys.* **39**, 2915 (1968).
13. B. V. Deryagin, D. V. Fedoseev, V. M. Luk'yanovich, B. V. Spitsyn, V. A. Ryabov, and A. V. Lavrent'er, *Sov. Phys. "Doklady"* **13** (6), 783 (Feb. 1969); translated from *Doklady Academiy Nauk SSSR* **181**, 1094 (1968).
14. R. H. Wentorf, Jr., and H. P. Bovenkerk, *J. Chem. Phys.* **36**, 1987 (1962).
15. "Thermistor Senses Red Heat Temperatures," *Materials Engineering*, p. 85 (Aug. 1968).
16. R. H. Wentorf, Jr., "Some Studies of Diamond Growth Rates," *J. Phys. Chem.* **75** (June, 1971).
17. H. M. Strong, "Further Studies on Diamond Growth Rates and the Physical Properties of Man-Made Diamonds," *J. Phys. Chem.* **75** (June, 1971).

ROBERT H. WENTORF, JR.
General Electric Company

E

ELECTROMIGRATION

The term electromigration refers to mass motion under the influence of high-current density. By usage it has come to be distinguished from electrolysis by referring only to those systems where the mass-transport number is small, as for example metals and alloys. The process depends directly on the diffusion coefficient and is therefore highly temperature dependent. In the region where the temperature is around $9/10$ of the melting temperature for a solid one can expect electromigration-transport numbers of the order of 10^{-8}. Interestingly enough the partial currents carried by the ions in such a case are of about the same order of magnitude as the electronic currents carried in undoped semiconductors.

Historical Background Before 1950. The oldest recorded investigation of volume electromigration was carried out by Gerardin (1) in 1861 when he first investigated the effect in molten alloys. Experimental studies on both solid and liquid metals begin to appear in literature in the 1920s almost exclusively by German investigators. The names of Schwarz, Seith, and Jost are particularly prominent; the work of that period has been reviewed by each (2–4). Particularly recommended is Schwarz's small volume, *Elektrolytische Wanderung in festen und flüssigen Metallen* (2). During the 1930s other contributors include C. Wagner and Kremann.

Work of Seith and Wever. The modern period of research in this area may be said to begin with the work of Seith and Wever (5) from 1953 to 1955. They introduced two new features into the investigations: first, they inscribed marks onto the surface of the specimen which allowed one to observe lattice motion with respect to the laboratory and secondly they showed that in moving across several of the Hume-Rothery diagrams the direction of the mass motion of the alloy with respect to the lattice reversed direction on going from a predominately electron-type to a hole-type conductor. Previously the other investigators had relied only on analyzing the changes in chemical composition caused by the high current density and did not attempt to determine any mass motion with respect to the lattice as a frame of reference. The introduction of the moving markers made available additional information so that one could deduce a motion of each of the alloy constituents with respect to fixed-lattice frame. In addition, it was soon apparent that experiments could be carried out on pure materials by this technique which had previously been unavailable for study. The fact that for the electron-type metals the net mass transport was directed toward the anode, whereas for the hole-type metals toward the cathode, suggested strongly that the interaction with the charge carriers provided the dominant drive for the mass movement. Almost all the prior thinking had been in terms of electrostatic forces driving the atom motion, with the one interesting exception of the suggestion by Skaupy (6) around 1914, who emphasized the interaction, or friction force, between the moving atoms and electrons. This force from electron friction, or "electron wind" force as it has been called, was presented of course in simple classical language. With the findings of Seith and Wever this point of view again became popular and was reformulated in more modern terms.

Current Scope. In the succeeding fifteen years a considerable number of investigations have been carried out to explore electromigration in both pure metals and alloys in liquid and solid state. While the field enjoyed no widespread popular vogue there were several groups in the scientific community in different countries that maintained an active interest in this area. In particular the work in Germany continued to develop at Münster under the leadership of Heumann, Seith's successor, and Hehenkemp, and Wever at the Technical University in Berlin. In Russia there have also been several active groups, particularly the one under Kouz'menko in the Ukraine. In France the principal investigators have been those in Adda's group at Saclay. Interest in electromigration in liquids has been fostered by Lodding at Gothenberg, Sweden, and by Klemm at Mainz, Germany. In the United States one notes Verhoeven and Peterson at Iowa State University, Oriani at United States Steel, Guy at the University of Florida, and Huntington at Rensselaer Polytechnic Institute. Liquid studies have been carried out at the Brookhaven National Laboratory. An excellent and comprehensive review of the work during the first part of this period has been furnished by Verhoeven (7).

Technological Aspects. This situation has changed somewhat in the late 1960s due to greater technological interests in the area. There has always been some involvement because of the possibility of using electromigration as a purifying device, but the recent developments stemmed rather from the deleterious effects associated with the phenomena. It was found about 1966 that many of the connecting aluminum stripes in the integrated circuitry were failing with rather short lifetimes because of voids developed from electromigration. Because of the dividends from greater miniaturization and higher current densities it was not feasible to solve this problem by any simple palliative. As a result, crash programs sprang up in several industrial laboratories and the manpower on electromigration studies rapidly multiplied. It should perhaps be emphasized in this connection that the problems intrinsic to the integrated circuitry deal with a rather complicated system; the results from the basic studies of pure bulk materials were not always helpful in interpreting the difficulties. Specifically, it has now become quite clear that the principal problem arises from the rapid diffusivity along grain boundaries or the free surface.

Basic Concepts

Driving Forces. Conceptually basic to this whole area is the understanding of the driving forces for the electromigration. They appear to be of two sorts, first the electrostatic drive which is experienced by the charged ions in transit and secondly the "electron wind" force mentioned above. As we shall see, the latter is proportional to the density of electrons and the strength of their interaction with the moving ion as measured by a hypothetical incremental resistivity.

$$F_i = F_{el} + F_{wd} \tag{1}$$

Knowing the strength of the interaction force, one can deduce the ionic velocity with respect to the lattice by a straightforward application of the Nernst-Einstein relation,

$$v_i = F_i D_i / kT \tag{2}$$

where for pure materials the D_i is the uncorrelated diffusion coefficient. (For the electromigration of substitutional impurities, correlation considerations enter into equation 2 in a more complex way.)

Reference Frames. In an alloy it usually happens that each constituent has a different intrinsic velocity, v_i. The velocities given by equation 2 are with respect to the lattice which itself may be moving with respect to the laboratory frame of reference. The determination of this particular relative velocity depends upon the boundary conditions under which the transport takes place. For example, liquid in a capillary is subject to the condition of constant volume, or

$$\Sigma n_i v_i \Omega_i = 0 \tag{3}$$

where n_i are the atomic fractions of the various constituents and the Ω_i are respectively the atomic volumes. In the case of a lattice, say under isothermal conditions, the restriction is to conserve lattice sites.

$$\Sigma n_i v_i = 0 \tag{4}$$

As a result the experimenter's task is simpler if he can measure the transport with respect to the lattice directly.

Experimental Techniques. At this point we discuss briefly the experimental techniques that can be used to study electromigration. Where one is concerned with a chemical difference between the moving constituents, two standard sets of initial conditions are available. In one the specimen initially contains a uniform distribution, but due to the imposition of the electrically driven transport a concentration gradient is built up with time. Interpretation requires that the boundary condition at the specimens ends be well defined and that diffusion be rapid. Consequently this technique is most useful in dealing with liquids in capillary tubes (8). For this application a short run will provide the basis for determining the electromigration flux (Fig. 1(**a**)); a long time run, wherein a steady-state condition is allowed to establish itself, gives a concentration profile to some extent independent of mobility and can therefore be used to measure the electromigration drive directly (Fig. 1(**b**)).   More generally suitable for solids, where diffusion is slower, is an arrangement where specimens of different compositions are welded together in two or three segments and the concentration profile is measured after the electromigration anneal.   The effect of electromigration and diffusion are jointly evident in these specimens, the former causing the composition discontinuities to be displaced in the direction of motion, the latter rounding out the discontinuities.   Besides straightforward chemical analysis several other techniques have been used to determine the variation of chemical composition in specimens undergoing electromigration.   Some of these are optical atomic absorption, radioisotope counting, and electron microprobe analysis (9).

As has been remarked before, it is important not only to know the change in the chemical composition, but also to be able to detect mass motion with respect to the lattice.   There are two main methods for carrying this out: one of these we shall call the isothermal-isotope method and the other the vacancy-flux method.

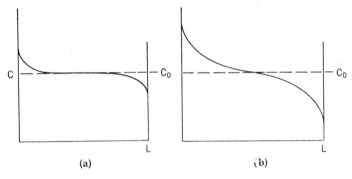

(a)   (b)

Fig. 1.   Typical concentration profiles following electromigration runs in semiclosed capillary tubes of
length L.   (**a**) After a relatively short run.   (**b**) Steady-state condition after a long run.

The isothermal-isotope method (7) consists in incorporating in the specimen a radioactive isotope which remains practically immobile in the matrix and acts as an inactive marker (10).   A second isotope of the material whose motion one wishes to study is also plated at the same point.   The simultaneous plating of both isotopes on the ends of rods, later butt-welded together, has proved to be a satisfactory technique, but it is important that the weld be sound and carefully made.   Later the specimen can be analyzed by a sectioning technique to determine the separation of the centers of the two isotopes distributions (Fig. 2).   In this way the velocities of the atoms moving with respect to the lattice are directly determined.   The technique, although it requires some care particularly in the making of the weld, has several important advantages.   First of these is the fact that the crucial part of the experiment is performed under nearly isothermal conditions which simplifies temperature characterization and eliminates thermomigration.   Second, there are no corrections to take into account because of transverse dimensional changes in the specimen.   Third, the effective temperature of operation can often be determined with very high precision if the diffusion constant is well known for the moving atoms.   Simply by calculating the diffusivity from the observed broadening of the moving isotope distribution a very precise value of the temperature can be established.

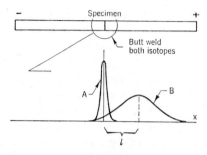

Fig. 2. Electromigration as measured (schematic) by the isothermal isotope method. Legend: A, Inert marker concentration; B, Concentration of self-isotope, $v_a(T) = l/t$, use shape of $B \sim \exp -(x^2/4\mathbf{D}(T)t)$ to determine T; $e\mathcal{E}Z^* = v_a(T)fkT/D^*(T)$.

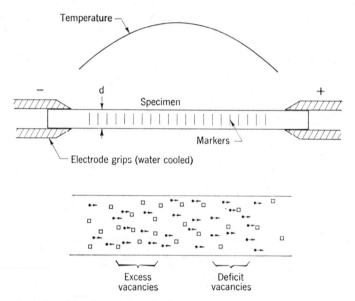

Fig. 3. Vacancy flux induced by electromigration in specimens with nonuniform temperature distribution. LEGEND: · electron; □ vacancy.

The situation for the vacancy-flux method is illustrated in Figure 3. Here the specimen is usually heated by direct current with densities of approximately 10^4 A/cm² and the ends are held in water-cooled vises. As a result the specimen takes on a nearly parabolic temperature distribution. During the course of the run one observes with a traveling microscope the lengthwise displacements of surface-inscribed marks and also monitors with a bifilar eyepiece the transverse diameter of the specimen. In this way a record is kept of all dimensional changes throughout the specimen. Substantial displacement of the lattice with respect to the laboratory system can only come about when there is a heavy vacancy flux. If, as shown in Figure 3, the flow of electrons to the right induces a mass flow in that direction, then there must also be a counterflow of vacancies going to the left. This vacancy flow is not uniform but has a marked divergence in the cold regions, because both the number of vacancies and their mobility are strongly temperature dependent. In such a situation as shown, vacancies will tend to collect over on the left and a deficit of vacancies to develop on the right (Fig. 3). The

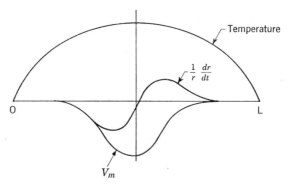

Fig. 4. Measurement of electromigration by the vacancy-flux method.

excess vacancies will become annihilated and in so doing annihilate part of the lattice. Conversely, in those regions where vacancies are being generated extra lattice sites are also being generated and the region will tend to swell. Part of the shrinkage, or swelling, as the case may be, will be in a longitudinal direction and as a result the marks will tend to move to the left. A plot of displacement as a function of position is shown in Figure 4. Experience has shown, however, that it is not sufficient simply to measure the displacement of the surface markers. The full story can only be obtained when these measurements are coupled with additional measurements of the changes in transverse dimensions. Also in Figure 4 is plotted the relative change of specimen diameter in a schematic manner, consistent with the notion that mass transport in this specimen is moving to the right. From a knowledge of both longitudinal and transverse dimensional changes combined, one can deduce not only the volume change as a function of position, but also the vacancy flux as a function of position and time. Such flux, of course, has a maximum in the high-temperature region and tails off towards the low-temperature ends.

When thermomigration occurs also in the specimen, the curves for marker displacement and relative diameter change are no longer respectively purely symmetric and antisymmetric with respect to thermal center. The electromigration effect turns out to be described by the symmetric part of the marker displacement and the antisymmetric part of the relative diameter change. Justification for this procedure rests on the fact that ac runs giving the same thermal distribution reproduce the antisymmetric part of the marker motion curve, etc.

Depending on the temperature range, optical or infrared pyrometry can be used to study the relative temperature variation throughout the specimen. Calibration with external thermocouples, internal thermocouples, and melting-point checks are useful in obtaining absolute calibration, although this phase of the technique often leaves something to be desired. Finally, the data on vacancy flux can be directly correlated with temperature, so that in one run it is possible to determine the flux from electromigration as a function of temperature over an appreciable range. It is customary to plot the log of the vacancy flux versus the reciprocal temperature in order to check how closely the slope of this curve agrees with the activation energy for diffusion.

The ratio of the relative longitudinal dimensional change to that in the transverse dimension can be expected to be close to one for long thin specimens of a fairly soft material. However, short thick specimens of low ductility will show considerably smaller transverse change in the center region where the expansion and contraction tend to mutually hinder one another. Toward the cooler temperature regions in such specimens the effect will be to enhance the transverse dimension change even in parts of the wire where the marker motion has not been evident.

As a comparison between these two approaches it can be said that the isothermal isotope method is best suited for very precise measurements at one particular temperature. It has the advantages of high-temperature precision and no thermal gradient. On the other hand, separate runs must be made at different temperatures to cover a temperature range. The vacancy flux-type measurement is ideal for initial study in that it gives quite approximate results over a wide temperature range in one run. The difficulties with it consist mainly in low-temperature precision and the need for coordinating both longitudinal and transverse dimensional changes in the same run.

Theory

Electrostatic Force. Before discussing the recent relevant theories for the wind force it should be pointed out that the concept of the electrostatic drive also has been subject to some uncertainty. The question in point is whether the free-electron cloud effectively shields any moving ion in the matrix. There is some thought that the situation may be different for an interstitial atom than for a substitutional one. On the other hand, it has been established on a classical continuum model (11) that the free charge does not effectively shield the moving ion. The model treats the electron charge as a continuous fluid and assumes an Ohm's law that is microscopically valid. On the basis of this limited model it can be shown quite plausibly that the electrostatic force is $\mathcal{E}$ times the nominal ionic Z_{el}, where $\mathcal{E}$ is the electric field strength.

Wind Force. There have been three rather recent treatments of the wind force all of which give effectively about the same prediction. Perhaps the simplest of these is a direct kinetic treatment by the Russian theorist, V. B. Fiks (12). Accordingly, each moving atom in the lattice interacts with the flowing charge carriers with a certain intrinsic cross section for scattering, σ_i. The number of such collisions experienced by each moving ion per unit time is given by the product of n, the charge-carrier density, v, the average velocity of the charge carrier, and σ_i. On the average every charge carrier gives up with collision an average momentum equal to the impulse supplied by the electric field $\mathcal{E}$ during a relaxation time, τ, or $e\mathcal{E}\tau$. On combining one finds for the electron wind force,

$$F_{wd} = -e\mathcal{E}n \cdot \lambda\sigma_i \tag{5}$$

where $\lambda = v\tau$.

Later this formula was extended to include the effect of the hole carriers

$$F_{wd} = e\mathcal{E}(n_h\lambda_h\sigma_{ih} - n_e\lambda_e\sigma_{ie}) \tag{5a}$$

It has become a rather common notation to represent the complete force for electromigration as

$$F = e\mathcal{E}Z^* \tag{6}$$

where Z^*e gives the effective charge that the moving atom would have in order to feel the same total force from pure electrostatic consideration. On the basis of the Fiks analysis Z^* would be given by

$$Z^* = Z_{el} - n_e\lambda_e\sigma_{ie} + n_h\lambda_h\sigma_{ih} \tag{7}$$

An alternative approach to the same end point was pursued by Huntington and Grone (13), where they considered the total momentum transfer from the charge-carrier system to the moving ions in terms of the transition probability arising from the scattering process. Although the original formal expression involved a double integration over the initial and final states of the electrons that were being scattered, it turned out to be possible to reduce the expression considerably by introducing under certain approximations a fractional contribution to the reciprocal relaxation time, $1/T_d$, that arose primarily from scattering by the moving defects. In this development the final expression for Z^* turned out to be quite equivalent to that developed by Fiks, but was couched in somewhat different terms. The final expression involved the ratio of the incremental resistivity per moving defect (ρ_d/N_d) to that resistivity attributable to an average matrix atom (ρ/N), as shown in equation 8,

$$Z^* = Z_{el} - z \left(\frac{\rho_d}{N_d} \right) \left(\frac{N}{\rho} \right) \frac{|m^*|}{m^*} \tag{8}$$

where z is the electron–atom ratio. Still a third approach, that of Bosvieux and Friedel (14), appeared to start from a very different point of view but ended up with very nearly the same end result. In their approach the polarization of the electronic charge around a defect was found to have an asymmetrical contribution in the event that there was a current in the metal. This asymmetrical charge distribution gave rise to a potential gradient at the position of the charge defect which, in turn, exerted the force of the electron wind. All three theoretical approaches were essentially limited to the Born approximation, dependent on first-order perturbation theory for their validity, and assumed a free-electron model for the metal in question. The final restriction is particularly serious if one is concerned with attempting to evaluate in a fairly rigorous way the competing contributions of the electrons and the holes to electromigration.

Experiment

Electromigration of Interstitials. A review of the experimental situation for electromigration starts naturally with the study of interstitial impurities. From the theoretical point of view this problem is somewhat simpler to formulate because the moving entity does not change its state so drastically between equilibrium position and the saddle point as is the situation for a substitutional atom moving by the vacancy mechanism. Also the complications with correlation are absent. Although different interstitials presumably exist in different charged states in the same matrix one might expect that the wind force would be directed in the same direction for all of them. Oriani and Gonzalez (15) have summarized the experimental situation for several different metals and pointed out that in most cases for the same solvent all interstitial

Table 1. Directions for Interstitial Electromigrations

Solvent metal	Moves toward anode	Moves toward cathode
α-iron		H, D, C, and N
γ-iron	N	H, C, and B
nickel		H, D, and C
yttrium	C, O, N, and H	
thorium	C, N, and O	
β-titanium	O	C
vanadium		C, N, and O

solutes tend to move in the same direction. The experimental results are listed in Table 1. There are two exceptions to this rule in Table 1, but the general impact of the collection of data suggests that essentially the wind force dominates in the different structures. A good deal of quantitative work remains to be done in this area to explore the extent to which the magnitudes of electromigration drive can be correlated with the incremental resistivities of the respective interstitial impurities in accord with the Huntington-Grone formalism.

One puzzling result in this area is the observation of Oriani and Gonzalez that the Z^* for the electromigration of deuterium is appreciably ($\sim$40%) larger than that of H in both Ni and α-Fe. It is also of interest to point out that, while interstitials in Ni generally move toward the cathode, as if under the influence of a "hole-wind," the mass transport of pure nickel itself is toward the anode.

Electromigration in Pure Metals. Actually the situation for electromigration in pure metals is conceptually more complex than for the interstitial case. Here the vacancy mechanism will usually dominate. The saddle-point configuration for the mechanism is quite complex, consisting as it does of the moving atom in an essentially interstitial position with two adjoining semivacancies. It is not apparent in any simple way what influence the latter have on the wind force.

There has been a considerable effort to measure Z^* for several of the pure metals. Unfortunately the results from different measurements have frequently not agreed well, and in several cases the values for Z^* have tended to decrease on remeasurement! In Table 2 are listed several of the more recent measurements. The second row indicates whether the technique was more closely allied to the isothermal isotope method, ii, or a measurement of the vacancy flux, vf. In several of the more reliable measurements the slope of $\ln v_i$ vs T^{-1} fitted well to the Q for diffusion and in these cases the value of Z^* is uniquely determined. In other cases where temperature dependencies do not agree, a temperature dependence for Z^* results (probably the result of experimental error) which explains the range of values listed.

The values for Au were among the first obtained by the vacancy-flux method where the extent of the transverse changes in dimension were inferred rather than directly measured. Under these circumstances the agreement with the latter measurements (10), carefully carried out by the isothermal-isotope method, may be considered satisfactory. Earlier measurements of Z^* in Ag gave much larger values, in part due to difficulties in temperature calibration. While the value listed under vf may actually be a little low, it is probably more reliable than the first value listed as judged by a comparison of the scatter in the two experiments. Curiously enough in the case of Cu the first measurements both in this country and in Germany reported a change in direction of the marker motion at high temperature, an effect completely out of keeping with expectations. A second measurement in our laboratory, where particular attention was paid to the purity of the ambient, revealed a normal behavior. The origin of the early anomaly is still in doubt.

The Z^* for Na should be a quite reliable measurement, although the value obtained seems a little small. It was with this soft material that the importance of continuously monitoring the specimen diameter during the runs first became particularly apparent.

The measurements on Al have particular significance in view of the technological problem of stripe failure. The In specimens were polycrystalline and hopefully single-crystal studies can be done eventually.

Inspection of the results for the transition metals reveals the wide degree of variability of Z^* for these materials.   The positive Z^* for Fe and Co are in keeping with their large, positive Hall coefficient.   Conversely, Ni, as has been remarked earlier, has a negative Hall coefficient.   The Hall coefficient of Pt is small and negative. Apparently it is not possible to tell directly from the sign of the Hall coefficient the sign of electromigration for metals with close competition between electrons and holes.

In this connection it should be pointed out that three other metals, Zn, Cd, and Pb, have shown the opposite behavior, that of a positive Hall effect and negative Z^*.   In addition, the anisotropy of Z^* in the hexagonal metals, Zn and Cd, has been explored using single-crystal specimens.   Although these metals have quite isotropic conductivities at room temperatures (for Zn $\rho_\perp/\rho_\parallel \simeq 1.1$; for Cd $\rho_\perp/\rho_\parallel \simeq 1.15$), the mass flow per unit electric field differs substantially in different crystallographic directions, being greater in the basal plane.   Since the anisotropy of diffusion in these metals is in the opposite sense $(D_\parallel/D_\perp \simeq 1.4)$ the corresponding Z^*'s are even more anisotropic (see Table 2).   Some theoretical effort has been expended to understand these results in terms of a nearly free-electron model using a fairly well-established pseudopotential for Zn, but the subject is still under study.

The refractory bcc (body-centered cubic) metals presented a special challenge to a forced-motion study because of the rather anomalous diffusion characteristics of some of these metals, ie Zn, Hf, γ-U, and V.   (These characteristics are principally a concave upward curvature of the Arrhenius plot coupled to exceptionally low values for Q_2 and D_{02}, the constants of the Arrhenius line fitted to the low-temperature data.)   These metals

Table 2. Z^* for Several Pure Metals (Solid)

Metal	Method	Z^*	Date of measure
noble			
Au	vf	-7.5 to -3.5	1961
	ii	-8	1966
Ag	vf	-5.5	1966
	ii	-16 to -28	1969
Cu	vf	-5.5	1966
alkali			
Na	vf	-2.4	1967
Li	vf	-10	1968
trivalent			
Al	vf	-20	1964
In	vf	-9	1964
transition			
Fe	vf	$+1$ to $+3$	1966
Co	vf	$+1.0$ to $+2.2$	1965
Pt	vf	0.24 to 0.32	1963
refractory, bcc[a]			
Zr	vf	$+0.3$	1969
U	vf	-1.2	1969
noncubic (single crystal)			
Zn	vf	-2.0[b], -4.4[c]	1968
Cd	vf	-1.6[b], -3.3[c]	1970

[a] Body-centered cubic.

[b] Refers to $Z_\parallel$ (along the c-axis).

[c] Refers to $Z_\perp$ (in the basal plane).

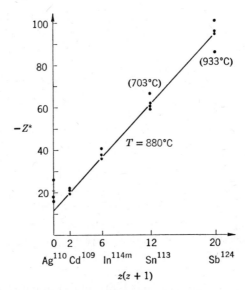

Fig. 5. The Z^* for dilute impurities in silver (according to N. V. Doan).

also have phase changes at low temperature where the low-temperature phases have practically no atomic mobility. As a result vacancy-flux studies of such metals show a large discontinuity in the surface-marker displacement curve at the phase boundary. For Zr the Z^* proved to be very small, barely observable, but the metal does exhibit a strong mass-motion response to thermal gradients (thermomigration). It was possible to use this effect to determine atom mobility over a wide temperature range. Interestingly enough the temperature dependence of the diffusivity so determined fitted a single Arrhenius line over the whole range with a slope in agreement with Q_2. While Ti also exhibits a sizable thermomigration and a small Z^*, γ-U has the reverse characteristic with electromigration to the anode dominating the thermomigration.

Dilute Impurities. The electromigration of dilute impurities has mainly been limited so far to multivalent solutes in the noble-metal solvents. For Sb in Au two different investigators found very considerable electron-wind effects indeed. One might expect that the electrostatic charge effect would increase linearly with the valence difference but that the electron-wind effect would vary as the square of the charge difference in accord with Mott's treatment of Born scattering and with Linde's rule for incremental resistivity from dilute alloying. Doan (16) has made a systematic study of the electromigration in Ag of several elements in the same row of the periodic table appearing as dilute solutes. His results for Z^* are plotted in Figure 5 and show an approximately parabolic dependence on valence z. Hehenkamp (17) and colleagues (18) have used dilute alloy studies as a way to make an evaluation of the strength of F_{el}. For this experiment they fashioned a three-part specimen with a short center piece of Cu alloyed with 0.5–5% Sb and the two outside pieces of pure Cu. The concentration profiles before and after electromigration are schematically shown in Figure 6. The crucial point is that electron wind effect varies with the current which is the same for all three sections of the specimen whereas the Z_{el} depends on the resistivity and is therefore higher in the central segment containing the Sb impurity. Its effect should bias the rising and falling slopes of the concentration profile so that they are not re-

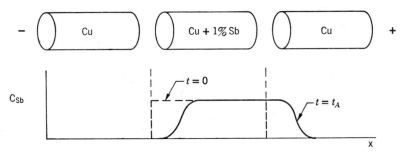

Fig. 6. Concentration profiles for Sb in Cu before and after electromigration. Legend: $F_a = ej$ $[\rho Z_{el} - n_e \{\rho_d/N_d \, |m^*|/m^*\}]$, $e \, \rho \, Z_{el} < 5\% \cdot n_e \, (\rho_d/N_d)$.

flections of each other. By careful measurements with an electron probe Hehenkamp was able to show the influence of Z_{el} and evaluate it as about $+4e$ for Sb in Cu.

In passing we might point out a quite different sort of experiment to evaluate Z_{el}, this time by looking for electromigration in the Hall field of a specimen carrying current in a magnetic field. Such an experiment was carried out by Y. Miller (19) for the diffusion of Fe in Ge at 825°C; Z_{el} of about three was reported. A similar experiment has also been carried on the Z_{el} for C in Fe (20) but there the interpretation is obscured by the coexistence of both holes and electrons in the metal.

Concentrated Alloys. In surveying the electromigration of concentrated alloys one thinks first of the original work by Seith and Wever (5,6) with the Hume-Rothery diagrams. Of the more recent investigations there has been a detailed series of measurements (21) of electromigration at a large number of temperatures and compositions for W–Mo systems. Electromigration in a strongly defected system, Cu_3Sb, has been observed and very rapid motion of the Cu toward the cathode is reported (22).

Semiconductors. At medium high temperatures in semiconductors electromigration operates primarily through the electrostatic drive. Among the first systems to be investigated (23,24) were Li and Cu in Si and in Ge. Of course lithium-drifted detectors have proved to be enormously useful technical devices for particle detection. Normally the Cu impurity in Ge acts as a deep electron trap and a poison, reducing carrier lifetime. In the case of Au in Si the motion is toward the cathode and is apparently reversed at higher temperature. The possibility for a change in the direction of electromigration at higher temperatures was pointed out by Fiks (25) as a natural result of increased carrier wind in the intrinsic region. Fiks estimated that the reversal temperature should come near 725°C for Ge and 1325° for Si. Other investigated systems which show reversal at high temperature are In in Si which goes toward the anode in the medium range and toward the cathode at high temperature and Sb in Si which moves in the reverse direction in both ranges (26). Clearly the situation is somewhat more complicated than what would follow from the Fiks' model since that would predict a common direction for all impurities driven by the carrier wind in the high-temperature region.

Liquids. For the electromigration of pure liquids there appears to be no analog of a vacancy-flux method. However, the separation of isotopes with electric current (Haeffner effect) (27,28) does serve to give a direct measure of the self-electromigration in a pure liquid metal. The general observation is that the lighter isotope becomes enriched at the anode. The effect was something of a puzzle for quite a while. If the force of electromigration was the same for all isotopes of a given metal, how could this force bring about a separation of mass centers of the atoms of the two (or more) isotopes. This paradox was eventually explained by Klemm (29). He suggested in effect that the mobility of an atom in a liquid varies with time, being greatest when its neighbors are most widely spaced, and that these fluctuations in mobility are correlated with fluctuations with the force of electromigration. Of course, all atoms in turn have the chance to respond to the electron wind force but those with the lighter mass respond the more readily. Hence the build up of the lighter mass at the anode. (Nearly all liquid metals are electron conductors.)

There has been a considerable body of work on electromigration in molten binary systems which we do not have the space to review in detail here. For the most part these alloys were dilute, although some of the earlier work by Kremann dealt with concentrated systems. In general it appears that the constituent with the higher intrinsic resistivity would tend to move to the anode as though driven by the wind force. However, the composition has also a bearing. A good example of this is the Na–K system which was first studied at 100°C as a function of composition by Drakin and Maltsev (30). They found that the minor constituent moved always to the anode with the change-over composition at Na 48 wt %. This change-over has more recently been verified by Jousset and Huntington (31) working at two fixed compositions bracketing the sign reversal and over a broader temperature range. They find for both compositions a rapid increase in electromigration around 180°C. These results were also confirmed in the experiments of Epstein and Dicke (32). These authors also give a good theoretical treatment of the wind force as a function of composition, relating it to the pseudopotentials of the Na and K atoms.

Technical Aspects

Beneficial Uses. The phenomenon of electromigration would appear to offer two technological uses: isotope separation and metal purification. However, as a method for the former it turns out simply not to be competitive. As a method for purification, there appears to be some promise, particularly for special transition or rare-earth metals where one would like to purify rather small samples with several 100 ppm contamination to a higher level than attainable by zone refining. Several specific studies in this area have been performed in the metallurgy department of Iowa State University on Th (33), Y (34), and V (35). As the results in Table 1 indicate, in a given metal the interstitial impurities usually move together toward the same electrode which is an advantage in purification. In the case of Y the statement is made that this procedure is the most effective for purification. For example, in one case a reduction in O content from 780 ppm to 100 ppm was effected. Because of the higher mobility of the liquid state, purification by electromigration is much more rapid above melting. The possibility of using electromigration in conjunction with purification by solidification (zone refining) has been explored by Verhoeven (36) with the Bi–Sn system. In an actual zone-refining treatment the effective distribution coefficient k_e is always somewhat closer to unity than the equilibrium quantity k_o because of the concentration gradient established in the melt at the interface. It was hoped that this could be counteracted by an electromigration mass transport down the gradient. Apparently the main difficulty in so doing arose from convection in the liquid. Of the several possible causes for such convection the principal one turned out (37) to be the drive by the radial thermal gradient. By reducing the tube diameter from 5 mm to less than 2 mm the convection was greatly reduced and the purification substantially enhanced by electromigration over what would be possible by zone refining alone.

Deleterious Effects. It was noticed very early that tungsten light filaments under dc power tended to burn out always at the anode end. Microscopic observations by R. P. Johnson (38) that the surface texture of a current-carrying tungsten wire would be smooth under ac but become serrated with dc with a stepped structure that was polarized by the current, clearly showed the result of electromigration with mass transport toward the cathode. Those crystal planes which show a high atomic mobility become developed in a force field if they are oriented so that the ensuing mass flow tends to build up the corresponding surfaces. More recently the same problem reappeared as a short-lived failure in rocket-borne devices powered by solar cells. In the course of studying this form of failure O'Boyle (39) made several interesting observations with a scanning electron microscope of tungsten wire specimens serrated by both dc and ac. For ac the effect was only observable at the ends where a sudden drop in temperature to the cool support caused thermomigration, ie, mass motion under thermal gradient.

In 1966 or thereabouts, a far more serious technological problem developed with thin-film Al stripes used as connecting resistive elements in nearly all the integrated circuitry of the computing industry. These films are usually deposited to the depth of a few thousand Å on the insulating SiO_2 substrate. They are about 0.3 mil in width and of the order of 10 mil in length. A photo-etch procedure from template is usually used in this production. The films can carry current densities of 10^6 A/cm² without melting and run at temperatures of 100–200°C. Under these conditions their lifetimes are usually quite limited, as the stripes open and fail. The failure begins with small voids at grain boundaries or small holes in the films, sometimes at the edge. At the same time in other parts of the film, nearer the anode, mounds or hillocks develop, or even whiskers, as matter is deposited in these regions. It was soon apparent that the known characteristic for electromigration in bulk Al, if extrapolated to the lower temperature for operation of the integrated circuitry, failed by at least a couple of orders of magnitude to explain the observations. Clearly mobility along the grain boundaries or even the free surface must have been playing a role.

There have been two ingenious displays of electromigration in thin stripes. The first of these by Blech and Meieran (40) relied on transmission electron microscopy to show sections of stripe in the last stage before failure. To make transmission possible the specimens were prepared by etching away the underlying Si so that the stripe itself was supported only by a thin skin of SiO_2 in the middle. As the electrodes acted as heat sinks, a nearly parabolic temperature distribution was maintained so that the mass loss was concentrated on the cathode side and the hillocks appeared on the anode side. The first voids usually appeared at grain boundaries and often spread sidewise until the specimen failed. Many effects were reversible, ie, voids could be healed by reversing the current. A short Ciné film of these observations has been an effective display. The second presentation has been recently developed by J. R. Black who observed essentially the same phenomenon with a scanning electron microscope. This instrument has the advantage of three-dimensional presentation rather than silhouette. Also since transmission was not involved, the stripe would be completely supported and maintained under nearly isothermal conditions. As a result the occurrences of voids and hillocks were not so clearly separated into cathode and anode regions respectively, but occurred more nearly at random throughout the stripe. One could also see that in the more nearly isothermal specimens the voids no longer tended to stay in a fixed region and broaden but instead oozed along toward the cathode, usually following the grain boundaries.

There is not yet complete agreement on the details by which the Al stripes fail in actual use. Resistivity measurements (41) show two stages; the first is a period of relatively slow increase, then followed by more rapid rise as the void becomes microscopically observable. Thermal gradients, even if present only locally, will accelerate failure (41). Variations in mobility over a small scale can be also most important as voids tend to form in regions where there is a transition in grain size. The research group with Rosenberg at the IBM Research Laboratory has tended to emphasize the role of grain mobility as against that of the free surface. Experiments (42) with stripes of different grain size show marked differences in lifetime. These differences seem to be the result of different energies for motion rather than any simple change in the total grain boundary area. Apparently large grains tend to show a preferred orientation (111) and are intrinsically more stable against atom motion. On the other hand, there is some evidence that the free surface is also important. J. R. Black (43) has concluded from a statistical survey of mean time to failure as a function of temperature under various conditions that small-grain stripes do show a lower-activation energy ($\sim$0.5 eV as against $\sim$0.8 eV for large-grain stripes), but that coating the free surface with $\sim$1 μ of SiO_2 increases the activation energy to the neighborhood of the bulk value ($\sim$1.2 eV) with consequent increase in lifetime. These results seem to be borne out by other investigators (44) who find that the effect of the surface treatment becomes negligible as the stripes are thickened at about 4000 Å.

Although there are many measures which can be taken to increase component lifetime in any particular situation, as of 1970 there appears to be as yet no universally satisfactory solution. Certain obvious palliatives include reducing current and maintaining a lower operating temperature, but these measures would be in the face of ever-increasing demands for larger loads and faster performance on the part of circuitry designers. Thicker or wider stripes could be used to lower current densities but at the cost of miniaturization. Clearly deposition at higher temperatures with consequent increase in grain size will bring some improvement. There are several other metals which provide stripes of longer lifetime than Al, but do not really compete with it in several other important respects, such as high conductivity, good resistance to corrosion (particularly oxidation), mechanical toughness, thermal compatibility with the SiO_2, ease of handling in evaporation, etc.

Since no single metal can match Al for all-round usefulness, some consideration has been given to composites although those would clearly be more expensive. One promising possibility is a Cr–Ag–Au metallization system (45), which shows some aging effects above 300°C, but low resistivity and good compatibility with n- and p-type Si and no failure from electro migration. The Cr film is for adherence, the Au for protection and the intervening Ag prevents intermetallic compound formation. In addition to three separate films careful precleaning is required but the processes are really not too difficult and the films can be easily patterned later by the standard techniques.

It appears, nevertheless, that the problem of the electromigration-caused failure may stay a vexing technological problem in integrated circuitry for some time to come.

Bibliography

1. M. Gerardin, *Compt. Rend.* **53**, 727 (1861).
2. K. E. Schwarz, *Elektrolytische Wanderung in flüssigen und festen Metallen*, Johann Ambrosius Barth, Leipzig, 1940; translation published by Edwards Bros., Ann Arbor, Mich., 1945.
3. W. Seith, *Diffusion in Metallen; Platzwechselreaktionen*, Springer-Verlag, Berlin, 1955.
4. W. Jost, *Diffusion in Solids, Liquids and Gases*, Academic Press, New York, 1952.
5. W. Seith and H. Wever, "Über einen neuen Effekt bei der Elektrolytischen Überfuhrung in Festen Legierungen," *Z. Elektrochem.* **57**, 891–900 (1953); H. Wever and W. Seith, "Neue Ergebnisse bei der Elektrolyse festen metallischen Phasen," *Z. Elektrochem.* **59**, 942–946 (1955).
6. F. Skaupy, "Die Elektrizitätsleitung in Metallen," *Verhandl. Deut. Phys. Ges.* **16**, 156 (1914).
7. J. Verhoeven, "Electrotransport in Metals," *Metallurgical Rev.* **8**, 311–368 (1963).
8. A. Lodding, "Isotope Transport Phenomena in Liquid Metals," *Gothenburg Studies in Physics*, Almquist and Wiksell, Gothenburg, 1961.
9. T. Hehenkamp, "Measurement of Transport Phenomena of Dilute Impurities in Metals," *J. Appl. Phys.* **39**, 3928–3930 (1968).
10. H. M. Gilder and D. Lazarus, "Effect of High Electric Current Density on the Motion of Au[196] and Sb[125] in Gold," *Phys. Rev.* **145**, 507–518 (1966).
11. H. B. Huntington, "Current Problems in Electromigration in Metals," *Trans. Met. Soc. AIME* **245**, 2571–2579 (1969).
12. V. B. Fiks, "On the Mechanism of the Mobility of Ions in Metals," *Soviet Phys.—Solid State (English Transl.)* **1**, 14–28 (1959).
13. H. B. Huntington and A. R. Grone, "Current Induced Marker Motions in Gold Wires," *J. Phys. Chem. Solids* **20**, 76–93 (1961).
14. C. Bosvieux and J. Friedel, "Sur l'Electrolyse des Alliages Metalliques," *J. Phys. Chem. Solids* **23**, 123–136 (1962).
15. R. A. Oriani and O. D. Gonzalez, "Electromigration of Hydrogen Isotopes Dissolved in Alpha Iron and in Nickel," *Trans. Met. Soc. AIME* **239**, 1041–1046 (1967).
16. N. V. Doan, "Electromigration et Structure Electronique des Ions en position de Col dans l'-Argent," *J. Phys. Chem. Solids* **9**, 2079 (1970).
17. T. Hehenkamp, "Ermittlung der Ladung von Fremdatomen in verdünnter Lösung mit Mikro-sondenmessungen des Materietransports in Metallen," *Mikrochem. Acta Suppl.* **4**, 147–157 (1970).
18. T. Hehenkamp, C. Herzig, and T. Heuman, *Julich Conf. Proc. 2*, Vol. I., 1968 p 69.
19. Y. Miller, "An Investigation of Electrical Transport in Metals and Semiconductors under the Influence of the Hall Electric Field," *Soviet Phys.—Solid State (English Transl.)* **3**, 1728–1732 (1962).
20. M. J. Bibby and W. V. Youdelis, *Can. J. Phys.* **44**, 2363–2386 (1966).
21. I. N. Frantsevich, D. F. Kaleinvich, I. I. Kovenskii, and M. D. Smolin, "Electrotransport and Diffusion in Molybdenum-Tungsten and Iron-Nickel Alloys Over a Wide Range of Temperatures," *J. Phys. Chem. Solids* **30**, 947–958 (1969).
22. H. Meiners, *Elektrotransport und Diffusion in der β-Phase des Systems Kupfer-Antimon*, private communication of abstract of doctoral thesis, University of Münster, West Germany.
23. C. S. Fuller and J. C. Severiens, "Mobility of Impurity Ions in Germanium and Silicon," *Phys. Rev.* **96**, 21–24 (1954).
24. C. J. Gallagher, "Electrolysis of Copper in Solid Silicon," *J. Phys. Chem. Solids* **3**, 82–86 (1957).
25. V. B. Fiks, "Entrainment of Ions by Electrons in Semiconductors," *Sov. Phys.—Solid State* **1**, 1211–1214 (1959).
26. B. P. Konstantinov and L. A. Badenko, "An Electrical Diffusion Study of the Behavior of Indium and Antimony Impurities in Germanium," *Soviet Phys.—Solid State* **2**, 2400 (1961).
27. E. Haeffner, "A Method of Changing the Isotope Abundance in Mercury," *Nature* **172**, 775–776 (1953).
28. A. Lodding, "New Measurements of the Haeffner Effect in Rb, K and In," *Z. Naturforsch* **16a**, 1252–1253 (1961).
29. A. Klemm, "Isotopenüberführung und Selbstüberführung in Metallen," *Z. Naturforsch.* **A9**, 1031–1035 (1954).
30. S. I. Drakin and A. K. Maltsev, "Electrodiffusion in Alloys of Potassium and Sodium," *Zhur. Fiz. Khim.* **31**, 2036–2041 (1957).

31. J. C. Jousset and H. B. Huntington, "Electromigration in Liquid Na-K Alloys," *Physica State Solida* **31**, 775–786 (1969).

32. S. G. Epstein and J. M. Dicke, "Study of Electromigration in Liquid Na-K Alloys," *Phys. Rev.* **B1** 2442 (1970).

33. D. T. Peterson, F. A. Schmidt, and J. D. Verhoeven, "Transport of Carbon, Nitrogen and Oxygen in Thorium," *Trans. Met. Soc. AIME* **236**, 1311–1315 (1966).

34. O. N. Carlson, F. A. Schmidt, and D. T. Peterson, "Electrotransport of Interstitial Atoms in Yttrium," *J. Less.-Common Metals* **10**, 1–11 (1966).

35. F. A. Schmidt and J. C. Warner, "Electrotransport of Carbon, Nitrogen and Oxygen in Vanadium," *J. Less.-Common Metals* **13**, 493–500 (1967).

36. J. D. Verhoeven, "The Effect of an Electric Field Upon the Solidification of Bismuth-Tin Alloys," *Trans. Met. Soc. AIME* **233**, 1156–1163 (1965).

37. J. D. Verhoeven, "The Effect of an Electric Field Upon Solute Redistribution During Solidification of Bi-Sn Alloys," *Trans. Met. Soc. AIME* **239**, 694–702 (1967).

38. R. P. Johnson, "Construction of Filament Surfaces," *Phys. Rev.* **54**, 459–467 (1938).

39. D. O'Boyle, "Observation of Electromigration and the Soret Effect in Tungsten," *J. Appl. Phys.* **36**, 2849–2853 (1965).

40. I. A. Blech and E. S. Meieran, "Direct Transmission Electron Microscope Observation of Electrotransport in Aluminum Thin Films," *Appl. Phys. Letter* **11**, 263–266 (1967).

41. R. Rosenberg and L. Berenbaum, "Resistance Monitoring and Effects of Non-adhesion During Electromigration in Aluminum Films," *Appl. Phys. Letter* **12**, 201–204 (1968).

42. M. J. Attardo and R. Rosenberg, "Electromigration Damage in Aluminum," to appear in *J. Appl. Phys.*

43. J. R. Black, "Electromigration, A Brief Survey and Some Recent Results," *IEEE Trans.* **ED 16**, 338–347 (1969).

44. S. M. Spitzer and S. Schwaltz, "The Effects of Dielectric Overcoating on Electromigration in Aluminum Interconnections," *IEEE Trans.* **ED 16**, 348–350 (1969).

45. K. Dong Kang, R. R. Burgess, M. G. Coleman and J. G. Keil, "A Cr-Ag-Au Metallization System," *IEEE Trans.* **ED 16**, 356–360 (1969).

H. B. HUNTINGTON
Rensselaer Polytechnic Institute

ENZYME DETERGENTS

The idea of using enzymes in laundry detergents dates back to the early years of the 20th century. The first known reference to their use for this application is a German patent issued to Otto Röhm in 1915 (1). The patent describes the use of tryptic enzymes, such as pancreatin, in laundry compositions and toilet soaps for degradation of protein and fatty residues. The enzymes of that time, however, lacked stability under laundering conditions, and compositions for the optimum enzyme performance were not well understood. As a result, the laundering compounds lacked sufficient effectiveness to attract any great attention from the industry.

The first U.S. reference to the use of enzymes in a laundry product is a patent issued to Frelinghuysen in 1932 for a process of making a soap compound with a diastase enzyme for improved cleansing action (2). In 1939, a study was conducted under the sponsorship of the Office for German Raw Products and Materials on the use of pancreas enzymes in washing preparations (3). The purpose of this work was to determine whether or not these enzymes would permit a reduction in the soap content of the formulations. This was an important consideration at that time since it offered a means to conserve fat, a valuable raw material to Germany during the war years. The tests, which were conducted in the laundry of Adolf Hitler's personal SS regiment, showed the effect of the enzyme to be quite impressive and indicated that a reduction of 80% in the soap content of the washing powders was feasible. Some laundry products were sold in Germany during the war that contained enzymes but no soap or other surfactant (4).

The developments that led to the large-scale commercialization of enzyme detergents started in Switzerland in the 1940s. A Swiss firm, Gebrueder Schnyder, introduced a product called BIO-37 which eventually was replaced with an improved formulation, BIO-40. This product was sold in Switzerland for several years, and finally through the combined efforts of this Swiss firm and a Dutch firm, Kortman and Schulte N. V., an enzyme presoak product called Biotex was introduced in Holland in 1963. This product has the credit of being the first successful enzyme-detergent soak product for the home laundry. Within two years it had captured a substantial 20% of the detergent market in Holland, a popularity which sparked demand for these enzyme soakers and prewash products, first throughout Europe, and then finally worldwide.

In 1967 several detergent manufacturers in Europe introduced enzyme-containing detergents for the complete wash cycle, ie, one which can act as a prewash agent during the heating cycle of the machine and as a conventional detergent during the subsequent washing cycles. These products differ from the enzyme prewash agents in that they contain sodium peroxyborate. They have been readily accepted in the United Kingdom, probably because the enzyme prewash products hold little interest there since the English housewife is not accustomed to practice soaking. However, in countries where soaking and prewash practices with enzyme-containing formulations are established, the penetration by these enzyme-containing, heavy-duty wash products has been slower. It seems reasonable to expect that these products, since they can be used for soaking and prewash, as well as the regular wash cycle, will eventually replace the specialty products.

In the United States, enzyme detergents appeared in test market areas for the first time in 1966. In the years since the appearance of the first product, which was Tide XK, the major detergent producers have introduced approximately twenty different enzyme laundry detergents and presoak products. At the present, all known enzyme laundry products in the United States and Europe are dry products although there is considerable research effort being expended to develop liquid formulations.

The impact of enzymes on the detergent industry has not been restricted to United States and Europe. Enzyme-containing detergent formulations have appeared in many other parts of the world. Neither has the use of enzymes been restricted to household laundry detergent products. Enzyme dishwashing products can be found in the United States, Germany, and Japan. Also, institutional and commercial detergents are in use in many parts of the world, specifically for the removal of blood stains from garments used by slaughterhouse workers and from hospital bed linens and gowns.

Description of Detergent Enzymes

The enzymes used in laundry preparations prior to 1960 were primarily animal-derived proteases, such as pancreatin or pepsin. These enzymes lacked stability in the presence of detergent components and were low in activity, of variable composition, and limited in supply. Technological developments of the early 1960s showed that bacterial proteases, which were more stable toward detergent ingredients, could be produced in commercial quantities with controlled activity and composition.

TABLE 1. Typical Properties of Enzymes Used in Detergent Applications

Producer	Trade name	Typical Activity in M units/g			Subtilo-peptidase variety[b]	Density, g/ml	Inorganic components
		Protease, pH 7[a]	Protease, pH 10	α-Amylase[b]			
Miles Laboratories, Inc.	Milezyme	650–700	350–400	450–520	B	0.4	Na_2SO_4
Monsanto Company	Enzyme AP	1500–2700	400–900	300–900	B	0.3	Na_2SO_4
	Enzyme AP-100	700–1200	250–300	250–350	B	0.6	Na_2SO_4
	Enzyme ALK	200–250	350–400	<5	A	0.7	Na_2SO_4, $CaSO_4 \cdot 2H_2O$
Novo Industries A/S,	Alcalase	200–250	350–400	<5	A	0.7	Na_2SO_4, $CaSO_4 \cdot 2H_2O$, NaCl
Denmark	Alcalase	200–250	350–400	<5	A	0.6	$Na_5P_3O_{10}$, Na_2SO_4, $CaSO_4 \cdot 2H_2O$
Pfizer & Co. and Royal Netherland Fermentation Industry	Maxatase	200–250	350–400	8–12	A	0.6	Na_2SO_4, $CaSO_4 \cdot 2H_2O$
Premier Malt Products, Inc.	Exzyme P	180–250	300–400	<5	A	0.6	Na_2SO_4, $Ca(C_2H_2O_2)_2 \cdot H_2O$
	Exzyme WT-2	120–180	3–6	200–250	B	0.6	Na_2SO_4, $Ca(C_2H_2O_2)_2 \cdot H_2O$
Rohm and Haas	Protease 57	150–175	300–350	40–60	B	0.3	$CaSO_4 \cdot 2H_2O$
Société-Rapidase, France	Rapidase	170–225	330–360	8–12	A	0.7	Na_2SO_4
Wallerstein Co., div. of	Protease 201	150–200	300–350	<5	A	0.7	NaCl
Baxter Laboratories, Inc.	Protease HA	150–200	300–350	150–200	A	0.6	NaCl

[a] Method of Kunitz (7) in casein units. [b] Method of Kollomich (8) in maltose units

The specific protease enzymes adopted widely by the detergent industry today are produced in a fermentation process using *Bacillus subtilis* organisms. The properties of the enzymes sold in the United States are listed in Table 1. Keay and Moser (5) have shown the alkaline protease component of these enzymes form two different groups, which are categorized as subtilopeptidase A or B.

The typical alkaline protease enzymes sold for use in detergent products can be classified as the subtilopeptidase A variety. These enzymes contain a high casein activity at pH 10 and a lower casein activity at pH 7. This fact means that these enzyme products contain essentially no neutral protease. The enzyme products of this category also are characterized by their low α-amylase activity and a higher esterase-to-protease-activity ratio than the subtilopeptidase B alkaline protease. Esterase activity is defined as the ability of an enzyme to hydrolyze low-molecular-weight esters.

The enzymes which are classified as subtilopeptidase B contain a high casein activity at pH 7 and comparable levels of alkaline protease and α-amylase activity. The high pH 7 casein activity means the enzyme product contains neutral protease. An estimate of the neutral protease activity can be obtained by subtracting the pH 10 casein activity of the enzyme from its pH 7 casein activity. A better quantitative number for neutral protease activity can be obtained by inactivating the alkaline protease component of the enzyme with diisopropyl fluorophosphate, $(C_3H_7)_2FPO_4$, before determining the protease activity. Also proper choice of the substrate can permit the assay of the neutral protease in the presence of alkaline protease activity. Feder (6) has shown 3-(2-furylacryloyl)-glycol-L-leucine amide to be a suitable substrate for this purpose. The neutral protease can also be distinguished from alkaline protease in that the neutral protease does not possess esterase activity. A typical substrate used to demonstrate this difference is *p*-nitrophenyl acetate ester of glycine. Still another important difference between these two proteases is the fact the neutral protease is a metallo-enzyme whereas alkaline protease is not. Such enzymes require the presence of metal ions in their structure to activate them, and usually different metals result in different activities. These metallo-enzymes are readily deactivated by strong sequestrants, such as EDTA (ethylenediaminetetraacetic acid).

Mechanical blends of the subtilopeptidase A alkaline protease and α-amylase are also being offered by enzyme producers for use in detergent products. The reason for these mixtures is that the A variety of alkaline protease products generally do not contain sufficient α-amylase to produce carbohydrase functional benefits in detergent systems, and some detergent manufacturers think that some α-amylase activity is necessary in their formulations. The α-amylase activity of the enzyme mixtures ranges from 50,000 to 150,000 units per 300,000 to 400,000 units of alkaline protease (7,8). These blends can be recognized by the combination of high α-amylase activity and subtilopeptidase A variety of alkaline protease.

The physical form of the enzymes varies from a light fluffy powder with a density of 0.2–0.3 g/ml to densified granules with densities of 0.6–0.8 g/ml. The more dense enzyme products are generally preferred because they are less dusty to handle. Dedusted enzyme products have been developed to reduce the dust problems in handling and mixing. They contain some water-soluble organic binders, such as a nonionic surfactant, to bind the small particles together and thereby reduce the dustiness.

The enzymes, in addition to the enzyme protein and components from the fermentation liquors, contain a variety of inorganic components. These are added to the enzyme for standardization of activity and to provide stability of the enzyme in solution.

Production and Handling of Detergent Enzymes

Wallerstein (9) and Beckhorn, Labbee, and Underkofler (10) have reviewed the commercial production of a wide variety of microbial enzymes. The general principles discussed in these reviews apply to the production of protease enzymes for detergent applications. The process consists basically of the following operations:

1. Organism selection.
2. Preservation of culture.
3. Inoculum buildup.
4. Plant fermentation.
5. Product isolation.

Organism Selection. The first step in the production of any commercial microbial enzyme is the selection of an organism that produces the desired enzyme in good yield. For detergent proteases, specially selected mutants of *Bacillus* species organisms are used. These organisms generally produce both proteolytic and amylolytic enzymes, the ratio dependent on the particular strain of organism used and process variables such as the composition of the medium, pH, and temperature.

Culture Preservation. Whatever the specific strain of organism, it is preserved as a pure culture by accepted microbiological techniques such as storage as lypholized or soil cultures. Purity of the cultures is assured by using methods to exclude contaminating organisms and to avoid development of substrains from within the culture itself. As an additional precaution in routine manufacture, a practice is frequently followed whereby single spore or cell isolates are made and tested for morphological and biochemical characteristics to assure purity of strain and maximum enzyme production.

Inoculum Buildup. Inoculum buildup is required to supply a sufficient amount of cells to serve as a starter for the production-scale propagation of the protease enzymes. The buildup process usually starts with the inoculation of small flasks or bottles containing the fermentation media from a slant from the pure culture. The fermentation medium for protease propagation usually contains a balance of protein and carbohydrate with minor ingredients such as calcium, phosphorus, and nitrogen. The exact composition of the medium will vary with the manufacturer, the strain of organism, the enzyme system desired, and production techniques. The inoculum cultures are grown in the laboratory under controlled temperature conditions. After the cell population has reached the optimum level, the contents of the containers are transferred to a series of larger containers, sometimes referred to as seed tanks, for further cell buildup.

Plant Fermentation. The content of the seed tanks is used to inoculate the production fermenters when the cell population has again reached an acceptable level. Agitation and aeration of the growing culture are controlled carefully, as are temperature, pH, disappearance of certain media ingredients, purity of culture, and level of enzyme. The optimum harvest time is the point at which the maximum production of protease activity has been achieved. Bacterial proteases are less stable in the fermentation media than other enzymes such as α-amylase, and hence, considerable care has to be exercised not to allow the fermentation to continue for too long a period of time.

Product Isolation. When the protease assays indicate that the maximum enzyme yield has been achieved, the fermented "beer," which contains the enzyme in solution along with suspended solids from the medium and microbial cells, is treated with a variety of reagents for special purposes such as stabilization, flocculation, and improvement in filtration rate. The beer is then clarified by either filtration or centrifugation. The clarified filtrate is usually concentrated several-fold at this point in a low-temperature vacuum evaporator.

Precipitation of the protease enzyme from the concentrated beer is accomplished either with a volatile organic solvent or by salting out with such agents as ammonium or sodium sulfate. The precipitated mass is then filtered. The filter cake can either be redissolved for additional purification or can be dried directly in atmospheric or vacuum driers at low temperature. After drying, the product is ground, if necessary, assayed for protease activity, and usually standarized to some activity designated by the customer by adding sodium sulfate or some other inert ingredient.

Handling. Precaution must be taken with the handling of protease enzymes to avoid inhalation of enzyme dust which could result in a range of respiratory allergic manifestations in susceptible individuals not unlike those seen in other industrial exposures to other dusts with antigenic properties. Handling instructions are generally available from the enzyme producers and are usually based on their own plant experience. One producer recommends that personnel in contact with their protease enzyme wear clean coveralls, rubber gloves with cloth liners, and a combination dust mask and face shield, and, as a routine practice, shower following a shift completion or a serious contact with the enzyme (11). These precautions pertain to the handling of the enzyme in detergent plants as well. Some reports of respiratory symptoms have appeared among workers in enzyme detergent manufacturing in Europe (12–14). In the United States improved dust-control measures in the detergent plants coupled with the use of proper personnel protective equipment has essentially eliminated the problem.

Methods of Enzyme Incorporation. The addition of enzymes to detergent products is accomplished either by blending the enzyme directly with the dry detergent base or by spraying a solution or suspension of the enzyme onto some base material and then blending this premix with the detergent base. Protease and α-amylase enzymes cannot be processed in detergent slurries used in spray-drying since they are deactivated at the temperatures encountered in such operations.

The dry-blending of the enzyme or enzyme premix with the detergent base is carried out in blending equipment such as a ribbon blender, rotary drum, or "V" shell blender. Caution is usually taken to prevent physical attrition of the detergent product during mixing to avoid a large increase in the bulk density of the final product. The base detergent should also be cool and void of any free moisture to avoid unnecessary degradation of the enzyme. The addition of the enzyme is usually the final step in processing prior to packaging.

Koch (18) describes a process for the manufacture of an enzyme premix. In this process the enzyme is mixed with a nonionic surfactant, which is liquid at the processing temperature but solid at room temperature, in ratio of enzyme to nonionic not to exceed 1:1. The suspension formed by this mixture is added to a Loedige mixer with sodium tripolyphosphate to form the premix. This premix is then added to the detergent from the spray tower by means of a continuous weighing mechanism in a manner similar to that used for sodium peroxyborate.

Several patents (19–25) also exist describing procedures for sticking the enzyme to the surface of some base material utilizing either aqueous solutions of the enzyme or suspension of the enzyme in some water-soluble organic liquid. In all of these processes the product is considered as a premix and must be blended with the detergent base. The advantage of this type of process is the reduction in the amount of enzyme dust generated in the blending of the enzyme with the detergent base.

Enzyme Detergents

The majority of the enzyme detergent products sold worldwide in 1969 for household use can be classified into two groups, laundry presoak products and heavy-duty laundry detergents. Specialty products, for such uses as soaking cooking utensils, washing baby diapers, and general-purpose cleaning, are beginning to appear in the market place but represent only a small portion of the enzyme consumption for this industry. A listing of the enzyme products sold in the United States in 1969 and their manufacturers is given in Table 2.

Table 2. Enzyme Detergent Products Sold in the U.S. for Household Use (1969)

Manufacturer	Presoak	Laundry detergent	Specialty use
Amway Corporation	Tri-Zyme		
Calgon Corporation	Sure		
Colgate-Palmolive Co.	Axion	Ajax, Cold Power, Fab, Punch	
Economics Laboratory, Inc.			Pan-Dandy
General Foods Corp.			Discover
Johnson & Johnson			Diaper Wash
Lever Brothers Company	Amaze	Drive	
Neo-Life Co. of America			Neo-zyme
North American Chemical Co.	N-zyme		
Procter and Gamble Co.	Biz	Bold, Cheer, Dash, Gain, Oxydol, Tide XK	
Purex Corporation, Ltd.	Brion	Brillo, News	Beads O'Bleach
Sears, Roebuck and Co.	Enzyme laundry presoak		

Presoak Products. The purpose of presoak detergents is to loosen or remove heavy stains from items prior to laundering them in the conventional washing machine. The time for presoaking will vary from 30 min to overnight, depending on the severity of the stains to be removed.

The presoak products sold in the United States (as listed in Table 2) contain sodium tripolyphosphate (STP), and either an alkylbenzenesulfonate or a nonionic surfactant. Only a portion of these products contain sodium silicate and only one contains sodium peroxyborate. The enzyme level in these products ranges from 0.5–1.0% enzyme based on the 350,000 casein units/g alkaline protease enzyme (7).

The enzyme presoak formulations sold in Europe typically contain STP and higher levels of surfactant than those sold in the United States. They do not contain sodium peroxyborate. These products are used in the prewash cycle in European washing machines, as well as for the longer presoaking applications.

Heavy-Duty Laundry Detergents. Enzymes have been incorporated into U.S. heavy-duty laundry detergent without any major changes in the formulation of the detergent. The enzyme level in these products is in the range of 0.3–0.6% of the 350,000 casein units/g alkaline protease enzyme. It is estimated that about 50% of the heavy-duty laundry detergents will be converted to enzymic products by the end of 1969.

The use of enzymes in European heavy-duty detergents developed more slowly at first than in the United States primarily because of concern over the stability of the protease enzyme in the presence of sodium peroxyborate, a constituent of most European detergents. The enzyme content of the European detergents is in the range of 0.8–1.2%. This high level of use provides a safety factor against loss of enzyme activity caused by the highly alkaline sodium peroxyborate. It has been reported that various manufacturers have resorted to coating the enzyme with a nonionic surfactant or soap to prevent undue loss of protease activity from contact with the sodium peroxyborate during storage. Although it was originally reported that sodium peroxyborate inactivates protease enzymes this is no longer felt to be the case. European detergent manufacturers advertise that the protease enzymes function in the early stages of the wash cycle while the water is heating and that sodium peroxyborate does not begin to function until the water has reached a temperature at which the protease has been deactivated thermally.

Specialty Products. Specialty products containing enzymes will probably grow in number rapidly by taking advantage of the present popularity of the word "enzymes" with the American housewife. To date no automatic dishwashing products with enzymes have appeared in the United States although a presoak product for cooking utensils is available. Automatic dishwashing products with α-amylase are known to exist in Germany and Japan and several patents have been issued indicating a benefit from enzymes in this type of product (15–17). Other specialty products include an enzyme detergent directed specifically for stain removal from baby diapers, an enzyme dry bleach for general stain removal problems, and a detergent booster. The first liquid product claiming enzyme activity in the United States is an all-purpose cleaner.

Performance Test Methods

Standard Soil Test Cloths. The EMPA standard soil test cloths (26) are used widely for performance evaluations and screening tests. These test cloths do not give practical performance results, but are used to provide guidance of potential enzyme performance and are useful for comparing the enzyme activity of two or more enzyme-containing detergents or different enzymes.

The EMPA cloth used most frequently for proteolytic enzyme performance is EMPA-116. The soil on this cloth is a mixture of blood, milk, and Japanese ink, and is highly responsive to proteolytic enzyme activity. This particular soil, however, is set by the presence of sodium peroxyborate in the detergent solution. For this test cloth to be useful for evaluation of peroxyborate-containing detergents with enzymes, the peroxyborate must be decomposed before introducing the test cloth into the detergent solution. This can be accomplished by the addition of an enzyme that catalyzes the decomposition of hydrogen peroxide, such as catalase.

The EMPA soil cloth used for amylolytic enzyme performance is EMPA-112. This cloth is stained with a cocoa–milk–sugar mixture. It is highly responsive to α-amylase activity and is not affected by sodium peroxyborate. The soil also responds slightly to proteolytic activity, but this is a small response compared with that for

α-amylase activity. The fact that there is a small response from a protease enzyme is not surprising in light of the milk component in the soil.

An EMPA cloth soiled with hemoglobin (EMPA-111) is also available for protease testing. This soil cloth, however, is not widely used because a high percentage of the soil is removed by the detergent base without enzyme. Many other standard soil test cloths have been mentioned in the literature (3,27–29). For the most part the soil composition is a mixture of proteins and sugar, and quite similar to the EMPA cloths.

The test cloths are cut into small swatches and washed in a detergent solution using small-scale washing equipment, such as the Terg-O-Tometer or Launder-ometer. Generally, several swatches are washed at one time to improve the reliability of the test results. A typical procedure is described by Langguth and Mecey (30). Following the wash, the reflectance of the swatches is measured and the reflectance of the corresponding unwashed swatches subtracted. The average difference in reflectance is a measure of the performance of the enzyme detergent. The performance of the enzyme can be measured under different test conditions by washing swatches of the test cloth in the detergent with and without enzyme. Then the difference between the reflectance of the washed swatches is the performance on the particular soil cloth due only to the enzyme. This latter method is useful when enzyme activity measurements are desired under varying conditions where the performance of the base detergent can vary, as well as the effect of the enzyme. Figures 1 and 2 illustrate the type of data obtained with EMPA-116 and EMPA-112 soil test cloths for different concentrations of alkaline protease and α-amylase activity respectively in a detergent solution. Reflectance data reported in these figures were obtained with a Gardner Color Difference Meter.

Natural Stains. The preparation of natural stains for enzyme performance testing has been described in several articles (31–34). The natural stains referred to in these articles include a variety of protein and food soils. Examples of the protein soils

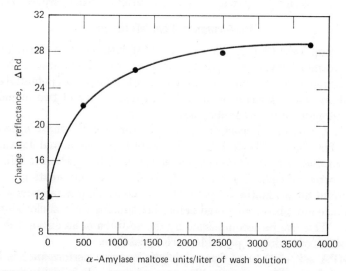

Fig. 1. Effect of the alkaline protease content of a detergent solution on stain removal from EMPA-116 test cloth (conditions: 0.15% anionic detergent, 120°F, 150 ppm water hardness, 10-min wash in Terg-O-Tometer).

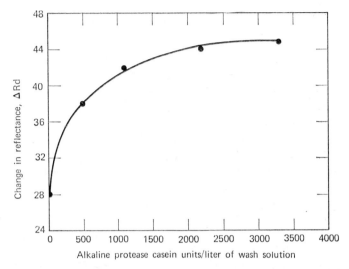

Fig. 2. Effect of the α-amylase enzyme content of a detergent solution on stain removal from EMPA-112 test cloth (conditions: 0.15% anionic detergent, 120°F, 150 ppm water hardness, 10-min wash in Terg-O-Tometer).

are blood, gelatin, serum albumin, globulin, casein, and collagen. Food soils include egg yolk, oatmeal, gravy, chocolate pudding and sauces, vegetables, coffee, tea, and fruit stains. The stained fabrics containing these soils are prepared either by staining the total surface area of the swatch or by staining only a portion of the swatch. The latter method is preferred by some because it permits an easy visual evaluation of the degree of stain removal. In cases where the soil is not colored, some form of tracer, such as carbon black (21,28), is used so that reflectance measurements can be taken. Both single-stain and multistained swatches are used, the multistained swatches being preferred where a large number of screening tests are required.

An interesting technique used with natural stains for performance comparisons is to prepare a large, nearly circular stain on a piece of fabric, and before washing cut the fabric so that equal pieshaped portions of the stain are formed (35). Then pieces are washed in different detergents, or under different conditions, and following the wash the pieces are fit back together in their original position. Visual examination can then readily detect performance differences.

Skin sebum soils are also used to demonstrate the ability of enzymes to remove stains formed on collars and cuffs of shirts. The soiling procedure for obtaining skin sebum stains is described by Trowbridge et al. (36).

Protease Activity Measurements. Many methods have been suggested for the determination of activity of protease and amylase enzymes (7,8,37–41). These methods for the most part, while effective for assaying the enzymes by themselves, have certain drawbacks for determining activity of the enzyme detergents under practical use conditions. Paixao et al. have developed an automated bioassay method for proteolytic enzymes which can be used satisfactorily in the presence of detergent products (42). Jaag has suggested a method for determining the activity of protease enzymes that reflect more closely the actual conditions that are employed in the laundry operation (43). In this test the enzyme reaction occurs in a two-phase system in which the enzyme is in solution and the substrate is present in solid form. The substrate is a specially prepared water-insoluble protein or water-insoluble starch chemically bound to a water-soluble determinable reagent component.   The enzyme detergent solution and a known weight of substrate are reacted under the desired conditions of concentration, time, temperature, and agitation.   The enzyme cleaves the substrate molecules, freeing the chemically bound water-soluble component.   A determination of the quantity of this component that has been solubilized can be used to indicate the extent of enzyme activity.   This method was proposed since it employs a technique in which the enzyme reaction with the substrate occurs on the surface of the substrate in a manner similar to the conditions that prevail in stain removal in the actual washing process.

Performance of Enzyme Detergents.   It is widely recognized that a sound technical basis exists for putting enzymes in laundry detergents.   Qualitative descriptions of enzyme detergent performance are abundant in the literature (3,27,31,44–57). These articles for the most part discuss the performance of the enzyme detergents in the usual terms of "splitting" of proteinaceous material such as blood, milk, egg yolk, excrement, and other proteinaceous materials into water-soluble proteoses and peptones which can then be washed out of the fabrics easily by effective detergent compositions. Most of these articles point out that the enzyme detergents are more effective than the enzyme-free detergents in getting rid of hard-to-remove stains and soils, and are particularly effective on soils, such as blood and milk-based stains, which bleach will not remove.   An alphabetical list of the problem stains which the manufacturers of enzyme detergents and enzyme presoak products claim are removed with their use appears in Table 3.   Although removal of most of these stains is improved by protease and amylase enzyme action, some of them can be removed by detergent action alone.

Published quantitative information on the performance of enzyme detergents on natural household stains, on the other hand, is limited.   Terry and Groves discuss the removal of natural stains such as blood, chocolate milk, grass, etc, from different fabric substrates under wash and presoak conditions, but use a subjective rating system to indicate performance (31).   They concluded that enzymes are helpful in removing protein stains such as blood and grass and that presoaking with the enzyme is required in most instances for complete stain removal.   Oldenroth studied the removal of a number of stains under a variety of European laundry conditions using reflectance measurements and protein analysis to quantify stain removal (32).   Some stains responded favorably to the enzyme detergents while others did not show any difference between the enzyme and enzyme-free detergents.

Several papers have been published which show the effect that various factors, such as wash temperature, detergent pH, wash time, and detergent ingredients, have on

Table 3.   Problem Stains Claimed to be Removed with the Use of Enzyme Detergents or Presoaks

baby food	egg yolk	licorice
barbecue sauce	fruit juice	meat
blood	grape juice	milk
blueberry juice	grass	perspiration
body soil	gravy	sauces
catsup	grease	scorch
chocolate	ground-in	spaghetti sauce
coffee	dirt	spinach
collar and cuff grime	ice cream	tea
cream	ink	tomato juice
diaper stains	iodine	wine

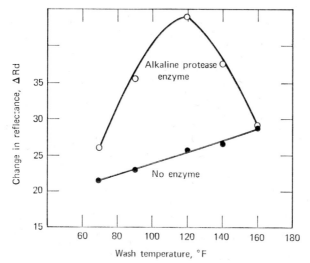

Fig. 3. Effect of temperature on stain removal from EMPA-116 test cloth by a typical commercially available alkaline protease (conditions: 0.15% anionic detergent, 2500 alkaline casein units/liter of wash solution, 150 ppm water hardness, 10-min wash in Terg-O-Tometer).

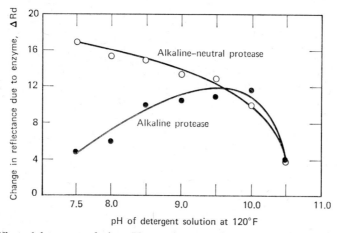

Fig. 4. Effect of detergent solution pH on stain removal from EMPA-116 test cloth by typical, commercially available alkaline protease and alkaline-neutral protease enzymes (conditions: 0.15% anionic detergent, 2500 alkaline casein units/liter of wash solution, 150 ppm water hardness, 10-min wash in Terg-O-Tometer).

enzyme performance (4,28,29,58–61). In all cases the protease enzyme performance was indicated from reflectance measurements on EMPA-116 standard soil cloth.

Temperature is an important factor in the performance of protease enzymes. Figure 3 shows that the greatest benefit from typical, commercially available, protease enzymes is realized at wash temperatures around 120°F, which coincides with the average wash temperature used by housewives in the United States (61). Cold-water wash temperatures reduce the enzyme action somewhat and temperatures higher than 120°F cause degradation of the protease in the presence of the detergent. The coincidence of data points at 160°F indicates that there has been essentially complete inactivation of the enzyme at this temperature.

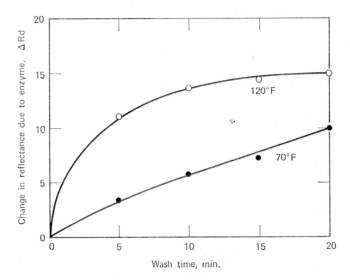

Fig. 5. Effect of wash time on stain removal from EMPA-116 test cloth by a typical, commercially available alkaline protease at cold- and hot-water wash temperatures (conditions: 0.15% anionic detergent, 2500 alkaline casein units/liter of wash solution, 150 ppm water hardness, 10-min wash in Terg-O-Tometer).

The importance of the pH value of the detergent solution to protease enzyme performance is shown in Figure 4 (61). Enzyme A, the commonly used alkaline protease, gives optimum performance in the pH range of 8.5–10.0. The majority of the laundry detergents sold in the United States have pH values within this range. The greater performance of enzyme B at the lower pH values results from the presence of a neutral protease in combination with alkaline protease in an enzyme product. At detergent pH values above 10, the stain-removal performance of both enzymes is reduced.

Enzyme performance, as expected, is also a function of the time during which the enzyme is in contact with the stain. Figure 5 shows the effect of wash time at two different temperatures on alkaline protease performance (62). The performance continues to increase with wash time at both temperatures. The same amount of stain is removed by the enzyme in 5 min at 120°F as is accomplished in 20 min at the cold-water temperature.

The effect of these laundry variables on α-amylase performance has been reported by Liss and Langguth (61). Their data show that α-amylase behaves similarly to alkaline protease in response to the different factors except that its activity is not as temperature sensitive as the subtilopeptidase A alkaline protease.

The compatibility of the alkaline protease enzyme with the various detergent ingredients has been studied using both assay techniques (28,63,64) and performance measurements (61) to determine any effect on protease activity. There is a general agreement between these studies that good enzyme activity can be obtained in the presence of detergent ingredients, and that high concentrations of sodium tripolyphosphate and anionic surfactants can be detrimental to protease activity under certain conditions of temperature and time of contact. Nonionic surfactants, on the other hand, have essentially no effect on enzyme activity. Langguth and Mecey show that highly alkaline ingredients such as sodium carbonate, sodium sesquicarbonate, sodium metasilicate, and sodium nitrilotriacetate [N(CH₂COONa)₃] (see Complexing agents) are detrimental to protease activity because of their alkalinity, and when the pH of these detergent ingredients is adjusted to 9.5–10, they no longer produce any inactivation of the protease (30). Wieg has shown that protease enzymes vary in their stability toward sodium peroxyborate, a fact which may account for the complicating reports in the literature on the stability of peroxyborate (64).

Alkaline protease and α-amylase enzymes show good stability on storage even under highly exaggerated conditions of temperature and relative humidity (61). Messing et al. have reported on a stabilized protease complex for use in detergent formulations, which gives improved stability of high temperatures and relative humidities over typical detergent alkaline proteases, but they did not describe the composition of the stabilizing agent (65).

Safety of Enzyme Detergents

Studies on the oral and cutaneous toxicity, irritancy, and skin sensitization of en zyme detergents are reported by Griffith et al. (66) and in a bulletin of the National Clearing-house for Poison Control Centers (67).

The LD_{50} of 20% aqueous solutions of two different commercial protease enzymes on rats was found to range from 3.7–10.3 g/kg of body weight. It was demonstrated that these values were directly related to levels of inorganic salts present as diluents in the enzymes. The LD_{50} on rats for enzyme laundry detergents and presoak products was shown to be less that 5 g/kg, and not significantly different from the enzyme-free formulations. These same enzyme laundry detergents and presoak products showed no toxic effects on dogs and the addition of the enzyme to the detergents did not alter the detergent's emetic properties.

Dermal toxicity results from 4-week and 13-week applications of enzyme–detergent mixtures to abraded or intact skin of albino rabbits showed no adverse systemic effects. At enzyme levels commonly encountered in enzyme detergents, mild-to-moderate irritation of the skin was observed but again, this did not differ from that observed with the nonenzyme controls. Extensive eye irritation studies on rabbits with the application of aqueous solutions, as well as granular forms of the enzyme detergents, showed no effect of any consequence when the protease enzymes were added to the formulations.

Primary irritation and cutaneous sensitization tests using human subjects and an occlusive patch test procedure were also conducted. A representative detergent product with exaggerated levels of enzyme showed slightly more irritation under these conditions than the formulation without enzymes. There was no evidence of cutaneous sensitization. Also other tests of above normal skin exposure showed that these products were not greatly different from the enzyme-free formulations.

Consumer use tests involving more than 11,000 housewives for periods from 2–4 weeks showed no adverse skin reactions related to the presence of the enzymes in the detergents. Other tests with housewives and babies also uncovered no skin irritation problems.

Studies on the characteristics of detergent dust and enzyme dust generated during the home use of laundry detergents have been reported by M. H. Hendricks (68). It is concluded that laundry detergents containing agglomerated enzymes are safe from the standpoint of potential consumer exposure to enzyme dust. It was found that even under conditions of excessive home use, consumer exposure is extremely low and can be compared to only a minute fraction of the industrial exposures which are considered to be safe.

Environmental Acceptability of Detergent Enzymes. Swisher has reported on a variety of tests used to show the biodegradation characteristics of a typical detergent-grade protease enzyme (69). The studies were conducted at enzyme activities 100-fold greater than that which would be expected in domestic sewage due to the sensitivity limits of the enzyme assay methods. Rapid degradation of the enzyme occurred in all instances. Swisher concluded, in view of the ready biodegradability of the enzyme and the natural occurrence of similar enzymes at comparable levels, that it would be unlikely that these enzymes would cause environmental reactions either from direct actions or from second-order effects.

Bibliography

1. Ger. Pat. 283,923 (May 1915), O. Röhm.
2. U.S. Pat. 1,882,279 (Oct. 1932), G. G. Frelinghuysen (to P. Ballantine & Sons).
3. A. Zscharn, *Chem.-Tech. Rundschau Fette Seifen* **10**, 463 (1940).
4. A. Suter, *Riv. Ital. Sostanze Grasse* **43**, 581–584 (1966); *Chem. Abstr.* **67**, 4017s (1966).
5. L. Keay and P. Moser, *Biochem. Biophys. Res. Commun.* **34**, 600 (1969).
6. J. Feder, *Biochem. Biophys. Res. Commun.* **32**, 326 (1968).
7. M. Kunitz, *J. Gen. Physiol.* **30**, 291 (1947).
8. S. P. Colowick and N. O. Kaplan, eds., *Methods in Enzymology*, Vol. 1, Academic Press, Inc., New York, 1955, p. 149.
9. L. Wallerstein, *Ind. Eng. Chem.* **31**, 1218–1224 (1939).
10. E. J. Beckhorn, M. D. Labbee, and L. A. Underkofler, *Agr. Food Chem.* **13**, 30–34 (1965).
11. Monsanto Company, *Technical Bulletin 1-301*, October 1969.
12. M. L. H. Flindt, *Lancet* **1**, 1177–1181 (1969).
13. J. Pepys et al., *Lancet* **1**, 1181–1184 (1969).
14. T. J. Franz et al., *paper presented at American Academy of Allergy, New Orleans, 1970.*
15. Brit. Pat. 5,099,887 (November 1967), to Unilever Ltd.
16. Dutch Pat. Appl. 6,715,387 (May 15, 1968), to Unilever N.V.
17. Ger. Pat. 1,285,087 (Dec. 1968), to Miele & Cie.
18. O. Koch, *Seifen-Oele-Fette-Wachse* **95**, 446 (1969).
19. Ger. Pat. 1,801,119 (May 1969), F. Pasztor (to Unilever, N.V.); *Chem. Abstr.* **71**, 23162j (1969).
20. U.S. Pat. 3,451,935 (June 1969), A. S. Roald and N. T. deOude (to Procter and Gamble Co.).
21. Fr. Pat. 1,520,948 (April 1967), A. S. Roald and N. T. deOude (to Procter and Gamble Co.).
22. Belg. Pat. 697,480 (April 1967), to Procter and Gamble Co.
23. Ger. (East) Pat. 14,296 (Jan. 1958), F. Leidholt; *Chem. Abstr.* **55**, 1036e (1961).
24. Ger. (East) Pat. 20,291 (Nov. 1960), F. Leidholt; *Chem. Abstr.* **55**, 27927c (1961).
25. Polish Pat. 41,847 (April 1959), O. Tauer; *Chem. Abstr.* **54**, 14734h (1960).
26. Obtained from Eidgenössiche Material Prüfungs- und Versuchsanstalt für Industrie (EMPA), Bauwesen und Gewerbe, St. Gallen, Switzerland, or Testfabrics, Inc., New York.
27. E. Jaag, *Chimia (Arrau)* **1**, 57–63 (1947); *Chem. Abstr.* **41**, 5312b (1947).
28. T. Cayle, *J. Am. Oil Chem. Soc.* **46**, 515–519 (1969).
29. O. Viertel, *Fette Seifen* **51**, 145–148 (1944); *Chem. Abstr.* **41**, 7778h (1947).
30. R. P. Langguth and L. W. Mecey, *Soap Chem. Specialties* **45**, 60 pp. (1969).
31. B. W. Terry and W. L. Groves, "Stains, Fabrics, Detergents," *paper presented at Am. Oil Chemists' Soc. Meeting, San Francisco, April 1969.*
32. O. Oldenroth, *Fette, Seifen, Anstrichmittel* **70**, 24–29 (1968); *Chem. Abstr.* **68**, 106276p (1968).
33. A. K. Ulcek, D. Krkoskova, and J. Mansfield, *Chem. Obzor.* **18**, 41–42 (1943); *Chem. Abstr.* **38**, 56167.
34. Rohm and Haas Co., *Technical Bulletin SAN 503*, 1968.
35. Private communication from Colgate-Palmolive Co.
36. J. R. Trowbridge, R. T. Hunter, and H. L. Marder, "Factors Affecting the Performance of Hydrophobic Textile Fibers in Laundering," *paper presented at Gordon Res. Conf. on Textiles, New London, N.H., July 1965.*

37. M. L. Anson, *J. Gen. Physiol.* **22**, 79 (1938).
38. W. L. Nelson, E. I. Ciaccio, and G. P. Hess, *Anal. Biochem.* **2**, 39 (1961).
39. H. Rinderknecht, P. Wilding, and B. J. Haverback, *Experientia,* **23**, 805 (1967); *Chem. Abstr.* **67**, 105374m (1967).
40. H. Rinderknecht, M. C. Silverman, and B. J. Haverback, *Clin. Chim. Acta* **21**, 197 (1969).
41. S. D. Friedman and S. M. Barkin, *J. Am. Oil Chemists' Soc.* **46**, 81–84 (1969).
42. L. M. Paixao et al., *J. Am. Oil Chemists' Soc.* **46**, 511–514 (1959).
43. H. R. Jaag, Jr., *Fette, Seifen, Anstrichmittel* **71**, 404–406 (1969); *Chem. Abstr.* **71**, 36020m (1969).
44. Anonymous, *Detergent Age* **5**(12), 38–39 (1968).
45. Anonymous, *Detergent Age* **4**(1), 47–49 (1967).
46. K. P. Duesing, *Fette, Seifen, Anstrichmittel* **69**, 738–741 (1967); *Chem. Abstr.* **68**, 359c (1968).
47. Anonymous, *Soap Chem. Specialties* **43**, 86 (Nov. 1967).
48. P. Mannheim, *Fette, Seifen, Anstrichmittel* **70**, 30–35 (1968).
49. Anonymous, *Chem. Week* **102**, 89–90 (June 22, 1968).
50. Anonymous, *Chem. Eng.* **75**, 108–110 (Sept. 23, 1968).
51. Anonymous, *Business Week*, 148 (Sept. 21, 1968).
52. Anonymous, *Business and Finance*, 89–90 (Oct. 7, 1968).
53. Anonymous, *Consumer Bulletin*, **4**, 39–40 (Oct. 1968).
54. Anonymous, *Consumer Report*, **34**, 44 (Jan. 1969).
55. Anonymous, *Chem. Eng. News*, **47**, 16–17 (Feb. 3, 1969).
56. Anonymous, *Detergents Specialties* **6**, 20–21, 56 (Aug. 1969).
57. R. Kessler, *Wall Street Journal*, 30 (Oct. 9, 1969).
58. J. C. Hoogerheide, *Fette, Seifen, Anstrichmittel* **70**, 743–748 (1968).
59. J. C. Hoogerheide, P. K. Bogerman, and R. J. Vogels, *Kem. Teollisuus* **24**, 207–212 (1967); *Chem. Abstr.* **67**, 55341 (1967).
60. J. C. Hoogerheide, "Enzymes as Additives to Laundry Detergents," *paper presented at Am. Oil Chemists' Soc. Meeting, Chicago, October 1967.*
61. R. L. Liss and R. P. Langguth, *J. Am. Oil Chemists' Soc.* **46**, 507–510 (1969).
62. R. P. Langguth, unpublished data of Monsanto Co.
63. D. Tsuru, *Kagaku To Kogyo (Osaka)* **43**, 199–211 (1969); *Chem. Abstr.* **71**, 79183j (1969).
64. A. J. Wieg, *Process Biochem.* **4**(2), 30–34 (1969).
65. R. A. Messing, D. J. Fischer, and J. R. Hutchins III, *Detergents Specialties* **6**(12), 22–23, 56 (1969).
66. J. F. Griffith et al., *Food Cosmetic Toxicol.* **7**, 581–593 (1969).
67. B. Golden, *Bulletin of National Clearinghouse for Poison Control Centers*, July–August 1969.
68. M. H. Hendricks, *J. Am. Oil Chemists' Soc.* **47**, 207–211 (1970).
69. R. D. Swisher, *Bioscience* **19**, 1093–1094 (1969).

ROBERT P. LANGGUTH
and RAYMOND L. LISS
Monsanto Company

ETHYLENE

References 1–3 present some new information on ethylene, including revisions of the values for some of its properties.

Manufacture

Thermal pyrolysis of petroleum fractions remains virtually the sole process commercially employed for the production of ethylene. Although any petroleum fraction from ethane to crude oil can be used, in this country the predominant feeds have been ethane and propane derived from natural gas. Less than 15% of the total ethylene produced in the U.S. is derived from liquid feedstocks such as light hydrocarbon condensates, natural gasoline, naphthas and gas oils. The rapid growth of propylene derivatives has encouraged recent interest in the U.S. in using some of these liquids as supplementary feedstocks, because propylene is an important by-product of feedstocks heavier than ethane (4). See also Olefins in this volume.

Outside of the U.S., where ethane and propane generally have not been available, naphtha feedstocks continue to be predominant. As the demand for naphtha increases, not only for ethylene feedstocks but also for ammonia feedstock and for motor gasoline, heavier feedstocks such as gas oils (crude oil fractions with boiling ranges from 400 to 800°F) are being employed commercially. It is also possible that the growing transport of liquefied natural gas (LNG) from North Africa and the Middle East to Europe may make ethane and propane commercially available to European manufacturers. See Gas, natural, in this volume.

High-Temperature Pyrolysis

The fired tubular heater remains the primary tool for the pyrolysis of hydrocarbon feedstocks to produce ethylene. For this reason, considerable effort has been expended by the industry to improve its design and operation.

The first major class of improvements involved investigations into fundamentals, using advanced techniques for measurement of yields, conversions, and heat-transfer coefficients both in pilot and commercial plants (5). These measurements and newly available computer techniques permitted the development of mathematical models for describing the kinetics and heat-transfer performance. Thus it became possible to make systematic studies of the effects of changing the main variables in physical design and in operation conditions and to apply the results with confidence to commercial plants.

The second major class of improvements involved investigation of yields from a wide variety of feedstocks, such that the effects of feed composition and reactor conditions (residence time, temperature profile, and partial pressure of hydrocarbons) could be correlated and predicted quantitatively.

The third class of improvements involved investigation into the relationship between feed composition, reactor conditions, and run length. It was found that the configuration of the reactor system, and the metal used for the tube, and its surface finish all have important influences upon coke deposition and tube carburization. As a result, it was necessary to develop standards of quality control for the metal composition, grain structure, and finish of the tube (6).

Armed with these tools, the industry is currently able to offer tubular reactor systems with larger capacities, lower residence times, and longer run lengths than previously available. The reactor characteristics can be selected to provide the desired yield of main and coproducts, from the available feedstocks. For example, if feedstock is limited or expensive or if maximum ethylene is desired, then a high-severity, low-residence-time design is appropriate. If high coproduct (propylene, butadiene) yields are desired, then a low-conversion, moderate-residence-time design is to be preferred.

The quench and heat-recovery section of the reactor system has also been improved. Transfer-line exchangers are now available in a variety of configurations and have been applied successfully to feedstocks as heavy as gas oil. For many feedstocks, the run length is limited by the fouling of the transfer line exchanger rather than the coking of the cracking coil.

Yields

The composition of the feedstock and the operating conditions in the reactor control the composition of the product mixture. Although the actual chemical reactions occurring in the reactor are very complicated, some useful generalizations can indeed be drawn (4).

One important measure of the ethylene potential of a feedstock is its hydrogen content—the higher the content (generally the lower-molecular-weight hydrocarbon), the higher the potential. The explanation for this is that the major light by-products, hydrogen and methane, have hydrogen contents higher than the feed. As cracking becomes more severe, there is a corresponding lowering of the hydrogen content of the heavier fractions which are converted to tars, polynuclear aromatics, and similar condensed compounds. Experience has shown that when the hydrogen content of the C_5 and heavier fractions in the product mixture falls below 7–8 wt %, the reactor and quench systems become fouled with coke and tar. This "limiting severity" is reached at a lower conversion for feedstocks with lower hydrogen contents.

A second measure is the hydrocarbon analysis by structure, known as PONA in the hydrocarbon industry [PONA is an acronym for paraffins, olefins, naphthenes, (alicyclic) aromatics]. Of these, the straight-chain paraffins are generally more favorable for the production of olefins. Branched paraffins are generally less favorable for ethylene production, but do give high yields of propylene and butylene.

Naphthenes are favorable for ethylene when pyrolyzed at optimum conditions by themselves. When part of a mixed feed, however, they are only moderately converted under normal commercial pyrolysis conditions and, therefore, their net effect is to reduce the overall yield of ethylene. However, they give yields of by-product butadiene and aromatics that are more favorable than from paraffins.

Aromatics are essentially inert in the pyrolysis reactor and contribute very little to the yield of olefins.

For gas-oil feeds, the PONA does not sufficiently characterize the yield and therefore pilot plant runs are usually made (5).

Table 1 presents some typical commercial yields for gas oils (8). By comparison with Table 3, Vol. 8, p. 509, it will be seen the yield of components heavier than the 400°F gasoline is an order of magnitude larger than when processing naphthas. This pyrolysis "fuel oil" stream does not meet specifications for commercial distillate or residual fuels. Thus there is a strong inducement to use as much as feasible by recycling to the pyrolysis furnaces. Beyond this, a gas-oil fed plant must develop other outlets such as feedstocks for carbon black or coking units.

Table 1. Typical Commercial Yields from Gas Oils

	Feed			
	Light gas oil		Heavy gas oil	
feed properties ASTM boiling range, °F	400–690		440–780	
	Gas-oil feed			
Pyrolysis product, % of feed	Light[a]		Heavy[b]	
	Moderate	High	Moderate	High
hydrogen	0.5	0.65	0.53	0.6
methane	8.9	10.80	8.2	10.7
acetylene	0.14	0.25	0.17	0.3
ethylene	20.0	23.0	18.0	21.0
ethane	3.6	3.9	3.4	3.6
propadiene	0.32	0.35	0.27	0.3
propylene	13.3	13.2	12.5	12.9
propane	0.52	0.5	0.55	0.55
butylenes–butanes	9.5	8.2	8.7	7.85
C_5-400°F gasoline	23.7	20.4	22.7	17.7
fuel oil	19.5	18.8	25.0	24.5
butadiene in butylenes– butanes stream, %	38	44	37	45
aromatics in gasoline, %	23	39	20	38

[a] ASTM boiling range, 400–690°F.
[b] ASTM boiling range, 440–780°F.

Recovery and Purification

The recovery and purification process schemes most frequently employed in current plants are low-temperature, high-pressure straight fractionation, and low-temperature, low-pressure straight fractionation; these are identified as (a) and (c) in Vol. 8, p. 511. Scheme (a) is still the dominant process although there has been increasing acceptance of (c) in Europe. The trend to very large plants (450,000 metric tons/year or more), to heavier feedstocks, and to more rigorous product specifications has inspired some variations in details of the process but the typical scheme (a) remains as previously described (9,10). Some plants have used solvents such as monoethanolamine instead of caustic soda for acid gas removal. This solvent can be recovered, thus giving an economic incentive as well as reducing the problem of disposing of the spent caustic.

In recent years, there has been a tremendous growth in the ocean transport of liquefied natural gas (LNG), which is carried out at essentially atmospheric pressure and −260°F. The implications for ethylene manufacture are two-fold: (1) the "cold" of the LNG can be used to provide at least part of the refrigeration for the low-temperature fractionation of ethylene; and (2) some LNG contains significant quantities of potential feedstocks, ie, ethane, propane, and butane. As regards the refrigeration, the maximum recoverable work would be on the order of 100 kW per million cubic feet per day of LNG vaporized, but this is not realizable in an actual plant because of nonideal conditions. Studies indicate that for a delivery rate of 125 million scfd (standard cubic feet per day) of a lean (high methane) LNG, there would be approximately a 25% savings in the investment and production costs for an associated 160,000 short ton per year ethylene plant. A richer (high ethane, propane, and butane) gas could support a larger plant, say on the order of 250,000–300,000 short tons per year. For optimum exploitation of the refrigeration potential, the ethylene plant production capacity should be about double that derivable from the LNG; in other words, a significant quantity of outside supplementary feedstocks would be necessary.

Some modification of the ethylene plant recovery scheme would be required to achieve the most efficient use of the available refrigeration but the technological problems are easily solved. Certain operational aspects such as seasonal variations in natural gas send-out rates and the necessary coordination between shipping terminal authority, a gas-utility company, and a chemical-plant operator may require some effort to solve (11).

Economics and Uses

Ethylene continues to be one of the most important and largest-volume petrochemicals in the world. Its production growth in the period 1960–1970 exceeded the forecasts; it is expected to continue to grow rapidly during the period 1970–1980, as shown in Table 2.

Table 2. Forecasted Ethylene Production in the Non-Communist World

Location	Annual production, short tons		
	1970	1975	1980
United States	7,800,000	12,000,000	17,600,000
Western Europe	5,500,000	9,500,000	14,500,000
Japan	2,500,000	4,700,000	7,300,000
other	1,200,000	3,300,000	8,000,000
total	17,000,000	29,500,000	47,400,000

This growth of production has encouraged the building of economical large plants. The minimum capacity now is 250,000 tons per year, but this size range is mainly of interest in Asia and in developing countries. In Western Europe, the new plants are mostly in the 400,000-ton-per-year range. The maximum practical single-train capacity is dictated by the availability of compressor machinery and is on the order of 600,000 tons per year. The investment benefit is beginning to diminish in sizes above 450,000 tons per year, and it is likely that few plants of larger capacity will be built (4).

The manufacturing costs before taxes for large ethylene plants in the U.S. fall in the range of 2.1–3.8¢/lb of ethylene. It is to be noted that these costs do not differ significantly from those of five years ago. The reason for this is that the economy of the larger plants has offset the inflation in materials and labor costs. The costs are very sensitive to credits for coproducts, especially for feedstocks heavier than ethane. Thus with unfavorable (low) values for the coproducts, it would be cheaper to make ethylene in the U.S. from ethane. On the other hand favorable high values for the coproduct make butane an interesting feedstock in the U.S., and heavy gas oil in Europe (4,7).

Derivatives and End Use. The projected U.S. growth rate for ethylene derivatives for the decade 1970–1980 is given in Table 3.

Table 3. Projected Growth Rate for 1970–1980 for Ethylene and Derivatives in the U.S.

Product	Rate, %/yr
polyethylene	9
ethylene oxide	7
styrene	8
vinyl chloride	11
others	8
ethylene	9

It is to be noted that these rates of growth generally are higher than for the decade 1960–1970.

Demand vs Capacity. As of 1970, there is a shortage of ethylene worldwide. The demand projection for the decade 1970–1980 indicates that 10–15 new plants will be required each year. Some of this capacity will be used to replace a number of older plants which will be retired.

Ethylene has virtually displaced acetylene and very few acetylene plants are being built, even of the kind that produce both acetylene and ethylene.

Transportation

Ethylene pipeline networks have been extended not only throughout the Gulf Coast of the U.S. but also in other parts of the world such as Germany and Holland. These networks combined with underground storage caverns offer protection to consumers against the failure of any single plant. Where geology does not permit cavern storage, above-ground cryogenic storage has been employed. The example of successful ocean transport of LNG has inspired consideration of tanker shipping of ethylene. Small-volume (50,000–100,000 metric tons/yr) routes have been commercially operated up to distances of 1000 nautical miles. Large volumes and larger distances are technically feasible but probably cannot compete with the local manufacture of ethylene from naphtha.

Bibliography

1. S. A. Miller, ed., *Ethylene and Its Industrial Derivatives*, Ernest Benn, Limited, London, 1969.
2. "Selected Values of Properties of Hydrocarbons and Related Compounds," *American Petroleum Institute Research Project 44*, Chemical Thermodynamic Properties Center, Agricultural and Mechanical College of Texas (Loose-leaf Data Sheets), 1968.
3. *Technical Data Book—Petroleum Refining*, American Petroleum Institute, New York, 1966.
4. J. G. Freiling, B. L. Huson, and R. N. Summerville, *Hydrocarbon Process.* **47**, 11 (1968).
5. J. R. Lambrix, B. A. Wallace, and J. C. Yarze, *Paper, World Petroleum Congress, Mexico City, Mexico, April, 1967.*
6. M. W. Clark, *Paper, Meeting National Association of Corrosion Engineers, Philadelphia, Pa., March 4, 1970.*
7. J. R. Lambrix, C. S. Morris, and M. J. Rosenfeld, *Chem. Eng. Progr.* **65**, 11 (1969).
8. Unpublished data, The Lummus Company, Bloomfield, N. J.
9. R. D. Harvey, *Oil Gas J.* **67**, 51 (1969).
10. L. Marshall and H. B. Zasloff, *Chem. Eng. Progr.* **65**, 10 (1969).
11. L. Kniel, *Oil Gas J.* **65**, 9 (1969).

D. L. CALDWELL
The Lummus Company

EUTROPHICATION

The fertilization of natural waters may result in the production of excessive growth of algae and higher plants. These crops may cause a serious deterioration of water quality. Today, the excessive fertilization (eutrophication) of natural waters is one of the most significant causes of water-quality problems in North America. It is likely that, as other sources of pollution are abated, the problems of excessive fertilization will assume a greater role in the deterioration of aquatic environmental quality. Eutrophication problems are not restricted to lakes; they also occur in rivers, impoundments, estuaries, and other coastal waters. This paper discusses the general aspects of the eutrophication of natural waters. Emphasis is placed on factors that influence aquatic plant production, effect of eutrophication on water quality, methods of measurement, sources of aquatic plant nutrients, and methods of controlling or reducing the rate of eutrophication. Additional information on these topics can be obtained (1–18).

Classification of Lakes

Lakes and other surface waters are frequently divided into one of two types, oligotrophic and eutrophic. Although the exact meaning of these two terms depends on the user, it is generally agreed that oligotrophic lakes are relatively unproductive and receive small amounts of aquatic plant nutrients, while eutrophic lakes are highly productive and receive high fluxes of aquatic plant nutrients. Eutrophication is the process of increasing the flux of materials to a water body in a way that promotes the growths of aquatic plants.

The problem of defining these terms, oligotrophic and eutrophic, is related to the fact that some aquatic scientists use these terms to refer only to the flux of aquatic plant nutrients, while others use these terms to describe the amounts of plant and/or animal production. Still another definition for eutrophication that is receiving increasing acceptance is that eutrophication is the process of excessive discharge of aquatic plant nutrients to a water body that results in a deterioration of water quality. This latter definition relates nutrient flux to water-quality deterioration. In reality with few exceptions, the various definitions all are essentially the same since high nutrient fluxes result in higher plant and animal production and decreased water quality.

Table 1 summarizes the general characteristics of oligotrophic and eutrophic lakes. Examination of this table shows that oligotrophic lakes contain small amounts of organisms but many different species of aquatic plants and animals and low nutrient fluxes. Eutrophic lakes are generally characterized as highly productive with large numbers of aquatic plants and animals of a few species. Normally lakes that are sufficiently deep enough to develop a thermocline (two-layer system due to density differences as a result of the thermal structure) and show a partial or complete depletion of dissolved oxygen in the hypolimnion (bottom layer) are classified as eutrophic, while those that maintain the oxygen in the hypolimnion throughout the period of thermal stratification are oligotrophic. This oxygen depletion in the bottom waters of a lake is dependent on amounts of aquatic plants that develop in the surface water and on the morphology of the lake. Lakes with a large hypolimnion volume tend to have the oxygen concentration depleted to a lesser degree than those with a smaller hypolimnion volume for a given amount of aquatic plant production in the surface layer or epilimnion. With few exceptions, the amount of aquatic plants produced in a lake is re-

Table 1. General Characteristics Frequently Used to Classify Lakes

Parameter	General characteristics	
	Oligotrophic	Eutrophic
aquatic plant production	low	high
aquatic animal production	low	high
aquatic plant nutrient flux	low	high
oxygen in the hypolimnion	present	absent
depth	tend to be deeper	tend to be shallower
water quality for most domestic and industrial uses	good	poor
total salts or conductance	usually lower	sometimes higher
number of plant and animal species	many	fewer

stricted to the surface waters since light penetration is usually restricted to epilimnetic waters.

In addition to changes in the total amounts of aquatic plant and animal production and the numbers of types (species) of each, the eutrophication of a lake is usually accompanied by a change in the kind of organisms produced. Although no indicator species have been found that are only present in one type of lake, it is generally observed that eutrophic lakes have greater numbers of blue-green algae and rough fish such as carp. At times, statements appear in the popular press that a eutrophic lake, like Lake Erie, is dead. Actually, this is exactly the opposite of the real situation in that eutrophic lakes suffer from problems due to excessive amounts of life of all forms. The fertilization of a body of water increases all forms of life from the planktonic (free floating) algae, attached algae, and rooted higher plants that develop in nearshore water to the zooplankton, benthic organisms, and fish.

Oligotrophic lakes are usually deeper than eutrophic lakes. However, this characteristic is highly variable and it is probably best to state that shallow lakes are frequently eutrophic and that as an oligotrophic lake fills due to deposition of sediments, it will become more eutrophic.

Another characteristic that is sometimes used to classify lakes is the total dissolved salt content or specific conductivity. The use of this parameter is based on an empirical correlation between the general levels of plant and animal production and total dissolved salts. Frequently lakes with a higher content of dissolved salts tend to be more productive. Beeton (19) has presented as evidence for the eutrophication of the St. Lawrence Great Lakes an increase in the dissolved salt content of these waters. Chemical species that make up the bulk of the total salts in most lakes are $Ca^{2+}, Mg^{2+}, Na^+, K^+, SO_4^{2-}, HCO_3^-$, and Cl^-. Sometimes nitrate concentrations are encountered in ground waters in amounts that contribute to the dissolved salts or specific conductance of the water. With the exception of nitrate, all of these species play minor roles in aquatic plant production of a lake, ie, their concentrations are in sufficient excess so that they do not limit the plant production. Therefore, the high total salts in a lake indicates a high probability of a high aquatic plant-nutrient flux by nitrogen and phosphorus and other trace compounds. In the case of the St. Lawrence Great Lakes, the increase in dissolved salts with time observed by Beeton indicates a greater degree of cultural activity in the lakes drainage basins with the result that the flux of many of the common cations and anions normally found in lakes is increased. As will be shown later, associated with the increase in cultural activity, a higher nitrogen and phosphorus flux will also occur.   Although the total amounts of nitrogen, phosphorus, and other aquatic plant nutrients is insufficient to be determined as a part of the dissolved salts or specific conductivity, they are sufficient to cause excessive growths of algae and other aquatic plants in Lake Erie and parts of the other Great Lakes.   Even though these salts probably do not significantly contribute to the nutrients for aquatic plants, their buildup in the Great Lakes is of major concern and will require their removal from some waste waters in the foreseeable future.

Limnologists use many other terms to classify lakes such as dystrophic, mesotrophic, hypereutrophic, etc.   Some of these terms bear little or no relationship to the nutrient flux, while others are subdivisions of the oligotrophic-eutrophic classification. For the purposes of this discussion, the oligotrophic and eutrophic classification is adequate to describe the relationship between nutrient flux and water-quality problems.

Factors that Influence Lake Production

The productivity of a given body of water is dependent on the solar radiation, temperature (to some degree), morphology of the basin, and the concentration of aquatic plant nutrients present in the water and available to organisms.   In eutrophication problems, primary concern is focused on the control of the aquatic plant nutrients entering the water, since objectionable conditions can be created by a sufficiently high nutrient flux, with normal light, temperature, basin morphology, and residence time of the water.   Excessive algal populations are found in waters near the freezing point, although some of the more objectionable forms of algae, such as the blue-greens, are generally considered warm-water organisms.   Occasionally very high numbers of these forms will be found in temperate lakes growing under a meter or more of ice.

The discharge of waste heat from large electric generating stations, such as nuclear power plants, is often alleged to cause an increased eutrophication of the lake.   While it is true that blue-green algae tend to be more prevalent in warm waters, there is no reason to believe that the total biomass of the organism would change significantly as a result of heating the water.   Normally the biomass of a certain type of algae is more dependent on availability of aquatic plant nutrients and other factors than on the temperature.   There is serious doubt that the highly localized heating of water resulting from large nuclear power electric generating stations located on large lakes should have an effect on the overall degree of eutrophication of the lake as a whole.   It is possible that where suitable substrates for the attached algae exist in the region of the discharge plume of the electric generating station, these forms might develop a little earlier each spring and persist slightly longer each fall.   However, it is doubtful that the total amounts of these organisms would be increased during the critical recreational use in the summer months.

The amounts of planktonic algae would not be expected to increase due to discharge of waste heat to large lakes since their rate of growth is normally much slower than the period of exposure of the algae to elevated temperatures in the thermal plumes of most electric generating stations.

Light does limit the aquatic plant production in those waters that have large amounts of suspended solids that increase turbidity or have high color.   Normally lakes of this type are very shallow and are subject to strong mixing by wind or animals such as fish, or they receive large amounts of marsh or swamp drainage.   The role of morphology of a lake in determining its productivity will be discussed below.

The amount of photosynthetic production in a lake is, therefore, frequently controlled by the flux to the water of chemical compounds that influence algal growth. Although the nutritional requirements of algae and higher aquatic plants are poorly understood, it is generally agreed that they all have large requirements for carbon, nitrogen, hydrogen, oxygen, phosphorus, and need lesser amounts of many different trace elements (20–27). Aquatic plant-nutrient requirements are much the same as terrestrial plant-nutrient requirements except for the terrestrial need for potassium. The fixation of potassium by clay minerals causes a deficiency in soils, while in water there is generally sufficient potassium to meet the needs of the aquatic plants. Aquatic plants are different in one important respect from some terrestrial plants in that they can use either NO_3^- or NH_4^+ with about equal facility, while some terrestrial plants are reported to use only NO_3^-. Some algae will take up NH_4^+ in preference to NO_3^-. Some of the blue-green algae also have the ability to use N_2 gas as a source of nitrogen. Since the dissolved N_2 content is always present in large excess, the process of nitrogen fixation gives this group of algae the ability to grow at very low NO_3^- and NH_4^+ concentrations. Orthophosphate is the form of phosphorus that is readily available for algal growth although it is possible that other organic or inorganic forms of phosphorus, may also be available to algae. The role of these compounds in the growth of algae will be discussed in a subsequent section.

Natural Versus Cultural Eutrophication. Some lakes and other surface waters are naturally eutrophic, ie, they receive sufficient aquatic plant nutrients from natural sources to produce excessive blooms of algae and macrophytes. Many references in the literature state that lakes start out as infertile bodies of water; with time they accumulate nutrients, become more fertile, eventually fill with sediments, and become a marsh and then dry land (11). Lakes are short-term features of the landscape in terms of geological time. However, it is highly questionable that the natural eutrophication of a lake is a time-dependent process (28,29) in which a lake becomes more fertile with time due to natural causes. Studies on the chemical characteristics and organism remains in lake sediment cores indicate that lakes do not become more fertile with time. In fact, the available evidence indicates that in the absence of cultural activities of man in the watershed, many lakes become less fertile with time.

Since for a given nutrient flux shallow lakes are thought to be more productive than deep lakes, the thermocline must play an important role in controlling nutrient recycling from a lake's sediments. In contrast to the frequently presented view that

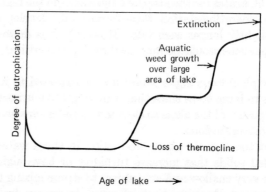

Fig. 1. Natural eutrophication of lakes. The degree of eutrophication is determined by the frequency and severity of excessive algal blooms and weed growth.

lakes proceed from oligotrophic to eutrophic under a natural progression, it is likely that lakes are highly fertile immediately after formation and lose this high fertility as the easily leachable nutrients are removed from the watershed. The lake would maintain a certain degree of fertility until it is sufficiently full so that it loses its permanent thermal stratification, ie, there is no permanent thermocline. At this point, the lake becomes more fertile since the lake recycles its nutrients more rapidly from its sediments, ie, there is no trapping of nutrients below the thermocline. A final major transformation in the development of a lake is the point where the lake is sufficiently shallow so that macrophytes occupy a major part of the lake basin. At this point in time, the lake starts to fill at a markedly different rate due to partial degradation of higher aquatic plant remains. Whether the natural eutrophication of lakes follows the sigmoid growth curve or proceeds in a stepwise manner, as proposed here, will await further research (see Fig. 1).

It might be argued that the shape of the natural eutrophication curve should have a break in it to correspond to the time that the hypolimnetic waters of the lake become anoxic to any significant degree. While it is clear that deoxygenation of the hypolimnion does lead to large releases of many aquatic plant nutrients such as nitrogen and phosphorus, it is doubtful that this release plays an important role in fertilizing the lake during the critical use period of the summer. The thermocline appears to be a very effective barrier to the transport of nutrients from deeper sediments of lakes to the overlying water. Overturn fall or mixing in the lake results in the mixing of high-nutrient hypolimnetic waters with the epilimnetic waters. This will often result in an algal bloom. Normally by this time of year the water has cooled sufficiently so that the algae that cause the severe summer blooms (blue-greens) do not develop. Although the fall blooms can cause serious water-quality problems, from a water supply-use point of view, these blooms rarely cause serious recreational use problems because generally the waters are not used as intensively in the fall as in the summer.

The high-nutrient level that develops at the beginning of fall overturn rarely persists for any period of time since the fall algae blooms tend to carry the nutrients to the sediments and, more important, the ferrous iron that was present in the hypolimnion is oxidized to ferric iron by dissolved oxygen which precipitates as ferric hydroxide, carrying with it coprecipitated and occluded phosphorus to the sediments. Based on the current degree of understanding of the aqueous environmental chemistry of phosphorus, it is unlikely that the aquatic plant nutrients brought to the surface waters at this time play a major role in increasing the degree of eutrophication of a lake and therefore no provision has been made to include a break in this natural eutrophication diagram (Fig. 1) to reflect the time in a lake's history that the hypolimnion becomes anoxic to a significant degree. It should be pointed out that for the research in systems models of the water chemistry of plant nutrient will produce changes in the shape of this diagram.

Even though it is impossible to predict the course of natural eutrophication accurately, there is general agreement among investigators that the change in fertility of a lake due to natural causes is a very slow process. On the other hand, the activities of man in a lake's watershed can change the degree of eutrophication of a lake in a period of a few years, whereas natural eutrophication can be measured in terms of hundreds to thousands of years. Because of this marked difference it is likely that any measurable change in trophic state of a lake in the past 50 years is due to cultural rather than natural causes.

Effect of Eutrophication

The eutrophication of a water may have a significant effect on domestic, industrial, recreational, and agricultural uses of the water. Typical effects in each of these areas are discussed in this section.

Domestic and Industrial Water Supplies. The presence of excessive amounts of nitrogen and phosphorus compounds can have a direct effect on water quality by such means as ammonia exerting an increased chlorine demand and by the various phosphate species, particularly the condensed phosphates, affecting the coagulation of particulates in the water with iron and aluminum salts. It is possible that the nitrogen content of the water in the form of nitrate could be increased significantly so that problems of methemoglobinemia are encountered. However, usually it is found that the direct effects of nitrogen and phosphorus species of water quality are minimal as compared to the indirect effects which are the result of the growth of excessive amounts of aquatic plants in the water. The excessive amounts of aquatic plants such as algae can significantly decrease water quality. For example, the algae will cause an increased turbidity or reduced light penetration in water with the result that they have to be removed in water treatment. Generally, their removal involves the addition of coagulants, such as iron or aluminum salts, followed by filtration through sand or other media filters. Whenever large concentrations of algae are present in the water, the rate of clogging of these filters increases significantly with the result that the filters have to be cleaned at more frequent intervals than would normally be expected.

The presence of algae and other plant remains in a water supply will increase the chlorine demand of the water since chlorine species will react with the remains of these organisms to form organochlorine compounds and oxidation products. It is believed by some that the presence of algae and other organisms in a water supply could protect pathogenic organisms from being destroyed by chlorine. For example, various kinds of higher animals could protect various kinds of pathogenic bacteria in their intestinal tract from destruction by chlorine normally added for disinfection purposes.

Probably the most significant effect of eutrophication of water supplies is the increased frequency of taste and odor problems. Many algae are notorious for causing tastes and odors in water supplies at very low concentrations of the organisms. Some algae when present on the order of a few cells per liter are said to impart a distinct odor in the water. Some water-plant operators can tell the type of algae present in the water supply by their odor. Some algae have characteristic odors such as cucumber-like, pigpen-like, and others. The removal of these tastes and odors from water supplies often involves the addition of activated carbon and/or various kinds of oxidizing agents, such as chlorine, ozone, or permanganate, in an attempt to either sorb or oxidize the odor. Algal odors arise either from direct excretion of various organic compounds from the algae while they are alive or shortly after their death, or by the growth of various kinds of fungi on the remains of algae. The actinomycetes are prime examples of this; they seem to grow in large numbers under certain circumstances shortly after the death of algal blooms.

The growth of algae and aquatic plants can increase the color of the water. In general, upon death these materials release organic compounds which cause a pale yellow color in the water. The removal of color from the water often involves the addition of various oxidizing agents and coagulants with or without activated carbon for sorption of the organic matter.

The location of the depth of a water supply intake in a lake is dependent upon the degree of eutrophication of the lake. Generally, in oligotrophic lakes, the overall water quality is better in the hypolimnetic (bottom water) of the lake than in the epilimnetic or surface water. The bottom waters are colder, and contain less algae and particulate matter. However, in eutrophic lakes, the loss of oxygen from the bottom waters results in anaerobic conditions which lead to the formation of reduced species of iron, manganese, and sulfur. The oxidized forms of iron, Fe (III), and manganese Mn (IV), in natural water are the predominant forms in the presence of dissolved oxygen. Since these forms are insoluble as $Fe(OH)_3$ and MnO_2 in natural waters they settle to the bottom of the lake and become incorporated in the sediments. Under oxidizing conditions sulfur is present as sulfate and does not cause any water-quality problems in most water supplies. In eutrophic lakes that experience the loss of all dissolved oxygen during periods of thermal stratification, anaerobic conditions develop that promote biochemical-chemical production of ferrous iron, manganous manganese, and H_2S. Since these reduced forms of iron and manganese are highly soluble, the concentrations may increase to levels which cause serious water-quality problems.

From a water-quality point of view for water supplies, the surface waters of all lakes tend to be of much poorer quality. However, in eutrophic lakes the presence of large amounts of iron, manganese, or H_2S causes very serious water-quality problems with the result that the water supply intake must be adjusted to take the surface waters of the lake in order to avoid the high Fe, Mn, and H_2S found in the bottom waters.

There are reports that organics, such as those present in natural color, cause an increased fouling of ion-exchange resins. Although work in this area to date has not clearly demonstrated the relationship between frequency of fouling and eutrophication, it is reasonable to suppose that further studies may show that more eutrophic waters tend to foul ion-exchange resins at a greater rate.

In summary, the eutrophication of domestic and industrial water supplies causes significant problems in water quality which results in an increased cost for water treatment.

Recreational Uses. Probably the most significant effect of eutrophication on recreational uses of water is with respect to its aesthetic quality. In general, excessive growths of aquatic plants cause a significant decrease in the aesthetic quality of the water. Certainly some plants, such as water lilies, are pleasing to the eye. However, when they become sufficiently thick so it becomes impossible to swim, boat, or fish in the area, then their qualities rapidly become undesirable. One of the factors that should be pointed out with respect to effects of eutrophication on recreational uses is that in general the areas where man's contact with the water are the greatest are also the same areas where the effects of growths of excessive amounts of aquatic plants are the most pronounced. The nearshore environment, the shallow waters near the edge of a lake or stream, can become completely choked with various kinds of rooted aquatics and attached algae. The thickness of growth of these plants can be such that it becomes almost impossible to use the water in this area for any purpose. Even the planktonic algal growth that develops in the middle of the lake often under certain conditions accumulates along the shorelines so that at times thick mats of decaying algae will be present. In severe cases these mats can be sufficiently thick so that turtles, ducks, and other aquatic animals can walk on top of them. These accumulated algae along the shore create serious water-quality problems, particularly because of the fact that in a short period of time they begin to decay and their high protein content results in production of hydrogen sulfide which develops into an extremely foul-smelling condition that is sometimes mistaken for the discharge of untreated municipal waste. The situation can become sufficiently severe at times so that property values along the shore of some lakes decrease while the property value away from the shore is increasing.

The effects of eutrophication on fishing deserve special attention. The fisheries in a lake, in terms of total production, depend on the total input of aquatic plant nutrients. Through the food web the plant nutrients combine through photosynthesis to produce the aquatic plants which feed the aquatic animals which eventually become fish food. Most eutrophic lakes have the greatest production of fish. Eutrophication, in addition to increasing the total fish production in the lake, also changes the type of fisheries. This change is generally one of complete loss of the cold-water fish, such as trout and cisco, and almost complete dominance of the less desirable warm-water fish such as carp and various kinds of bullheads. The loss of cold-water fisheries is the result of the depletion of oxygen below the thermocline during the summer stratification period. In an oligotrophic water, oxygen is present at the bottom of the lake throughout the year. In eutrophic waters oxygen is lost during summer stratification below the thermocline so that a fish that would normally inhabit cold waters simply cannot survive in eutrophic lakes because of the complete depletion of its oxygen. In summary, the effect of eutrophication on fisheries is one of increasing total fish production but this production results in less desirable fish.

Agricultural Uses. The eutrophication of a water can have a significant effect on the agricultural uses of water. First in this area is toxicity. Some blue-green algae are reported to excrete highly toxic substances which can cause death of waterfowl, cattle, sheep, and other animals. Although the record in this area is not clear as to the frequency of this kind of problem, it does appear from studies that toxins produced by these algae could be significant in certain situations. With respect to human health, however, it is estimated that the average human being would have to consume about one to two quarts of the "pea soup" that results from an excessive bloom of blue-green algae before he would be adversely affected. Another factor to consider in the agricultural effects of eutrophication is the transmission of water in canals. The transmission of water in irrigation canals can be greatly inhibited by excessive growths of aquatic weeds. The weeds increase the frictional resistance for transmission. In addition, these same weeds can cause significant losses of water through increased evapotranspiration. This problem is particularly present in the western United States where long irrigation canals are used in arid areas.

Measurement of Eutrophication

At the present time, there is no one single analytical tool to determine the current degree of eutrophication of a given body of water. Instead, most experts in this area feel the best approach is to measure many different parameters and to synthesize the results into a general pattern which will give an overall, somewhat average degree of eutrophication for the water. This situation is likely to change within a few years since it may be possible to develop numerical scales through the use of systems models for the eutrophication of water which will have some meaning with respect to the problems of excessive fertilizations of water in terms of comparing one lake to another. However, even this approach will require large numbers of different parameters to be measured in order to assess the current degree of eutrophication.   Fruh, Stewart, Lee, and Rohlich have reviewed this topic (30).   Many of the parameters that should be measured are mentioned below.

Standing Crop of Algae and Aquatic Plants.   Since the problems of eutrophication are caused by excessive numbers of planktonic and attached algae and higher aquatic plants, it is logical to use the total numbers of these organisms present as an estimate of the current degree of the eutrophication of the water.   Unfortunately, this is extremely difficult to do since it requires a team of scientists to collect the samples and enumerate and identify the organisms present in the water.   In order to circumvent this difficulty in obtaining this kind of information, numerous methods have been proposed for assessing the total biomass of planktonic algae.   For example, the suspended solids in the water are sometimes used as a measure of the algal populations.   The problem with suspended solids is that a large part of the suspended solids in most waters is nonliving. In some lakes, for example, the living to nonliving ratio is $1:10$, ten times as much nonliving particles of organic matter present in the sample as living.   Others have proposed that the volume of algae be used, the volume being the amount that would be obtained in the graduated centrifuge tube.   Under extreme conditions of eutrophication this can give some estimate of the total numbers.   Again, though, the problem of living versus nonliving must be considered.   One of the most frequently used methods is a method employing the extraction of chlorophyll from the sample.   Chlorophyll is present in all plants in sufficient amounts that it can be extracted with various solvents and estimated using spectrophotometric means.   The problem with chlorophyll is that it works reasonably well for relatively pure cultures of one type of organism.   However, with mixed populations of organisms, particularly where there is one type of organism one week and another the next week, it is found that frequently the correlation between the chlorophyll content and the total numbers or mass of algae in the water is very poor.   Using the ratio of chlorophyll b to chlorophyll a has been tried in an attempt to overcome this problem.

Blooms of Algae.   In advanced stages of eutrophication, one of the somewhat subjective types of measurements that could be used to assess the degree of eutrophication is the number of objectionable blooms of algae.   A bloom of planktonic algae usually lasts on the order of a week or so during the summer period in a moderately eutrophic lake.   Many lakes have half a dozen or more of these blooms per summer where the numbers of algae will fluctuate widely from week to week.   If some estimate of the frequency and severity of obnoxious blooms were recorded, it would be an important measure of the degree of eutrophication.   Many investigators are proposing now that a measure of the photosynthesis of the organisms present in the water be used as criteria for determining the degree of eutrophication of a body of water.   Here, the problem is primarily one of trying to correlate the activity as measured by photosynthesis with water-quality problems.   Some groups of organisms present in lakes could be photosynthesizing at a high rate, yet not cause significant water-quality problems.   Probably one of the better approaches to this is the combination of primary production measured by photosynthesis and of standing crop.   A productivity index, as has been proposed by Strickland (31), in which the primary production is divided by the biomass is a reasonable approach.   This would eliminate some of these problems and might give a better correlation between the degree of eutrophication and its effect on man.

Some of the more frequently used parameters for assessing the eutrophication of lakes are the oxygen in the hypolimnion and light penetration.   **Hypolimnetic oxygen**

depletion in lakes that are sufficiently deep to stratify is probably the most widely used index separating oligotrophic from eutrophic lakes. However, there are many problems with this index. The rate of depletion of oxygen from the hypolimnion of a lake depends to a significant degree on the morphology of the lake; that is, the area-to-volume ratio. Lakes that have large hypolimnetic volumes compared to their surface area will lose their oxygen at a significantly lower rate than lakes that have large surface areas and small hypolimnion volumes. One of the complicating factors is the fact that in many lakes the most significant source of oxygen demand is the accumulated reduced iron, manganese, and sulfide species in the lake sediments. Often eutrophic lakes will contain thousands of parts per million on a dry weight basis of iron and sulfur species. These materials will react rapidly with dissolved oxygen. The lakes which are not stratified generally have a thin layer of oxidized iron hydroxide on the surface of the sediments. However, once the stratification takes place and renewal of oxygen from the atmosphere can no longer take place, this layer of oxidized iron oxide will be reduced, and, in turn, it is generally found that the oxygen in the hypolimnion is fairly rapidly depleted by abiotic chemical reactions. This statement should not be interpreted to mean that the primary production in the surface waters of a lake does not control the hypolimnetic oxygen depletion; it does, particularly in oligotrophic and moderately eutrophic lakes. However, at some point in the eutrophication of a lake there will be significant accumulation of reduced iron and sulfur species which can exert the major oxygen demand during periods of thermal stratification. Under these conditions the epilimnetic production of aquatic plants may be changed significantly through the years, yet the rate of depletion of the hypolimnetic oxygen will not change since it is controlled by abiotic reactions.

Light penetration is probably the most widely used measure of eutrophication. Although sometimes criticized as being an extremely crude instrument, the Secchi disc, which consists of a plate about a foot or so in diameter painted in black and white quadrants attached to a metered rope or line, is an important tool in limnological investigations involving eutrophication. One of the most significant effects of eutrophication on water quality is a decreased clarity of water. This decreased clarity of water results from light scattering from the microscopic plants that are produced in the water. The depth at which a Secchi disc can be seen is an estimate of the amount of phytoplankton present in the water. There are many problems with this technique. However, since it is an inexpensive technique and can be readily performed by almost any individual, it deserves significant attention as a tool for measurement of eutrophication. In almost every case where it has been used, it is clearly shown that, as a lake becomes more eutrophic, the Secchi-disc depth decreases significantly.

One of the methods that can be used to assess the degree of eutrophication of waters is the **aquatic plant-nutrient content.** Although it is difficult to establish meaningful, critical concentrations that are applicable to many different waters, there are critical nitrogen and phosphorus concentrations that are often cited as being the critical levels that separate oligotrophic from eutrophic waters. These critical concentrations are discussed in a subsequent section. It is important to point out that these critical concentrations are often based on the excessive growths of aquatic plants that produce aesthetically unpleasing water. It is quite possible that concentrations considerably less than these amounts could cause significant deterioration in water quality, particularly with respect to the use of the water for water supplies. The use of these critical concentrations as dividing oligotrophic from eutrophic lakes must be viewed with caution.

Another parameter that could be used to estimate the degree of eutrophication of a lake is the **regression of higher plants** in the water. Here, we are concerned with the question of what is the maximum depth at which a rooted aquatic plant can grow in a given lake. This maximum depth is determined to a significant degree by light penetration. In some lakes it has been found that as the lake becomes more eutrophic the maximum depth at which higher plants can grow becomes less. For example, plants may grow at 20–30 ft of water during the more oligotrophic stages of a lake, while in the eutrophic stages they may be restricted to the 5–10-ft depths of a lake. This is because the phytoplankton develops in sufficient numbers each year to block off so much light that plants that would normally develop in deeper waters in more oligotrophic conditions simply cannot develop because they do not receive sufficient light.

Effects on Water Treatment. One way to assess the economic significance of eutrophication is to examine the decrease in water quality associated with its use for domestic and industrial water-supply purposes. Many water plants keep accurate records of chemical doses used to treat the water. As explained earlier, eutrophication results in increased activated carbon demand, increased chlorine demand, increased coagulants, etc, so that a parameter of eutrophication can be derived which is based on the amounts of chemicals that have been used at a given water plant in order to treat the water.

Composition of Sediments. The sediments of a lake offer the possibility of assessing the current degree of eutrophication and determining the rate at which the lake has become eutrophic. The sediments of a lake provide a geological record of the events that have occurred within a lake. Unfortunately, these sediments also provide a record of the events that have occurred within a watershed. It is extremely difficult at the present time to determine the sources of materials in the sediment. There is ample evidence that the carbon present in lake sediments, particularly the organic carbon, is derived primarily from the watershed; yet, it is reasonable to suspect that, as a lake becomes more eutrophic, the total amounts of organic carbon deposited in the sediments increases. Normally it is expected that as a lake becomes more eutrophic, greater amounts of the phosphorus, nitrogen, and other aquatic plant nutrients would be deposited in the sediments. Yet, at the present time work in this area has not clearly demonstrated a relationship between the chemical composition of the sediments and the degree of eutrophication. A more fruitful approach is to examine the sediments for specific types of organisms, particularly those with parts which are well preserved in the sediments. Probably one of the best groups of organisms for this purpose is the diatoms. The diatoms are a group of algae which have siliceous shells, many of which are well preserved in the sediments. By taking the sediments and determining the numbers of types of diatoms, it is possible to gain some inference about the rate of eutrophication of a given body of water.

Sources of Aquatic Plant Nutrients

The aquatic plant nutrients often considered to be the most significant factors determining the growth of aquatic plants in surface waters are orthophosphate, nitrate, nitrite, and ammonia. Other species of phosphorus and nitrogen, such as the organic forms, can and do contribute to the fertility of the water, either directly through uptake by the organisms or indirectly through their conversion to the other previously mentioned forms by abiotic and biotic chemical reactions. There are some who feel that carbon should be listed as one of the critical elements in terms of the fertilization of natural waters. However, the evidence to date in this area seems to indicate that carbon in the form of CO_2 only becomes limiting under excessive or massive blooms of algae and that under these conditions the degree of eutrophication is exceedingly high. Water quality is deteriorated to such a degree that further production is of limited consequence. Under high-population density, the aquatic plants can use CO_2 at a rate that causes the pH of the solution to increase, thereby decreasing the CO_2 concentration in water. Except under conditions of high turbulence, the rate of resupply of CO_2 from the atmosphere and from respiration of aquatic plants, bacteria, and other organisms is generally slow compared to the rate at which it can be used by large populations of algae.

With regard to the trace elements, it is known that some are essential for growth of plants; for example, the diatoms need silica for growth. However, even with the diatoms, the evidence seems to indicate that in general the silica content is in excess of what is needed for production of large numbers of these organisms.

Probably the next most frequently mentioned element that could possibly limit or control the populations of algae in lakes is iron. Iron is present in the epilimnion of lakes in the ferric form and in this oxidation state is extremely insoluble as a hydrous oxide resulting in rapid precipitation and transmission to the sediments of the lake. Some investigators have found an apparent iron deficiency in some waters. Other elements that are mentioned as essential for growth of algae and other aquatic plants include sulfur, potassium, magnesium, calcium, boron, zinc, copper, molybdenum, manganese, cobalt, sodium, and chlorine. With respect to eutrophication, the important question is, do they control the growth of algae, or are the concentrations that are normally found sufficient to provide for excessive crops of aquatic plants? The same questions can be asked with respect to various organic components such as vitamins, hormones, chelating agents, etc. It is fair to state that nitrogen and phosphorus are probably the key elements in controlling aquatic plant growths and that the other elements may be important under certain conditions in certain types of waters. However, further research will be necessary to fully delineate their roles in the eutrophication of natural waters. This discussion on nutrient sources will be restricted to nitrogen and phosphorus sources.

The question may be asked, what are the critical concentrations of nitrogen and phosphorus in most natural waters? This is a topic of great concern today in terms of attempting to manage the nutrient input to lakes. If the nutrient input can be limited so that the total concentrations in the lake are less than the critical concentrations, then it would be possible to control the degree of eutrophication of the water. Although few studies have been made in this area, the work of Sawyer (32) for Wisconsin lakes and Vollenweider (17) for Swiss lakes has shown that when the inorganic nitrogen content, ammonia plus nitrate nitrogen, is equal to or greater than 0.3 mg nitrogen per liter and the orthophosphate content is equal to or greater than 0.01 mg phosphorus per liter (or one part per hundred million), then the lake is likely to have excessive crops of algae and other aquatic plants. These numbers represent, to some degree, the best estimate available today for the critical concentrations of elements. Unfortunately, the situation is not simply one of taking critical concentrations, such as those given, and using them in all types of waters. In fact, this approach could lead to quite erroneous results. The productivity of a given body of water, as pointed out previously, depends on many factors in addition to the concentrations of nutrients. In this case, where it is not certain at the present time that nitrogen and/or phosphorus is the controlling element, the evidence obtained in the last few years seems to show that nitrogen controls certain populations at certain times during the year while phosphorus in the same lake may be controlling other populations at other times. Until additional information is gained it will be impossible to answer the question of what controls populations and therefore what are the critical elements. One of the major difficulties in the existing critical concentrations is that they are based on excessive growths of algae as the criterion of quality. It has been found that some eutrophication problems can occur at much lower numbers of a specific form of algae which cause taste and odors in water supplies or clog the sand filters in water-treatment plants. It is likely that the critical concentrations of nitrogen and phosphorus would be lower if these conditions were used to determine objectionable water quality conditions.

At the present time, the federal government and many states, following the lead, have taken the approach that what should be done is to limit the phosphorus going into a given body of water. This is based to some degree on these critical concentrations. For example, in the case of Lake Erie, it is believed that it may be possible to limit the phosphorus input to the lake so that it will become less than the critical concentrations cited by Sawyer and others. However, there is virtually no evidence to show that this would be the case. The aqueous environmental chemistry of phosphorus is sufficiently complex to make it impossible to predict what concentrations would result in a given lake for a certain nutrient input. The complexity here rises primarily from the fact that the sediments of a lake act as a sink and as a source for many of the nutritive elements. The role of sediments in supplying nutrients to the overlying waters will be discussed in a subsequent section.

One of the problems that complicate the relationship between the concentrations of nutritive elements in the water and the growth of certain crops of aquatic plants is the fact that the stoichiometric concentrations of some of the primary elements in algae varies within fairly wide limits. Typically algae contain about 106 carbon atoms for each 16 nitrogen and 1 phosphorus. This is the average composition that is found in both fresh and marine waters. Algae, however, have the ability to store some nutrients in great excess of their needs. For example, algae can store what is often termed surplus phosphorus which ranges from five to approaching ten times the minimum requirements for the particular cell. Therefore, the composition of algae is highly variable and dependent on the composition of the water. In addition, the situation is further complicated by the fact that the specific phosphorus and/or nitrogen requirements of some algae are markedly different for other algae. Some algae grow at phosphorus levels which are greatly below the critical concentrations found by Sawyer; indeed for these same algae it is found that phosphorus on the order of the critical concentrations may be toxic to them. In addition to the concentrations in the water, as related to their needs, it appears that the ratios of the various elements, such as nitrogen, phosphorus, and trace elements, may play an important role in determining the species of algae and other plants present in the water. Therefore, not only is the total biomass controlled by the aquatic nutrients but also the species diversity as influenced by both the organic and inorganic trace compounds present in the surface waters (see references 20–27). With this background, it is appropriate to examine the various sources of nitrogen and phosphorus compounds in an attempt to gain some insight into the potential causes of water-quality problems due to excessive fertilization (see references 30–36).

Domestic Wastewaters. One of the foremost sources of nitrogen and phosphorus for natural waters is domestic wastewaters. Domestic wastewaters often contain tens of mg nitrogen per liter and 5–20 mg phosphorus per liter, but these concentrations are highly variable, depending on the time of day and day of week. If these concentrations are compared to the critical concentrations, it is readily apparent that domestic wastewaters must be diluted manyfold in order to reduce the fertilizing potential below that normally cited for critical concentrations. One of the areas of major concern today is the sources of phosphorus in domestic wastewaters. Several studies have shown that approximately 50% of the phosphorus present in domestic wastewaters is derived from the phosphorus that is used in various cleaning compounds such as detergents. Many detergent formulations contain builders in which the primary forms of phosphorus used are pyrophosphate and tripolyphosphate. These condensed phosphates have been shown to hydrolyze to orthophosphate during domestic wastewater treatment or in natural waters. Some attempts are being made today to try to limit the amounts of phosphates used in detergents in an endeavor to reduce the fertilizing potential of domestic wastewaters. A crude estimate of the amounts of nitrogen and phosphorus contributed by domestic wastewaters can be made in terms of a population equivalent. Various studies have shown that two pounds per person per year of phosphorus and seven pounds per person per year of nitrogen are contributed in typical domestic wastewaters. These figures then can be used to obtain crude estimates of the potential significance of a given wastewater in terms of contribution of nitrogen and phosphorus to a water course.

One of the complications often encountered in wastewater treatment that can cause eutrophication problems is the disposal of sludge and other solids. Usually it is placed on the ground or in a pit and therefore represents potential sources of nutrients. In a similar manner, garbage disposal may also cause eutrophication problems since disposal sites are frequently low lands which have high water tables. Waters with high nitrogen and phosphorus content are associated with both domestic wastewater, sludge disposal and garbage-and refuse-disposal areas. Nutrients from these areas can be carried into the ground water and during periods of heavy rains into lakes via surface-water flow.

The individual household septic-tank wastewater-disposal system may also contribute nutrients to surface waters. In general, nitrogen is readily transported in ground waters and, therefore, a significant part of the nitrogen going to septic tank systems will be transported to the ground water if it is oxidized to nitrate and does not become denitrified. Phosphate is usually strongly sorbed by aquifer materials except in sandy areas. Quartz and other sands that have low iron, carbonate, aluminum, clay mineral, and organic content will readily transport phosphate in ground waters which could contribute nutrients to surface waters. In nonsandy soils septic tanks frequently fail in a short period of time due to the plugging of the tile field. When this occurs surface discharge results and nutrients are transported via overland flow to the nearby water course.

Industrial Wastewaters. Industrial wastewaters can have very large or very small amounts of aquatic plant nutrients. For example, some wastewaters which cause serious water-quality problems, such as pulp and paper wastes, are deficient in nitrogen and phosphorus compared to carbon. Other wastewaters, such as those associated with phosphate mining, can contribute large amounts of phosphorus to the water. Industrial wastewaters are highly variable in aquatic plant-nutrient content and are dependent on the particular industry.

Urban Drainage. The runoff from urban areas is beginning to be recognized as an important source of aquatic plant nutrients. Frequently, storm-water runoff contains on the order of several mg nitrogen and phosphorus per liter. Weibel et al. (36) have found that in Cincinnati approximately nine pounds per acre per year of nitrogen and 0.8 pound per acre per year of soluble phosphorus are contributed in storm-water run-off. To date, essentially no information is available on the sources of these high concentrations in streets. Fertilizers used on lawns, normal dust fall, contributions from dogs, cats, gasoline automobile engines and other combustion processes, and leaves, etc, must be considered. Further research, though, will be necessary to delineate the relative significance of these sources.

Agricultural Drainage. Agricultural drainage, because of the fact that large quantities of fertilizers are often used on various crops, is often thought to be a significant source of nutrients for surface waters. Although this could be the case, it is also fairly certain that under proper soil, water, and fertilizer management, it is possible to control the amounts of nitrogen and phosphorus derived from fertilizers applied to croplands. One the other hand, misapplication of large amounts of these materials can bring about a very large release or loss of these materials to the surface waters, particularly during times of heavy rainfall and overland flow. Studies of farmlands located near Madison, Wisconsin, have shown that the nutrient content of farmland drainage can range from that essentially associated with natural sources, with concentrations on the order of 0.03 and 0.003 pound per acre per year of nitrogen and phosphorus, respectively, to values many times these amounts where applied fertilizers are used in great excess of their needs, and also under conditions which tend to promote their runoff to the nearby surface waters. One of the most significant agricultural sources that has been found in the area located near Madison, Wisconsin, is the manure derived from dairy-farm operations. In this part of the country, the dairy farmers maintain approximately 100 cows per square mile, each cow producing 15 tons of manure per year which is then spread on the land. It is reasonable to expect that during late spring, summer, and early fall the nutrients present in this manure will be carried into the soil and in general become associated with the crops that develop. However, during the winter period the manure spread on the land cannot release its nutrients to the soil since it is frozen. At the time of spring thaw and rain, the snow melt and rainwater combine in a heavy overland flow carrying with it all of the nutrients derived from manure spread on frozen land. In general, the manure problem associated with dairy operations is small compared to animal feedlots since the density of animals is much higher in the latter. Feedlots often have animal densities approaching 50–100 animals per acre. Some feedlots contain 100,000 animals. Drainage from these large feedlots requires treatment similar to domestic wastewaters. In the western U.S. the irrigation return waters have high concentrations of nitrogen which are likely to cause eutrophication problems. Some irrigation return waters have been found to contain concentrations of nitrate approaching 50 mg nitrogen per liter. These waters require treatment to remove the very high concentrations of nitrogen.

Natural Sources. Many lakes are naturally eutrophic, ie, they receive sufficient quantities of nitrogen, phosphorus, and other plant nutrients which produce excessive crops of aquatic plants. Under these conditions the watershed of the lake must serve as the source of nutrients for the lake and under conditions of natural eutrophication large amounts of nitrogen and phosphorus are derived from the watershed. Some soils, such as many in the Midwest, are highly fertile and contain large amounts of nitrogen and phosphorus with the result that small lakes which receive drainage from large land areas are often naturally eutrophic.

Lake Sediments. Sediments of a lake often contain thousands of parts per million (mg/kg dry weight) of phosphorus and nitrogen. Potentially very small amounts of these sediments, if mixed with the water and if the nutrients present in the sediments are leachable, could fertilize large quantities of water. Fortunately, however, most of the nitrogen and phosphorus present in lake sediments are bound in refractory (non-leachable) forms. Recent studies have shown that some lake sediments do act as phosphate buffers. If the phosphorus concentration in the overlying waters is decreased, the sediments will contribute phosphorus to the overlying waters to make up for this decrease. The same type of situation exists for nitrogen, although in the case of nitrogen it appears to be controlled more by the aerobic versus anaerobic conditions than with phosphorus, where phosphorus is leached under both aerobic and anaerobic conditions (37). In general, the amount of leaching from anaerobic conditions is significantly greater than under aerobic. Further studies on the role of lake sediments as a source of nitrogen and phosphorus for lakes are urgently needed.

Atmospheric. Precipitation in the form of rainfall and snowfall is a significant source of nitrogen in some parts of the world. In the Midwest typical rainfall contains on the order of 1 mg nitrate nitrogen per liter. When this is compared to the normal 0.3 mg/liter, often cited as the critical concentration of nitrogen, rainfall rather than diluting the nutrients in a lake is actually contributing to them. Phosphorus, however, is fairly low in most rainfall.

Ground Water. Ground water rarely contains significant concentrations of phosphorus since phosphorus species tend to be strongly sorbed on aquifer materials. On the other hand, nitrate is very poorly sorbed by most aquifer materials, with the result that ground waters may contain large concentrations of nitrate nitrogen. It is not uncommon to find that nitrate nitrogen is present in ground waters at 1 per liter mg nitrogen. In some situations this concentration can reach 40–50 mg/liter. Ammonia nitrogen and various phosphate species tend to be sorbed in most clay soils. However, in sandy soils, such as those frequently encountered around lakes, it may be found that the adsorption capacity of sand is exceedingly small, with the result that septic-tank sewage-disposal systems located adjacent to a lake in a sandy soil rarely have problems of plugging. However, these systems also readily transmit the nutrients from the household to the nearby water course via ground water.

A special but frequent cause of ground contamination is sanitary landfills and other solid-waste, garbage, refuse, sludge, and disposal systems. Often community solid waste materials and wastewater sludges are deposited on low-lying land, frequently on wet land areas. Recent studies have shown that very serious ground water contamination problems have resulted from such practices. In order to avoid this type of problem, solid waste and wastewater sludge disposal systems must be arranged to avoid ground water contamination by various types of aquatic plant nutrients.

Marshes. In general, marshy areas contain large populations of aquatic plants. It is reasonable to expect that these areas would act as nutrient traps and remove nutrients from inflowing waters during the growing season. However, during the winter and spring period in cold climates, it has been found that a marsh will discharge large quantities of nitrogen and phosphorus so that a marsh probably acts on a short-term basis to delay nutrient transport coming to it during the late spring, summer, and fall. These trapped nutrients are released at the time of high spring flows. Therefore, it is reasonable to question whether a marsh is a significant nutrient trap over an annual cycle. A special case with respect to marshes that deserves attention is the drained marsh. The drainage of marshes to convert the area into either urban or agricultural areas can result in a significant release of nitrogen species, particularly nitrate. The marsh environment is a typical anaerobic environment in which the nitrogen is present in the form of organic nitrogen and ammonia, both of which tend to remain associated with soil particles and plant debris within the marsh. However, draining a marsh results in converting it from an anaerobic to an aerobic environment. The aerobic environment promotes biochemical conversion of organic nitrogen to ammonia and the conversion of ammonia to nitrate. Nitrate is highly soluble in water, poorly sorbed by soil particles, and is rapidly transported from the marsh system. The drainage of a marsh is likely to result in a significant increase in the nitrogen content in the effluent water.

Nitrogen Fixation. Nitrogen fixation is restricted in natural waters to a few forms of algae, particularly certain members of the blue-green algae and a few bacteria. These organisms can take nitrogen gas and convert it to ammonia and organic nitrogen.

Table 2. Estimated Nutrient Sources for Lake Mendota (35)

Source	Annual contributions, lb		Estimated contribution[a] %	
	Nitrogen	Phosphorus	Nitrogen	Phosphorus
municipal and industrial wastewater	47,000 (total)	17,000 (total)	10	36
urban runoff	30,300 (soluble)	8,100 (soluble)	6	17
rural runoff	52,000 (soluble)	20,000 (soluble)	11	42
precipitation on lake surface	97,000	140–7,600	20	2
ground water	250,000	600	52	2
nitrogen fixation	2,000		0.4	
marsh drainage	?	?		
total	478,300	47,000[b]		

[a] These calculations are based on 1,000 pounds per year of phosphorus in precipitation on the lake surface.

It is difficult at the present time to estimate the significance of this. Certain forms of algae, eg *Aphanizomenon* and *Anabaena*, which are frequently associated with highly eutrophic waters, are nitrogen fixers. On the other hand, *Microcystis* is also associated with highly eutrophic waters and it is not a nitrogen fixer. It is possible that nitrogen fixation occurs at such a rate as not to affect significantly the overall nitrogen balance of a given body of water.

Miscellaneous. Among the miscellaneous sources of nutrients to lakes are ducks, geese, and other organisms. In the case of ducks, naturally maintained populations probably do not contribute significant amounts of nutrients to the water since they feed primarily in the water. These populations do, however, increase the rate of recycling the nutrients within the water. On the other hand, ducks which are maintained in an area as a result of feeding by individuals, in parks, zoos, etc, can contribute nutrients to the water in direct proportion to the amount of feeding that takes place. A similar problem exists with maintaining large herds of deer and other animals where these animals are fed near the lake shore. Geese feed primarily on land and, therefore, can increase the flux of nutrients from the land to the water.

From the above discussion, it will be seen that aquatic plant nutrients are derived from many different sources. It is clear that for any given lake a detailed study of each of these potential sources must be made. A study of the nutrient sources for Lake Mendota, in Madison, Wisconsin, was made several years ago. Table 2 presents a summary of these data. Examination of this table shows that the phosphorus is primarily derived from the activities of man such as wastewaters, manure spread on frozen land, etc. Nitrogen for this particular lake is derived from noncultural sources, such as rainfall, ground water, etc. If this is the situation for many lakes, it is logical to proceed with an attempt to control phosphorus in this lake since it is going to be extremely difficult, if not impossible, to control nitrogen. In any type of control program it may not be possible to control the elements down to a critical level because of the wide variety of sources and particularly since some of these sources such as storm-water runoff are not amenable to control at the present time.

Methods of Reducing Rate of Eutrophication and Its Effects on Water Quality

The eutrophication of a lake can be controlled or its effects on water minimized by reducing the nutrient input to the lake, increasing nutrient output from the lake, immobilizing nutrients within the lake, or controlling excessive growths of algae and macrophytes within the lake. Various methods that have been proposed in each of these areas are summarized below.

Nutrient Removal from Wastewaters. Domestic wastewater represents a potentially significant source of aquatic plant nutrients. It is often the source that is looked to first for control. The nitrogen and phosphorus and to some extent the other trace elements can be removed from wastewaters so that they will not fertilize to the degree they do without removal. Various laboratory, pilot-plant, and field-scale experiments have shown that both nitrogen and phosphorus can be removed from wastewaters at a moderate cost. Phosphorus is fairly readily removed from wastewaters by alum flocculation, ferric iron flocculation, or lime precipitation. All three of these will remove 80–90% of the phosphorus present in wastewaters. In the case of ammonia and other nitrogen species, this can be done by such means as ion exchange for removal of ammonia and nitrate, or conditions can be established to bring about a deliberate bacterial denitrification in which the ammonia is oxidized to nitrate. The nitrate then may become denitrified to form nitrogen gas. Another scheme that is being used is to strip the ammonia at high pH in a gas-stripping tower. These various methods have been applied, and can bring about reduction in nutrients. But in general, this will cause a significant increase in the cost of waste-treatment in terms of conventional waste-treatment costs. In the case of phosphorus removal at the present time the cost is on the order of a few cents per thousand gallons, depending on the size of the plant, the larger plants being less expensive. This represents roughly a doubling of conventional wastewater treatment costs. Nitrogen removal is at the present time more expensive, although it is expected that the cost will be comparable if additional experience is obtained. It is likely that within the next few years significant amounts of funds will be spent for phosphorus removal, followed a few years later with nitrogen removal from wastewaters.

Diversion of Wastewaters. The most frequently used method to reduce the eutrophication of a lake caused primarily by wastewaters is to divert the wastewaters around or away from the lake. This approach has been used in Madison, Wisconsin. It is being used in Lake Washington, Seattle, Washington, and it is a procedure that is being used to some degree at Lake Tahoe. This method does eliminate the problem from the original lake that received the wastewaters. However, it also increases the problem for the receiving waters. From a long-range point of view, this approach is not satisfactory for the solution of these problems. Wastewater treatment will have to be practiced as a means of controlling nutrients.

Dredging. A procedure that can be used to remove nutrients from the lake is dredging of lake sediments. As previously pointed out, lake sediments represent potentially significant sources of nutrients for the lake. The lake undergoes a self-fertilization each year. This self-fertilization for some lakes may be important as one of the primary sources of nutrients. If nutrient-rich sediments could be dredged from the lake, it is possible that this self-fertilization would be decreased. One of the problems with dredging, however, is that in general the nutrient content of lake sediments does not change drastically with depth. Recently conducted studies show that for many lakes phosphorus and nitrogen contents of lake sediments are approximately the same at the surface as 10–15 ft below the surface, although there are some indications that the leachability of elements deep in the sediments may be somewhat less than in the surface sediments. Therefore, it is reasonable to question whether dredging will have a significant effect on nutrient release. Certainly any undertaking in which dredging is proposed should be preceded by studies on nutrient release from the various types of sediments that will be dredged. Another problem occurs with dredging; it is usually followed by a shift from the growth of rooted aquatic plants to planktonic algae because the rooted plants cannot develop in moderately deep water since the algae shut off the light available to them in the overlying waters. Thus, as a result of dredging, a lake may be changed from one with an aquatic weed problem to one with an algal scum problem. Dredging of lakes needs to be more properly evaluated before it can be used as an effective tool in the management of eutrophication. Care must be exercised in methods of disposal of the dredge materials so that the nutrients present in them are not leached out and carried to a nearby water course.

Considerable concern has been expressed about the effect of the disposal of material dredged from Great Lakes and from harbors in the lakes. The hopper dredges used to remove sediments from harbors by their method of operation do not remove large amounts of nutrients since the dredged materials are washed as part of the dredging operation to remove fines. In general, various studies have shown the fine sediments containing the largest fraction of plant nutrients.

Low-Flow Augmentation. Low-flow augmentation can be used effectively to control nutrients within a lake. If large volumes of water of low nutrient content are available, flushing the lake with this water will increase water quality and decrease the frequency and severity of algal blooms. However, it is only rarely that large quantities of nutrient-poor water are available for flushing purposes.

Zoning. It is possible that one of the best methods to control nutrient flux in a watershed is to control land use within the watershed. For example, marshes could be zoned to prevent their drainage or drying up for agricultural or urban purposes. The type of farming and the types and amounts of fertilizers used could be controlled through zoning regulations in order to protect a given watershed.

Control of Nuisance Plant Growths. Both algicides and herbicides are being used to control the excessive growths of aquatic plants in natural waters. Algicides such as copper sulfate can effectively control algae. Herbicides such as 2,4-D and sodium arsenite do control rooted aquatic plants. In general, the applications of these chemicals to a water requires close attention and supervision, and large expenditures of funds, and must be done at frequent intervals during the growing season. On some occasions it has been found that whenever a lake is treated to remove certain kinds of algae a few weeks later another type of alga will rapidly develop and replace that which has been killed off. A potentially quite important aspect of the use of algicides and herbicides is the question of the effects on other organisms present in the water or on users of the water. If these chemicals persist in the water, there are always questions concerning their toxicity to fish, fish-food organisms, or to man if the water is used for domestic or industrial purposes. This toxicity question may be broken down into two parts. There is an acute toxicity that is associated with the application of the materials. If any of these chemicals are applied in excessive doses, they can cause fish kills.   On the other hand, the more important question today, since in general the acute toxicity can be readily taken care of by proper application, is one of chronic toxicity. Will the presence of these chemicals cause genetic changes? Are they carcinogenic, etc? These kinds of questions cannot be answered at the present time because of insufficient knowledge to be certain that they will not have long-lasting effects on the aquatic populations present in natural waters. The use of biological control of excessive growths of algae and macrophytes has not been developed to the point where there are any potentially effective agents that are likely to found in the near future. The most promising result to date in this area has been the work on the isolation of a virus that shows promise of being specific for blue-green algae. If such a virus can be found and readily cultured, it may be possible to use it to control excessive blooms of blue-green algae.

Harvesting. Other methods of reducing the nutrient content or the flux of a given body of water include removal of weed, debris, and rough fish, and harvesting algae and aquatic weeds along the shore. Harvesting results in the removal of certain amounts of nitrogen and phosphorus. In general, however, the various types of harvesting procedures do not make significant inroads on the nutrient balance of a lake. They may be justified in terms of improving the aesthetic quality of the lake by making it useful for swimming, boating, and fishing. Sometimes harvesting may remove significantly large amounts of nutrients from the lake compared to the nutrient influx to the lake and, therefore, be justified as a nutrient removal procedure. Although the harvested weeds do have a good fertilizer and humus potential and could be used as an agricultural fertilizer, the problems of handling and hauling them greatly restrict their use for this purpose. Frequently, the harvested aquatic weeds and the rough fish removed must be buried in land fills since no one wants the material.

Many express the opinion that the excessive growths of aquatic plants could lead to a harvestable crop of fish or other organisms. As previously explained, larger crops of fish are produced in eutrophic lakes; however, the large fish crops do not occur until sufficiently large populations of algae cause serious deterioration of water quality. In Florida the manatee is used to keep some of the canals from becoming completely choked with macrophytes. The animals consume large quantities of aquatic plants, thereby clearing the canal but not removing significant amounts of nutrients from the water. The disposal of harvested plants, debris, etc, must be done so that the nutrients contained therein do not become leached out and return to the water course.

Mixing of Lakes. One of the methods that is sometimes proposed to control eutrophication is to mix the lake with air injected by various kinds of pumps. The basis of this method is that it is generally believed that aquatic plant nutrients such as phosphorus are not released under aerobic conditions. Recent studies at the University of Wisconsin Water Chemistry Laboratory have shown that this is not the case. Significant phosphorus release occurs in many types of lake sediments under aerobic conditions and, therefore, the aeration of a body of water for the control of algae is of questionable value, particularly if the aeration destroys the thermocline. The thermocline is an effective barrier to nutrient transport from the sediments. Very small amounts of chemicals are transported across it. The thermocline is present throughout the growing season which is the critical period of the year for transport of nutrients from the sediments to the overlying water. Therefore, rather than mixing a lake to bring about complete oxygenation and destroying the thermocline, it would be better to aerate the hypolimnion of a lake without destroying the thermocline. There are special devices which enable this to be done. This aeration of the hypolimnion with either air or gaseous oxygen would allow the cold-water fisheries to exist, at the same time as it would tend to control the nutrients to some degree. At fall overturn the amounts of nutrients circulated in these overlying waters would be less and it quite possibly would then take less energy to completely mix a body of water.

Agricultural Sources. Agricultural sources of nutrients can be controlled through education of the farmer, in terms of what are the best times to apply nutrients, what concentrations should be applied, and the best control of soil erosion and other conditions that tend to promote high nutrient fluxes from farmland. The manure problem that exists in Wisconsin and other nearby states can be controlled by having the farmer store the manure in tanks over the winter period and subsequently spreading it on the land after the ground has thawed in the spring.

Urban Drainage. Control of urban nutrient sources at the present time has little promise. The volume of storm waters that occur during normal thundershower activity is often such that it is impracticable to consider diverting these waters or even treating them by any of the conventional means readily available today. Here the future in control may lie in understanding the sources of nutrients and thereby controlling them at their source.

Hypolimnetic Withdrawal. Eutrophic lakes that are sufficiently deep to develop a permanent thermocline accumulate higher concentrations of nitrogen and phosphorus in hypolimnetic waters than present in the epilimnion. The higher concentrations are derived from the sediments under anoxic conditions. In some lakes, withdrawal of hypolimnetic water will result in a higher nutrient flux from the lake than would be obtained with removal of epilimnetic water. In some cases where withdrawal of hypolimnetic water from eutrophic lakes has been practiced, serious H_2S odor problems have developed near the point of water discharge due to the release of this gas from the anoxic waters of the hypolimnion of the lake.

Water-Level Management. Water-level manipulation in impoundments and where possible in lakes can reduce the crops of rooted aquatic plants. In cold climates a combination of lowering water levels and freezing will reduce macrophytes in lakes.

Immobilizing of Nutrients. Aluminum and iron salts may be added directly to the lake to remove phosphorus from the lake water and carry it to the sediments. This method of nutrient control needs study to define the required chemical dosages and the frequency of treatment that is needed.

Rate of Recovery of a Lake upon Application of Remedial Action. The rate of recovery of an excessively fertilized lake after a reduction in nutrient input is dependent on many factors, the more important of which are the morphology of a lake, and its drainage basin, hydrology of the lake (relative amounts of surface and ground water), the theoretical flushing period of the lake, amount of short circulating of inlet and outlet waters, the amounts, forms, and distributions of aquatic plant nutrients in the sediments of the lake, magnitude of nutrient input reduction, chemical composition of the water and the chemical processes occurring in the lake, etc. The interrelationship of the various factors is very poorly understood. About the best that can be done at this time to predict the rate of recovery of an excessively fertilized lake upon reduction of nutrient input is to assume that at least several theoretical flushing periods (volume of lake divided by throughput) will be necessary before the nutrients in a lake will reach a new steady state of concentration on an annual basis. This statement is based on the assumption that the lake is a completely mixed system, with all input water completely mixing with the total volume of the lake, and the flushing of the lake by low-nutrient water obeys a first-order (exponential) flushing curve. It also assumes that any nutrient exchange with the sediments will essentially be complete in several flushing periods. This figure is of great importance in lakes like the Great Lakes where because of the relatively small watershed of the upper lakes, Superior and Michigan, as compared with their volume, it results in very long flushing periods. With theoretical flushing periods in excess of 100 years for both of these lakes, many generations (several hundred years) would have to pass before these lakes would recover from any lake-wide excessive fertilization of them. Fortunately large lakes tend to show excessive fertilization problems in the nearshore environment before any lake-wide problems develop. If corrective actions are taken shortly after any signs of excessive fertilizations are found, it is likely that the significant recovery would occur before the time calculated based on the theoretical flushing period.

Conclusions

Eutrophication of natural waters is one of the most significant water-quality problems that man faces today. The growth of excessive amounts of aquatic plants can cause a significant decrease in water quality, resulting in increased costs for water treatment, decreased quality for use in recreational purposes, and a hindrance to the use of water for agricultural purposes. The nutrients that cause this problem are nitrogen, phosphorus, and other trace elements. These elements are derived from many sources, the most important of which are domestic wastewaters, urban drainage, agricultural sources, the atmosphere, ground water, and to some degree from within the lake in terms of self-fertilization from the sediments. The control of eutrophication can best be effected on point sources, such as wastewater effluent, by nutrient removal. Other methods of control which show promise include weed, debris, and rough fish removal, dredging of lake sediments, low-flow augmentation, and zoning. Chemicals such as herbicides can be used to provide temporary relief from excessive growths of aquatic plants. However, their use may result in significant water-quality problems at some future date. There is an urgent need for additional research in all aspects of eutrophication, ranging from understanding the hydrodynamics, the hydrogeology, the hydrobiology, and the water chemistry of lakes and streams, to the various engineering aspects of nutrient control including the social, political, and economic aspects of water-resources management. The control of eutrophication of natural waters will require cooperative efforts of the aquatic scientists, engineers, and economists, and social, political, and legal experts. Only through the combined efforts of these individuals will it be possible to manage water resources for the betterment of mankind.

Bibliography

1. R. A. Taft, "Algae and Metropolitan Wastes," *Transactions of Seminar on Algae and Metropolitan Wastes, Cincinnati, Ohio, April 27-29, 1960.*
2. W. T. Edmondson, "Water-Quality Management and Lake Eutrophication: The Lake Washington Case," in *Water Resources Management and Public Policy.* University of Washington Press, Seattle, Wash., 1968.
3. D. E. Frey, *Limnology in North America,* University of Wisconsin Press, Madison, Wis., 1963.
4. G. E. Hutchinson, *A Treatise on Limnology,* John Wiley Sons, Inc., New York, 1957.
4a. *Geography, Physics, and Chemistry,* Vol. I of reference 4.
5. *Introduction to Lake Biology and the Limnoplankten,* Vol. II of reference 4.
6. D. F. Jackson, *Algae and Man,* Plenum Press, New York, 1964.
7. D. F. Jackson, *Algae, Man and the Environment,* Syracuse University Press, Syracuse, N.Y., 1968.
8. National Technical Advisory Committee to the Secretary of the Interior, *Water Quality Criteria,* Federal Water Pollution Control Administration, Washington, D.C., 1968.
9. K. M. Mackenthun, and W. M. Ingram. *Biological Associated Problems in Freshwater Environments Their Identification, Investigation and Control,* Federal Water Pollution Control Administration, Cincinatti, Ohio, 1967.
10. G. F. Lee and E. G. Fruh, "The Aging of Lakes," *Ind. Water Eng.* **3,** 26–30 (1966).
11. A. D. Hasler, "Eutrophication of Lakes by Domestic Drainage," *Ecology* **28,** 383–395 (1947).
12. K. M. Mackenthun, "A Review of Algae, Lake Weeds and Nutrients," *J. Water Pollution Control Federation* **34,** 1077–1085 (1962).
13. C. N. Sawyer, "Basic Concepts of Eutrophication," *J. Water Pollution Control Federation* **38,** 737–744 (1966).
14. K. M. Mackenthun, W. M. Ingram, and R. Porges, *Limnological Aspects of Recreational Lakes,* U.S. Dept. of Health, Education and Welfare, 1964.
15. K. M. Stewart and G. A. Rohlich, *Eutrophication—A Review,* Publ. No. 34, Calif. State Water Quality Control Board, 1967.
16. J. O. Veatch, and C. R. Humphrys, *Lake Terminology.* Dept. of Resource Development, Agricultural Experiment Station, Michigan State University, 1964.
17. R. A. Vollenweider, *Scientific Fundamentals of the Eutrophication of Lakes and Flowing Waters, with Particular Reference to Nitrogen and Phosphorus as Factors in Eutrophication,* Organization for Econ. Co-Operation and Development, Directorate for Scientific Affairs, Paris, 1968.
18. *Eutrophication: Causes, Consequences and Corrections,* National Academy of Science, Washington, D.C., 1969.
19. A. M. Beeton, "Eutrophication of the St. Lawrence Great Lakes," *Limnol. Oceanog.* **10,** 240–254 (1965).
20. K. M. Mackenthun and W. M. Ingram, *Algal Growth Factors Other than Nitrogen and Phosphorus,* Federal Water Pollution Control Administration, Washington, D.C., 1966.
21. E. J. Middlebrocks, T. E. Maloney, C. F. Powers, and L. M. Kaack, *Proceedings of the Eutrophication-Biostimulation Assessment Work, Federal Water Pollution Control Administration,* Corvallis, Ore., 1969.
22. R. A. Lewin, *Physiology and Biochemistry of Algae,* Academic Press, New York, 1962.
23. K. M. Mackenthun, *Nitrogen and Phosphorus in Water, An Annotated Selected Bibliography of Their Biological Effects,* U.S. Dept. of Health, Education and Welfare, 1965.
24. R. A. Vollenweider, *A Manual on Methods for Measuring Primary Production in Aquatic Environments,* International Biological Programme Handbook, No. 12, International Biological Programme, 1969.
25. Pacific Northwest Water Lab., "Environmental Requirements of Blue-Green Algae," *Proceedings of a Symposium, University of Washington and Federal Water Pollution Control Administration, Corvallis, Ore., Sept. 23–24, 1966.*
26. G. E. Fogg, *Algal Cultures and Phytoplankton Ecology,* University of Wisconsin Press, Madison Wis., 1965.
27. C. R. Goldman, *Premary Production in Aquatic Environments,* University of California Press, 1966.
28. D. A. Livingstone, "On the Sigmoid Growth Phase in the History of Linsley Pond," *Am J. Sci.* **225,** 364–373 (1957).
29. F. J. Mackereth, "Chemical Investigation of Lake Sediments and Their Interpretation," *Proc. Royal Soc. B,* **161,** 295–309 (1965).

30. E. G. Fruh, K. M. Stewart, G. F. Lee, and G. A. Rohlich. "Measurements of Eutrophication and Trends." *J. Water Pollution Control Federation* **38**, 1237–1258 (1966).

31. J. D. H. Strickland, "Measuring the Production of Marine Phytoplankton," *Bull. Fisheries Res. Board Can.* **122** (1960).

32. C. N. Sawyer, J. B. Lockey, and A. T. Lens, *Investigation of the Odor Nuisances in the Madison Lakes, Particularly Lakes Monona, Waubesa and Kegonsa from July 1943 to July 1944*, Report to Governor's Committee, Madison, Wisconsin, 1945.

33. *Effects of Fertilizers on Water Quality*, National Fertilizer Development Center, Tennessee Valley Authority, 1969.

34. *Excessive Water Fertilization*, Report to Water Subcommittee of Natural Resources Committee of State Agencies, Madison, Wisconsin, 1967.

35. G. F. Lee, *Report on the Nutrient Sources of Lake Mendota*, Lake Mendota Problems Committee, Madison, Wisconsin, 1966 (Revised 1969).

36. S. R. Weibel, R. J. Anderson, and R. L. Woodward, "Urban Land Runoff as a Factor in Stream Pollution," *J. Water Pollution Control Federation* **36**, 914–924 (1964).

37. G. F. Lee, "Factors Affecting the Exchange of Materials Between Waters and Sediments," *Presented at the American Chemical Society Meeting, New York, Sept. 1969*.

G. Fred Lee
University of Wisconsin

F

FERTILIZERS

World fertilizer consumption in 1969 (Fig. 1) maintained the remarkable rate of growth that began in 1945 and which is expected to extend for some time into the future. The rapid growth in population, the continuing decrease in the ratio of available land to population, and the ever higher standards of living all combine to increase the requirement for plant foods.

The increase in production has been accompanied by numerous changes in the production technology, concentrated mainly in the high-analysis fertilizers, such as ammonia, urea, and ammonium phosphate. Because of increasing costs of handling and shipping, these materials are becoming more and more economical in contrast to the older, less concentrated types.

It should be noted first, however, that possibly the most important development is the rapidly increasing trend to very large sizes of individual plant production units. The main objective is to reduce the investment per ton of product, a very important consideration because of the increasing "cost of money" and the high projected return on capital that investors insist on before putting their money into a project. For com-

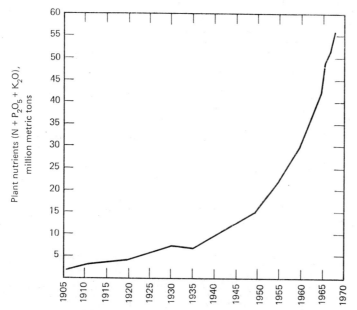

Fig. 1. World fertilizer consumption, 1906–1968 (FAO data; fiscal years).

plicated processes, such as ammonia and urea, the capital-related cost items—depreciation and return on investment—often make up the major portion of the product price that must be realized to make the project a financial success. As a result, both ammonia and urea plant units (single train) have been built that have capacities approaching 1500 tons of product per day. Further increase is projected, although problems, such as difficulty in shipping the large reaction vessels required and the heavy loss of production when accident or malfunction shuts down the large unit (as compared with having two or more smaller units), reduce the advantage of larger size.

Granulation of Multinutrient Fertilizers

Most of the fertilizer used is of the multinutrient type, containing two or more of the major plant nutrients, ie nitrogen (N), phosphate (P_2O_5), and potash (K_2O). Most of it is granulated (to a particle size of $1/12$ to $1/8$ in.) to improve the physical condition. Major developments in granulation technique have taken place in the last decade.

MELT GRANULATION

The granulation of multinutrient fertilizers in the past has generally involved the use of water or aqueous solutions to form the liquid phase necessary for sticking small particles together to form larger ones. After the water has performed this function, however, removing it from the solid granules requires a large and expensive dryer, generates a dust problem, and incurs considerable cost for recycling offsize particles. In contrast, melt granulation of ammonium nitrate or urea—normally carried out by evaporating water before granulation and finishing the resulting melt in one of several ways—requires no dryer and little, if any, recycling of fines.

The main problem in applying the melt-granulation technique to multinutrient fertilizers is that phosphates have high melting points. In recent developments, how-

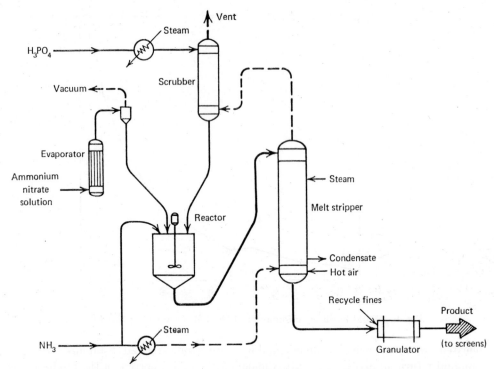

Fig. 2. Melt granulation of ammonium phosphate nitrate by the Fisons process (1).

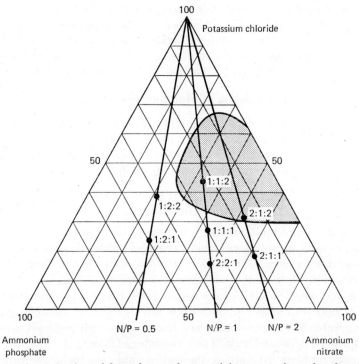

Fig. 3. Compositions of safe and hazardous melts containing ammonium phosphate, ammonium nitrate, and potassium chloride (2).

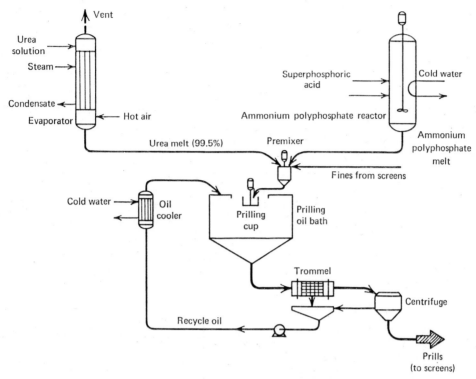

Fig. 4. Oil prilling of urea–ammonium polyphosphate (4).

ever, it has been found that mixtures of nitrogen compounds (ammonium nitrate or urea) with ammonium phosphate melt at low enough temperatures to make melt-granulation practical. Potassium chloride can also be included in the mix; it either dissolves in the melt or forms a manageable slurry.

In the Fisons Fertilizers Limited process (Fig. 2), which is used in a large plant in England, ammonium nitrate solution, phosphoric acid, and gaseous ammonia are introduced into a reactor tank and the resulting solution of ammonium nitrate and ammonium phosphate is pumped to a drying tower (melt stripper) where the water introduced with the raw materials is removed. The melt is then ready for granulation by any of the standard methods—flaking, prilling, or granulation in a pugmill, drum granulator, spray drum, or pan granulator. No drying step is needed. The waste gases from the drying tower are passed through the incoming phosphoric acid to recover ammonia.

When the melt to be granulated includes both ammonium nitrate and potassium chloride, there is some danger of fire or explosion because the chloride sensitizes the nitrate. If phosphate is also present, however, and the various materials are properly proportioned, there is little hazard. The "safe" area is shown on the phase diagram in Figure 3 (2).

Melt granulation has also been applied in the nitric phosphate field, particularly in conjunction with the Odda process (3). The main product from this process, a mixture of ammonium nitrate, ammonium phosphate, and dicalcium phosphate, can be prilled because the molten ammonium nitrate–ammonium phosphate mix can carry the precipitated dicalcium phosphate in suspension without interfering with prill formation.

The combination of urea and ammonium phosphate is a promising multinutrient fertilizer because of its high nutrient content (30–30–0, 20–20–20) (30% N, 30% P_2O_5, 0% K_2O; the second set of figures shows what it could be with KCl added), but the tendency of the urea to decompose at elevated temperature in the presence of phosphate makes it difficult to produce, either by standard methods or by most melt-granulation methods. In standard granulation, the drying step must be carried out at relatively low temperature—and therefore at a low rate—to minimize decomposition. In melt prilling, the evaporation of water cannot be carried out after the two materials are mixed as the phosphate would quickly decompose the urea.

In a prilling process developed by the Tennessee Valley Authority (TVA) (4), melts of urea and of ammonium polyphosphate (see Vol. 9, p. 130) are first formed separately and then mixed just before the prilling step (Fig. 4). The mixed melt flows into a rotating prilling cup that showers droplets downward into a cooled oil bath a short distance below. The oil chills the drops quickly and solidifies them into prills.

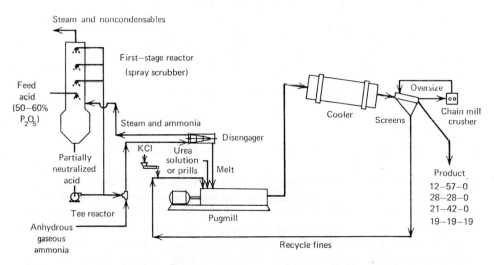

Fig. 5. Melt granulation of urea–ammonium phosphate in a pugmill.

The oil-prill slurry flows to a trommel screen where most of the oil is removed and then to a centrifuge to complete the de-oiling. After screening to size, the undersize particles are recycled to the prilling cup where they serve as nuclei for prill formation. The recycle is relatively low, about 0.2 pound per pound of melt.

Oil prilling is used rather than the usual air prilling because the polyphosphate crystallizes at a relatively slow rate. In the normal air-prilling operation, the prills would probably still be soft when they strike the bottom of the tower and would therefore deform, whereas the oil can receive the prills while still soft without causing deformation and hold them until rapid cooling, crystallization, and hardening occur. Ammonium polyphosphate is used in the TVA process both because it has a relatively low melting point and also because a high polyphosphate content in the product is desirable, particularly in supplying phosphate for liquid fertilizers. However, ammonium orthophosphate can also be used in this type of melt-granulation process.

In another TVA development (Fig. 5) wet-process phosphoric acid is reacted with ammonia under conditions designed to conserve the heat of reaction, thereby evaporating all of the water and producing a melt suitable for mixing with urea melt and subsequent granulation. About 15 to 25% of the orthophosphate is converted to polyphosphate in this operation. Potassium chloride may be added.

Melt granulation is used in commercial plants in Europe for ammonium nitrate–ammonium phosphate combinations and for nitric phosphate. TVA is building a demonstration plant in which urea–ammonium polyphosphate will be made by the oil-prilling method. It is expected that melt granulation will continue to grow in acceptance and eventually become the principal method for granulating multinutrient fertilizers.

FLUIDIZED-BED GRANULATION

Another way of eliminating the dryer in granulation of multinutrient fertilizers is to combine the steps of granulation and drying, in contrast to melt granulation where the "drying" is accomplished before granulation. The Spherodizer (see Vol. 9, p. 128) employs this principle; fertilizer slurry, still containing the water introduced with the raw materials, is sprayed onto solid recycled particles which are lifted by flights in a rotary drum and dropped repeatedly through the sprays. The slurry sticks to the solid particles and the water is removed by a current of hot gases passed through the drum. Drying is rapid because of the thin, "onion-skin" layers thus built up on the particles.

Another departure, now coming into use, is fluidized-bed granulation. One version of this, developed by Montecatini-Edison SA in Italy (5), is shown in Figure 6. Dilute phosphoric acid (unconcentrated product from a phosphoric acid plant) is first used to scrub off-gases and then reacted with ammonia in a series of reaction tanks. The resulting slurry is carried into the fluid bed by a current of hot gas (air plus NH_3), where it coats out on particles in the bed and is dried. The off-gas passes through a cyclone for dust recovery and then to the off-gas scrubber for ammonia recovery. As the particles grow in size in the fluid bed they escape and are screened; the fines are recycled to the bed to serve as nuclei.

Two plants have been built that use this method, one of 100- and the other 250-ton-per-day capacity. The developers claim that the process is applicable to mono-ammonium and diammonium phosphate (from 28% P_2O_5 acid), nitric phosphates, urea phosphate, ordinary superphosphate (from dilute H_2SO_4 and acid sludges), and triple superphosphate (from 28% $P_2O_5 \cdot H_3PO_4$).

Urea

The advantages of urea—high nutrient content, relatively good physical condition, and agronomic superiority for some crops—have given it a position of growing importance in modern fertilizer technology. Urea has presented some unique and difficult problems, however, in development of production methods. The reaction of ammonia and carbon dioxide must be carried out at high pressure and temperature, the reaction mixture is highly corrosive, the reaction cannot be completed in one pass, and the product decomposes at relatively low temperature.

Because of these problems, development of efficient production methods has lagged behind that for other nitrogen fertilizers, such as ammonium nitrate and ammonium sulfate. Only in the past decade have techniques been developed to bring investment and operating cost down to the low levels common for other fertilizers.

RECYCLE OF UNCONVERTED REACTANTS

Since the effluent from the urea reactor is an aqueous solution containing urea and unconverted ammonium carbamate ($NH_4CO_2NH_2$), the solution must be heated to decompose and remove the carbamate. The decomposition products are evolved as a hot, gaseous mixture of ammonia, carbon dioxide, and water vapor. Recycling of this corrosive gas probably can qualify as the most difficult problem that has been encountered in the development of urea synthesis.

Carbamate Solution. The principal recycle system of modern urea technology involves merely condensing the NH_3–CO_2–H_2O gas mixture and pumping the resulting

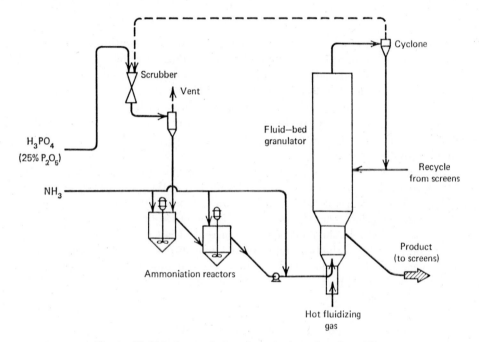

Fig. 6. Fluid-bed granulation of ammonium phosphate (5).

solution back into the reactor (Fig. 7). This general procedure is used in several of the commercial processes. These are called the conventional processes and have much in common, in reactor operation as well as in the recycle system. All use similar reactor conditions (temperature about 185°C and pressure about 200 atm), maintain an NH_3:CO_2 mole ratio of about 4:1 in the synthesis loop, and get about the same single-pass conversion (65–67%). All reduce the reactor-effluent pressure to an intermediate level and then pass the solution through two or three stages of decomposition (by heating) at successively lower pressure levels. In each stage the evolved gas mixture is condensed (or absorbed in weak solution condensed in a later stage) and the resulting solutions are worked back through the system to the reactor. The excess ammonia (from the excess used in the initial reactor feed) passes through the absorbers, is condensed, and is fed back to the reactor.

Although these major steps are common to the various conventional methods, there is considerable difference in the carbamate solution recycle systems—in pressure and temperature levels, equipment arrangement, and process flow. This phase of the development is still in a state of flux; even for a given company, the flowsheet for a current plant is likely to be somewhat different from the immediately preceding one.

The *number of decomposition stages* is one of the points of difference. The carbamate could be decomposed in a single stage to reduce investment, but this drops the pressure all the way from reactor pressure to atmospheric (or near to it) in one step, with the result that a relatively large amount of water evaporates (which must be returned to the reactor) and heat recovery is unattractive because of the low temperature level. Multistage operation removes most of the reactants at higher pressure levels and thus improves the water balance and makes heat recovery more economical.

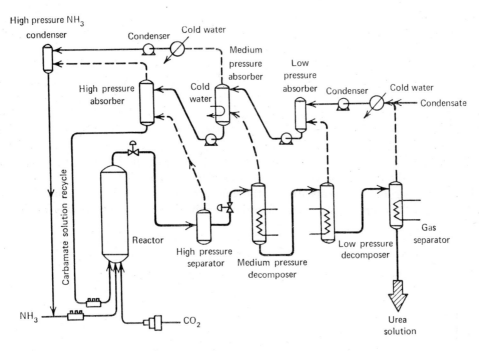

Fig. 7. Conventional carbamate solution recycling in urea synthesis.

The current trend is to three stages as the optimum number. The third stage generally involves both decomposition of carbamate and evaporation of water, with vacuum applied to remove the ammonia down to a very low level as a means of minimizing atmospheric pollution. The flashed gas is passed through a water-cooled condenser, the condensate is stripped of ammonia, and the stripped condensate preferably is discarded rather than returned to the reactor. Such a procedure gives only traces of ammonia in the gaseous and aqueous effluents.

The *point of heat recovery* also varies. Heat is available from two sources: the heat of reaction (carried out of the reactor with the products) and heat added to decompose the carbamate and convert it to gaseous products. Much of this considerable quantity of heat is released when the evolved gases are recondensed, so it is at this point that heat usually is recovered. The recovery is limited to the first decomposition stage, however, because the gases are at so low a pressure in the later stages that condensation temperature is uneconomically low for heat recovery.

The main variation is in the stream selected to absorb this heat; in some cases, water is heated, producing steam. In other published flowsheets a process stream is involved (1), as shown below:

Company	Heat-absorbing stream
Chemico	solution to second decomposer
Montecatini[a]	solution to first decomposer
Mitsui Toatsu[a]	solution to crystallizer
Weatherly	solution to evaporator

[a] Latest version not being offered.

The *pressure level in the first decomposition stage* is a very important point of variation because it has led to the so-called "stripper" processes, a new and somewhat radical development in urea technology. These processes still involve carbamate solution recycle but in an unconventional manner. High pressure is quite desirable because less water evaporates and the gases subsequently condense at a higher temperature level. However, decomposition and gas evolution become more difficult as pressure increases; the temperature must be raised until finally corrosion and urea decomposition become the limiting factors. Until recently, from 15 to 20 atmospheres was the accepted level in the conventional processes, as a compromise between the various effects. However, in one of the newest developments, Mitsui Toatsu Chemicals, Inc. (6) operates the first decomposer at 58 to 77 atmospheres. The evolved gases from this unit are scrubbed in an absorber at the same pressure with carbamate solution from later stages. The ammonia passing off of the absorber is condensed by contact with the

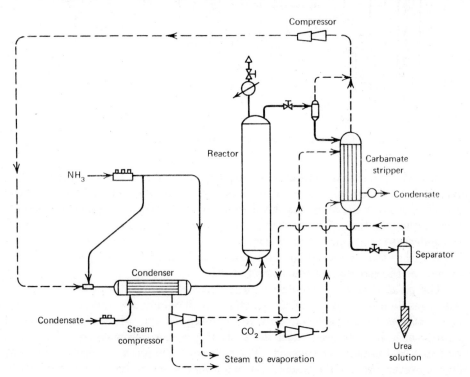

Fig. 8. Norsk Hydro stripping process for urea synthesis (7).

incoming liquid ammonia feed plus the solution from the absorber in the tube side of a mixer coming just before the reactor. The heat of condensation is recovered as steam from the shell side of the mixer.

Montecatini-Edison has also developed a "high-pressure decomposer" unit (1) in which the first decomposer operates at 80 atmospheres. Off-gases from this unit are reacted with about one-third of the carbon dioxide feed in a condenser; the heat evolved is used to produce steam at about 3 atmospheres. Part is compressed to 5–7 atmospheres for second- and third-stage decomposers; the remainder is used in evaporation. A 600-ton-per-day unit is in operation and larger units are under construction.

Because of the adverse effect of the high temperature necessarily associated with high-pressure decomposition, developers have sought some driving force other than the usual heat and decompression to help decompose carbamate. The answer has been found in a method analogous to water evaporation—an inert stripping gas is used, making the decomposer similar in principle to an air-swept evaporator. The "inert" gas is ammonia or carbon dioxide; although these are also the reactants, when one is present in excess over the carbamate ratio, it behaves as an inert and reduces the partial pressure of the other over the solution. As a result, the "reactant" can be removed almost entirely by the inert at high total pressures, but at acceptably low temperatures.

Both the stripping gas and the first-stage decomposition pressure vary between the various processes; the gases and pressures used are as follows:

Process	Stripping gas	Pressure in first decomposition stage, atm
Norsk Hydro	carbon dioxide	70–100
SNAM	ammonia	135
Stamicarbon	carbon dioxide	135–150
Weatherly	ammonia plus inert gas	230

Norsk Hydro-Elektrisk Kvaelstofaktieselskab (7) uses a relatively low pressure level but accomplishes fairly complete decomposition by the combination of heating (with steam recovered in the process) and stripping with the feed carbon dioxide (Fig. 8). The gases evolved in the first stage are further compressed to reactor pressure (190–230 atm) by centrifugal compression and then condensed in a "condenser-pre-reactor-boiler" (ammonium carbamate condenser). At this high-pressure level, the pressure of the steam generated is 5–8 atmospheres absolute; this is further increased, by a turbocompressor, to give steam hot enough (10–15 atm abs) for use in the stripper-decomposer. That part of the steam not needed in the stripper is used in the evaporator at the 5- to 8-atmosphere level. This is a combination of carbamate solution recycle and hot gas-compression recycle (see below).

The Norsk Hydro process has not yet been optimized and a practical demonstration has not been made; limitations are imposed by the size of the centrifugal compressors. It is claimed, however, that capital cost should be 10–20% lower than for established processes and that energy cost should be about $1 less per ton of urea.

SNAM Progetti SpA operates the stripper-decomposer at near-reactor pressure which is approximately about 147 atmospheres, much lower than normal (Fig. 9). Gaseous ammonia (part of liquid feed is vaporized) is the stripping gas. The lower pressure gives lower conversion but permits efficient stripping and cen-

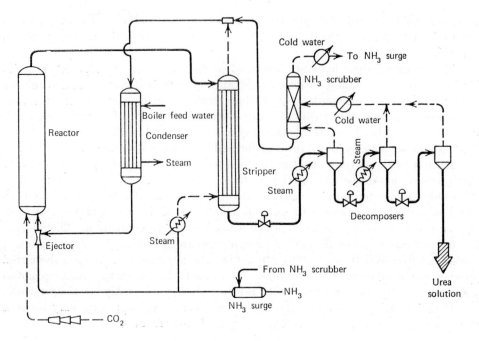

Fig. 9. SNAM ammonia-stripper urea process.

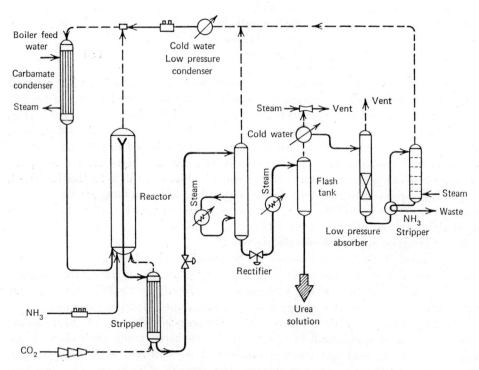

Fig. 10. Stamicarbon carbon dioxide-stripper urea process.

trifugal compression of the carbon dioxide feed (centrifugal compression to high reactor pressure is difficult). The pressure of the steam generated by condensing the carbamate is relatively low, about 3.5–5.5 atmospheres, but can be used in the plant. The solution from the carbamate condenser is injected into the reactor by a liquid ammonia ejector, thus eliminating the high-pressure solution pump. One SNAM plant has been built (1969) and five others are under construction.

Stamicarbon NV (Dutch State Mines) carries out stripping at full reactor pressure (Fig. 10) but again the pressure (135–150 atm) is much lower than in conventional processes. Gaseous carbon dioxide (feed) is the stripping gas. In a version developed later than that shown in Figure 10, the off-gas from the stripper goes to the top of the condenser, rather than to the reactor, as shown. This, together with the addition of

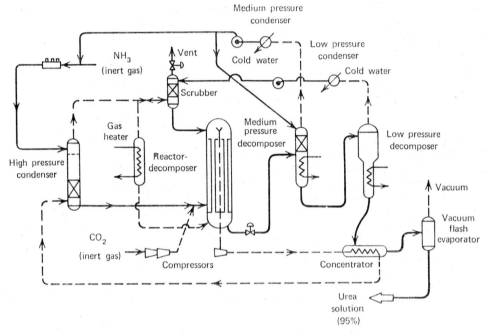

Fig. 11.   Weatherly urea process.

part of the ammonia feed to the condenser, permits positioning the condenser at the same level as the reactor, rather than high above it. The method was the first of the stripping processes and is the most thoroughly tested. About sixteen plants are in operation in Europe and Asia.

The D. M. Weatherly Company method (Fig. 11) is the newest of the stripper-type but has not yet been demonstrated on a practical scale. The process combines stripping and urea formation in a single shell-and-tube vessel, a unique arrangement. The feed reactants flow up the shell side, which corresponds to the urea reactor, and then down through the tubes where a flow of superheated gaseous ammonia (plus an inert gas such as nitrogen) strips out the carbamate. The stripped gases give up sensible heat to solution entering the evaporators at the end of the system and then return to the condenser, which operates at full reactor pressure; the condenser is cooled by evaporation of the incoming feed ammonia. This process also combines solution recycle and hot gas-compression recycle, though in this case only enough compression to overcome line pressure drops is required.

The main feature of the process is direct use of reaction heat (from carbamate formation on the shell side) to decompose carbamate (on the tube side); therefore, generation of high-pressure steam for decomposition is not required.

The stripper processes are equally divided between ammonia and carbon dioxide as the stripping gas. Ammonia has the advantages of (1) lower corrosion and biuret formation in the high-pressure system because of the high $NH_3:CO_2$ ratio; and (2) higher conversion and lower water recycle (also because of high $NH_3:CO_2$ ratio). However, with proper attention to temperature and retention time, it is said that carbon dioxide is satisfactory in these respects. In addition, carbon dioxide is basically the more effective (increase in CO_2 vapor pressure reduces NH_3 vapor pressure more than the reverse), is less soluble and therefore easier to remove from the liquor, and does not require heat to vaporize it initially as does ammonia. Further plant experience will be necessary to establish any clear-cut advantage of one over the other.

The foregoing sections indicate that most urea processes may be classified as (1) conventional, low-pressure decomposition; (2) nonstripping, high-pressure decomposition; or (3) stripping, high-pressure decomposition. The last two are the newer processes and are a step forward in urea technology. Published claims of utility requirements, some stated as guaranteed, others unspecified, for the various processes are given in Table 1 (1).

This indicates, assuming typical utility costs in the United States, a saving of about \$0.50 to \$0.80 per ton of urea for the newer methods. For a plant making 1000 –1500 tons per day, this is a major saving over the course of a year.

The stripping processes so far have not been applied in single plant trains larger than 600 to 700 tons per day. Design and construction problems for the high-pressure, tube-and-shell decomposer and condenser appear to have been limiting factors. However, progress in solving these problems seems to be under way. Single-train units of 1000- and 1400-ton-per-day capacity are reported to be under construction (1).

The relative merits of stripping versus nonstripping, high-pressure decomposition processes are difficult to evaluate. Operating and investment costs appear to be about

Table 1. Utility Requirements in Urea Processes

Process	Utility requirement, per short ton of urea		
	Steam, lb	Electricity, kWh	Cooling water, gal
conventional	2400–3200	132–170	16,000–29,000
SNAM	2200	110	18,500
Stamicarbon	2200	100	12,000
Weatherly[a]	1600[b]	130[b]	16,000[b]
	2800[c]	15[c]	23,000[c]
Montecatini	1980[b]	140[b]	
	2750[c]	10[c]	
Mitsui Toatsu (Process D)	1700	155	14,500

[a] Not yet fully demonstrated.
[b] Steam-driven compressor.
[c] Electric-driven compressor.

the same. Elimination of the high-pressure carbamate solution pump in the stripper process appears to be its main advantage.

Carbamate Slurry. Since water recycled to the reactor has an adverse effect on conversion, recycling of carbamate slurry rather than solution has been attempted in an effort to reduce the amount of water required. Montecatini has developed a process based on recycle of carbamate suspended in liquid ammonia (8). The method is like the conventional one except that the feed ammonia is brought in at the first-stage condenser; formation of a carbamate–ammonia slurry at this point makes it unnecessary to use condensate from later stages to keep the carbamate in solution. Gases from the second decomposition stage (the final one) enter a system where ammonia is recovered and recycled without the water. The method has been tested only on a pilot-plant scale.

Hot Gas Recycle. An obvious way to recycle the unreacted ammonia and carbon dioxide is merely to recompress them. This was the first method tried, in the early days of the industry, but was quite unsuccessful, since reciprocating compressors, the type commonly used then, are not suitable for such service because carbamate condenses in the intercoolers. Today, centrifugal compressors are widely used in many applications where the gas-flow volume is not too small to be a limiting factor. For the 1000- to 1500-ton-per-day plants in modern practice, gas recycle by means of centrifugal compressors may well be practical. It would have the advantages of eliminating the carbamate-solution pumps, requiring only one condensing stage, and recovering practically all the heat of carbamate decomposition. However, large-scale tests, which are expensive, have not yet been made, and small-scale testing is impractical.

Integration with Ammonia Plant. Integration of ammonia and urea production has long been a goal because it would allow use of energy from the exothermic ammonia reaction to help meet energy requirements in the urea plant. Although the process has not been used on a commercial scale, Mitsui Toatsu has operated a pilot plant for several years. The process involves: (1) heat exchange from shift-converter exit gas to urea reactor effluent solution in decomposer reboilers to decompose the carbamate; (2) compression of converter gas (H_2, N_2, CO_2) to full ammonia and urea reactor pressure (300 atm); (3) absorption of carbon dioxide at reactor pressure by liquid ammonia from the ammonia-synthesis loop (along with recycled carbamate solution from the condensers); and (4) feeding the resulting carbamate solution to the urea reactor. The energy saving comes from three sources: (1) elevated pressure of carbon dioxide at the shift-converter exit (about 24 atm); (2) heat normally required in the ammonia plant to remove carbon dioxide from the absorbent; and (3) pressure of liquid ammonia from the synthesis loop.

A considerable saving is possible from the integration. Net utility consumption claimed for the urea plant is 83 kilowatt-hours, 1040 pounds steam, and 24,000 gallons cooling water—all per short ton of urea. This is considerably lower than for standard processes and a reduction of 5–7% in investment is also claimed.

UREA FINISHING

Removal of unreacted carbamate in the urea plant decomposers leaves a urea solution from which the water (about 25% of the solution) must be removed before a solid product can be obtained. However, without free ammonia present, heating the solution promotes decomposition, both to the original reactants (hydrolysis) and to biuret. Hydrolysis products can be recovered but the biuret is mixed with the product where it is undesirable for some uses. Since biuret formation is a function both of temperature and retention time, the trend has been to evaporators that minimize the levels of these variables. Development effort has centered on the film type, both falling film (air-swept) and rising film (vacuum with high recirculation rate). The spinning-disc, air-swept type is also effective but may not scale up as well as the others. The vacuum type has the disadvantage that volatilized ammonia (residual ammonia from the decomposers or ammonia formed by hydrolysis) is collected in the evaporator condensate and therefore may cause a water-pollution problem (unless recovered), which usually is more troublesome than the air pollution resulting from use of an air-swept evaporator. The latter, however, requires a supply of dehumidified air reheated to about 140°C.

The biuret content can be kept below 1% (100% urea basis) by good evaporator operation, and, since very little biuret formation takes place during conversion to the solid form (usually by prilling), the final product also contains less than 1%. This has been a major accomplishment but for technical-grade product even lower biuret is desired. As a result, the crystal remelt method—in which the urea solution is crystallized in a vacuum crystallizer and the crystals are centrifuged, dried, melted, and prilled—has been developed. The product contains only 0.25 to 0.35% biuret because the biuret in solution does not cocrystallize with the urea. It is removed from the crystallizer in a purge stream of mother liquor that is generally fed back to the synthesis reactor where conditions are such that conversion back to urea takes place. The stream may go directly to the reactor or indirectly through the absorber system; SNAM feeds it back to the stripper (at synthesis pressure). The crystal remelt method seems to be growing in popularity, even though investment is on the order of 8 to 10% higher than for evaporation prilling.

Urea finishing by prilling is a fairly well developed technology. Most producers prefer multiple spray heads rather than spinning baskets, apparently because a wider range of particle sizes (mircoprills to agricultural prills) is possible with the sprays. The main development probably has been use of a fluidized bed in the base of the tower, both to cool the product in a convenient way and to prevent sticking of prills on the tower bottom. Alternatively, a rake-type prill-removal mechanism in a flat-bottom tower is preferred to the cone-bottom gravity-flow type.

Some progress has been made in developing finishing equipment which is smaller in size than prilling tower installations and which gives a larger product granule. TVA has tested pan granulation on a pilot-plant scale (9), and Cominco has developed and is using a Spherodizer type of operation (10).

Potassium Nitrate

Potassium nitrate (KNO_3; 13% N, 44% K_2O) is an excellent fertilizer material but its use has been restricted because of high production cost. It is one of the oldest chemicals known, used centuries ago by the Chinese in making gunpowder, but production cost has always been relatively high because of the complexity of the process. The usual raw materials are potassium chloride and nitric acid, which in itself is a problem. The potassium chloride is an inexpensive, efficient fertilizer without any chemical treatment and the nitric acid is valuable for its acid potential as well as its nitrogen content; if the hydrogen ion content is wasted, in effect, by reaction with potassium chloride the economics become doubly questionable. There are four processes in use for making potassium nitrate (Table 2) (11).

Table 2. Potassium Nitrate Production Processes

Manufacturer	Source of K^+	Source of NO_3^-	By-product	Approximate production rate, tons/yr
Auby, France	KCl	NH_4NO_3	NH_4Cl	8,000
Victor, Germany	K_2SO_4	$Ca(NO_3)_2$	$CaSO_4$	20,000
Southwest Potash, U.S.A.	KCl	HNO_3	Cl_2	75,000
Haifa Chemicals, Israel	KCl	HNO_3	HCl	100,000[a]

[a] Nominal rate; startup in 1969.

The Southwest Potash Corporation method is a complicated one. The problem is that the reaction of potassium chloride with nitric acid (under the basic processing conditions used) not only gives potassium nitrate but also several by-products such as $NOCl$, NO_2Cl, and N_2O_4. Southwest Potash takes care of these by converting the N_2O_4 to nitric acid, concentrating medium-strength nitric acid to 81%, and using this strong acid to oxidize NOCl to Cl_2 and NO_2. This difficult process is made possible by (*1*) a shift in composition of the nitric acid–water azeotrope, from about 70 to over 80%, in the presence of potassium nitrate at high concentration; and (*2*) the practicality of oxidizing NOCl with the strong acid at reasonable temperature and pressure.

The Southwest Potash method dissipates the acid value of the nitric acid, but offsetting this is the relatively high value of the chlorine by-product. The potassium nitrate has found a place in the fertilizer industry because of its applicability in agronomic situations, such as the growing of tobacco and potatoes, where the amount of chlorine must be limited.

The Haifa Chemicals method, generally known as the IMI (Israel Mining Industries) process, was developed later and is quite different. The method makes use of the following reaction:

$$KCl + HNO_3 \rightleftharpoons KNO_3 + HCl$$

An organic solvent—a C_5 alcohol—is used to remove hydrochloric acid from the system in order to allow the reaction to proceed, and to separate the acid and salt components of the system. The reciprocal-pair system K^+–H^+–Cl^-–NO_3^-, with the solvent added, is invariant when both potassium chloride and potassium nitrate are present in solid form; thus at a given temperature the solvent and aqueous phases will have a fixed composition as long as both solids are present. The weight ratio of the solids has no effect on the system so the amount of potassium chloride can be quite small, which makes it possible to convert solid potassium chloride to solid potassium nitrate in a single-stage, simple operation.

The reaction is carried out at 5–10°C in stirred reactors (Fig. 12) (*12*). Fertilizer-grade potassium chloride and 60–70% HNO_3 are fed into a salt solution of specified composition along with recycled solvent. Conversion takes place immediately and potassium nitrate crystallizes, while hydrochloric acid goes into solution in the solvent, along with the excess nitric acid. After separation and washing of the potassium nitrate, the solvent phase is treated in a series of liquid–liquid contacting steps to separate 22% HCl (coproduct) from the solvent–nitric acid solution, which is recycled.

Since the hydrochloric acid is recovered, the acid value of the nitric acid is not wasted; it is merely transferred to a new acid. Hydrochloric, however, normally is not a desirable acid; in the Haifa Chemicals installation, the acid will be used for treating

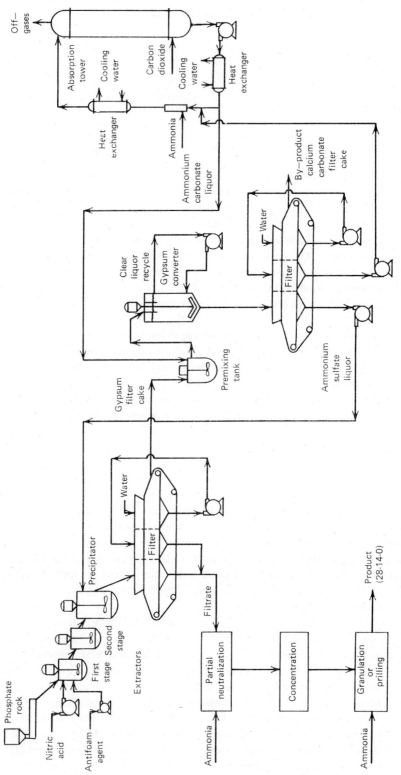

Fig. 12. IMI process for potassium nitrate (12) (Courtesy of Centre International des Engrais Chimiques).

Table 3. Raw-Material and Utility Consumption of The Potassium
Nitrate Process, Per Short Ton of Potassium Nitrate

	Amount
raw material	
potassium chloride, ton	0.74
nitric acid, 100% basis, ton	0.62
ammonia, ton	0.005
solvent makeup, ton	0.003
utilities	
steam, ton	0.65
electric power, kWh	63
process water, gal	235
cooling water, gal	9500

phosphate rock by another IMI solvent-extraction process, to make high-grade phosphoric acid.

The raw-material and utility consumption for the potassium nitrate process is listed in Table 3.

The Haifa Chemicals plant about doubled the world production of potassium nitrate. It remains to be seen whether premium uses in the agricultural industry, plus the somewhat limited industrial demand, will be able to absorb the increased supply. The advantages and drawbacks of the material are summarized below.

Advantages:

1. High analysis (13–0–44). However, the total nutrient content is lower than that of potassium chloride (60% K_2O) from which it was made.

2. Very low hygroscopicity.

3. It is a granulation aid for mixed fertilizer. The relatively high solubility at elevated temperature makes it possible to granulate with less water.

4. Good stabilizer for ammonium nitrate.

5. Agronomic advantage where chloride is harmful.

6. Less likely to burn plants.

7. Low salt index in the soil.

8. Reduction of carcinogenic hydrocarbon content in tobacco (13).

Disadvantages:

1. Processes are complicated and expensive. Investment is particularly high because corrosive-resistant materials must be used.

2. Economics depend on getting an adequate return from a by-product.

3. Economics are further adversely affected by the fact that all the nitrogen comes from nitric acid, a relatively expensive source.

It appears that potassium nitrate can be profitable only if a premium price can be obtained for it. Since the premium uses are limited, consumption is likely to be limited also.

Nitric Phosphate by Sulfate Recycle Method

Nitric phosphates, made by acidulating phosphate rock with nitric acid and ammoniating the acidulate, are important modern fertilizers. The main problem in pro-

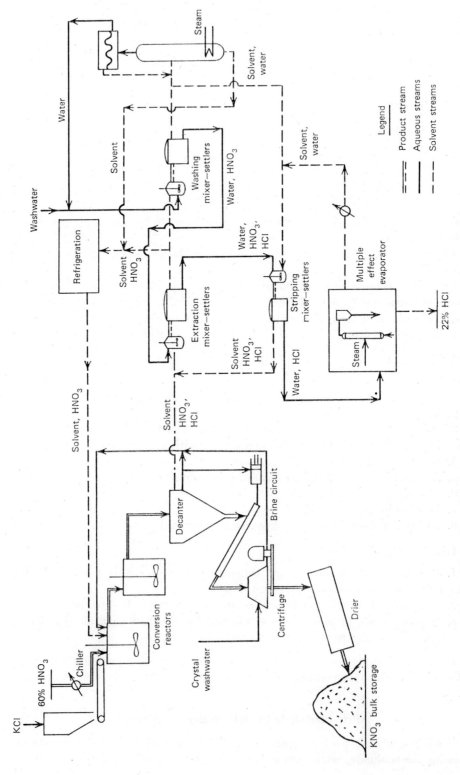

Fig. 13.   Ammonium phosphate nitrate by nitric phosphate route (sulfate recycle process) (15).

duction is that the calcium nitrate formed in nitric phosphate processes is not nearly so easily removed as is the calcium sulfate made in the standard process for phosphoric acid, where phosphate rock is treated with sulfuric acid and the resulting insoluble calcium sulfate is filtered out. If the calcium salt is not removed, the nutrient concentration is reduced and, more importantly, the high $Ca:P_2O_5$ ratio reduces the phosphate solubility to an unacceptably low level.

The two principal methods used in coping with the problem are: (*1*) removing most of the calcium by cooling the solution and crystallizing calcium nitrate; and (*2*) adding phosphoric acid to the reaction mixture to give an acceptably low $Ca:P_2O_5$ ratio. As neither is completely satisfactory, a considerable amount of research and development has been carried out on alternating methods. A leading one is adding ammonium sulfate to the acidulate (which is a mixture of $Ca(NO_3)_2$ and H_3PO_4) to precipitate the calcium as calcium sulfate. The sulfate is separated by filtration and reacted with ammonia and carbon dioxide to regenerate the ammonium sulfate for recycling; calcium carbonate is a by-product:

$$CaSO_4 + 2\ NH_3 + CO_2 + H_2O \rightarrow (NH_4)_2SO_4 + CaCO_3 \downarrow$$

Such a sulfate recycling method has been tested in a pilot plant by TVA (15). The process (Fig. 13) consists of five steps: (*1*) Acidulation of phosphate rock with nitric acid in two stages. (*2*) Precipitation of calcium by adding recycled ammonium sulfate solution, to the phosphate acidulate (H_3PO_4–$Ca(NO_3)_2$), followed by filtration to remove the calcium sulfate formed. (*3*) Treatment of the calcium sulfate with ammonium carbonate solution to precipitate calcium carbonate and regenerate ammonium sulfate for recycling. (*4*) Preparation of the ammonium carbonate solution from ammonia, carbon dioxide, and water. (*5*) Neutralization (with NH_3), concentration, and granulation of the filtrate from step (*2*) (mainly a solution of NH_4NO_3 in H_3PO_4), thereby making a 28–14–0 product.

The amount of nitric acid used is that required to give a $HNO_3:CaO$ mole ratio of 2:2. The excess over the ratio in calcium nitrate is required to give an adequate acidulation rate, an even grade (28–14–0), and good process operation. A small amount (0.1 lb/ton of product) of added antifoam agent controls foaming in the acidulation step. The temperature in the single-stage sulfate precipitator is maintained at about 160°F. Sulfate filtration is carried out in a stagewise, countercurrent wash system in which the first wash liquor is returned to the filtrate.

The gypsum converter is a single-stage unit designed by TVA to improve the crystal size and filtration rate of the calcium carbonate. In some of the other processes that include the $CaSO_4$–NH_3–CO_2 reaction, very finely divided calcium carbonate, difficult to filter, has been formed. In the TVA unit, the calcium sulfate and ammonium carbonate solution is first mixed and then introduced into a vertical, stirred reactor a few inches underneath the liquor surface. The liquor in the reactor is recycled continuously, overflowing from the top and reentering through a sparger arrangement (combined with a rake agitator) in the bottom of the vessel. A bleed stream is removed from this circuit to feed the calcium carbonate filter. The combination of slow stirring and solution recycling gives relatively large crystal agglomerates that are easy to filter.

The sulfate recycle method has not been used commercially; possibly the closest approach is by Dutch State Mines in Holland, where by-product ammonium sulfate from a caprolactam plant is used to precipitate calcium in a nitric phosphate plant.

The calcium sulfate is discarded rather than converted to ammonium sulfate for recycling.

One of the main drawbacks to the recycle process is the high $N:P_2O_5$ ratio in the product; since all the nitrogen from the nitric acid is retained, plus an equivalent amount of ammonia for neutralization, the product grade is about 28–14–0. However, the economics are competitive with other nitric phosphates and with wet-process acid-based ammonium phosphates. The process has a good chance of acceptance, particularly where sulfur prices are high.

By-product Sulfur for Phosphate Production

Sulfur is very important in the fertilizer industry as one of the raw materials in making superphosphate and phosphoric acid. Very large quantities are used in the manufacture of these phosphates.

The deposits of elemental sulfur in the Gulf Coast area of the United States have been the traditional source of sulfur for several decades, but there is some concern that these deposits are losing ground to the growing demand and that they must be supplemented in a major way in the foreseeable future. The main sources of such supplemental sulfur are pyrites, sour natural gas, crude oil, coal, and calcium sulfate (gypsum and anhydrite). Of these, the technology for obtaining useful sulfur compounds from pyrites and sour gas is well advanced and in use. Calcium sulfate has also been used as raw material in at least two plants. The main emphasis in research and development, however, is on the recovery of sulfur from oil and coal or from the combustion gases formed in burning these fossil fuels to produce energy.

Methods for desulfurizing oil are well developed, to the extent that desulfurization facilities have been built in Japan. For coal there is no established process but there are several developments under way that may be significant. For example, coal gasification methods which are aimed at making a substitute for pipeline natural gas incidentally remove sulfur in the process.

Particular emphasis has been placed on development of methods to remove sulfur oxides from combustion gases, especially from coal-burning power plants where the emission of sulfur oxides to the atmosphere is often quite large. For example, a 1,000,-000-kilowatt power plant (which is not unusually large) burning coal containing 3.5% sulfur (which is not unusually high) emits sulfur oxides equivalent to about 1000 tons of sulfuric acid per day. This pollution of the atmosphere has led to extensive research on methods for removing the sulfur from the gas before it leaves the power plant. Moreover, the fact that it is a valuable natural resource now being wasted is another good argument for recovery. Numerous development efforts aimed at recovering the sulfur are under way in various parts of the world, particularly in the United States, France, Czechoslovakia, Germany, and Japan. Because of the pollution aspect, governmental agencies are financing much of the work.

The problem of recovery is quite difficult because of the low sulfur oxide concentration (almost all sulfur dioxide) in the gas, usually 0.25 to 0.35%. Because of the tremendous quantities of combustion gas involved—over 100,000 tons per day for a 1,000,000-kilowatt plant—removal equipment must be quite large and expensive. In addition, there are various operational problems that make development of an economical process a major challenge.

The many different process approaches being tested—on a bench scale, in pilot plants, or on a prototype scale (gas-flow equivalent to 10,000–50,000 kW of power pro-

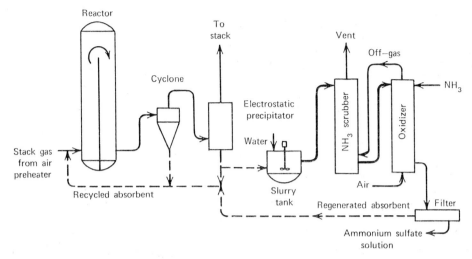

Fig. 14. Mitsubishi manganese dioxide absorbent process.

duction)—can be grouped under four main classifications: (*1*) absorption by metal oxides or salts in a dry absorption system; (*2*) absorption by ammoniacal or metal compounds in a wet system; (*3*) adsorption on activated carbon; and (*4*) catalytic oxidation.

One of the leading processes, developed by Mitsubishi in Japan, is injection of finely divided manganese dioxide into the gas stream at its coolest point (about 300°F), after heat removal for power production has been completed (Fig. 14). Rapid reaction of the metal oxide with sulfur dioxide and oxygen (present in the stack gas) occurs. The product manganese sulfate is recovered in dust-removal equipment and then treated with ammonia solution to give ammonium sulfate solution as the product and to regenerate the manganese dioxide for recycling. The process is being studied in a 55,000-kilowatt prototype test unit in Japan. The main drawback is that the ammonium sulfate produced has a limited market.

Other metal oxide dry systems are being studied on a pilot-plant scale. The *alkalized alumina* method, developed by the U.S. Bureau of Mines, involves use of sodium oxide impregnated in granular alumina as the absorbent. The absorption is carried out at a relatively high temperature (about 600°F) and therefore the recovery unit must be inserted in the power-plant heat-recovery sequence at an intermediate point. The loaded absorbent is reduced in a separate vessel to give sulfur as the product. The developers have encountered a major problem in physical and chemical deterioration of the absorbent after repeated recycling. The Atomics International *molten salt* method operates even farther back in the power plant train, at a temperature of 850°F. The absorbent, a molten mixture of sodium, potassium, and lithium carbonates, is partially converted to the sulfate form and then reduced to sulfur and regenerated carbonates in a separate step.

There are several large prototype test units, either in operation or operated within the past 3 or 4 years, that use solution or slurry scrubbing of gas at the end of the power-plant system. *Ammonia scrubbing* has received particular attention. Kuhlmann and Electricité de France have built a 35,000-kilowatt test facility in France (Fig. 15), in which the gas is scrubbed with a recycled solution of ammonium sulfite and bisulfite

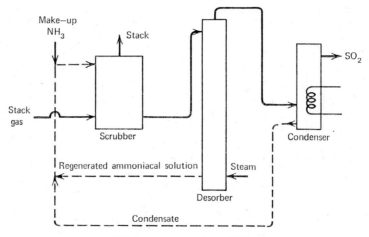

Fig. 15. Kuhlmann ammonia scrubbing process.

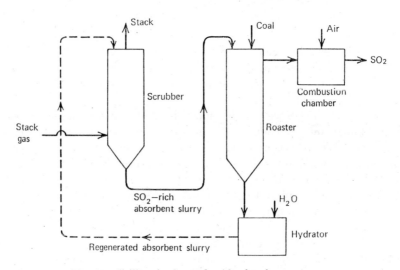

Fig. 16. Grillo mixed-metal oxide absorbent process

(converting sulfite to bisulfite). The scrubber effluent is heated to decompose bisulfite and evolve a rich stream of sulfur dioxide (suitable for conversion either to sulfuric acid or sulfur), and the stripped solution is recycled. The economics depend on the amount of heat required for stripping, which has not yet been reported. Showa Denko has also operated a prototype unit in Japan, with the difference that the sulfite and bisulfite in the scrubber effluent is oxidized with air to ammonium sulfate. A third effort has been in Czechoslovakia, where the process used involves treating the scrubber solution with sulfuric acid to evolve sulfur dioxide and converting the ammonia to ammonium sulfate. The sulfur dioxide is converted to sulfuric acid and part of it is recycled. Finally, TVA is building a pilot plant (supplied with gas from an operating power plant) to resolve some unanswered questions on the scrubbing step.

The production of ammonium sulfate in some of these processes is a drawback because of the limited market for the product; however, this problem can be reduced by recycling the ammonium sulfate in the production of nitric phosphate by the sulfate recycle process described earlier (Fig. 13). This would require building a large fertilizer plant adjacent to the power plant because ammonium sulfate solution cannot be shipped very far economically.

Other alkali-scrubbing solutions have been used also. For example, Wellman-Lord (U.S.) has operated a prototype unit at a Baltimore Electric power plant in which the absorbent is a potassium sulfite–bisulfite solution. The loaded scrubber effluent can be regenerated in much the same way as for an ammoniacal scrubbing solution, giving a rich stream of sulfur dioxide suitable for the production of sulfur or sulfuric acid.

Another approach is to use a *slurry of an insoluble compound* rather than a solids-free solution for scrubbing. A leading example of this is the process under development by Grillo (A.G. fuer Zinkindustrie vorm. Wilhelm Grillo) in Germany, in a prototype unit (Fig. 16). The absorbent is a slurry of manganese and magnesium oxides, hydrated before use. After absorption, the slurry is mixed with fine coal and reduced in a pyrites-type roaster to produce gases which are burned to give a rich stream of sulfur oxide suitable for sulfuric acid production. The regenerated oxides are hydrated and recycled. Chemico (Chemical Construction Corporation) has followed a similar course in the United States, using magnesium oxide as the absorbent. The resulting magnesium sulfite–sulfate is heated in a reducing atmosphere to give a rich stream of sulfur dioxide.

Activated carbon has been the absorbent favored by several companies, including Hitachi, Ltd., in Japan and Reinluft, Inc., Lurgi Gesellschaft für Chemie und Hüttenwesen mbH, and Bergbau-Forschung GmbH in Germany. The Reinluft method, once the leader but now abandoned or delayed, involved regeneration by heating; part of the carbon reacted with the sulfuric acid formed in the carbon pores and reduced it to a concentrated stream of sulfur dioxide. In all the other processes, the acid is removed by water washing with a different washing technique for each method. The main problem is low concentration of the product acid, less than 35%.

The fourth process category is *catalytic oxidation*, in which the entire gas stream is passed through catalyst at elevated temperature to convert sulfur dioxide to sulfur trioxide, much as is done in a standard sulfuric acid plant. The difference is that the sulfur dioxide concentration in stack gas is very low as compared with that in the gas fed to a sulfuric acid converter, thus requiring several times the investment in catalyst. Monsanto Company has treated the process in a 15,000-kilowatt prototype unit; dust is first thoroughly removed, the cleaned gas is then passed through the catalyst, and sulfuric acid (about 80% H_2SO_4) is produced by absorbing the sulfur trioxide in the moisture condensed during normal cooling of the gas. The T.I.T.-Kiyoura process in Japan, tested in a much smaller unit, involves the same first step of catalytic oxidation but ammonia is then introduced to form ammonium sulfate as a finely divided solid carried along in the gas to a solids-collection unit.

None of these processes appear close to commercial use. All are probably workable but a long period of research and development is necessary before such a radically different technology can be incorporated into the industry. One of the major problems is marketing the product; the very large quantities and the poor location, for fertilizers, of many power plants are major adverse factors. In time, however, the public pressure for pollution abatement may bring sulfur oxide recovery into a significant position as a source of sulfur. If this occurs the changed sulfur supply situation will have a major impact on the fertilizer industry.

Ultra-High Analysis Phosphate

Throughout the history of the fertilizer industry there has been a continuing effort to increase nutrient concentration in order to reduce handling and shipping cost. A ton of low-grade fertilizer costs as much to handle and ship as does a highly concentrated one, but less nutrient is delivered to the farmer.

Continuing progress has been made, but the modern combination of urea, ammonium phosphate, and potassium chloride—all high-analysis materials themselves—brings the industry almost to the ultimate that can be attained with the compounds customary in the field. New compounds therefore must be sought. A promising area, perhaps, is the phosphate portion of the fertilizer, because the oxygen in the PO_4^- anion has a major diluting effect.

An intensive research program is being carried out by TVA on this problem, with emphasis on compounds that have a P—N linkage and therefore contain little or no oxygen (16). Several classes of materials have been studied, including metaphosphimic and phosphonitrilic compounds. The metaphosphimic acids, a family of cyclic and linear compounds, are of greatest interest; trimetaphosphimic acid is the first member of the cyclic series (larger rings, such as tetra- and higher, are also known):

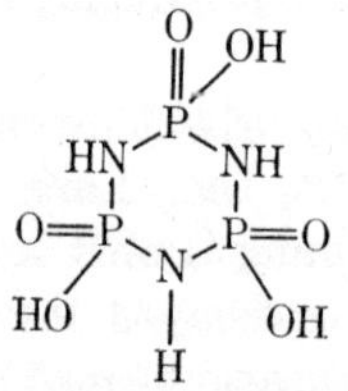

trimetaphosphimic acid

This acid and its derivatives are very concentrated materials. Expressing the phosphorus content in the usual way, as P_2O_5, the following grades are obtained:

Compound	Grade
$H_3(PO_2NH)_3$	18–90–0
$(NH_4)_3(PO_2NH)_3$	29–74–0
$K_3(PO_2NH)_3$	12–61–40

Unfortunately, these very high-analysis materials have been found to be very poor fertilizers. The trimetaphosphimic acid, for example, gave poor crop response even though it is quite soluble in water.

Much better results have been obtained with phosphonitrilic compounds. These are prepared by first treating phosphorus pentachloride with ammonium chloride:

$$n\ PCl_5 + n\ NH_4Cl \rightarrow (NPCl_2)_n + 4n\ HCl$$

Ammoniation then gives the amide:

$$(NPCl_2)_n + 4n\ NH_3 \rightarrow (NP(NH_2)_2)_n + 2n\ NH_4Cl$$

The $(NP(NH_2)_2)_n$ appears mainly as six- and eight-membered rings with some larger rings and some straight-chain material. The six-membered ring, phosphonitrilic hexaamide, has the following structure:

This compound is a remarkable material. It has a grade of 55–92–0, is water soluble, and is a very good fertilizer. Since the hydrogen weighs very little, it is almost all plant nutrient (94.7% N + P). In other words, the absolute ultimate in nutrient content has been closely approached.

The good fertilizer response is somewhat unexpected because it has been fairly well established that plants take up phosphorus mainly as the PO_4^- ion. The good availability is believed to result from rapid hydrolysis of the compound in the soil. The ring structure breaks up readily when exposed to water and forms three moles of phosphoryl triamide.

Then, through successive additions of water, diammonium phosphate [$(NH_4)_2HPO_4$] and free ammonia are finally formed.

In contrast, metaphosphimic acid, although water soluble, does not hydrolyze rapidly enough to form PO_4^- at an adequate rate. The saturated metaphosphimate ring resists breakage by water attack and is quite stable in comparison with the phosphonitrilic ring with its N=P bonds.

The phosphonitrilic hexaamide is almost an ideal fertilizer but unfortunately the known methods for making it are far too expensive. A search for less expensive methods is under way but nothing promising has yet been developed. Direct synthesis from phosphorus and ammonia is unpromising because of the inertness of these two materials to each other. Reaction can be obtained by addition of oxygen to the phosphorus–ammonia mixture, but oxygen then combines and dilutes the products. In further research at TVA, a two-stage reaction (at 1000 and 1400°F, respectively) of ammonia, air, and phosphorus gave typical product grades of 17–78–0 and 18–89–0; water solubilities were 70 and 35%, respectively. The products were mainly amorphous gels with some unidentifiable crystal phases; both P—N and P—N—O linkages appear to be present.

Hence there must be much more progress before a practical process is available for making ultra-high analysis phosphates with good agronomic and physical properties. The goal, however, is a worthy one.

Bibliography

1. A. V. Slack and G. M. Blouin, "Technology and Economics of Complex Fertilizer Production," *"Fertiliser Production and Technology National Seminar, 14th Annual General Meeting of The Fertiliser Association of India, New Delhi, India, Dec. 14–16, 1969.*

2. F. E. Steenwinkel and J. W. Hoogendonk, "The Prilling of Compound Fertilisers," *Meeting of The Fertiliser Society, London, April 24, 1969.*

3. A. V. Slack, *Farm Chem.* **130**(4), 28–30, 32, 34 (1967); *ibid.*, (5), 24, 26, 28–29, 62, 64 (1967); *ibid.*, (7), 30, 32, 40, 42, 44 (1967). A. V. Slack, G. M. Blouin, and O. W. Livingston, *Farm Chem.* **130**(6), 124–126, 128, 130, 132 (1967).

4. "New Developments in Fertilizer Technology," *7th Demonstration Booklet, Spec. Rept. No. 433,* Tennessee Valley Authority, Muscle Shoals, Ala., Oct. 1–2, 1968.

5. A. Arzani, "New Developments in Fluid-Bed Granulation of High-Analysis Fertilizers," *158th National Meeting of the American Chemical Society, New York, Sept. 7–12, 1969.*

6. *Chem. Eng.* **76**(21), 100 (1969).

7. P. H. Nilsen, L. Ylvisaker, and S. G. Terjesen, "Development of a Hot Gas Recycle Urea Process," *158th National Meeting of the American Chemical Society, New York, Sept. 7–12, 1969.*

8. G. Fauser, ed., *Chemical Fertilizers,* Pergamon Press, Inc., New York, 1969, pp. 49–62.

9. *Nitrogen* No. 44, 31–32 (Nov-Dec. 1966).

10. E. Pelitti, R. M. Reed, and G. C. Hildred, "Recent Developments in the Granulation of Nitrogenous Fertilizers," *158th National Meeting of the American Chemical Society, New York, Sept. 7–12, 1969.*

11. Y. Araten, A. Baniel, and R. Blumberg, *Proc. Fertiliser Soc.* (London) **99**, (1967).

12. A. V. Slack, *Fertilizer Developments and Trends 1968,* Noyes Development Corp., Park Ridge, N.J., 1968.

13. *Chem. Week* **101**(13), 84 (1967).

14. *Oil Gas J.* **66**(9), 45–46, 48 (1968).

15. R. S. Meline, H. L. Faucett, C. H. Davis, and A. R. Shirley, Jr., "Pilot-Plant Development of the Sulfate Recycle Nitric Phosphate Process," *158th National Meeting of the American Chemical Society, New York, Sept. 7–12, 1969.*

16. Z. T. Wakefield, S. E. Allen, J. F. McCullough, R. C. Sheridan, and J. J. Kohler, "New Phosphorus Nitrogen Fertilizer Compounds," *158th National Meeting of the American Chemical Society, New York, Sept. 7–12, 1969.*

A. V. Slack
Tennessee Valley Authority

FIRE EXTINGUISHING AGENTS

This article is printed by permission of the National Fire Protection Association which retains the right to reproduce the entire article or any part thereof at any time.

Dry Chemical Agents

Dry chemical agents are solids, such as sodium and potassium bicarbonates, that undergo a chemical reaction in the fire, releasing products that aid in its control. Thus they are contrasted with the dry powder agents, such as powdered graphite and mixtures of sodium chloride and tricalcium phosphate, which are merely inert materials for use on combustible metal fires.

There has been much research into the mechanism whereby dry chemical agents extinguish fire, and the reason why some materials are more effective than others. The following is a plausible explanation. Dry chemicals exert both a physical and chemical flame-killing effect—physical with respect to thermal shielding of the fuel supply, and chemical due to the interruption of the chain-reaction process. Formation of free radicals, particularly the hydroxyl radical, is the key to the existence of fire. Adsorption of the hydroxyl radical on the solid surfaces of the dry chemical particles will extinguish fire.

Sodium Bicarbonate-Base Agents. Sodium bicarbonate, $NaHCO_3$, has long been used as a fire-extinguishing agent. Additives are necessary to make it moisture-repellent, noncaking, and free-flowing. Some of these additives, such as the stearates of calcium, magnesium, and zinc were found to be destructive to protein foam to the point of rendering it completely ineffective. This deficiency has been overcome by treating the sodium bicarbonate mixture with silicone resins. By a reaction combining hydrolysis and oxidation there is formed a polysiloxane coating over all the granules which results in a heat-resistant, inert, noncaking, free-flowing, protein-foam-compatible dry chemical which will retain its purity for an indefinite period while in storage.

A further improvement in sodium bicarbonate dry chemicals was to reduce the particle size. Most agents on the market range in particle size from 10 to 75 μ. Particle size has been shown to have a definite effect on extinguishing efficiency. Therefore careful control is exercised in manufacture to prevent particles from exceeding the upper limit of the optimum performance range. Further dramatization of this phenomenon may be seen when it is realized that a 30-lb dry chemical extinguisher contains chemical particles with a surface area of approximately 45,000 ft^2 or over one acre. These large areas per unit mass exert strong extinguishing measures in the form of a heat barrier to protect the operator of the equipment.

Foam-compatible dry chemical may be procured under Federal Specification MIL-F-19563 (AER); its compatibility with all protein-base foaming agents conforming to Federal Specification O-F-555b has been established. It is listed and rated by Underwriters Laboratories, Inc., and Underwriters Laboratories of Canada.

Potassium Bicarbonate-Base Agents (KHCO$_3$). The basic information applying to sodium bicarbonate-base agents also applies here. Potassium bicarbonate-base agent is the product of long and extensive research, carried out by the United States Naval Research Laboratories, which indicated that the superior effectiveness of potassium-base material over sodium-base material could be as much as fifty percent. Why this is true is the subject of much debate and to date has not been scientifically explained. However, it is empirically accepted as a fact.

The hazard of reflash is ever present in the use of dry chemical extinguishing agents. The reluctance of fire to reflash when extinguished with a potassium bicarbonate-base agent as compared to a sodium bicarbonate-base agent is very pronounced. When evaluated on the basis of quantity required to extinguish a standard flammable-liquid fire, potassium bicarbonate-base dry chemical is the most effective extinguishing agent known at this time. It is being challenged by other agents which will be discussed later. This agent is not considered to be, nor has it been approved, for use by any nationally recognized fire testing laboratory as a foam-compatible agent even when treated with silicone. However, the United States Military Forces do use it as a companion agent with certain compatible protein-base foams. The deleterious effect on the foam is small enough to be considered tolerable even though it does not meet the foam compatibility tests of the laboratories. It may be procured under Military Specification MIL-F-22287A (WEP), "Fire Extinguishing Agent."

Monoammonium Phosphate-Base Agents (NH$_4$H$_2$PO$_4$) (MAP). This agent is the result of work carried on extensively in Germany since the end of World War II. Other dry chemical agents of the alkali type have been proven to be effective against burning flammable-liquid fires but are only temporarily effective in the extinguishment of fires in cellulosic materials. The purpose of this new development was to produce an agent that would be effective on the surface-type fire and not be reduced in effectiveness against the burning flammable-liquid fires, while maintaining its insulating properties against energized electrical equipment.

The monoammonium phosphate-base agent known as "all-purpose" dry chemical has been the result. The primary ingredient of this agent, regardless of the proprietary formulation, is ammonium dihydrogen orthophosphate, $NH_4(H)_2PO_4$. This is an acidic salt as opposed to the alkaline salts previously discussed. It is hygroscopic and must be carefully protected against moisture. It also requires considerably more grinding to obtain the 15–75 micron-size particle that is desired. The siliconizing treatment for moisture-proofing is required to be considerably stronger than for the sodium and potassium bicarbonate-base materials. The fire-extinguishment characteristic is thought to be due to the thermal decomposition of the phosphate into free ammonia and orthophosphoric acid. Through progressive steps these pass through the pyrophosphoric and metaphosphoric, to the ultimate formation of gaseous phosphorus pentoxide through dehydration. The reactions are all endothermic and therefore exert a strong cooling effect on the gas-phase flames. The released ammonia is effective in reducing the hydroxyl ion concentration. The surface burning extinguishing by this agent is due to the formation of crustaceous coating permeated with gaseous ammonia. The coating is flexible while hot but on cooling becomes more brittle. If not disturbed this coating becomes a flame retardant due to the exclusion of air (2). This agent is not compatible with foam and also should not be used in areas that contain delicate electronic equipment or other sensitive hardware subject to damage by the crustaceous coating. Monoammonium phosphate substances should never be mixed even in the smallest quantity with the sodium or potassium bicarbonate substances. They react, releasing gases that may build up dangerous pressures within the container.

Potassium Chloride-Base Agents. This substance is new to the fire-extinguishing agent family and as of 1970 shows great promise but is largely unproven. It is prepared for use in much the same manner as the sodium and potassium bicarbonate-base materials. Its composition resulted largely from research that was directed toward the development of an agent with maximum compatibility with protein-base foam conforming to Federal Specification O-F-555b. It has been tested and listed as foam-compatible by Underwriters Laboratories, Inc. The principal manufacturer of potassium chloride-base agent has made extensive capability comparisons with other dry chemical agents. Based upon its extinguishing capacity, as compared to potassium bicarbonate when used in portable fire extinguishers rated by Underwriters Laboratories, Inc., it appears to possess approximately 25% greater extinguishing capacity on an equal-weight basis. Due to the limited number of fire extinguishers available using potassium chloride-base agent the conclusion based upon these comparative tests may not be entirely reliable.

Other Dry Chemical Agents Under Study. A new dry chemical fire-extinguishing agent made by compounding potassium bicarbonate with urea has recently been introduced to the market. There is wide disagreement between those observers who have conducted comparative laboratory tests. Its producer, the Mond division of Imperial Chemical Industries in Runcorn, Cheshire, England, claim that when used in portable fire extinguishers operated by unskilled and untrained persons in comparison tests with sodium bicarbonate agents it has been proved to be sixteen times more effective. It is also said to be of low toxicity and compatible with protein foam. It functions by a novel mechanism that provides greater particle surface area needed for efficient flame extinction. When a particle of the size ranging from 20 to 75 microns is introduced to the heat of a fire it breaks into hundreds of particles ranging in size from 0.01 micron to 0.1 micron. Thus the important function of flame inhibition is significantly increased. This agent had not been tested and listed for fire-extinguishing capacity or foam compatibility by any of the recognized fire-testing laboratories in the United States, Canada, or Europe, as of 1969. Thus, while this substance offers exciting prospects, it is yet an unknown quantity.

Potassium sulfate-base dry chemicals were developed and are currently used on a limited basis in Europe. The primary goal in using this salt is to obtain compatibility with protein-base foam. It is not manufactured or used in the United States and its value is completely unknown in this country.

Dry Powder Agents

Dry powder agents (not to be confused with dry chemical agents) have been developed for the express purpose of extinguishing fires in combustible metals. A given agent does not necessarily control or extinguish all metal fires, and although some are valuable in working with several metals, others are useful in combatting only one type of metal fire. A limited number of these agents have been tested and listed by Underwriters' Laboratories, Inc., and the Factory Mutual Research Corp., for general use on burning metals. These agents include Met-L-X Powder manufactured by the Ansul Chemical Co., of Marinette, Wis., and "Pyrene" G-1 powder manufactured by Chemical Concentrates of Fort Washington, Pa., and distributed by Norris Industries of Newark, N.J. The formulation of these powders is considered proprietary by the manufacturers and is not available for public information.

Most agents have been developed for limited use on particular metals and have not been tested and listed by any fire-testing laboratory. Detailed discussion of these agents may be found in the Fire Protection Handbook, published by the National Fire Protection Association (1).

Carbon Dioxide

Carbon dioxide has been used for fire extinguishment for many years. It is noncorrosive, nondamaging, and leaves no residue to clean up after a fire. It will sublime at temperatures as low as $-100°F$ ($-73.3°C$) to produce pressures inside a closed container above atmospheric. For this reason, it provides its own pressure for discharge through pipes and nozzles. It is ideal for use in areas of extremely low temperatures. Since it is a gas heavier than air, it will penetrate and spread to all parts of the area it protects. It will not conduct electricity and is effective on both high- and low-voltage electrical installations. When installed as a full flooding system, it is particularly valuable in protecting large-volume cold-storage warehouses.

Carbon dioxide is effective as an extinguishing agent primarily because it reduces the oxygen content of the air to a point where it will no longer support combustion. Thus its smothering effect is paramount while the cooling effect is negligible. Because of the absence of any appreciable cooling, fires that have been extinguished may reignite after the smothering atmosphere has been dissipated if smoldering embers or hot metal surfaces remain. In such cases it may be necessary to reduce the oxygen content to about six percent and maintain this concentration until hot surfaces have cooled and all embers are dead.

Carbon dioxide should not be used to extinguish fires in chemicals containing their own oxygen supply, such as cellulose nitrate; reactive metals that react with carbon dioxide, such as sodium, potassium, magnesium, titanium, and zirconium; or metal hydrides (1).

Foam

Foam (qv) is used to form a fluid blanket floating on the surface of a flammable or combustible liquid to smother the fire by excluding the air and also by stopping further formation and reignition of burnable vapor–air mixtures. Foam contains water dispersed in very thin films which also gives it the property of cooling. Foam is useful as a fire prevention and extinguishing agent in widely varying situations involving flammable materials, as it meets the requirements for a fluid of very low density, high heat-removal capacity, and continuous film coalescense (1).

There are a considerable number of mechanical foam compounds which are based on synthetic surfactants. These include a variety of products which are identified by groups, such as high-expansion foams, wetting-agent foams, fluorinated-surfactant foams, and a unique type bringing together a fluorinated surfactant with a protein hydrolyzate. Among these are a variety of products originating largely from chemical companies who are in the soap or detergent business. Some of these are proving to be useful materials, particularly because they may be used in a wide variety of equipment. Frequently the solution is only 1 or 2% foam concentrate, but may also be applied in solutions up to six percent concentrate. See mechanical foam, p. 369. The technique of their use is generally determined by the expansion required for a given application. For example, the same synthetic surfactant may be used in different types of application hardware with the result that expansions from liquid solution to foam of 10:1, 100:1, 500:1, and even 1000:1 may be achieved. The degree of flooding required will determine the selection of the equipment to provide a given expansion.

Fire-fighting foams may conveniently be divided into five categories: (*1*) Conventional foam; (*2*) high-expansion foam (expansion ratios over 100:1); (*3*) fluorochemical-base foam; (*4*) fluorochemical-surfactant foam; and (*5*) wetting-agent foam. Some of these categories may be further separated by class and type.

Conventional Foam. There are two basic classes of conventional fire-fighting foam in general use, chemical and mechanical.

Chemical foam is formed by the reaction of an alkaline salt solution with an acid salt solution in the presence of a foam-forming agent. Aluminum sulfate ("A" solution) is usually reacted with sodium bicarbonate ("B" solution) which contains a foaming agent and a stabilizer to produce chemical foam. The stabilizer is mixed with the basic ingredients and serves to strengthen bubble walls and produce a tough long-lasting foam blanket.

$$6\ NaHCO_3 + Al_2(SO_4)_3 \rightarrow 2\ Al(OH)_3 + 6\ CO_2 + 3\ Na_2SO_4$$
$$\text{"A"} \qquad \text{"B"}$$

Stabilizers commonly used are derived from lignin, licorice, animal or vegetable proteins, or other chemicals having suitable properties. The carbon dioxide is trapped in the bubbles of the foam, giving it the necessary buoyancy to float on the surface of burning liquids. Chemical foam gains much of its consistency from the hydrated aluminum hydroxide in the reacted foam mass. Because of its high content of solids, the carbon dioxide-filled foam is very resistant to flame and mechanical disruption and has a marked tendency to set up and resist surface flow.

In the generation of chemical foam three varieties of charges may be used. The most common is separate packages of "A" (aluminum sulfate) powder and "B" (sodium bicarbonate) powder dissolved in water and stored in separate containers. The two solutions are brought together and mixed when foam is needed. This is referred to as the batch method. In some instances the mixed powder is stored dry and is mixed with water through hopper injectors at the time of need. This is known as the continuous method. This method is common in large installations. This combination is often called a combination charge or a 2-in-1 charge. It must be kept absolutely dry since any contact with water will immediately generate foam. The third variety is either of the other two, to which special soaps have been added which when diluted with water form a precipitate in the bubble wall, making the foam blanket resistant to breakdown by polar solvents and water-soluble liquids.

New chemical solutions or fresh chemical powders form the best quality of foam when reacted at solution temperatures between 60 and 85°F. Above and below these temperatures the quality of the foam produced deteriorates. Expansion ratios depend upon the volume of water used per unit weight of the powder but generally range between 7:1 and 16:1. Chemically generated foam is not suitable for transport through long pipes or application through nozzles under pressure.

Chemical foam-powder containers must be stored in a dry place and safeguarded against external corrosion of the container. Ambient temperatures should not exceed 100°F. The containers should be inverted, shaken, and restacked at six-month intervals to prevent possible caking. Stored solutions should be maintained between 50 and 100°F in tanks safeguarded against corrosion. Field tests for strength and deterioration should be conducted annually. Chemical foam systems are gradually becoming obsolete (1).

Mechanical (air) foam is formed by physical turbulence which mixes air into a dilute solution of a foam-forming concentrate. Air, mechanically entrained, is the gas phase of the foam bubble. Being completely encased in the bubble it cannot aid combustion. There are a number of liquid foam-forming compounds or surfactants available commercially which may be separated into two general types: natural surfactants such as proteins, and synthetic surfactants (see Surfactants). Both types develop their fire-extinguishing properties when applied on horizontal surfaces through the formation of a vapor-sealing blanket of foam which covers the surface of the fuel and excludes oxygen from the fire environment. Mechanical foam contains a high percentage of water and when applied to a fire the thermal decomposition of the aqueous foam produces an appreciable quantity of steam under certain conditions. This cools the surface of the burning fuel and reduces the available oxygen for combustion, thus aiding in the progressive control of the fire.

Protein-type foam concentrates contain high-molecular-weight hydrolyzates formed by the chemical hydrolysis of proteins of vegetable or animal origin. Ferrous compounds, and sometimes salt of other polyvalent metals, are added to these liquids to give added strength to the foam bubbles, when exposed to heat or severe mechanical action. Foam liquids must be homogeneous and fluid over a wide range of temperatures, must be free of sediment, and compounded under controlled conditions with materials which will ensure a stable liquid with long life. Their utility and stability are dictated by a number of factors. The pH must remain nearly constant to inhibit chemical change. Manufacturers usually compound their liquids with a pH of 7, allowing a fluctuation not greater than 6.5 to 7.5.

Natural or protein foam concentrates used in providing mechanical foam are manufactured in two different strengths: six percent concentrate and three percent concentrate.

Six percent concentrate is a protein-base agent of the low expansion range (expansion ratio 8:1 to 10:1 depending on the hardware used.) It produces a heavy-walled bubble that is extremely resistant to breakdown by heat and holds its water content for long periods of time. Six gallons of this concentrate in solution with ninety-four gallons of water aspirated by air through the required hardware will produce from 800 to 1000 gal of high-efficiency foam. It is used on spill fires and tank fires involving petroleum hydrocarbons.

Mechanical concentrate of six percent strength is also formulated from synthetic-detergent substances which makes more bubbles per gallon and therefore has a higher expansion ratio (expansion ratio 16:1 to 20:1). When expanded to its ultimate, one gallon of solution (0.06 gal of concentrate and 0.94 gal of water) will produce 20 gallons of foam. The amount of water is the same as in the protein-base foam, but the foam lacks the protective action of protein and the bubble wall is much thinner and much less resistant to breakdown by heat. Its use is usually limited to ground-spill fires of flammable liquids because the concentrate is soluble in hydrocarbons, and, since there is less protein, there is greater likelihood of reflash.

The six percent protein-base concentrate for use by the U.S. government is described under Federal Specification, Foam Liquid, Fire Extinguishing, O-F-555c, Jan. 3, 1969, and is the standard military and industrial foam and other formulations are judged by comparison with it.

Three percent concentrate is a protein-base liquid containing organic additives and metallic salts to give it greater foam volume and to increase its resistance to breakdown by fire. It is a different blend of the same substances that make up 6% concentrate, but though it is concentrated, it is not twice as concentrated as the 6% as this would make it a semisolid. Three gallons of this concentrate in solution with 97 gal of water aspirated by air through the required hardware will produce approximately the same quantity of foam as 6 gal of 6% concentrate with 94 gal water, ie, 800–1000 gal.

"Alcohol-resistant" foams are usually formulated for use in 6% or greater concentrations. These special formulations are suitable for use on polar solvents, such as alcohols, ketones, esters, aldehydes, and ethers. They are not effective on deep-layer, low-molecular-weight amines. These foams are made from a protein hydrolyzate containing an organometallic soap and when diluted with water and mixed with air, they form an insoluble chemical barrier between the bubbles of the foam and the surface of the burning liquid. The formation of this barrier is immediate and complete upon mixing of the concentrate with water. Therefore, expansion and application must be within a critical time limit after dilution with water. The maximum transit or premix time is about one minute, depending on the fuel, water temperature, and nature of the concentrate.

Some manufacturers are producing foams that are effective on low-molecular-weight amines and can be used in less gentle application devices. The production of this foam combines four ingredients: foaming concentrate, catalyst, water, and air. The concentrate contains a low-molecular-weight polymer. This concentrate is then injected into the water stream in conjunction with a catalyst. Only 3 or 4% of catalyst is required. In some formulations regular 6% foam concentrate will serve as the catalyst. The catalyst increases the molecular weight of the polymeric material and a semi-gelled solution is formed. This solution is made up of 20% concentrate, 3% catalyst, and 77% water. These percentages may vary slightly according to the particular manufacturer's formulation. The solution is then discharged through standard foam-making hardware which aspirates air into the solution stream and the foam is formed. When the foam comes in contact with a polar solvent, a portion of the water is drawn out of the foam. This results in an even tougher bubble and causes an impervious polymeric foam to blanket the surface of the flammable liquid. It should be remembered that this is not a protein-base material and, whereas the hydrophilic character of polar solvent tends to destroy other types of foams, this same characteristic performs a useful and stabilizing function with polymeric-type foam.

Low-temperature foam concentrate may be of either the hydrolyzed protein base or the synthetic detergent base. To either base concentrate a stabilizing metallic salt compound is added. Other additions which serve to depress the freezing point are introduced in quantities sufficient to lower the freezing point to $-30°C$ ($-22°F$).

Protein-base mechanical foam compounds may promote corrosion in the vapor space of a steel tank. Corrosion does not occur below the liquid level. Detergent-base foams have a wetting and detergent effect and are more corrosive both above and below the liquid level.

High-Expansion Foam. High-expansion foam (expansion ratio 100:1 to 1000:1) is a new agent of the synthetic detergent base which is particularly effective as a flooding agent used in confined spaces. The development of its use for fire-fighting purposes started with the work of the Safety in Mines Research Establishment of Buxton, England, upon the difficult problem of fires in the coal mines of Wales. By expanding an aqueous surfactant solution to a semistable foam of about 1000 times the volume of the original solution, it became possible to force the foam down long corridors, thus producing a vehicle for transporting water to fires in locations that were otherwise inaccessible.

The effectiveness of this ultrahigh expansion-foam extinguishing agent clearly indicated a need for and resulted in the development of specialized generating equipment that is adaptable for use in fighting fires in mines, for municipal and industrial fire-fighting applications, and for protection against other special hazard. High-expansion foam is produced in special generating equipment by a semipressure fan driving a high-volume air stream through a metal or cloth grid which is continually sprayed with an aqueous solution of surface-active agents at a predetermined rate and in dilute concentrations of 1.5–2.0%.

There are three types of prime movers in common use to drive the semipressure fan: the electrically powered unit, the hydraulically powered unit, and the gasoline or diesel engine powered unit. Hydraulic units may be further classified into the reaction-motor type and the turbine-powered type. Both types of hydraulic units are equally efficient and have the advantage over the electrically powered units of the absence of electrical hazards. Gasoline or diesel power is used only on portable high-expansion-foam generators.

While it is possible under proper conditions to generate fire-fighting foams of expansion from 100:1 to 1000:1, large-scale field tests conducted about 1968 have given strong indication that optimum expansion ratios vary from 500:1 to 800:1, depending upon the chemical composition of the synthetic-detergent and foam-concentrate system used in their manufacture. Hand-operated units, having no moving parts, do not normally produce foams with expansion ratios greater than 200:1.

Such foams provide a unique agent for transporting water to inaccessible places, for total flooding of confined spaces, and for volumetric displacement of vapor, heat, and smoke. Tests have shown that under certain circumstances high-expansion foam when used in conjunction with water sprinklers, will provide more positive control and extinguishment than either extinguishing system by itself. High-piled storage of rolled paper stock is an example. Optimum efficiency in any one type of hazard is dependent, to some extent, on the rate of application and also on the foam expansion and stability.

High-expansion foam is particularly suited to fight indoor fires in confined spaces. Its use outdoors is limited because of the effects of weather. High-expansion foam has several effects on fires:

1. When generated in sufficient volume, it can prevent air from reaching the fire.

2. When forced into the heat of a fire, the water in the foam is converted to steam, reducing the oxygen concentration by dilution of the air. For example, the water in a foam having an expansion ratio of 1000:1 can provide enough steam to reduce the oxygen concentration of the resultant air–steam mixture to about 7.5% by volume.

3. The conversion of the water to steam absorbs heat from the burning fuel. Any hot object exposed to the foam will continue the process of breaking the foam, converting the water to steam, and of being cooled.

4. Because of its relatively low surface tension, solution from the foam, which is not converted to steam, will tend to penetrate Class A materials (see Vol. 9, p. 297). However, deep-seated fires may require overhaul (opening up and inspections to establish with certainty that the fire is out).

5. When accumulated in depth, high-expansion foam can provide an insulating barrier for protection of exposed materials or structures not involved in a fire and can thus prevent the spread of the fire.

Current research has shown that using air from inside a building for generating high-expansion foam has an adverse effect on the volume and stability of the foam produced. Combustion and pyrolysis products can reduce the volume of foam produced and increase the drainage rate when they react chemically with the foaming agent. The high temperature of the air in the vicinity of an interior fire also decreases the amount of foam produced, and physical disruption of the foam is probably caused by vapor and solid particles from the combustion process. If foam could be successfully generated from inside air-containing combustion and/or pyrolysis products, the gases trapped in the foam would cause the foam to be toxic (5).

Fluorochemical-Base Foams. These foam concentrates, frequently referred to as *fluorocarbon* or *fluoroprotein* foams, are a class of fire-fighting foams which are produced from mechanical foam liquid concentrates containing fluorinated surface-active agents, polymeric foam stabilizers derived from purified hydrolysis products of proteins, and freezing-point depressants. They have the ability to provide quicker knockdown of many types of fires and are more versatile than conventional foams when used in conjunction with dry chemical extinguishing agents. This foam has good thermal resistance and resists fuel pickup. It sheds hydrocarbons. The most probable structural formula for the fluorochemical molecule employed in these foaming agents can be represented as $X(CF_2)_7CF_3$ where the X grouping is hydrophilic, with limited solubility, while the fluorocarbon moiety $(CF_2)_7CF_3$ is both water and oil shedding with low aqueous solubility (6).

Specifically, fluorochemical-base foams possess three particular advantages: (1) appreciably less breakdown than regular mechanical foams when used in conjunction with dry chemicals, particularly the potassium bicarbonate-base chemicals; (2) capability of forming secure blankets over flammable hydrocarbons for twice the length of time attainable with regular foams; and (3) ability to provide protection against fuel pickup, and also to permit burn-off of petroleum product trapped in the foam without total destruction of the foam itself.

The fluorochemicals protect the protein foam from destruction by dry chemical extinguishing agents by lowering the surface tension of the aqueous phase of the foam and also the fluorocarbon end of the molecule is extended outward and forms an oleophobic barrier at the interface between the foam and a fuel, such as gasoline and other hydrocarbons. This prevents the migration of a monomolecular film of the fuel over the surface of the foam blanket. This fuel film is harmless to the foam, but when in contact with silicone-treated dry chemical, it establishes a foam destructive mechanism. This dynamic system requires an appreciable time to establish the optimum interfacial equilibrium between the foam and the fuel surface.

The oleophobic characteristic also permits the injection of foam below the surface of a burning tank of fuel. This may be done through existing product lines at expansion rates low enough (2:4 expansion ratio) to prevent excessive occlusion of hydrocarbons. Thus the cost of installation of the system is greatly reduced (6).

These foams are available as concentrates for use at 3 or 6% in fresh or seawater.

Fluorochemical Surfactants (aqueous-film-forming foam, AFFF). A fluorinated surfactant has been developed for controlling fires in certain flammable petroleum products. When initially developed, the surfactant was "twinned" with potassium bicarbonate-base dry chemical in specially designed, commercially available equipment. This same surfactant can also be used by itself, in limited application, as an alternative agent to protein mechanical foam. In the original equipment, designed and developed by the U.S. Naval Research Laboratory, dichlorodifluoromethane was used in the system to act as a foaming agent for the surfactant. More recently, the foaming agent was eliminated, the chemical composition of the surfactant slightly changed, and now the material produces an aqueous-film-forming foam when mixed with air either in a foam pump or at an aspirating type nozzle.

"Twinned" equipment discharging fluorinated surfactant and dry chemical is useful in obtaining quick knockdown of flammable liquid fires (achieved principally by the potassium bicarbonate-base agent) and in providing a vapor-sealing effect for reducing subsequent flash-over of fuel vapors exposed to lingering open flames or heated surfaces (achieved principally by the fluorinated surfactant). The surfactant solution drained from the foam floats on the surface of some hydrocarbon fuels, creating a barely visible film that reduces the release of vapors and the subsequent reignition hazard. This type of fire extinguishing agent is sometimes referred to as "Light Water."

Selective discharge of the agents from dual nozzles connected by a bar requires training to obtain optimum use of the combined agents, particularly the sequencing and timing of application of the two media. When used alone, the surfactant is applied and utilized as mechanical foam. The rates of application and techniques employed to gain maximum effectiveness are being extensively researched.

The fluorochemicals used are quaternary ammonium compounds, with a fluoro-carbon radical, C_7H_{15} or C_8H_{17}, and hydrophilic groups. The fire-extinguishing mechanism of this type of agent has been explained in the following manner:

"The aqueous fluorocarbon solution, which drains rapidly from aqueous-film-forming foam, may actually have a surface tension lower than that of the fuel and, therefore, be capable of spontaneous spreading and floating (hence the trade name "Light Water") upon the hydrocarbon fuel surface, thereby suppressing the vaporization of the hydrocarbon below its combustible limit in air.

"According to the theory of Harkins and Langmuir concerning the spontaneous spread of insoluble films on liquids, the following equation prevails:

$$\gamma_o - \gamma_w - \gamma_i = SC$$

where SC is the spreading coefficient (aqueous fluorocarbon solution, ie, "Light Water"), γ_o is the surface tension of the fuel, γ_w is the surface tension of the aqueous fluorocarbon solution, and λ_i is the interfacial tension between fuel and aqueous fluorocarbon solution. (This unfortunately only predicts initial spread as γ_o and γ_w change rapidly.)

"If the spreading coefficient has a value greater than zero (ie, positive), the aqueous phase can spread spontaneously upon the fuel. A coefficient below zero (ie, negative) indicates that it cannot spread. When the spreading coefficient is zero, the liquids are spontaneously miscible.

"The effect of heat on a liquid or solution is to cause a reduction in the surface tension. The rate at which the surface tension is lowered over a given temperature range is a physical function of that particular liquid or solution. Hydrocarbons in general show a more rapid reduction in the surface tension with increasing temperature than do aqueous solutions. This implies that an aqueous film that has a sufficiently low surface tension to float upon a hydrocarbon liquid at one particular temperature, may be completely dissipated as the temperature of the system is raised. This inversion in surface tension values would result in gross lensing of the aqueous phase and subsequent removal from the hydrocarbon surface by gravity.

"The variation of surface tension with temperature is only one of the important parameters that must be considered in conducting a comprehensive fire-fighting performance evaluation of this complex system. Another equally important function to be considered, is the exacting balance that must be maintained at all times between the hydrophilic and oleophobic properties of the fluorocarbon molecule when used with hard water or seawater or when large changes in solution concentration and pH value occur" (6).

Wetting-Agent Foams (1). Foams made from wetting-agent solutions and air are designated wetting-agent foams and usually break down into the original liquid state at temperatures below the normal boiling point of water. In this respect, wetting-agent foams differ from the tough persistent mechanical and chemical foams previously discussed.

Water, for many years, has been accepted as the most practical fire-fighting agent because of its universal availability and its high specific heat. Being naturally a liquid, it can perform its greatest cooling effect by undergoing only one change of state. Both tests and experience have shown that the addition of a proper wetting agent to plain water will increase the efficiency of that water with respect to quantity used and time saved. Certain types of fires, such as those in densely packed cellulosic materials, which do not ordinarily respond to treatment with plain water, may be extinguished when a proper wetting agent is used. This property may be contributed to the lowering of the surface tension of the water which increases its penetrating, spreading, and emulsifying properties. Treated water thus has the ability to penetrate small openings and enter concealed recesses which plain water will flow over by the simple bridging action of the surface film. Such solutions possess not only penetrating and spreading qualities, but also increased speed of absorption and superior ability to adhere to solid surfaces.

Wetting agents with foaming characteristics, when mixed with water and air, produce a foam which retains the wetting and penetrating qualities of the wetting agent, as well as providing an efficient smothering action for fire extinguishment together with a fluid insulation for protection against fire exposure. Foam of this type breaks down at approximately 175°F, returning to its liquid state while retaining its penetrating and wetting qualities.

Air admixed with a wetting-agent solution of the synthetic-detergent type forms an opaque cellular structure that can intercept and reflect radiant heat. The foam acts as an insulation. This insulating property, combined with the heat-absorbing ability of the solution, provides a threefold protection to structures against exposure to fire: (1) heat from the exposure fire is reflected by the white opaque surface of the foam; (2) the flow of heat through the wetting-agent foam is retarded; and (3) heat is absorbed by the foam and is carried away from the structure by the continuous flow of the foam as it breaks down to a liquid. Large-scale fire-exposure tests have demonstrated that wetting-agent foam, expanded at a ratio of 10:1 and delivered at a flow rate one-half that of plain water, afforded protection to an above-ground tank containing flammable liquids.

There are numerous chemicals which fulfill the primary function of a wetting agent, which is to lower the surface tension of plain water. However, most of these substances are not suitable for fire-control work because of toxicity, corrosivity, and unstability. It is therefore extremely important that water-wetting agents do not affect the water adversely, nor render it harmful to personnel, property, or equipment. The most dependable way to ensure that, is to use only those materials that have been tested and accepted by a nationally recognized laboratory specializing in the testing of fire protection equipment and materials.

Halogenated Extinguishing Agents

A halogenated compound is one which contains one or more atoms of an element from the halogen series, fluorine, chlorine, bromine, and iodine. Generally, the presence of fluorine in the compound increases its inertness and stability; the presence of other halogens, particularly bromine, increases the fire extinguishing effectiveness of the compound (4). Only the following five halogenated compounds are used to a significant extent as fire extinguishing agents:

> *Halon 1011*—bromochloromethane, CH_2BrCl
> *Halon 1211*—bromochlorodifluoromethane, $CBrClF_2$
> *Halon 1202*—dibromodifluoromethane, CBr_2F_2
> *Halon 1301*—bromotrifluoromethane, $CBrF_3$
> *Halon 2402*—dibromotetrafluoroethane, $CBrF_2CBrF_2$

See also Vol. 9, p. 739.

The halon system for naming halogenated hydrocarbons was devised by the U.S. Army Corps of Engineers to provide a convenient and quick means of reference to fire extinguishing agents. The first digit in the number represents the number of carbon atoms in the compound molecule; the second digit, the number of fluorine atoms; the third digit, the number of chlorine atoms: the fourth digit, the number of bromine atoms; and the fifth digit, the number of iodine atoms. Terminal zeros are dropped. Valence requirements not accounted for are assumed to be hydrogen atoms (number of hydrogen atoms = 1st digit times 2, plus 2, minus the sum of the remaining digits).

The only agent recognized in the United States thus far is halon 1301. Halon 1211 is widely used in Australia and Europe. Halon 2402 is being developed, refined, and promoted by a large industrial firm in Milan, Italy. Halon 1301, bromotrifluoromethane, is often shortened to "bromotri" or "BT." It is used as a low-temperature refrigerant and as a cryogenic fluid, as well as a fire-extinguishing agent. Under normal conditions, halon 1301 is a colorless, odorless gas with a density approximately five times that of air. It can be liquefied upon compression for convenient shipping and storage. Unlike carbon dioxide, halon 1301 cannot be solidified at temperatures above $-270°F$.

Table 1 lists some of the more important physical properties of halon 1301.

Table 1. Physical Properties of Halon 1301

Property	Value
boiling point at 1 atm.	
°F	−71.95
°C	−57.75
freezing point,	
°F	−270
°C	−168
crit temperature,	
°F	152.6
°C	67.0
crit pressure,	
psia	575
atm	39.1
specific heat	
of liquid[a] at 77°F, Btu/(lb)(°F)	0.208
of vapor at const pressure of 1 atm and at	
77°F, Btu/(lb)(°F)	0.112
heat of vaporization at boiling point, Btu/lb	51.08

[a] Heat capacity.

Halon 1301 is an effective fire extinguishing agent that can be used on many types of fires. It is effective in extinguishing surface fires, such as flammable liquids, and on most solid combustible materials except for a few active metals and metal hydrides, and materials which contain their own oxidizer, such as cellulose nitrate, gunpowder, etc.

The mechanism by which halon 1301 extinguishes fires is not thoroughly known; neither is the combustion process of the fire itself. It appears, however, to be a physiochemical inhibition of the combustion reaction. Halon 1301 has also been referred to as a "chain-breaking" agent, meaning that it acts to break the chain reaction of the combustion process. Halon 1301 dissociates in the flame into two radicals:

$$CBrF_3 \rightarrow CF_3 \cdot + Br \cdot$$

Two inhibiting mechanisms have been proposed, one which is based on a free-radical process, and another based on ionic activation of oxygen during combustion.

The free-radical theory supposes that the bromide radical reacts with the fuel to give hydrogen bromide,

$$R-H + Br\cdot \rightarrow R\cdot + HBr$$

which then reacts with active hydroxyl radicals in the reaction zone:

$$HBr + OH\cdot \rightarrow H_2O + Br\cdot$$

The bromide radical again reacts with more fuel, and so on, with the result that active $H\cdot$, $OH\cdot$, and $O\cdot$ radicals are removed, and less reactive alkyl radicals are produced.

The ionic theory supposes that the uninhibited combustion process includes a step in which O^{2-} ions are formed by the capture of electrons which come from ionization of hydrocarbon molecules. Since bromine atoms have a much higher cross section for the capture of slow electrons than has O_2, the bromine inhibits the reaction by removing the electrons that are needed for the activation of the oxygen.

The discharge of halon 1301 to extinguish a fire may create a hazard to personnel from the halon 1301 itself, or, what is worse, from the products of decomposition that result from exposure of the agent to the fire or other hot surfaces. Unnecessary exposure of personnel to either the agent itself or to the decomposition products should be avoided.

Undecomposed halon 1301 has been determined to be safe to humans in concentrations up to about 10% by volume in air for short exposures. Much greater exposure levels have been found nonlethal to animals, with an approximate lethal concentration (ALC) of 83.2% by volume for a 15-minute exposure. Anesthetic effects have been reported in animals at concentrations above 30%, and a similar effect on humans has been found beginning at about 7½%. Underwriters' Laboratories, Inc., has classified halon 1301 in Group 6, their least toxic classification, which requires that the compound not produce injury to test animals as a result of a 2-hr exposure to a concentration of 20% by volume of the compound.

Halon 1301 is colorless and odorless. Discharge of the agent may create a light mist in the vicinity of the discharge nozzle, resulting from condensation of moisture in the air, but the mist rarely persists after discharge is completed. Thus, little hazard is created from the standpoint of reduced visibility. Once discharged into an enclosure, it is difficult to detect its presence through normal human senses; though in concentrations above 3%, voice characteristics are changed due to the increased density of the agent–air mixture.

Perhaps the greatest hazard to personnel from unchanged halon 1301 is dilution of oxygen. Concentrations about 20% will reduce the oxygen concentration in air below the 16% level necessary to sustain life. The concentrations used for total flooding are usually well below this level. However, the high density of halon 1301 vapor (5 times that of air) requires the use of discharge nozzles that will achieve a well-mixed atmosphere in order to avoid local pockets of higher concentration. It is also possible to develop local pockets of higher concentration in pits or low-lying areas adjacent to local application systems. Once mixed into the air, the agent will not settle out.

Although the vapors of unchanged halon 1301 are low in toxicity, products of decomposition can present a hazard to personnel. At about 900°F, halon 1301 becomes unstable and breaks down in the presence of moisture to give, predominantly, hydrogen fluoride (HF), free bromine (Br$_2$), and carbonyl halides (COF$_2$ and COBr$_2$). These decomposition products have a characteristic sharp, acid odor, even in minute concentrations of only a few parts per million. This characteristic provides a built-in warning system for the agent, but at the same time creates a noxious, irritating atmosphere for those who must enter the hazard following the fire.

The amount of halon 1301 which can be expected to decompose in extinguishing a fire depends to a large extent upon the size of the fire, the size of the enclosure, and the rapidity with which the agent is discharged. For example, extinguishment of a 25-ft^2 heptane fire in a 10,000-ft^3 enclosure within 0.5 seconds produced only 12 ppm HF. A similar test having an extinguishment time of 10 seconds produced an average HF level of 250 ppm over a 9-minute period. Equivalent tests taking up to one minute for extingishment would probably produce an atmosphere which would be quite hazardous to personnel. From this standpoint, it is advantageous to employ the most rapid detection system possible and to discharge the agent in the minimum possible time.

Water and Water Additives

Water is the most commonly used extinguishing agent (1) and has been employed for centuries on the basis of its cooling, smothering, diluting, and emulsifying properties. Its ability to extinguish fire is so well known that it scarcely deserves discussion, but its use with other substances and the various methods of its application through specialized hardware for particular purposes make mandatory its discussion in detail.

The physical properties of water important to the extinguishment of fire are:

1. At ordinary temperatures it is a heavy, stable liquid.

2. Its heat of vaporization is 970.3 Btu/lb.

3. When it changes from the liquid to the vapor state it expands approximately 1700 times by volume. This large volume of steam displaces an equal volume of air, reducing the oxygen content necessary to sustain combustion.

4. It has high specific heat, requiring one Btu of heat to raise the temperature of one pound one degree fahrenheit.

Water is most effective as an extinguishing agent through the medium of cooling which takes full advantage of all of its physical properties. The quantity of water required for extinguishment depends on the amount of heat which must be absorbed. The speed of extinguishment depends on the rate of application in relation to the heat generated, the degree of coverage, and the form in which the water is applied. It is best to apply water to a fire in a form that will permit its change to the vapor state in the shortest period of time. The water can be heated to its boiling point more readily if finely divided, thus exposing more surface area to the heat of the fire.

Water can also be used to extinguish a fire by smothering.

If steam is generated in sufficient amounts (dependent upon the rate of water application, particle size, and the heat of the fire), air can be displaced or excluded. Smothering action is of course aided by confinement of the steam generated in the combustion zone. The process of heat absorption by steam ends when the steam starts to condense, which releases heat from the steam.

When immiscible liquids are agitated together one liquid may be dispersed throughout the other in the form of minute droplets, thus forming an emulsion. When water is applied to certain viscous flammable liquids, extinguishment can be achieved by the emulsification process since the effect is to cool the surface of the liquid below its flash point and thus prevent release of flammable vapors. With some viscous liquids, such as fuel oil, the emulsification appears in the form of a "froth" which retards the release of flammable vapors. Care must be exercised in utilizing this technique as the frothing may be violent and result in the spread of burning liquids over the side of an open tank. A relatively strong, coarse water spray is usually employed to obtain the emulsifying effect.

Fire in flammable materials which are soluble in water may, sometimes, be extinguished by dilution. The percentage of dilution necessary to effect extinguishment varies greatly, and the volume of water and the time necessary for extinguishment will likewise vary. For instance, in a fire involving a spill of ethyl or methyl alcohol this dilution technique can be used successfully where it is possible to get an adequate mixture of the two liquids. In tanks, the addition of water to achieve extinguishment by dilution is not commonly practiced, due to the large amount of water that would be required, the possibility of overflow, and the danger of frothing should the mixture become heated to the boiling point of water.

Water additives are used to depress the freezing point in localities where freezing weather is common. Calcium chloride with a corrosion inhibitor is frequently used. It is manufactured for this use in either flake (77%) or pellet (94%) form. In wet pipe sprinkler systems, chemically pure glycerol, or propylene glycol is used. Precautions must be taken to prevent the solution from entering the public water supply.

The relatively high surface tension of plain water slows its ability to penetrate burning combustibles and to spread throughout any closely packed, baled, or stacked materials. Immersion of burning combustibles in water is rarely practical, and when a fire originates or burrows into a mass of combustibles it is frequently necessary either to dismantle the mass and apply water to the interior portions, or to employ a wetting-agent additive to lower the surface tension of the water and thus facilitate extinguishment.

By decreasing the surface tension of the water, a wetting agent tends to increase the amount of free surface of the water available for absorption of heat while decreasing run-off, thus, in effect, increasing the efficiency of the extinguishing properties of the water by increasing the rate of heat absorption for a given volume. For continuous storage the use of such materials as cast iron, aluminum, zinc, galvanized steel, lead or lead-coated iron, die-cast alloys (such as white metal, zinc, etc), or "air-dried" types of coating (which may include plastics, oil paint, lacquers, or asphalt) should be avoided. The storage and use of wetting-agent solutions should be limited to equipment for which the suitability of the wetting agent has been determined.

The greatest use of "wet water" (formed by the addition of a wetting agent to plain water) is to penetrate porous surfaces and thus allow the solution to reach any hidden areas of burning combustibles, such as may be present in a bale of cotton or in stacked hay, and to penetrate the subsurface of layers of ordinary combustible materials to prevent rekindling. Wet water has some application on outdoor fires (such as grass, brush, or forest fires) but, in the main, these latter types of fires are more properly and easily handled by "thickened" water.

The viscosity of plain water limits its ability to penetrate a burning mass, makes it tend to run off surfaces quickly, and limits the ability of water to blanket a fire by forming a barrier on the surface of combustible materials. Additives to make water more viscous (thickened water) have been developed to make the use of water more efficient on certain types of fires.

Viscous water is water to which one of several viscosity agents has been added. In proper proportions, viscous water seems to have the following advantages over plain water in certain fire-fighting operations:

1. Sticks and clings more readily to the burning fuel.
2. Spreads itself out in a continuous coating over the fuel surface.
3. Develops in a layer several times the thickness of plain water.
4. Absorbs heat proportional to the amount of water present.
5. Projects somewhat further and higher from straight-stream nozzles.
6. Forms a tough, dry film after drying which helps seal the fuel from oxygen.
7. Resists wind drift in some applications (as from aircraft in forest fire fighting).

Disadvantages of viscous water may be:

1. Does not penetrate the fuel as well as plain or wet water.
2. Increases friction loss in hose or pipe.
3. Increases water-droplet size (where fine sprays are needed they cannot be secured as readily).
4. Increases the slipperiness of coated surfaces making it more difficult to walk with safety in areas where it has been applied, and increases handling problems and logistics of fire control operations because of need to handle and mix viscosity agents in water. (Under some conditions, stored solutions can lose viscosity, principally through water temperature changes and possible bacterial or chemical contamination.)

A new agent developed in Germany, referred to as Organ-O-Sil (Degusa Chemical Works, West Germany), consists of a combination of 90% water and a 10% water-absorbing silicone dioxide which produces an unwettable white powder called "dry water." This agent is said to be effective both as a dry chemical agent and a vapor suppressant by floating on the surface of a flammable fuel.

One of the reasons for discussing water as an extinguishing medium under the subject of new extinguishing agents, is not that water offers anything new, but that there are new and startling methods of applying water to a fire. One of the first to be discussed is the high-speed application of water to a burning solid propellant that is liable to detonate.

Recent advances in the technological field, particularly in solid propellants for missiles and rockets, have created a need for fire-protection systems having a capability for extreme speed of operation. Many fires, consuming the rapidly burning materials used in this field, can be controlled or extinguished, if the extinguishing media can reach the seat of the fire soon enough after ignition.

Conventional fire-protection systems have been considered fast acting when measured against the burning characteristics of ordinary combustible materials and have an excellent record for efficiency over many years of extensive use. However, they have proved to be too slow for the special conditions inherent in the burning of the new high-energy fuels.

There are two phases to the problem of speeding up a fire-protection system. The first is speed of detection and the second is getting the extinguishing agent to the burning surface in the least possible time.

Conventional fire-protection systems depend for their operation on the heat, smoke, or products of combustion produced by a fire. These things are, of course, present in every fire. However, the phenomena by which evidence of their presence is transmitted from one point to another, are relatively slow. Another evidence of fire which is not slow and is always present with the fuels being considered here, is light. Therefore, systems of this type are designed to be actuated by photosensitive cells. The principal problem involved with such fire detectors is the fact that light, in its many forms, is universally present, and it is essential to discriminate between light from a fire and light from other sources. This has been done by selecting a solid-state photosensitive cell with a sensitivity limited to the infrared band of the spectrum. This cell is mounted in a housing in such a manner that its field of view is directional, so that it is affected only by light originating from a known area. Discrimination is further improved by using various filters, depending on the light characteristic of the flame to be detected, to further narrow the band of light reaching the detector. Light intensity is another factor taken into consideration. The detection equipment is designed to cause operation only when the cell sees light above a certain intensity, which makes it possible to override ambient light conditions.

The signal from the detectors is carried to a control panel which contains, among other things, a miniaturized amplifier made up from solid-state devices. Since there are no moving parts involved, the current passes through the amplifier with extreme speed.

The second phase of the problem, that of getting the extinguishing agent to the seat of the fire, also required some new equipment. The extinguishing agent used on solid propellants is water, so the first problem is to find a fast-acting water-control valve. The principles of operation of valves used in conventional fire-protection systems do not fit the requirement for extreme speed of operation. Therefore, it was decided to develop a new valve using an explosive force for operation.

The valve body is designed so as to accommodate a piston-type enclosure. This piston is held in the closed position against the water pressure by a latch which rests against the piston stem. An explosive primer is so placed that the end rests against the latch in its closed position. Firing the primer forces the latch off the end of the piston stem, allowing the piston to rise, thus opening the valve. Since the supply water and the priming water fill all cavities of the valve, the first movement of the piston starts the water in motion. The only moving parts are the latch and piston-stem assembly. Travel distances are short and motion is caused by relatively high explosive and hydraulic forces. Therefore, action is almost instantaneous.

Hazards of the type requiring this kind of protection will invariably require high rates of water applications per square foot for control or extinguishment, and the entire area should be flooded at one time. This means that all the nozzles protecting the area must discharge together. In conventional fire-protection systems, this is accomplished by using a deluge system. The nozzles are of the open type; that is, without individual fusible elements. The piping is empty, being open to the atmosphere through the open nozzles. Water flow is controlled by a deluge valve in the main supply. In an ultrahigh-speed system, it is not only desirable, but necessary to preserve the deluge concept. However, the empty pipe cannot be tolerated, since the time required to fill the piping with water would make the system too slow. Fortunately, this problem has previously been solved and spray nozzles are available that are fitted with caps capable of holding priming water under gravity pressure which will blow off when line pressure is released into the system by operation of the valve. Using nozzles of this type, the piping between the nozzles and the valve can be filled with water so that this delay is eliminated.

The components described can be combined into a system which will operate in the millisecond range. The number of milliseconds will vary from installation to installation, depending on such factors as available water pressure, size and configuration of the piping system, etc. The experience gained from the test work during development of the system and from installations already made, make it possible to predict, within reasonable limits, what the operating time for any given installation will be.

Many auxiliary functions can be initiated by the systems, such as stopping a machine or process, fans and conveyors, and sending out alarms, etc. The system can also be integrated with an operation or process to be in or out of service, as required.

The components making up the system are sufficiently flexible so that, with proper job engineering, the varying physical arrangements of different hazards can be successfully dealt with.

This new system gives the fire-protection engineer one more tool to work with in his constant effort to keep abreast of the ever-growing complexity of fire-protection problems in American industry.

Another new system utilizing water as the extinguishing agent is such a departure from all conventional applications that it deserves attention in a discussion of fire-extinguishing agents and equipment. At the heart of this system are a number of rugged, highly sophisticated heat sensors or detectors located strategically throughout the area being served. These detectors are connected in series by means of an electrical cable—consisting of a solid copper wire surrounded by magnesium oxide insulation and enclosed by a specially formulated and fabricated copper sheath—to a relay in an electrical panel. This circuit is energized to 24 V which is sustained by nickel–cadmium batteries in case of interruption of the normal power supply. When ambient temperatures are sufficient to raise the skin temperature of any detector to 140°F, the electrical flow is interrupted, causing the relay to trigger and activate two solenoid pilot valves. The water-supply flow-control valve is a double-chamber arrangement that is held closed by a pressure-differential diaphragm. When activated the solenoid control valves exhaust the water from the top chamber of the flow-control valve which allows water to enter the piping system. While the detectors operate at 140°F, the sprinkler heads are not opened until they reach 165°F. This variance in temperature permits the water to be available at the fire when the sprinkler fuses. In this manner only those sprinklers in the fire area operate. When the detector or detectors that have been exposed to the heat of the fire are cooled to 140°F, the detector circuit closes. This activates a time-delay relay switch that allows the water to flow an additional five minutes, at which point, the dual solenoid valves close and pressure builds up in the upper part of the water-supply flow-control valve, causing it to close. If the fire should rekindle, the detectors will again function at 140°F, causing the entire cycle to repeat itself.

Another highly sophisticated system in which water is the extinguishing agent is a spin-off of the space industry. In the oxygen enriched atmospheres of a hyperbaric chamber fire burns with much greater speed and intensity than it does in normal atmosphere. The fire-extinguishing system developed to meet this need is capable of supersonic speed of detection, activation in milliseconds time, and discharge in deluge quantities.

This is a dual pipe system connected to specially designed and engineered discharge heads. Each discharge head functions as an independent valve. The valve is held closed by a pressure-differential poppet valve, in which the pressure in the pilot line keeps the valve closed. When the system is activated the pilot line is bled to the atmosphere, reducing the pressure on the poppet valve which allows it to open. Water from the main supply line, being at the point of discharge, immediately begins to flow. Detection may be pneumatic (rate of rise), electronic (solenoid), or manual (control valve). When high-speed activation is desired, the electronic detection device is used. The infrared detector sees the fire and activates the system. The pilot valve releases the pressure in the pilot line, and water begins to flow from the heads at a rate of 7 gal/ft^2 floor space/min. The elapsed time from detection to discharge is under 200 milliseconds. All discharge heads on the system discharge simultaneously. The system may be restored for service by repressuring the pilot line, causing the poppet valves in the discharge heads to close. No parts require replacement.

Bibliography

1. *Fire Protection Handbook*, 13th ed., National Fire Protection Association, Boston, 1969.
2. Walter M. Haessler, *The Extinguishment of Fire*, The Fyr-Fyter Company, Dayton, Ohio, 1962.
3. Arthur B. Guise, *The Chemical Aspects of Fire Extinguishment*, The Ansul Company, Marinette, Wisconsin, 1960.
4. *Tentative Standard on Halogenated Fire Extinguishing Agent Systems*, National Fire Protection Association, Boston, May 1968.
5. J. R. Williams, "Effect of Combustion Products on High Expansion Foam," *Fire J.* **62** (6), 32 (1968).
6. George B. Geyer, "Extinguishing Agents for Hydrocarbon Fuel Fires," *Fire Technol.* **5** (2), 151 (1969).

JAMES M. HAMMACK
National Fire Protection Association

FUEL CELLS

The modern history and development of fuel cells can be neatly illustrated by their treatment in this Encyclopedia. Under Cells, electric, in Vol. 3 of the first edition, 1949, there was no mention of fuel cells. But in 1960 the Second Supplement to the first edition had 22 pages on Fuel cells, by Howard L. Recht (1) of Atomics International. In the second edition, Vol. 3, 1964, fuel cells were treated (under Batteries), in 22 pages by Ernest B. Yeager of Western Reserve University (2). This article described the involvement with fuel cells of companies such as General Electric, Union Carbide, Pratt & Whitney, and Allis-Chalmers.

The chemistry of fuel cells was reviewed and the first attempts at constructing serious, but admittedly impractical hardware were described. Since 1964 the use of fuel cells has in fact become a reality (3–11b). The space missions were possible because of the fuel cells on the Gemini and Apollo flights. Many specific fuel-cell applications can now be considered in detail.

Units. In this field, as in many other branches of engineering, there is much confusion between U.S. (and British) engineering units, and the metric system.

There is much use of hybrid expressions such as W/ft^2, lb/kW, Wh/lb. Some conversion factors are given below:

To convert	To	Multiply by
W/ft^2	W/dm^2	0.10764
lb/kW	kg/kW	0.4536
Wh/lb	Wh/kg	2.2046

Fuel Cells for Space Travel

In evaluating the fuel cell as a power source for space flight, the weight of the fuel battery (collection of cells), together with the associated equipment, as well as the tanks of hydrogen and oxygen for the duration of the mission, must be considered. Fuel cells offer the lightest total weight for missions requiring substantial amounts of power over periods ranging from 1–2 days to 1–4 months. The General Electric hydrogen–oxygen solid-polymer electrolyte fuel cells were selected to power the Gemini spacecraft with missions up to 14 days and the Pratt & Whitney Bacon-Chambers type was selected in March 1962 to power the command and service modules of the Apollo lunar missions. To meet the needs of space environment—zero gravity, thermal vacuum (since the cells are mounted in a cylindrical can outside of the space capsule), vibration, acceleration shock, etc—these fuel cells offer:

1. Extreme simplicity—no rotating parts or other complex auxiliary apparatus.
2. Independence from gravity effects.
3. High energy density due to thin-cell construction, with simple, light electrodes.
4. High shock and vibration resistance.
5. Self-regulation—consumes fuel only on load demand.
6. Direct production of water.

Gemini Solid-Polymer Electrolyte Fuel Cell. The fuel cell developed by General Electric is characterized by use of a thin, tough sheet of polymer plastic—an ion-exchange membrane—as the electrolyte. By bonding a simple catalytic electrode structure to each side of this sheet a simple and lightweight fuel cell can be constructed. Because the membrane rejects water above a fixed amount, this by-product of operation can be easily removed by condensing the vapor on cool wicks which carry it off by capillary action.

Individual cells can produce up to about 1 V and are normally operated from 0.8 to 0.9 V, depending on the current density desired.   General Electric spacecraft cells measure approx 13 W each, that is about 7×8 in., and deliver $35 \ W/ft^2$, with peak power capability up to $75 \ W/ft^2$. In the fuel battery for the Gemini spacecraft 32 fuel cells were stacked into a series-connected module.

A 1-kW fuel-cell battery contains 3 modules of 32 fuel cells, pressure regulators and sensors, and a product water separator. Fuel: hydrogen, approx 0.1 lb/kWh (21 psia); oxidant: oxygen, approx 0.8 lb/kWh (22 psia); by-product: Water, approx 1 lb/kWh; weight: 70 lb; size: (of the cylindrical can) 12.5 in. diameter, 25 in. long; efficiency: 50–60%.

Apollo Power Cell. The Pratt & Whitney Aircraft PC3A-2 fuel-cell power plant uses hydrogen and oxygen, and produces potable water as a by-product. It uses "dual-porosity" nickel electrodes (macropores graded to micropores on the reverse side) with a potassium hydroxide electrolyte.

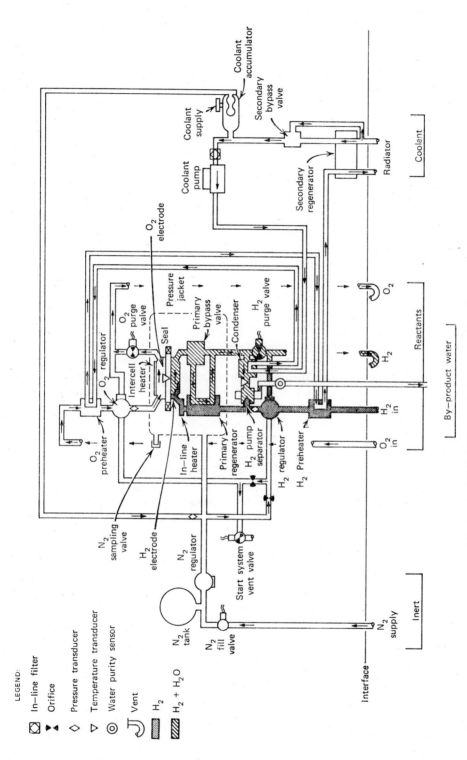

Fig. 1. Apollo fuel-cell power-plant model PC3A2 flow diagram.

The Apollo fuel-cell power plant consists of a power section, a reactant control system, a waste heat and water removal system, and flight instrumentation. A schematic diagram of the power plant (Fig. 1) shows the power section consisting of 31 Bacon-type fuel cells (see Vol. 3, p. 146) having dual-porosity nickel electrodes and using highly concentrated aqueous potassium hydroxide as the electrolyte. The cells operate at temperatures up to 500°F, combining hydrogen and oxygen to produce electrical energy, water, and waste heat. Gaseous hydrogen and oxygen are provided to the power section through reactant regulators which maintain the pressure of the reactants in the fuel cell at desired levels independent of electrical power demand. Preheaters in the reactant supply system utilize a portion of the waste heat to warm the reactants before they enter the pressure regulators.

A flow of hydrogen in excess of the instantaneous demand of the fuel cell is maintained to carry water and waste heat away from the cells. If the cell temperature is too low at a given operating condition, the return flow of hydrogen passes through a regenerator. In this primary regenerator the hydrogen supplied to the cells is heated to maintain the temperature of the cells at the desired level. The proportion of the hydrogen return flow passing through the regenerator is controlled by the primary regenerator bypass valve.

The return flow of hydrogen-bearing water vapor then passes through a condenser where the water vapor is condensed to a liquid. The condenser is cooled by an ethylene glycol–water mixture which is pumped through the spacecraft radiator. A portion of the return flow from the radiator is bypassed to the secondary regenerator to maintain a constant temperature at the condenser. The amount of coolant bypassed to the regenerator is controlled by the secondary regenerator bypass valve.

Hydrogen and water leaving the condenser pass through a centrifugal separator where the water is removed from the cool hydrogen and discharged to the spacecraft water system. A redundant water-discharge-valve diaphragm ensures that no free hydrogen enters the water manifold. The dry hydrogen exiting from the separator is pumped back to the fuel cell through the primary regenerator.

Reactant purge valves are included in the power plant to permit venting of the reactant systems and fuel cells. This is necessary to remove inert constituents of the reactant gases which are concentrated by the removal of hydrogen and oxygen in the fuel cells. Instrumentation is included to permit significant operating variables to be monitored during checkout and operation of the power plant.

Hydrogen–Air Fuel Cells

Although considerable attention has been given to fuel cells utilizing hydrogen as the fuel and oxygen as the oxidant, much less attention has been given to the engineering complexities introduced when ambient air is used as the oxidant. The variable temperature and humidity of the incoming air necessitates a much more extensive consideration of moisture balances. Several attempts have been made to adjust moisture levels and to maintain a uniformity of air flow to allow the use of a matrix-held electrolyte. The present discussion is limited to the state-of-the-art of hydrogen–air fuel-cell hardware of a high energy density. A high degree of compactness is required in fuel-cell power plants which are to be competitive in power density to internal-combustion-driven engine-generators (50–120 lb/kW) and which have the high energy-conversion efficiency (30–60%) which one expects of a fuel-cell system.

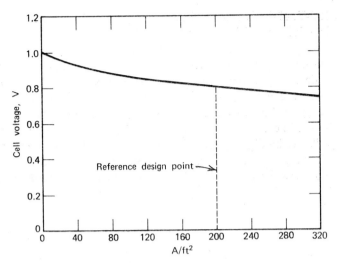

Fig. 2. Hydrogen–air fuel-cell performance.

45-kW Fuel-Cell Power Plant(12) The fuel-cell system for this power plant was selected because of its ability to meet the low specific weight and volume requirements of a vehicle. It consists of a cell stack with thin-screen electrodes and a matrix impregnated with an aqueous solution of potassium hydroxide. Each cell is separated from the next, in an assembly, by a cooling plate. This plate serves the role of current collector and gas housing, as well as providing a passage for circulating a coolant through the cell assembly. Water removal from the cell is accomplished by allowing the fuel-cell product water to evaporate from the electrolyte into the air stream which is supplying oxygen for the cell.

Figure 2 (13) plots the cell voltage against the current obtainable with current hydrogen–air electrodes. Taking 200 A/ft² (160 W/ft²) as the reference design point

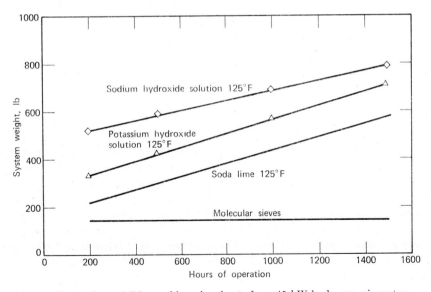

Fig. 3. Comparison of CO_2 scrubber absorbents for a 45 kW hydrogen–air system.

means that a 120-V, 45-kW battery will weigh approximately 450 lb and occupy 6 ft³ if eight identical modules of 0.6 ft² cell size are used.

Carbon Dioxide Scrubber.   One of the difficulties in using the more highly developed alkaline electrolyte hydrogen–air system is the requirement of an air scrubber. When process air contacts the potassium hydroxide electrolyte in the fuel cell, the carbon dioxide in the air reacts with the electrolyte to form potassium carbonate which causes a precipitate to form in the electrolyte and on the fuel-cell electrodes, causing a reduction in cell performance.   To prevent this condition, the CO_2 in the air is removed or "scrubbed" to trace amounts prior to the air entering the fuel cell. The CO_2 scrubber represents an appreciable fraction of the total weight of the power plant.   Figure 3 gives the weight of scrubber systems as a function of operating time.

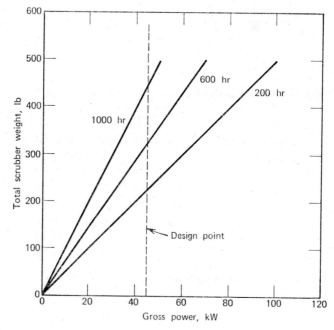

Fig. 4.   Total scrubber weight as a function of gross power and of mission time at maximum load (200 A/ft², 0.8-V cell).

The molecular-sieve-type scrubber absorbs carbon dioxide and is regenerated by heating.   Since the molecular sieve also absorbs water vapor and requires a regeneration temperature of 450°F, large amounts of prime fuel are required to heat the regenerating gas stream.   This method is not feasible because it leads to a substantial drop (15–20%) in overall operating efficiency.   Both potassium and sodium hydroxide solutions lead to large weights due to the large contact volumes required.   Soda lime, a solid granular adsorbent, is easy to handle and is effective in removing the CO_2 from the incoming air to less than 10 ppm.   The scrubber weight is less than for liquid scrubbers.   The soda lime can remove CO_2 from 900–1000 lb of air per hour per pound of soda lime.   Figure 4 shows the total scrubber weight as a function of gross power for a given time duration at a maximum rated power.

Hydrocarbon–Air Fuel Cells

The hydrocarbon mixture obtained commercially from a petroleum refinery is the world's most compact, easily transportable, and yet economical form of energy for most portable power requirements. Chemically speaking, however, ordinary gasoline is a heterogeneous mixture of many hydrocarbon species. The total energy which can be delivered from this valuable fuel form is drastically limited by the heat cycle utilized in today's internal combustion engines. The fuel cell is the hope to provide a doubling of the world's petroleum energy potential because of its twofold increase in conversion efficiency. There are, however, complexities in utilizing petroleum hydrocarbons simply and efficiently to provide electrical power by means of the fuel cell.

CHEMISTRY

The practical use of hydrocarbons as a fuel form for fuel cells involves either the direct utilization of the hydrocarbon fuel by electrochemical oxidation at an anode or the indirect means of preparing more easily oxidizable fuel forms external to the anode compartment. Hydrogen of course is the most easily oxidized and preferred fuel form but is also difficult and expensive to prepare in pure form.

Direct Oxidation. The electrochemical oxidation of hydrocarbon molecules directly at an electrode is possible, using platinum and platinum-alloy catalysts. Much effort was spent to greatly increase reactivity and in fact to utilize gasoline directly for the generation of electrical power. Feasibility has been demonstrated but the current densities were too low and the voltages (efficiency) too low to be of economic interest. At the present rate of about 1 g of catalyst to produce 1 W, 1000 g of platinum (about $4000) would be required per kW of generating capacity. An excellent account of the extensive hydrocarbon fuel-cell research has been recorded by Liebhafsky (3). This author states that "The importance of hydrocarbon fuels is so great that the fuel-cell effort may fall far short of complete success if a fuel battery is not developed in which a hydrocarbon can be introduced directly into the anode chambers." He lists the processes occurring at a hydrocarbon anode as follows: (*1*) adsorption of fuel and of water; (*2*) breaking of C—H and C—C bonds; (*3*) transfer of electrons to external circuit; (*4*) oxygenation of intermediates; and (*5*) removal of products (H^+ and CO_2 in an acid electrolyte).

The complete oxidation of normal alkanes is possible because the intermediate products (all of the species derived in the chain from the first electron transfer to the last electron transfer) are strongly held on the anode while the end products of the reaction, the hydrogen ion and the carbon dioxide, are easily liberated. The hydrogen ion is drawn toward the cathode and the carbon dioxide is readily desorbed in gaseous form. For hydrocarbon molecules containing double bonds or branched chains the situation becomes more complex. Molecules with aromatic rings involve reactions so complex that not even preliminary data are available to try to interpret their oxidation mechanisms. It must be understood that even simply listing the processes given above does not in any way take into account the physical complexity of the hydrocarbon anode. Mass transport, wetting, electrode structure, and the dynamic character of the electrode all play a part. The invention of thin-screen electrodes using polytetrafluoroethylene (PTFE) wet-proofing agents began the start of the investigation of direct oxidation in 1961 and 1962. Since then an enormous amount of effort has been devoted to the solution of the problem of direct hydrocarbon oxidation. Very much work must yet be undertaken. The book by Liebhafsky and Cairns (3) is the best source of information on the status of this endeavor.

Hydrocarbon Reforming Systems. To obtain hydrogen as a fuel from hydrocarbons one has the choice of using *thermal cracking, partial oxidation,* or *steam reforming.* The routes can be presented in a somewhat simplified manner by equations 1–3.

Partial oxidation: $C_nH_{2n} + {}^n/_2 O_2 + n H_2O \rightarrow 2n H_2 + n CO_2$ (1)

Steam reforming: $C_nH_{2n} + 2n H_2O \rightarrow 3n H_2 + n CO_2$ (2)

Thermal cracking: $C_nH_{2n} \rightarrow n C + n H_2$ (3)

The above equations presume that carbon monoxide is reduced to a low level by a shift reaction $CO + H_2O \rightarrow CO_2 + H_2$ following the gasification step.

Two major factors are involved in the selection of a hydrocarbon reforming process. On one hand the efficiency of hydrogen preparation must be very high if the total overall efficiency of the fuel cell utilizing the hydrogen is to remain attractive. On the other hand a reforming process must be used which is highly tolerant to the low level of sulfur impurities generally found in common hydrocarbon fuels. If for instance a very highly purified hydrocarbon fuel must be utilized, much of the advantage of utilizing a hydrocarbon from a refinery is lost.

Thermal Cracking. The extraction of hydrogen from hydrocarbon fuels by thermal cracking results in the lowest efficiency of the three processes because none of the energy value of the carbon is involved in the hydrogen-producing process. Hardware to accomplish this thermal cracking on a small scale is relatively simple but can suffer high heat loss and is dependent on a regenerative process wherein the carbon is burned off the catalyst by air oxidation. Thermal cracking is, however, fairly tolerant to sulfur impurities, the sulfur being retained on the catalyst cracking bed. Principally because of its low efficiency, thermal cracking will be utilized only in cases where extremely lightweight and highly simple fuel cells are required.

Partial Oxidation. Partial oxidation with oxygen is routinely used in refineries for the inexpensive preparation of hydrogen. However, a major disadvantage of the oxidative process is that, since it involves combustion, particles of elemental carbon are produced which are almost impossible to eliminate from the system without extensive treatment. Such particles vary in size from several microns down to a few angstroms in diameter and are extremely difficult to filter from the gas stream. Cyclone processes, though attractive for major installations, are difficult to adapt to small, highly portable fuel-cell systems. In addition, oxygen would be uneconomical to provide in its pure form for use with portable fuel-cell systems. The use of air as a source of oxygen is feasible but introduces large amounts of nitrogen into the process gas stream which greatly reduces the hydrogen partial pressure in the anode chamber. A fuel-cell system based on air partial oxidation has been constructed mainly because of its very high tolerance to sulfur and other impurities in the fuel (Fig. 5). The hydrogen–air cell stack in this case (a molten carbonate electrolyte system) (14) is fed with a 28% by volume hydrogen. The diluents (28% carbon dioxide; 44% nitrogen) are from the air partial oxidation of the hydrocarbon fuel. The main adaptation in this hydrogen–air system is to obtain high current density with the low partial pressure of fuel gas obtainable by air partial oxidation (15).

Steam Reforming. Steam reforming has been the preferred method of preparing pure hydrogen for fuel cells because of its high efficiency. A simple look at the equation above indicates the basis for the higher efficiency. Notice that the hydrogens

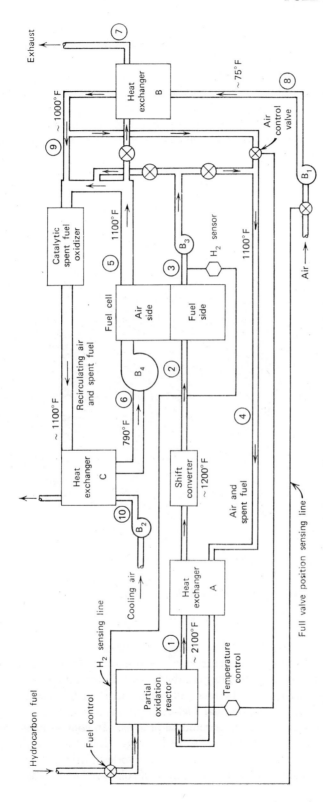

Fig. 5. Hydrogen–air fuel-cell system using air partial oxidation of fuel.

of the water (steam) which are introduced into the reaction end up as product hydrogen. Conventionally, the reforming process is carried out at higher pressures (140 psi) and uses a silver–palladium diffuser to obtain pure hydrogen. The silver-stabilized palladium foil is selective to the diffusion of the hydrogen product and retains the excess water and the product carbon dioxide within the reactor chamber. This steam reforming is normally done at temperatures of approximately 1500°F, the reactor being heated by burning the bleed-off excess hydrogen in the impure effluent stream. The selection of the exact temperature depends on the space velocities desired and the equilibria involved.

The steam-reforming reaction can be written:

$$C_nH_{2n} + n\ H_2O \rightarrow 2n\ H_2 + n\ CO \tag{4}$$

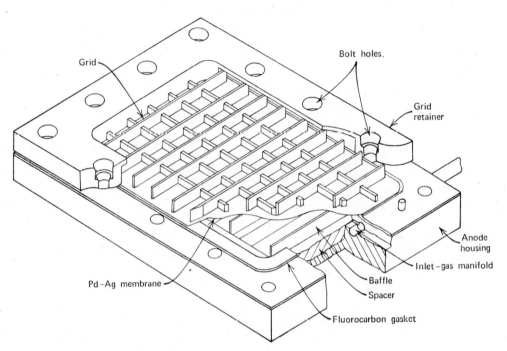

Fig. 6. Cutaway view of internal reforming anode assembly.

This can be followed by the water gas shift reaction,

$$H_2O + CO \rightleftharpoons CO_2 + H_2 \tag{5}$$

when excess water is present. When a diverse mixture of hydrocarbons is utilized care must be taken to provide the correct water-to-hydrocarbon ratio to prevent carbon deposition on the steam-reforming catalyst. One disadvantage is that these highly reactive, largely nickel-based catalysts will react with and be deactivated by sulfur impurities in the fuel. In a practical fuel-cell system it is necessary to precede the steam-reforming reaction by a sulfur removal process. In conventional steam-reforming operations this is done by feeding some hydrogen into the incoming fuel stream and converting the sulfur to hydrogen sulfide by hydrodesulfurization procedures. The hydrogen sulfide is easily removed on a variety of solids-removal beds.

·The utilization of steam reforming in fuel cells has followed three distinct paths:

1. A high-pressure, silver–palladium diffuser reformer is used for the production of pure hydrogen. This type of reformer has been shown to be approxi 65–66% efficient in converting the heating value of input fuels (kerosene) to the heating value of hydrogen supplied to the fuel cell. Because of the purity of the hydrogen, alkaline electrolyte fuel cells have been utilized in this configuration.

2. A low-pressure (5 psi over ambient) reformer can be coupled directly with the fuel cell, eliminating the costly silver–palladium diffuser. In this case the total effluent, including carbon dioxide, the excess water, and minor amounts of carbon monoxide are allowed to flow directly to the anode of the fuel cell. This has the advantage of simplicity but requires the use of a carbon dioxide-rejecting fuel-cell electrolyte. Phosphoric acid electrolytes have generally been chosen for this type of fuel-cell system.

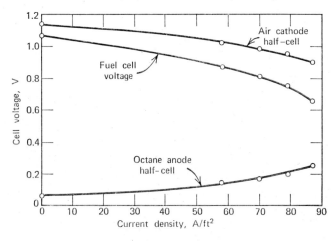

Fig. 7. Experimental performance of air–octane fuel cell. Space velocity $\sim$ 200 per hr; temperature $\sim$500°F.; electrolyte $\sim$ nominal 80% KOH; electrode spacing $\sim$0.59 in.; losses included.

3. Steam reforming must be carried out at about 1500°F to produce a high equilibrium partial pressure of hydrogen in the product stream. One method for operating at a lower temperature is an internal reforming cell where the steam reaction occurs in a catalyst bed which is in direct contact with the fuel-cell anode. A cell with potassium hydroxide electrolyte can be operated at 500°F, and at this temperature the equilibrium for hydrocarbon–steam reactions is such that only a small percentage of hydrogen is produced. However, as the fuel-cell anode consumes the hydrogen the equilibrium is shifted so that it is possible to convert a high proportion of the fuel to hydrogen and to utilize this hydrogen in the anode reaction. The reform reaction, being endothermic, can take heat directly from the waste heat of the cell. The details of the experimental anode assembly are shown in Figure 6. A performance curve for octane is shown in Figure 7 (16). In general, the greater the catalyst-bed depth, the higher the maximum current density and the lower the fuel utilization. For a bed depth of 0.6 in., current density is 180 A/ft² at 20% fuel utilization. For a bed depth 0.15 in., 65 A/ft² are obtained at 67% fuel utilization. The main adaptation in this case to a 500°F (Bacon-type) hydrogen–air system is to use an activated silver–palladium membrane anode.

HARDWARE

The ability to construct and operate a hydrocarbon–air fuel cell which can convert 30–40% of the energy content of a hydrocarbon fuel to electrical power has been demonstrated. Two systems, the first a 500-W power unit and the second of 4-kW electrical output, have been constructed by the Pratt & Whitney fuel-cell group. Both of these power plants use an alkaline electrolyte cell stack with a high-pressure reformer and silver–palladium diffuser for providing the pure hydrogen. The flow diagram of the hydrogen generator for the 500-W power source is shown in Figure 8 (17). The fuel and water are fed in a premixed ratio and pressurized by the feed pump. The feed mixture is preheated and fed into a reactor chamber. A pressure of approximately 240 psia is required to drive the palladium–silver tube purifier. The purifier assembly is composed of two concentric rings. The inner ring contains a standard Milton-Roy Model C-50D tube bundle with the annulus between the inner and outer ring containing a shift catalyst. The principal feature of this type of hydrogen generator, operating at the high pressure required as the driving force for the hydrogen purification process, is the dual temperature reactor (reforming with shift at 1400°F and hydrogen purification at 700°F). A sketch of the assembly is shown in Figure 9. The thermal efficiency of the hydrogen generator is 63%. The purified hydrogen is fed from the reformer to the anode. The flow scheme of the fuel-cell assembly of the 500-W system is shown in Figure 10. The reactant air is first scrubbed to remove carbon dioxide which could form harmful carbonate deposits in the cell stack. Figure 11 is a photograph of the 36 cells in the stack for the 500-W unit, showing the external air manifold for cooling of the cells. Heat is conducted through the cell fixture, from the reaction zone to the external configuration where cooling air is blown across the fin structure. This system is characterized by (1) a requirement for an air scrubber be-

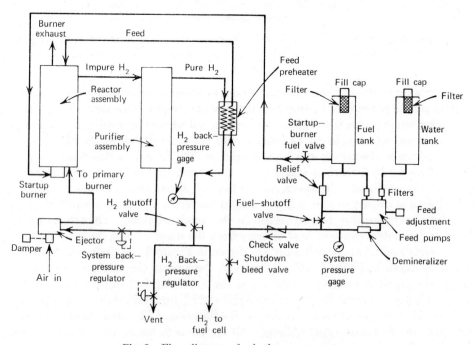

Fig. 8. Flow diagram of a hydrogen generator.

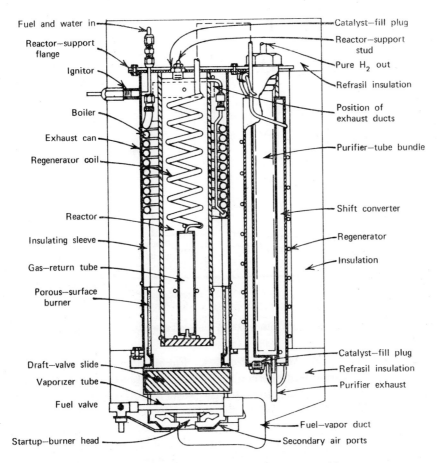

Fuel and water in — Catalyst—fill plug

Reactor—support flange — Reactor—support stud

Ignitor — Pure H₂ out

— Refrasil insulation

Boiler — Position of exhaust ducts

Exhaust can —

Regenerator coil — — Purifier—tube bundle

Reactor — — Shift converter

Insulating sleeve — — Regenerator

Gas—return tube — — Insulation

Porous—surface burner —

Draft—valve slide — — Catalyst—fill plug

Vaporizer tube — — Refrasil insulation

Fuel valve — Purifier exhaust

— Fuel—vapor duct

Startup—burner head — Secondary air ports

Fig. 9. Prototype of a hydrogen generator assembly.

cause of the alkaline electrolyte; (*2*) the use of air convective cooling; and (*3*) no recovery of product water in the exit process air stream.

The system design of the hydrogen generator for the 4-kW liquid hydrocarbon–air fuel cell which has been built by Pratt & Whitney is somewhat different. The principal difference is to modulate the fuel- and water-feed rate to provide varying hydrogen-generation rates, depending upon the electrical load on the fuel cell. A feed control pump is used to vary the rate of fuel and water flow.

The 500-W and 4-kW Pratt & Whitney units described above are the only hydrocarbon–air fuel-cell systems capable of exceeding 30% efficiency over appreciable portions of their operating range. Two additional hydrocarbon–air fuel-cell systems which are being developed or planned have limitations, allowing approximately 20% overall efficiency. The 1.5-kW system developed by the General Electric Company is limited in overall efficiency because of the high internal resistance of the dual ion-exchange-membrane electrode system which lowers the single-cell voltage at maximum power operation. The 15-kW system based on a molten carbonate fuel-cell stack being developed by Texas Instruments is limited in efficiency principally because of the partial oxidation process used to gasify the hydrocarbon fuel and the low voltage per single cell at the system's design point.

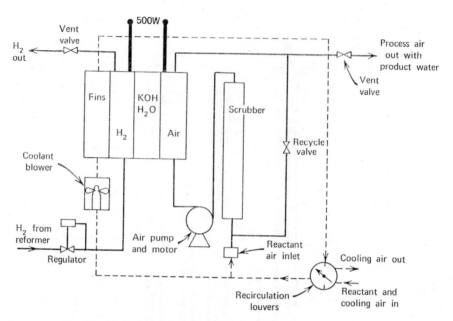

Fig. 10. Pratt & Whitney 500-W fuel-cell assembly flow diagram.

Cells with Phosphoric Acid Electrolytes. For military applications the weight (power density) of a total hydrocarbon fueled electrical power source is, of course, of extreme importance. The goal is to match the power densities of conventional internal-combustion-engine generators, and at the same time provide higher operating efficiency and also silence. The best way to approach the first major reduction in weight (increase in power density) is by simplifying and redesigning the system to eliminate excess components. For this reason a new fuel-cell concept which utilizes a phosphoric acid electrolyte offers a highly compact fuel-cell stack assembly in a very highly simplified system. A simple atmospheric pressure prereactor of the conventional

Fig. 11. Pratt & Whitney 500-W fuel-cell stack assembly with external air manifold.

hydrocarbon–steam-reformer type, using more active reformer catalysts, can be operated at 500°C. At this temperature the shift conversion can occur in the primary reactor bed, thus eliminating the need for a separate shift converter which would operate at a lower temperature from the main reactor. The hydrogen from this single-bed reformer, including some carbon monoxide, carbon dioxide, methane, and excess water, is fed directly into the anode of a phosphoric acid electrolyte fuel cell. The acid electrolyte also allows the direct use of ambient air in the cell stack (18). Only a simple dust filter need be provided on the inlet stream. Operating the cell at 150°C allows the reformed water and part of the fuel to be vaporized by the heat created in the cell stack, therefore increasing efficiency. The use of a phosphoric acid electrolyte at this operating temperature permits a higher single-cell operating voltage on direct reformer effluent (2–4% CO) than would be possible with systems using sulfuric acid. The principal advantage of this advanced hydrocarbon–air fuel-cell system using a phosphoric

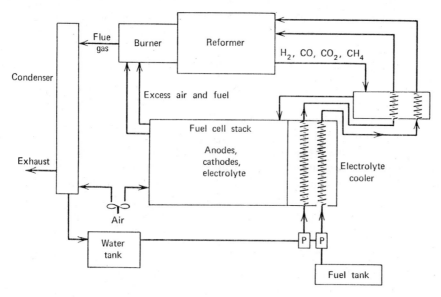

Fig. 12. Phosphoric acid electrolyte hydrocarbon–air fuel-cell system.

acid electrolyte at 150°C is the extreme simplicity of the system. Many of the complexities of an alkaline electrolyte matrix fuel-cell system are eliminated; for example:

1. The bulky air scrubbers required in alkaline systems to reduce the carbon dioxide content of the incoming process air are not required. The acid electrolyte allows the direct use of ambient air.

2. In the larger alkaline systems the cell-stack temperature control and cooling is accomplished by a coolant circulating through the cell stack and into a heat-rejection radiator. By using a cell stack which operates above the normal boiling point of water, the principal amount of heat which must be rejected by the cell electrolyte can be used to vaporize the reformer water. The fuel-feed stream to the reformer (as shown in the system diagram in Fig. 12) can be directly passed through the cell stack with the net effect of converting the product heat to latent heat of evaporation for the fuel and water, thus conserving heat in the system and reducing the cooling required for the cell stack. The additional cooling required, if any, could be accomplished either

through finned extensions on the cell stack with an external air coolant flow or by evaporative cooling of the product water from the electrodes in the fuel-cell stack.

3. The reformer product gas is directly utilized in the cell stack, thus eliminating the need for the bulky and costly hydrogen diffusion purifiers required in the alkaline electrolyte systems. The alkaline systems demand ultra-pure hydrogen and thus require silver–palladium membrane purifiers. This results in a very high-cost component in the fuel-cell system and also the necessity of operating the reformer at an elevated pressure. The use of the lower temperature and lower pressure reformer allows a lower weight and better transient response for the reformer section.

4. Because the excess water from the reformer and the fuel-cell product water is contained in the air and fuel exhaust, it is directly fed to the burner of the reformer. A single condenser on the burner flue gas is all that is required to recondense the water required for the reformer process, eliminating the multiple condensers often required in alkaline systems.

This simplified hydrocarbon system is the closest approach to a lightweight, highly efficient, and silent converter of gasoline or similar fuel to electrical power.

Zinc–Air Hybrid Fuel Cell

A fuel cell is understood to be one in which the electrodes are supplied with a continuous feed of fuel; such a cell can theoretically deliver power indefinitely as long as the fuel supply holds out. This is in contrast to a conventional cell, in which the electrodes are supplied with limited amounts of active material and can deliver power only until these supplies are used up. The zinc–air system has a combination of these properties in that it contains a cathode which can consume oxygen from the air on a continuous basis when coupled in a potassium hydroxide solution with a zinc anode which has a limited life but is renewable. This cell is therefore, strictly speaking, a hybrid, rather than a fuel cell, but nevertheless may be usefully discussed here.

The overall cell reaction is generally regarded as follows:

$$Zn + \tfrac{1}{2} O_2 + 2 KOH \rightarrow K_2ZnO_2 + H_2O$$

The cell has an open-circuit voltage over 1.4 V and generally operates at approximately 1.25 V. A typical voltage vs current curve is shown in Figure 13. As can be

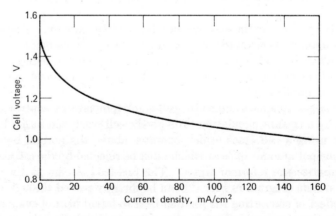

Fig. 13. Current–voltage characteristics of zinc–air cells (electrolyte concentration, 30%; ambient temperature, 70°F).

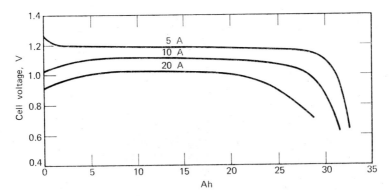

Fig. 14. Capacity vs rate of discharge in zinc–air cells (ambient temperature, 70°F; active surface area, 200 cm²).

seen there is a considerable activation polarization but a fairly level plateau voltage is found from 10 to 150 mA/cm².

Based on zinc alone, the theoretical energy density is about 464 Wh/lb. However, extraneous hardware, electrolyte, case, terminals, etc, reduce this figure. In hardware where ruggedization is an important factor, energy densities of 50 to 100 Wh/lb can be achieved, depending upon battery size and the particular application. Where weight is the all-important factor and more fragile structures can be tolerated, 200 Wh/lb appears to be a practical limitation.

The mechanically rechargeable communications-type battery (19) consists of 22 series-connected cells resulting in a nominal voltage of 24 V. Capacity of this battery is rated at 25 Ah. This service is obtained at a discharge rate of 10 A. Since considerably more active anode material (zinc) is actually put into the cells (enough for 37–39 Ah), service can be extended beyond the rated capacity at lighter loads. Cell discharge curves in voltage vs ampere hours are shown in Figure 14. Each cell consists of two cathodes connected in parallel and supported by a plastic frame; a porous zinc anode enclosed in a separator inserted between the cathodes; and electrolyte, a potassium hydroxide solution which is mainly absorbed into the porous anode and absorbent separators. Any excess of electrolyte is contained within the framed cathodes which also serve as the outer cell walls. Figure 15 is a sketch of one of the

Table 1. Battery Characteristics of Radio 1 and Radio 2 Batteries of Zinc–Air Cells

Characteristic	Radio 1	Radio 2
voltage, nominal	24	24
capacity, rated, Ah	25	25
no. cells	22	22
discharge rate (receive-transmit), A	2–3	0.6–12
duty cycle, min	9.1	9.1
weight, lb	10.75	12.4
volume, in.³	351	454
Wh/lb	60	53
Wh/in.³	1.9	1.4
rechargeability	mechanical	mechanical
recharge weight (22 anodes), lb	4.30	4.30

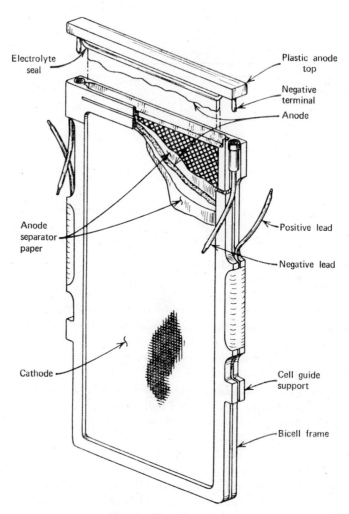

Electrolyte seal

Plastic anode top

Negative terminal

Anode

Anode separator paper

Positive lead

Negative lead

Cathode

Cell guide support

Bicell frame

Fig. 15. Zinc–air unit cell.

22 cells used in this battery. Intercell structures of expanded nickel screen separate the cells from one another, allowing air flow between each cell.

The communications battery has two interchangeable covers. One cover incorporates a centrifugal fan and a voltage regulator. The blower is automatically activated on transmit to provide the air flow needed for high power requirements. Peak power of 340 W has been obtained in this fashion. The voltage regulator is used to keep the battery in close control because some radio sets have a voltage limitation of 22–28 V.

Table 1 shows some of the battery characteristics when used with two different radio sets (20).

Recharging of the battery is accomplished by mechanical replacement of the anodes. The charge consists of 22 porous zinc anodes which have been impregnated with a quantity of solid potassium hydroxide to constitute the 31% liquid electrolyte. The recharge kit weighs 4.30 lb. Mechanical recharging is effected by removing the discharged zinc anodes, adding water to each cell, inserting fresh anodes into the cell,

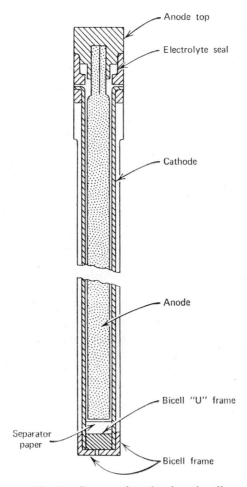

Fig. 16. Cross section of a zinc–air cell.

and reclamping. The battery is designed to operate from −40 to +125°F. However, at the lower temperatures some short amount of start-up time is required to stabilize air flow and internal cell-heat balance.

After successful demonstration of these two batteries the zinc–air battery system was selected for full development because of its very attractive energy density (over 100 Wh/lb), good power density (30 W/lb), long shelf-life when unactivated, and an acceptable method for mechanically recharging, ie, the replacement of the zinc anode.

The new standard battery was designed as a nominal 24-V unit, with 20 cells at 1.2 V per cell. (Advanced designs gave the slightly higher voltage per cell, allowing reduction in the number of cells to 20 for a 24-V dc unit.) Using the 12.2-in. length of the battery box, and allowing sufficient space at one end for the connector, a thickness of 0.508 in. is available for each cell, including the air space. Figure 16 shows the cross section of the zinc–air cell, and the location and size of each of the major component parts.

In the design of this cell, specific consideration was given to several critical points. It was desired to make the zinc anode comparatively thick, 0.200 in., in order to contain a large amount of active material. This should give the highest possible battery energy output, provided that the optimum thickness had not been exceeded, excessively increasing the anode resistance and decreasing anode efficiency.

The air spacing is another critical factor and represents a compromise between the need to provide sufficient air to handle heavy loads, yet to minimize air flow to prevent drying out—or partial drying out—when running for long periods of time at light loads. The use of blowers could simplify this design, but this approach is not advantageous because of the undesirability of using rotating devices in an otherwise silent battery. The spacing of 0.230 in. that was available for air with the cell design selected was found to be adequate to handle a load as high as 10-A or 240-W on a continuous or intermittent basis.

At light loads, 1 A or lower, the cell was able to operate for over 48 hr, without drying out. In the cell design, anode porosity, separator absorption characteristics, and the size of the cell cavities will be selected to assure the availability of sufficient water to maintain operation over the required period.

Another design consideration was the total capacity of the battery, which is directly related to the battery size (or height with a fixed cross section) and battery weight. Based on a study of typical communications applications for portable power, batteries of three sizes, approximately 150 Ah, 48 Ah, and 20 Ah in capacity, were selected in the standard formula to fill most of the major requirements for portable applications where the use of these mechanically rechargeable batteries is appropriate. The design details of these three batteries are given in Table 2. The actual batteries are currently under development.

Table 2. Comparison of Three Batteries

Characteristic	Battery 1	Battery 2	Battery 3
capacity (rated), Ah	150	48	20
voltage (nominal)	24	24	24
no. cells	20	20	20
discharge rate, A max	25	10	4
weight without cover, lb	35	13.3	7.0
size, in.	$12.3 \times 6.7 \times 10.0$	$12.2 \times 4 \times 9$	$12.2 \times 4 \times 4.5$
volume, in.^{3}	831	440	220
W/hlb	100	87	69
Wh/in.^{3}	4.3	2.8	2.2
recharge	mechanical	mechanical	mechanical

The expected performance characteristics of the batteries are shown in the discharge curves in Figure 17. The curves are applicable for several battery designs and illustrate their flat discharge curve and their capabilities over a wide range of discharge load. The voltage level is maintained within $\pm 10\%$ of the nominal voltage from the 4–100 hr discharge rate. Even higher currents can be drawn for pulse-power application, and for special uses, the performance can be improved if air movement is accelerated by a blower. (See Table 3.)

The curves illustrate the batteries' performance when air stabilization and operating temperature of cells have been attained immediately at temperatures of 70°F and above. At the higher loads, or at low temperature the battery will not respond immediately, but will require a finite time to "bootstrap" itself to operating temperature

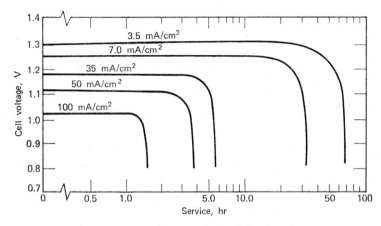

Fig. 17. Performance characteristics of the zinc–air system.

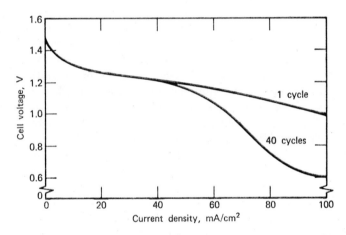

Fig. 18. Effect of cycling in zinc–air batteries (electrolyte concentration, 30%; ambient temperature, 70°F).

and performance.   Pulse-discharge curves were taken at 70°F and show the effect of using a blower for special applications.

The air electrodes and the complete battery, except for the anode-electrolyte replacement, will have a service life in excess of 1000 hr in normal use, or about forty 24-hr cycles.   Figure 18 illustrates the voltage current curve of a fresh battery and

Table 3. Zinc–Air System

Current density, mA/cm²	Total Current		
	20-Ah cell	48-Ah cell	150-Ah cell
3.5	0.3	0.7	1.8
7.0	0.6	1.4	3.5
35.0	3.0	7.0	17.5
50.0	4.3	10.0	25.0
100.0	8.3	20.0	50.0

one that has been through forty such cycles. The figure shows that performance degradation occurs at the heavier discharge loads.

Fuel Cells for Lightweight Portable Power

Fuel cells, for the first time, are becoming sufficiently simple, reliable, and low cost for consideration in a wide variety of practical applications. To determine where it is economically feasible to employ fuel cells to add to the capabilities of and extend the range of usefulness of existing power sources, takes very serious consideration. Both the initial cost of the fuel-cell power source and its use cost per kWh must be taken into consideration. The cost of a power source must be considered in relation to the cost of equipment which it is powering and the specific job that it is doing. To match the cost of central-station power for general-purpose uses or even of Diesel auxiliary power would be a very difficult challenge. There are, however, many applications where a high price per kWh is now paid for usable electrical power. Power for lightweight portable equipment is purchased at a premium price. The conventional Leclanché cell is an example of fairly expensive electrical power. It costs about \$30.00/kWh in the packages of carbon–zinc cells commonly used to power radios, hand lanterns, and other lightweight portable equipment. The power sources used to power the high-intensity lights used for color television coverage of the national political conventions form an example of a requirement for high portability in mobile manpack type of operation. The remote relay station or weather-telemetry station is another example where direct energy-conversion devices look most attractive.

For most commercial uses, secondary batteries, such as the vented or sealed nickel–cadmium alkaline types (see Vol. 3, p. 172), are highly convenient and desirable if economical recharging procedures and power are available to renew their energy at the end of a full discharge. Because of our existing use patterns for highly mobile and portable electric power, one of the first applications of the economical fuel cell will be as a battery charger either to replenish discharge cells or to be used with conventional secondary batteries in hybrid applications. This is the most attractive way to provide electrical power in those locations where power is not normally available. Energy can be distributed in easily packaged and transportable fuels for fuel cells. Since the total amount of fuel involved is actually very small, in fact a reduction in both volume and weight over the equivalent amount of zinc–carbon primary batteries, any fuel can be used which can be successfully packaged for safe storage, safe handling, and safe transfer to the fuel cell in the field. Any fuel-cell fuel is economical if it is less expensive than the equivalent form of electrical power which would be utilized.

Fuel Cells as Battery Chargers. The fuel cell is becoming sufficiently simple and reliable to be used as a portable power source for communications and surveillance equipment. It is interesting to note that those lightweight fuel cells now being developed are not replacing batteries, but are assisting conventional secondary batteries by providing extended life in special fuel-cell–battery hybrid configurations. A favorable combination of virtues stems from the fact that the secondary battery has a satisfactory power density (W/lb) and can instantly provide power for the equipment while the fuel-cell portion effectively converts a primary fuel to electrical power at a steady continuous rate to provide a high energy density after its initial warm-up. The attractiveness of this combination of power sources is seen when one analyzes the traditional batteries used in lightweight communications equipment, their limitations, and the effect that microminiaturization of lightweight man-portable equipment has on the selection of a power source.

The bulk of the electrical power consumed in communications and surveillance equipment comes from the discharge of primary zinc–carbon batteries. At drain rates of approximately 10 W or less, these batteries give very trouble-free service for service periods of the order of 10–20 hr. At the end of a battery's discharge it is discarded and a new supply of chemical energy in the form of these zinc–carbon cells is inserted in the equipment to power it for an additional service period. The present conversion from the zinc–carbon cell to the magnesium–carbon Leclanché cell promises to give an increase in energy density and improved high-temperature storage capability (20a, b,c). This is possible because of the higher voltage and energy of magnesium metal and its ability to form surface films which effectively resist surface corrosion on standing. The increased energy density often allows twice the period of service from a battery of the same equivalent volume and weight as the conventional zinc–carbon battery. No significant increase in power density (W/lb) has been achieved with these magnesium cells.

Microminiaturization of components has greatly reduced the amount of electrical power required in the normal radio for equivalent performance. For example, the receive or standby power requirement of a typical radio may be as low as 2–3 W. But since microminiaturization has also allowed the designer to incorporate extended range and improved performance in a very small man-portable package, greatly increased amounts of electrical power are required for transmit periods. A radio may have only a 3-W standby requirement but require as much as 120–150 W during transmit.

For these applications where periodic higher peaks of power are required than can be accommodated within the low rate limitations of the standard dry batteries, secondary batteries, principally of the vented nickel–cadmium type, must be used. These secondary batteries have very good characteristics for supplying the large pulses of energy such as may be encountered in these several-minute transmit loads within well-prescribed voltage limits. The principal difficulty is that in rugged packaging they have energy densities of only approximately 10 Wh/lb. If a total lightweight package is required their energy content is soon depleted, requiring a recharging.

It is quite evident that the optimum method of renewal for a power source in communications and surveillance applications should use chemical energy which can be carried in a disposable container. Whether this is the traditional packaging of carbon–zinc cells in a radio battery, or whether it is a container of fuel for fuel cells, makes very little difference. It therefore became apparent that one very attractive application for fuel cells is to use them in combination with a secondary battery where the secondary battery provides the peak pulses, while the fuel cell efficiently converts the chemical fuel into electrical energy at a continuous rate. This combines the attractiveness of a disposable fuel container (fuel of several hundred Wh/lb) with the ability to meet high periodic electrical-power requirements in an extremely small power-source package. For mobile operations where weight reduction is extremely significant, a premium price can be paid for a fuel cell which offers these advantages.

Hybrid Power Source. The combination of a radio with a 30-W fuel cell and a nickel–cadmium storage battery is an example. Drawing power directly from the storage battery, the operator has power instantly available to operate his radio under any type of field condition. This instant load capability is not inherent in a fuel cell operating alone because it has a start-up lag since its normal optimum operating condition is different from the ambient environment in which it is stored. If the operator contemplates continued use of his radio in both the receive and transmit conditions he will activate the fuel cell by providing it with fuel from a disposable container and allow it to provide the power he requires and the power for recharging of the battery automatically after its initial warm-up. The size of the fuel cell and the capacity of the battery must, of course, be properly selected for the equipment to be powered so that full operating performance can be maintained over the total time required and that the smallest and lightest weight power-source unit can be assembled. A wide range of communications and surveillance equipment was analyzed to determine the power level which would be most attractive if only one fuel cell was picked to mate with a variety of batteries. The first analysis, which covered a range of highly portable radios, radars, and night-vision equipment, indicated that an average power of 20–30 W was encountered with peaks usually not exceeding 100–140 W during high-intensity power periods. Based on this, a very simple 30-W fuel cell was designed to work in a hybrid configuration with batteries at 12 and 24 V.

Chemical Fuel Forms. For the 30-W fuel cell the total amount of fuel consumed in 8–12 hr is only a fraction of a pound, hence large quantities of fuel are not involved. Actually a reduction in both volume and weight over the equivalent supply of zinc–carbon primary batteries can be achieved. This means that any fuel that can be successfully packaged so that it can be safely stored, safely handled, and safely transferred to the fuel cell, can be utilized in the field. A special fuel for the fuel cell is considered to be lighter or heavier, more expensive or less expensive compared to the equivalent weight and cost of conventional zinc–carbon batteries. Because of the high cost per kWh of electrical power supplied from Leclanché batteries, almost any type of nonexotic chemical fuel could be cost competitive. The use of gaseous fuels has not been considered because of possible safety considerations. However, since most fuel cells use hydrogen as the active material for oxidation at the anode, a solid or liquid chemical form of hydrogen is preferable. A solid chemical form of hydrogen, lithium hydride, or sodium aluminum hydride, was selected as the fuel for the 30-W fuel cell. Hydrogen is generated by action of water in a system which needs no moving parts.

$$LiH + H_2O \rightarrow LiOH + H_2$$

Hydrazine, which can be regarded as a liquid form of chemical hydrogen, reacts directly in a fuel cell in an alkaline electrolyte. It requires a somewhat more complicated system but it was selected for the higher power 60-to-100-W range because it can provide very low impedance and a high overload capability.

Approximately 1 kWh/lb is obtained from lithium hydride at a cost of about $10.00/kWh and 350 Wh/lb from hydrazine at a cost of about $3.00/kWh. In comparison, standard military zinc–carbon Leclanché cells provide approximately 30 Wh/lb at a cost of about $44.00/kWh.

30-Watt Metal Hydride–Air Fuel Cell. The photograph of the 30-W fuel cell (Figure 19) shows an experimental model packaged in the hybrid configuration compatible with mounting directly to the radio and to the auxiliary secondary battery. In the left-hand portion of the fuel-cell package is the hydrogen generator. The cylindrical aluminum hydride fuel tablet (4 ounces) is inserted into the core of the

Fig. 19. General Electric 30-W fuel cell.

hydrogen generator, the core attached to the top closure, water added to the outer chamber, and the hydrogen generator assembled for use.

The fuel cell consists of two 14-V hydrogen–air modules which can be used in series or series-parallel to interface with 24 or 12-V batteries. A simplified electrical diagram is shown in Figure 20. The single on-off control releases hydrogen to the fuel-cell modules and opens the air louvers. A light indicates positive operation and a refill indicator tells the operator when the hydrogen generator must be disassembled for refueling.

The current-limit control located in the output circuit allows the fuel cell to be used at a set constant current in recharging the battery during periods when no external load is applied or during periods when the external load is less than the full output of the fuel cell. This current limitation was employed so that sealed as well as vented nickel–cadmium batteries could be utilized without exceeding their continuous overcharge rate. During normal float operation of the battery, recharge rates limited only by the excess power available from the fuel cell could easily be used. However, since the operator has no knowledge of the condition of the battery used in the fuel-cell–battery configuration, it is impossible to protect a small, sealed battery from possible damage during extended overcharge unless this type of current limitation is employed. A coulometer or other means of charge control could be used to feed information from the battery back to the fuel cell to automatically regulate the amount of this charging

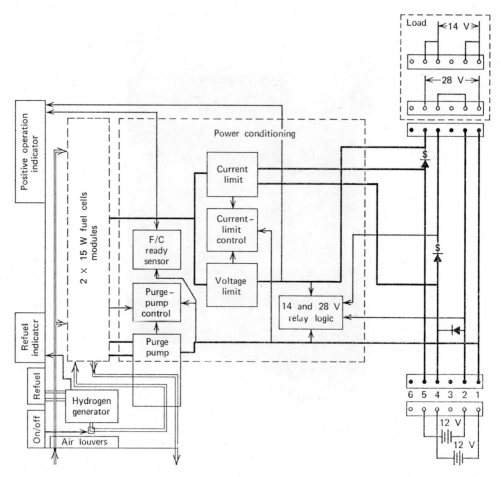

Fig. 20. Simplified schematic diagram of a 30-W fuel cell. LEGEND: → signals; —— power; ═══ gas; ---- base unit.

current. This has not been used in this case, since a prime consideration in the selection of the fuel-cell hybrid component is its ability to use any type of battery. The fuel cell must, therefore, be compatible with, and recharge, any secondary batteries in the same way as any other external battery charger.

Electrical Output Characteristics. The use of a hybrid power source for powering electronic equipment is of course not new. Electronic equipment mounted on vehicles use power from the battery (normally at 24 V), but are also capable of being powered at 28 V dc when the generator or alternator is operating. Since most portable electronic equipment is designed for vehicular use, it was decided that the fuel-cell–battery hybrid should employ the same voltage characteristics.

The 30-W fuel cell which has an ion-exchange membrane electrolyte has a high impedance and can provide a highly regulated 28 V for direct powering of the equipment and for recharging of the battery only by extensive power conditioning using a voltage limiter. It is, therefore, not well suited for the type of load which would benefit from a fuel-cell overload during the peak load periods. For this higher output a fuel cell utilizing a lower impedance system is preferred.

Hydrazine Fuel Cells. Hydrazine fuel cells have been in development for several years (21). A 60-W hydrazine fuel cell weighed 14 lb and produced approximately 390 Wh/lb of fuel. The chemical process system used is shown in Figure 21. Hydrazine fuel is injected into an electrolyte tank to provide a constant level of hydrazine concentration in the anolyte. The anolyte is circulated through the anode compartment of the fuel cell module and air blown through the cathode compartment. Other components are required to maintain heat and moisture balances. More recent models have a simplified fuel-feed-control system which feeds fuel in proportion to the amount of gas evolved. An anolyte compartment gas exhaust pump maintains a negative pressure on the anolyte which improves the operation of the air cathode and also removes the nitrogen formed as a reaction product. This reduced pressure can also be used to introduce fuel as required into the anolyte chamber.

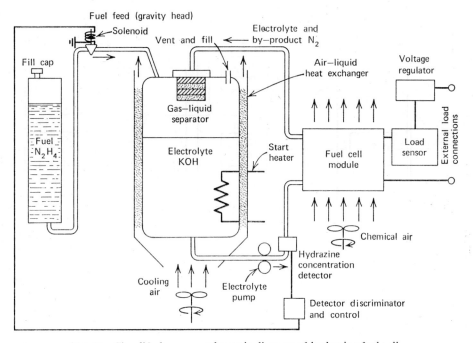

Fig. 21. Simplified process schematic diagram of hydrazine fuel cell.

The inherent regulation of the hydrazine fuel cell is better, the voltage–ampere curve being highly regulatable by controlling several of the operating variables (fuel concentration, temperature, air flow). To allow high flexibility in control and the use of a lower operating voltage from the fuel-cell stack, a dc-to-dc converter and regulator has been incorporated into the system. The output of this converter regulator is adjustable from 28 to 32 V to compensate for lower temperatures of operation where the battery must be floated at a high voltage to obtain the desired recharge rates. A simplified diagram of how the battery is interfaced with the dc-to-dc converter and the fuel-cell stack is shown in Figure 22.

Vented batteries which can safely take up to 5 A of recharge current can provide 24 V directly to the output and will be recharged at 28 V dc (28–32 V dc adjustable) from the output of the dc-to-dc converter regulator when no external load is applied. In this mode the fuel cell can be used as a battery charger for any battery (constant potential charge), not necessarily in a hybrid configuration.

Sealed batteries can also be used as a 12-V input in parallel with the fuel-cell power-system input to the converter regulator. The charge control and battery gate allow recharge of the 12-V dc battery directly from the fuel-cell stack. In this hybrid configuration power for the startup processor is taken from the 12-V dc battery. This 12-V dc source also serves to stiffen the input to the converter regulator during transients when the fuel-cell stack voltage may drop to 12-V. This startup and stiffening function is independent of whether a 12-V dc (paralleled sections of a sealed battery) or 24-V dc vented battery (12-V dc tap across one side) is used.

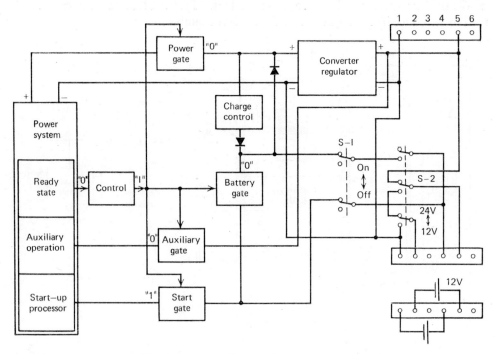

Fig. 22. Simplified electrical schematic diagram of hydrazine fuel cell.

Instant load capability is possible at 24 V from an attached vented nickel–cadmium battery or at 24 V dc through the converter-regulator from the sealed batteries. In either case the fuel-cell power gate is closed when the control indicates a ready state (fuel cell at operating temperature). The output voltage jumps to 28 V dc and is maintained there within the current limits and for as long as the fuel cell has fuel to maintain its output voltage.

A hydrazine fuel cell of the type described in combination with an appropriately sized vented battery can provide extremely high electrical output for short periods of time (1–2 min) without compromising the voltage stability of the whole system. Up to 5 A the output is held at 28 V by the converter regulator. At 150 W the current limiter on the converter regulator drops the voltage to the normal plateau of the attached 24-V vented nickel–cadmium battery. The output voltage will remain at this plateau level depending only on the polarization characteristics of the size of battery employed.

Fuel Cells for Electric Cars

The electric car is seen as a possible attractive alternative to the existing internal combustion engine because of its far lower emission of polluting by-products. The big question is whether an electric car can provide a transportation means which will be accepted by the American public and which will become a vital factor in the planning of transportation patterns within our big cities or across the country in general. Since in almost all cases the electrical power for the future electrical cars will come from energy stored within the car, rather than from a trolley-like overhead wire or third rail, it comes down to a consideration of how the energy can be stored. The power source which may become possible for future electric cars and the means for recharging them with the energy required will be considered here in detail.

The first vigorous public debate on electric cars was associated with the Senate hearings in 1966–1967 to explore the possible alternatives in vehicle transportation. During this debate two basic groups emerged, both of which saw the electric car as the answer to particular transportation problems. The first group, the here-and-now group, sees the electric car meeting a variety of short-range transportation needs in specific urban and suburban situations. They study the average distance and rate of travel of a vehicle in Manhattan and determine that there are many deep urban zones which could be fully converted to electrical cars and meet the requirements for business and pleasure transportation in "smog-free" zones. This group has also considered the housewife in her daily trips to and from the shopping centers, schools, and family recreation areas, and foresees an application for a short-range electrical car. In most of these studies the total energy capacity of the car is between 10 and 20 kWh so that an overnight recharge in the family garage, or a plug-in at parking meters or combination commuter parking and recharge stations is completely feasible. Discussions extend to the all-rental fleet of cars where a person simply places his charge card in the vehicle's ignition system and is billed at the end of the month for the extent of use of the "core of city" fleet of transportation vehicles. The design challenge in the local, short-range, limited-energy use of electrical cars is not in the creation of new power sources or even new power trains, but in the way in which people would use cars and in the total planning of interchange and localized integrated transportation systems. Most of the electrical cars now being offered to the public by a number of companies as semi-experimental lines are of this type and utilize conventional batteries, usually of the lead–acid type, which have been successfully used for many years in golf carts.

The second major group is endeavoring to extend the range of electric cars by increasing the energy-storage capability of existing power sources and by making major adaptations and modifications in the design of an automobile to optimize its design around the concept of electrical propulsion. Press announcements by the automobile companies, together with some battery development groups, all promise the electric car which can go a little faster, a little farther, and be a little more comfortable. It is in this area where the real design challenge lies and where concerted improvements of both the power source and the power train, and mechanical design of the vehicle, can be expected to lead to drastically improved electrical cars.

When one considers the fully competitive electric car most of the discussion comes down to the battery. Can we provide in the battery sufficient power and energy to have an electric automobile which can do all the things and provide all the conveniences which the present gasoline-engine-powered car does for the average person today? One can dismiss the possibility of using the low-performance local electric car since it will not be acceptable as a total solution because it asks people to make major changes in the way they would go about their daily routine. Therefore, for major conversion and wide impact over the total general transportation system, the much more difficult technical problem must be undertaken, ie to develop the electrical automobile which has all the capabilities of our present high-power, gasoline-driven cars. This means that the scientists and engineers must invent new battery systems which will allow us to overcome some of the limitations which have been present in electric cars since the days of Thomas Edison. To accomplish this, not only are new batteries required, but also considerations must be given to the whole aspect of applying a power source to do the best job to give optimum performance on the specific-duty cycle which our vehicle demands. The design challenge is then to determine how one would use high-energy battery systems most effectively in powering a full-performance electrical car.

What Is Expected of the Family Car. Normally our cars have gasoline tanks which are large enough so that we can travel approximately 300 miles before refueling at a gas station. Thus, a battery should carry enough electrical energy to run the car the same distance. Normally, automobile engines are designed with a large energy reserve for overtaking; the full horsepower is very rarely used. The engine in normal driving is almost at idle. The battery for the future electric car must therefore be capable of allowing electrical current to be drawn at a normal rate, but also must provide high rates of electrical current when racing away from a stop light, climbing steep grades, or for high-speed passing.

When the automobile runs out of energy, the owner stops at a gasoline service station, and in 5–10 min is ready to go again for another 300 miles. This is the point where use of batteries becomes most difficult. Normally, batteries which are used in small vehicles, such as lift trucks in industrial plants, are allowed to recharge overnight or during the shift when they are not being used. This means that in the conventional manner the electric car would have to be plugged in overnight to be ready to move the next day. This, of course, would put a serious limitation on long cross-country traveling because one could only travel 300 miles during the day and then must plug in at a friend's house or at a service station overnight so that one could go again the 300 miles for the next day's trip. What is needed, then, is a new type of battery which would not only have the full energy reserve for 300 miles of traveling, but which also could be fully charged in about 5–10 min, equivalent to the time taken to fill a car with gasoline.

New Batteries. Both the Ford Motor Company (22) and General Motors Corporation (23) have worked on new batteries for use in future electric cars. Both of these batteries, which are still at very early stages of development, use completely new battery principles. These new batteries run at temperatures equivalent to those now found in the inside of gasoline engines so that the conversion of chemical to electrical power can go much more readily. The chemicals normally used in these batteries are lithium or sodium metal as the anode materials, and sulfur or chlorine materials as the depolarizers or cathodes. Melted salts of these chemicals all have very high electrical-energy equivalents and are very lightweight. If packaged properly and used efficiently, these chemicals can provide a battery which could propel the normal automobile beyond the present 300-mile range with a weight of total battery less than the present weight of the engine and the fuel tank combined. Because these batteries run at higher temperatures ($250-600°C$) they allow the conversion of chemical to electrical energy to proceed very rapidly and therefore result in a battery which can deliver very high currents. Another advantage of the ease of chemical reaction is that not only can the chemicals be converted to electrical current, but also that electrical current from the outside can be applied to the battery to recreate the chemicals and therefore recharge the total battery system. Because this reaction proceeds very quickly, it is possible with proper design and packaging of the battery to produce a battery which can be fully recharged in 10–20 min. This, however, creates a very serious problem. The electrical distribution system in a normal household is designed for a normal usage not to exceed approximately 3 kW of power. If we design the system to accomplish an overnight recharge of an electric automobile, this would increase the requirements to about 15–20 kW to be drawn during the overnight recharging period. The electrical distribution and switches required for this overnight recharging could be easily contained in the average garage. If, however, we use the battery's capability to be recharged in a period of approximately 10–20 min, this means that a major substation must be installed in every garage. To have a distribution system for from 600 kW to over 1000 kW in each individual residence is of course, impractical because of the cost alone, if for no other reason. This means that these new batteries in future vehicles would have to be recharged at special recharging stations, which would require a new capital investment in a whole series of electrical recharging stations similar to what we now have invested in our nation-wide chain of gasoline stations. But let us first examine what the requirement to recharge these new batteries in 10 min does to the design of the batteries themselves and the way they are placed in an electric car. If the car is to have equal range and capability with present automobiles, this means that we must have in the battery approximately 200 kWh of stored electrical energy. If the battery system is designed to run at approximately 200 V, this means that in recharging within 10–20 min, 3000–6000 A must be passed through the wires connecting the battery with the recharge station. For this quantity of current, the switch alone may weigh as much as the present engine in the car, and the weight of metal required to carry the current inside the car from the switch to the battery would be so heavy that very little space and weight would be available for the battery. Even with the very high energy and lightweight chemicals of these new battery systems, it would not be practical to try to incorporate all the metal and conductors needed to try to recharge these batteries at the very high rate. It is, therefore, obvious that batteries alone are not sufficient to solve the power source problem.

Fuel Cells. Another approach to creating the electrical power needed to drive an electric automobile is the fuel cell. Fuel cells have been used in space explorations, using hydrogen and oxygen which were liquefied and kept stored in cooled containers. They provided the power required over extended periods in orbit of from 4 to 14 days. For fuel cells to work on the ground, the oxygen can be obtained directly from the air around us. Likewise, hydrocarbon fuels, such as presently used in existing engines, can be a source of hydrogen to be used in the fuel cell. Even though the fuel cell can very efficiently convert the energy contained in a gasoline fuel to electric power, the fuel cell itself is relatively heavy and bulky compared to the present gasoline engines. So, even if we should have available a fuel cell which would have the same ability to convert gasoline to energy as the existing gasoline engine, it would be far too heavy to carry in an automobile. This is assuming that we would pick the size of the fuel cell to be identical to that of the existing engine, ie, to give fast acceleration, permit the climbing of step grades, and high-speed passing in turnpike traffic. But, combining the advantages of both of these approaches, the new higher-energy, lighter-weight batteries and the hydrocarbon-converting fuel cell, it appears that the best way to solve the problem of the most versatile and best type of electrical-power plant for future cars is to combine both the new type of battery and the new type of fuel cell together in a hybrid system. The fuel cell is best when it continuously converts gasoline and air to electrical power at a steady, constant rate. The battery is best for providing a wide range of currents to meet small or large electrical demands of the motors, but has the limitation that it only carries a small amount of total reserve energy. Therefore, to overcome the immense problem of charging the battery, each electric car of the future would carry a gasoline tank and a small fuel cell which can convert this gasoline to electrical power continuously to recharge the batteries, and the stored energy of the battery would be used for the sudden spurts of energy that are so necessary. The fuel cell would be used to supply an average level of electrical power which could be used to sustain normal driving under normal highway conditions and which would be used to recharge the batteries while the automobile is motionless in traffic or during periods when the car is parked, waiting for the next trip. Because the battery and the fuel cell are both electrochemical systems, and have similar characteristics, they can be made to work together very well. The fuel cell will automatically keep the battery at its full charge of electrical power and instantly ready to provide the power required for any function of the automobile. Even under the most adverse weather conditions, no additional warm-up would be required. The parts of the fuel cell and the storage battery could be so arranged in a common package that each would be extremely simple and would require only a minimum of auxiliary controls and accessories. Since the fuels which would be used in this hybrid battery and fuel-cell package would be the same fuels which are now used in existing gasoline-engine cars, the same nation-wide network of service stations could be used. A traveler making a long-distance trip across country could be refueled in the same time that it now takes him to refuel his car at a service station. Because the fuel cell is not dependent on rejecting heat at a lower temperature, it has a much higher energy-conversion efficiency and therefore can provide much more electrical energy per gallon of fuel. For the type of total system, including fuel cell and battery, which would be used in a private automobile, 37–47% of the energy in the gasoline would be converted to motion of the car, depending upon the efficiency of the particular drive train used to deliver power to the wheels of the car. This means that the future electric car would go at approximately 60 miles per gallon of gasoline and therefore represent a great saving in cost to its owner, as well as contributing to conservation of petroleum resources.

The particular fuel cell which would be used in this system would have to be low in cost and very simple to operate. This type of fuel cell has not yet been built, except in the laboratory.

The technology is available, but as of this date, no concerted effort is being directed at developing this new type of new vehicular power source.

Hybrid Power System. A hybrid power-source system (Fig. 23) would consist of approximately an equal weight of hydrocarbon fuel, fuel-to-electrical converter (fuel cell), and energy storage (battery). The theoretical energy of the fuel, 5.5 kWh/lb, becomes useful when the fuel cell converts it for immediate needs or stores it in a battery for later use. The fuel cell's high conversion efficiency (40–50%) will allow more miles to the gallon using an equivalent refinery-produced liquid-hydrocarbon fuel. The fuel cell and battery elements could be configured in the series-parallel ar-

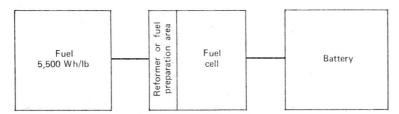

Fig. 23. Hybrid power-source system.

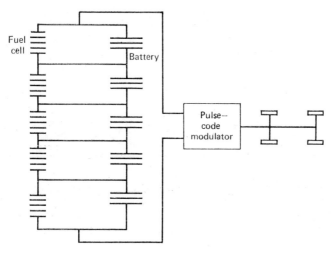

Fig. 24. Series-parallel configuration.

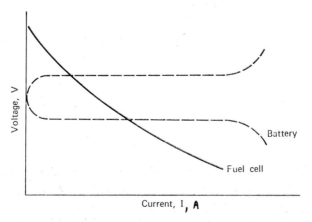

Fig. 25. Voltage vs current curve for hybrid system.

rangement shown in Figure 24. The voltage across this parallel arrangement of battery and fuel cell would be applied to the pulse code modulator in the vehicle propulsion-control system. The voltage at these bus terminals will be a function of the current drawn. Figure 25 shows the fuel-cell voltage-vs-amperage curve which would be followed until sufficient amperes are drawn to reduce the fuel-cell module voltage to the battery-discharge voltage. From this point to maximum rated power the voltage across the pulse code modulator will be the battery's discharge voltage. As the re-

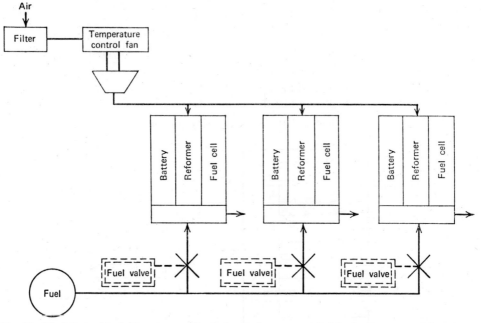

Fig. 26. Modularized hybrid system. The fuel valves are controlled by hydrogen partial pressure.

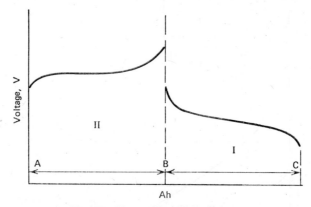

Fig. 27. Charge-discharge efficiency.

quired external current is reduced the voltage rises to the point where the fuel cell starts to recharge the battery. When the external load is reduced to zero, internal current flows as the fuel cell fully recharges the battery.

Figure 26 is a diagram of a possible modularized hybrid system. Each module would consist of a hydrocarbon-to-hydrogen reformer, the fuel cell, and the battery-storage unit. A typical system may use the molten electrolyte lithium–chlorine battery which operates at 450–600°C, together with a reformer and a molten carbonate matrix-electrolyte fuel cell operating at the same temperature. For control simplicity, the fuel-cell fuel feed could have a variable flow pump regulated to maintain a constant excess hydrogen partial pressure at the exit of the fuel-cell converter. The small amount of excess hydrogen could be combusted in a catalytic burner to provide the quantity of heat needed to keep the hybrid system at its operating temperature. Like-

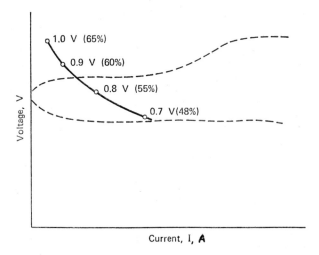

Fig. 28. Battery charger efficiency.

wise, the flow of air in the fuel-cell combustion air stream could be adjusted to maintain the proper temperature during periods of activity when heat must be dissipated. Since excellent electrical transient response is provided by the storage-battery energy, the lag time of the reformer and fuel cell can be rather lengthy, thus allowing very simple, largely self-regulating controls.

By proper attention to design criteria, a battery–fuel-cell power source can be (*1*) less polluting; (*2*) more silent; (*3*) more efficient in using energy from liquid hydrocarbons; (*4*) lighter weight; (*5*) simpler; and (*6*) more reliable than internal-combustion-engine vehicle power plants. The most important design criteria for optimizing the hybrid power source are (*1*) minimum power-plant weight by proper sizing of the fuel cell and battery component; (*2*) proper efficiency matching; and (*3*) thermal integration and control simplicity.

In the hybrid system the battery would principally be floated between 25 and 90% of full capacity. In this regime the principal energy loss is due to resistances in the cell's current collectors and electrolyte resistivity, particularly where porous electrode materials are utilized, assuming that self-discharge rates have been reduced to negligible proportions. Chemical polarization losses which are present in all lower temperature systems can be significantly reduced in molten electrolyte batteries. The only true measure of a battery's energy-storage efficiency (Fig. 27) is to determine the Whr of useful energy which are discharged from the battery during its normal operation and compare that to the watt hours of energy required to bring it back to its previous charged state. Many conventional batteries (lead–acid, for example) have far too low energy-storage efficiencies and would not be suitable in a hybrid application. The most attractive battery for hybrid use appears to be a molten-salt system where Faradaic efficiencies of 100% and duty-cycle energy-storage efficiencies of 70–80% should be achievable.

The efficiency with which a fuel cell can directly generate electrical power for supply to the drive train or for recharging of the energy periodically removed from the battery is determined by (*1*) the single-cell operating voltage at the load point; (*2*) the fuel preparation efficiency; and (*3*) the amount of parasitic power which must be wasted in the conversion process.   Figure 28 shows the voltage-amperage curve for the fuel-cell battery charger.   The single-cell voltages are shown together with the total fuel-cell system thermal-conversion efficiencies corresponding to these single-cell voltages.

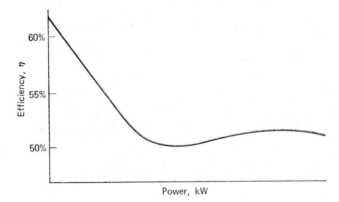

Fig. 29.   Efficiency vs power to drive train.

One of the principal advantages of the fuel-cell–battery hybrid system is that it significantly reduces the complexity of the fuel-cell portion.   By achieving complete thermal integration and a simplified control system, the fuel preparation section (hydrocarbon–steam reformer) can maintain a high efficiency even at very low levels of

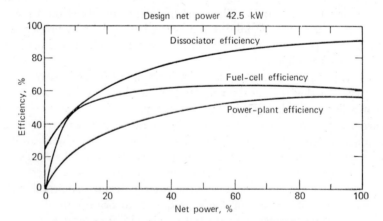

Fig. 30.   Efficiency vs load; design net power, 42.5 kW.

gas production.   Also since the total parasitic power requirements are negligible the overall thermal-conversion efficiency is in direct proportion to single-cell voltages. Since the fuel cell and the battery are directly connected in parallel to the load, the lowest single-cell voltage which the fuel cell would experience is the preselected battery crossover voltage.   This means that the lowest thermal-conversion efficiency of fuel to electrical power can be set at a fuel-cell maximum-overload point of 0.7 V per single cell and is 48%. At zero or very low external power demands the fuel-cell system will internally recharge the battery at a single-fuel-cell voltage between 0.9 and 1.0 V where the battery charger efficiency is between 60 and 65%. Based on the synthesis of these two efficiency patterns the efficiency of the total hybrid system vs the power to the drive train is shown in Figure 29. The initial decreasing portion of the efficiency curve is in direct proportion to the reduction of the single-cell operating voltages of the fuel cell. The minimum in this curve indicates the full participation of the fuel cell at its maximum overloaded point. As the power requirements increase even higher, more of the energy is withdrawn from the battery with a slight increase in overall thermal efficiency because of the combination of higher efficiency involved in the initial placement of this energy in the battery and its efficient delivery for this application. As power requirements increase to overload the complete hybrid system, the thermal efficiency will, of course, drop again as the battery seriously polarizes. It must be noted that this curve is for external power to the drive train. During periods of reduced vehicle activity the hybrid system will have a significant internal current for battery recharging operations.

Because the fuel-cell–battery hybrid system is highly regenerative, using its own waste heat for fuel preparation and to maintain operating temperatures, the severely lowered efficiencies which are characteristic of fuel cells by themselves are not experienced with this system. Figure 30 is an efficiency-vs-load curve for an ammonia–air fuel cell. Note that the power-plant efficiency drops significantly when operating below 30% of rated operation. This is partially due to the parasitic power required for the auxiliaries which must be sized to operate at the 40-kW level, but is principally a function of lower efficiency of the hydrogen generator. This same loss in efficiency at part load will be encountered in a hydrocarbon–air fuel cell which is not integrated in a hybrid system.

Hybrid System Design. All of the design calculations are based on a hydrocarbon–air fuel-cell portion which would weigh 30–35 lb/kW and a battery with an energy density of approximately 150 Wh/lb (24). As previously indicated, any fuel cell with this power density, or any battery with this energy-storage density, would not necessarily be the optimum candidate for the best hybrid system for vehicle propulsion applications. Maximum advantage is obtained when the fuel preparation, the fuel-cell reaction, and the battery reactions are all carried out at the same temperature. According to this concept the unit building block contains the fuel-reforming, fuel-cell conversion, and energy-storage components. These hybrid modules could be standard repeatable units which could be paralleled in larger power sources. The fuel-preparation section contains a conventional reformer catalyst which is located in thermal contact with the heat stored in the heat capacity of the battery electrolyte. The fuel cell could utilize a molten-salt electrolyte immobilized in a suitable high density matrix. Laboratory models of these fuel cells have been fabricated and shown performance equivalent to the voltages, currents, and efficiencies described in Figure 30. The battery could utilize the lithium molten-salt reactions, preferably in a design which would use sealed single cells.

A large amount of attention must still be given to the high-temperature materials, the devising and optimizing of specific cell configuration, and total system integration and control schemes.

Bibliography

1. A. Standen, ed., *Encyclopedia of Chemical Technology*, Interscience Publishers, a div. of John Wiley & Sons, Inc., New York.

1a. H. L. Recht, *Fuel cells*, in reference 1, 1st ed., Suppl. 2, 1960, pp. 355–376.

2. E. B. Yeager, *Fuel cells*, in reference 1, 2nd ed., Vol. 3, 1964, pp. 139–160.

3. H. A. Liebhafsky and E. J. Cairns, *Fuel Cells and Fuel Batteries*, John Wiley & Sons, Inc., New York, 1968.

4. C. Berger, ed., *Handbook of Fuel Cell Technology*, Prentice-Hall, Inc., Englewood Cliffs, N.J., 1968.

5. J. Bockris and S. Srinivasan, *Fuel Cells: Their Electrochemistry*, McGraw-Hill Book Co., Inc., New York, 1969.

6. W. Mitchell, Jr., ed., *Fuel Cells*, Academic Press, Inc., New York, 1963.

7. W. Vielstich, *Brennstoffelemente*, Verlag Chemie Weinheim, Germany, 1965; *Fuel Cells, Modern Processes for the Electrochemical Production of Energy* (English Transl.), John Wiley & Sons, Inc., 1970.

8. L. Austin, *Fuel Cells—A Review of Government Sponsored Research, 1950–1964*, NASA SP-120, Washington, D.C., 1967.

9. B. Baker, ed., *Hydrocarbon Fuel Cell Technology*, Academic Press, Inc., New York, 1965.

10. B. Baker, ed., *Fuel Cell Systems II*, American Chemical Society, Washington, D.C., 1969.

11. D. Collins, ed., *Power Sources 1966*, Pergamon Press Ltd., London, 1967.

11a. A. Hart and G. Lomax, *Fuel Cells: Theory and Applications*, Chapman and Hall Ltd., London, 1967.

11b. K. Williams, ed., *An Introduction to Fuel Cells*, Elsevier, Amsterdam, 1966.

12. *Ammonia-Air Fuel Cell System for Vehicle Propulsion, PWA-2636*, Final Technical Report, July 5, 1965, U.S. Army Contract SA-44-009-AMC-747(T).

13. G. Frysinger, "Hydrogen-Air Fuel Cells," *Rev. Energ. Primaire* **1**(3), 3 (1965).

14. G. Frysinger, J. Truitt, and C. Peattie, "A Molten Carbonate Fuel Cell Systems Using Air and Liquid Hydrocarbons," *Proc. 18th Annual Power Sources Conference, Red Bank, N.J., 1964*, p. 14.

15. F. Gray, "Small Hydrocarbon-Air Fuel Cell Systems Using a Molten-Carbonate Electrolyte," *Deuxièmes Journées Internationales d'Étude des Piles A Combustible, Brussels, 1967*, p. 385.

16. D. Gregory and H. Heilbronner, "Feasibility Studies on a Hydrocarbon Fuel Cell," *Hydrocarbon Fuel Cell Technology*, Academic Press, Inc., New York, 1965, p. 509.

17. R. F. Buswell, "500-Watt Hydrocarbon–Air Fuel Cell System," *Proc. 19th Annual Power Sources Conference, Red Bank, N.J., 1965*.

18. G. Frysinger, "High Efficiency Hydrocarbon-Air Acid Electrolyte Fuel Cell System," *Deuxièmes Journées Internationales d'Étude des Piles A Combustible, Brussels, 1967*, p. 314.

19. D. Linden and H. Knapp, "Metal-Air Primary Batteries," *Proc. 21st Annual Power Sources Conference, Red Bank, N.J., 1967*, p. 109.

20. *Sixth Status Report on Fuel Cells*, U.S. Army Electronics Command, Ft. Monmouth, N.J., May 1967.

20a. L. Urry, *Optimization of BA-4270/U and BA-4386/PRC-25 Magnesium MnO₂ Primary Batteries*, Final Report, Contract DA28-043-AMC-02565(E) (USAEC), Union Carbide Corporation, April, 1968.

20b. P. F. Albert, *Development of Magnesium Flat Cell Battery*, Final Report, Contract DA28-043-AMC-02136(E) (USAEC), Ray-O-Vac Division, October, 1968.

20c. L. W. Eaton, *Development of Magnesium Wafer Cells*, Final Report, Contract DA28-043-AMC-02135(E) (USAEC), Burgess Battery Company, December, 1968.

21. R. Salathe et al., "Fuel Feed Techniques for Hydrazine–Air Fuel Cell Systems," *Proc. 22nd Annual Power Sources Conference, Red Bank, N.J., 1968*, p. 6.

22. N. Weber and J. Kummer, "Sodium–Sulfur Secondary Battery," *Proc. 21st Annual Power Sources Conference, Red Bank, N.J.* 1967, p. 37.

23. H. Wilcox, "Lithium–Chlorine Molten Electrolyte Battery," *Proc. 21st Annual Power Sources Conference, Red Bank, N.J.*, 1967, p. 39.

24. G. Frysinger, "Battery-Fuel Cell System," *Proc. 21st Annual Power Sources Conference, Red Bank, N.J.*, 1967, p. 54.

GALEN R. FRYSINGER
ESB Incorporated

G

GAS, NATURAL

Tremendous strides have occurred since 1960 in the world natural gas industry. Proved reserves alone have doubled and marketed production has risen from 16.887 trillion ft³ to 36.083 trillion ft³ in 1968—an increase of more than 100%. Consumption of natural gas is expected to be 36.374 trillion ft³ in 1970 (1–3). (1 billion = 10^9, 1 trillion = 10^{12}, 1 quadrillion = 10^{15}).

Natural gas is being recognized for the role it can play in reducing air pollution. Efforts are under way chiefly in the U.S. and Japan to supplement other hydrocarbon fuels with natural gas to reduce particulate matter, sulfur oxides, and other gaseous pollutants. Efforts in the U.S. are being severely hampered by a shortage of indigenous natural gas supplies. Proved reserves fell by 12.241 trillion ft³ in 1969 due to the imbalance of production and supply additions. This was the second straight year that production exceeded additions to supply. While residential and commercial customers are in no danger of being without natural gas, this does mean that the supply for industrial customers, particularly those on interruptible rates, will be curtailed.

Although U.S. national gas sales will be depressed in the 1970s due to the shortage of natural gas supplies, events should begin to offset this situation by 1980. Production of domestic natural gas should be increased, importation of liquefied natural gas (LNG) will be expanded, and coal and oil gasification plants may begin to come on-stream. Thus, the shortage of natural gas is viewed as temporary until alternative sources of supply and additional domestic reserves are developed. As world demand for energy continues to increase, the natural gas industry must continue to develop new and more efficient ways of meeting this demand and maintaining the quality of the environment.

Gas Reserves, Production, and Consumption

Reserves, consumption, and production of natural gas have been fairly well documented for the United States and Canada (Table 1). However, such statistics in the rest of the world, especially the developing nations, are more difficult to ascertain. The distribution of natural gas reserves indicates that the U.S.S.R. has the largest reserves for any single country, followed by the U.S. On a regional basis, the Communist bloc possesses over 445 trillion ft³. The U.S.S.R. alone possesses almost 425 trillion ft³ of this with a total of 177 trillion ft³ being claimed for Siberia. Second in overall

421

reserves are North America and the Middle East with approximately 340 trillion ft^3 each. Large reserves in the North Slope of Alaska have yet to be evaluated, but unofficial estimates put them at over 427 trillion ft^3 (4). Table 2 presents a breakdown

Table 1. Estimated Proved Recoverable Reserves of Natural Gas in the U.S. and Canada (10^6 ft^3)

					United States	
State	Proved reserves, Jan. 1, 1969	Extensions and revisions	New fields and new pools	Production, 1969	Proved reserves, Jan. 1, 1970	Change from Jan. 1, 1969
Alaska	5,252,324	+37,155		87,336	5,202,143	−50,181
Arkansas	2,715,065	+19,513	58,289	166,061	2,632,773	−82,292
California^a	7,316,329	+168,063	48,105	644,770	6,870,946	−445,383
Colorado	1,660,103	+31,302	13,169	108,711	1,596,286	−63,817
Illinois	297,908	−1,432		3,470	337,812	+39,904
Indiana	75,458	+764		1,312	77,561	+2,103
Kansas	14,511,173	+487,812	12,875	886,178	14,125,125	−386,048
Kentucky	923,289	+68,650	6,030	79,304	920,520	−2,769
Louisiana^a	88,015,624	+3,030,626	1,264,448	7,277,564	85,056,639	−2,958,985
Michigan	757,426	+23,609	9,130	34,468	750,964	−6,462
Mississippi	1,434,078	+51,009	92,239	165,507	1,410,898	−23,180
Montana	911,533	+226,063	11,791	43,995	1,110,208	+198,675
Nebraska	56,768	+5,685	121	7,278	56,594	−174
New Mexico	15,143,204	+182,783	47,254	1,087,675	14,281,503	−861,701
New York	124,087	−670	400	4,861	120,540	−3,547
North Dakota	866,810	−176,061	1,877	44,062	648,564	−218,246
Ohio	783,875	+70,500	22,100	51,443	809,293	+25,418
Oklahoma	18,368,265	+605,856	282,600	1,679,654	17,593,197	−775,038
Pennsylvania	1,344,996	+21,000	5,000	79,134	1,303,907	−41,089
Texas^a	119,001,106	−801,831	1,848,611	7,658,970	112,392,622	−6,608,484
Utah	1,156,556	−13,241	114	52,874	1,090,768	−65,788
Virginia	34,341			2,903	31,438	−2,903
West Virginia	2,585,581	+53,716	30,875	213,609	2,447,324	−138,257
Wyoming	3,768,535	+426,233	57,547	318,395	3,937,045	+168,510
miscellaneous^b	245,418	+45,124	201	3,656	304,165	+58,747
total	287,349,852	+4,562,228	3,812,776	20,723,190	275,108,835	−12,241,017

					Canada			
Province	Proved reserves, Jan. 1, 1969	Extensions	Revisions	Discoveries^c	Production, 1969	Proved reserves, Jan. 1, 1969	Change from Jan. 1, 1969	Probable reserves, Jan. 1, 1970^d
Brit. Col.	7,462,938	462,539	556,767	114,006	256,903	8,339,347	876,409	8,875,460
Alberta	39,119,502	1,367,471	1,489,337	771,446	1,239,459	41,508,096	2,388,594	45,895,144
other	1,084,021	860,593	−2,289	219,000	60,171	2,103,452	1,019,531	3,697,359
total	47,666,461	2,690,603	2,043,815	1,104,452	1,556,533	51,950,995	4,284,534	57,467,963

^{a} Includes offshore reserves.

^{b} Includes Alabama, Arizona, Florida, Minnesota, Missouri, South Dakota, Tennessee, and Washington.

^{c} The 1969 net production figures were compiled from records of actual production for whatever period such were available, with estimates for the remainder of the year.

^{d} Includes proved reserves.

SOURCE: *Oil & Gas Journal.*

Table 2. Distribution of Estimated World Natural Gas Reserves, Trillion ft³

Region	1961	1966	1968	1970 (est)
North and Central America	334.6	345.5	356.0	339
South America	44.8	51.8	51.7	54
Western Europe	55.5	108.1	145.6	152
North Africa	0.3	118.6	160.0	171
West Africa	54.2	4.8	12.1	12
Middle East	178.3	303.6	342.7	343
Far East	19.6	28.2	43.8	44
Oceania		14.9	23.4	21
Communist Countries	84.2	183.6	406.0	445
Total	771.5	1159.1	1541.3	1581

of reserves by region. The estimates of natural gas reserves presented here include associated gas and are based on published data supplemented by data gathered from oil companies and government agencies (5–7).

Compared with 1961, there is a total increase in reserves of more than 100%. This vast increase comes from natural gas fields in the North Sea off England, Norway, and the Netherlands; from Europe's enormous field at Groningen in the Netherlands; from huge fields in the center of Bass Straits in Australia; and isolated discoveries in Mozambique, in the Red Sea off Saudi Arabia and Ethiopia, in coastal areas off South Africa, Norway, and northwestern Sumatra, and in New Zealand. Estimates of some of these fields are listed in Table 3.

Table 3. Estimates of Reserves Found in Recent Major Discoveries, 10^{12} ft³

Location	Proved reserves	Estimated ultimate reserves
North Sea	31.0	
Groningen (Netherlands)	65.3	
Australia (Bass Straits)	8.6	
North Slope (Alaska)		427
Siberia (Tyumen)	176.6	207
Libya	24.0	
Algeria	141.3	
Canada	52.0	509.7
Iran (Sarakha)	18.0	
Brunei	4.0	

Many of the fields, however, lie far from any major consumer of energy. It is for this reason that an international gas industry was conceived on a scale never imagined before 1960. It was born in 1964 when the first shipments of liquefied natural gas (LNG) were begun on a commercial basis between Arzew, Algeria, and Canvey Island, located east of London in the Thames River mouth.

Liquefied Natural Gas

The most dramatic development in the natural gas business has been the meteoric growth of liquefied natural gas, LNG. LNG at −260°F (−162°C) and 1 atm is composed chiefly of methane and ethane with small percentages of propane, butanes,

Table 4. Conversion Table for Liquefied Natural Gas[a]

To convert from	To	Multiply by
barrel	ft³, liquid	5.615
barrel	1000 ft³, gas[b]	3.478
ft³, liquid	ft³, gas[b]	619.5
ft³, liquid	pound, liquid	27.82
metric ton	1000 ft³, gas[b]	49.10
metric ton	cubic meters, liquid	2.244
U.S. gallon	pound	3.718
U.S. gallon	ft³, gas[b]	82.82
U.S. gallon	ft³, liquid	0.1337
ft³	liters	28.316
lb	kg	0.45359

SOURCE: *LNG Conversion Tables.* Texas Eastern Transmission Corp., Process Engr. Div., Shreveport, La., 1968.
[a] Assumed molecular weight of gas = 17.
[b] At 14.696 psi and 60°F.

heavier hydrocarbons, and nitrogen. The composition of the liquefied gas and the method used to liquefy it contribute to the variance in composition. By liquefying natural gas the ability to store and transport it economically is tremendously increased, since the volumetric ratio of gas to liquid is approximately 620:1. Table 4 lists some conversions for an LNG composed of natural gas with a molecular weight of 17. These conversions will vary slightly, depending on the gas composition.

History of Growth and Development. LNG has done much since 1964 to revolutionize the natural gas industry all over the world. The ability to produce, transport, and store natural gas at approximately −162°C has given an entirely new dimension to the industry.

In 1940, the first U.S. facility was built to liquefy and store natural gas. This plant, constructed by the Hope Natural Gas Company in West Virginia, had a capacity of 0.3 million ft³/day and storage for 1.2 million ft³ equivalent of LNG. It was essentially a pilot-plant operation, but the insight obtained from it was used to construct a facility in Cleveland, Ohio, in 1941. The Cleveland plant—owned and operated by the East Ohio Gas Company—had a liquefaction capacity of 4 million ft³/day and total storage equivalent to 56 million ft³.

The plant was successfully operated until 1944 when a storage tank failed, resulting in a fire and explosions. The U.S. Bureau of Mines investigated the accident. Its published report (8) cited several possible causes for the disaster. The principal reason cited was the use of 3.5% nickel steel, which proved to be an unsatisfactory alloy for service at −162°C.

Despite this setback in the United States, the U.S.S.R., under a lend-lease arrangement with the United States, built an LNG plant near Moscow in 1947. The facility had an initial capacity of 4.25 million ft³/day and a storage capacity of 120 million ft³. Production of LNG for the original purpose of peakshaving was never realized and in the mid-1960s a nitrogen loop was added to enable the separation of helium from the feed gas stream.

The next significant event took place in 1955 when the Union Stockyard and Transit Company of Chicago combined with Continental Oil Company to construct a 7 million ft³/day, barge-mounted expander liquefaction plant at Lake Charles, Loui-

Table 5. World LNG Import–Export Projects

Supply source	Destination	Capacity, million ft³/day	Status
Arzew, Algeria	Canvey, United Kingdom	100	operational (1964)
	Le Havre, France	50	operational (1965)
Kenai, Alaska	Tokyo, Japan	140	operational (1969)
Marsa el Brega, Libya	Barcelona, Spain	110	operational (1970)
	La Spezia, Italy	235	operational (1970)
Skikda, Algeria	Fos, France	350	construction (1972)
Brunei	Tokyo	520	construction (1972)
Arzew, Algeria	United States East Coast	1000	planniug (1975)
Abu Dhabi, Persian Gulf	Japan	400	planning
Nigeria	United States East Coast	1000	planning
Venezuela	United States East Coast	1000	negotiation, planning
Alaska and Canada	United States West Coast	500	planning
Saudi Arabia	Japan, South Africa, India	1000	planning

siana. The intention was to barge LNG up the Mississippi River to Chicago, but the availability of pipeline gas switched the emphasis to overseas shipment. Thus, in 1959, a converted liberty ship, the Methane Pioneer (now the Aristotle), began successful test shipments of LNG between Lake Charles and Canvey Island, England.

As a result of these tests, the British Government, in 1961, approved a plan for liquefying natural gas at Arzew, Algeria, and shipping it by tanker to Canvey Island. This scheme, conceived before the discovery of large reserves in the North Sea, was to provide base-load natural gas to the United Kingdom. Consequently, in 1964, the first international commercial shipments of LNG were made from Algeria to the United Kingdom and France. This project is still underway and is now successfully supplying 100 million ft³/day to the United Kingdom and 50 million ft³/day to France. Other operational and planned schemes are shown in Table 5.

International shipments of LNG beginning in 1964 totaled an equivalent 150 million ft³/day. In 1970, worldwide shipments increased to 635 million ft³/day with an additional 4770 million ft³/day in the planning stage.

LNG Peakshaving. The expression "peakshaving" refers to the practice of using stored LNG to help meet the peak demand in the winter months.

In 1970 the commercial shipments of LNG started, and the first commercial LNG peakshaving plant (except for the smaller earlier unit at Cleveland, O.) was constructed in the United States. Built at Oak Creek, Wisconsin, by the Chicago Bridge & Iron Company for the Wisconsin Natural Gas Company, this plant has a capacity of 1 million ft³/day and storage for an equivalent 250 million ft³ (72,000 bbl).

Since 1964, the growth rate of LNG peakshaving plants has been meteoric. The United States in 1970 had a total of 15 plants in operation with an additional 9 in the construction or planning stage. This, combined with international base-load plants, results in a total of 29 liquefaction facilities with a combined capacity of 750 million ft³/day.

As regards feed preparation for the U.S. plants, molecular sieves for removing CO_2, H_2S, and sulfur compounds, and some means for heavy hydrocarbon stripping are generally in use. Either the cascade- or expander-cycle liquefaction system or some modification of these cycles is used. Storage is done almost exclusively in aboveground, double-walled, metal tanks. Submerged-combustion vaporization systems

Table 6. Dehydration Processes

System	General description
glycol	Generally triethylene glycol (TEG) used in an absorber column where the gas is dehydrated. A regeneration system is required to reclaim diluted glycol.
amine–glycol	Generally either monethanolamine (MEA) or diethanolamine (DEA) can be used for bulk H_2O removal but must be supplemented for NG liquefaction.
molecular sieves	Generally Linde type 4A arranged in either two- or three-column systems to allow for a continuous cycle of dehydration, regeneration, and cooling.
other dry dessicants	These include silica gel, activated alumina, activated bauxite, magnesium perchlorate, and calcium oxide usually arranged in two columns, one for dehydration and one for regeneration.

are the preferred means for regasifying the liquid, although several other methods are available.

Gas Purification Processes. Irrespective of the type of liquefaction cycle employed, small traces of contaminating gases that might solidify on cooling and plug piping or foul heat exchangers must be removed. Thus, as a general rule, the natural gas entering a liquefaction plant must be treated for the removal of water, carbon dioxide, sulfur compounds, and other natural gas constituents that could form solids as the gas is cooled for liquefaction.

The various processes for the removal of water are listed in Table 6. Notice that the amine–glycol dehydration system is considered useful for bulk H_2O removal only. A backup system is required to reduce the water content sufficiently for liquefaction. It has been specified that water concentration be reduced to 1 ppm (9), approximately 0.0416 lb of water/million ft^3 gas. By contrast, most high-pressure transmission lines carry gas dehydrated to a water-vapor level of 5–7 lb/million ft^3.

Removal of hydrogen sulfide and carbon dioxide can be accomplished in a number of ways (Table 7). Except for the iron oxide dry-box treating and the caustic treating processes, all of those listed have found general acceptance in the industry. The dry-box process requires an enormous amount of material for treatment of large-volume gas streams and two reactors for continuous operation. Thus, high capital charges plus high operating costs make this process unattractive in most cases.

The caustic treating or "lime" process is a once-through operation with a non-regenerable product. It is, therefore, suitable only for handling small quantities of gas with low quantities of impurities. As far as can be determined, caustic treating has never been applied to natural gas.

Table 7 lists CO_2- and H_2S-removal techniques. Other techniques are also available. These, however, are generally considered uneconomical and do not purify the acid gas sufficiently for liquefaction. An exception could be the Lacy-Keller process for which there are insufficient data to make a proper analysis. The process consists of an unidentified chemical solution that contacts the sour gas in an absorber. Colloidal sulfur is produced by reaction with this sweetening agent and the solution flows to flotation cells where the sulfur is flocculated and skimmed off the surface as a thick slurry. The remaining solution is passed to a regeneration cell that is operated without the addition of heat. The solution is then pumped to the absorber.

Table 7. H$_2$S and CO$_2$ Removal

System	Comments
molecular sieves	Generally, Type 4A molecular sieves are used to simultaneously remove CO$_2$ and H$_2$S in either two- or three-tower systems. Occasionally, Type 13X are used to remove cyclic sulfides and mercaptans used as odorants.
amine treating	Generally, monoethanolamine (MEA) in aqueous solution reacts with H$_2$S and CO$_2$ to form salts which readily decompose upon heating.
glycol–amine	Mixture of monoethanolamine (MEA) and diethylene glycol (DEG) and water used to simultaneously dehydrate and "sweeten" (remove H$_2$S and CO$_2$) acid gas. Dehydration not sufficient for LNG.
Giammarco-Vetrucoke	Uses two distinct processes, one for CO$_2$ removal, one for H$_2$S removal. Both processes are based on absorption of acid gases in an alkaline solution containing organic or inorganic additives. Typically, CO$_2$ removal uses arsenic oxide (As$_2$O$_3$) and selenious and tellurous acids, H$_2$S uses sodium and potassium carbonate solutions containing trivalent and pentavalent arsenic.
hot potassium carbonate	Very similar to amine treating, but absorption and regeneration take place at the same temperature. No liquid heat exchangers required.
iron oxide dry-box treating	Uneconomical for LNG plant pretreating.
caustic treating	Neither practical nor economic for LNG plant pretreating.

Process plants using the Lacy-Keller process remove both H$_2$S and thiols (mercaptans), but not CO$_2$. Two plants employing this process (10) have been built, one treating 12–20 million ft^3/day of sour gas and recovering 300 lb/day of sulfur. The sour gas contains 1.1 grams of sulfur per 100 ft^3 (0.4 g/m^3). Initial investment cost for the plant is reportedly comparable to that for an amine plant designed for the same service. However, operating costs are expected to run about one-tenth of that required for the amine plant.

Stripping of hydrocarbons can be accomplished in a number of ways. Associated with natural gas liquefaction, the separation of the heavier components, C$_{2+}$, in an LNG mixture can be accomplished by fractionating.

Liquefaction Cycles. In natural gas liquefaction cycles energy in the form of sensible and latent heat is removed. There are two widely used methods for heat removal:

1. In the cascade cycle heat is transferred through refrigerants to a high-level heat sink, such as cooling water or air.

2. In the expander cycle cooling is accomplished as the gas does work in an expansion engine.

There are also three modifications of these two basic cycles, all of which are explained briefly in Table 8.

Two additional methods of liquefaction are also included in Table 8, liquid-nitrogen exchange and the cold-gas refrigeration. In the case of nitrogen exchange, it would appear at this time that large capital investments necessary for the liquid nitrogen plant and storage tend to wash out any economic advantages. The cold-gas refrigerator system is inefficient for large-scale liquefaction plants, but could find application in small-scale operations.

Table 8. Liquefaction Cycles

Type	Process description	Major system components
cascade	Uses a series of refrigerants to obtain low temperatures until liquefaction of methane results. Principle first conceived by Pictet, later carried out by H. Kamerlingh Onnes and W. H. Keesom.	compressor; heat exchanger; cooling tower; instrumentation; control unit
modified cascade	Series of refrigerants found in conventional cascade cycle combined into one refrigerant stream, usually ethane and LPG, enriched with N_2 extracted from the feed gas stream. Liquefaction is accomplished by progressive cooling; condensation obtained by successive cooling steps with the single refrigerant stream.	refrigerant compressor; heat exchangers; throttling valves; instrumentation; control unit
expansion	High-pressure feed gas expanded through either a turbine or reciprocating engine to produce cooling effect. A portion is withdrawn to fuel the compressor; the remaining is further cooled by the expander effluent and finally throttled. Liquid then separated from the flash vapors and stored.	compressor; expander turbine or engine; heat exchanger; flash tank
combined cycles	Uses Joule-Thompson expansion, cascade, and expansion refrigeration techniques. Medium-pressure gas compressed, then cooled by a refrigerant stream, then split and passed through expander where some liquid is formed. Remaining vapor is throttled, liquefying more of the stream.	compressor; expanders; heat exchanger; Joule-Thompson valve; separator tanks
liquid-nitrogen exchange	Involves heat exchange between methane and a medium (nitrogen) at lower temperature than $-162°C$. Theoretically 2.14 lb of liquid nitrogen will liquefy 1 lb LNG.	heat exchanger
cold-gas refrigerator	Based on Stirling cycle, uses a fluorochemical refrigerant for precooling; for larger-capacity systems (greater than 500,000 ft³/day) some compression with intermediate Joule-Thompson expansions	precool refrigerant; cold-gas refrigerator; separator; compressor

Technological Trends in Liquefaction Systems. Since liquefaction represents such a large portion of the total cost, there are continual and extensive research programs underway to devise new liquefaction systems. These are primarily designed to reduce the horsepower requirements and/or heat-exchanger surface. A great number of complex schemes have been proposed. The single-refrigerant loop cycle, the so-called autorefrigerated cascade (ARC) cycle or single-duty compressor cycle, is presently finding increasing acceptance in large plants because of its simplicity of operation. Even though it does have a somewhat lower efficiency, the reduced complexity of plant construction and operation is a prime advantage in countries where labor skills are low.

Storage Systems. Two areas of interest have indicated a definite need for large-volume storage of LNG. In transporting gas from energy-rich to energy-poor areas in insulated tankers, the need for large storage depots at both the loading and the market ports is evident. In such base-load operations the storage facility is essentially a surge tank smoothing out the nonuniform base-load demand and fuel-delivery operations. It is not necessary to preserve the LNG in the surge tank for long periods because it is passed on to distribution within a short period of time. Consequently, a higher heat influx, resulting in greater boil-off rates, can be tolerated than in other situations.

In the second area, the continued growth and expansion of the natural gas industry has created the necessity for large-volume storage near metropolitan areas to meet the winter peak loads. In this case, LNG is stored for relatively long periods of time and used (ie, vaporized and distributed) during only a few days of the winter. Consequently, heat influx must be held to a minimum.

Whether the LNG plant is to be used for base-load operation or peakshaving, a large portion of the cost is the storage facility. Also, the large volume of storage associated with LNG plants represents a high concentration of energy. It is for these reasons, ie, economics and reliability, that recent research and development efforts have been concerned with storage concepts.

Various storage systems now in use or under development are listed in Table 9. At present (1970), installations based on the first three concepts are in service or being planned. Although the in-ground frozen pit concept has been a failure in the U.S., two different cavern-system concepts have been developed: (1) The Institute of Gas Technology atmospheric-pressure storage utilized primarily for peakshaving operations, and (2) The Gaz de France pressure storage for base-load operations. Both systems, as in the case of frozen pits, are highly dependent on geologic conditions at the site for establishing both technical feasibility and economics.

Table 9. Storage Systems

Type	Description
aboveground or belowground double-walled metal tanks	Tanks generally flat-bottomed, cylindrical, dome-roofed, with outer shell of carbon steel and inner shell of 9% nickel steel or aluminum. Insulation usually perlite with nitrogen or dry natural gas atmosphere in annular space.
prestressed concrete (belowground) tanks	Both circumferential and vertical stressing to eliminate ring forces and vertical bending stresses in concrete wall are applied. Floor construction may be of several types, all of which must provide for contraction during initial cooling. Wall insulation may be exterior or interior, provided an impermeable barrier is used on either wall surface. Roofs may be either metal or concrete.
prestressed concrete (aboveground) tanks	Similar to aboveground metal tanks except prestressed concrete is used as inner shell; can be either double- or single-walled. Insulation may be either external or internal. If outer shell desired, can be either carbon steel or concrete.
frozen in-ground pits	Excavated cavity made in frozen earth with no insulation or liner. Roof structure generally metal with various insulations. No success with pits constructed in rock.
mined cavern	Either atmospheric or pressure storage can be used. Atmospheric uses horizontal shaft entry with room-and-pillar cavern construction; pressure storage uses a vertical shaft. Both use insulation-liner system to contain LNG and reduce heat flux.

Table 10. Vaporization Systems

Type	Description
direct-fired	Uses flue gases from combustion of gas–air mixture as heat source to vaporize LNG. Flue gas circulated at 1000°F directly around tube banks at a velocity of about 400 ft/sec.
submerged combustion	Combustion gases from high-pressure fuel–air mixture bubbled up through water bath. Gas–water mixture circulates around tube banks at about 130°F to vaporize LNG.
indirect-fired	Uses heated water–glycol mixture to vaporize and superheat LNG in a heat exchanger. Water–glycol mixture heated by natural-gas-fired furnace.
ambient	Uses either atmospheric air or water to provide heat source to vaporize LNG. Very large surface areas required. Not recommended for large-scale use.

Vaporization Systems. It has been traditional to vaporize LNG before burning it. Whether this will be necessary or desirable in all applications in the future is open to question. Existing LNG base-load plants serve gas pipelines and, therefore, vaporization of LNG is mandatory. However, short LNG pipelines between a tank and a power-plant boiler, for example, may provide some simplification of equipment, though this would require special burners. Fortunately, there are a variety of reliable vaporizers available and these do not represent an inordinate part of the invested capital of the LNG system. Fired vaporizers absorb approximately 2% of the Btu that they transmit to the pipeline, so that the operating cost is not large. The primary requirements for a regasification system are: (1) LNG pumps; (2) heat exchangers; (3) controls; and (4) odorants (thiols or organic sulfides, about 0.5–1.0 lb/million ft^3).

Among the systems listed in Table 10, the pumps, controls, and odorants are quite similar. The main differences, as described in the table, are in the methods of heat exchange.

LNG Transportation Systems. After natural gas is converted to a liquid by cooling, it is readily transportable as a cryogenic liquid. The transportation equipment must meet the requirements imposed by the chemical composition and physical state of the liquid, but beyond that it poses no problems other than those found in transporting any other liquid fuel.

LNG Ocean Tankers. LNG tankers are unique among deepwater tankers in several respects. They are rated to operate at lower temperatures than any other liquid-gas carriers, ie −162°C. The cargo space is heavily insulated, reducing the effective cargo volume. The low-density cargo necessitates special ballasting systems. Tankers presently in use or under construction use a conventional steam-turbine propulsion system, but the fuel system is usually modified to allow the use of boil-off natural gas from the cargo tanks. The boil-off gas quantity when fully laden amounts to about 0.25–0.3%/day of the total volume for the LNG tanks and generally provides for a large part of the propulsion system (11).

The first LNG tankers in service, other than the experimental Methane Pioneer, were of modest size. The Methane Progress and Methane Princess have capacities approximately 27,400 m^3, or 172,000 bbl. The capacity is steadily increasing; the Descartes, constructed for Gazocean to be used for charter service, has a capacity of 314,500 bbl; the latest ships to be constructed by the Phillips-Marathon group for the Alaska-Japan project have a capacity of 450,000 bbl.

Future tanker orders indicate that LNG vessels will benefit from the economies of size that oil tankers have. El Paso Natural Gas Co. has already ordered tankers of 120,000 m³ (750,000 bbl) capacity, and Phillips Petroleum has indicated that it is considering 1 million-bbl tankers (167,000 m³).

Freestanding Tanks. The first LNG tankers built utilized the so-called freestanding tank construction. That is, conventional self-supporting insulated tanks were prefabricated and mounted in the hull of the ship. The Methane Progress, typical of this class of construction, carries 9 separate aluminum cargo tanks. The insulation installed between the cargo tank wall and the steel bulkhead is comprised of balsa wood panels sandwiched between layers of fiberglass.

The freestanding tank construction combined with the low density of LNG requires that LNG tankers have larger hulls with low draft and high freeboards. Since the cargo tanks cannot be used to carry water ballast as oil tankers do, separate ballast tanks must be provided at some cost and sacrifice of space.

The low temperature requires special materials, usually aluminum or 9% nickel steel, for the cargo tanks, and special arrangements must be made to accommodate the large expansion and contraction induced by thermal cycling of the tanks. The tanks, as well as all other equipment on board, must meet not only the containment and cryogenic requirements but also the shipboard environment. They must be able to withstand continuous vibration, sustained pitching and rolling—up to 35% from the vertical—and dynamic forces as great as 1.6 g. They are subjected to stresses induced by the hull deflection, and are constantly attacked by the corrosive seawater.

Membrane Tankers. In an effort to reduce tanker costs and give better utilization of the hull space, several companies undertook development of a new storage-tank concept in which the tank could be more nearly molded to the contours of the ship's hull. Since the inner tank need not be self-supporting, it can be made of a very thin, although impermeable, metal barrier. Thus the term "membrane tanker" developed. This type of tank was fully tested in the Pythagore and is installed in the two tankers which are being used for the Alaska-Japan trade, the Polar Alaska and the Arctic Tokyo (12).

The load, ie the weight of the liquid in the membrane-type tank, is transferred by the load-bearing insulation to the outer hull. The so-called Gaz Transport membrane system consists of an inner-membrane containment vessel made of Invar (36% nickel steel), perlite insulation, and an outer, wooden box that contains the perlite and transmits the cargo load to the hull. To conform to Coast Guard regulations a secondary barrier, which is designed to contain the cargo in the event of failure of the primary barrier, is installed.

Spherical Tanks. A third tank concept, which reportedly will reduce the cost of tankers from that of the membrane design, is the spherical tank system. Two such systems have been designed. One system, designed by Kvaerner Brug A.G. of Norway, will be incorporated into ships being built by Moss Rosenberg at Stavanger, Norway. The other is designed by Technigaz, a subsidiary of Gazocean. The Euclides is the prototype ship which incorporates the Technigaz design. A ship of 4000 m³ capacity, it has four 9%-nickel–steel 1000-m³ spherical tanks supported by three large circles situated in three perpendicular planes (horizontal, transversal vertical, and longitudinal vertical). Two rods and one articulated arm are fastened between the circles and ship hull. They transmit the stresses and forces caused by the expansion and contraction of the tanks and deformation of the hull to the ship's structure (13). Advantages of the Technigaz design are said to include better utilization of hull space, thinner steel plates, and the elimination of a secondary liquid barrier.

LNG Trailers and Tanker Trucks. Liquefied natural gas can be transported overland by either pipeline, tank trucks, or tank cars. Tank trucks, designed for road transport of LNG, have been operated successfully in the Soviet Union for a number of years. These trucks are used to distribute LNG to areas far removed from pipelines and to fuel trucks that are designed to run on natural gas. In the United States, as a logical consequence of the development of tank trucks for cryogenic usage with liquid oxygen, nitrogen, and hydrogen, tank trucks have recently been constructed for transporting LNG. Great Britain also has a number of urethan-foam-insulated trailers in operation.

LNG tanker trucks and trailers must meet the same criteria of safe containment of a flammable cryogenic liquid that ocean tankers must meet. Over-the-road trailers also must stay within stringent dimensional and weight limitations, but otherwise are quite similar in design concept to any other transportation equipment. An inner containment vessel made of cryogenic metal is surrounded by an insulating space. This may be a vacuum insulation or filled with a suitable insulating material such as perlite or urethan foam. An optimized trailer design which has been developed in the U.S. is a trailer having a capacity of 10,000 gal, equivalent to 918,000 ft^3 of natural gas. The tank has an operating pressure of 30 psig. Other trailers, ranging in size from 3000 to 11,000 gal, have been designed (14).

The trailer can be fitted with a gravity-fed vaporizing coil so that a pressure-transfer system can be used for unloading. In the event that the receiving vessel is at a higher pressure than the trailer-tank operating pressure, a cryogenic liquid transfer pump mounted on the truck can be used.

Railroad Tank Cars. Although LNG has not yet been transported by railroad tank car in the United States, tank-car designs have been prepared. A tank car designed for LNG service in accordance with the Department of Transportation Specification DOT 113C60W would carry 113,750 lb of LNG, equivalent to approximately 2.75 million ft^3. This is the largest sized tank car which can be used in unlimited interchange service. The internal stainless steel vessel is suspended within a carbon steel outer shell. The annular space is filled with perlite and evacuated. The inner tank suspension system is designed to minimize heat leak. The heat leak is so low that the total through the insulation, supports, and piping will result in a pressure rise of only 30 psi over a 40-day period.

Cryogenic Barges. Another mode of water transportation that has been considered is that of barging the LNG. Barges may be designed for either seagoing service or inland waterways, and while each has its own structural needs, stiffening members, etc, most design features are common to both. Barges have been designed that essentially consist of double-walled metal tanks with insulation in the space between the walls, similar to those built to transport the liquid hydrogen for NASA. These barges could be used as a means of distributing LNG from large central liquefaction plants to smaller local storage facilities.

Cryogenic barges offer an attractive and economic extension of the waterborne LNG transportation system. Deepwater tankers can serve only those ports with suitable berthing facilities, but shallow-draft barges could easily receive LNG from the tanker and, at low cost, move the fuel inland to river or lake ports. Their use has been considered by a number of companies. The first plan of Constock International,

Methane Ltd. in the U.S. was to move LNG from the Gulf Coast to Chicago via barge; at least one company has seriously considered using a seagoing barge. Although no LNG barges have as yet been built (excluding the barge-mounted trailers used by Boston Gas Co. to transfer LNG from the Aristotle to its plant in 1968), the cryogenic technology in hand should allow for their design and construction when needed.

Liquid Pipelines. The concept of liquid pipelining has been suggested as a means of reducing natural gas transportation costs. Since it is possible to move approximately $2\frac{1}{2}$ times the energy through a pipeline of the same internal diameter if the fluid is in the liquid rather than in the gaseous state, there would appear to be some possible economies of pipeline construction. However, these are largely offset by the need for cryogenic materials and insulation, and the costs of the outer containment shell. Also, since the line itself has a constant heat influx, the line must be operated either at supercooled conditions or with two-phase flow. Materials suitable for LNG pipeline construction are available. Presently existing insulation systems could be adapted to pipeline service. However, much more work must be done before an economically competitive LNG pipeline system could be developed.

Natural Gas as a Motive Fuel

The use of natural gas as an engine fuel is not necessarily new to everyone. The installation of compressed gas cylinders in automobiles was written into the Italian motor vehicle code as early as World War I. It was not until 1967 that much interest was shown in the United States and then, at first, only by two gas utility companies in California. It was not just compressed natural gas that was the subject of tests, however. LNG was tested in a Dodge pickup truck by San Diego Gas and Electric Company. Other interests have developed since the feasibility of operating an engine with LNG was proved. Because of its particular characteristics, LNG lends itself very well for use as a turbine fuel. As such it may well be used in supersonic transports (SST), helicopters, and perhaps even subsonic fixed-wing aircraft.

As a fuel it compares favorably with other liquid fuels, such as propane, gasoline, and diesel fuel, on a Btu/lb basis. For example, the heating value of LNG—assuming pure methane—is 23,885 Btu/lb (1010 Btu/ft^3), compared to 20,400 Btu/lb for diesel fuel. The drawback, however, is that LNG has a much lower density—3.54 lb/gal—so that the heating value per gallon is significantly lower than that of diesel fuel or gasoline, as shown below:

Fuel	Heating value, Btu/gal
LNG (pure methane)	84,700
diesel fuel, no. 2	136,000
propane	91,250
gasoline, regular grade	125,000

As has been explained, LNG is a mixture of methane, ethane, and perhaps some propane and butanes (more rarely heavier hydrocarbons), as well as nitrogen in most cases. The methane content of LNG can vary from as low as 85% to as high as 99%. A high-methane LNG poses no problem for use as a vehicular fuel, but LNG containing a large percentage of heavier hydrocarbons experiences a problem called "weathering." The lower-boiling components, usually methane and ethane, preferentially boil off, leaving a liquid richer in the heavier hydrocarbons. If provisions are not made, either to rapidly deplete the stock, install reliquefaction equipment, or periodically flush the storage tank, this change in composition can lead to engine knock due to the lower octane number of the heavier hydrocarbons.

Automobiles, Trucks, and Buses. The use of natural gas, in particular, as a fuel for motor vehicles has been prompted by the acute air-pollution problems in the U.S. as a whole, but particularly in major metropolitan areas where vehicular congestion is the greatest. According to a report published by the U.S. Department of Health, Education, and Welfare Public Health Service (15), the automobile accounts for 91% of all carbon monoxide, 63% of the unburned hydrocarbons, 48% of the oxides of nitrogen, as well as 8% of the particulate matter and 4% of the sulfur oxides. In the U.S. automobiles dump more than 90 million tons of pollutants into the atmosphere each year. This confirms the notion that the automobile is the prime polluter when compared with 30 million tons for industry, 15 million tons for coal and oil power generation, 8 million tons for space heating, and 3 million tons for refuse burning.

Natural gas has exhibited superior qualities for reducing exhaust emissions (Table 11). Although it is doubtful that natural gas (compressed natural gas, CNG) will

Table 11. Natural Gas Emissions Tests Compared to California Standards (17)

	Compressed natural gas, g/mile		1968 standards	1971 standards, g/mile	1974 standards, g/mile
	1968 Ford Ranchero	1965 Rambler Ambassador			
carbon monoxide	0.13% or 3.65	0.14% or 3.07	1.5%	23.0	23.0
hydrocarbons	88.0 ppm or 1.30	133.0 ppm or 1.81	275.0 ppm	2.2	1.5
oxides of nitrogen	554.0 ppm or 2.74	337.0 ppm or 1.29	no standard	4.0	1.3

ever capture the private-automobile fuel market, significant inroads can probably be made in fleet operations. According to a representative of Pacific Lighting Service Company of Los Angeles (16), 75 vehicles in its fleet had been converted as of December, 1969. All of their CO emissions measured about 1.3% prior to conversion and 0.13% after conversion. Hydrocarbon emission allowed by 1968 standards was 270 ppm; 78 ppm was achieved with CNG as compared to 217 ppm on gasoline. Gasoline exhausts contain approximately 50% olefins, the most active hydrocarbons, 15% aromatics, and the remainder paraffins. With natural gas, 10% of the exhaust emission is olefins and the remainder is methane, which is nonreactive and nontoxic. The third contaminant in exhaust emissions consists of the oxides of nitrogen. A Ford Ranchero emitted 1070 ppm oxides of nitrogen on gasoline and 114 ppm on natural gas. The average level of oxides of nitrogen emitted by the whole converted fleet was from 100 to 200 ppm. A second program has shown that this performance of natural-gas-fueled engines is maintained even after 42,000 miles of vehicle operation (17).

In addition to a decrease in exhaust emissions, there has been a noticeable reduction in engine maintenance (17). According to officials at the San Diego Zoo, this was one of the primary reasons for converting their tour buses to run on LNG. Tests to determine the actual maintenance benefits, however, have not as yet been documented. Trucks equipped with spark-ignited engines (Otto cycle) will, of course, gain the same benefits as the automobiles. However, at present, the conversion of diesel-engine trucks or buses has not been shown to be either economically or technically feasible. On the other hand, turbine-powered trucks and buses should prove to be an excellent application for the use of LNG as a fuel. Tests have been conducted on off-the-road ore carriers proving the technical feasibility of such ventures.

The aircraft-fuel market offers an even greater opportunity for LNG. Here there are sound technical reasons why high-performance supersonic aircraft at Mach 2 or greater need to use liquid methane. At speeds above Mach 3.5, heat buildup due to skin friction is so great that JP-4 and JP-5 (jet fuel) start to decompose and deposit carbon in the engine system. The fuels which should adapt best are LPG (liquefied petroleum gas), good to about Mach 4; LNG, good to Mach 6 or 7; liquid hydrogen, good at any speed above Mach 7; or highly exotic fuels that absorb heat by chemical change.

At present, the National Aeronautics and Space Administration is conducting a five-year development program to demonstrate the flyability of methane-fueled aircraft. Several industrial organizations are conducting in-house research on engines and airframes for LNG-powered aircraft. Technical reasons for using LNG in supersonic aircraft are to its favor, but LNG could also be used in conventional aircraft or helicopters. Particularly in helicopters, LNG's 15% greater energy-to-weight ratio can increase payloads by an amount equal to the weight saved.

Synthetic Food from Natural Gas

Natural gas may also be a source of high-protein and vitamin—particularly B vitamin—biosynthetic products (18). Many microorganisms have the ability to "eat" or metabolize simple hydrocarbons and convert them to a wide variety of products. Synthetic proteins suitable for livestock and poultry foods have already been introduced. These are produced from liquid petroleum fractions and natural gas by microbiological reaction.

Natural gas or methane is considered to be one of the best feedstocks for synthetic food supplies for human consumption (19). This is generally true, since there is virtually no problem in separating the product from unreacted feedstock and the elimination of off-flavors caused by other feedstock. On the average one pound of methane can "grow" one pound of foodstock (19). See also Proteins in this volume.

Fuel Cells

One major development associated with the space industry which may benefit the natural gas industry is the fuel cell. Considering the nature of its operation it might, however, be better classified as a "continuous battery" (20). The National Electrical Manufacturers Association defines a fuel cell as an "electrochemical cell which can continuously change the chemical energy of a fuel and an oxidant to electrical energy by an isothermal process involving an essentially invariant electrode–electrolyte system." By this NEMA definition, then, as long as fuel and oxidant are supplied to this continuous battery, it will not run down.

The operation of a hydrogen–oxygen fuel cell is similar to that of a lead–acid battery (20). Hydrogen is fed to the anode and is converted to hydrogen ions with the discharge of electrons. At the cathode, hydrogen ions from the electrolyte react with oxygen and electrons from the external circuit to form water. In this type of cell, the energy of the hydrogen fuel is recovered by forcing the necessary electron transfer to take an external path rather than recovering it as heat by simple combustion. As long as hydrogen and oxygen are fed to the fuel cell, it will continue to produce electricity.

Unlike conventional heat engines, fuel cells are not limited by Carnot efficiencies. In fact, for most common fuels and oxidants (reformed natural gas and air included), efficiencies up to 83% are theoretically possible (20).

Generally, all types of fuel cells work on the principle described above. There are, however, various types of fuel cell. High-temperature fuel cells operate at about 1000–1300°F (20). In this type of cell, methane can be used directly since steam reforming is presumed to take place on the surface of the anode (20). The molten carbonate "breathes" flue gas rather than straight air, since both carbon dioxide and oxygen must be present to form the carbonate ions. In this system, sponge nickel can be used as the anode catalyst and silver paint or copper oxide for the cathode (20).

Intermediate-temperature fuel cells operate near 500°F, at which temperature 85% potassium hydroxide melts to form an active electrolyte (20). Carbon dioxide must be eliminated in this type of cell to prevent the formation of carbonates which will precipitate out of the electrolyte. Reforming is then necessary to change methane and air into hydrogen that must be purified through palladium–silver diffusion membranes (20). Nickel is a satisfactory catalyst if reformed methane is used (20). Modifications of this cell, operating on pure hydrogen and oxygen, were used on board Apollo moon flights.

Plans call for the field testing of several modified intermediate-temperature fuel cells in 1970–1971. Results from this study will determine the economic potential and engineering viability of the fuel cell in commercial use. If proved successful, the most dramatic use would be in power packs for dwellings. In many areas of the United States, to a residential customer, the cost of a unit of energy in the form of natural gas is one-sixth to one-eighth as much as that of the same unit of energy in the form of electricity. Other uses for fuel cells should not be discounted, however. Mobile applications, while a long way off, are not out of the question. See also Fuel cells in this volume.

Environmental Conditioning

Total conditioning of the indoor environment is being recognized as a major goal of the natural gas industry in the United States. There is then a need for a completely integrated environmental control system capable of heating, cooling, filtering, humidity control, and ventilating. While great strides have been made over the last ten years on conventional cooling units—most noteworthy is the ammonia-absorption air-conditioning unit now on the market—recent activities bring the promise of a completely new system that should do much to revolutionize the residential air-conditioning market.

This system is the Munters Environmental Control (MEC) system, which is also known as the "Lizenzia" machine. Covered by numerous international patents owned by Carl Munters Co. of Sweden, technical development of the unit has been licensed to Gas Developments Corp. of Chicago and the commercial developments rights sublicensed to the Arkla Corp.

The mechanics of the MEC system are basically simple (21). Two parallel chambers make up the basic design. These are the air-intake and air-return passages. In separate sections of the passages, at right angles to the airflow, are two porous wheels that are the heart of the unit. Constructed of corrugated asbestos wound into tight rolls, thousands of parallel air passages permit air to flow through the wheels. One wheel, used for drying, is treated with LiCl to absorb moisture. The second wheel is treated to repel moisture and acts as a heat exchanger between the air intake and exhaust streams. Other components include air intake and exhaust fans, which supply air velocity for circulation through house ductwork as well as through the unit itself, and also a gas burner and water saturation pads. These pads are used to cool air through evaporation during the cooling cycle and humidify during the heating cycle.

The MEC system possesses a number of points not exhibited by any other single, integrated units. These are:

1. Three tons of air conditioning (36,000 Btu/hr), 100,000 Btu/hr of heating, humidity control, air filtration and ventilation.

2. Automatic compensation for the above design conditions. The unit's cooling capacity increases when inside or outside temperatures exceed design (21). When indoor temperature is 85°F and and the outdoor is at design (95°F), the MEC unit will perform at greater than double its design capacity (21).

3. Faster cool-down time is provided than by any other cooling unit.

4. The system can be designed for 80% efficiency during the heating cycle with humidification compared to 70% seasonal efficiency for a conventional gas furnace without humidification.

5. No water supply is necessary during winter humidification. Water recovery from the drying wheel and water formed by combustion are sufficient to maintain the proper humidity level.

6. Dehumidification can take place when ambient temperatures are 70–75°F, but the air is very humid. Conventional air conditioners can do this only with the addition of a reheat cycle.

7. The system can be operated at full fan capacity to supply a continuous flow of fresh outdoor air, and can be operated to deliver 100% fresh makeup air with no sacrifice in operating efficiency.

Bibliography

1. H. R. Linden, "Current Trends in U.S. Gas Demand and Supply," *Public Utility Fortnightly* **86**, 27–38 (1970).
2. *Energy Supply and Demand in Canada, and Export Demand for Canadian Energy, 1966–90*, National Energy Board, Ottawa, Canada, 1969.
3. "Forecast for the Seventies," *Oil Gas J.* **67**, 160–181 (1969).
4. "Natural Gas Supply Study," *U.S. Senate Committee on Interior and Insular Affairs Hearings November 13 and 14, 1969*, U.S. Government Printing Office, Washington, D.C., 1970.
5. *Am. Assoc. Petrol. Geologists Bull.* **53** (8) (1969).
6. *International Petroleum Encyclopedia 1970*, Petroleum Publishing Co., Tulsa, Oklahoma, 1969.
7. *World Oil* (1969).
8. M. A. Elliott, et al., "Report on the Investigation of the Fire at the Liquefaction, Storage, and Regasification Plant of the East Ohio Gas Co., Cleveland, Ohio, October 20, 1944," *U.S. Bur. Mines Rep. Invest.* **3867** (1946).
9. R. J. Schoofs, "Natural Gas Clean-Up Prior to Liquefaction," *Gas* **42**, 85–91 (1966).
10. "Gas-Sweetening Process Leaves in CO_2," *Oil Gas J.* **64**, 58–59 (1966).
11. J. W. Hunt, "The Techniques and Rudimentary Economics of Transporting Liquefied Natural Gas by Sea." *Paper presented at an Ordinary General Meeting of the Institute of Petroleum, London, March 2, 1966*.
12. W. L. Culbertson and J. Horn, "The Phillips-Marathon Alaska to Japan LNG Project," *Paper No. 13* in J. W. White and A. E. S. Neumann, eds., *Proceedings of the First International Conference on LNG*, Institute of Gas Technology, Chicago, 1968.
13. "Tanker Will Store LNG in Spheres," *Ocean Industry* **5**, 50–51 (1970).

14. "LNG: A Sulfur Free Fuel for Power Generation," *Final Report prepared for the National Air Pollution Control Administration, Public Health Service, and Department of Health, Education, and Welfare, under Contract No. PG 22-68-58*, Institute of Gas Technology, Chicago, Ill., 1968.

15. "Sources of Air Pollution and Their Control," *Public Health Service Publ. No. 1548*, U.S. Department of Health, Education, and Welfare, U.S. Government Printing Office, Washington, D.C., 1966.

16. R. Corbeil, *Paper presented at the Institute of Gas Technology Natural Gas-Fueled Vehicle Seminar, IIT*, December 4, 1969.

17. San Diego Gas & Electric Co., Press release of November 1968.

18. D. L. Klass and J. J. Iandolo, "Man, Microbes, Methane, and Food," *Amer. Gas J.* **194,** 30–34 (1967).

19. L. Hart, "Natural Gas Future's Food," *Chicago Am. Mag.*, August 6, 1967.

20. D. K. Fleming, "Progress in Developing Commercial Fuel Cells," *J. Petrol. Technol.* **19,** 749–755 (1967).

21. W. F. Rush and R. A. Macriss, "Munters Environmental Control System," *Appliance Engr.* **3,** 23–28 (1969).

N. Biederman
Institute of Gas Technology

GREAT SALT LAKE CHEMICALS

The Great Salt Lake, located in northwestern Utah, USA, has been mainly of geologic, historic, and touristic interest since its discovery in 1776. The mineral wealth of this highly saline body of water, estimated by some authors to have a value of 75 billion dollars, has been virtually untouched until recent years. To date, only a limited amount of common salt has been extracted and converted to saleable products. Reduction in the level of the lake increased the concentration of dissolved minerals, and advances in technology utilizing low-cost solar energy have combined to make the Great Salt Lake an attractive source of potash, salt cake, magnesium metal, and Li compounds. A number of companies have entered into mineral leases and options, which encompass a majority of the solar-pond area available on the lake. Three companies have constructed solar ponds and commercial production of K_2SO_4, Na_2SO_4, and $MgCl_2$ is planned to commence in late 1970.

History and Present Status of the Lake

The Great Salt Lake, GSL, is the largest lake in the western hemisphere that does not drain to an ocean. Approximately 30,000 yr ago, however, when the lake was considerably larger, there was an overflow to the Snake River Valley at Red Rock Pass, and the lake drained to the Pacific Ocean (1,2). Due to a change in climate more water

Table 1. The Climate of the Great Salt Lake Valley

Location	Total yrs recorded	Temperature, °F			Annual pptn, in.		Days/yr[b]	
		Mean annual	Extremes max	min	rain	snow	90°F and above	32°F and below
Antelope Island	14	51.6[a]	111	−14	15.06[a]	16.3	72	140
Bear River Refuge	29	49.9	105	−26	11.78	21.4	54	144
Salt Lake City (airport)	32	50.9	107	−30	13.90	51.4	56	138
Tooele	65	51.5	104	−16	15.48	72.8	23	131

[a] Extrapolated.   [b] Recorded from 1951 to 1960.

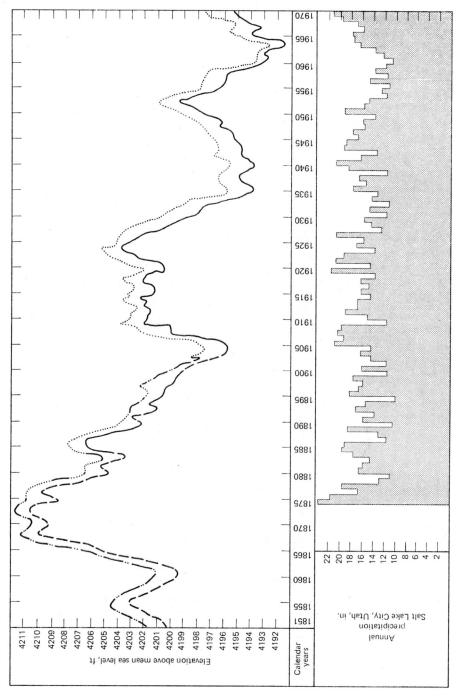

Fig. 1. Lake Level and Precipitation. Annual maximum and minimum elevation from 1851 through 1970. Annual precipitation from 1874 through 1970.

was evaporated than replaced by rain and inflow from the surrounding mountains. The history of the lake has been reconstructed by intensive geological research. Its level was carefully watched by the early settlers in the Great Salt Lake valley beginning in 1850 and accurately recorded since 1875 (1,2), as shown in Figure 1.

The area covered by the lake in fall 1969, when the level was at 4195.2 ft, is shown in Figure 2 (3). The climate in the valley is characterized by rather large fluctuations.

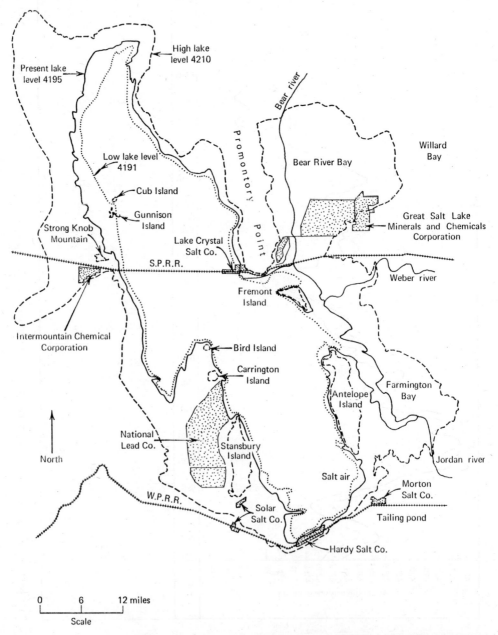

Fig. 2. The Great Salt Lake, shorelines vs lake level. Dotted areas: Operating companies. S.P.R.R: Southern Pacific Railroad. W.P.R.R: Western Pacific Railroad.

Table 2. Ranges of Concentrations[a] of Typical Brines Sampled from the Great Salt Lake, 1963–1965

Constituent or property	At inflow area[b]	Remainder of southern part of lake		North arm of lake	
		Min	Max	Min	Max
silica	11	2.0	5.1	1.1	4.2
calcium	62	126	342	164	312
magnesium	805	7,100	11,300	11,200	13,500
sodium	7,330	65,100	86,100	76,000	85,600
potassium	616	4,170	6,700	6,780	7,740
lithium	0.0	34	58	42	66
bicarbonate	303	369	473	477	523
carbonate	14	0	0	0	0
sulfate	1,430	11,400	24,800	20,000	27,400
chloride	12,900	113,000	149,000	141,000	155,000
fluoride	0.6	3.8	5.8	4.8	6.0
boron	0.0	19	46	29	52
bromide[c]		80	140	100	160
dissolved solids[d]	25,200	212,000	286,000	277,000	296,000
density, g/liter	1.011	1.153	1.218	1.214	1.223
pH	8.3	7.5	7.8	7.4	7.7

[a] In ppm, unless stated otherwise.
[b] Between Promontory Point and Fremont Island, October 1965.
[c] Determinations by GSLM & CC.
[d] Residue on evaporation at 180°C.

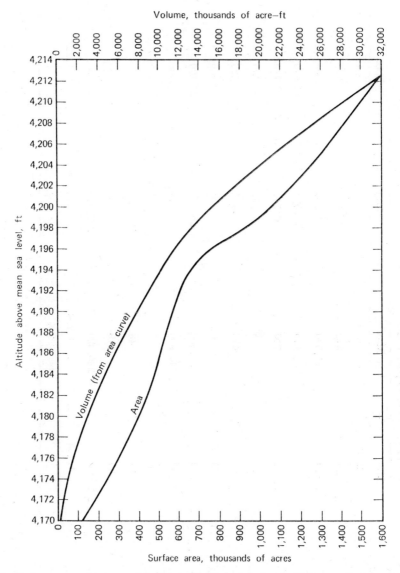

Fig. 3. Surface area and volume of the great salt lake vs lake level.   Data smoothed from various sources.

The summer is usually hot and dry.   The precipitation occurs mainly during winter and spring as shown in Table 1 (2,4).

The lake-level change is always accompanied by a change of the mineral concentration in the brine, but at a given level the brine concentration has always varied considerably at the different points and the different depths of the lake (4,5).

Most of the surface water inflow is from the northeast, east, and southeast through the Bear, Weber, and Jordan rivers, whereas the inflow from the other direction is almost negligible (Fig. 2).   This has been known for a long time, but the effect on the lake composition was not identified in detail until extensive sampling was started in 1963 at different locations and depths.

The interest in brine concentration may have been stimulated by the tremendous activity at the Great Salt Lake in the late 1950s, when the Southern Pacific Railroad completed a railroad causeway across the lake, dividing it into a northern portion, comprising approximately 35% of the total area, and a remaining portion to the south. The causeway was intended to be permeable; there are two culverts between the two portions of the lake which equalize the lake level (4,6). Table 2 shows the differences between the north and the south arm (2).

Due to the lack of information on the composition of the north arm brine before the causeway was built, it is very difficult to assess the effect of the causeway. It could be an accentuation and a stabilization of an already existing phenomenon. The latest detailed sampling of the lake has identified at least four different coexistent brines, as well as a flow of concentrated brine from north to south through the porous causeway and culverts. North of the causeway there is at least one type of brine, and three general brine concentrations have been identified south of it (4).

The north arm brine is the highest in concentration of most components, although it is lower in sulfate than the brine in most of the south arm. The exact material balance of salts is in question because concentrated brine which flows from the north to the south arm does not mix well. Investigations show that the upper 5 ft are more dilute than the underlying brine. In the deeper sections (5–20 ft) two different brines can be distinguished: One type immediately south of the causeway. The brine obviously leaked in from the north arm. The other type at the south end of the lake. This type in contrast to most of the south arm is greatly depleted in sulfate. The source of this brine is not known.

Estimating the mineral content of the lake is quite difficult, since depth and concentration show a wide variation. The situation is further complicated by the division of the lake into two arms. Figure 3 gives a survey of the surface area and the volume depending upon the lake level (7,8).

Table 3 shows the total amount of salt present in the lake for various years (7,9). This table indicates that this amount is not constant as might be anticipated, but becomes smaller if the lake level decreases. This strange effect has been explained by the flatness of the lake shore. If the lake level decreases, brine pools are separated from the main lake and are completely dried out, and it appears the remaining salt is carried away by the wind, a great deal of which drops on the Wasatch Range east of the GSL by prevailing winds and is subsequently recycled to the lake.

The inflow of dissolved minerals to the lake has been investigated by D. C. Hahl (5). This inflow includes recycle as well as amounts given up by erosion of native soils. The similarity of the ratio of dissolved solids in the Great Salt Lake and the ocean (see Table 4) have led to the belief that salts in the lake originated from the ocean. It is postulated that winds physically carried ocean brines to the basin where runoff water then has carried the salts down to the lake.

Table 3. History of Great Salt Lake Mineral Inventory (9)

Year	Millions of tons
1873	6,390
1896	5,873
1961	4,129
1963	4,198

Table 4. A Typical Brine Composition.

Constituent	Concentration in the brine, wt %			g/100 g dissolved solids		
	GSL	Dead Sea	Ocean	GSL	Dead Sea	Ocean
chloride	14.1	17.5	1.94	55.2	65.1	55.4
sodium	7.6	3.3	1.08	29.8	12.3	30.8
sulfate	2.0	0.7	0.27	7.8	2.6	7.7
magnesium	1.1	3.4	0.13	4.3	12.6	3.7
potassium	0.7	0.6	0.04	2.7	2.2	1.1
calcium	0.016	1.4	0.04	0.06	5.2	1.1

Commercial development of the lake has always been considered. The earliest settlers obtained their table salt from the lake and at the present time salt is produced for commercial sales by four companies (see Fig. 2): Hardy Salt Co., Lake Crystal Salt Co., Morton Salt Co., and Solar Salt Co. Production by these companies amounts to approx 400,000 tons/yr of NaCl.

There have been a number of attempts to recover other valuable minerals. During World War I, when potash was in great demand, the Diamond Match Co. started potash production near Grantsville at the south end of the lake, but could not compete because of high production and freight costs.

Much attention has been given to the recovery of sodium sulfate from Glauber's salt, $Na_2SO_4.10H_2O$, which crystallizes from the Great Salt Lake brine during winter time. In 1932 the Salt Lake Sodium Products Co. was formed to produce Na_2SO_4. A plant was built, but soon abandoned, because it also turned out to be uneconomical (8).

In recent years there has been considerable new activity concerning the development of a minerals industry on the lake. Interest has been directed mainly towards the more valuable constituents of the lake brine. This interest might be explained by the decrease in lake level in the early 1960s, exposing wide areas around the lake useful for solar ponding, and by the increasing demand for Mg and Li.

Consumption of Mg metal has steadily increased since 1964 and has exceeded production for the past 3 yr. Civilian and military aircraft, automobile industry, and Al alloying account for most of the present use and the expected future growth. Li metal and its various compounds find increasing applications in the production of lubricating greases, glass and ceramics, aluminum, swimming-pool sanitizer, air conditioning and refrigerating systems, and most recently as drugs for the control of manic-depressive psychosis. Total world demand for lithium has doubled during the last 5 yr.

Several companies have retained rights to lands around the lake (see Fig. 1) and to extract minerals. National Lead Co. has shown a strong interest (10) which recently resulted in the announcement of plans to construct a $70 million facility for a 1972 startup. Great Salt Lake Minerals & Chemicals Corporation built a solar evaporation complex in 1967 (11). The processing plant is due on-stream late 1970. Combined facilities investment by the company will be in excess of $30 million by 1971.

A large part of the ponding land available around the Lake is land exposed as a result of the lowering of the water level of Great Salt Lake. A procedure for resolving a dispute between the State of Utah and the U.S. Government as to title to this land was established by the passage in 1966 of legislation by which the U.S. Government granted title conditionally to the State of Utah. As a result of such legislation, industrial enterprises are able to make economic use of the leased land and will not be materially affected should title to the land revert to the U.S. Government. The final decision on ownership is presently pending in the U.S. Supreme Court.

Solar-Pond Operation

The complexity of a solar-pond system is dependent upon the type of minerals to be recovered from the Great Salt Lake brines. All solar ponds are affected to some degree by the following variables: (1) meteorology (evaporation, temperature, wind, radiation, humidity); (2) brine concentration entering and leaving the pond; (3) pond depth; (4) pond area; (5) leakage of pond liquors into the ground; (6) entrainment of pond liquors in crystallized salts; (7) type and amount of salts crystallized in the pond.

The significance of each variable is dependent upon the total amount of evaporation and the type of minerals to be crystallized. Pond leakage, for example, is always of concern, but is less important in areas of high evaporation, or when sodium chloride is the only salt produced.

Pond leakage results in lost production and generally is undesirable. In a system of ponds where brine must be preconcentrated and then flowed from pond to pond to make magnesium chloride, the total time lapse from the time it enters the first pond to the time it leaves may be 2 yr. If the average depth of a pond is 12 in. and leakage causes the level of brine to drop 0.01 in./day, then over 60% of the brines will be lost to the ground. Leakage in NaCl crystallizing ponds is not as significant if the brines in these ponds are not to be held for crystallization of other salts later. The longer brines are held, the more significant is the leakage consideration. The residence time in a NaCl pond will range from 1 to 3 months. A leakage of 0.01 in./day in this case would cause a loss of less than 8%. Actual leakage rates are determined by the permeability of the soil. Because sealing of vast pond areas is uneconomical, a very extensive soil investigation program has to prove the suitability of a given area for solar ponding before constructing the pond.

Another problem associated with leakage is the total entrainment in the salt floor. Brine entrained in the voids between salt crystals is lost for further production unless it is released. This entrainment may be 50% or more by weight in the crystallized salts.

Net evaporation is a function of all meteorological conditions, the two most important being solar radiation and precipitation. Evaporation is greatest where it is hot and dry. Other factors affecting the evaporation are wind, humidity, and concentration of the brine. The latter has a profound effect on the evaporation of the brines. As the brine becomes higher and higher in dissolved solids, the vapor pressure of the brine is reduced and the evaporation is, therefore, reduced. Depending upon concentration, the quantity of water evaporated from a highly concentrated brine may be only 10% of what would be evaporated from seawater.

The chemical composition of the feed brine determines what type of salts will crystallize as evaporation begins. A typical brine composition of the Great Salt Lake is shown in Table 4. The composition of the ocean and the Dead Sea is also shown.

Some brines, such as ocean water, are not saturated in any salt and must be concentrated before saturation occurs. Figure 4 shows a system of solar ponds that might be used with almost all brines with ion concentration similar to that of Great Salt Lake and ocean water.

The preconcentration ponds are used to bring the brines to saturation of sodium chloride. At this point, brines are transferred to another pond to crystallize the salt.

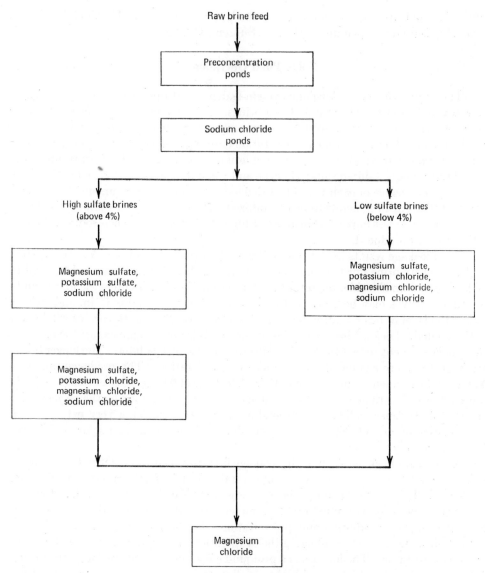

Fig. 4. Flow diagram for solar evaporation.   The names in the blocks indicate the compounds in the salts that are crystallized.

The brines leaving the preconcentration ponds will contain about 19–21% NaCl and about 28–30% total dissolved solids.   Only NaCl will crystallize until one of the other constituents becomes concentrated, through evaporation, to saturation.   Companies producing only NaCl usually discard the brine well before saturation of other salts. This is done to reduce contamination of the NaCl by entrained brine containing high concentrations of undesired ions (mostly Mg).   Potash producers, who are interested in the potassium salts, use the NaCl ponds as a purification step to reduce the Na content in the brine as much as possible before saturation of the potassium ion begins.   Some brines, pumped from underground sources, are already at or near saturation of the potassium ion, and the preconcentration pond and the NaCl ponds are not necessary.

Saturation of the potassium ion occurs at 2–2.5% at ambient temperatures. If the SO$_4$ ion is near 4% or above, the potassium will crystallize in the various forms of K–Mg double salts. Low-sulfate brines will yield KCl and carnallite. The phase diagrams shown in Figures 5 and 6 indicate the salts that are stable in equilibrium with lake brine or higher concentrated brines resulting from evaporation of lake brine.

Lake brine has a composition in the astrakanite field close to point U. By evaporation the brine follows the crystallization path V–W–X–Y–R–Z and salts adjacent to these lines may crystallize. Solubility of MgSO$_4$ in warm brines (100°F) may be twice

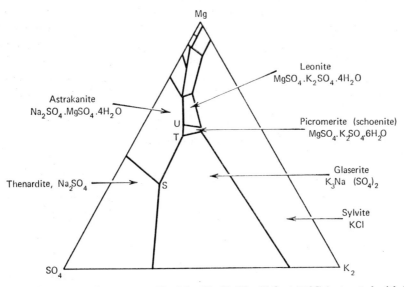

Fig. 5. Phase diagram of the system: Na, Mg, K, Cl, SO$_4$, H$_2$O at 25°C (saturated with NaCl).

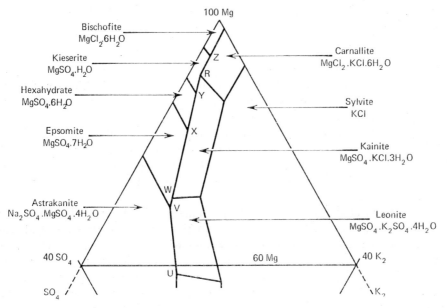

Fig. 6. Enlargement of phase diagram shown in Figure 5 at high magnesium concentrations.

as high as its solubility in cold brines (30°F). This is significant and must be considered during the temperature increase and decrease at the beginning and end of an evaporation season. The solubilities of all of the ions are affected by the temperature of the brine.

Material-balance calculations are sometimes quite difficult, but must be made frequently when a large array of salts is to be crystallized. In a simplified system of a salt pond (NaCl) feeding a potash pond, care must be taken not to feed the potash pond with brine from the salt pond too soon. The dilute brine will not be saturated with potassium, and introduction into the potash pond will contaminate it with unwanted NaCl. If the brine is pumped too late, then some of the potassium salts will crystallize and be lost to the salt pond. The salt pond must be sized so that it will feed just the right amount of brine to the potash pond. A salt pond too large will make too much brine for the potash pond and either the potash-pond area must be increased or some of the brine must be discarded. Too small a salt area will not supply enough brine to the potash area, resulting in over-concentration of the potash brines and insufficient use of pond area.

Table 5. Salts That May Crystallize from Great Salt Lake Brines

Mineral	Formula
astrakanite (bloedite)	$Na_2SO_4 . MgSO_4 . 4H_2O$
bischofite	$MgCl_2 . 6H_2O$
carnallite	$KCl . MgCl_2 . 6H_2O$
epsomite (bitter salt)	$MgSO_4 . 7H_2O$
glaserite (apthitalite)	$Na_2SO_4 . 3K_2SO_4$
Glauber's salt	$Na_2SO_4 . 10H_2O$
halite	$NaCl$
magnesium sulfate hexahydrate	$MgSO_4 . 6H_2O$
kainite	$KCl . MgSO_4 . 2.75H_2O$
kieserite	$MgSO_4 . H_2O$
langbeinite	$2MgSO_4 . K_2SO_4$
leonite	$MgSO_4 . K_2SO_4 . 4H_2O$
schoenite (picromerite)	$MgSO_4 . K_2SO_4 . 6H_2O$
sylvite	KCl

A delicate balance exists between all of the variables, and if brine concentrations are to be controlled, then all of the variables must be known. One variable that is estimated, but never really known, is the evaporation rate. High rainfall may occur during a particular month or year, completely changing the status of the solar pond and the production forecasts. Although the weather forecasts may have reversals, with appropriate meteorological equipment the type of weather just passed can be measured accurately and appropriate action taken to keep pond concentration in control.

Of all the variables considered in the pond design, the weather will be the hardest to predict and, therefore, an over-design is sometimes used to correct for "bad years." Often sales commitments cannot be met because of an unexpected wet season. This places the company as an unreliable supplier. The pond design should, therefore, be made to bridge lean years by holding in reserve extra salts made in good years. Good pond design will provide a constant supply of salts to meet sales commitments regardless of the weather.

The total array of salts that may crystallize depends again on the concentration. Table 5 shows some of the typical salts that may crystallize in solar ponds, using Great Salt Lake brine.

Harvesting Salt from the Solar Ponds.   After the desired salt has crystallized and collected on the pond floors, there remains the logistical problem of removing it and taking it to the processing plant. Salt companies around Great Salt Lake do not all use the same method. Hardy Salt Co. harvests NaCl with a self-loading scraper, carries it to the plants, dumps it, and then returns for another load. Lake Crystal Salt Co. uses a road grader to windrow the salt. A front-end loader is then used to stockpile the salt into the pond. Trucks are then loaded from the stockpile or windrows and the salt is carried into the processing plant. Morton Salt Co. and Solar Salt Co. both use a harvester specially designed to remove the salt from the floor, convey it, and load a truck running next to it.

The equipment used depends on the subsoil under the layer of salt to be harvested. If soils are made of soft clays and mud, then a sufficiently strong salt floor must be there to support the equipment harvesting it. Some companies require that there is a separation between the salt to be harvested and the salt left behind and needed to support the equipment. Such a cleavage plane is made by dragging the ponds during the spring with heavy weights. The weights crush the crystals of salt on the top of the floor and prevent salt that will crystallize during the summer from fusing to the old floor used as the equipment-supporting base. It may take 2 or 3 yr to build this base in new ponds before any product can be removed from the pond.

Problems encountered in harvesting the salts are compounded when minerals, other than NaCl, are produced. Many of the potash and Mg salts are much harder than NaCl. More energy is needed to break the salts and lift them away from the base floor. Equipment specially designed for the harder salts is used. The corrosive nature of the brines also increases and precaution must be taken to protect and care for the equipment. Figure 7 is an illustration of a harvesting machine.

Solar-Pond Design and Construction.   The main features of pond facilities constructed to utilize solar evaporation techniques for the recovery of minerals include: (1) impervious base soils and dikes to retain the brine; (2) canals to transmit brine from the source to appropriate ponds; (3) pumps to elevate the brine over dikes and existing land gradients; and (4) structures to facilitate flow between ponds. The design and construction of ponds and dikes in the Great Salt Lake basin must also consider fluctuations in the lake level (see Figs. 1 and 2), and must be so constructed that in the event of a substantial increase in the lake level dikes can be increased in height conveniently and at low cost to protect the solar ponds from intrusion of lake brine.

The choice of material to construct dikes is related primarily to cost of construction, required permeability and erosion resistance, and the availability of materials. Dikes can be economically and conveniently constructed by excavation and piling the material adjacent to the dike location, utilizing draglines or backhoes. The amount of local material is determined by the dike height and slope, which in turn are dictated by depths of the brine. In some cases where material is readily available near the pond site, rock or gravel materials can provide low-cost dike construction which resists erosion more effectively than the local clay materials. A combination of local material in the center of the dike and imported granular covering can sometimes provide the best means of dike construction by providing maximum leakage and erosion resistance at minimum cost. All three methods are utilized on the shores of the Great Salt Lake for

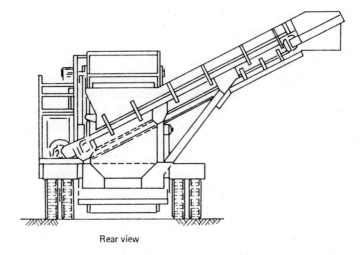

Rear view

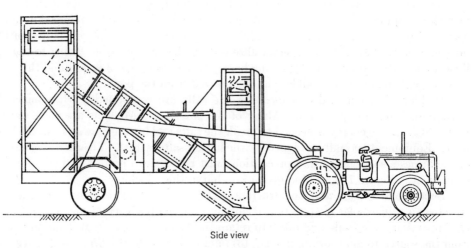

Side view

Fig. 7. Harvesting machine, model Palmer-Richards. The cutting edge of the longitudinal conveyor is height adjustable and controls the thickness of the harvested layer. The harvested material is transferred to the transversal conveyor and discharged into a truck (not shown), running with equal speed alongside the harvesting machine.

solar ponds. The choice of dike construction depends on the location and the process, and operating and maintenance requirements. The same type of construction used to build pond dikes is also utilized for the construction of canal dikes. In locations where canals carry brine over permeable ground, a plastic lining—polyethylene or poly(vinyl chloride)—is oftentimes employed to prevent leakage of brine. Pumps for transporting brine from the lake to the solar-pond system, and in some cases for subsequent use between ponds, are usually of a vertical turbine type. Operators on the lake have successfully used pump-construction materials ranging from plastics to stainless steels and bronze alloys. Weir structures to regulate flow between canal and ponds and from pond to pond vary, depending on the layout of the pond system. Many facilities have been built that utilize little or no control weir structures; others have a significant number. The structures are normally constructed of wood and the weirs designed to regulate an overflow from pond to pond or, in some instances, submerged weirs are used to control flow when an overflow design is not a desirable feature for controlling pond levels.

As with dike construction, the design of auxiliary solar-pond facilities depends largely upon the location, quality of soil, the elevation of the pond system in respect to the lake elevation, the process function of the ponds, and the type and concentration of the brines being processed.

The purpose of the Great Salt Lake Minerals & Chemicals Corporation solar-pond system is to evaporate brines so that Na and K salts and $MgCl_2$ brines can be recovered and processed. The project is contained in the Bear River Basin in the northeast end of the lake, adjacent to Promontory Point (see Fig. 2). The initial development utilizes 14,000 acres of land east of Promontory Point. The brine is taken from the north arm of the lake and transported by means of pumps and an 8.5-mile canal system to a solar-evaporation-pond system. The evaporation pond area is divided into salt ponds, potash ponds, sodium sulfate ponds, and various storage ponds (13).

The area of the various ponds was determined from a material-balance study and the location was established by topography, soils, access to fresh water, and accessibility for operating personnel. The Bear River passes through the project area near Promontory Point and is separated by peripheral dikes that protect the ponds from high stages of the Great Salt Lake and the river. The heights of dikes are designed to be increased in the event the lake level should rise. The pumping station at the Bear River is designed to pump brine from the north arm over the Bear River to the upper northeast reaches of the pond system during the evaporation season, and is also arranged to take fresh water from the Bear River for washing unwanted salt from the pond system. The disposal of unwanted NaCl is a key feature of any development designed to recover potash or magnesium from Great Salt Lake brines. If provision is not made to dissolve salt, the operator on the lake must consider plans to construct additional ponds after the ponds are filled with salt. The facilities were constructed in 1967 and operated successfully during 1968 and 1969.

During the 1967–1968 construction period, over 6,000,000 yd^3 of material were handled in constructing 150 miles of dikes and roads and over 3,000,000 board ft of lumber used to construct bridges, flumes, flow structures, and pump stations.

Beneficiation Processes

Potash. It may be noted that the term "potash" is often applied to any commercial potassium compound. See Vol. 16, p. 369. During World War I the Diamond Match Co. built a potash plant at Grantsville at the south end of Great Salt Lake. This was the only early plant designed to produce potash directly from the brines of the lake. The brine was preconcentrated in solar ponds and then fed to evaporators. In 1916, however, the plant was abandoned, because it could not compete (14). Progress was not really made until basic research was done in the very complicated system containing Na, K, Mg, SO_4, Cl, and water. The classical work is that of Van't Hoff and D'Ans (15).

There was a growing interest in the Great Salt Lake in the early 1960s, and consequently many articles were published (12,16,17). Glassett (12) evaporated lake brine stepwise at 25 and 80°C and tried to separate the various salts crystallizing. He concluded that evaporation steps alone are not a satisfactory method to isolate the different salts. Actually, potassium chloride has been produced in Utah for many years at Wendover from underground brines. These brines, however, are very low in SO_4, and therefore differ considerably from the Great Salt Lake brine. When evaporated, these brines yield KCl as the first potassium salt which is harvested and separated from NaCl by flotation (17).

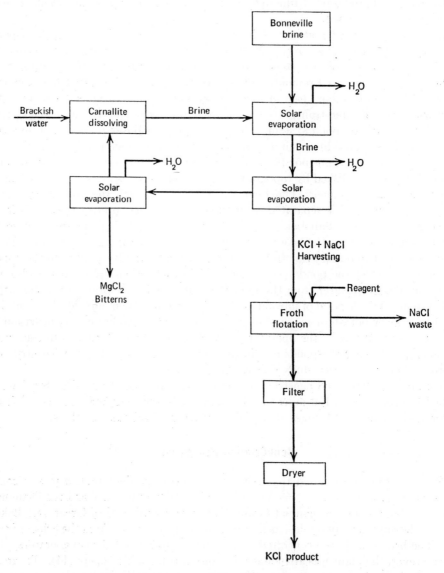

Fig. 8. Production of KCl at Wendover, Utah (17).

Since the technique for the production of KCl at Wendover (see Fig. 8) is well known, it has been suggested that the sulfate be removed from the Great Salt Lake brine, followed by use of the Wendover method. One possibility is the addition of calcium salts (18,19) (see Fig. 9).

If the Great Salt Lake brine is cooled to below about 0°C, Glauber's salt crystallizes and takes considerable amounts of SO_4 out of the brine (12). If the temperature is lowered enough, the resulting brine, when evaporated, produces KCl as the first potash salt (12,19,20).

George et al. (21) suggest precipitation of the SO$_4$ with BaCl$_2$, followed by reduction of BaSO$_4$ to BaS which can then be used to produce sulfur from the lake brine.

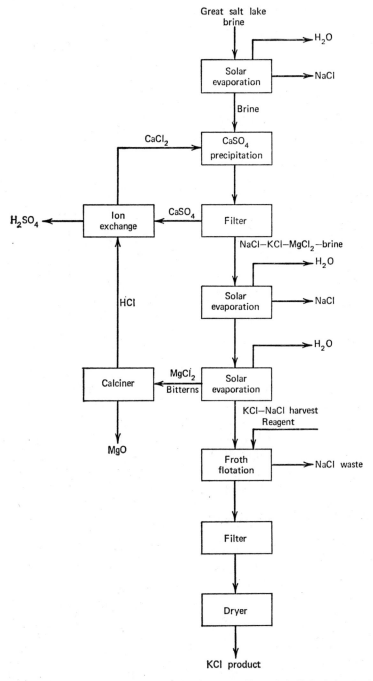

Fig. 9. Sulfate removal and KCl production from Great Salt Lake brine (18).

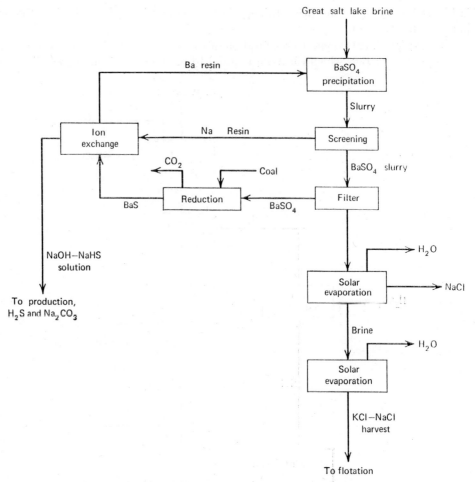

Fig. 10. Sulfate removal by BaSO₄ precipitation and ion exchange (21).

The Ba salts are regenerated by ion exchange.   KCl can be produced from the desulfated brine (see flowsheet Fig. 10).

Another method (22) to extract potassium from Great Salt Lake brine is described by a patent. Potassium is precipitated potassium as $KClO_4$ and the perchlorate regenerated by ion exchange.

Although many publications concentrate on the removal of sulfate from the brine, there are also studies to find out what happens during evaporation if the sulfate remains in the brine. Using phase diagram data, Hadzeriga (17) calculated the salts that theoretically should crystallize if Great Salt Lake brine is evaporated at 25°C as follows:

	Percent of total available	
Mineral	*K*	*Mg*
as astrakanite		12.4
as leonite	38.6	7.1
as kainite	46.3	17.0
as carnallite	11.6	4.3
in residual brine	3.5	59.2

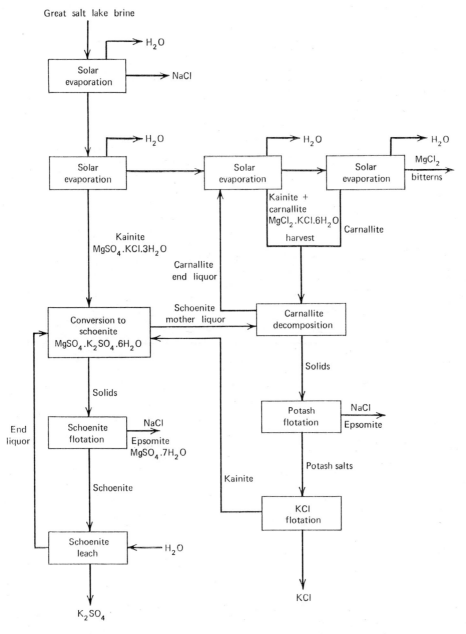

Fig. 11. Production of KCl and K$_2$SO$_4$ from potash harvest (24).

The potassium crystallizes as leonite, kainite, and carnallite. The Mg appears in 4 different salts; if the residual brine is further evaporated, bischofite ($MgCl_2 \cdot 6H_2O$) crystallizes. In a later publication (23) Hadzeriga studied the formation of the different salts in evaporation tests and found that actually astrakanite, leonite, and kainite could not be identified, and that schoenite ($K_2SO_4 \cdot MgSO_4 \cdot 6H_2O$), sylvite (KCl), and epsomite ($MgSO_4 \cdot 7H_2O$) formed instead.

A process following the general solar-evaporation outline has been published (24). Complicated mixtures of schoenite, kainite, KCl, carnallite, and MgSO$_4$ salts are

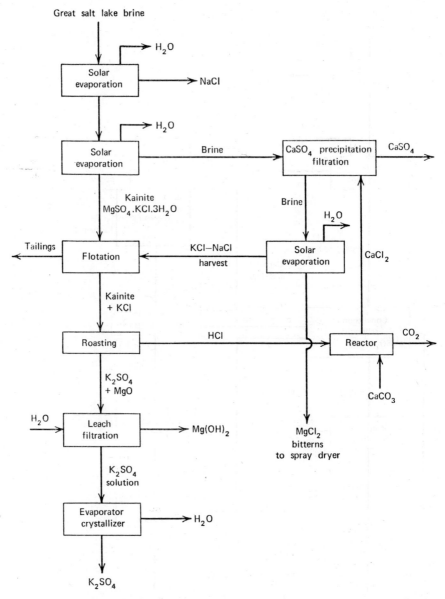

Fig. 12. Production of K_2SO_4 and bitterns with partial sulfate removal (19).

crystallized if Great Salt Lake brine is evaporated (Fig. 11). Separation of these minerals is essential for recovering the potash values. Separation of kainite and KCl is described in reference 25, the separation of schoenite from NaCl and $MgSO_4$-hydrates in reference 26. Clean schoenite can be converted to K_2SO_4; this was reported as early as 1881 (15,27).

Kainite can be converted to K_2SO_4 by a different process (19). Kainite mixed with KCl is roasted at 1250°F, thereby developing HCl gas. The resulting solids are slurried in water, Magnesium hydroxide is filtered off, and K_2SO_4 crystallized from the remaining brine (see Fig. 12).

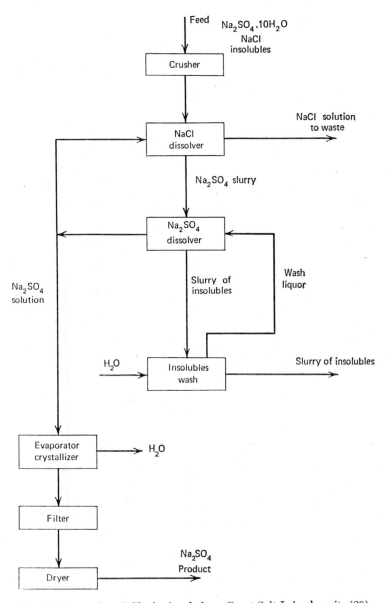

Fig. 13. Processing of Glauber's salt from Great Salt Lake deposits (29).

The first large-scale production of potash has been announced by Great Salt Lake Minerals & Chemicals Corp. in 1967 (13).   A solar-pond system (see Fig. 2) is already in operation.   A processing plant with a capacity of 240,000 tons K_2SO_4 per year is under construction; startup is scheduled for fall 1970.

Sodium Sulfate Processes. Production of sodium sulfate from the Great Salt Lake was suggested as early as 1890 (1).   It was recognized that Great Salt Lake brine is saturated with respect to sodium sulfate during the cold season (2).   Thus large quantities of Glauber's salt, $Na_2SO_4 \cdot 10H_2O$, crystallize during wintertime in the north arm of the lake and to a lesser extent in the south arm as well, forming large reefs adja-

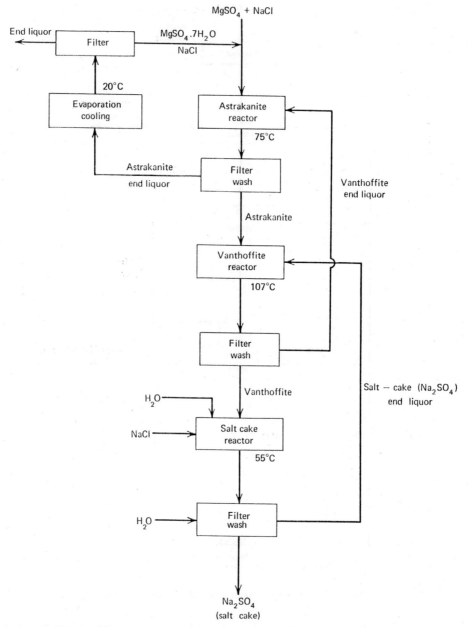

Fig. 14. Production of sodium sulfate from magnesium sulfate salts (30).

cent to the shore line (8). These deposits of Glauber's salt could be harvested and processed if there were economical methods to pick it up. Glauber's salt is dehydrated to obtain Na_2SO_4.

Deposits of Glauber's salt have been found at the bottom of the lake as well (28). Covered with layers of clay, they are separated from the lake waters. It has been suggested to mine a Glauber's salt deposit at the south end of the lake (29). (Analysis on a dry basis: 52% Na_2SO_4, 40% NaCl, and 8% insolubles.)

The raw material is crushed (see flowsheet Fig. 13) and treated with a solution of sodium sulfate (produced later in the process), thereby dissolving the NaCl completely and obtaining a Na_2SO_4 slurry, which is thickened. The main portion of the liquor is rejected; the salt cake slurry is transferred to a second reaction step where Na_2SO_4 is dissolved in water. The clarified solution is partly used in the NaCl dissolving step and partly evaporated to obtain Na_2SO_4.

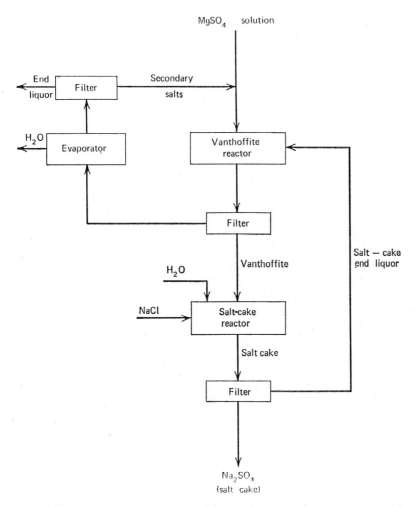

Fig. 15. Production of sodium sulfate from magnesium sulfate salts (32) (two-step process).

It is also possible to obtain Glauber's salt by cooling Great Salt Lake brine in special holding ponds, taking advantage of low winter temperatures. The chemistry of the cooling process has been described by Glassett and Anderson (12).

If Great Salt Lake brine is evaporated, $MgSO_4$ salts are deposited, which can be used as a source for producing Na_2SO_4 as well. A process is described by Conley and Partridge (30). Epsomite and NaCl are converted to astrakanite ($Na_2SO_4 \cdot MgSO_4 \cdot 4H_2O$) at a temperature of 75°C. The filtered astrakanite is reslurried and converted to vanthoffite ($MgSO_4 \cdot 3Na_2SO_4$), at a temperature of about 107°C. The vanthoffite,

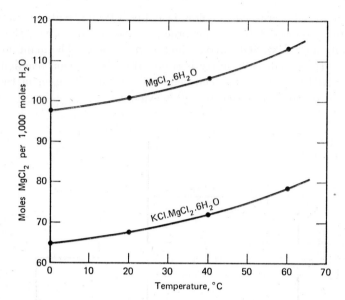

Fig. 16. Solubility curves of carnallite, KCl.MgCl$_2$.6H$_2$O, and bischofite, MgCl$_2$.6H$_2$O (D'Ans (15)).

again, is filtered and treated with NaCl and H$_2$O to crystallize Na$_2$SO$_4$ which is filtered and washed (see Fig. 14).

The astrakanite step can be skipped, and the MgSO$_4$ salts directly converted to vanthoffite, as described by Schwarzenauer (31) and Dancy (32). (See Fig. 15.)

Detailed studies of the stable and metastable equilibria in the aqueous system Na$_2$Cl$_2$ and MgSO$_4$ in the temperature range between -5 and 90°C have been published by Autenrieth (33).

The first large-scale facility to produce salt cake from the Great Salt Lake is being built by Great Salt Lake Minerals and Chemicals Corporation (GSLM&CC) and is due on-stream in fall 1970 (13). GSLM&CC harvested feedstock is a mixture of NaCl hydrated MgSO$_4$ (epsomite), and Glauber's salt. It is first upgraded to improve the SO$_4$ content and, under carefully controlled concentration and temperature conditions, is then converted to a high-quality Na$_2$SO$_4$. Purity ranges between 99.5 and 99.7%. Annual capacity will be 150,000 tons of product. The major markets for this compound are manufacturers of paper and detergents. Paper mills employing the Kraft process use Na$_2$SO$_4$ as a reagent in the digestion of wood pulp. Large quantities of high-purity Na$_2$SO$_4$ are also used by detergent manufacturers in compounding their products. Other applications include ceramic and glass manufacturing.

Magnesium Chloride. The Mg concentration in the Great Salt Lake ranges from 0.71 to 1.13% by weight in the south arm and 1.12 to 1.35% by weight in the north arm. During the solar evaporation of the lake brine (34), MgCl$_2$ stays in solution until the brine reaches a concentration of about 70 moles MgCl$_2$ per 1,000 moles H$_2$O. Further evaporation causes the crystallization of carnallite, KCl.MgCl$_2$.6H$_2$O, together with salt. At about 110 moles MgCl$_2$ per 1,000 moles H$_2$O, the brine becomes saturated with respect to MgCl$_2$.6H$_2$O (15). (See Fig. 16.)

The brines with higher MgCl$_2$ concentrations, generally called bitterns or bischofite, represent a very suitable raw material for the production of purified MgCl$_2$, which consequently is used as feed for the electrolytic Mg metal and Cl production. (See

Vol. 12, pp. 661 and 719 and Chlorine in this volume.)   The relatively high $MgCl_2$ concentration in the Great Salt Lake together with the low-cost solar energy, provides the basis for a highly competitive bulk $MgCl_2$ production (35–38).   Several companies with magnesium interests have entered the lake area.   The following appear to be the most advanced (39,40).

The National Lead Company.   The Mg project, a former joint venture of National Lead Company, Hooker Chemical Co., and Hogle-Kearns of Salt Lake City, is now 100% owned by National Lead and called The Magnesium Division.   A solar-evaporation-pond system, consisting of 3 ponds covering a total area of about 11 by 8 miles and 2 pump stations, has been in operation since 1966.   The company announced plans to produce up to 45,000 tons per year of Mg metal and 80,000 tons per year of chlorine at the Great Salt Lake.   Total investment for ponds and plant is estimated at 60–70 million dollars.   The ponds are located at the south arm in Tooele County between Stansbury Island and Lakeside Mountains.   The proposed plant site is about 25 miles northwest of Grantsville, Tooele County.   Up to 80 MW of interruptible power will be delivered by Utah Power & Light Company for 3.1 mills per kWh, and there is additional capacity of 40 MW in a company-owned power plant.   Waste heat from the gas turbines fired with natural gas will be utilized in spray dryers to dehydrate $MgCl_2$ brine.   Startup of the plant is scheduled for late 1971 to early 1972.   Both major products, Mg and Cl, have to be shipped to customer areas.   Potential by-products include potash, salt, gypsum, and lithium compounds.

A process for the production of $MgCl_2 \cdot 2H_2O$, NaCl, K_2SO_4, $CaSO_4$, MgO, and HCl starting with Great Salt Lake brine and $CaCO_3$ has been described above (see Fig. 12). Kainite precipitated in solar ponds is purified by flotation and thermally decomposed into HCl gas and a mixture of MgO and K_2SO_4.   The latter is leached and crystallized. The HCl gas reacts with $CaCO_3$ to form $CaCl_2$, which is used to precipitate the SO_4 contents of the combined mother liquors as gypsum.   The desulfated brines are further concentrated by solar evaporation, yielding carnallite and a high $MgCl_2$ brine, which is finally spray-dried to obtain a solid $MgCl_2$ with about 1.5–2 moles H_2O.   McCormick (41) modifies this to a product with approximately 5% water and 5% oxide, which is consequently molten and purified to remove both water and oxide.   This material is fed to an electrolytic cell similar to the Magnesium-Elektron Ltd. cell (MEL-cell), in which National Lead has large-scale experience from its jointly owned subsidiary Titanium Metals Corporation of America.   These cells are designed to operate on a bath composition approximately as shown in Table 6.

Table 6. Typical MEL-Cell Bath.

Electrolyte	Wt %
$MgCl_2$	13.0
$CaCl_2$	34.0
NaCl	30.5
KCl	22.5

Great Salt Lake Minerals & Chemical Corporation (GSLM & CC).   GSLM & CC is jointly owned by Gulf Resources and Chemical Corporation of Houston, Texas (51%), and by Salzdetfurth A. G. of Hannover, West Germany (49%) (13).   Lithium Corporation of America, a subsidiary of Gulf, started feasibility studies on the Great Salt Lake in 1963.   Test ponds were operated from 1965 to 1967, and a commercial pond system of 12,000 acres constructed in 1967. This system has been in operation since 1968 and has been increase to 14,000 acres.

Bitterns resulting from this operation contain up to 600,000 tons per year of $MgCl_2$. The company entered into a 15-yr contract with The Dow Chemical Co. for delivery of 100,000–200,000 tons per year of $MgCl_2$ as purified magnesium chloride hexahydrate commencing in late 1971. Dow will construct a plant to further dehydrate this product and ship it to its new magnesium-metal plant to be constructed at Dallesport, Washington, where very inexpensive hydroelectric power is available, presumably at about 2 mills per kWh (42).

Plant output is 48,000 tons magnesium metal per year and 100,000 tons elemental chlorine per year, with investment of 20 million dollars at Dallesport and an additional 6–10 million dollars at the Great Salt Lake to be shared almost equally by Dow and GSLM & CC (43). Only a very simplified flowsheet has so far been published (13), showing that bitterns are processed in a steam-evaporating plant. The effluent, probably enriched in Li and Br, is shown to be processed together with bitterns from the ponds in a Li and Br extraction plant.

Intermountain Chemicals Corporation. This company is 90% owned by International Chemicals Development Corporation. In early 1969, 2,500 acres of ponds were constructed on the west side of the lake just south of the Southern Pacific Railroad. The company announced plans to produce $MgCl_2$, MgO, and Li salts.

A patent granted to J. G. Macey (20), now president of this company, describes a combined process to recover Li and K values from Great Salt Lake brine, which also yields bischofite and high $MgCl_2$ brine.

Sodium Chloride. Solar evaporation is the primary step in the recovery of NaCl from the Great Salt Lake. Washing and drying of the crude salt are performed as required by the market. Annual production from the lake is approximately 400,000 tons.

All of the salt producers, except one, take their feed from the southern end of the lake. Methods employed for producing the crude salt are all similar. Lake brine is pumped into preconcentrating ponds where, by solar evaporation, the saturation point, with respect to NaCl, is reached. The saturated brine is then transferred to crystallizer ponds (garden ponds) where the crude NaCl is deposited. The brine becomes saturated at about 1.20% Mg and is rejected at between 2.70 and 4.00% Mg. Higher Mg in the brine results in a contaminated product and one of a smaller crystal size. Normally, the ponds are operated 3–10 in. deep. The dikes of the garden ponds are lined with wood to prevent contamination with clay. In size the ponds vary from 20 to 150 acres. One producer has ponds that vary from 20 to 1,800 acres.

The salt is harvested each year. A deposit of one season is 2–5 in. thick. Generally, the harvest begins in September and is completed sometime in November. If the harvest is not completed by the time cold weather sets in, the salt hardens due to formation of the dihydrate $NaCl.2H_2O$ and harvesting becomes more difficult.

Beneath the annual harvest are 12–18 in. of base salt that is used to support the harvesting and hauling equipment. This base salt is deposited by operating the pond for several years without harvesting. The production season is relatively short. Actual crystallization of recoverable salt begins sometime in June and lasts until the harvest begins in September. As the production season begins, a cleavage plane is made by dragging the ponds. The dragging smooths the pond floor and helps to ensure easy separation of the year's crop from the base salt.

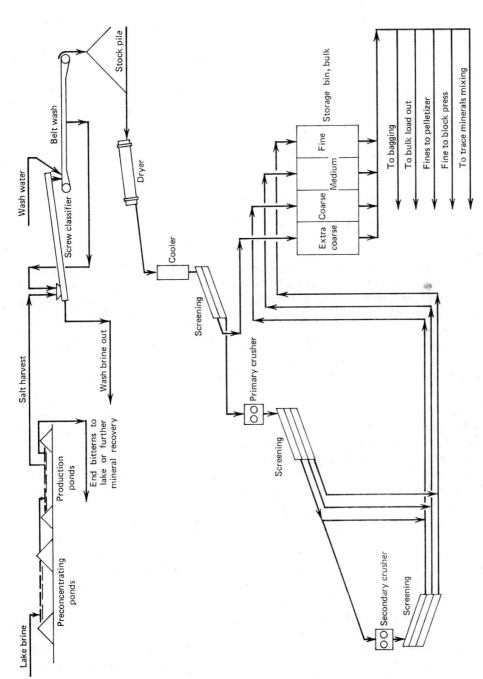

Fig. 17. Typical facilities for the production of salt at the Great Salt Lake.

During the harvest, the salt is brought into the area near the processing plant where it is stockpiled as crude salt, or washed and then stockpiled. An alternative is for the salt washing to be done before the stockpile. The crude salt is reclaimed from the stockpile, washed, dried, and cooled. The dried salt is crushed and screened into several grades. The crushing and screening step is usually done in two to four stages in order to obtain the desired control of size. See Figure 17. See Sodium chloride under Sodium compounds.

Lithium Salts. The economical recovery of Li from the Great Salt Lake brine presents a difficult task considering the low concentration of Li present and the mixture of other materials in solution as shown in Table 2. However, after the Li values are concentrated in the $MgCl_2$ bitterns following potash recovery, the problem is simplified somewhat. Typical bitterns analysis is the following:

Wt %	Wt %
Mg, 8.6	Cl, 24.2
K, 0.13	SO_4, 2.6
Na, 0.18	H_2O, 64.3
Li, 0.04	

It is readily apparent that the major problem is that of separating the Li from the major cationic impurity, Mg. The Mg cannot be separated from the Li by crystallization, and therefore it must be recovered by some other method or alternatively the Li must be extracted from the bitterns mixture.

Evaporation-Crystallization, Thermal decomposition. This process employs mechanical evaporation to produce a $MgCl_2 \cdot 6H_2O$ crystalline product and a strong LiCl (6%) liquor (44). Further concentration of Li would result in loss of LiCl in the $MgCl_2 \cdot 6H_2O$ product. The Mg is then removed from the LiCl-rich liquor by thermally decomposing the $MgCl_2$ to form HCl gas and MgO. The soluble LiCl is leached from the insoluble MgO and can be recovered as Li_2CO_3 by carbonation with Na_2CO_3 or as LiCl by evaporation-crystallization.

Ion Exchange. Acid retardation and ion retardation have been suggested for the separation of Li from the Mg and other alkaline metals in solution (45). However, investigations by the Lithium Corporation of America (LCA) and Dow Chemical (46) (46) led to the conclusion that these methods do not give sufficiently good separation.

Hansford and Raabe (47) concluded from their studies that ion exchange can be adapted to separate Li, Na, and K but that in actual practice where Li exists in solution with large amounts of alkali metal, alkaline earth metal, and other metal cations so many complicated variables are introduced that these impurities would have to be first sorbed on the resin. It would be extremely difficult to operate an efficient ion-exchange system where the Li content is much smaller than that of the other cations.

Lithium Aluminate Complex. It is known that an insoluble aluminate of lithium ($LiAlO_2$) can be obtained, from solutions containing Li and other alkali metals. Recent investigators (48–50) have developed processes for the recovery of Li contained in small concentrations from aqueous solutions containing alkaline earth metal salts. The processes involved reacting an aqueous solution containing Li and alkaline earth metals with a soluble aluminum salt such as $AlCl_3$ and precipitating a major portion of the Li as lithium aluminate complex without concomitantly precipitating substantial quantities of alkaline earth metals. Control of temperature and alkalinity are necessary for optimum formation of the aluminate. Neipert and Bon (50) discuss a method producing a granular form of lithium aluminate which is easier to filter than the gelatinous product formed by the process of Goodenough (48).

The recovery of the Li from the aluminate complex may be accomplished by several means. Suggested methods are a hydrothermal digestion followed by an ion exchange concentration of the resulting LiCl (51) and a dissolving of the complex with an acid, adding ammonium to precipitate ammonia alum NH_4Al $(SO_4)_2 . 12H_2O$, followed by recovery of the Li (49).

Solvent Extraction. The solvent extraction of lithium from solutions containing other metal cations has been reported as an analytical method for the separation of Li primarily from alkaline earth metals. Guter and Hammond (52) found that a chelating agent, dipivaloylmethane $((CH_3)_3CCO)_2CH_2$, binds Li ions selectively under alkaline conditions. Ether was found to be the best common organic solvent.

Lee's method for extraction of Li values from an alkaline solution of other alkali metals employs a chelating agent and a Lewis base solvating ligand (53). The chelating agent is selected from β-diketones and analogs thereof and the solvating ligand is an amine or organophosphorus compound, with an organic aliphatic or aromatic solvent capable of dissolving the chelating agent and solvating ligand.

However, these solvent extraction processes are not applicable for recovery of Li values from Great Salt Lake bitters, because of the high pH required, which would precipitate the Mg as $Mg(OH)_2$. LCA (54) found that Li can be selectively extracted from an acid solution into an organic phase as a complex. Best results were obtained when a mixture of solvents was used in order to obtain synergistic effects. The Li is subsequently recovered in a Mg-free aqueous solution from which it can be removed as LiCl by crystallization or as Li_2CO_3 by addition of Na_2CO_3.

Bromine. Bromine can be recovered from the $MgCl_2$ bitters prior to recovery of $MgCl_2$ and other values. This process consists of chlorination of the brine to oxidize the bromides to bromine and subsequent steam stripping to remove the liberated bromine. These operations are carried out simultaneously in a suitable column. The brine is acidified to a pH of 3–3.5 in order to avoid losses of halogen and to improve the liberation of bromine. The theoretical Cl_2 requirement is about 0.46 lb Cl_2/lb bromine liberated; however, the actual requirement can increase to 0.6 lb or higher if the brine contains organics or other reducing substances. Some organics are contained in the Great Salt Lake bitters. The steaming-out process is considered suitable for brines with bromide contents as low as 1 g/liter (55). See also Bromine.

Bibliography

1. G. K. Gilbert, "Lake Bonneville," U.S. Geological Survey, Vol. 1 (1890).
2. *Guidebook to the Geology of Utah*, No. 20, Utah Geological Society, Salt Lake City, Utah, 1966.
3. A. J. Eardley, *The Great Salt Lake*, a map published by Utah Geological and Mineralogical Survey, Univ. of Utah, 1961.
4. D. C. Hahl and A. H. Handy, "Chemical and Physical Variations of the Brine," *Water Resources Bulletin 12*, Utah Geological and Mineralogical Survey, 1969.
5. D. C. Hahl, "Dissolved Mineral Inflow to Great Salt Lake," *Water Resources Bulletin 10* (1968), Utah Geological and Mineralogical Survey.
6. T. C. Thomas, "Salt Migration to the Northwest Body of Great Salt Lake, Utah," *Science* **143** (3610) 1027–29 (1964).
7. A. J. Eardley, V. Gvosdetsky, R. E. Marsell, "Hydrology of Lake Bonneville and Sediments and Soils of its Basin," *Bull. Geol. Soc. Am.* **68** (9), 114–1202 (Sept. 1957).
8. "Geology of Salt Lake County," *Bulletin* **69**, Utah Geological and Mineralogical Survey (1964).

9. R. E. Cohenour, A. J. Eardley, W. P. Hewitt, and H. R. Bradford, *Report of Investigation No. 3*, Utah Geological and Mineralogical Survey, 1963.
10. *Chemical Week*, **98** (9) 15–16 (Feb. 26, 1966).
11. *Chem. Eng.* **75** (13), 106 (June 17, 1968).
12. J. M. Glassett and B. J. Anderson, "Recovery of Salts from Waters of Great Salt Lake," *Bulletin No. 128* of the University of Utah, Eng. Experiment Station, Salt Lake City, Utah, 1964.
13. "The Great Salt Lake Project," pamphlet by Great Salt Lake Minerals & Chemicals Corporation, Ogden, Utah, 1969.
14. M. C. Gardner, "Chemical Industry Potential of the Great Salt Lake," *paper presented to Seventeenth Annual Industrial Development Conference, State of Utah, Salt Lake City, 1966.*
15. J. D'Ans, *Die Loesungsgleichgewichte der Systeme der Salze ozeanischer Salzablagerungen*, Verlag Fuer Ackerbau, Berlin, 1933.
16. D. E. Garrett, "Crystallization of Potash," *Chem. Eng. Prog.* **59** (10) 59 (1963).
17. P. Hadzeriga, "Some Aspects of the Physical Chemistry of Potash Recovery by Solar Evaporation of Brines," *Trans. AIME* **229**, 169 (1965).
18. U.S. Pat. 3,099,528 (July 30, 1963), P. Hadzeriga (to Standard Magnesium Corp.).
19. U.S. Pat. 3,432,258 (March 11, 1969), L. W. Ferris (to National Lead Co.).
20. U.S. Pat. 3,342,548 (Sept. 19, 1967), J. G. Macey (to Signal Oil & Gas Co.).
21. D. R. George, J. M. Riley, and L. Crocker, "Preliminary Process Development Studies for Desulfating Great Salt Lake Brines and Sea Water," *U. S. Bur. Mines, Rept. Invest.* (1967). **6928**
22. U.S. Pat. 3,429,657 (Feb. 25, 1969), D. R. George, J. M. Riley, and J. R. Ross (to U.S. Government).
23. P. Hadzeriga, "Dynamic Equilibria in the Solar Evaporation of the Great Salt Lake Brine," *Soc. Mining Eng. Trans.* **238** (4) 413–419 (1967).
24. French Pat. 1,514,676 (Jan. 15, 1968), D. E. Garrett.
25. U.S. Pat. 3,447,681 (June 3, 1969), J. Ramirez.
26. U.S. Pat. 3,456,791 (July 22, 1969), J. Ramirez.
27. H. Precht, *Dinglers Polytech. J.* **241**, 456–464 (1881).
28. A. J. Eardley, "Glauber's Salt Bed West of Promontory Point, Great Salt Lake," *Special Studies* **1** (1962). Utah Geological and Mineralogical Survey.
29. K. G. Larsen, "Optimum Design of an Anhydrous Sodium Sulfate Plant," Thesis 1965, Brigham Young University, Provo, Utah.
30. J. E. Conley and E. D. Partridge, "Anhydrous Sodium Sulfate from Saline Deposits or Brine by a Four-stage Process," *U.S. Bur. Mines Rept. Invest.* **3299** (1936).
31. Ger. Pat. 406,555 (April 3, 1921), W. Schwarzenauer.
32. U.S. Pat. 2,952,515 (Sept. 13, 1960), W. B. Dancy (to International Minerals and Chemical Corp.).
33. H. Autenrieth and G. Braune, *Kali Steinsalz* Nos. 1,3 (1960).
34. A. F. Nylander and J. H. Jensen, *Mining Eng.* November 1964, p. 64.
35. *Metals Week*, May 27, 1968, p. 14.
36. *Utah Desalination Study*, State of Utah, Atomic Energy Commission, Salt Lake City, Utah, Dec. 1968.
37. Utah Power and Light Company, *Testimony given in Public Service Commission, Raft River Hearing*, Exhibit 186, January 1968.
38. D. A. Elkins et al., "Economic Aspects of Magnesium Production," *AIME, Extraction Metallurgy Div. Operating Conf., Cleveland, Ohio, Dec. 2–4, 1968.*
39. *Chemical Week*, September 6, 1969, p. 15.
40. *Chemical Engineering*, August 25, 1969, p.60.
41. W. R. McCormick, *paper No. A-70-50, presented at the TMS-AIME Annual Meeting*, Denver, Colorado, Feb. 16–19, 1970.
42. *Metals Week*, June 16, 1969, p. 5.
43. *Metals Week*, December 9, 1968, p. 3.
44. Studies by Lithium Corporation of America (LCA), unpublished.
45. M. J. Hatch, J. A. Dillon, and H. B. Smith, *Ind. Eng. Chem.* **49** (11), 1812–1819 (1957).
46. Unpublished correspondence and studies by LCA and The Dow Chemical Co., 1964.
47. U.S. Pat. 3,101,246 (August 20, 1963), D. L. Hansford and E. W. Raabe.
48. U.S. Pat. 2,964,381 (Dec. 13, 1960), R. D. Goodenough.

49. D. Kaplan, *Israel J. Chem.* **1**, 115–120 (1963).
50. U.S. Pat. 3,306,700 (Feb. 28, 1967), M. P. Neipert and C. K. Bon.
51. U.S. Pat. 2,980,497 (April 18, 1961), R. D. Goodenough and V. A. Stengh.
52. G. A. Guter and G. S. Hammond, *J. Am. Chem. Soc.* **78**, 5166–5167 (1956).
53. U.S. Pat. 3,479,147 (Nov. 18, 1969), DeWayne A. Lee.
54. Studies by LCA, unpublished.
55. Z. E. Jolles, *Bromine and Its Compounds*, Academic Press, New York-London, 1966.

G. FLINT
Great Salt Lake Minerals & Chemical Corp.

H

HALOGENATED FIRE RETARDANTS

With the increasing acceptance of plastics in all phases of modern construction, flammability or lack thereof is becoming of greater and greater concern to government and private interests. Further expansion of plastic production and sales, particularly in construction materials, is therefore dependent to a large extent on solving this problem. In early plastics applications, the small size of fabricated articles made fire retardancy a secondary consideration, but as applications on a larger scale present themselves, this factor assumes a role of increasing importance. Improvements over the first non-flammable plastics have been made, but further large-scale development requires even more effective methods. In addition to emphasis on nonburning, it is becoming more and more apparent that polymers which do not smoke under ignition conditions are needed. See also Fire resistant textiles under Textile technology in this volume.

Imparting fire-retardancy to flammable compositions has been largely provided by the incorporation of halogen and/or phosphorus compounds, although a wide variety of other elements and compounds have also been suggested. Often a combination of elements has been used to obtain a synergistic increase in fire-retardant efficiency. These elements have been used as simple additives mixed with the basic polymer or they have been incorporated by one means or another into, or grafted onto, the polymer backbone.

Commercial halogen products currently used are chlorendic acid, tetrachloro-phthalic anhydride, and chlorinated waxes (and other hydrocarbons). More recently, the commercial importance for tetrabromophthalic anhydride, tetrabromobisphenol-A, and 2,2-bis(bromomethyl)-1,3-propanediol has increased because of the greater efficiency of bromine.

The economic importance of halogenated fire retardants is illustrated by the estimated 17 million lb of reactive fire retardants used in 1968 for unsaturated polyesters alone (approximately two thirds of which was chlorendic acid). Sales of chlorinated waxes during this period were estimated to be 9.5 million lb (1). The phenomenal growth that can be expected for these products is illustrated by the market for fire-retardant reinforced polyester laminates, consumption of which is expected to increase from about 100 million lb in 1969 to more than 1.5 billion lb in 1975, a phenomenal fifteen-fold increase. It is growth of this kind that results in the increased industrial research in these areas.

The main topic of this article is the application of the halogen products in polymers. Phosphorus additives are included only where they have a bearing on the subject. Only problems of bulk polymers are considered, while special problems of fibers, fabrics, coatings, and elastomers are mentioned only in passing.

Because of the voluminous literature on fire retardancy, a complete survey is not attempted here. Some of the more general information has been drawn from several excellent review articles (2,3,3a).

Terminology. The application of such terms as fireproof, flameproof, or flame resistant to organic polymers which burn, pyrolyze, or char at flame temperatures has often led to ambiguity about relative flammabilities of different materials. Therefore the precise definitions of terms as applied in this article are listed below.

Fire retardant—used to describe plastics whose basic flammability has been improved or reduced by some modification as measured by one of the accepted test methods.

Burning—used to describe plastics which are essentially entirely consumed by a flame under test conditions.

Self-extinguishing—applies to those plastics which ignite under the test conditions, but which stop burning within a short period after removal of the ignition source.

Nonburning—applies to those plastics which do not ignite under the test conditions. This is sometimes difficult to differentiate from self-extinguishing.

Noncombustible—refers to refractory materials which do not "burn" except under the most severe conditions.

Smoke—airborne vapor and particulate matter emitted from fires, especially in sufficient quantity to pose a problem in toxicity or visibility.

Testing

Common test methods (4,5) used for plastics are listed below, with a brief description of each.

SCREENING TESTS

ASTM D 635-68, Test for Flammability for Rigid Plastics. This is a standard method for obtaining comparative data on rigid, moderately fire-retardant polymeric materials, 0.127 cm thick, or thicker. Although no limit is specified on thickness, 0.5-in. injection molded bars are recommended. A flame is touched to one of the lower corners of a rectangular specimen placed at 45° from the vertical, as shown in Figure 1, for 30 sec. A second 30-sec ignition is applied if the specimen extinguishes after the first flame application. The sample is rated "nonburning," "burning," or "self-extinguishing," according to its behavior after the second ignition. For self-extinguishing materials, the distance burned is the "extent of burning." This is a relatively mild test, but results can vary significantly if comparison is not made between samples of the same shape and dimensions. The ASTM D 635 is commonly used to rate rigid plastics.

Underwriter's Laboratories Modification. The above test does not distinguish between polymers that extinguish by their inherent fire-retardant nature and those that extinguish when the flame front is carried away by the dripping of molten polymer. Underwriter's Laboratories, Inc. (UL) has suggested a modification of the ASTM D 635–68 to overcome this difficulty. The modification consists of placing a wad of cotton beneath the specimen during the test. A distinction is made between those samples which ignite the cotton and those that do not.

UL Subject 94, Burning Test for Plastics Classed as Self-Extinguishing. Test specimens are 6 in. long and $\frac{1}{2}$ in. wide in both $\frac{1}{16}$ in. and $\frac{1}{8}$ in. thickness. Two sets of specimens of each thickness, three specimens per set, are provided for each test. One set of each thickness is tested in the "as-received" condition; the other set is tested after being aged in an oven at 70°C for a duration of seven days. The burning test is conducted in an area free from drafts. The test specimen, supported vertically by its upper end, is ignited at the lower end for 10 sec by a bunsen burner (tube placed

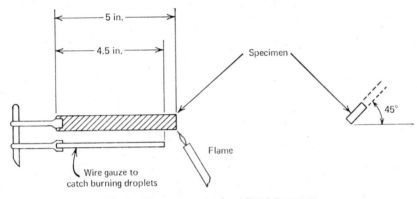

Fig. 1. Test apparatus for ASTM D 635-68.

$\frac{3}{8}$ in. below specimen, blue flame, $\frac{3}{4}$ in. high). If flaming or glowing combustion stops within 30 sec after removal of the flame, the specimen is reignited for 10 sec. The duration of flaming or glowing is again noted.

If the specimen drips flaming particles, these are allowed to fall into a layer of surgical cotton placed 1 ft below the sample. The particles are considered significant if the cotton ignites.

To qualify as "self-extinguishing" the average duration of flaming or glowing shall not exceed 25 sec after each ignition. Materials which comply and do not drip flaming particles are classified "Self-Extinguishing, Group I." Those which comply, but do drip are "Self-Extinguishing, Group II."

ASTM D 757-49, Flammability Test for Self-Extinguishing Plastics. This test was developed for further classification of those plastics which are found to be self-extinguishing by ASTM D 635–68. The test specimen is brought into contact with an igniting bar maintained at 950 ± 10°C by a suitable electric circuit, as indicated in Figure 2. Any remaining flame is extinguished at the end of a 3-min ignition period and the burning rate in in./min is calculated. Highly fire-retardant compositions extinguish before the end of the 3-min period, while good fire retardancy is indicated by burning rates of less than 0.3 in./min.

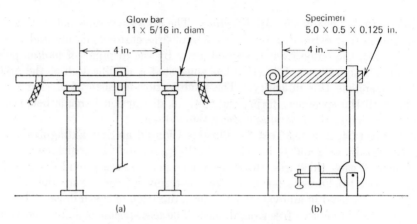

Fig. 2. Test apparatus for ASTM D 757-49.

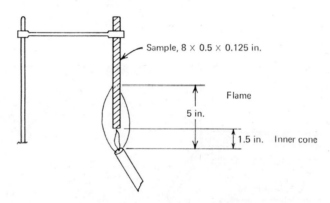

Fig. 3. Test apparatus for HLT-15.

Intermittent Flame Test. This test, often designated as HLT-15 (Hooker Laboratory Test), is a more severe test capable of distinguishing between materials rated as nonburning by the above tests. This is principally useful for evaluation of glass-mat and cloth-resin laminates and, in general, highly fire-retardant materials (6). In this test a flame is applied, in the manner indicated in Figure 3, to a specimen for increasingly longer periods. The time of burning is noted after each application. In this way, a rating of 0–100 is calculated with increasing fire retardancy indicated by higher ratings.

ASTM D 1692-59T, Test for Flammability of Plastic Foam. Materials which shrink or cure under the test conditions cannot be evaluated by this test. A flame is applied to the test specimen for a given time and, according to the result, the polymer is designated "burning," "nonburning," or "self-extinguishing," depending upon the position of the char area relative to bench marks on the sample. For samples judged to be burning, the burning rate is noted, while in the case of nonburning or self-extinguishing polymers, the cause of extinguishment, dripping, etc, is also noted. This tends to be a relatively mild test.

ASTM D 1360-59, Test for Fire Retardancy of Paints. A flame is impinged, under controlled conditions, onto a weighed wooden panel coated on one side with the paint to be tested. After cooling the panel at the end of the test, the loss in weight is determined and the char volume calculated. The test does not measure flame spread on the panel and determination of the char volume is uncertain. Also this test does not correlate well with ASTM E 84-68, which is the final criterion for any coating requiring a fire-retardant rating. The standard ASTM procedure does not attempt to assign different categories under this test, but Interim Federal Specification TTPP 0026-B defines a coating as fire retardant by this test if the weight loss is not greater than 15.0 g and the char volume is not greater than 4.5 in.[3]. This is actually a very lenient definition.

USE-EVALUATION TESTS

Test for Surface-Burning Characteristics of Building Materials (Tunnel Test), ASTM E 84-68. This test is used to determine surface-burning characteristics of any material that is capable of supporting itself in position on the roof section of the test furnace. This is an especially important test since it is used as a criterion for the Underwriter's label, which is required by Government codes for general use of material in public buildings. The test apparatus consists of a chamber 25 ft long and 17.5 × 12 in. in cross section, one end of which contains two gas burners. A test sample (25 ft × 20 in.) attached to the roof is exposed to the gas flame for 10 min while the maximum flame spread and temperature are observed down the tunnel.

The Oxygen-Index Test, ASTM D 2863-70 (7). A polymer sample (6 × 3 × 80 mm) is placed vertically in a chimney with a controlled atmosphere and the upper end is ignited with a gas flame. By varying the oxygen:nitrogen ratio, the ratio which just supports a flame is determined and the oxygen index is defined as follows:

$$\text{oxygen index} = O_2/(O_2 + N_2)$$

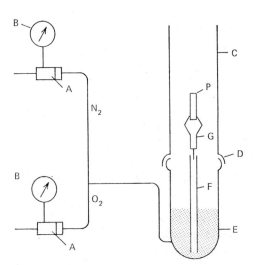

Fig. 4. Test apparatus for ASTM D 2863-70.

LEGEND: A = calibrated jeweled orifice   E = glass beads
         B = pressure gage, 0–100 psig   F = glass tube
         C = glass column   G = specimen clamp
         D = ground glass joint   P = test specimen
                                                    (6 mm × 3 mm × 8 cm)

The more fire-retardant polymer yields the higher index values by this test. A diagram of the apparatus is shown in Figure 4. This is an accurate and simple test.

OTHER TESTS

Other tests that are or have been used to determine the flammability of plastics are listed in Table 1.

Table 1. Medium and Small-Scale Tests for Flammability

Designation	Description	Data obtained[a]
ASTM D 568-68	flammability of plastic film and sheeting	BR, SE, or NB
D 1361-58	test for fire-retardancy of paints[b]	
D 1433–58	flammability of flexible thin plastic sheeting	BR, SE, or NB
D 299[c]	flammability of rigid sheet and plate insulation	time to ignite
D 1929-68	ignition properties of plastics	flash-ignition temp, self-ignition temp
E-162-67	surface flammability of materials using a radiant heat source (radiant panel)	flame spread, fuel contribution, smoke weight, and density
USBM Test[d]	penetration of torch flame through plastic material	burn-through time
Fed Test Method[f]		
2021	flammability of plastics over 0.050 in. thick[e]	BR, SE, or NB
2022	flammability of plastics under 0.050 in. thick	burning time, burned area
2023	flame resistance, ignition of vapors from heated sample by spark plugs	time to ignition, flame spread, burning time

[a] BR = burning rate; SE = self-extinguishing; NB = nonburning.
[b] Stick and wick method.
[c] Section 45–50.
[d] See *U.S. Bureau of Mines* (*USBM*) *Report of Investigation* **6366**.
[e] Analogous to ASTM D 635.
[f] Standard No. 406.

Fire-Retardancy Problems and Theories

A clear idea of the basic processes of ignition and burning and the effect of halogens on these processes may help in understanding the importance of these halogen-containing compounds to the plastics industry (8,8a). The theoretical aspect of polymer fire retardance is complex and not much has been published on the subject. Starting with the hypothesis that all organic material can be destroyed by burning, an effective fire retardant must retard ignition and inhibit subsequent flame spread.

In the burning of any material, heat first reaches it by radiation, convection, or conduction. At the decomposition point, pyrolysis leads to the production of small, volatile fuel particles which escape as a gas, creating porosity, and increasing the surface area. A greater surface accelerates the absorption of heat and the volatilization process. With increasing temperature, the ignition point is reached and a flame develops, producing additional heat for pyrolysis. Whether a self-sustaining flame develops depends upon the transfer of enough heat from the flame front to the hot substrate to maintain fuel production. The shape or state of subdivision of the sample is an important variable in this latter process.

In view of the complexity of the reactions involved, it is not surprising that the precise mechanism is still uncertain. Also, a particular mechanism may be the most important in a given situation and only supplemented by the other modes of action. There is, however, a body of well-founded empirical data that is useful in formulating suitable fire-retardant compositions. Some of the most important of these are listed below.

1. The incorporation of halogen atoms into a polymer decreases the flammability of the composition.

2. The efficiency of halogen in fire-retardant additives is $F < Cl < Br$.

3. Halogens on aromatic structures are less efficient than those in aliphatic hydrocarbons.

4. A combination of antimony oxide and halogen is more efficient than either of these compounds alone (synergism) (9,10).

5. Some combinations of phosphorus and halogen exhibit a considerable synergism in specific polymers (11).

6. The degree of effectiveness of a fire retardant varies markedly, depending upon polymer composition.

7. The amount of fire retardant required to obtain a constant degree of fire retardancy varies, depending on the physical form (ie molding laminates, foam, or film) of the polymer composition.

8. Many fire-retardant compositions leave large amounts of charred, difficultly combustible residues when exposed to a flame.

9. The pyrolysis of a halogen-containing polymer composition containing hydrogen generally results in conversion of most of the halogen into gaseous products, of which the largest constituent is hydrogen halide.

The Chemistry of Flames. Thermally decomposing plastics form smaller molecules in complex fast reactions. A simple example is the oxidation of ethane, shown below.

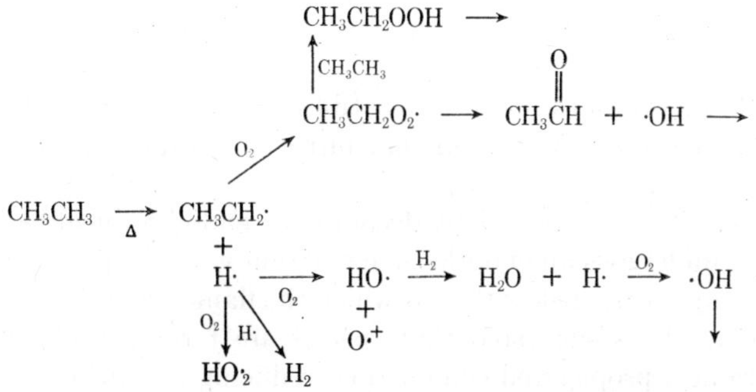

The key to the burning velocity is the proliferation of the highly reactive $\cdot$OH radicals. The reaction between these and atoms and molecules of hydrogen leads to chain branching and a highly exothermic autocatalytic reaction. By dissipating the energy of the ·OH radicals, the flame velocity can be greatly reduced. The halogens, particularly Br and Cl, are particularly effective in this process.

The mechanism for inhibition of radical chain reactions by halogens is substantiated by a body of experimental evidence, but the assumption that this is the only or the most important mechanism does not appear justified. The hydrogen halide may alter the pyrolytic decomposition and change the amount and/or the flammability of the volatile gases, since, for example, they induce coking in poly(methyl methacrylate) (13–16) and other compositions. Moreover, hydrogen bromide itself has been found to be a catalyst for the oxidation of hydrocarbons (13). The halogens have been observed to react with polymer fragments, as shown by analysis of pyrolysis products of a self-extinguishing polystyrene composition (14); a variety of halocarbons and halohydrocarbons were found in addition to hydrogen halide. Burning, therefore, depends to a large extent on energies and rates of pyrolysis, on the energy available from the flame, and the rates of heat absorption and diffusion. The effect of fire-retardant compounds on these processes is of great interest so that accurate predictions may be made for tailoring products to needs.

Heats of combustion must be considered as factors in the burning of individual polymers. Theoretically, substitution of a sufficient amount of highly endothermic C—X bonds for the C—H bonds (the breaking and oxidation of which is exothermic) should render a polymer thermodynamically incapable of sustaining oxidation. This has been substantiated in the case of chlorine-containing unsaturated polyesters (17). However, little correlation has been found between heat of combustion and practical fire-retardant applications (18). For example, highly combustible cellulose nitrate has a low heat of combustion (4134 cal/g) whereas a self-extinguishing grade of polyethylene has a heat of combustion of 9970 cal/g. This value is, however, 11% lower than the nonfire-retardant polyethylene. The difficulty in using heats of combustion to predict fire retardancy is not surprising since even under controlled test conditions there is incomplete combustion, and the heat of combustion is only one of many important factors. However, the fire-retardant effect of many inert, inorganic fillers may very well depend on the reduction of the overall heat of combustion (19).

Use of halogen compounds in polymers, either as additives or as comonomers, is thought to alter the flammability of the composition by several general mechanisms listed below.

Coating Theory. The fire-retardant additives intumesce or cause the formation of carbonaceous foam or char which acts as a thermal insulator in addition to preventing access of oxygen.

Gas Theory. Large volumes of incombustible gases are produced which dilute the oxygen supply. Examples are ammonia, nitrogen, sulfur dioxide, and halogen acid.

Thermal Theory. The fire retardant decomposes endothermically, eg by fusion or sublimation, or it undergoes an endothermic reaction with the flammable substrate which reduces the temperature below that at which the flame is self-sustaining.

Chemical Theory. It is suggested that species are formed which influence the course of the free-radical propagated combustion, reducing the ultimate flammability of the system.

Antimony–Halogen Synergism. No satisfactory theory is yet available to account for the synergism of antimony compounds as halogen fire retardants. Antimony trichloride (11) or antimony oxychloride (20) have been suggested as the active inhibitor under burning conditions. Pitts and co-workers give differential thermal and thermogravimetric data on antimony oxychloride and suggest that the formation of volatile antimony trichloride may be important (21).

It has been shown that the combination of antimony and chlorine in polyethylene has no inhibiting effect in a nitrous oxide atmosphere which suggests that inhibition in oxygen occurs by poisoning of the flame (16). This is supported by the fact that 75% of the antimony is vaporized during burning. The possibility, however, that antimony enhances the catalytic effect of halogen on pyrolytic decomposition cannot be discounted since antimony–halogen fire-retardant compositions always produce a carbonaceous residue, even with such polymers as polypropylene which produces none in the absence of fire retardants.

Afterglow. As practical methods for controlling the flammability of polymers became available, afterglow, an especially difficult type of fire to extinguish, has become more important. In this process the carbonaceous residue, left from pyrolysis in the diffusion flame, burns in the manner of charcoal. Oxidation of carbon may occur by two different mechanisms:

$$C + \tfrac{1}{2} O_2 \rightarrow CO \quad \Delta H = -26.4 \text{ kcal} \tag{1}$$

$$C + O_2 \rightarrow CO_2 \quad \Delta H = -94.4 \text{ kcal} \tag{2}$$

The first reaction is probably not sufficiently exothermic to maintain combustion, while the second is. Thus, to minimize afterglow, it could be desirable to divert reaction 2 to reaction 1.

An interesting set of data is presented by Coleman and Thomas (22) which show that combustion of chlorinated plastics at low temperature (about $300°C$) yields about equal amounts of carbon monoxide and carbon dioxide, but at higher temperatures (about $900°C$) the carbon dioxide reaction is by far predominant. The afterglow phenomenon may well be related to the carbon dioxide reaction.

Smoke. One of the most important aspects of fire retardancy, which has not received proper attention in the past, is smoke generation (23). It has been suggested that as many fire deaths may be attributable to smoke as to the heat of the fire. There seems to be general agreement that vapors and particulate matter from smoldering or burning materials present three kinds of hazards.

1. They are irritating to the eyes and the respiratory system.

2. They impede escape from burning locations and make the entrance of fire fighters or rescue teams difficult.

3. They are toxic either directly by virtue of their components or indirectly by reducing the amount of oxygen in the environment.

Despite the admitted need, the prospect of developing low-smoke fire-retardant organic plastics in the near future is not bright because the fire-retardant methods currently available appear to interrupt the combustion processes predominantly in such a manner as to yield visible carbonaceous by-products which enter the atmosphere as smoke.

Toxicity of Gases Evolved. The toxicity of gaseous products evolved from the pyrolytic decomposition of fire-retardant polymer compositions has been a subject that has concerned many investigators and public agencies over the past years. This concern has stemmed from the fact that smoke and fumes spread much faster in building fires than the flame itself. Fires in which deadly gases were generated by the pyrolysis of such materials as cellulose nitrate have resulted in an unusually heavy loss of life (24). The accuracy of some of these conclusions regarding the toxicity of gases is not always certain, however, since the gaseous decomposition products from many commonly used building materials are toxic in one degree or another. Carbon monoxide is the most common and most insidious because of its lack of odor or taste.

Several studies of the gaseous pyrolysis products from halogen-containing polymer compositions have been carried out to determine the degree of toxicity to be expected from the pyrolysis of common fire-retardant polymers (14,25,26). In all cases, the halogen has been shown to be evolved almost exclusively as hydrogen halide. Only traces of free halogen and no significant amounts of phosgene have been detected. Generally, the poisonous gas found in the highest concentration has been carbon monoxide. These studies have indicated fairly conclusively the absence of any special hazard of this nature in the use of halogen-containing polymer compositions.

The corrosive effect the hydrogen halide pyrolytically produced from halogen-containing fire-retardant plastics has become a major problem in the building industry (27). More serious damage has resulted in many cases from the corrosive damage to building contents from the hydrogen halide than from actual fire damage. The evolution of hydrogen chloride during the disposal of chlorine-containing polymer waste has also led to a corrosion problem in municipal incinerators. The economic importance of corrosion from halogen-containing polymers is not yet fully determined.

A study (28) of the gaseous decomposition products obtained from the pyrolysis of nitrogen-containing polymers, such as polyurethans, nylons, and polyacrylonitrile, indicates that hydrogen cyanide was a pyrolytic product in all cases. The hydrogen cyanide concentrations were found to vary from 200 to 3000 ppm, depending upon the polymer structure. The practical toxicity of these pyrolytic gaseous mixtures was not evaluated, however.

Commercial Halogenated Fire Retardants

By far the most common method of making polymers fire retardant is by the incorporation of halogen compounds into the polymer composition, either alone or together with antimony or phosphorus synergists. The increasing economic importance of these fire-retardant methods is indicated by sales of fire-retardant chemicals which have risen from 68 million lb in 1960 to over 150 million lb by 1967 as illustrated in Table 2 (29). Halogenated chemicals are by far the largest part of this market, the largest uses being for small appliances, electronics, refrigerator insulation, toys, furniture, and applications in the transportation industry.

Antimony oxide is an important part of the halogenated fire-retardant market because of its synergistic enhancement of the fire retardance of halogenated plastics. Approximately 14 million lb of this chemical were consumed in 1968 in fire-retardant

Table 2. Sales of Fire Retardants, Million lb (29)

Year	Reactive	Coadditive	Additive
1960	15	11	42
1964	27	13	56
1965	33	21	63
1966	42	20	71
1967	43	21	75
1968	50	20	85

plastics (30). An unstable supply picture for this important material and a resulting rapid increase in price has led to a considerable effort to find substitutes and will undoubtedly lead to a decline in the importance of antimony in this market.

The number of companies actively engaged in supplying fire-retardant chemicals is increasing rapidly and newer ones are continually entering the market. Some of those most active in the field are Hooker Chemical Corp., Stauffer Chemical Co., Mobil Chemical Co., The Dow Chemical Co., Michigan Chemical Corp., Monsanto Co., Diamond-Shamrock Chemical Corp., M. & T. Chemicals, Inc., U.S. Borax & Chemical Corp., and Harshaw Chemical Co.

Fire retardants can be grouped into the three following categories:

1. Reactive types. Generally involves the chemical combination of the flame-retardant agent into the basic polymeric structure. Compounds included in this group are bromoethyl acrylate, halogenated styrenes, chlorendic acid, vinyl bromide, tetrachlorophthalic anhydride, tetrabromophthalic anhydride, tetrabromobisphenol-A, unsaturated phosphonates, and tetrakis-(hydroxymethyl)phosphonium chloride.

2. Additive types. These flame-retardant agents are generally incorporated by physical blending with the base polymer. Included among these are ammonium bromide, diammonium phosphate, hexabromocyclododecane, chlorinated waxes, poly(vinyl chloride), poly(vinylidene chloride), tris-(2,3-dibromopropyl) phosphate, pentabromotoluene, and 1,5-bis(chlorendo)cyclooctane (see p. 485).

2. Coadditive types. Included are those compounds which by themselves are ineffective flame retardants, but in the presence of halogens give good self-extinguishing properties. By far the most important in this group are the oxides and sulfides of antimony, zinc borate, and phosphorus esters.

REACTIVE FIRE RETARDANTS

The main advantages of the reactive types of fire retardants are permanence and the absence of a substantial degrading effect on the physical properties of treated polymers. The polymer compositions are usually more costly, however, because of the additional step and, in some cases, more expensive processing.

Among the first reactive fire retardants were chlorendic acid and the anhydride, which were introduced in the 1950s for use with unsaturated polyesters and epoxy resins, and later for rigid polyurethan foams. Tetrabromobisphenol-A and tetrachlorobisphenol-A are used in the epoxy resins and unsaturated polyesters. Common reactive types are summarized in Table 3. The more commonly used fire retardants are discussed below in more detail.

Chlorendic Acid (1). The best known and most widely used of the fire-retardant polyesters are based on chlorendic acid, 1,4,5,6,7,7-hexachlorobicyclo(2,2,1)hept-5-ene-2,3-dicarboxylic acid.

Since this and many other fire-retardant compounds are based on hexachlorocyclopentadiene, a brief discussion of this reagent might be in order. The compound does not appear formally in the literature until 1930 (31), although Prins states that he started work on it in 1912 (32). Commercially, hexachlorocyclopentadiene is prepared by a two-stage process from pentanes by photochemical chlorination followed by a thermal treatment (350–400°C) in a chlorine atmosphere over a porous surface-active catalyst, such as fuller's earth, to give a better than 90% yield (33). This excellent commercial preparation gives an outstanding source of a low-cost highly chlorinated precursor for fire-retardant plastics.

Table 3. Some Common Commercial Reactive Fire Retardants

Systematic name	Common generic or trade name	Manufacturer
1,4,5,6,7,7-hexachlorobicyclo(2.2.1)-hept-5-ene-2,3-dicarboxylic anhydride or dicarboxylic acid	chlorendic anhydride, HET acid	Velsicol Chem. Corp. Hooker Chem. Corp.
tetrabromophthalic acid	Firemaster PHT4	Michigan Chem. Corp.
tetrachlorophthalic acid	Niagathal Tetrathal	Hooker Chem. Corp. Monsanto Co.
4,4′-isopropylidenebis(2,6-dichlorophenol)	tetrachlorobisphenol-A	
4,4′-isopropylidenebis(2,6-dibromophenol)	tetrabromobisphenol-A, Firemaster BP4A	Michigan Chem. Corp.
2,3-dicarboxy-5,8-endomethylene-5,6,7,8,9,9-hexachloro-1,2,3,4,4a,-5,8,8a-octahydronaphthalene anhydride	Cloran	Universal Oil Products Co.
α,α′-bis(ethoxy)-2,3,4,6-tetrachloro-1,3-dimethylbenzene		Diamond Shamrock Chem. Corp.
α,α′-2,3,5,6-hexachloro-1,4-dimethylbenzene		Diamond Shamrock Chem. Corp.
diallyl chlorendate		FMC Corp., Organic Chemicals Div.

Chlorendic acid was first reported in 1947 by Prill (34) who effected the Diels-Alder reaction of maleic anhydride and hexachlorocyclopentadiene in toluene followed by hydrolysis of the anhydride with aqueous or alcoholic base.

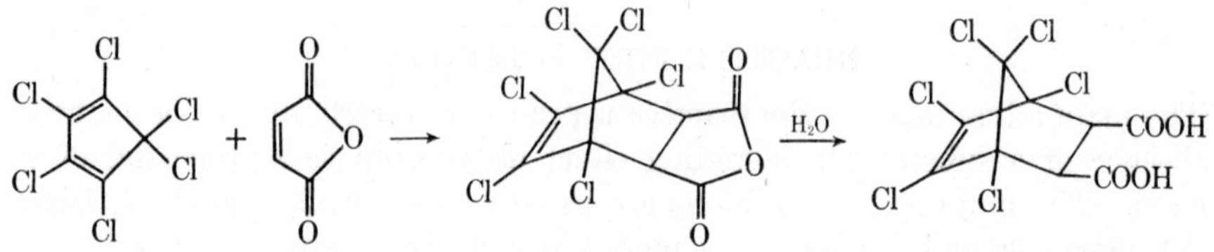

chlorendic anhydride

chlorendic acid (1)

The commercial process remains unchanged in essential details. It is carried out in a high-boiling solvent, such as chlorobenzene, to accelerate the reaction and to assist in subsequent purification (34,35). The anhydride can be hydrolyzed in situ by the addition of measured amounts of water if the dicarboxylic acid is desired.

A summary of its preparation as described in the patent literature follows (35). Equimolar amounts of hexachlorocyclopentadiene and maleic anhydride in chlorobenzene were heated at 140–150°C for 8–10 hr. The hot anhydride solution was then added to water to effect hydrolysis and provide chlorendic acid as the monohydrate in better than 90% yield (after washing with chlorobenzene and water). Drying at 100–105°C yields an essentially anhydrous product of 99.6% purity.

Chlorendic Acid Polyesters. The success of chlorendic acid as a reactive fire-retardant monomer in polyesters can be largely attributed to the high level of thermally and hydrolytically stable chlorine in this relatively inexpensive compound. In addition, esterification rates are comparable to those of phthalic anhydride, allowing ready substitution of this common reagent in commercial polyester preparations.

The chlorine substituents on the double bond of chlorendic acid not only render it inert to most reagents, but also prevent its use as a crosslinking site. Other reactive monomers, such as maleic anhydride, must be included to achieve crosslinking. Despite the relative stability of the chlorines in the bicyclic compound, the inherent weakness of the carbon–chlorine bond limits the esterification reaction to 180°C if colorless resins are to be obtained.

Chlorendic acid polyesters are generally prepared by bulk polymerization using the following general procedure (10):

After blanketing the reaction vessel with an inert gas (nitrogen or carbon dioxide) the glycol or glycol mixture is charged and heated to 100°C. Chlorendic acid and maleic anhydride are then charged and the temperature is increased while water of esterification is removed through a steam-heated condenser (to minimize loss of glycol). The reaction is continued at 165°C until an acid number of 25–55 mg KOH/g is reached. Inhibitor is added during the latter stages of the reaction to prevent gelation. The total esterification reaction can be completed in 12–24 hr, depending on the equipment. The molten resin is cooled, blended with the required amount of styrene, and additional inhibitor is added for the required storage stability. The completed resin usually has a viscosity of about 2000 cP and is light yellow in color. It is essential that all traces of iron be eliminated from the reaction process if a good color is to be obtained.

The fire retardancy of these polyesters decreases with increasing styrene content, thus limiting the amount of inexpensive monomer that can be added. However, antimony oxide can also be used to extend the effectiveness of the chlorinated polyester. The high chlorine content and efficiency of chlorendic acid allow the formulation of polyester laminates with flame-spread ratings in the noncombustible range. Table 4 compares the ASTM E 84 flame-spread ratings of typical chlorendic acid polyester laminated sheets to some common building materials. The excellent fire retardance possible with these compositions is apparent.

Table 5 summarizes the results of fire-retardancy tests with some typical polyester resins containing phthalic, tetrachlorophthalic, or chlorendic acid. These resins were formulated, with an identical mole ratio of acids or anhydrides to maleic anhydride, to yield resins with equivalent amounts of unsaturation. The high chlorine content of chlorendic acid results in a more highly fire-retardant resin as indicated. A similarly high fire retardance cannot be obtained by simply increasing the amount

Table 4. Comparative Flame-Spread Ratings (ASTM E 84-68) of Chlorendic Acid Polyester, Laminates, and Some Common Building Materials

Material	Thickness, in.	Rating
asbestos-cement board		0
red-oak flooring		100
white pine		130
plywood		100–180
nonfire-retardant polyester sheet	$\frac{1}{16}$	400
FRP[a] corrugated sheet		
chlorendic acid	$\frac{1}{16}$	30–35
chlorendic acid + 5% Sb_2O_3	$\frac{1}{16}$	35
flat FRP sheet, chlorendic acid		
+ 5% Sb_2O_3 + 20% Ca_2SO_4	$\frac{1}{10}$	21

[a] Fire-retardant polyester.

of tetrachlorophthalic anhydride because the reduction in maleic anhydride necessitated by such an approach results in unacceptable losses in desirable physical properties.

Chlorendic acid polyesters have an exceptional heat resistance and an unusually high resistance to corrosive chemicals (36). The high chlorine content, however, causes the weathering resistance and light stability to be reduced appreciably. This can be minimized by the addition of suitable light stabilizers or by the application of a suitable coating. Other problems associated with the use of chlorendic acid containing polyesters are the high working viscosity and the tendency towards brittleness (37).

Coatings. Although chlorendic acid finds major use in unsaturated polyester resins, it has also attained commercial importance as a fire-retardant monomer in coatings, epoxy resins, and polyurethan foams. Its use in coatings is well-established, though limited because of the lack of an intumescent property (38). Oil modified alkyds containing chlorendic acid find use primarily in military applications as coatings for metal surfaces (a market estimated to use 500,000–700,000 lb/yr of chlorendic acid).

Table 5. Fire Retardancy of Polyester Resins (10)

	Chlorendic acid based resin	Phthalic acid based resin	Tetrachlorophthalic acid based resin
chlorine content of polyester, wt %	38.0	0	29.9
styrene content of resin, % by wt	23	23	23
ASTM D 757-49			
in. burned per min	0.18	burns freely	0.79
time to flame out, sec	150		>180
ASTM D 635-68			
self-extinguishing	yes	burns	yes
flame out time, sec	0		150

Epoxy Resins. The use of chlorendic anhydride as a fire-retardant curing agent for epoxy resins was originally investigated by Robitschek and Nelson (39). Although fire-retardant compositions with high heat resistance were obtained, the high melting point and insolubility of the anhydride resulted in difficult processing and short pot life. It has subsequently been shown that lower viscosity mixtures with pot lives greater than 8 hr can be obtained by the use of a low-melting coanhydride mixture (40). Hexahydrophthalic anhydride seems to be the preferred coanhydride. Its use, however, lowers the fire and heat resistance of the composition to some extent.

Polyurethan Foam. After some initial failures, chlorendic acid was incorporated into polyurethan foams in about 1956 (41). Despite the excellent fire and heat resistance, the high melting points of the initial polyesters required high processing temperatures which were commercially unacceptable. A reduction of the molecular weight of the polyol and modification with a low-molecular-weight epoxide has eliminated these difficulties (42).

Cloran (Universal Oil Products) Brand Flame Retardant. A relatively new addition to the list of commercially useful reactive fire retardants is 2,3-dicarboxy-5,8-endomethylene-5,6,7,8,9,9-hexachloro-1,2,3,4,4a,5,8,8a-octahydronaphthalene anhydride (**2**), the use of which has been reviewed by Roberts et al. (43). It is prepared according to the following equation:

butadiene   maleic   4,5-dicarboxy-1-
            anhydride   cyclohexene
                            anhydride

Cloran is claimed to give better thermal and light stability and weatherability because of the increased stability of the hydrogens on the bicyclic ring which are not activated by adjacent carboxyl groups as are those of chlorendic acid. This difference is thought to minimize degradation reactions, such as indicated below.

Despite this advantage of Cloran a very large market in fire-retardant applications has not developed, perhaps because of its relatively low chlorine content and high cost.

Tetrabromophthalic Anhydride. This compound, $C_6Br_4(COOH)_2$ (29), is an excellent fire-retardant monomer in thermoset polyester and epoxy resins (44). It shows good fire retardancy at a bromine level of 12.5% compared with greater than 20% chlorine needed for chlorendic acid. It may be used with a range of diluent diacids and glycols. In the preparation of polyesters, monoesterification is easy, but esterification of the second group requires temperatures of 185°C. It is important to remove even trace amounts of iron and inorganic acids. This can be accomplished by the addition of a basic inorganic salt, such as sodium acetate (45).

Another problem encountered with polyesters containing tetrabromophthalic anhydride is the tendency to discolor under light, probably due to the labile C–Br bond. This is especially true when the brominated acid groups are at the chain end. This may be minimized, however, by end-capping the free carboxyl groups or by use of uv light stabilizers.

As mentioned above, one of the problems with the use of the tetrabromophthalic anhydride in polyester syntheses is the need for high-purity material. The commercial product is not suitable without the special treatment outlined below (46).

Tetrabromophthalic anhydride is dissolved in dilute caustic, filtered, and acidified with dilute hydrochloric acid. The precipitated acid is washed several times with hot water and the pure anhydride is then obtained by heating at 150°C for several hours.

An example of polyester preparation is as follows: To a 500-ml three-neck flask, equipped with a reflux-column, nitrogen inlet, and condenser were charged 116 g (0.25 mole) of purified tetrabromophthalic anhydride, 38 g (0.26 mole) of phthalic anhydride, 69 g (0.70 mole) of maleic anhydride, and 132 g (1.60 moles) of 1,2-propanediol. The reaction mixture was blanketed with nitrogen and heated with stirring while removing water by distillation. The temperature was raised slowly to 180°C and after $4\frac{3}{4}$ hr the acid number was 29 mg KOH/g, indicating esterification was 93% complete. The resin can be styrenated in the usual manner.

Brominated Tetrahydrophthalic Maleate Esters. A development that appears to be of future commercial importance in the field of fire-retardant polyester resins has been disclosed in a patent (47). In this process an unsaturated polyester is first prepared in the conventional manner from a glycol, an α,β-unsaturated anhydride (eg maleic anhydride), and a saturated anhydride, such as tetrahydrophthalic anhydride. The resin is then dissolved in a chlorinated solvent and brominated at low temperature (-25 to $40°C$). The fact that addition to the cyclic double bond is ten times as fast as addition to the conjugated double bond of the maleate leads to a brominated resin in which the maleate unsaturation remains for the subsequent curing reaction with styrene. This process is advantageous because it allows the esterification to proceed rapidly at optimum temperatures without the danger of discolorization often encountered with halogenated monomers. The addition of bromine is essentially quantitative without the need for recycling hydrogen bromide.

The fire resistance can be varied widely, depending upon the amount of bromine incorporated into the final resin. The greater efficiency of the bromine also allows the formulation of fire-retardant materials without the necessity of using insoluble antimony oxide so that highly fire-retardant translucent products can be made.

2,2′-Bis(bromomethyl)-1,3-propanediol. A reactive fire-retardant monomer that has been suggested for use in unsaturated polyesters and polyurethans is 2,2′-bis-(bromomethyl)-1,3-propanediol, $HOCH_2C(CH_2Br)_2CH_2OH$ (3) (48).

This is one of few brominated diols to show significant commercial promise. Its advantages are a high bromine content (61%), good resistance to dehydrobromination, and good light resistance. This permits its formulation into unsaturated polyesters where the efficiency and stability of the bromine allows esterification under conventional conditions with good color. The small quantity required as a result of the high bromine level permits a wide flexibility in the choice of properties through use of a variety of modifying polyols and acids. Probably the most unusual commercial property of this material is its excellent light stability. Wheatherometer tests have shown the weather resistance of these resins to approach the nonhalogen-containing products in performance. This has not yet been substantiated by full-scale outdoor weathering tests, however. These unique properties are probably a result of the aliphatic neopentyl structure which would be expected to have unusual stability.

Although the specific commercial manufacturing process is not known, an adequate method, giving an 85% yield, is available (48a). Pentaerythritol is dissolved in glacial acetic acid and treated with a slight excess of dry hydrogen bromide. After removal of the excess acetic acid, the diacetate of 2,2′-bis(bromomethyl)-1,3-propanediol obtained is transesterified with methanol to give the desired product (mp, 109–110°C).

Tetrachlorophthalic Anhydride. This monomer has long been commercially available as a fire retardant. It is prepared by the direct chlorination of phthalic anhydride in a suitable solvent. Although it finds its largest market in unsaturated polyester resins, the lower fire-retardant efficiency of the aromatic halogens and its relatively low chlorine content has limited its use to those formulations not requiring the maximum possible fire retardance. (See Table 5 for comparison with chlorendic acid polyesters.)

Antimony oxide can be used to increase the fire retardance as in other halogenated compositions but at the expense of transparency. A lesser improvement in fire retardance without the loss of transparency can be obtained by the addition of various phosphorus compounds, such as triethyl or triallyl phosphate (49). Triethyl phosphate, like most other monomeric phosphorus esters, is relatively rapidly leached from the cured resin, however, by exposure to water or aqueous solutions with a resulting loss in fire retardance. The ability of triallyl phosphate to copolymerize reduces the migration tendency considerably.

Miscellaneous Compounds. Many other halogenated monomers are available in addition to the more important ones discussed above. New halogenated monomers and compositions are continually being introduced, as the need for polymer fire retardance increases. A few of these less important fire-retardant monomers are tetrabromobisphenol-A, vinyl bromide, chlorostyrene (mixed ortho and para), diallylchlorendate, 2,3-dibromo-1-propanol, and pentabromophenol and its allyl ether.

Many others are also available—mainly used in urethan foams—which contain phosphorus as an additional fire-retardant element.

Tetrabromobisphenol-A and diallyl chlorendate have been in use for some time and are of some commercial importance. Tetrabromobisphenol-A finds its largest use in fire-retardant epoxy resins while diallyl chlorendate is predominantly used as a comonomer in diallyl phthalate molding compounds.

ADDITIVE TYPES

The use of unreactive additives has been the historical method of choice for obtaining polymer fire retardance. The ideal additive should be inexpensive, colorless, easily blended, compatible, heat and light stable, efficient, permanent, and have no negative effects on the physical properties of the base polymers.

The available additives are not ideal, and the most important limitations are the adverse effects on physical properties and a tendency to undesirable migration. Some of the disadvantages can be overcome by using polymeric additives, such as polychloroprene, chlorinated polyethylene, poly(vinyl chloride), and chlorosulfonated polyethylene. This approach seems to have attained its greatest commercial significance in the blending of polychloroprene with other elastomers. However, some of the more general disadvantages of this approach are the following: (a) the low halogen content of the polymers usually requires a massive amount of the additive; (b) the low thermal stability of most of the available halogen-containing polymers limits processing temperatures; and (c) expensive processing techniques may be needed for suitable blending.

Despite these disadvantages, poly(vinyl chloride) (PVC) has attained a degree of commercial utility as a fire-retardant additive for acrylonitrile–butadiene–styrene (ABS) resins. The low cost of PVC is a sufficient economic advantage to overcome the need for the large amounts of PVC required to obtain the desired degree of fire retardance. In addition the high impact strength and reasonable heat-distortion temperature of the blend are properties not simultaneously attainable with other conventional fire retardants. The thermal instability of the PVC–ABS blend, however, limits its use in injection-molding applications and has seriously limited its commercial utility.   The amount of PVC required for fire retardance can be reduced by the addition of antimony oxide with only minor changes in other properties.

Halogenated Hydrocarbons.   Poly(vinyl chloride) provides the largest single market for fire-retardant additives.   Although the bulk of the additives used in this market are phosphorus esters or antimony oxide, about 10 million lb of chlorinated paraffins were forecast to be used as secondary plasticizers to enhance the fire retardance of flexible compositions (50).   Chlorinated paraffins are by far the biggest sales item of the halogen compounds in this market.   They are generally used in place of some of the standard plasticizer in a flexible composition so that the total chlorine content is not reduced to the flammable level.   The amount of chlorinated paraffin used in a given composition is generally limited because of its lack of compatability at higher concentrations.   Major applications for these compounds are in wire and cable coatings, calendered products, and profile extrusions.   Other nonfire-retardant applications are as components in printing inks, rubber compositions, lubricants, and metal-working compounds.

Chlorinated biphenyls and polyphenyls also find considerable use in poly(vinyl chloride) and many other fire-retardant compositions.   These materials are marketed with a range of chlorine contents and vary from pourable liquids to resinous solids, depending upon the extent of chlorination and the number of aromatic rings.   Like the chlorinated paraffins, however, these products generally lower the heat resistance of the polymer composition because of their plasticizing action.   Although the aromatic halogen is significantly more thermally stable than the aliphatic chlorine of the paraffinic waxes, it is less efficient as a fire retardant and thus requires higher concentrations.   Their relative compatibility in a wide variety of polymers has suggested their use as fire-retardant additives in epoxy resins, polyesters, polyurethans, and chlorinated rubbers.

Several new brominated derivatives have been introduced as fire-retardant additives for a variety of polymer systems.   Hexabromobenzene, pentabromotoluene, and hexabromobiphenyl are three aromatic compounds that have been suggested as fire retardants for both thermoplastic and thermosetting polymers and resins.   Their high bromine content makes them very efficient fire retardants in many polymer systems.   Although their aromatic character makes them sufficiently thermally stable for many molding operations, their relatively high volatility and sublimation tendency may preclude their use in applications requiring a high resistance to migration at elevated temperatures.   These fire retardants have not yet demonstrated their commercial utility (2,3,3a).

Fillerlike Additives.   Halogenated fire-retardant additives have been developed which do not exhibit the reduction in thermal properties generally associated with the chlorinated paraffins and halogenated polyphenyls.   These products are high-melting solids which, because of their incompatibility in the polymer phase, act as reinforcing fillers in contrast to the plasticizing action of the other additives.   The result is often

(4)

bichlorendo

an increase in the heat resistance of the fire-retardant composition. One of the first additives of this type was bichlorendo (4) which has a chlorine content of 78% and a melting point of 480°C (51). Not only does (4) produce compositions more thermally stable than the chlorinated waxes but it also does not deleteriously affect the electrical properties. The aliphatic character of the halogen also results in a higher fire-retardant efficiency than that of the chlorinated polyphenyls.

Bichlorendo has been replaced in many applications by 1,2,3,4,7,8,9,10,13,13,14,-14-dodecachloro-1,4,4a,5,6,6a,7,10,10a,11,12,12a-dodecahydro-1,4:7,10-dimethano-dibenzo[a,e]cyclooctene (1,5-bis(chlorendo)cyclooctane) (5), because of the higher processing conditions possible without discoloration. In addition, the considerably lower vapor pressure of (5) in most polymer compositions essentially eliminates the tendency of the additive to migrate at elevated temperatures. The latter property has opened many new applications for fire-retardant polymers in applications where stability at elevated temperatures is required. Compound (5) can be easily prepared by a Diels-Alder reaction of two equivalents hexachlorocyclopentadiene and 1,5-cyclooctadiene, as indicated in the equation below (52).

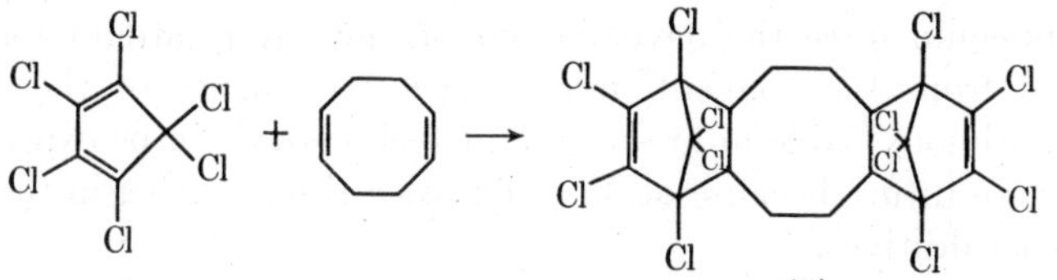

(5)

1,5-bis(chlorendo)cyclooctane

Bis(chlorendo)cyclooctane is used extensively with antimony oxide in fire-retardant polypropylene. The enhancement in physical properties possible with such fire-retardant additives is indicated in Table 6.

The fillerlike action of these additives generally increases the heat-distortion point and modulus with only minor degradation in other properties. In high-impact ABS compositions, however, there is a severe reduction in impact strength (see Table 6). Despite this disadvantage, hexachlorocyclopentadiene Diels-Alder adducts are

Table 6. Bis(chlorendo)cyclooctane fire-Retardant Compositions

	Polyproylene		ABS	
composition, %				
polymer	100	60	100	61.9
bis(chlorendo)cyclooctane		26.7		24.7
antimony oxide		13.3		12.4
properties				
flammability (ASTM D 635)	burning	self-ext.	burning	self-ext.
self-extinguishing time, sec		2–5		2
heat distortion temp, °C				
66 psi	102	117	92	89
264 psi	63	74	82	82
tensile strength yield, psi	5400	4000	6400	4200
flexural strength yield, psi	8300	7500	11700	8700
modulus, psi $\times 10^5$	2.8	3.9	3.6	4.9
impact strength, notched				
Izod, (ft)(lb)/in.	0.9–1.0	0.4–0.7	3.4–5.0	0.4

used commercially in fire-retardant ABS compositions. The diadduct of vinyl cyclohexene and hexachlorocyclopentadiene has attained a degree of commercial utility. To date it has been marketed only in proprietary compositions, however.

(The names bichlorendo for (4) and (1,5-bis(chlorendo)cyclooctane for (5) are suggested here as convenient "handles," since the systematic names are entirely inconvenient. It is hoped that they will be regarded with favor.)

Future Trends

Although considerable progress has been made over the years in the development of fire-retardant plastics, major problems remain to be solved if these materials are to find large-scale uses in the construction industry. Some of the more important deficiencies of halogenated materials are high cost, and high smoke and corrosive fumes on exposure to fire. The smoke and corrosivity of fumes are inherent in halogenated plastic compositions and may limit their future growth. The U.S. Government is assuming increasing responsibility in setting fire-retardant standards for industrial products. The future adoption of low-smoke and noncorrosive requirements for plastic products could force the development of new fire-retardant techniques completely divorced from the conventional halogen technology of the present. The importance of antimony oxide in fire-retardant technology can be expected to decline considerably in the future because of its rapid price rise resulting in the development of new synergistic additives.

The inherent fire retardance of the newer thermally stable polymers, such as polybenzimidazoles and aromatic polyamides, may already be pointing the way to future fire-retardant polymers. See Polyimides in this volume. Some of these newer compositions have physical properties not appreciably affected by the application of an ordinary flame and very little smoke and fumes are produced. The extremely high cost of these polymers, however, limits their use to those applications where cost is a secondary factor. However, they are already finding appreciable markets in aircraft applications, at least partly because of their superior flammability characteristics.

Bibliography

1. *Mod. Plastics* **46** (9), 99 (1968).
2. "Flame Resistance with Polymers," *Plastics Inst. Trans. J., Conf. Suppl.* **2** (Jan. 1967).
3. C. J. Hilado, *Flammability Handbook for Plastics*, Technomic Publishing Co., Inc., Stamford, Conn., 1969. J. W. Lyons, *The Chemistry and Uses of Fire Retardants*, Interscience Publishers, a div. of John Wiley & Sons, Inc., New York, 1970.
3a. "Flammability Characteristics of Polymer Materials," *Polymer Conf. Ser., University of Detroit, June 16–20, 1969*.
4. "Plastics—General Methods of Testing," *ASTM Stds. (Plastics)* **27** (1964).
5. "Burning Tests for Plastics," *Underwriter's Bull., Subject 94*, Underwriter's Laboratories, Inc., Skokie, Ill., Dec. 9, 1965.
6. R. C. Nametz and R. S. Nulph, *Proc. 20th Ann. Tech. Conf. SPI Reinforced Plastics Div., Chicago, Feb. 1965*, Sect. 11-C; W. J. Connolly and A. M. Thornton, Sect. 11-B.
7. C. P. Fenimore and F. J. Martin, *Mod. Plastics* **44,** 141 (Nov. 1966); *Combust. Flame* **10,** 295 (1966).
8. K. M. Bell, in reference 2.
8a. S. L. Madorsky, *Thermal Degradation of Organic Polymers*, Interscience Publishers, a div. of John Wiley & Sons, Inc., New York, 1964.
9. B. Parkyn, *Brit. Plastics* **32** (1), 29 (1959).

10. U.S. Pat. 2,909,501 (Oct. 20, 1959), P. Robitschek and J. L. Olmstead (to Hooker Chemical Corp.). P. Robitschek and C. T. Bean, *Ind. Eng. Chem.* **46** (8), 1628 (1954). J. R. Lawrence, *Polyester Resins*, Reinhold Publishing Corp., New York, 1960, p. 67. U.S. Pat. 2,779,701 (Jan. 29, 1957), P. Robitschek and C. T. Bean (to Hooker Chemical Corp.).
11. Japan. Pat. 10,644(61) (July 15, 1961), J. Kokura and K. Matsumoto.
12. W. G. Schmitt, *Plastics Inst. Trans. J.* (*London*) **33**, 247 (1965).
13. F. F. Rust and W. E. Vaughn, *Ind. Eng. Chem.* **41** (11), 2595 (1949).
14. R. E. Dufour, *Bull. of Research, No. 53*, Underwriter's Laboratories, Inc., Skokie, Ill., July 1963, p. 20.
15. R. R. Hindersinn and N. D. Blair, unpublished results, Hooker Chemical Corp.
16. C. P. Fenimore, "Flammability Characteristics of Polymeric Materials," *Polymer Conf. Ser., Wayne State University, June 1966*.
17. I. M. Al'shits and I. E. Flis, *J. Appl. Chem. USSR* (*English Transl.*) **34** (3), 618 (1961).
18. K. Krekeler and P. M. Klimke, *Kunststoffe—Plastics* **55** (10), 758 (1965).
19. W. J. Connolly and A. M. Thornton, *Mod. Plastics* **43** (2), 154 (1965).
20. S. Gross, ed., *Modern Plastics Encyclopedia*, McGraw-Hill Book Co., Inc., New York, 1966 p. 470.
21. J. J. Pitts, P. H. Scotts, and D. G. Powell, *J. Cellular Plastics* **6**, 35 (1970).
22. E. H. Coleman and C. H. Thomas, *J. Appl. Chem.* (*London*) **4**, 279 (1954).
23. J. R. Gaskell, in reference 3a.
24. C. H. Yuill, *Bldg. Res.* **2** (4), 45 (July–Aug. 1965).
25. A. Fish, N. H. Franklin, and R. T. Pollard, *J. Appl. Chem.* (*London*) **13**, 506 (1963).
26. R. I. Thrane, *A. Chem. Soc., Div. Org. Coatings Plastics Chem. Preprints* **23** (1), 15 (1963).
27. *Mod. Plastics* **45**, 49 (1968); *Plastics World* **27** (12), 5 (Dec. 1969).
28. B. Bott, J. S. Firth, and T. A. Jones, *Brit. Polymer J.* **1**, 203 (1969).
29. J. DiPietro, in reference 3a,
30. *Mod. Plastics* **45** (13), 98 (1968).
31. F. Straus, L. Kullek, and W. Heyn, *Chem. Ber.* **63B**, 1868 (1930).
32. H. Gerding, H. J. Prins, and H. van Brederode, *Rec. Trav. Chim.* **65**, 168 (1946).
33. C. W. Roberts, *Chem. Ind.* (*London*) **1958**, 110. U.S. Pat. 2,509,160 (May 23, 1950), E. T. McBee and C. F. Baranauckas (to Purdue Research Foundation.) U.S. Pat. 2,650,942 (Sept. 1, 1953), A. H. Maude and D. S. Rosenberg (to Hooker Chemical Corp.).
34. E. Prill, *J. Am. Chem. Soc.* **69**, 62 (1947).
35. U.S. Pat. 3,112,339 (Nov. 26, 1963), R. H. Kimball and G. W. Darling (to Hooker Chemical Corp.).
36. W. A. Syzmanski and R. C. Talbot, *Ind. Eng. Chem.* **56** (4), 38 (1964); *Chem. Eng. Progr.* **61** (4), 53 (1965).
37. *3rd Intern. Reinforced Plastics Conf., London, 1962*, p. 11.1.
38. W. M. Ewalt and A. W. Hopton, *Paint Varnish Prod.* **51** (12), 53 (1961).
39. P. Robitschek and S. J. Nelson, *Ind. Eng. Chem.* **48** (10), 1951 (1956).
40. C. S. Ilardo and B. O. Schoepfle, *SPE* (*Soc. Plastics Engrs.*) *J.* **16**, 953 (1960).
41. U.S. Pat. 3,156,659 (Nov. 10, 1964), P. Robitschek (to Hooker Chemical Corp.). U.S. Pat. 2,865,869 (Dec. 23, 1958), R. R. Hindersinn and S. M. Creighton (to Hooker Chemical Corp.).
42. U.S. Pats. 3,275,606 (Sept. 27, 1966) and 3,297,596 (Jan. 10, 1967), F. M. Kujawa and M. Worsley (to Hooker Chemical Corp.).
43. C. W. Roberts, D. H. Haigh, and R. J. Rathsack, *J. Appl. Polymer Sci.* **8**, 363 (1964).
44. S. M. Spratz, H. Stone, M. Koral, R. I. Steiner, and H. W. Ackerman, *Ind. Eng. Chem. Prod. Res. Develop.* **8**, 381 (1969).
45. *Chem. Eng. News* **42** (9), 56 (March 2, 1964).
46. Brit. Pat. 988,304 (April 7, 1965), to Michigan Chemical Corp.
47. U.S. Pat. 3,536,782 (Oct. 27, 1970), V. Toggweiler and F. Roselli (to Diamond Shamrock Chemical Corp.).
48. W. C. Weaver and E. R. Larsen, *Am. Chem. Soc., Div. Org. Coatings Plastics Chem. Preprints* **28** (1), 196 (1968); E. R. Larsen, *Am. Chem. Soc., Div. Org. Coatings Plastics Chem. Preprints* **29** (2) 375 (1969).
48a. M. Saucier, C. Souriol, and R. L. Salvado, *Can. J. Chem.* **44** (13), 1599 (1966). C. H. Issidorides, R. C. Gulen, and N. S. Aphramian, *J. Org. Chem.* **21**, 997 (1956).

49. *Tech. Bull. O/RE-19*, Org. Chem. Div., Monsanto Co. H. W. Meggos and Y. C. Chae, *Preprint Book, 25th Anniv. Conf., SPI Reinforced Plastics/Composites Div., Washington, D.C., Feb. 1970*, Sect. 9A.

50. *Mod. Plastics* **44** (1), 104 (1966).

51. E. V. Gouinlock, F. W. Long, and S. M. Creighton, *Plastics Technol.* **8** (12), 40 (1962).

52. U.S. Pat. 3,403,036 (Sept. 24, 1968), R. R. Hindersinn and J. F. Porter (to Hooker Chemical Corp.).

V. A. Pattison and
R. R. Hindersinn
Hooker Chemical Corp.

HEAT PIPE

The heat pipe is a new heat-transfer device that shows great promise for providing the stringent temperature control commonly required in chemical processes. In its simplest form the heat pipe possesses the property of extremely high thermal conductance, often several thousand times that of the metals. As a result of this high conductance, the heat pipe can produce nearly isothermal conditions. In another form it can provide positive, rapid, and precise control of temperature under conditions which vary with respect to time.

The heat pipe is self-contained, has no mechanical moving parts, and requires no external power other than the heat that flows through it. A typical heat pipe may require as little as one thousandth the temperature differential needed by a copper rod to transfer a given amount of power between two points. For example, in a recent test a heat pipe and a copper rod of the same diameter and length were heated to the same input temperature (approx 1400°F) and allowed to dissipate the power in air by radiation and natural convection. The temperature differential along the rod was 540°F and the power flow was 250 Btu/hr. The heat-pipe temperature differential was less than 1°F; the power was 1030 Btu/hr. The heat pipe has been called a "thermal superconductor." In this illustration the ratio of effective thermal conductance was approximately 2500:1.

The heat pipe was initially described by Gaugler (1). However, commercial use did not follow and the device was unknown when Grover (2) and his associates at the Los Alamos Scientific Laboratory of the University of California subsequently described the same basic structure in 1963 in conjunction with the space nuclear-power program. The name "heat pipe" is attributed to Grover. For several years development efforts in the field were conducted almost exclusively in connection with high-temperature thermionic and thermoelectric space power systems. During this period the basic physics received considerable scrutiny, long-life devices were developed, and a variety of geometries were demonstrated. More recently, the operating range has been extended downward through and below room temperature. Cryogenic heat pipes have been operated at −320°F. Heat pipes are currently being marketed in limited quantities for a range of applications, including experimentation in the chemical and semiconductor-material manufacturing fields.

Principles of Operation

The heat pipe achieves its high performance through the process of vapor heat transfer. A volatile liquid employed as the heat-transfer medium absorbs heat in the input area by means of the latent heat of vaporization. The vapor thus formed moves to the heat output area, where condensation takes place. Energy is stored in the vapor at the input and released at the condenser. The liquid is selected to have a substantial vapor pressure, generally greater than 20 mm Hg, at the minimum desired operating temperature. The highest possible latent heat of vaporization is desirable to achieve maximum heat transfer and temperature uniformity with minimum vapor flow.

The tendency toward isothermal operation results from the energy-storage property of the latent heat of vaporization. When an atom or molecule receives sufficient thermal energy to escape from a liquid surface, it carries with it the heat of vaporization at the temperature at which evaporation took place. Condensation (return to the liquid state accompanied by release of the latent heat of vaporization) occurs upon contact with any surface that is at a temperature below the evaporator temperature. The effect, then, is to cause preferential condensation to occur at all points which are at temperatures below that of the evaporator, so that the temperatures of the condenser areas are increased until they approach the evaporator temperature. In other words, the effect is a strong tendency to produce isothermal operation and a high effective thermal conductance.

To this point, the process as described is widely employed; indeed the steam heating system for a building is such a system. The unique aspect of the heat pipe lies in the means of accomplishing return of the condensed working fluid from the heat output area, or condenser, to the heat input end, or evaporator. Without a return mechanism, the fluid starting in the evaporator would quickly accumulate in the condenser. It is necessary to return the liquid from the condenser to the evaporator by a pumping mechanism. This pumping action is supplied by means of a specially designed wick. The surface tension of the liquid is the active force that produces wick pumping. (Such wick pumping is a familiar process in lamp wicks and sponges.) With proper design, a substantial flow rate can be sustained against the pressure head of the counter-flowing vapor or even against an appreciable gravitational head or other acceleration.

The heat pipe consists, then, of the following components: a closed chamber evacuated before admission of the working fluid (evacuation is required to establish a contaminant-free system and to prevent air or other gases from interfering with the desired vapor flow), a wick structure of appropriate design, and a thermodynamic working fluid with a substantial vapor pressure at the desired operating temperature. A schematic drawing of an elemental heat pipe is shown in Figure 1. The following base condition must be satisfied for proper operation:

$$\Delta P_l > \Delta P_v + \Delta P_l(g) + \Delta P_l\ (F) \tag{1}$$

That is, for liquid return, the condenser-to-evaporator pressure difference in the liquid, ΔP_l, must exceed the sum of the evaporator-to-condenser pressure differential in the vapor, ΔP_v, plus the pressure differential in the liquid caused by gravity, $\Delta P_l(g)$, plus that caused by frictional losses, $\Delta P_l(F)$. Under this condition, there is liquid flow toward the evaporator, and heat can be transferred. It can be seen intuitively that the pressure difference in the vapor is a direct function of the mass flow rate and an inverse function of the cross-sectional area and length of the vapor space. In turn, the mass flow rate is related directly to the power being transferred and inversely to the latent heat of vaporization. The gravitational head is the elevation of the evaporator with respect to the condenser. It can be either positive or negative, depending upon whether it aids or opposes the desired flow in the wick. At low vapor velocities, the frictional losses are caused primarily by viscous drag in the liquid as it passes through the channels or passages in the wick. The extent of this drag is controlled by the viscosity of the liquid at the operating temperature, the hydraulic radius of the passages (cross-sectional area of each channel or pore divided by its perimeter), a factor representing the tortuosity of the passages, and the cross-sectional area and length of the wick. It is of interest to examine the roles of the variables which affect the functioning of the wick.

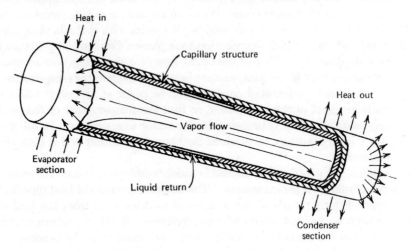

Fig. 1. Cutaway view of a heat pipe.

In general there is an optimum value of wick dimensions for each application. This results primarily from the opposing effects of the characteristic pore size of a given wick structure. If the wick is a woven mesh the capillary pressure which can be developed, ΔP_c, is inversely proportional to the pore radius (3):

$$\Delta P_c = 2\gamma \cos \theta / r_c \tag{2}$$

The surface tension of the fluid is given by γ; θ is the contact angle between the fluid and wick; and r_c is the effective pore radius.

In operation the pressure drop in the liquid is inversely proportional to the square of the pore radius, as follows (3):

$$\Delta P_l(F) = \frac{b\eta_l l Q}{2\pi \ (R_w{}^2 - R_v{}^2) \ \rho_l e r_c{}^2 L} \tag{3}$$

where b is a dimensionless constant descriptive of the wick tortuosity and extent of pore interconnection, η_l is the liquid viscosity, l is heat pipe length, Q is the heat transfer rate, R_w and R_v are the outer radii of the wick and vapor spaces, respectively, ρ_l is the liquity density, e is the fraction of the wick occupied by liquid, and L is the latent heat of vaporization of the fluid.

Thus the pore radius tends to govern both the maximum capillary pressure which induces liquid flow and the resistance to that flow. At high vapor velocities, friction at the liquid–vapor interface can become significant. In the extreme case, liquid wave formation and liquid entrainment in the vapor stream can occur.

Design Features

The heat pipe has properties of considerable interest to equipment designers. The first such property is the tendency to assume a nearly isothermal condition while carrying notable quantities of thermal power. An example was cited above of a small heat pipe carrying 300 W, somewhat more than 1 ft, with a total temperature differential of less than 1°F.

A second property, closely related to the first, is the ability of the heat pipe to effect what has been called heat-flux transformation. The vapor and liquid streams connecting the evaporating and condensing regions are essentially unaffected by the local power densities in these two regions so long as the total heat flow is in equilibrium. Thus the heat pipe can accommodate a high evaporative-power density coupled with a low condensing-power density, or vice versa. The result is a valuable property. It is common in heat-transfer applications for the intrinsic power densities of heat sources and heat sinks to be unequal. This condition may force undesired performance compromises on the equipment or process in question. The heat pipe can be used to accomplish the desired matching of power densities by simply adjusting the input and output areas in accordance with the requirements. Heat-flux transformation ratios exceeding 12:1 have been demonstrated in both directions; ie, concentration and dispersion of power density. An example may be illustrative. It is not uncommon in chemical applications for flame heat sources to be employed to establish desired reaction temperatures and rates. The natural power density from the flame can be appreciably greater than that desired locally within the reaction vessel. A heat pipe can collect the power at high density from the flame and distribute it at low density over large areas within the vessel.

The third major property grows directly from the first. That is, the high thermal conductance of the heat pipe can make possible the physical separation of the heat source and the heat consumer (heat sink). Heat pipes exceeding 8 ft in length have been constructed and shown to behave predictably. Separation of source and sink is especially important in those applications in which chemical incompatibilities exist. For example, it may be necessary to inject heat into a reaction vessel. The lowest-cost source of heat may be combustion of hydrocarbon fuels. However, the existence of an open flame or of the combustion products might jeopardize the desired reaction process. In such a case it might be feasible to carry heat from the flame through the wall of the reaction vessel by use of a heat pipe.

The fourth heat-pipe property makes use of all three of the preceding properties. Through the combination of these properties, it is possible to accomplish what has been called "temperature flattening." It is possible to regard the evaporation region of a heat pipe as consisting of many small subelements, each receiving heat and an influx of liquid working fluid and each evaporating this fluid at a rate proportional to its power input. Within the limitations discussed in the following sections, each such incremental unit of evaporation area operates independently of the others, except that all are fed to a common vapor stream at a nearly common temperature and pressure. The temperature of the elements is, therefore, nearly uniform. It can be seen that the power input to a given incremental area can differ widely from that received by other such areas. Under other circumstances, a nonuniform power profile would produce a nonuniform temperature profile. In the case of the heat pipe, however, uniformity of temperature is preserved; only the local evaporation rate changes. In this fashion the heat pipe can flatten the very nonuniform power-input profile from a flame, delivering heat to the sink with the same degree of uniformity as if the heat source were uniform. Another example is the use of a heat pipe to cool simultaneously, and to nearly the same temperature, a number of electronic components operating at different power levels.

A modified version of the basic heat pipe has a series of unique properties of considerable value in the regulation of temperature and heat flow. This device, known as the constant-temperature heat pipe, operates so that its access to the heat sink varies in proportion to changes in power input, while preserving its operating temperature at a very nearly constant value. Changes of power input by a factor exceeding 30:1 have been recorded with a change in temperature of less than 2°F. This extremely precise temperature regulation is accomplished through simple principles and without resort to external sensing and control mechanisms. The operation is as follows: The heat-pipe vessel is extended to include a volume of inert gas at a predetermined pressure (Fig. 2).

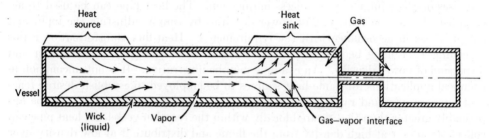

Fig. 2. Schematic diagram of a gas-controlled heat pipe.

The effect upon the heat pipe of this gas over-pressure is similar to the effect on the boiling point of water of the ambient air pressure; ie the operating temperature is established as the point on the fluid vapor-pressure–temperature curve where the vapor pressure equals the gas pressure. During heat-pipe operation the kinetic energy of the highly directional vapor flow sweeps the gas to the condenser end of the heat pipe. The gas and vapor remain highly segregated so long as the mean free path of a vapor molecule in the gas is short, corresponding to a pressure of a few tenths of an atmosphere or more. Under these conditions the gas–vapor interface is extremely sharp, and heat-pipe action ceases beyond this point. An abrupt drop in temperature indicates the location of the interface.

As the heat input to such a gas-controlled, constant-temperature heat pipe is increased, the operating temperature tends to remain constant because the location of the interface moves so as to expose an increased access area to the heat sink. The degree of temperature control is determined by the ratio of the total gas volume to the displaced gas volume. Because the temperature is a very slow function of the fluid vapor pressure, this volume need not be large to effect very precise control. A device of this type provides similar regulation under conditions where the heat-sink properties vary with time. It also starts quickly and smoothly from a cold, frozen condition under which a conventional heat pipe might stall. The control point of a gas-controlled heat pipe can be varied at will by varying the pressure of the gas. Devices of this type have been used for measuring vapor pressures and regulating the temperature of semiconductor devices.

Operational Limits

Analytical and experimental work has established with some accuracy the limitations on heat-pipe operation. These limitations are discussed below in the order in which they appear most commonly in practice.

The wick is a pump. As such it has a finite pumping capacity for returning the condensed liquid working fluid from condenser to evaporator. The product of the latent heat of vaporization and maximum mass flow rate of the fluid that can be sustained by the wick is the measure of the total thermal power-transfer capability of the heat pipe. Operation at power levels beyond this point results in complete evaporation of the returning fluid before it reaches the end of the heat pipe. The resulting loss of coolant can lead to an uncontrolled rise in temperature in the uncooled section of the evaporator, and ultimate failure. In general this factor is within the control of the designer. The effect of gravity is similar. If the desired operation requires that the liquid flow be "upward" against gravity or other acceleration, operation is affected adversely to a degree that is a function of the lift height and the mass flow rate. It is of interest to note that, under the zero gravity conditions of space flight, heat-pipe operation is unimpaired.

In many applications, especially in the chemical and semiconductor fields, the closest possible approach to isothermal operation is desired. Under these conditions the effects of several factors must be considered. In general, these factors are related to power per unit area being transferred into and out of the heat pipe and to the location of the operating point on the vapor-pressure–temperature curve of the working fluid.

The power density, or power per unit of input or output area, is a factor in eight of nine additive, series-connected temperature differentials which exist in a heat pipe. These differentials are, in order: (1) the interface temperature loss at the external input surface between the heat pipe and the heat source; (2) the conductive loss through the heat-pipe wall; (3) the conductive loss inward through the fluid-saturated wick; (4) the evaporative interface loss at the wick–vapor interface; (5) the temperature equivalent of the vapor-pressure loss caused by vapor motion from evaporator to condenser; (6) the condensing interface loss at the vapor–wick interface in the condenser; (7) the conductive loss outward through the saturated wick; (8) the conductive loss through the heat-pipe wall; and (9) the external heat-pipe–heat-sink interface loss. Although the number of losses is large, many are negligibly small in absolute value. Heat pipes with overall temperature losses of less than 1°F are not uncommon. All but two losses, the external interface losses, are to some degree under the control of the heat-pipe designer. Selections of high-conductivity structures can minimize the conductive losses. The evaporating and condensing losses are generally small. The vapor-pressure drop is a function of total power rather than power density, and is determined by the vapor velocity and mass-flow rate. The pressure drop and associated temperature loss can become appreciable at high mass-flow rates or at low vapor pressures. In the latter case, even modest heat-flow rates can imply mass flows which demand velocities approaching the sonic limit, where heat-pipe behavior ceases. For this reason, heat pipes are generally designed to operate at vapor velocities below Mach 0.6 or 0.7.

As heat flows inward through the saturated wick structure, a temperature differential appears across the wick. This temperature difference increases with increasing power density to quite high levels. At a point depending on the fluid and wick properties (about 500,000 Btu/(ft²)(hr) for water; more than 3,500,000 Btu/(ft²) (hr) for some alkali metals as working fluids), the liquid–vapor interface becomes blanketed with a stagnant vapor layer which retards further evaporation. The consequent reduction in heat transfer results in a rapid temperature increase and often in failure of the heat pipe. This onset of vapor blanketing is called the critical heat-flux density of the heat pipe, and is generally an absolute limit. The level at which it occurs is usually sufficiently high to permit a wide range of operating conditions. Additionally, with the existence of a large temperature differential across the wick, appreciable superheating of the liquid occurs. In the presence of suitable nucleation sites, bubbles can form in the wick, blocking both longitudinal liquid flow and radial heat flow. The effects of vapor blanketing and bubble formation are similar as are the operating conditions under which they may occur.

An absolute upper limit on operating temperature exists for any given fluid and vessel combination. This limit is determined by the creep or rupture strength of the vessel, ie, the ability of the vessel to contain the increasing vapor pressure of the working fluid. Limitations may be encountered at somewhat lower than the absolute limit temperatures as a result of chemical incompatibility or decomposition of the working fluid.

The final limitation can be imposed by environmental conditions. If, in the non-operating condition, the working fluid is frozen, start-up may or may not occur smoothly. If the energy expended in evaporating all of the working fluid stored in the evaporator is insufficient to raise the temperature of the balance of the heat pipe above the melting point of the working fluid, then the vapor may freeze in the condenser and heat-pipe action will not start.

If the heat pipe is short, longitudinal thermal conductivity through the vessel and wick may aid starting and prevent stalling. Use of a gas-controlled heat pipe can assure smooth start-up because the vapor–gas interface forms first at the evaporator and moves toward the condenser only as the heat pipe is able to raise its own temperature above the fluid melting point. The presence of the interface prevents vapor loss into thermally inaccessible areas of the heat pipe. Thus, although there are several limits which apply to heat-pipe operation, they generally lend themselves to specific design solutions or occur at sufficiently high levels of performance to permit a wide latitude in practical applications.

Selection of Materials

Thermodynamic Working Fluid. Several fluid properties have been discussed in conjunction with the basic heat-pipe operating principles. Quantitatively, the latent heat of vaporization, L, surface tension, γ, liquid density, ρ_l, vapor density, ρ_v, and viscosity, η_l, determine the total heat-transfer capacity of the heat pipe, Q, as follows:

$$Q = K \left(\frac{L^3\gamma^2\rho_l\rho_v}{\eta_l}\right)^{1/3} \qquad (4)$$

where K represents the geometrical factors associated with the particular wick structure and heat-pipe size and shape. Each of the factors in equation 4 is a function of temperature. A given heat pipe must, therefore, be evaluated for its performance throughout the desired temperature range from start-up to the maximum anticipated conditions. The fluid vapor pressure, a contributor to the vapor density, is one of the fastest changing functions of temperature. The melting point of the fluid is not only important in determining the minimum operating temperature, but also influences the start-up and storage characteristics. If solidification of the fluid is expected, care must be taken to avoid stresses, caused by density changes, which may distort the vessel or wick. The relationship of the liquid density to the surface tension determines the lifting height of the fluid in a given wick structure and, therefore, the extent to which operation can be expected in opposition to an accelerative force such as gravity.

A most important factor is the wetting angle (contact angle) which forms between the liquid working fluid and the wick and wall materials. This angle is a measure of the adhesive forces between the liquid and solid materials. The application of the surface tension of the liquid to the capillary pumping process is proportional to the cosine of the wetting angle. It is a requirement, therefore, that the angle be less than 90°. Material systems such as mercury on glass, in which the wetting angle exceeds 90°, are unsuited to heat pipes.

The operating lifetime of a given heat pipe is usually determined by corrosion mechanisms. The repetitive distillation or refluxing of the working fluid can cause rapid mass transport of dissolved material unless careful attention is paid to compatibility. The process is cyclic; the condensing vapor is at maximum purity and therefore has maximum dissolving power for the wick and/or vessel materials. If solution takes place, the dissolved material is carried along to the evaporator where it is left behind as the liquid is reevaporated. The result can be solution of the wick or vessel in the condenser region and clogging of the wick in the evaporator. It has also been shown that small quantities of impurities can vastly accelerate the corrosive action in some systems. A number of pairs of materials have been shown to have long undegraded life (thousands of hours), when properly processed. The pairs listed in Table 1 are representative.

Wick. The selection of a suitable wick for a given application involves consideration not only of the material itself, but also of its form factor or geometry. The basic material is generally chosen on the basis of the wetting angle and compatibility considerations discussed above. To minimize electrochemical effects, the wick and vessel

Table 1.   Pairs of Material with Long, Undegraded Life

Fluid	Wick-vessel material
ammonia	aluminum
acetone	304 stainless steel
water	copper
mercury	304 stainless stee
potassium	nickel
	304 stainless steel
sodium	304 stainless steel
	316 stainless steel
	Inconel
	Hastelloy X
	nickel
	molybdenum alloy TZM[a]
sodium chloride	aluminum oxide
lithium	molybdenum alloy TZM[a]
bismuth	molybdenum alloy TZM[a]

[a] Climax Molybdenum Co.

materials are generally the same. The factors which must be considered in wick design are often conflicting, with the result that each specific heat pipe requires a separate study to determine the optimum structure. Compromises must be made between the small capillary-pore size desired for maximum pumping pressure and the large pore size required for minimum viscous drag. These considerations may become particularly significant for very long heat pipes or for those required to pump against gravity.

Several wick structures are in relatively common use. First is a fine-pore woven screen (typically 60–100 mesh) which is rolled into an annular structure consisting of one or more wraps inserted into the heat-pipe bore. The mesh wick is a satisfactory compromise, in many cases, between cost and performance. Where high heat transfer in a given diameter is of paramount importance, a fine-pore screen is placed over longitudinal slots in the vessel wall. Such a composite structure provides low viscous drag for liquid flow in the channels and a small pore size in the screen for maximum pumping pressure.

Where complex geometries are desired, the wick can be formed by powder metallurgy techniques, ie a dry powder is sintered in place, often around a central mandrel, which is then removed. Such wicks can be made with extremely small pore sizes, providing good pumping pressures, but tend to have high viscous drag properties. For heat pipes of considerable length where minimum viscous drag is required, an arterial wick geometry has been employed. In this case a tubular "artery," often formed of screen, is attached to the wick which lines the inside walls of the heat pipe. The inside of the artery provides a low drag passage for liquid flow. At the evaporator fluid flows outward at the point of attachment to the wall and from there circumferentially throughout the heat-input region. Careful design is required to assure proper "priming" of the artery, that is, to achieve the proper balance of forces to assure that the artery will be filled.

The cross-sectional area of the wick is determined by the required liquid flow rate and the specific wick properties of capillary pressure and viscous drag. The flow rate is equal to the desired heat-transfer rate divided by the latent heat of vaporization of the fluid. Thus the transfer of 540 cal/sec (at 2260 W) requires a liquid flow of 1 cc water/sec at temperature of 100°C. Because of their porous character, wicks are relatively poor thermal conductors. Radial heat flow through the wick is often the dominant source of temperature loss in a heat pipe. Therefore the wick thickness tends to be constrained and rarely exceeds $\frac{1}{8}$ in.

Vessel. The vessel in which a heat pipe is enclosed must be strictly impermeable to assure against loss of the working fluid or leakage into the heat pipe of air or other undesired materials in the external environment. The first consideration in vessel design is its status as a pressure vessel across which the pressure may vary not only in magnitude, but also in direction. In the quiescent, cold state, the heat pipe is evacuated except for the working fluid and is generally under an external pressure because of the atmosphere. As operation is initiated, the vapor pressure of the working fluid rises and offsets the external atmospheric pressure. Frequently the heat pipe operates at a vapor pressure exceeding the external pressure. Under these conditions, a heat pipe may be designed to conform with established pressure vessel codes, considering both rupture and creep strengths.

The vessel, as well as the wick, must be compatible with the working fluid. Where possible, the wick and vessel are made of the same material to avoid the formation of galvanic corrosion cells in which the working fluid can serve as the electrolyte.

In addition to its role within the heat pipe, the vessel also serves as the interface with the heat source and the heat sink. Design of these interfaces is often of great importance because high local power densities can exist which will determine the temperature and temperature uniformity that apply at the source and sink.

As the container of an evacuated structure, the heat-pipe vessel wall is a heated membrane across which a pressure differential exists. Under these conditions, diffusion or permeation of contaminants can be a factor. At elevated temperatures, for example, all metals are permeated rapidly by hydrogen. Therefore, heat pipes for operation in hydrogen-containing environments must be protected by a nonmetallic material, eg glass or ceramic.

Simple corrosion is a factor limiting the maximum temperature of operation in air, or other reactive gases, of heat pipes made of copper, stainless steel, nickel, molybdenum, and other materials.

Applications

The extent to which the technical potential of the heat pipe will be realized in practice will be determined by its versatility and the economics associated with its use —not only direct cost, but replacement and warranty costs, as well as the cost of items which it replaces.

Geometrically, the heat pipe has been shown to have considerable versatility. In addition to the basic right circular cylinder, it has been fabricated in a variety of sizes and shapes, such as a right-angled structure, a reentrant heat pipe designed with an internal cavity to slip over the anode of an electron tube, a "Y"-shaped heat pipe, and many others.

Heat pipes have been designed for operation from the cryogenic region to more than 3000°F. The power transferred has varied from a few Btu/hr to a current maximum of 57,000 Btu/hr. Dimensions have varied from $\frac{1}{16}$ to 6 in. in diameter and from $\frac{1}{4}$ in. to more than 8 ft in length. These data represent the state of the art in late 1970. There is no intrinsic limitation to prevent extension to other dimensions, temperatures, and power ranges.

Heat sources have included nuclear energy, electron bombardment, electrical resistance heaters, flowing liquids, hot gases, open flames, and thermal radiation. Heat pipes have been cooled by forced and natural convection of liquids and gases, by radiation and conduction, by thermoelectric coolers, by radiation, and by the thermionic emission of electrons from the condenser surface.

Heat pipes are in service or under development in a growing number of practical fields. The following applications are representative: Chronologically, the first use of heat pipes was in prototype commercial refrigerators to provide cooling remote from the compressor unit (1). This use was followed, many years later, at the other temperature extreme by high-temperature uses in transferring power to thermionic and thermoelectric thermal-to-electrical power-generation systems.

In addition to these uses, current applications include the use of the heat pipe as an "isothermalizer" in chemical reactions involving flowing gas-feed stream, the transport of heat from a flame source, the cooling of electron tubes and semiconductors, temperature control of electronic subsystems such as printed-circuit boards, and the cooling of electric motors and transformer windings.

The special attributes of the heat pipe would appear to qualify it for several additional applications as yet unexplored. Processes requiring unusually high spatial uniformity of temperature may be enhanced by the use of a heat pipe. An example might be an annular heat-pipe furnace-muffle heater for use in the growth of single-crystal materials or in the formation of epitaxial layers in the semiconductor field. Metallic heat pipes are subject to the deleterious effects of hydrogen permeation, but can be protected by quartz or ceramic permeation barriers. Ceramic heat pipes can be fabricated as well.

There appear to be applications in the chemical manufacturing and pharmaceutical industries for reaction or culture-growing vessels in which an unusual degree of temperature uniformity is desired. Such a vessel could include heat pipes in its walls or could itself be a specialized heat pipe. In a number of these categories of use, the precise temperature regulation of the gas-controlled, constant-temperature heat pipe may prove most useful because, in addition to its precision, it requires no electronic or other external sensing and control mechanism for its operation.

In many geographical areas, gaseous or liquid hydrocarbon fuels are appreciably less costly than electricity per Btu of delivered heat. However, electricity is often used as a heat source in these areas because of the superior temperature control and uniformity which can be obtained. In such applications the use of hydrocarbon fuels with heat pipes shows promise as an approach in which a slightly higher investment in facilities may result in an appreciable long-term saving in fuel costs.

Bibliography

1. U.S. Pat. 2,350,348 (June 6, 1944), C. S. Gaugler (to General Motors Corp.).
2. G. M. Grover et al., "Advances in Heat Pipe Technology," *LA-DC-9619*, Los Alamos Scientific Laboratory, University of California, Los Alamos, N. Mex.
3. T. P. Cotter, "Theory of Heat Pipes," *LA-3246-MS*, Los Alamos Scientific Laboratory, University of California, Los Alamos, N. Mex., 1965.

General References

NOTE: The following references, although far from complete, provide additional background in the theory and practice of heat pipe operation.

G. M. Grover et al., "Structures of Very High Thermal Conductance," *J. Appl. Phys.* **35**, 1990 (1964).

T. P. Cotter, "Theory of Heat Pipes," *LA-3246-MS* Los Alamos Scientific Laboratory, University of California, Los Alamos, N. Mex., 1965.

T. P. Cotter, "Heat Pipe Startup Dynamics," *LA-DC-9026*, Los Alamos Scientific Laboratory.

J. E. Deverall, "Mercury as a Heat Pipe Fluid," *LA-4300-MS*, Los Alamos Scientific Laboratory.

J. E. Kemme, "Heat Pipe Design Considerations," *LA-4221-MS*, Los Alamos Scientific Laboratory.

H. Cheung, "A Critical Review of Heat Pipe Theory and Applications," *UCRL-50453*, Lawrence Radication Laboratory, University of California, Livermore, Calif.

R. C. Turner, "Feasibility Investigation of the Vapor Chamber Fin," *AD839-469*, RCA Electronic Components, Lancaster, Pa.

G. Y. Eastman, "The Heat Pipe," *Sci. Am.* **218** (5) 38–46.

G. Y. Eastman, "The Heat Pipe - A Progress Report," *ST-4048*, RCA Electronics Components, Lancaster, Pa.

R. A. Freggens, "Experimental Determination of Wick Properties for Heat Pipe Applications," *ST-4086, RCA* Electronics Components, Lancaster, Pa.

W. L. Haskin, "Cryogenic Heat Pipe," *Report AFFDL-TR-66-228, AD-657-025*, Flight Dynamics, Lab., Wright Patterson Air Force, Case, Ohio.

J. Bodhansky and H. E. J. Schins, "A New Method for Vapor Pressure Measurements at High Temperature and High Pressure," *J. Appl. Phys.* **36** (11) 3683–3684.

K. T. Feldman and G. H. Whiting, "The Heat Pipe," *Mech. Eng.* **89** (2) 30 (1967).

K. T. Feldman and G. H. Whiting, "Application of the Heat Pipe, *Mech. Eng.* **90** (11) 48 (1968).

E. K. Levy, "Theoretical Investigation of Heat Pipes Operating at Low Vapor Pressures," *Am. Soc. Mech. Eng. Trans. Proc. of Annual Aviation and Space Conf., 1968*, p. 671 (1968).

S. Katzoff, "Heat Pipes and Vapor Chambers for Thermal Control of Spacecraft," *Paper No. 67-310*, American Institute of Aeronautics and Astronautics.

G. Yale Eastman
Radio Corporation of America

HYDRIDES

This article deals with recent advances in metal hydrides, and particularly with their applications. The main subjects covered are: broader use of sodium borohydride; two new hydrides, sodium cyanoborohydride and sodium dihydro-bis(2-methoxyethoxy)aluminate; hydroboration; and certain electrophilic reductions.

Sodium borohydride is a less vigorous reducing agent for organic functional groups than lithium aluminum hydride, but this gives it an advantage, stemming from the fact that aldehydes, ketones, and acid chlorides can be selectively reduced to alcohols in the presence of other groups, such as esters and amides, that would be reduced by aluminohydrides. For this reason sodium borohydride has become a basic tool in organic synthesis, permitting the chemist greater flexibility in tailoring organic molecules efficiently. It has also been especially valuable in the pharmaceutical and fine-chemical areas, where selectivity and the resulting improved yields of product are particularly desirable. An outstanding example is the selective reduction of steroid keto groups with sodium borohydride.

Larger-volume uses of sodium borohydride have been developed since the 1960s in such diverse areas as vat-dye technology and pulp bleaching. Vat dyeing commonly employs sodium hydrosulfite (dithionite, $Na_2S_2O_4$) as the reducing agent. But at the dyeing temperature, $\sim100°C$, considerable decomposition of the reducing agent occurs, requiring that a substantial excess be used. But sodium borohydride undergoes minimal losses under dyeing conditions in the highly alkaline solutions used, and this makes it competitive. Sodium borohydride is also competing in the reductive bleaching of groundwood pulp, where zinc hydrosulfite has been used.

Intermediate volumes of sodium borohydride are being consumed in removing trace organic impurities from numerous process streams, such as alcohols, glycols, ethers, oxides and amines. The impurities, which are usually aldehydes, ketones, or peroxides, are normally present in ppm quantities and have been proved to contribute greatly to undesirable properties in these materials, which may be destined for surfactant or polymer manufacture. Treatment with sodium borohydride at low ppm levels results in improved color, odor, resistance to oxidation, thermal stability, and recycle characteristics. Frequently as little as ten pounds of $NaBH_4$ can effectively purify a million pounds of a process stream.

Broader Use of NaBH₄

Recent developments in hydride chemistry have included more diversified use of sodium borohydride in organic synthesis. Economic considerations have been important. The lower cost per reducing equivalent of $NaBH_4$, compared with $LiAlH_4$, has provided the incentive for chemists to devise ways of accomplishing many of the same reductions with the borohydride. The greater ease of handling sodium borohydride and its stability in alkaline aqueous solutions have also enhanced its attractiveness as a commercially useful chemical.

Over the years, organic chemists have generally become familiar with the use of sodium borohydride for the reduction of aldehydes and ketones to the corresponding alcohols. The reduction of organic peroxides and ozonides, Schiff bases, diazonium fluoborates, and azides by $NaBH_4$ is less well known. Recent applications, which are discussed below because of their extensive use or unusual potential, include the reduction of acids, amides, quaternary heterocyclics, nitro and nitroso groups, and a variety of double bonds.

Acids. Carboxylic acids are not reduced by $NaBH_4$. In fact, acids usually accelerate destruction of borohydrides by solvolysis. Yamada and co-workers (1) have circumvented this difficulty by forming in situ a mixed anhydride with ethyl chloroformate and then reducing the anhydride to the alcohol with $NaBH_4$.

$$RCOOH + ClCOOEt \rightarrow HCl + \begin{matrix} RCO \\ \diagdown \\ O \\ \diagup \\ EtCO \end{matrix} \xrightarrow{NaBH_4} RCH_2OH$$

Because the reduction takes place under mild conditions, selectivity is retained. Only the carboxyl group is reduced in acids containing nitro, cyano, amido, and ester groups, and conjugated double bonds. Yields of better than 70% are obtained.

Amides. Amides have been considered nonreducible by $NaBH_4$ under normal reaction conditions. More recently it has been found that at higher temperatures they are quite reactive. Dehydration of primary amides to nitriles occurs in refluxing diglyme, dimethyl ether of diethylene glycol (bp, 162°C) (2).

$$R\text{—}CONH_2 \rightarrow RCN + H_2O$$

A more complete investigation (3) shows that in refluxing pyridine (bp, 115°C) primary amides form the nitrile, secondary amides do not react, and tertiary amides are reduced to the amine.

$$R\text{—}CONR_2' \rightarrow RCH_2NR_2'$$

Demercuration. The oxymercuration of olefinic double bonds has been known for some time, but it is only recently that H. C. Brown's group developed a procedure for reducing the organometallic with $NaBH_4$ (4). The reduction, which takes place rapidly at room temperature, is essentially quantitative. The combined reactions affect stereoselective Markovnikov hydration of double bonds.

$$RCH{=}CH_2 + Hg(OAc)_2 \rightarrow RCH(OH)CH_2\text{—}HgOAc \xrightarrow{NaBH_4} RCH(OH)CH_3$$

It should be noted that anti-Markovnikov hydration of double bonds to form the primary alcohol is available through hydroboration (see page 505) and oxidation with alkaline hydrogen peroxide.

Oxymercuration–demercuration has been utilized in the presence of alcohols to synthesize ethers and in the presence of acetonitrile to synthesize amines (5).

Double Bonds. Isolated carbon–carbon double bonds are inert to $NaBH_4$. When such unsaturation is activated, however, usually by an aromatic ring at one end and a polar functional group at the other, $NaBH_4$ affects hydrogenation. This reaction has become increasingly useful in compounds containing other functional groups which would be destroyed by catalytic hydrogenation. Cyanostilbenes are converted to diphenylcyanoethanes in excellent yield (6).

$$PhC(CN)=CRPh \rightarrow PhCH(CN)CHRPh$$

Kadin (7) has studied the hydrogenation of a variety of systems exhibiting α,β-unsaturation with $NaBH_4$, ncluding acrylates, atropates, and alkylidene malonates. Similar saturation of α,β-unsaturated cyanoacetates and alkylidene cyanoacetates has been reported (8). This type of reaction is now used commercially to convert a dihydropyridine to the tetrahydro form in the manufacture of substituted benzazocines (9), which are used as analgesic agents.

A slightly different variation is the conversion of α,β-unsaturated carboxylic acids, which are inert to aqueous $NaBH_4$, to the saturated acids by catalyzing the reaction with cyanocobaltate (10).

Saturation of the carbon–nitrogen double bond in Schiff bases by sodium borohydride under mild conditions has been known for many years.

$$ArN=CHR \rightarrow ArNH-CH_2R$$

More recently, $NaBH_4$ has been used to saturate carbon–nitrogen double bonds in a wide variety of heterocyclics, including isoquinolines (equ. 1), 1,3-oxazines (equ. 2), diazocines (equ. 3), and thiazines (equ. 4).

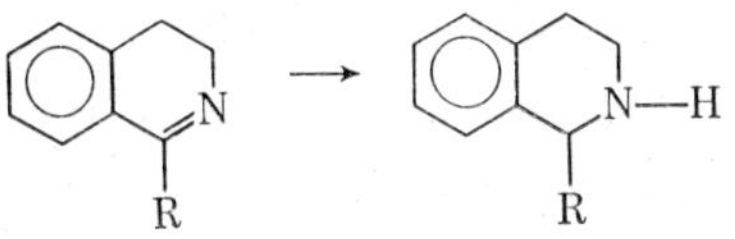

(1)

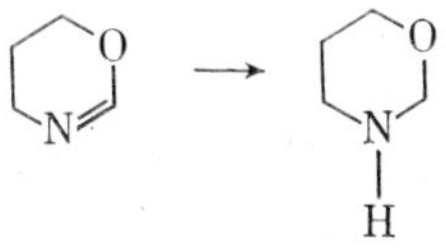

(2)

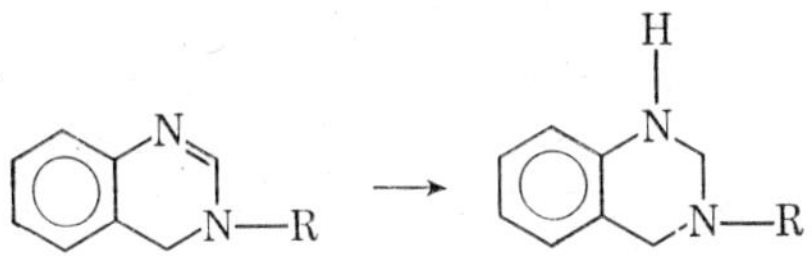

(3)

(4)

Nitro Compounds. The nitro group is not reactive with $NaBH_4$ except in a few special cases; nitrobenzene is reduced to azoxybenzene only slowly, even in a refluxing diglyme. When catalyzed by palladized charcoal, however, aromatic nitro and nitroso compounds are reduced to the amine in good yield (11). No evidence was found of azo, azoxy, or hydrazo intermediates being formed. This reduction has been applied in the synthesis of porphyrins and phenetidines (12). The phenetidines, particularly the acetoxy derivative, are used as analgesics and antipyretics. The starting material is 4-ethoxy-2-hydroxynitrosobenzene; the product, 2-hydroxy-p-phenetidine.

Quaternary Compounds. A large variety of cyclic quaternary ammonium salts have been reduced with $NaBH_4$, including pyridinium, isoquinolinium, pyrazinium, and thiazolium compounds. In these the $>C=\overset{+}{N}<$ is effectively hydrogenated to the amine. One of the most interesting reactions of this type is the complete reduction of quaternized 4-aminopyridines to the 4-aminopiperidines (13), a reduction impossible to carry out by catalytic hydrogenation.

Even nitrilium salts, $(-C\equiv\overset{+}{N}-)$, by way of the imino ester are reduced in good yield to the secondary amine (14). The equation for reduction of nitrilium salts with sodium borohydride via the iminoester is the following:

$$RC\equiv N + Et_3O^+BF_4^- \rightarrow RC\equiv\overset{+}{N}CH_2CH_3BF_4^- \xrightarrow{EtOH} RC\underset{|}{\overset{OEt}{=}}NCH_2CH_3 \xrightarrow{NaBH_4} RCH_2NHCH_2CH_3$$

Mixed naphthopyrans result from the similar reduction of naphthopyrilium salts (15).

In this case a ternary oxonium ion is involved.

Reductive Cleavage. Among the varied uses which $NaBH_4$ has found in organic synthesis is the reductive cleavage of heterocyclic rings, such as the lactone ring in 3-dehydrobufalin.

Also the cleavage of imidazolium rings (equ. 5), (16), benzoxazinones (equ. 6), (17), and glutarimides (equ. 7), (18), to name but a few.

$$(5)$$

$$(6)$$

$$(7)$$

Reductive Cyclization. In direct contrast with the foregoing, $NaBH_4$ has also been applied to many cyclization reactions in recent years. Cyclizations are reported in the stereospecific synthesis of *cis*- and *trans*-dihydrotoxol (equ. 9) (19), and in the

$$(8)$$

formation of diazasteroid systems (equ. 9) (20).

$$(9)$$

Coutts has used $NaBH_4$, catalyzed by palladized charcoal, to prepare heterocyclic hydroxamic acids (equ. 10) from *o*-nitroesters, such as nitrocinnamates, and as a preferred route to benzothiazine hydroxamic acids (equ. 11) from *o*-nitro-thioesters (21).

$$(10)$$

$$(11)$$

Sodium Cyanoborohydride

Sodium cyanoborohydride, $NaBH_3CN$, is a hygroscopic white, solid derivative of $NaBH_4$, which has been introduced very recently. This compound (d = 1.20 g/cc) is soluble in tetrahydrofuran, alcohols, and amines and extremely soluble in water. It promises to be a particularly useful reducing agent because of its stability in aqueous acid solution to a pH of 2–3. Since $NaBH_4$ is hydrolytically stable only in aqueous alkali, the two compounds complement each other, permitting reduction over nearly the entire pH scale.

The corresponding lithium salt, LiBH₃CN, was first prepared in 1951, by Wittig and Raff, who noted its unusual hydrolytic stability. Shortly thereafter, a brief note appeared, indicating general utility of this compound for aldehyde reductions only. Recent reinvestigation has shown that ketones, as well as aldehydes, are reduced, although more slowly than with NaBH₄ (22).

In acid solution the imine group ($>C{=}N{-}$) is reduced much more rapidly than the carbonyl group. This permits reductive amination of aldehydes and ketones under extremely mild conditions.

$$R_2CO + HNR_2' \xrightarrow{H^+} R_2C{=}\overset{+}{N}R_2' \xrightarrow{NaBH_3CN} R_2CHNR_2'$$

Reductive amination of substituted sodium pyruvates opens up a convenient route to amino acids in good yield.

$$\underset{R-C-C-ONa}{\overset{O\ \ \ O}{\underset{\|\ \ \ \ \|}{}}} + NH_3 \xrightarrow[H^+]{NaBH_3CN} \underset{R-C-C-OH}{\overset{H_2N\ \ O}{\underset{|\ \ \ \ \|}{}}}$$

Sodium Dihydro-bis(2-methoxyethoxy)aluminate

Another new arrival on the hydrides scene is a dialkoxy derivative of sodium aluminum hydride, sodium dihydro-bis(2-methoxyethoxy)aluminate, NaAlH₂(OC₂H₄-OCH₃)₂, which, for brevity's sake, has been called SDMA. It was first prepared in 1965 by Vit, Casensky, and Machacek at the Czechoslovak Academy of Sciences in Prague (23). The pure compound (d = 1.12 g/cc) is a slightly yellow, glassy solid which is soluble in ethers and aromatic hydrocarbons. Because its physical form causes some difficulty in handling and transfer, SDMA is supplied as a 70% solution in benzene.

The unusual solubility of this complex hydride in aromatic hydrocarbons and its significantly less vigorous reaction with water and alcohols, compared to lithium or sodium aluminum hydride, result in a more convenient aluminohydride. These factors are the principal advantages of SDMA.

Like lithium aluminum hydride, SDMA reduces a wide range of organic carbonyl and carboxyl compounds, including aldehydes, ketones, acid chlorides, carboxylic acids and anhydrides, esters, lactones and lactams, amides, oximes, nitriles, and nitro compounds (24). It also dehalogenates both aliphatic and aromatic halides.

It is as yet too early to predict what impact SDMA will have in the market place. It will surely find some uses where its greater convenience in handling or its unique solubility in aromatic hydrocarbons is the most important criterion. But it must be remembered that economic comparisons must be made on the basis of cost per reducing equivalent. The reducing equivalent weights, ie, molecular weight divided by the number of hydride atoms per molecule, of aluminohydrides are as follows:

LiAlH₄	9.5
NaAlH₄	13.5
NaAlH₂(OC₂H₄OCH₃)₂	101.1

All other factors being equal, the cost of SDMA must be about one-tenth that of LiAlH₄ or one-eighth that of NaAlH₄, to give comparable economics. It must also be remembered that SDMA is supplied as a solution in benzene.

Hydroboration

The addition of borane, BH_3, to organic unsaturation, called hydroboration, was discovered and studied extensively by H. C. Brown and his co-workers (25). Their efforts have opened up a new avenue to synthetic organic chemistry whereby unsaturation can be converted to a large variety of functional derivatives by suitable treatment of the organoborane initially formed.

Diborane, B_2H_6, the simplest boron hydride, is most conveniently handled as a solution in tetrahydrofuran (THF), in which it exists as the monomeric coordination complex, $THF \cdot BH_3$. The use of this solution overcomes the toxicity problem inherent

Table 1. Organoborane Reactions

Reaction	Reagent	Product
amination	H_2NOSO_3H	$-\overset{\shortmid}{\underset{\shortmid}{C}}-B< \quad \rightarrow \quad -\overset{\shortmid}{\underset{\shortmid}{C}}-NH_2$
coupling	alk $AgNO_3$	$2(-\overset{\shortmid}{\underset{\shortmid}{C}}-B<) \quad \rightarrow \quad -\overset{\shortmid}{\underset{\shortmid}{C}}-\overset{\shortmid}{\underset{\shortmid}{C}}-$
cyclization	heat	$-\overset{\shortmid}{C}-H \;\; H-B' \rightarrow -\overset{\shortmid}{C}-B<$
displacement	$R'CH{=}CH_2$	$R-\overset{\shortmid}{C}-\overset{\shortmid}{C}-B< \rightarrow R'-\overset{\shortmid}{C}-\overset{\shortmid}{C}-B<$
homologation		
1 C	CO	$-\overset{\shortmid}{\underset{\shortmid}{C}}-B< \quad \rightarrow \quad -\overset{\shortmid}{C}-\overset{\shortmid}{C}-B<$
2 C	α-haloester (+ $KOBu^t$)	$-\overset{\shortmid}{\underset{\shortmid}{C}}-B< \quad \rightarrow \quad -\overset{\shortmid}{\underset{\shortmid}{C}}-CH_2COOR'$
3 C	$CH_2{=}CHCHO$	$-\overset{\shortmid}{\underset{\shortmid}{C}}-B< \quad \rightarrow \quad -\overset{\shortmid}{\underset{\shortmid}{C}}-CH_2CH_2CHO$
4 C	$CH_2{=}CHC(O)CH_3$	$-\overset{\shortmid}{\underset{\shortmid}{C}}-B< \quad \rightarrow \quad -\overset{\shortmid}{\underset{\shortmid}{C}}-CH_2CH_2C(O)CH_3$
isomerization	heat	$-\overset{\shortmid}{C}-\overset{\shortmid}{\underset{B}{C}}-\overset{\shortmid}{C}- \rightarrow -\overset{\shortmid}{C}-\overset{\shortmid}{C}-\overset{\shortmid}{C}-B<$
metalation	alk M salt	$-\overset{\shortmid}{\underset{\shortmid}{C}}-B< \quad \rightarrow \quad -\overset{\shortmid}{\underset{\shortmid}{C}}-M$
oxidation		
to alcohols	alk H_2O_2	$-\overset{\shortmid}{\underset{\shortmid}{C}}-B< \quad \rightarrow \quad -\overset{\shortmid}{\underset{\shortmid}{C}}-OH$
to ketones	H_2CrO_4	$-\overset{\shortmid}{\underset{\shortmid}{C}}-B< \quad \rightarrow \quad >C{=}O$
to acids	1. H_2CrO_4 2. RCOOOH	$-\overset{\shortmid}{\underset{\shortmid}{C}}-B< \quad \rightarrow \quad -\overset{\shortmid}{\underset{\shortmid}{C}}-COOH$
protonation	RCOOH, heat	$-\overset{\shortmid}{\underset{\shortmid}{C}}-B< \quad \rightarrow \quad -\overset{\shortmid}{\underset{\shortmid}{C}}-H$

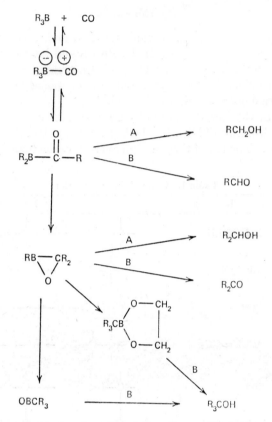

Fig. 1. Intramolecular transfer steps in carbonylation of organoboranes. LEGEND: A, alkaline H_2O; B, alkaline H_2O_2.

to diborane and permits handling at ambient temperature without cumbersome vacuum lines. The solution is stable indefinitely when refrigerated. It can be handled in air, but exposure is best minimized since it is subject to hydrolysis.

The hydroboration reaction

$$>B{-}H + CH_2{=}CHR \rightarrow >B{-}CH_2CH_2R$$

takes place rapidly and quantitatively at room temperature. It is an anti-Markovnikov addition in that the boron atom adds to the least substituted carbon atom. It has the advantages of retaining stereoconfiguration and of being compatible with a large number of functional groups. Hydroboration can be applied not only to olefins and acetylenes, but also to carbonyls, imines, and nitriles.

As would be expected, three moles of a simple olefin react with one of borane, BH_3.

$$BH_3 + 3\,CH_2{=}CHR \rightarrow B(CH_2CH_2R)_3$$

Such is the case for mono- and disubstituted terminal olefins ($CH_2{=}CHR$ and $CH_2{=}CR_2$) and disubstituted internal olefins ($RCH{=}CHR$) where the R's are n-alkyl. The reaction with branched olefins may, for all practical purposes, stop at the diorganoborane (R_2BH) or the monoorganoborane (RBH_2), depending on the degree of branching. The steric requirements of the organic compound determine the extent of reaction. Mono- and polycyclic olefins react in an analogous way, depending on the degree of steric hindrance in the molecule.

The organoboranes formed by the hydroboration are quite versatile. By proper choice of reagents and reaction conditions (see Table 1), they can be converted to a large number of diverse functional types, usually without isolation of the intermediate. Alcohols, ketones, amines, carboxylic acids, hydrocarbons, and organometallics are among the compound types which can be prepared.

Carbonylation of Organoboranes. The utility of hydroboration has recently been augmented by H. C. Brown's discovery that organoboranes could be carbonylated with carbon monoxide (26) at atmospheric pressure by employing elevated temperatures. This reaction, like hydroboration, is tolerant of many functional groups, such as ester, nitrile, and halogen, which are not compatible with Grignard reagents. The carbonylation reaction is generally carried out in diglyme because of the temperature required, 100–125°C. Reactions of the carbonylated organoboranes have been developed which permit conversion to primary, secondary, and tertiary alcohols, and aldehydes, and ketones.

The key to the various product types lies in controlling the intramolecular transfer of organic groups from boron to carbon. The proposed transfer intermediates and routes to various products are shown schematically in Figure 1. Alkyl transfer is limited to one by use of a complex hydride, LiBH$_4$, or LiAlH(OMe)$_3$ during carbonylation. This also catalyzes the carbonylation, permitting reaction at 25–45°C, instead of the usual higher temperature. If it is desired to stop alkyl transfer with two groups, the carbonylation is performed in the presence of water which greatly inhibits transfer of the third group. Complete transfer is accomplished at 100–125°C in the absence of either additive. However, the completely transferred intermediate is sometimes difficult to oxidize; carbonylation in the presence of ethylene glycol overcomes this problem.

Selective Hydroboration. Mono- and dialkylboranes formed by hydroboration of sterically hindered olefins have been found useful in their own right for the stereoselective hydroboration of other olefins. They provide a source of high-purity stereoisomers, as shown below for *cis*-4-methyl-2-pentene and styrene. The isomer distribution is shown compared with that obtained using borane.

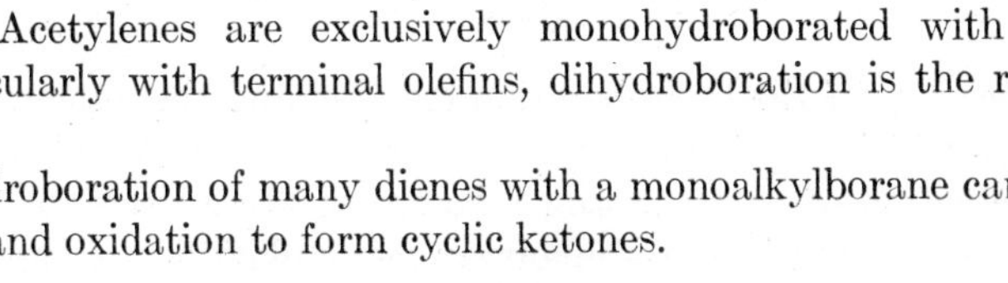

% BH$_3$:	43	57	19	81
% R$_2$BH:	3	97	2	98

Alkylboranes also permit selective monohydroboration of dienes containing double bonds of different reactivities, such as the exocyclic unsaturation in 4-vinylcyclohexene. Acetylenes are exclusively monohydroborated with alkyl boranes, whereas, particularly with terminal olefins, dihydroboration is the rule with borane itself.

Cyclic hydroboration of many dienes with a monoalkylborane can be followed by carbonylation and oxidation to form cyclic ketones.

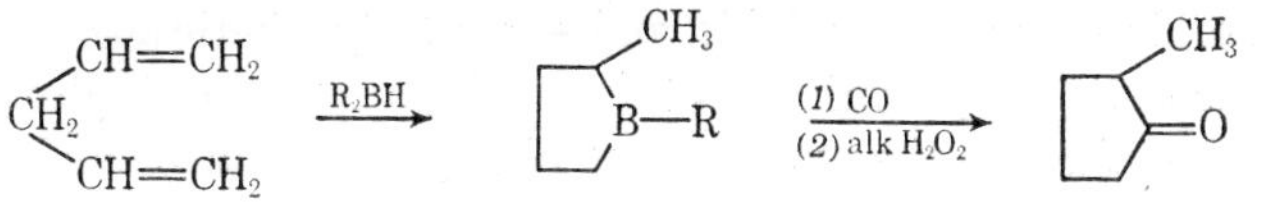

Annelation reactions of appropriate and accessible dienes lead to polycyclics such as *trans*-1-decalone.

Electrophilic Reductions

Besides the hydroboration reactions discussed above, borane and its mono- and disubstituted derivatives are also useful for the reduction of functional groups. In contrast to the complex hydrides which are nucleophilic and attack the carbon atom of largest positive charge, the boranes are Lewis acids and operate electrophilically. They therefore have different reducing properties, as summarized in Table 2, where the most reactive group heads each column. Sodium borohydride reduces acid chlorides, which are reduced only very slowly by borane. On the other hand, borane reduces carboxylic acids, nitriles, epoxides, and esters, which are not readily reduced by sodium borohydride. Such markedly different reactivities of typical functional groups with the two boron hydride reagents permit reduction of one group in the presence of another. In a compound containing both an acid chloride and an ester group, for example, either function can be reduced exclusively by the proper choice of reagent.

Table 2.   Reactivity of Functional Groups

MBH₄	BH₃
acid chloride	carboxylic acid
aldehyde	olefin
ketone	aldehyde
epoxide	ketone
ester	nitrile
nitrile	epoxide
carboxylic acid	ester
	acid chloride

Alkylboranes are much milder reducing agents than the parent BH_3. They provide steric control of reduction to give predominantly *cis*-alcohols. Their selectivity allows selective reduction of an aldehyde or ketone in the presence of a disulfide or epoxide, half-reduction of lactones to hydroxyaldehydes, and reduction of carboxylic dimethylamides to aldehydes, in the presence of free carboxylic acids.

Uses

Since the discovery of the hydroboration reaction and the numerous reactions of the organoboranes which are formed, many uses have been found for the valuable selectivity and retention of configuration inherent in these reactions. As would be expected, these are centered in areas involving manipulation of complicated organic structures, eg steroids, terpenes, alkaloids, and sugars. Synthetic hormones (27), 6-keto steroids (28), gonenes, and gonatrienes (29) are prepared using hydroboration. The reaction has been applied to the synthesis of pinenes (30), citronellol (31), menthols

(32), tricyclic sesquiterpenes (33), and others. Recent synthesis in the prostaglandin series has used hydroboration in the synthesis of prostanoic acid precursors (34).

Bibliography

1. K. Ishizumi, K. Koga and S. Yamada, *Chem. Pharm. Bull.* (Tokyo) **16**, 492 (1968); *Chem. Abstr.* **69**, 58805g (1968).
2. S. E. Ellzey, C. H. Mack, and W. J. Connick, *J. Org. Chem.* **32**, 846 (1967).
3. Y. Kikugawa, S. Ikegami, and S. Yanada, *Chem. Pharm. Bull.* (Tokyo) **17**, 98 (1969); *Chem. Abstr.* **70**, 87491c (1969).
4. H. C. Brown et al., *J. Am. Chem. Soc.* **89**, 1522, 1524, 1525 (1967).
5. H. C. Brown and M.-H. Rei, *J. Am. Chem. Soc.* **91**, 5646 (1969). H. C. Brown and J. T. Kurek *J. Am. Chem. Soc.* **91**, 5647 (1969).
6. J. Knabe, P. Herbort, and N. Ruppenthal, *Arch. Pharm.* **229**, 534 (1966); *Chem. Abstr.* **65**, 8815a (1966).
7. S. B. Kadin, *J. Org. Chem.* **31**, 620 (1966).
8. J. A. Meschino and C. H. Bond, *J. Org. Chem.* **28**, 3129 (1963). J. A. Marshall and E. D. Carroll, *J. Org. Chem.* **30**, 2748 (1965).
9. U.S. Pat. 3,250,678 (May 10, 1966), S. Archer (to Sterling Drug Inc.).
10. A. Kasahara and T. Hongu, *Yamagata Daigaku Kiyo, Shizen Kagaku* **6**, 263 (1967); *Chem. Abstr.* **65**, 2120c (1966).
11. T. Nielson, H. C. S. Wood, and A. C. Wylie, *J. Chem. Soc.* **1962**, 371.
12. M. J. Namkung and T. L. Fletcher, *J. Med. Chem.* **12**, 348 (1969).
13. G. N. Walker, *J. Org. Chem.* **26**, 2740 (1961).
14. R. F. Borch, *J. Org. Chem.* **34**, 627 (1969).
15. Z. Muljiani and B. D. Talik, *Indian J. Chem.* **7**, 28 (1969); *Chem. Abstr.* **70**, 87449v (1969).
16. E. F. Godefroi, *J. Org. Chem.* **33**, 860 (1968).
17. I. W. Elliott, F. Hamilton, and D. K. Ridley, *J. Heterocycl. Chem.* **5**, 707 (1968).
18. Y. Kondo and B. Witkop, *J. Org. Chem.* **33**, 206 (1968).
19. L. H. Zalkow and M. Ghosal, *J. Org. Chem.* **34**, 1646 (1969).
20. J. H. Burckhalter et al., *Chem. Commun.* **1968**, 1274.
21. R. T. Coutts, *J. Chem. Soc.* **1969**C, 713. R. T. Coutts and E. M. Smith, *Can. J. Chem.* **45**, 975 (1967); *Chem. Abstr.* **67**, 11467s (1967).
22. R. F. Borch and H. D. Durst, *J. Am. Chem. Soc.* **91**, 3996 (1969).
23. Fr. Pat. 1,515,582 (March 1, 1968), J. Vit, B. Casensky, and J. Machacek (to Czechoslovak Academy of Sciences).
24. M. Capka et al., *Tetrahedron Letters* **1968**, 3303; *Collect. Czech. Chem. Commun.* **34**, 118 (1969); *Chem. Abstr.* **70**, 67807g (1969). M. Cerny et al., **34**, 1025 (1969); *Chem. Abstr.* **70**, 96346m (1969). M. Kraus and K. Kochloefl, *Collect. Czech. Chem. Commun.* **34**, 1823 (1969); *Chem. Abstr.* **71**, 38480k (1969). M. Cerny and J. Malek, *Tetrahedron Letters* **1969**, 1739. J. F. Corbett, *Chem. Commun.* **1969**, 1257.
25. H. C. Brown, *Hydroboration*, W. A. Benjamin, Inc., New York, 1962.
26. H. C. Brown and M. W. Rathke, *J. Am. Chem. Soc.* **89**, 2737–2739 (1967).
27. H. Smith et al., *J. Chem. Soc.* **1968**C, 2647.
28. J. F. Bagli, P. F. Morand, and R. Gaudry, *J. Org. Chem.* **27**, 2938 (1962).
29. Brit. Pats. 1,115,635 (May 29, 1968); 1,115,954 (June 6, 1968); 1,128,041 (Sept. 25, 1968), to H. Smith.
30. G. Zweifel and C. C. Whitney, *J. Org. Chem.* **31**, 4178 (1966).
31. Brit. Pat. 1,031,302 (June 2, 1966), A. H. Turner and J. M. Vickers (to Shell International Research. U.S. Pat. 2,990,422 (June 27, 1961), E. L. Woroch and J. W. Cole (to Glidden Co.).
32. J. Katsuhara et al., *Bull. Chem. Soc. Japan* **39**, 617 (1966); *Chem. Abstr.* **64**, 19690h (1966).
33. J. E. McMurry, *J. Am. Chem. Soc.* **90**, 6821 (1968).
34. I.S. Pat. 3,435,053 (March 25, 1969), P. F. Beal, F. H. Lincoln, and J. E. Pike (to Upjohn Co.).

EDWARD A. SULLIVAN
Ventron Corporation

I

INFORMATION RETRIEVAL SERVICES AND METHODS

Man's knowledge of chemistry and chemical technology is growing at an exponential rate; the total store is doubling about every 10 years. Those who are active in this field are no doubt familiar with many of the traditional and time-tested tools available for retrieval of this information. However, the sheer volume of information to be handled, together with the changing patterns of information use in recent years has created a need for new and more effective means of processing and disseminating the information.

The professional societies and the information industry are responding to this challenge by utilizing modern technology to create new information retrieval tools and services which are responsive to the present-day needs of their users. As might be anticipated, computer technology is used extensively in the creation and use of these newer tools. As a consequence a new breed of publications has emerged which in most instances is available in both printed and computer-readable form. Furthermore, the use of computer technology provides a heretofore unattainable degree of flexibility in packaging the information so that a wide spectrum of tools and services is rapidly becoming available, each of which is tailored to some specific need or to some specific group of users.

Chemists' information needs may be categorized in several different ways. In traditional information retrieval the most common approach is to differentiate between the need for "current awareness" as contrasted to the need for "retrospective searching." Current awareness relates to those activities, products, or services which enable the chemist to keep up with the current literature and to keep aware of recent developments in his field. Retrospective searching, on the other hand, embodies those activities, products, or services required to locate and retrieve a specific item of information from the entire body of literature (from past to present), or to establish whether or not a particular item of information has ever been reported in the literature. The value of a current-awareness tool is primarily a function of the timeliness of the information it contains, whereas the value of a retrospective searching tool depends very much on the quality of its indexes. (Adequate coverage of the subject matter is assumed in both instances.)

Another interesting way of categorizing the chemist's information needs is to view the information retrieval process in terms of *information discovery* and *information recovery*. Current-awareness tools, in this sense, help him to *discover* those things that he cannot request because he does not know they exist. On the other hand, retrospective tools enable him not only to discover information that was not known to exist but also to *recover* information that is known or presumed to exist.

Some modern current-awareness and retrospective chemical information retrieval tools are described below. The discussion is organized in three sections: the first section describes printed publications; the second deals with computer-based search services which utilize computer-readable forms of some of the printed tools; the last section is devoted to a discussion of recent developments in an area of special interest to chemists, ie substructure searching.

Printed Forms of Modern Information Retrieval Tools

Current Contents (CC), a set of pocket-sized weekly publications produced by the Institute for Scientific Information (ISI), is probably the pacemaker among the newer current-awareness information tools available to chemists, scientists, and technologists. Five editions of interest to chemists and chemical technologists are *Current Contents, Chemical Sciences (CCCS)*; *Current Contents, Physical Sciences (CCPS)*; *Current Contents, Life Sciences (CCLS)*; *Current Contents, Agricultural, Food & Veterinary Sciences (CCAF&VS)*; and *Current Contents, Engineering and Technology (CCE&T)*. (In 1971 the *CCCS* and *CCPS* merged into *Current Contents, Physical & Chemical Sciences*.) Each edition reproduces the table of contents (in most instances in the original format) of all the important journals in the fields which they cover. *CCLS* covers about 1000 journals (approximately 3000 articles per week) in biochemistry, medicine, botany, zoology, pharmacology, cytology, genetics, systematics, ecology, and other life science disciplines; *CCPS* covers about 700 journals (approximately 2000 articles per week) in experimental and theoretical physics, astrophysics and astronomy, space engineering, earth sciences, nuclear physics and engineering, mathematics, information and computer sciences, electronics, instrumentation, metallurgy, and pure and applied chemistry; *CCCS* covers approximately 1000 articles per week in all areas of pure and applied chemistry, chemical engineering, and chemical technology. *CCAF&VS* and *CCE&T* are two of the more recent additions to this family of current-awareness tools. Each covers about 700 journals (approximately 2000 articles per week) for the respective fields covered. There obviously is some degree of overlap between each of these separate editions of *Current Contents*, but this is done purposely to make each edition as self-contained as possible for the population of users whose interests lie in any one of the designated fields.

The tables of contents reproduced in each weekly issue of *Current Contents* often arrive before the journals from which they are obtained. With this timeliness of coverage, *CC* thus provides an effective and convenient solution to journal routing problems. Also, the pocket-size form makes it possible to scan a manageable amount of information either systematically in a library or at odd moments in the laboratory, or while on the move attending business or professional meetings. Through such browsing the chemist can simultaneously see what is new in the world of chemical research and allied fields, and also watch for items of particular interest in his current work.

A unique feature of *CC* is a computer-produced alphabetical index and address directory of the principal authors of the papers noted in each weekly issue. This makes it easy to request reprints of articles without delay, particularly for articles published in journals which are not easily accessible.

Another modern current-awareness tool is *Chemical Titles (CT)* which is published biweekly by *Chemical Abstracts Service (CAS)*. Generally recognized to be the first computer-produced periodical, *CT* alerts chemists and chemical technologists to current information published in approximately 650 of the world's leading chemical journals. Each issue contains bibliographic data for approximately 5000 articles. The particular articles selected from each journal covered in any given issue of *CT* are listed in the Bibliographic Section of the periodical. Articles of interest are easily located by searching the Author Index or the KWIC (Key-Word-in-Context) Index (1, 1a), or by browsing through the Bibliography Section. Timeliness of coverage allows one in many instances to learn about publication of an article before the arrival of the journal in which it is published.

Both *Current Contents* and *Chemical Titles* owe their existence to the need for current-awareness service to help bridge the gap between publication of articles in primary journals and their subsequent processing in traditional secondary publications such as *Chemical Abstracts* (see below) and *Chemisches Zentralblatt* (2). As the proliferation of new chemical knowledge gradually began to outpace the capabilities of conventional information handling and publishing techniques, the time lag between the appearance of an article in a primary publication and its indexing and abstracting in a secondary publication began to widen. Hence the need for intermediate, less comprehensive current-awareness services such as those just described.

More recently another type of current-awareness tool has appeared on the scene in fulfillment of yet another need. It arises from the fact that the earliest manifestation of progress in research or advances in technology is usually a paper presented at a meeting or a conference. Since presentation of such a paper usually precedes the publication of an article in a scientific journal by as much as two years, there is often a lengthy delay between the actual research and the dissemination of the resulting scientific and technical information. This communication bottleneck is bypassed by *Current Index to Conference Papers* (*CICP*), a set of monthly publications produced by CCM Information Corporation, a subsidiary of Crowell, Collier, and Macmillan.

CICP alerts the scientific and technological community to the contents of papers delivered at important scientific and technical meetings throughout the world, in most cases doing so by the time the meeting takes place. It is available in three subject areas of interest to specialists in the fields of chemistry and chemical technology— namely, chemistry, life sciences, and engineering. *CICP in Chemistry* covers approximately 25,000 papers annually from more than 250 professional meetings; *CICP in Life Sciences* covers approximately 45,000 papers annually from more than 400 professional meetings; and *CICP in Engineering* covers approximately 50,000 papers annually from more than 800 professional meetings. Every paper is indexed by subject and by author(s).

Each monthly issue of *CICP* for a particular subject area (eg, chemistry) includes papers that have been and are about to be delivered. A typical issue is likely to cover a time span of four or five months both preceding and following the publication date. The subject-index entries provide the complete title of the paper, the author's name and address (if available), the paper number, and the registry number of the meeting at which the paper is being (or has been) presented. The meetings section provides all of the particulars for the meeting to which an index entry is keyed. Since the contents of any one issue are unlikely to be a reliable guide to whether a particular meeting has already been reported, each succeeding issue of a volume (12 issues per year) includes a listing of meetings that have been previously indexed in that volume. Semiannual accumulations of the subject and author indexes and of the meetings sections are also provided.

The group of secondary publications described up to this point are strictly current-awareness tools. Their principal objective is to provide up-to-date, timely information to their subscribers to fulfill a need which may not be adequately served by other information tools. As already noted, the only information they contain consists of bibliographic listings of recently published articles or meeting presentations together with some appropriate indexes to facilitate retrieval of the desired information at this level of information transfer. These publications have little or no shelf value after one or two years (except for an occasional historical trackdown) because by that time most information of lasting value has been repackaged in more useful ways for retrospective searching.

The next group of secondary publications to be described have permanent value as retrospective search tools, but since the retrospective search value is primarily a function of the quality of the indexes, the contents of the individual issues are designed with current awareness in mind. In general, because of the greater intellectual effort required to produce these publications, the information contained in each current issue is slightly less up-to-date than the information found in the first group. However, because they provide more information (usually in the form of abstracts and/or better indexes) and because the information is still reasonably current, these publications are also widely used as current-awareness tools, particularly for gaining access to more indepth information on articles published in less accessible primary journals or in less familiar languages.

Chemical Abstracts (*CA*) is probably the best known information retrieval tool in this group, and it will probably acquire even more stature now that *Chemiches Zentralblatt* (*CZ*), the German counterpart to *CA*, has ceased publication as a result of a recent agreement between the American Chemical Society (ACS) and the Gesellschaft Deutscher Chemiker (GDCh) to unite their efforts in processing secondary chemical and chemical-engineering information (3). *CA*, which is now published weekly, is the most comprehensive abstracting and indexing service devoted to chemistry in the world. At present about 275,000 abstracts are published annually in *CA*, approximately 90% of which come from articles published in about 2000 journals. To attempt complete coverage of chemical science and technology, however, nearly 12,000 periodicals from over 100 countries in more than 50 languages must be monitored by the CAS staff. Additional abstracts come from patents issued by 26 nations and from 600 to 700 monographs which are published each year. The present median currency for abstracts (elapsed time between publication of an article or patent and appearance of the abstract in *CA*) is approximately 100 days.

Long before *CA* attained its present size, it was evident that the publication was becoming far too large and too costly to be fully useful as a current-awareness tool for the individual scientist. Consequently, since 1963, *CA* has been partitioned into five topical areas each of which is published separately as well as in the regular complete edition of *CA*. Each topical edition contains a proportionate share of the classified sections into which the abstracts published in *CA* are located (presently 80 sections). The topical areas consist of the following: *Biochemistry Sections* (sections 1–20), *Organic Chemistry Sections* (sections 21–34), *Macromolecular Sections* (sections 35–46), *Applied Chemistry and Chemical Engineering Sections* (sections 47–64), and *Physical and Analytical Chemistry Sections* (sections 65–80). Each topical edition (or section grouping) is available to the individual subscriber without volume indexes at a fraction of the cost of the complete edition. They are useful both as current-awareness tools and for "browsing" because they are restricted to manageable amounts of information in five broad areas of specialization, one or more of which should coincide with the specialized interests of each chemist.

Another significant change in the CA issues, introduced at the same time as the section groupings, was the expansion of the issue indexes to include a keyword subject index and a patent concordance index (discussed below) in addition to the previously provided author and numerical patent indexes. The expanded issue indexes (not to be confused with the volume indexes discussed below) now provide a greater number and a wider variety of access points to the abstracts contained in each current issue of the complete edition of CA. This simultaneously enhances the current-awareness aspects of the CA issues and facilitates retrospective searching during the time interval between publication of the CA issues and the CA volume indexes. The keyword indexes (but not the other issue indexes) are also included in the topical editions of CA.

The value of a retrospective search tool is a function of the quality of its indexes. CA's volume and collective indexes have been acclaimed as models in this regard both within and without the chemical community. Some of the evolutionary changes which these indexes have undergone in recent years to improve (and sometimes maintain) their usefulness are described here. One group of changes pertains to the frequency of publication. Prior to 1962 a volume index covered a 12-month period of CA issues; from 1962 to the present a volume index covers a 6-month period. Similarly, prior to 1957 the volume indexes were cumulated at 10-year intervals to form the CA *Collective Indexes;* since 1957 they have been cumulated at 5-year intervals. These changes in time cycles, which reflect the burgeoning growth of the literature, kept the respective indexes down to manageable sizes and helped to keep the time lags between the CA issues, the volume indexes, and the collective indexes within reasonable bounds.

The second group of changes pertains to improvements in the quality and type of indexes provided. Most chemists are no doubt thoroughly familiar with CA's subject, author, formula, and numerical patent indexes. The subject and author indexes have been published for each volume since CA's inception in 1907; the formula indexes since 1920; and the numerical patent indexes (on a continuing basis) since 1935. Three other indexes (Fig. 1) have been added in recent years which are probably less familiar to most chemists. These are the index of ring systems introduced in 1957; the patent concordance index in 1963; and the HAIC (hetero-atom-in-context) formula index in 1967. The Index of Ring Systems enables one to determine all ring systems which have been reported during the index period. The ring notations used in this index conform to those used in the *Ring Index* (4) and its supplements. The patent concordance index enables one to identify all patents which cover a given claim and to identify which patent was first described in CA. The HAIC index, a molecular-formula index in which the formulas are permuted on successive noncarbon nonhydrogen atoms (ie, a KWIC index of molecular formulas) enables one to locate all molecular formulas having a given type and number of heteroatoms. The formulas so located are then used as cross-references to the regular formula index to locate the names of the compounds and the abstracts in which they are described.

Still another change introduced in 1969 is the CA index guide which includes a compilation of CAS indexing policies, and directions for use of the indexes. It also gathers in one place all of the cross-references, scope notes, synonyms, and illustrative structural diagrams that have appeared previously in the subject indexes; the latter now contain just the index entries themselves, devoid of the above material. Sub-

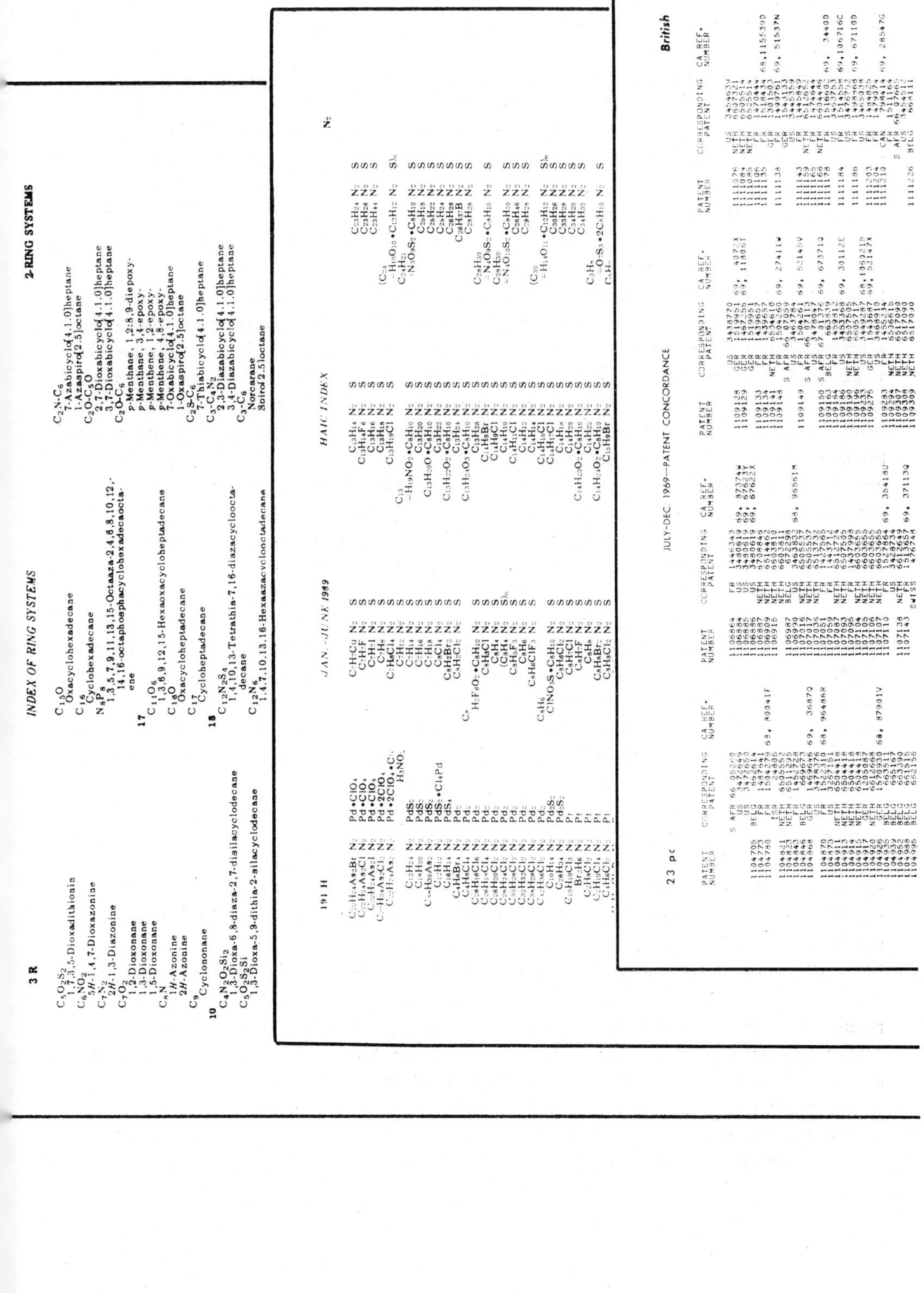

Fig. 1. Sample portions of three indexes which have been added to the CA Volume Indexes in recent years to improve access to information frequently sought by many members of the profession.

division of the *CA* subject index in this manner was initiated to simplify the editing and manufacturing tasks and, as a consequence, make the indexes available at an earlier date. (Each segment can now be compiled, edited, and composed for printing separately and, to a considerable degree, simultaneously rather than sequentially.) Other changes being contemplated, beginning with the ninth collective indexing period (1972–1976), involve extensive use of CAS registry numbers (discussed below under the CAS publication *CBAC*) in the *CA* subject and formula indexes (5).

Despite the comprehensiveness of *CA* and the generally good quality of its indexes, there are certain areas in which some chemists consider the format of the abstracts to be somewhat less than optimal. One such area is in the use of graphic formulas and flow diagrams to depict chemical compounds and chemical reactions. The relatively sparce number of such diagrams in *CA* is no doubt dictated by pragmatic reasons of trying to limit the space requirements of the abstracts.

A reference tool which has emphasized graphic descriptions rather than narrative is *Index Chemicus (IC)*, a publication initiated by ISI in 1960. In 1970, *IC* was replaced by another publication, *Current Abstracts of Chemistry and Index Chemicus*, discussed below. Since both the old and the new publication have retrospective value, a knowledge of the difference between the two is worthwhile. *IC* is a comprehensive yet concise tool reporting information on new chemical compounds and new synthetic reactions described in the world's more important chemical journals. Equally important, the format (Fig. 2) has been geared to the scanning chemist. Author summaries are used only to supplement structural diagrams and equations. Other graphic devices are also used to produce what is essentially a completely graphic abstract. One such device summarizes the analytical methods used to define the compounds described in the abstract. Another is the "use profile" which summarizes those uses and activities of compounds supported by actual test data in the original article.

Index Chemicus has proved to be particularly useful as a current-awareness tool for synthetic chemists, pharmacologists, and others interested in the new compounds appearing in literature. In 1969 nearly 185,000 new compounds were described in approximately 20,000 abstracts with a median currency of about 65 days. Indexes, for subject, author, journal, and molecular formula, have been provided monthly and cumulated semiannually and annually. The annual indexes thus provide ready access to information on over 1,000,000 compounds and their syntheses reported since 1960. Some of this information is not indexed in any other system.

As mentioned earlier, *IC* has recently been replaced by *Current Abstracts of Chemistry and Index Chemicus (CAC&IC)*, a similar publication with broader coverage. Whereas *IC* dealt only with articles containing information on new compounds and new reactions, *CAC&IC* abstracts all articles from the core journals covered regardless of whether or not new compounds or new reactions are described. *CAC&IC* consists of two components which have different publication schedules. The *CAC* component is a weekly publication containing graphic abstracts in the format described above for *IC* (1960–1969); it is divided into two sections—one for articles describing new compounds and new reactions (this section is equivalent to the weekly issue of the old *IC*), and one for articles which do not describe new compounds. Thus the reader can scan each weekly issue to keep abreast of all important chemical developments or limit himself to that portion of the literature describing new compounds or reactions (information of special significance to many industrial organizations). The new *IC* is strictly the indexing component of *CAC&IC*. It is published monthly with semiannual and annual

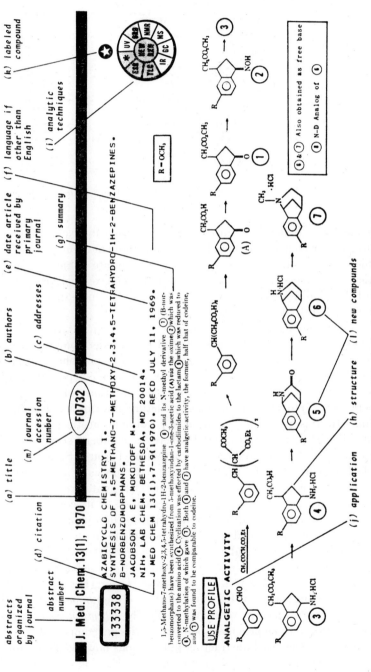

Fig. 2. Annotated samplea bstract from *CAC&IC*.

```
INDIUM.
    ELECTROSEPARATN FROM AMALGAM  - -144772
    IONIZATN ROTARY ELECTRODE        136918
    TELLURIUM MELT. EMF  - - - - -  -136933
    TL ALLOY. ELECTROLYSIS           144805
INDOGENIDES. 2-ALKYLIDENE-3-ONE   - -140076
INDOLEACETALDEHYDES. PHARMACOL       137927
INDOLEACETIC ACIDS. ESTERS - - - - -135907
INDOLECARBOXYLIC ACIDS.
    ALKYLAMINO-                      135171
    ETHANOLYAMINE  - - - - - - - -  -138268
    3-. HO-. TLC                     145901
INDOLEDIONES. ALKYLAMINO-  - - - -  -135171
INDOLENINES.
    2.3.3-TRI-ME-                    130089
    3-HYDROPEROXY  - - - - - - - -  -142459
    3-HYDROPEROXY-                   142459
INDOLES.
    ACYL-. ETHANOLAMINE  - - - - -  -138268
    ALKALOID. DERIV                  143295
    ALKALOID. VINCA ROSEA.
      CATHARANTHINE DERIVS - - - -  -143496
    ALKALOIDS                        140100
    AUTOTRANSFER CHROMATOGRAMS - -  -146031
    CHEMILUMINESCENCE                126328
    DI-CL-. DERIVS - - - - - - - -  -136667
    ET ESTERS                        142441
    EXCITED STATES - - - - - - - -  -129622
```

Fig. 3. Sample portion of a Subject Index from *Index Chemicus*.

cumulations. It includes author indexes, journal indexes, subject indexes, standard molecular formula indexes, and Rotaform (rotated molecular formula) indexes (6). The subject index (Fig. 3) is created from appropriate subject terms assigned to each article by professional chemists. Rotaform indexes perform the same function as the HAIC indexes which now appear in the *CA* volume indexes (see above), but they utilize a slightly different format.

A new companion index to *CAC&IC*, which is an outgrowth of the *Index Chemicus Registry System* (*ICRS*) to be discussed later under computer-based services, is the *ICRS-Substructure Index*. Basically, this index is an alphabetical listing of Wiswesser Line Notation (WLN) descriptions of new chemical compounds described in *CAC&IC*. The WLN is one of several types of linear notations which have been developed in recent years (7) to represent chemical structural information in computer manipulatable form. In this particular notation, for example, acetic acid (CH_3COOH) is represented by the character string QV1, where the number 1 stands for a methyl group, the V for a carbonyl group, and the Q for a hydroxyl group. Similarly, benzoic acid (C_6H_5-COOH) is represented by QVR, where the R represents a benzene ring. Thus with a defined set of symbols and an appropriate set of syntax rules (8) it is possible to represent virtually any chemical structure, regardless of its complexity, in terms of such a notation. Also, by permuting the notation (9) in a manner similar to the HAIC and Rotaform indexes described earlier, it is possible to create index entries for all functional groups in the structure and thereby not be restricted to index entries for those functional groups which enjoy indexing prominence on the basis of the hierarchical rules of the notation (10). The *ICRS Substructure Index* (Fig. 4), includes some selective permuted listings of the WLN's in addition to the nonpermuted listings. (In 1971 the *ICRS-Substructure Index* was replaced by the *Chemical Substructure Index* (*CSI*), a permuted index which provides about six entries per compound.)

A set of specialized abstracting publications now available from CAS in conjunction with the trend towards increased computerization of their services are *Chemical-Biological Activities* (*CBAC*), and *Polymer Science and Technology* (*POST*). The latter comes in two editions, one covering the journal literature, *POST-J*, and the other the patent literature, *POST-P*.

T3NTJ

```
                                                CDC      CDP
                                                ABSTR.   NO.
                                                NO.
T3NTJ APO&O2&N2&2# . . . . . . . . . . .127833-  2
T3NTJ APO&O4&N2&2#                                1
T3NTJ AVR BM1#                          126645-  4
T3NTJ AVR BZ# . . . . . . . . . . . . .           3
T3NTJ AVR CNW ENW#                                2
T3NTJ AVR DNW#                                    1
T3NTJ AVYR&UYZR& BR& CR# . . . . . . .126642-  3
T3NTJ AVYR&UYZR& BR#                              1
T3NTJ AVYR&UYZR& B1R& CR#                         4
T3NTJ AV2VM2# . . . . . . . . . . . . .127800-  7
T3NTJ AV2VZ#                                      5
T3NTJ B BR#                             125923-  2
T3NTJ# T5OJ BNW EYUNOV1V1&- A . . . . .125929-17
T3NXJ# L B656 HXJ H-& B                 125826-  1
T3OS CHJ CR# L66J B- C                  127688-  3
```

T3OTJ

```
T3OTJ B B C# . . . . . . . . . . . . . .127149-  1
T3OTJ B B CV2XNW#                       125975-  8
```

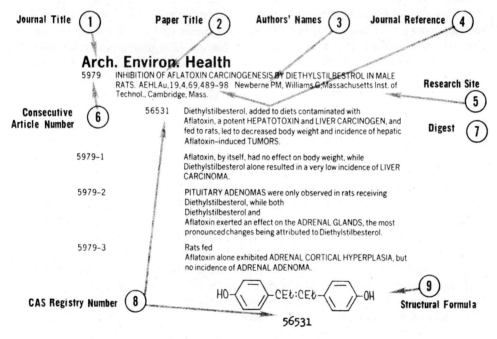

Fig. 4. Sample portion of the *ICRS Substructure Index.*

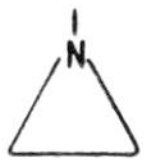

Fig. 5. Annotated sample digest from *CBAC.*

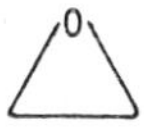

CBAC, which was introduced in 1965, is a biweekly publication containing digests (abstracts) of current technical articles related to the field of biochemistry appearing in approximately 600 journals. More specifically, it covers the scientific literature that reports on the interactions of organic compounds with biological systems; related metabolism and in vitro chemical studies are also included (see Fig. 5 for representative abstract). Each issue is accompanied by a KWIC subject index, a molecular formula index, an author index, and two registry number-faceted number cross-reference indexes. These indexes are accumulated for each volume (every 6 months).

The KWIC indexes for *CBAC* are derived not only from the titles of the articles, but from each sentence in the digest. The index entries, consequently, are keyed to the digest number and sentence number for each sentence in the digest to facilitate location of the subject matter being sought. The registry numbers appearing next to the names for each compound mentioned in the digest are unique identification numbers assigned to these compounds on the basis of unique computer representations of their chemical structures (11) by the CAS chemical compound registry system (to be discussed later). Once the identity of a registry number for a particular compound is known, it can be used to locate information on that compound in a registry number Index without having to recall the myriad names by which it may otherwise be known. This facility, being able to circumvent nomenclature barriers to access of information on chemical compounds, is important to many areas of chemistry and chemical technology as attested to by the availability of several compendia in which lengthy lists of synonymous trade names have been compiled for various compounds via such a registry system (12,13).

The faceted numbers appearing in the registry number-faceted number cross-reference indexes provide a means of interrelating the various topological isomers (ie, stereoisomers, isotopically labeled isomers, etc) of a given chemical structure, and also provide a means of interrelating salts with the acids or bases from which they are derived. For example, the registry number for 2,3,4,5,6-pentahydroxyhexanal with undefined stereochemistry (ie, for its constitution only) is 7,005,198. This registry number then becomes the base number of the faceted numbers for D-glucose (7,005,-198g), D-galactose (7,005,198e), and D-mannose (7,005,198c), where the letters after the numbers are the facets for description of the various stereoisomers. In a similar way, the registry number for benzoic acid (65,850) becomes the base number of the faceted numbers for sodium benzoate (65,850.02) and potassium benzoate (65,850.03), where the numbers after the decimal point are the particular facets for description of sodium and potassium salts, respectively, of organic acids. The faceted-number system is described in detail in the introduction to each issue of *CBAC*.

POST-J and *POST-P* are similar in design to *CBAC*, but they cover literature related to the field of polymer chemistry. *POST-J* is a biweekly publication covering the worldwide journal and report literature (approximately 500 primary sources), while *POST-P*, also a biweekly, covers the patent literature of 26 countries. The digests contain information on research, development, production, uses, equipment, and other aspects of polymer chemistry. In both publications the digests are grouped into six categories: synthetic polymers, plastics technology, textiles, elastomers, coatings, and cellulose and other carbohydrates.

Each issue of *POST-J* contains a keyword subject index, an author index, a molecular formula index, and a *CA* keyword index to related material (eg, biopolymers) abstracted in *Chemical Abstracts*. These indexes are accumulated for each volume (every six months). A registry number index is provided with the cumulative indexes only. A similar set of indexes are included with *POST-P* with the exception of the *CA* keyword index mentioned above. In its place, a numerical patent index and a patent concordance are included.

Citation Index

To find citations to a specific paper:

1. *locate cited author*
2. *locate reference year*
3. *locate reference publication, volume and page*
4. *note that source citations follow reference lines*

The data shown here simulate the type of material which appears in the Science Citation Index.

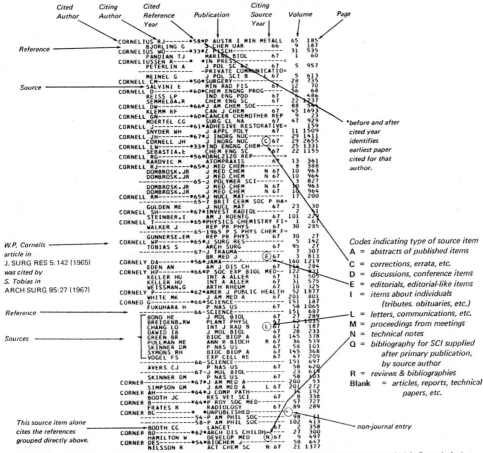

To locate sources which cite a particular paper, first look for the cited or reference author or patent number, located on the left. For each cited paper by that author there is a dashed line which continues to the column reserved for the year of reference publication, followed by journal, volume and page. To the right of each cited patent is the year and country. When a given reference has been cited more than once, the sources are arranged alphabetically by author. Each type of source item is further identified by a code. Note: only the first author is listed in the *Science Citation Index* proper. See the *Source Index* for all citing co-authors and full article titles.

Patent Citation Index

When a patent is cited in a source item the arrangement of the information is altered slightly. As shown in the example below, the cited patent number is used in place of the authors last name. The Patent Section is numerically arranged. Additional information is displayed in sequence as: Cited Reference Year, Inventors name, Country of issuance, and application or reissue status.

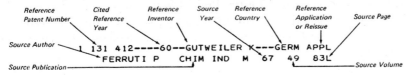

Fig. 6. Annotated sample portion of the Citation Index from *SCI*.

Perhaps the most remarkable of the newer search tools to appear on the scene in recent years (14) is the *Science Citation Index*, published quarterly by ISI on a regular basis since 1964. In contrast to all the other tools described up to this point, which provide conventional *current-awareness* and/or *retrospective* search capabilities as defined earlier in this article, the *Science Citation Index* (*SCI*) also provides a *prospective* search capability—ie, the capability of *searching forward in time*. This unique search capability is possible because one of the indexes included in the *SCI* is a citation index (Fig. 6), an alphabetized list of cited references each accompanied by a list of the later documents (citing sources) which refer to it. The citation index thus enables one to use an important article, a book, or a patent as a starting point for a search on a given topic and to be actually *brought forward in time* to subsequent articles which cited the earlier reference. Needless to say this type of indexing provides access to information which is difficult to retrieve by conventional indexes.

In addition to the citation index, the *SCI* also includes ISI's unique Permuterm Subject Index (PSI), a corporate index (since 1967), and a source index in which all of the source items are listed by author. Primary entries in the source index provide all coauthors of articles (maximum of ten), journal title, volume, page, year, type of source item (review, letter, correction, etc), number of references in the bibliography of that source, the issue number, part, or supplement number for that journal issue, all followed by the title of the article. Cross-references are provided in the source index for every coauthor, even though the primary entries only list a maximum of ten authors. The Permuterm Subject Index, consists of index terms (significant words) derived from each title and subtitle of the source index entries. A computer program generates and then alphabetizes all possible pairs of these terms. To use the Permuterm Index one simply looks up a specific subject under that primary term. Under the primary term all other concepts used to index the articles are also arranged in alphabetical order as co-terms (see Fig. 7). By coordinating any repetitions of page and item numbers under any one entry, the search can be narrowed even further on the basis of those terms assigned to a given article. PSI was produced only as an annual through 1970, but it will also be available on a quarterly basis in 1971.

The *Science Citation Index* has been used as a basis for many studies (15). Literature describing some of the unusual searches which can be performed with this new retrieval tool is available from ISI.

The printed tools which have just been described represent only a small segment of the total number of tools available to the chemist to help him with his information retrieval problems (1,2). The particular ones which have been described have been chosen partly because of the special impact which they have had on the information-gathering habits of chemists and partly because they are representative of some of the trends which have taken place within the past decade both with regard to the creation of completely new tools such as the *Science Citation Index* and to the modernization of staid, old tools such as *Chemical Abstracts*. Present indications are that both of these trends will continue for some time to come until a new steady state is reached in the information management problem as a result of the new technology which is just now beginning to be applied.

Computer-Based Search Services

As mentioned in the introduction to this article, the widespread use of computer technology for creation of the newer printed tools has given rise to a new breed of

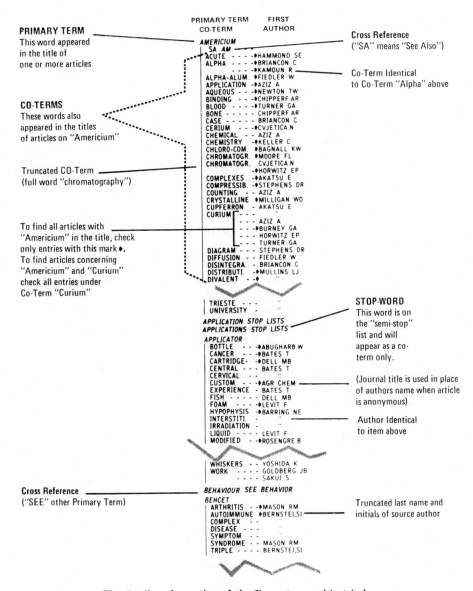

Fig. 7. Sample portion of the Permuterm subject index.

secondary publications available in both printed and computer-readable form. With the availability of these computer-readable data bases, a rapidly growing number of automated search services have emerged which provide capabilities of retrieving the recorded information at various levels of sophistication. These search services are available on a current-awareness basis, for which the descriptive phrase "selective dissemination of information (SDI)" has been coined, and for retrospective searching as well.

The fundamental principles involved in information retrieval are the same whether one is conducting an automated search or a manual search. Essentially, information retrieval may be categorized as a look-up operation wherein words, phrases, or other data elements of a search query (ie, the search terms) are matched against words, phrases, or data elements of a search file (ie, the index terms). Manually these operations are usually performed with the aid of conventional indexes—ordered lists of terms used to describe the important concepts covered in the data base being searched, arranged alphanumerically (letters precede numbers in the ordering sequence). However, because of the speed with which the look-up operations can be performed by computer, the concept descriptors do not necessarily have to be ordered alphanumerically, thereby eliminating many of the constraints superimposed on manual indexes. The net effect is that every character, word, phrase, or numerical quantity described in a computer-readable data base represents a potential index term, or access point, to the information being sought. Obviously certain data elements will be more expensive to search than others, but the important point being stressed here is that the technology is now available to retrieve information which heretofore was virtually irretrievable regardless of what one was willing to pay for it.

There is virtually no limit to the degree of sophistication with which one may query an automated search system (provided the system has been built to handle it). The range of sophistication usually varies from simple queries based on a single concept to more sophisticated queries based on complex relationships between several concepts. The required relationships between the data elements of a query are usually specified in terms of Boolean logic (16), the fundamental aspects of which are embodied in AND, OR, and NOT operators. To illustrate a few simple examples, suppose one were interested in the topic *biosynthesis of cholesterol;* one would most likely phrase a query specifying that both the words *biosynthesis* AND *cholesterol* would have to be present in the search item in order to satisfy the request. This technique would be preferable to using the phrase *biosynthesis of cholesterol* as the search term because of the possibility of excluding retrieval of inverted descriptions such as *cholesterol biosynthesis*, or compound phrases such as *biosynthesis of androsterone and cholesterol.*

To handle problems of synonymy, the OR operator is used. For example, since the phrase *in vivo synthesis* is synonymous with *biosynthesis* it would be appropriate to rephrase the query to include the *biosynthesis or in vivo synthesis of cholesterol*, in which case the Boolean logic expression would specify that *cholesterol* AND (*biosynthesis* OR *in vivo synthesis*) would have to be present in the search item to satisfy the request. Finally, there are many situations where one may wish to exclude retrieval of certain items such as articles published by a particular author, or articles published in a particular journal. For example if one wished to exclude retrieval of articles by L. Fieser on the above topic, the Boolean expression would specify that only those articles containing the terms *cholesterol* AND (*biosynthesis* OR *in vivo synthesis*) AND NOT L. Fieser will satisfy the search request. (Just as in manual indexes, subject terms and author names can be handled distinctly from each other, or not, depending on how the system is set up.)

A powerful technique that can be incorporated into the logical expressions for most automatic search systems involves the use of term truncation. This allows one to use word roots (also referred to as word stems) as search terms to obviate the need of having to use variant word forms to search on a given concept. For example, the word root *biosynthe* would match satisfactorily against *biosynthesis, biosynthetic, biosynthesize, biosynthesized, etc*, and obviate the need of having to phrase a Boolean expression with OR between each of the specific words. (Some systems permit truncation only to the right of a search term whereas others permit truncation on both the left and right.)

ISI®

INSTITUTE FOR SCIENTIFIC INFORMATION
325 Chestnut St Philadelphia Pa 19106 USA

ASCA IV Account No. __ISI01__
Name __CHEMICAL INTERMEDIATES__
Address __325 CHESTNUT STREET__
City __PHILA.__ State __PA.__ Zip __19106__ Phone____

ASCA IV PROFILE ENTRY FORM

	LEAVE BLANK	NAME & INITIALS of cited first author, or other TERM	CITED PUBLICATION, or (CLASS), for other terms	VOLUME or (TYPE OF USE)	CITED ITEMS FIRST PAGE	CITED ITEMS LAST PAGE	YEAR	ASCA IV DOLLAR UNITS	
01		CARBEN//	(FLOATING STEM)	TP 1				20	
02		METHYLENE	(WORD)	TP 1				11	
03		CADOGAN JIG	CHEMISTRY ALKENES	(BOOK)			1964	4	
04		CLOSS GL	TOPICS STEREO CHEMIS	(BOOK)			1968	4	
05		FREY HM	PROGRESS REACTION KI	(BOOK)			1964	4	
06		HINE J	DIVALENT CARBON	(BOOK)			1964	4	
07		KIRMSE W	PROGRESS ORGANIC CHE	(BOOK)			1964	4	
08		KIRMSE W	CARBENE CHEMISTRY	(BOOK)			1964	4	
09		MOSS RA	SELECTIVE ORGANIC TR	(BOOK)			1969	4	
10		PARHAM WE	ORGANIC REACTIONS	(BOOK)			1963	4	
11		KOBRICH G	ANGEW CHEM	6	41		1967	3	
12		MOSS RA	CHEM ENG N	47	50		1969	3	
13		BENZYNE//	(FLOATING STEM)	TP 1				40	
14		NUCLEOPHIL/	(INITIAL STEM)	TP 1				11	
15		HOFFMAN RW	DEHYDROBENZENE CYCLO	(BOOK)			1967	4	
16		HABERFIELD P	J ORG CHEM	34	1508		1969	3	
17		KORNBLUM N	J AM CHEM SOC	77	6269		1955	3	
18		WITTIG G	CHEM BER	95	2729		1962	3	
19		HUISGEN R	CHEM BER	92	192		1959	3	
20		MACK W	CHEM BER	93	608		1960	3	
21		CARBONIUM	(WORD)	TP 1				7	
22		CARBANION	(WORD)	TP 1				7	
23		BROWN HC	(CITED AUTHOR)					12	
24		WINSTEIN S	(CITED AUTHOR)					42	
25		CRAM DJ	(CITED AUTHOR)					32	

MAKE COPY FOR YOUR OWN FILES, SEND ORIGINAL TO ISI   continued

Fig. 8a. Sample query (or search profile) illustrating the query-language format for ISI's ASCA Service.

The actual manner in which the queries have to be phrased for a particular search system constitutes what is known as the *query language*. The formats of these query languages may vary slightly from system to system as do the various output options and formats for the answers to a query (which may also be printed on various types of paper or cards to suit the fancy of a particular group of users). Since these vary but

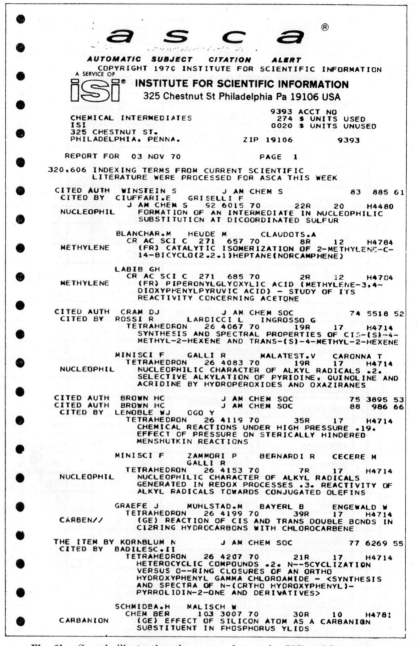

Fig. 8b. Sample illustrating the answer format for ISI's ASCA service.

slightly from one system to the other and can be altered as needed without too much difficulty, details concerning the variations in query languages and output formats will not be dealt with here (see Fig. 8 for a representative query and the answers). Rather, attention will be focused on a few of the different types of data bases and services available (primarily from CAS and ISI), and the differences in the data elements that can be searched from each.

One of the first computer-readable data bases to become widely available to chemists was *Chemical Titles* on magnetic tape. Its searchable data elements are (*1*) all author names, (*2*) all words in the titles of the articles, and (*3*) journal coden for the journals covered in *CT*. (Journal coden are compact journal abbreviations developed by the American Society for Testing and Materials (ASTM) (17) to reduce the storage requirements for describing journal names in computer-readable data bases. The coden for all of the journals covered in *CT* are listed in the inside front and back covers of each printed issue of *CT*.) Computer programs to search *CT* on magnetic tape are supplied by CAS to those subscribers who have the necessary facilities to perform their own searches. Otherwise searches are performed by CAS in accordance with the specifications described in the CAS catalog of information services.

Shortly after the introduction of *CT* on magnetic tape, CAS began to offer other computer-readable data bases on a similar basis. Most of them provide for a much greater depth of search than is possible with *CT*. The particular data bases and services presently available from CAS are summarized in Table 1 along with the data elements which are searchable in each of them. For a clearer understanding of much of the information summarized in Table 1, it is suggested that the reader refer back to the section on Printed tools where most of the corresponding printed versions were described. However, several items require further elaboration here. For example, *Basic Journals Abstracts (BJA)* is strictly a computer-readable service (issued biweekly) which contains abstracts of chemical and chemical engineering interest published in 35 selected journals. The list includes journals such as *Analytical Chemistry, Chemische Berichte, Journal of the American Chemical Society, Journal of Organic Chemistry*, and *Journal of Physical Chemistry*. (The complete list of journals is published in the CAS 1970 Catalog of Services.) A printed version of *BJA* is included with a subscription to the computer-readable service, but it is not available solely as a printed service.

Another item requiring further elaboration in Table 1 is *CA* condensates, a weekly computer-readable service which coincides with the weekly printed issues of *CA*. It contains the bibliographic heading information (ie, author names, title of article, journal reference, etc) for each of the abstracts published in *CA*, together with the index terms which were used to index each article in the *CA* issue indexes.

Several computer-readable services are available from ISI. One is the ASCA (Automatic Subject Citation Alert) search service (Fig. 8), the first automatic search service ever to become available on a personal subscription basis. The search service utilizes the *Science Citation Index* source tapes and citation tapes. The data elements

Table 1. Searchable Data Elements in CAS Computer-Readable Data Bases

	Data base				
Data element	Chemical titles	Chemical biological activities	Polymer science and technology	Basic journal abstracts	*CA* condensates
words in title	yes	yes	yes	yes	yes
words in digest		yes	yes	yes	
keyword-index terms					yes
author names	yes	yes	yes	yes	yes
journal coden	yes	yes	yes	yes	yes
molecular formulas		yes	yes		
registry numbers		yes	yes		

Table 2. Information Centers for Computer-Based Search Services

Country and company	Administrative officer	Location
United States		
Aerospace Research Application Center	Assistant Director	Bloomington, Ind.
American Petroleum Institute	Assistant Manager, central abstracting and indexing service	New York, N.Y.
The Dow Chemical Co.	Project Leader, information sciences	Midland, Mich.
University of Louisville, Speed Science School, Greater Louisville Technical Referral Center	Director	Louisville, Ky.
IIT Research Institute, Information Sciences Computer Search Center	Director	Chicago, Ill.
Institute for Scientific Information	Vice President, marketing	Philadelphia, Pa.
3I Company, Information Interscience, Inc.	Executive Vice President	Philadelphia, Pa.
The Ohio State University, Mechanized Information Center	Director	Columbus, Ohio
University of Georgia, Computer Center	Information Scientist	Athens, Ga.
University of Iowa University Computer Center	Head of Special Services	Iowa City, Iowa
University of Pittsburgh, Knowledge Availability Systems Center	Assistant director	Pittsburgh, Pa.
Canada		
Research Council of Alberta, Alberta Information Retrieval Association		Edmonton, Alberta
National Research Council of Canada, National Science Library	Library Systems Analyst	Ottawa, Ont.
Denmark		
Danish Technical Library Dokumentationsafdelingen		Copenhagen
Great Britain		
United Kingdom Chemical Information Service	Technical director	Nottingham
West Germany		
Gesellschaft Deutscher Chemiker Chemie Information und Dokumentation	Chefredakteur	West Berlin
Netherlands		
The Royal Netherlands Chemical Society, Netherland Organization for Chemical Information	Director	The Hague
Sweden		
The Royla Institute of Technology, Swedish Council for Information and Documentation	Head Librarian	Stockholm
Biomedical Documentation Center	Director	Stockholm

which can be searched include (*1*) author names, (*2*) titles of articles, (*3*) journal names, (*4*) organization names, (*5*) cited references (ie, books, papers, symposia, conference reports, etc), and (*6*) cited author names. The SCI source tapes and citation tapes can also be procured from ISI for in-house searching by organizations who have the computer facilities required.

Another automated search service which ISI has introduced in 1970 is the ICRS search service which utilizes the ICRS tapes. These tapes contain the bibliographic heading information for all of the abstracts published in *CAC&IC*, the subject-index terms used for each abstract, and the WLN's and molecular formulas for all the chemical compounds reported therein. The searchable data elements are (*1*) author names, (*2*) titles of articles, (*3*) journal names, (*4*) organization names, (*5*) WLN's (for substructure searches), (*6*) molecular formulas, (*7*) analytical techniques used by authors, and (*8*) applications data terms. This search service is available by personal subscription, or the tapes can be procured for in-house searching with the ISI search program called RADIICAL (*R*etrieval and *A*utomatic *D*issemination of *I*nformation from *I*ndex *C*hemicus *a*nd *L*ine Notations).

As was the case for the newer printed tools, there are many other computer-based search services, too numerous to mention, which provide information of interest to the chemist or chemical technologist. Many of these other services augment those which have already been described and they include some which provide capabilities of retrieving various types of physical properties data. A number of directories are available (18) describing the range of these services. In addition, a number of information centers are being established both nationally and internationally to provide a much needed interface for the users of these automated services at the local level. See Table 2. Recently, these centers have begun to establish organizations designed to facilitate the exchange of ideas among users of tape services. Two such organizations are ASIDIC (Association of Scientific Information Dissemination Centers) in the U.S.A. and CHEOPS (Group of Operators of Chemical Information Systems) in Europe.

Substructure Search

Most of the retrieval tools described up to this point, in general, involve the same basic information processing techniques that are used in other disciplines. However, chemistry is unique in that much of its literature deals with chemical structure information, for which the structural diagram has become the basic medium of communication. It is not surprising, then, that chemists have always felt a need for searching information on the basis of structural characteristics, utilizing search techniques which, in modern jargon, have come to be known as *substructure search*.

Since the structural diagram is a routine part of the chemist's day-to-day communications, verbalized equivalents of the diagrammatic language, ie, chemical nomenclature, have also become an essential part of the communication system. However, the deficiencies of traditional systematic nomenclature for substructure searching have long been recognized (7,19). Naming of compounds is necessary for oral communication among chemists, but names provide a poor basis for the classification or grouping of compounds that have similarities in structure.

Difficulties with traditional methods of storing and retrieving chemical structure information have stimulated the development of alternative techniques for representing structures and substructures (7). These techniques fall into three categories based on the type of coding used, namely, (*1*) fragment codes; (*2*) linear notations; and (*3*) connectivity tables.

Fragment codes usually involve assignment of descriptors (often arbitrary numbers) to functional groups or other more complex substructural units (fragments) for the purpose of indexing and retrieving structures having specified generic characteristics. For example the descriptor 100 might be assigned to all compounds containing the fragment COOH. Through the use of such codes one can index and retrieve each compound under as many defined fragments as are present in the structure, a task which is virtually impossible with traditional nomenclature.

Fragment codes became very popular with the introduction of punched card systems, both hand and machine-sorted (1,20), because of the ease with which the coding, sorting, and searching operations could be performed on these systems. Many fragment codes have been developed in the past few decades (7,21), one of the most publicized being the CBCC (Chemical-Biological Coordination Center) Code (22). They have proved to be adequate and very practical for many classification and correlation purposes, particularly for small files, and their continued use is evidence of their value. However, such descriptions are only a partial representation of structure based on an aggregate of predetermined fixed segments for which appropriate fragment codes have been defined. Thus, for some structures there may be no suitable fragments to use. Also, when searching for structures containing combinations of fragments, there may be many false retrievals because the fragments do not have the desired relationships. Because of these limitations fragment codes have generally been considered to be inadequate as the sole method of retrieving structural information from large files. However, they play an important role in breaking large files down into smaller subsets prior to the more detailed analysis allowable by other coding techniques.

Linear notations employ letters and symbols in linear sequence to describe the complete structure. The Wiswesser Line Notation (WLN), discussed earlier under *CAC&IC* and the *ICRS Substructure Index*, is representative of, and no doubt the most popular among, a wide group of such notations (7) which differ primarily in the prominence and precedence given to particular structural features (10,21). They combine the ability to identify structures uniquely and unambiguously for printed indexes, and to delineate substructure components for classification and for substructure search. The searches can be accomplished manually through permuted indexes (9), some partial listings of which were shown in Figure 4, or through the use of automated search systems such as ISI's RADIICAL search program described above under Computer-based search systems. The outputs from such a search would be printed line notations (in the above case, WLN's) or structural diagrams. The structural diagrams could be obtained from a stored record or generated directly from the notation (23).

Although linear notations in principle permit searching for all details of chemical structure, there are certain types of substructure searches which are very difficult to perform directly on the notation (24). In such situations it is preferable to perform the search on a connectivity table which provides the greatest flexibility for substructure searching (25) because it contains all of the structural details in the most expanded form.

Connectivity tables provide complete topological descriptions (ie, atom-by-atom, bond-by-bond descriptions) for known chemical structures. Just as is true for fragment codes and linear notations, there are a wide variety of connectivity tables. Most of them are based on techniques which involve explicit or implicit numbering of all nonhydrogen atoms of a structure together with a defined set of bond codes to facilitate tabular description of a structure as illustrated in Figure 9. The tabular descriptions also usually include explicit or implicit information on the valence of each atom, the number of hydrogen atoms attached to each nonhydrogen atom, and other structural details such as atomic mass, ionic charge, and stereochemistry. Although this particular type of connectivity table is suitable for unambiguous clerical input of the structural data, it is generally considered to be too redundant and too bulky for permanent

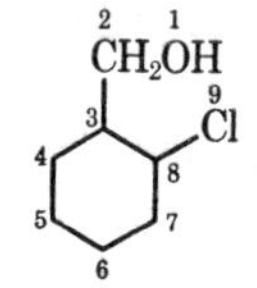

Atom no.	Element	Group	Bond 1	Attachment 1	Bond 2	Attachment 2	Bond 3	Attachment 3	Bond 4	Attachment 4	Charge	Abnormal valence	Abnormal mass	H count	Atom no.
1	O		1	2										1	1
2	C		1	1	1	3								2	2
3	C		1	2	1	4	1	8						1	3
4	C		1	3	1	5								2	4
5	C		1	4	1	6								2	5
6	C		1	5	1	7								2	6
7	C		1	6	1	8								2	7
8	C		1	7	1	9	1	3						1	8
9	Cl		1	8											9

Fig. 9. Sample of a connectivity table used for clerical input of structural data. The atom numbers for the non-hydrogen atoms are arbitrarily assigned by the person preparing the table.

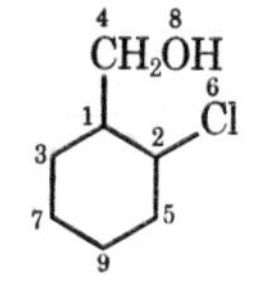

Atom no.	Element	Attachment	Bond
1	C	—	—
2	C	1	1
3	C	1	1
4	C	1	1
5	C	2	1
6	Cl	2	1
7	C	3	1
8	O	4	1
9	C	5	1
Ring closure:		7–9	1

Fig. 10. Sample of a compact (or nonredundant) connectivity table which can be derived by computer program from the input connectivity table shown in Figure 9. The original non-unique numbering scheme can also be converted to a unique numbering scheme such as the above by various techniques. The above numbering scheme is that which would be generated by the technique of Morgan (11).

storage of the information on magnetic storage media. Furthermore, the resulting structural representations lack the uniqueness usually desired for handling large files of structural information to assure that all information on a particular chemical structure is located in the same place in the file. To overcome these drawbacks, the above nonunique redundant connectivity table can be converted by computer program to a more compact canonical (or unique) connectivity table of the type illustrated in Figure 10 (11,26), a variation of which is used in the CAS chemical compound registry system (27) mentioned earlier under the discussion of the printed version of *CBAC*.

In reality, connectivity tables of any desired type can be automatically generated with little difficulty from any form of input which provides unambiguous description of the complete chemical structure. As has already been suggested, connectivity tables have been generated from linear notations (24,28). Other methods by which they have been produced include mechanical translation from chemical nomenclature (29), automatic encoding from structural formulas which have been directly keyboarded by chemical typewriters (30), automatic encoding from optically scanned structural formulas (31), and automatic encoding from structural formulas drawn on the screen of a cathode-ray tube (32). The reverse transformations are generally somewhat more difficult to accomplish because most of the connectivity tables now used have fewer constraints than do most of the other forms of representation (eg, hierarchical rules for nomenclature or linear notation, esthetic problems for graphic display, etc). Nevertheless, considerable progress has been made towards effecting the reverse transformations as well.

An example of a type of search that would be difficult to perform by conventional methods, but which would be comparatively easy to perform on linear notations or connectivity tables is a search for compounds containing three nitrogens in sequence. Formulas (1–4) are representative of the types of structures retrieved, subject to the exact specifications of the query.

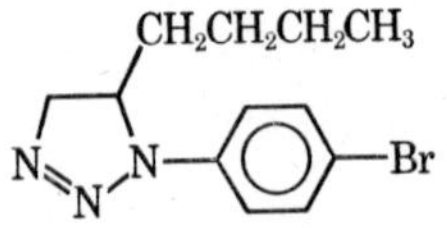

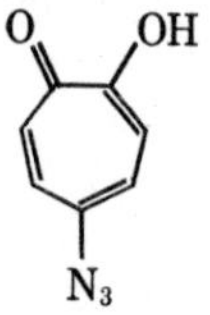

If no restraints were placed on the environment in which the desired atom-bond network was embedded, all four of the indicated structures would be retrieved. However, the specifications of the query can be altered to restrict the range of structures that would be retrieved. For example if the NNN could not be part of a ring structure, (1) would not be retrieved. If the query further specified that the NNN could not be attached to a ring, (2) and (3) would not be retrieved. It should be obvious that appropriate restrictions could limit the results to any one of the four structures shown.

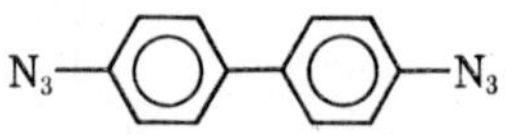

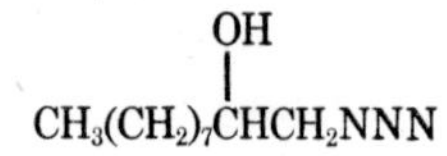

It must be pointed out that some searches are easier to perform on linear notations while others are easier to perform on connectivity tables. The economic factor will certainly play an important role as to which approach is used under a given set of circumstances.

Also, concerning the "completeness" of the structural information stored in linear notations and connectivity tables, no system as yet includes an adequate quantitative treatment of stereochemistry to permit quantitative searching for substructures having specific stereochemical requirements. Methodology is available to accomplish this however (33), and incorporation of such a capability into existing systems will have a salutary effect on their usefulness for substructure search and other related studies in the years ahead.

As to the availability of automated substructure search services, it was mentioned earlier that ISI introduced a commercially available substructure search service in 1970 based on the index chemicus registry system where the structural information is stored in Wiswesser Line Notation. Also, several of the information centers cited in

Table 2 are experimenting with, and providing a limited amount of service through, the CAS substructure search system where the searches are performed on the connectivity tables stored in the CAS chemical compound registry system.

CAS has registered more than 1.5 million structures since 1965, but only a subset of the registry file is being searched with the more sophisticated CAS substructure search programs, pending the results of feedback from the experimental search services

Table 3. List of Abbreviations

Name	Abbreviation
American Chemical Society	ACS
Automatic Subject Citation Alert	ASCA
Association of Scientific Information Dissemination Centers	ASIDIC
American Society for Testing and Materials	ASTM
Basic Journal Abstracts	*BJA*
Chemical Abstracts	*CA*
Current Abstracts of Chemistry and Index Chemicus	CAC&IC
Chemical Abstracts Service	CAS
Chemical-Biological Activities	*CBAC*
Chemical Titles	*CT*
Chemisches Zentralblatt	*CZ*
Current Contents	*CC*
Agricultural, Food and Veterinary Sciences	*CCAF&VS*
Chemical Sciences	*CCCS*
Engineering and Technology	*CCE&T*
Life Sciences	*CCLS*
Physical Sciences	*CCPS*
Physical and Chemical Sciences	*CCP&CS*
Group of Operators of Chemical Information Systems	CHEOPS
Current Index to Conference Papers	CICP
Gesellschaft Deutscher Chemiker	GDCh
Hetero-Atom-in-Context	HAIC
Index Chemicus	IC
Index Chemicus Registry System	ICRS
Institute for Scientific Information	ISI
Keyword-in-Context	KWIC
Permuterm Subject Index	PSI
Polymer Science and Technology	*POST*
Journal Literature	*POST-J*
Patent Literature	*POST-P*
Retrieval and Automatic Dissemination of Information from Index Chemicus and Line Notations	RADIICAL
Rotated molecular formula	Rotaform
Science Citation Index	*SCI*
Selective Dissemination of Information	SDI
Wiswesser Line Notation	WLN

now being provided. ISI has registered more than 800,000 unique structures since 1967, all of which are searchable by ISI's RADIICAL programs mentioned previously (subject to some of the limitations discussed earlier concerning the degree of sophistication with which substructure search questions can be phrased). Widespread usage of both of the above substructure search services is needed to provide feedback that will determine the direction these systems should take in the years to come. Table 3 gives a list of frequently used abbreviations.

Bibliography

1. A. Standen, ed., *Encyclopedia of Chemical Technology*, 2nd ed., Interscience Publishers. a div. of John Wiley & Sons, Inc., New York.

1a. T. J. Devlin and B. J. Weil, *Literature (Documentation)*, in reference 1, Vol. 12, 1967, pp. 511–529.

2. M. D. Schoengold, *Literature (Sources)*, in references 1, Vol. 12, 1967, pp. 500–511.

3. "ACS Links with Germans in Information Network," *Chem. Eng. News* **47** (40), 15–16 (1969).

4. *Ring Index*, 2nd ed., Chemical Abstracts Service, Columbus, Ohio, 1960.

5. *Report on Twelfth Chemical Abstracts Service Open Forum, New York, New York, September 7, 1969*, Chemical Abstracts Service, Columbus, Ohio, January, 1970.

6. E. Garfield, "Generic Searching by Use of Rotated Formula Indexes," *J. Chem. Doc.* **3**, 97 (1963).

7. National Research Council—National Academy of Sciences: (a) "Survey of Chemical Notation Systems," *Publication No. 1150* (1964); (b) "Survey of European Nonconventional Chemical Notation Systems," *Publication No. 1278* (1965), (c) "Chemical Structure Information Handling—A Review of the Literature 1962–1968," *Publication No. 1733* Washington, D. C., 1969.

8. E. G. Smith, *The Wiswesser Line-Formula Chemical Notation*, McGraw-Hill Book Co., New York, 1968.

9. C. E. Granito, et al., "Rapid Structure Searches via Permuted Chemical Line Notations (III): A Computer Produced Index," *J. Chem. Doc.* **5**, 229 (1965).

10. H. T. Bonnett, "Chemical Notations: A Brief Review," *J. Chem. Doc.* **3**, 235 (1963).

11. H. L. Morgan, "The Generation of a Unique Machine Description for Chemical Structures—a Technique Developed at Chemical Abstracts Service," *J. Chem. Doc.* **5**, 107 (1965).

12. *Synthetic Organic Chemical Manufacturers Association (SOCMA) Handbook*, Chemical Abstracts Service, Columbus, Ohio, 1966.

13. *Desktop Analysis Tool*, Chemical Abstracts Service, Columbus, Ohio, 1969. Available from U.S. Clearinghouse for Federal and Scientific Information, Springfield, Va., *PB 179 900*.

14. E. Garfield, "Citation Indexes for Science," *Science* **122**, 108–111 (1955); E. Garfield, "Science Citation Index—A New Dimension in Indexing," *Science* **144**, 649–654 (1964).

15. J. Martyn, "An Examination of Citation Indexes" *Aslib Proceedings* **17**, 184 (1965); J. Margolis, "Citation Indexing and Evaluation of Scientific Papers," *Science* **155**, 1213 (1967); C. C. Spencer, "Subject Searching with *Science Citation Index:* Preparation of a Drug Bibliography using *Chemical Abstracts, Index Medicus*, and *Science Citation Index* 1961 and 1964," *American Documentation* **18**, 87 (1967); E. Garfield, "Citation Indexing for Studying Science," *Nature* **227**, 669–671 (1970).

16. J. Becker, and R. M. Hayes, *Information Storage and Retrieval*, John Wiley & Sons, Inc., New York, 1963, pp. 335–343.

17. *Coden for Periodical Titles*, American Society for Testing and Materials (ASTM), Philadelphia, Pa., 1966, and Supplements.

18. L. Cohan, *Directory of Computerized Information in Science and Technology*, Science Associates International; *A Guide to a Selection of Computer-Based Science and Technology Reference Services in the U.S.A.*, American Library Association, Chicago, 1969; *Commercially Available Information Products, Services, and Systems for the Chemical and Pharmaceutical Industries*, Information Industry Association, Washington, D.C., September, 1970.

19. F. A. Tate, "Handling of Chemical Compounds in Information Systems," in C. Cuadra, ed., *Annual Review of Information Science and Technology*, Vol. 2, John Wiley & Sons, Inc., New York, 1967, pp. 285–309.

20. R. S. Casey, et al., *Punched Cards*, 2nd ed., Reinhold Publishing Corp., New York, 1958.

21. M. L. Huber, "Chemical Structure Codes in Perspective," *J. Chem. Doc.* **5**, 4 (1965).

22. *A Method of Coding Chemicals for Correlation and Classification*, Chemical-Biological Coordination Center, National Research Council, Washington, D.C., 1950.

23. L. H. Thomson, E. Hyde, and F. W. Matthews, "Organic Search and Display Using a Connectivity Matrix Derived from Wiswesser Notation," *J. Chem. Doc.* **7**, 204 (1967).

24. E. Hyde, et al., "Conversion of Wiswesser Notation to a Connectivity Matrix for Organic Compounds," *J. Chem. Doc.* **7**, 200 (1967).

25. W. E. Cossum, M. L. Krakiwsky, and M. F. Lynch, "Advances In Automatic Chemical Substructure Searching Techniques," *J. Chem. Doc.* **5**, 33 (1965).

26. D. J. Gluck, "A Chemical Structure Storage and Search System Developed at Du Pont," *J. Chem. Doc.* **5**, 43 (1965).
27. D. P. Leiter, H. L. Morgan, and R. E. Stobaugh, "Installation and Operation of a Registry for Chemical Compounds," *J. Chem. Doc.* **5**, 238 (1965).
28. G. M. Dyson et al., "Mechanical Manipulation of Chemical Structure: Molform Computation and Substructure Searching of Organic Structures by the Use of Cipher-directed, Extended and Random Matrices," *Information Storage and Retrieval* **1**, 69 (1963).
29. G. G. vander Stouw, I. Naznitsky, and J. E. Rush, "Procedures for Converting Systematic Names of Organic Compounds into Atom-Bond Connection Tables," *J. Chem. Doc.* **7**, 165 (1967).
30. J. M. Mullen, "Atom-by-Atom Typewriter Input for Computerized Storage and Retrieval of Chemical Structures," *J. Chem. Doc.* **7**, 88 (1967).
31. W. E. Cossum, M. E. Hardenbrook, and R. N. Wolfe, "Computer Generation of Atom-Bond Connection Tables from Hand-Drawn Chemical Structures," *Proc. Amer. Doc. Inst.* **1**, 270 (1964); E. Meyer, "Mechanization of Chemical Documentation," *Angew. Chem. Intern. Ed. Engl.* **4**, 347 (1965).
32. E. J. Corey, and W. T. Wipke, "Computer-Assisted Design of Complex Organic Synthesis," *Science* **166**, 178 (1969).
33. A. E. Petrarca, M. F. Lynch, and J. E. Rush, "A Method for Generating Unique Computer Structural Representations of Stereoisomers," *J. Chem. Doc.* **7**, 154 (1967); A. E. Petrarca and J. E. Rush, "Methods for Computer Generation of Unique Configurational Descriptors for Stereoisomeric Square-Planar and Octahedral Complexes," *J. Chem. Doc.* **9**, 32 (1969).

Eugene Garfield and Charles E. Granito
Institute for Scientific Information
Anthony E. Petrarca
The Ohio State University

IRON BY DIRECT REDUCTION

The term "direct reduction" is here used to mean processes for obtaining iron from its ores without going through the molten state. Direct reduction of iron ore appears enticingly simple and has attracted the attention of a host of scientists, engineers, and inventors. Nearly 100 years ago (1874), T. S. Blair (1), in speaking before the American Institute of Mining and Metallurgical Engineers said, "The whole literature of the art, so far as it relates to the direct process, is, up to this time, but a history of failure. It is safe to say that more money, time, and talent have been fruitlessly spent in the pursuit of this object than in all the other unsuccessful efforts in the whole line of iron metallurgy. A distinguished authority on patent law has remarked that the invention records of the United States and of foreign countries are filled with the waifs and abandoned relics of the abortive efforts."

Nevertheless, prior to the development of the blast furnace, about 600 years ago, crude devices were used for the reduction of iron ores to yield directly a solid metal product that could be hammered and wrought into useful shapes. A blast furnace accomplishes the reduction of the iron ore, but it melts the reduced iron so that it is drawn from the furnace in liquid form. The product, called pig iron, has some usefulness when cast into shapes, but for almost all purposes serves only as an intermediate material for subsequent refining into steel. Through the centuries since the blast furnace was developed, a relentless search has continued for a practical method that would reestablish direct reduction for recovering iron from its ores. During the past two decades, substantial progress has been made and several of the new developments are on the threshold of large-scale commercial operations.

Many writers define direct reduction as any method for recovering iron from its ores other than by the conventional blast furnace. This is a convenient distinction only when one is discussing alternatives to the blast furnace. However, blast-furnace smelting and electric-furnace smelting have many common features and have only one distinguishing feature. Both use coke as the reductant, and both produce a molten product. The difference is that in the blast furnace the combustion of coke with pre-heated air is used to provide the energy for the reduction, whereas in the other it is supplied electrically. All the direct reduction processes discussed here produce a solid product by operations carried out at temperatures substantially below the melting point of pig iron (1160°C).

From an economic point of view, perhaps the most significant feature of direct reduction is that it uses readily available fuel, ie natural gas or fuel oil, and does away with the necessity of the complex operation of preparing metallurgical coke. There are conditions in many countries that are causing steel producers to give serious consideration to direct reduction as an alternative to the blast furnace or as a complementary process for recovering iron from its ores. This is so, for example, in Venezuela, where there is abundant iron ore, but no coal suitable for coking.

Sponge iron has become a generic term meaning any kind of iron obtained from the direct reduction of iron ore without going through the molten stage. Accordingly, there are many kinds of sponge iron. For example, freshly produced sponge iron has the same shape and size as the original ore particles from which it was produced. When fine ores are used, the freshly produced sponge iron is in the form of a powder which may be agglomerated by rolling it into a plate form or by compressing it into briquettes or special shapes. If the starting materials are highly pure and special processing is used, a high-purity sponge can be produced for specialized end uses, such as laboratory and electronic equipment, and coating for use in sewing machines, typewriters, and similar lightly stressed equipment. This specialized market consumes many thousand tons of powdered iron annually, but if the direct reduction methods are to become an important method for processing iron ores, they must establish themselves competitively in the large-volume operations of the world iron and steel industry.

In recent years, several hundred processes have been described in technical journals, patent literature, and other publications (2,3), but only a few have been used commercially or have undergone pilot-plant investigations. These attempts have embraced practically every known type of apparatus suitable for the purpose, including pot furnaces, reverberatory furnaces, regenerative furnaces, shaft furnaces, retorts, rabbled-hearth furnaces, rotary-hearth furnaces, rotary kilns, tunnel kilns, traveling grates, fluidized beds, electric furnaces, and various combinations of these devices. A great variety of reducing agents have also been tried, such as coal, coke, graphite, fuel oil, tar, producer gas, water gas, coke-oven gas, natural gas, as well as carbon monoxide and hydrogen, and mixtures of these two gases. All of the foregoing reductants are basically carbon, hydrogen, or hydrocarbons.

Despite the overwhelming importance of the blast furnace for smelting iron ores, there are varying conditions and reasons from country to country that justify the serious consideration of direct reduction processes as an alternative to the blast furnace or as a complementary process to produce a superior burden material for subsequent use in blast furnaces. In most iron- and steelmaking centers throughout the world the principal ingredients for iron- and steelmaking (iron ore, coking coals, and limestone) do not all occur in the proper quantity or quality and thus it becomes necessary to transport one or more of these raw materials, sometimes over thousands of miles, to obtain the proper blend to support iron- and steelmaking operations. Both highly industrialized and underdeveloped countries contribute to this flow and cross-flow of raw materials so that a world map of iron and steel transport shows a network tying together all continents for the exchange of iron ores, coal, coke, scrap, ferroalloys, and steel products (4). Only a few areas in the world, such as the Ruhr and Saar valleys, mid-England, southeastern United States, and India are fortunate to have abundant quantities of iron ore, coking coals, and limestone in close proximity but, unfortunately, the ores and coals in these areas are not always of the highest quality. A combination of such local conditions particularly favors the blast furnace as a low-cost method for processing iron ore. However, in other geographic areas, and particularly those that have economical access to large supplies of natural gas or fuel oil, it is logical to critically examine the economic aspects of replacing coke with natural gas or fuel oil for the partial or nearly complete reduction of iron ore. Some of the direct reduction processes have been specifically designed to accommodate these conditions and to produce a material for subsequent use in steelmaking furnaces.

Equilibria. The primary chemical reactions involved in recovering iron from its ores, whether in a blast furnace or by direct reduction, are those concerned with the removal of oxygen from the ore. Accordingly, a knowledge of the fundamental physical and chemical properties of the oxides of iron and their equilibria with available reductants is necessary for an insight into the technical limitations of any scheme for the direct reduction of iron ore. The only reductants of practical importance are carbon monoxide and hydrogen. Although carbon, as coal or coke, is used as a reductant in direct reduction processes employing rotary kilns, the rate of reduction attained in such devices is far greater than could be accomplished by the reaction of solid carbon with solid Fe_2O_3, which shows that even when using solid carbon as the primary reductant, the mode of removing oxygen from the iron oxide is provided by carbon monoxide.

The equilibria and thermodynamics of the reactions of CO and H_2 with the oxides of iron have been studied intensely, and data from Elliott and Gleiser (5) are shown in Figures 1 and 2, covering the iron–oxygen–carbon system and the iron–oxygen–hydrogen system over the temperature range of 500 to 1200°C, respectively. These two sets of curves reveal important similarities and differences in the reaction of CO and H_2 with the various oxides of iron. For example, Fe_2O_3 is not shown on either diagram because the presence of very small amounts of either CO or H_2 in the furnace atmosphere will cause Fe_2O_3 to be reduced to Fe_3O_4. At all temperatures below 570°C, Fe_3O_4 is reduced directly to Fe by either CO or H_2, but above this temperature the Fe_3O_4 is first reduced to ferrous oxide, FeO, which can be subsequently reduced to Fe. For reduction of Fe_3O_4 to FeO, the utilization of CO and H_2 is greatly improved by increased reaction temperature. However, for the subsequent reduction of FeO to Fe, the situation is different for the two gases because increased reaction temperature leads to greater utilization of H_2 but to a lesser utilization of CO.

Table 1 shows the equilibrium ratios of H_2–H_2O and CO–CO_2 required for reduction of iron oxides to Fe over the temperature range from 600 to 1200°C.

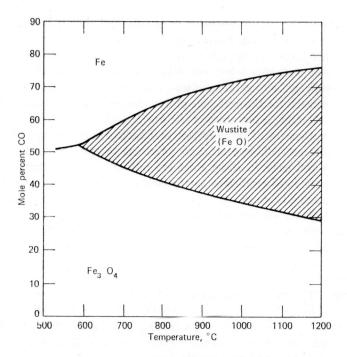

Fig. 1. Iron–oxygen–carbon system.

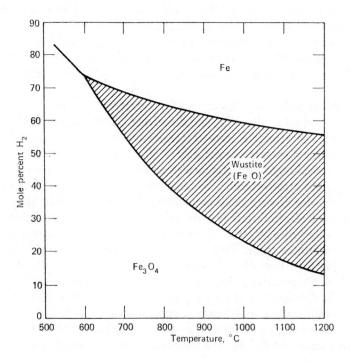

Fig. 2. Iron–oxygen–hydrogen system.

Table 1. Equilibrium Ratios of H_2–H_2O and CO–CO_2 for the Reduction of Iron Oxides

Temperature		Equilibrium with Fe	
°C	°F	H_2–H_2O	CO–CO_2
600	1112	2.8	1.1
700	1292	2.2	1.5
800	1472	1.9	1.9
900	1612	1.6	2.2
1000	1832	1.4	2.6
1100	2012	1.3	3.0
1200	2192	1.2	3.2

At about 800°C, hydrogen and carbon monoxide are equally effective, but above this temperature H_2 becomes more efficient than CO for the reduction of iron oxides to Fe. Below 800°C the situation is reversed. Although CO appears to be an efficient reductant for iron oxides at temperatures of 500–600°C, in this temperature range, however, dissociation of carbon monoxide can occur according to the reaction $2CO \rightarrow C + CO_2$ and thereby prevent the reduction of iron oxide to a lower form than Fe_3O_4. Dissociation of H_2O is not a problem in the temperature ranges being considered, and the reduction of Fe_3O_4 to Fe by hydrogen will occur below 650°C.

Thermal Effects. Offsetting the favorable equilibrium of H_2 with the oxides of iron and the freedom from dissociation of H_2O in the temperature range of interest is the fact that all the reactions of H_2 with the various oxides of iron are mildly endothermic, whereas the corresponding reactions with CO are slightly exothermic. The heats of reaction for reduction of Fe_2O_3, Fe_3O_4, and FeO to Fe by either CO or H_2 are shown in Table 2 over the temperature range of practical interest for most direct reduction processes, roughly 600–1000°C. The data are presented as Btu/lb of Fe and were calculated from those published by Elliott and Gleiser (5). (The thermodynamic convention is used in which the plus sign indicates an endothermic reaction, and the minus sign indicates an exothermic reaction.)

The data in Table 2 pertain only to heats of reaction and do not include enthalpy effects in bringing the reactants to the indicated temperature and the equilibria requirements which demand substantial amounts of CO and H_2 in excess of stoichiometric relations. These enthalpy effects substantially affect the total heat required to

Table 2. Heats of Reaction of Some Reduction Processes

Temperature			Btu/lb Fe[a]					
			$Fe_2O_3 \rightarrow Fe$		$Fe_3O_4 \rightarrow Fe$		$FeO \rightarrow Fe$	
°K	°C	°F	H_2	CO	H_2	CO	H_2	CO
900	627	1161	+245	−169	+250	−118	+115	−160
1000	727	1341	+230	−172	+245	−112	+115	−150
1100	827	1521	+231	−160	+248	−100	+120	−140
1200	927	1701	+229	−151	+248	−89	+122	−130
1300	1027	1881	+217	−152	+238	−90	+124	−134

[a] Divide by 1.8 to convert to kcal/kg.

carry on the reduction reactions and amount to 600–700 Btu/lb of Fe reduced in the temperature range considered in Table 2.

Kinetics. While reaction equilibria and the thermal aspects of iron oxide reduction are important, the rate at which equilibrium is approached has a vital influence on the choice of reductants and operating temperatures for use with practical direct reduction processes. Because of the practical importance, a great deal of work has been done on the gaseous reduction of iron oxides, but progress has been slow in understanding the rate-controlling mechanisms. In general, reaction rates increase with increasing temperature and with decreasing particle size. However, at high temperatures sintering or agglomeration of the solids takes place more easily and thereby may decrease the surface available for contact with the gaseous reductant. In fluidized-bed, direct reduction processes, the occurrence of sintering would cause the bed to defluidize and thereby completely disrupt the process. Conversely, if reduction is carried out at low temperatures, not only are the reaction rates slow, but also the iron product may be pyrophoric (spontaneously combust in air) and require subsequent processing before it can be stored, transported, and used. The use of higher pressure permits the use of more compact equipment, and also gives an increase in reduction rate.

Studies on the kinetics of reduction of iron oxides (6) show that the rate of reduction of Fe_2O_3 to FeO increases rapidly with temperature and becomes progressively faster than the reduction of FeO to Fe as the temperature of the reaction rises above 570°C. (At 570°C and lower temperatures, the reduction of Fe_2O_3 proceeds directly to Fe without traversing the FeO region, see Figures 1 and 2.) Moreover, Visnyovsky showed that reaction rates obtainable with H_2 as the reductant are substantially higher than those observed for CO at all temperatures applicable to the direct reduction processes (6). The following reaction rates were observed at 600 and 1000°C for the reduction of Fe_2O_3 to FeO, and of FeO to Fe using either H_2 or CO as the reductant (Table 3).

Table 3. Reduction of Iron Oxides

	O_2 removed per min per ton of iron oxide, lb			
	With H_2		With CO	
	600°C	1000°C	600°C	1000°C
$Fe_2O_3 \rightarrow$ FeO	10	52	4	16
FeO $\rightarrow$ Fe	9	24	4	8

The rates of reduction in Table 3 do not indicate the total time required for the stoichiometric reduction of iron oxides to Fe because the rate of oxygen removal slows noticeably as the reduction reaction proceeds, so that it is impractical to attempt to achieve complete stoichiometric removal of oxygen by any direct reduction process. For example, for the reduction of Fe_2O_3 by hydrogen at 800°C, the rate curves show that it takes as long to proceed from 50% reduction to 75% reduction as it did to attain the first 50% reduction. Beyond 75% reduction, the reaction rates proceed at even slower speeds so that to attain 90% reduction requires roughly four times as long as to remove the first 50% of the oxygen from the ore. Moreover, to go from 90 to 95% reduction will again double the amount of processing time required. These reduction rate relations may be summarized as follows:

Oxygen removal, %	Unit time
50	1
75	2
90	4
95	8

Use of Prereduced Iron. Of the 750 million tons of iron ore processed annually in the world, only about 0.2 to 0.3 percent of this total is currently being treated by direct reduction techniques. Currently several commercial-scale plants, capable of processing 500 to 4000 tons of ore daily, are in the early stages of operation or are nearing completion of construction. These various installations include the technologies of shaft reduction, static reactors, rotary kilns, and fluidized beds. Economic success of these new ventures will give them the long-needed impetus required to establish direct reduction as a viable method for processing iron ore. By far the greatest enthusiasm for using directly reduced iron is shown by steelmakers who employ electric arc furnaces. Here the product, either in lump, pellet, or briquette form, has several distinct advantages among which are: (*1*) consistency of chemical analysis, (*2*) low and known amounts of undesirable elements, and (*3*) uniformity of size.

With the small quantities of material so far available, a number of very useful demonstration melts and pilot experiments have been run in several countries. An important attribute of the prereduced materials is that they can be fed continuously to the melting furnace while melting of the entire charge is progressing. The proving of various techniques of reduction coupled with the technical success of continuously feeding the directly reduced iron to the electric-arc melting furnace can be expected to encourage greater consideration for direct reduction as an economical means for processing large tonnages of iron ores and concentrates.

Bibliography

1. T. S. Blair, "The Direct Process in Iron Manufacture," *Trans. AIME* 2, 175–199 (1874).
2. E. P. Barrett, *Sponge Iron and Direct Reduction Processes, Bull. No. 519*, United States Bureau of Mines, Washington, D. C., 1954.
3. J. H. Strassburger, D. C. Brown, R. L. Stephenson, and T. E. Dancy, *Blast Furnace Theory and Practice*, Vol. 2, Gordon & Breach, Science Publishers, Inc., New York, 1969, pp. 1024–1040.
4. "Structural Change in World Ore," *Steel Review*, April 1963.
5. O. Elliott and O. Gleiser, *Thermochemistry for Steelmaking*, Vol. 1, Addison-Wesley Publishing Co., Inc., Reading, Mass., 1960.
6. L. Visnyovszky, "Mechanismus und Kinetik von Reductionsreaktion," *Arch. Eisenhüttenw.* 39, 733 (1968).

DAVID L. McBRIDE
United States Steel Corporation

M

MERCURY, RECOVERY BY ELECTROOXIDATION

Mercury is recovered from its ores by roasting sulfide minerals and condensing the vapors to obtain the metal. The process is efficient from the standpoint of mercury extraction from the calcine; however, vapor and particulate losses in the condensing system, as well as recombination of the mercury with sulfur, can represent substantial losses. These losses are usually aggravated by the use of low-grade or wet ores, because vapor and particulate losses are directly proportional to the flue-gas volume.

A hydrometallurgical approach to mercury recovery from cinnabar, HgS, as well as from materials containing native mercury, offers several advantages: (1) Environmental pollution in the form of SO_2 and mercury vapor in the flue gas is eliminated; (2) similarly, health hazard to plant employees by accidental exposure to mercury vapors is minimized; (3) mercury recovery from low-grade ores is more efficient; and (4) the method is simple and can be applied to operations of varying size.

Hydrometallurgical treatment of mercury ores has been considered by several investigators. The dissolution of cinnabar by sodium sulfide and hypochlorite solutions is well known (1–4) and attempts have been made in the past (5–7) to use this reaction to develop commercially acceptable processes for mercury recovery. G. A. Parks (8) was issued a patent for a process employing the leaching of cinnabar with sodium hypochlorite, followed by carbon adsorption of the mercury from solution.

An electrooxidation process, originally developed by the U.S. Bureau of Mines for pretreatment of carbonaceous gold ores (9), was effective in dissolving mercury present in small amounts in the gold ore. Subsequent investigations and pilot-plant studies have shown that this electrooxidation can be used for the extraction of mercury from a variety of ores and concentrates (10).

The Process

Basically, the technique consists of crushing and grinding ore, forming a pulp with brine solution, and electrolyzing the pulp to oxidize minerals of mercury and some other metals to form water-soluble products. Conventional liquid–solid separation techniques are then employed to obtain a reasonably clear pregnant solution from which the mercury is precipitated as an amalgam by an active metal such as zinc. Recovery of mercury from the ore is 88–90%, depending on the particular ore processed. The flow diagram in Figure 1 shows the essential details of the process and the sequence of operations, as developed in experiments conducted by the Bureau of Mines.

Pilot-plant experiments were conducted with equipment consisting of a rod mill (18 in. by 3 ft), four rubber-lined 55-gal electrolysis tanks fitted with marine-type

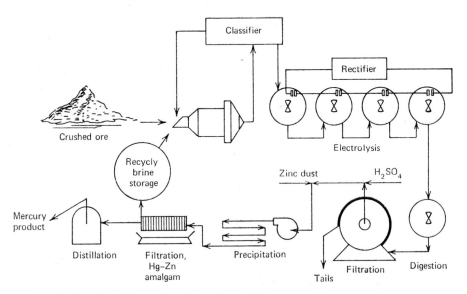

Fig. 1. Flow diagram for the electrooxidation process for mercury ores.

agitators, an agitated digestion vessel (a 55-gal drum), five thickeners (3 by 3 ft), (not shown in Figure 1), a rotary vacuum filter (1 by 3 ft), a precipitation unit, and supplemental pumps, piping, valves, etc. Each electrolysis tank was fitted with a five-electrode unit (4 by 20 in.). Direct current was supplied by an appropriate recti-fier. Mill capacity ranged from 1.4 to 1.8 tons/24-hr day, depending on the ore being processed. Table 1 gives operating conditions and data obtained in pilot-plant opera-tion on six different mercury ores from Utah and Nevada.

The ore was wet ground to 90–96%-65 mesh in a brine solution of 4–10% salt. In the cell, oxidation of cinnabar occurs as a result of the controlled production of hypochlorite during electrolysis of the brine solution containing the finely ground ore. The anode reactions involved in forming the oxidizing species are shown in the follow-ing equations:

$$2 \text{ Cl}^- - 2 \, \epsilon \rightarrow \text{Cl}_2$$
$$\text{Cl}_2 + \text{H}_2\text{O} \rightarrow \text{OCl}^- + 2 \text{ H}^+ + \text{Cl}^-$$

The hypochlorite ion formed as a result of the anode reactions oxidizes the cinna-bar to the sulfate, which is then hydrolyzed to the basic sulfate.

$$\text{HgS} + 4 \text{ OCl}^- \rightarrow \text{HgSO}_4 + 4 \text{ Cl}^-$$
$$3 \text{ HgSO}_4 + 2 \text{ H}_2\text{O} \rightarrow \text{HgSO}_4 . 2 \text{ HgO} + 2 \text{ H}_2\text{SO}_4$$

These mercury compounds have limited solubility in relatively neutral solutions; however, they react with the sodium chloride electrolyte to form the soluble tetra-chloro mercury complex as follows:

$$\text{HgSO}_4 + 4 \text{ Cl}^- \rightarrow \text{HgCl}_4{}^{2-} + \text{SO}_4{}^{2-}$$
$$\text{HgSO}_4 . 2 \text{ HgO} + 12 \text{ Cl}^- + 2 \text{ H}_2\text{O} \rightarrow 3 \text{ HgCl}_4{}^{2-} + \text{SO}_4{}^{2-} + 4 \text{ OH}^-$$

Two types of electrode systems were evaluated, one utilizing an iron cathode and a lead dioxide-coated titanium anode and another using an all-graphite system. A salt concentration of about 8–10% is desirable with the graphite–graphite electrode

Table 1. Summary of Pilot-Plant Operating Conditions and Extraction Data

Cinnabar matrix	Ore assay, lb Hg/ton	Tons processed	Solids in pulp to elec cells, %	Power consumption, kWh/ton	Tail assay, lb Hg/ton	Soluble Hg lost in tails, lb Hg/ton	Hg extracted from ore, %	NaCl lost in tails, lb/ton	Total metallic Hg recovery, %[f]
opalized[a]	4.2	2.8	37	29	0.1	0.06	97.4	92	94.6
in silicified									
sinter[a]	0.7[b]	2.3	43	35	0.07[c]		90.0	30[e]	89
in dolomite[a]	2.3	3.2	44	23	0.07[c]		96.9	22[e]	96.0
in silicified									
volcanic[g]	1.0	2.6	30	38.3	0.09	0.04	90.1	71	88
opalized									
with clay[d]	2.5	3.2	30	59	0.14	0.04	94.6	68	92
in silicified									
sinter[d]	1.5[b]	6.2	35	17.1	0.04	0.03	96.4	32	93.5

[a] Graphite–graphite electrode system.
[b] Elemental sulfur present.
[c] Including soluble Hg.
[d] Lead dioxide anode–iron cathode electrode system.
[e] Liquid–solid separation conducted on an Oliver rotary drum filter (1 by 3 ft).
[f] Based on ore assay.
[g] With 45% clay; lead dioxide anode–iron cathode electrode system.

system to prevent oxidation of the anode, whereas a 3–4% salt solution can be used with the iron–lead dioxide electrode system without degradation of the anode. Power consumption in the 4% salt solution was about 20% higher than that required with the 10% salt solution. Under conditions of proper salt concentration, no degradation of either electrode system was noted during the course of the experiment.

It was necessary to agitate the pulp during electrolysis to make sure that the mineral particles came in close contact with the anode. The electrodes were immersed into the pulp so that the agitator continuously pumped the pulp through the electrode system. By this active agitation hypochlorite ion reacted as rapidly as it was formed, thus effectively maintaining hypochlorite concentration at a minimum.

The ore particles inhibit the conduction of current through the cell and so it is necessary to have the anode and cathode spaced so that effective transport of material between the electrodes and adequate electrical conduction can both be obtained. It was found that electrode spacing for a graphite–graphite system of about $\frac{1}{4}$–$\frac{1}{2}$ in. for electrodes about 3–4 in. wide gave the most satisfactory results. The electrode design and spacing in the cell are shown in Figure 2. In operations on a larger scale the cell consisted of a 55-gal drum, with agitation provided by a 10-in. diam impeller. This particular cell design consisted of four graphite cathodes positioned between five graphite anodes. All electrodes were made from $\frac{3}{4}$-in. graphite sheet and were 4 in. wide. Electrodes were immersed about 20 in. in the brine pulp. Continuous flow of the pulp through four electrolytic cells was effective in treating the ores. These cells were either in series or in a series-parallel circuit. The circuitry was changed, depending on the ore-flow rate and type of ore treated. In a series circuit, about 20 V was required, or about 4 V/cell. A fifth barrel with an agitator, referred to as a digester, was placed at the end of the circuit to ensure that the chemical reaction was

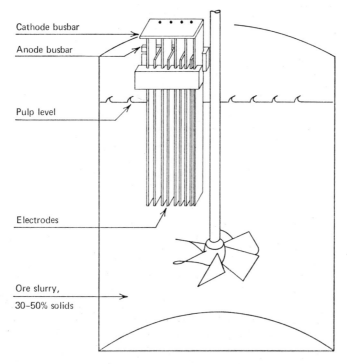

Cathode busbar

Anode busbar

Pulp level

Electrodes

Ore slurry,
30–50% solids

Fig. 2. Electrooxidation cell and agitation vessel.

complete before the pulp entered the liquid–solid separation system. The rate of flow of the ore gave a total retention time of 4–6 hr of electrolysis, depending on the ore being treated. The kWh used for electrolysis varied with the difficulty of treating each specific ore, ranging from 17 to 60 kWh/ton of ore treated. The current density ranged from about 0.3 to 0.7 A/in.^{2} of electrode surface.

The pH of the electrolyte was generally allowed to follow the natural pH obtained on contact of solution with the ore. This usually fell in the range of pH 6 to 7 and is consistent with efficient production of hypochlorite in the electrolysis of salt solution.

It was found that the rate of reaction depends somewhat on temperature. The rate of oxidation of the minerals increases with temperature; however, the stability of hypochlorite decreases with increasing temperature so that the optimum operating temperature is in the range of 25 to 40°C.

The technology of liquid–solid separation for the recovery of a pregnant solution closely follows a conventional practice used in countercurrent slimes circuits. If the ore contains considerable quantities of clay, countercurrent decantation or washing is usually required to minimize the loss of mercury as soluble salts in the mill tails. Liquid–solid separation by filtration is generally favored whenever permitted by the character of the ore. Whereas soluble mercury losses to the tails are approximately equal to those obtained with countercurrent decantation, the sodium chloride losses obtained by filtration are half of the losses in a countercurrent-decantation circuit. Since salt losses in the tails can represent an important economic factor, careful operation of the tailings pond is necessary. Fresh makeup water added to the system should be repulped with exiting filter cake or countercurrent-decantation tails and reclaimed from the tailings pond to assure maximum recovery of salt, as well as of any soluble mercury compounds. (Exciting pulp is pulp that is leaving the system.) This reclaimed salt solution is then recycled through the system.

Precipitation of the mercury from the chloride solution by an active metal is readily accomplished without the degassing and clarification required by the classical Merrill-Crowe process for gold precipitation from cyanide solution (11). Precipitation is rapid, effective, and essentially complete at a pH of 2.5 by contacting the pregnant solution with 200-mesh metallic zinc dust in the amount of 1.5 lb Zn/lb Hg. Copper is also effective for mercury precipitation; however, precipitation on copper appears to be a surface phenomenon so that a much greater surface area is required than with zinc. The gold and silver dissolved during electrolysis follow the mercury through the system and are coprecipitated with the mercury. Barren brine solution, resulting from the mercury precipitation step, is recycled through the system after addition of sufficient lime to return the pH to 7. The same brine-electrolyte solution was utilized and recycled in experiments on all of the ores. No buildup of deleterious components in the brine was noted after four months of recycling.

The resultant precipitate consists of a zinc–mercury amalgam with a nominal composition of 40% mercury and 60% zinc, including minor amounts of lead, silver, gold, copper, etc. Essentially complete mercury recovery from the amalgam is readily accomplished by distillation at 500–600°C and condensation of the vapors. The zinc calcine is washed with ammonium hydroxide to remove the portion of zinc oxidized during distillation of the mercury and is then recycled to effect further precipitation of mercury from pregnant solution.

The process merits consideration for industrial application. Its advantages lie in the simplicity of the chemistry, the high extractions, and the ease of controlling the various steps. Operation and handling of materials are simple and costs and procedures parallel those encountered in large-scale gold cyanidation mills.

Bibliography

1. U.S. Pat. 1,119,377 (Dec. 1, 1914), E. B. Thornhill.
2. W. W. Bradley, "Quicksilver Resources of California," *Calif. State Div. Mines Bull.* **78** (1918).
3. U.S. Pat. 1,637,481 (Aug. 2, 1927), W. Glaeser.
4. W. H. Butler, *The Hydrometallurgy of Mercury*, Ph.D. Thesis, Stanford University, Stanford, Calif., 1928.
5. L. H. Duschak, *Trans. AIME* **91**, 283 (1930).
6. E. Oberbillig, J. Fyfe, W. Aitkenhead, and J. Jackel, *Mining World* **20**, 53 (1958).
7. J. N. Butler, "Studies in the Hydrometallurgy of Mercury Sulphide Ores," *Nev. Bureau of Mines Rept. 5*, Mackay School of Mines, University of Nevada, Reno, Nev., 1963.
8. U.S. Pat. 3,476,552 (Nov. 4, 1969), G. A. Parks and R. E. Baker.
9. B. J. Scheiner, R. E. Lindstrom, and T. A. Henrie, *Electrolytic Oxidation of Carbonaceous Ores for Improving Gold Recovery*, U. S. Bur. Mines Tech. Progr. Rept. **8** (1969).
10. B. J. Scheiner, R. E. Lindstrom, D. E. Shanks, and T. A. Henrie, *Electrolytic Oxidation of Cinnabar Ores for Mercury Recovery*, U. S. Bur. Mines Tech. Progr. Rept. **26** (1970).
11. J. L. Bray, *Non-Ferrous Production Mettallurgy*, John Wiley & Sons, Inc., New York, 1947, pp. 263–265.

T. A. HENRIE AND R. E. LINDSTROM
Bureau of Mines, U. S. Dept. of the Interior

METHYLACETYLENE

Methylacetylene (propyne), $CH_3C \equiv CH$, is a colorless gas at ordinary temperature and pressure. It is isomeric with allene (propadiene), $CH_2 = C = CH_2$, and since the two are produced together, an adequate discussion of methylacetylene must deal also with the nature and reactions of its isomer.

In recent years considerable study has been devoted to the use of methylacetylene as a petrochemical building block, since it is the one remaining low-molecular-weight hydrocarbon which has not found extensive use. It may be expected that it will be used in some of the reactions which are characteristic of acetylene. It has the same reactive triple bond and one (but only one) reactive hydrogen atom in its structure so that propynylation reactions analogous to the vinylation reactions of acetylene occur.

Physical Properties

The physical properties of methylacetylene and allene are given in Table 1.

Table 1. Physical Properties of Methylacetylene and Allene (1,2)

Property	Methyl-acetylene	Allene
boiling point, at 1 atm, °C	−23.22	−34.5
dt/dp, at 1 atm, °C/mm Hg	0.030	0.033
freezing point in air, at 1 atm, °C	−102.7	−136.3
density of liquid, at 20°C, g/ml	0.6711	0.6575
critical pressure, atm	51.0[a]	54[a]
critical temperature, °C	121.6	120
critical volume, liter/mole	0.164	0.162[a]
heat capacity of gas at const pressure and 25°C, cal/(g)(°C)	0.3618	0.3520
heat of vaporization at saturation pressure,[b] cal/(g)(°C)	97.3	121
heat of formation (gas), at 25°C, kcal/(g)(mole)	44.39	45.92
free energy of formation (gas), at 25°C, kcal/(g)(mole)	46.313	48.37
surface tension, at 25°C, dyn/cm	11.4	9.4
viscosity of liquid, at 25°C, cP	0.140	0.140
standard enthalpy, H^0, at 77°F, Btu/lb	306.23	368.45
standard entropy, S^0, at 77°F, Btu/(lb)(°R)	2.480	2.455

[a] Estimated.

[b] At the normal boiling point (1 atm).

For low pressures (essentially ideal-gas conditions), the enthalpy of pure methylacetylene or allene is given by the following equation: $H^0 = H_0^0 + A(T/100) + B(T/100)^2 + C(T/100)^3 + D(100/T) + E$, where H^0 is the ideal gas enthalpy at T, referred to the base enthalpy of 0 Btu/lb; for the saturated liquid at −200°F, T is temperature in °R and A, B, C, D, and E are constants the values of which are given in Table 2.

The following equation gives the heat capacity of pure methylacetylene or allene (in the ideal state): $C_p^0 = A(T/100) + B(T/100)^2 + C(T/100)^3 + D(T/100)$, where T is in °R; the values of the constants A, B, C, and D are given in Table 2.

The corresponding equation for the ideal-gas entropy of methylacetylene or allene is the following: $S^0 = A(t/100) + B(t/100)^2 + C(t/100)^3 + D(t/100)^4 + E \log (t + 459.7) + 1$, where t is temperature in °F; the values of A, B, C, D, and E are given in Table 2.

Table 2. Values for the Constants in the Equations for Enthalpy, Heat Capacity, and Entropy

Constant	Enthalpy	Heat capacity	Entropy
methylacetylene			
A	15.52172	7.00117×10^{-2}	2.49878×10^{-2}
B	2.18521	-2.37587×10^{-3}	0.67851×10^{-3}
C	-2.54810×10^{-2}	3.20304×10^{-5}	-4.80120×10^{-5}
D	-15.21656	2.62752×10^{-1}	0.85920×10^{-6}
E	166.758		0.53497
allene			
A	13.88180	7.28484×10^{-2}	2.43380×10^{-2}
B	2.32156	-2.54153×10^{-2}	0.86985×10^{-3}
C	-2.80134×10^{-2}	3.47742×10^{-5}	-5.83404×10^{-5}
D	-7.67558	1.52903×10^{-1}	1.03999×10^{-6}
E	232.838		0.52593

Isomerization Equilibrium

As mentioned earlier, methylacetylene and allene are produced together. The study of the isomerization equilibria of the two is, therefore, of considerable interest as an aid in predicting the amount of methylacetylene produced and of the residual allene fraction (which may be subjected to further interconversion techniques, thereby increasing the overall yield of methylacetylene from the process).

The calculation of K_p for the reaction methylacetylene $\rightleftharpoons$ allene was made for several temperatures using 1969 data (3). The results, showing the percent allene in the mixture at equilibrium for each temperature, are listed in Table 3.

Table 3. Allene at Equilibrium at Various Temperatures

Temp, °K	Mole %	Temp, °K	Mole %
300	4.13	700	18.82
400	8.02	800	21.78
500	10.18	900	24.41
600	15.53	1000	26.80

The values obtained above agree fairly well, in the higher temperature range, with extrapolations from the experimental results obtained by Cordes and Günzler in the temperature range from 400 to 600°K (4). However, in the lower temperature range the discrepancy between the theoretical and actual values widens and becomes quite significant, as shown in Figure 1.

Chemical Properties and Reactions

The double bonds of allene and the fact that they are adjacent govern its chemistry. Its reactions are characteristic of this type of unsaturation. Similarly, methylacetylene undergoes all the reactions typical of the triple bond. A few of the more interesting reactions are given below. For further details, see references 5–11.

Alcohols.

$$CH_3C\equiv CH + CH_3OH \xrightarrow{BF_3/HgO} CH_3C\begin{smallmatrix} \diagup OCH_3 \\ \diagdown CH_2 \end{smallmatrix}$$

$$CH_3C{\equiv}CH + 2\ CH_3OH \xrightarrow{BF_3/HgO} CH_3C{\underset{OCH_3}{\overset{OCH_3}{-}}}CH_3$$

Halogen and Alkyl Halides.

$$CH_3C{\equiv}CH + Br_2 + H_2O \xrightarrow{Ag/KOH} CH_3C{\equiv}CBr$$

$$CH_2{=}C{=}CH_2 + Cl_2 \rightarrow CH_2{=}CClCH_2Cl + CH{\equiv}CCH\ Cl$$

$$CH_3C{\equiv}CH + HBr \xrightarrow[-40°C]{peroxides} CH_3CHBrCH_2Br$$

$$CH_3C{\equiv}CH + (CH_3)_3CCl \xrightarrow{AlCl_3} CH_3CCl{=}CHC(CH_3)_3$$

$$CH_3C{\equiv}CH + HBr \longrightarrow CH_3CBr_2CH_3 + \text{(structure 1)}$$
main product

(1)

cis and *trans*- 1,3-dibromo-
1,3-dimethylcyclobutane,
traces

Cyclodimerization products, such as (1), are also produced in substantial amounts from allene with HBr and with HCl, but not with HI (11).

Dimerization. The dimerization of allene to butadiene derivatives, or polymers thereof, based on

has been reported (12) to be catalyzed by the use of palladium compounds, such as palladium acetate or nitrate in glacial acetic acid.

Carboxylic Acids.

$$CH_3C{\equiv}CH + CH_3COOH \xrightarrow{BF_3} CH_3COOC{=}CH_2$$
$$\underset{CH_3}{|}$$

Aldehydes and Ketones.

$$CH_3C{\equiv}CH + HCHO \xrightarrow{KOH} CH_3C{\equiv}CCH_2OH$$

$$CH_3C{\equiv}CH + \underset{CH_3}{\overset{CH_3}{>}}C{=}O \xrightarrow{KOH} CH_3C{\equiv}C{-}C{\underset{OH}{\overset{CH_3}{<}}}CH_3$$

Sodium.

$$CH_3C{\equiv}CH + NaNH_2 \xrightarrow{liq\ NH_3} CH_3C{\equiv}CNa$$

$$CH_3C{\equiv}CNa + CO_2 \xrightarrow{15\ atm} CH_3C{\equiv}C{-}COONa$$

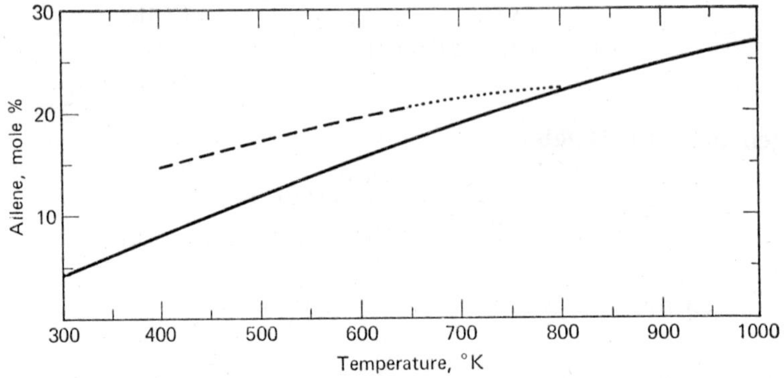

Fig. 1. Isomerization equilibrium of allene. Legend: —— theoretical values; - - - Cordes and Gunzler's experiment; . . . extrapolation of experimental results.

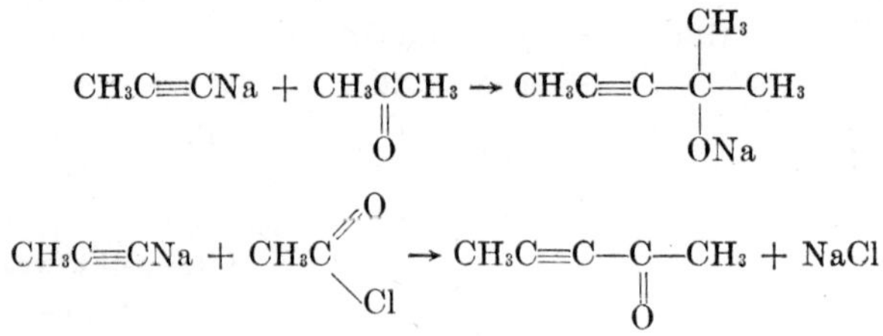

Miscellaneous.

$$CH_3C{\equiv}CH + HCN \xrightarrow[425°\ C]{Zn} CH_3C(CN){=}CH_2 + CH_3CH{=}CHCN + CH_2{=}CHCH_2CN$$

$$4\ CH_3C{\equiv}CH + Ni(CO)_4 + 2\ HCl + 4\ CH_3CH_2OH \xrightarrow{40\text{–}45°C} 4\ CH_2{=}C(CH_3)COOH + NiCl_2 + H_2$$

$$2\ CH_3C{\equiv}CH \xrightarrow{Cu^+ + O_2} CH_3{\equiv}C{-}C{\equiv}CH_3$$

$$CH_3C{\equiv}CH \xrightarrow{NaOBr} CH_3C{\equiv}CBr$$

$$CH_3C{\equiv}CBr + CuC{\equiv}CCH_3 \rightarrow CH_3{\equiv}C{-}C{\equiv}CH_3$$

Polymerization (13). Methylacetylene does not polymerize on long standing, (unlike acetylene which does, forming a solid condensation product known as "cuprene"). However, under the initiation of ultraviolet irradiation which breaks the triple bond, methylacetylene polymerizes, forming a white solid. The polymerization of allene (13) has been reported (12) to be catalyzed by various palladium compounds, yielding a polymer having conjugated unsaturation.

Analysis. Methylacetylene is determined in the presence of allene primarily by gas chromatography (14) and infrared spectroscopy (4).

Manufacture

Dehydrohalogenation of Propylene Dibromide (15). Propylene as the feed is brominated in the liquid phase, using propylene dibromide as the solvent. A certain amount of further bromination takes place by substitution.

$$CH_3CH{=}CH_2 + Br_2 \rightarrow CH_3CHBrCH_2Br$$

The reaction products are distilled to separate the higher bromides as bottoms (they are reacted with caustic to recover sodium bromide). The propylene dibromide overhead from the column is reacted with caustic, forming methylacetylene and allene, as shown below:

$$CH_3CHBrCH_2Br + 2\ NaOH \rightarrow CH_3C{\equiv}CH + 2\ NaBr + 2\ H_2O$$

$$CH_3CHBrCH_2Br + 2\ NaOH \rightarrow CH_2{=}C{=}CH_2 + 2\ NaBr + 2\ H_2O$$

The sodium bromide forms a slurry and is removed in a rotary filter. The gas mixture is compressed and liquefied and sent to a distillation column from which methylacetylene is removed as bottoms and stored. Allene is isomerized to a methylacetylene–allene mixture and recycled to the column. The sodium bromide is dissolved in water and sent to electrolytic cells for conversion to bromine and caustic.

Pyrolysis of Propylene (16). This process involves the thermal pyrolysis of propylene in the presence of steam.

$$CH_3CH{=}CH_2 \xrightarrow{\text{steam}} CH_3C{\equiv}CH + H_2$$

The feed mixture preferably contains 13–35 mole % propylene and about 65–87 mole % steam. It is essential for good yields to employ low contact times (on the order of 0.0030 to 0.010 sec). Temperatures of 950–1200°C are best. The operating pressure (ie the total pressure of the propylene and steam mixture) is usually kept as close to atmospheric as possible. The partial pressure of propylene in the reactor should be about 100–350 mm Hg.

The contact time is considered critical because it is believed that the temperatures at which methylacetylene and allene are formed thermally from propylene, are also the temperatures at which they themselves thermally decompose to other products. Thus, to minimize this secondary pyrolysis, the proper selection of contact time is essential.

In order to achieve the critical low contact time and to keep the decomposition and side reactions to a minimum, it is necessary to cool the gas stream quickly, immediately after it leaves the reaction zone, to a temperature of 350°C or less. This lowers the temperature of the gases below the pyrolytic temperature, thereby avoiding the decomposition of products and unwanted side reactions. It also lowers the temperature of the unsaturated hydrocarbons in the product gases to a point where polymerization of these materials is at a minimum.

One method of separating the products involves an absorption system using, for example, naphtha as the absorbing liquid. Methylacetylene, allene, propylene, butadiene, and other heavy ends are removed (temperature range 15–90°C; pressure range 1–3 atm). The effluent gas stream from the absorber contains hydrogen, ethylene, methane, and acetylene which may be further processed.

Methylacetylene, allene, and propylene (the latter for recycling to the feed) are recovered by stripping the naphtha which may then be recycled to the absorber.

Hydration of Magnesium Carbide (15). A low-melting eutectic of magnesium chloride–sodium chloride is fed continuously into a liquid-phase melt heated by hot gases in a regenerative furnace. Calcium carbide is also continuously fed into the furnace, and the molten product is tapped from the other end of the furnace and cooled in pigs. The solid is ground in a hammer mill under an inert atmosphere, screened, and then passed into a carbide generator. The resulting gas product which is a mixture of acetylene and methylacetylene (from Mg_2C_3, which is formed by decomposition of MgC_2, see Vol. 4, p. 72) is water scrubbed, dried, and passed to a reboiler absorber, using dimethylformamide as the solvent. The lean gas recovered is acetylene; the fat solvent is stripped of methylacetylene which is subsequently liquefied and stored.

Reaction of Sodium Acetylide and Dimethyl Sulfate in Liquid Ammonia (13). A solution of sodamide, $NaNH_2$, in liquid ammonia is prepared by passing ammonia over a bed of metallic sodium. The by-product gas, containing some vaporized ammonia, is passed on to a scrubber to absorb the ammonia, which is subsequently recovered by steam stripping. In a separate tower, ammonia is saturated with acetylene. This stream is then mixed with the sodamide stream.

$$NaNH_2 + C_2H_2 \rightarrow NaC_2N + NH_3$$

The mixture is passed to a hold-up tank to allow escape of the ethylene formed from the reaction of acetylene and hydrogen. Dimethyl sulfate is injected into the stream and the mixture passes to a reactor.

$$NaC\equiv CH + (CH_3)_2SO_4 \rightarrow CN_3C\equiv CH + NaCH_3SO_4$$

Methylacetylene gas containing some ammonia and acetylene is then scrubbed with water to remove the ammonia. The methylacetylene–acetylene mixture is passed to a reboiler–absorber, using dimethylformamide as solvent. Acetylene comes off as the lean gas, while the methylacetylene is recovered from the fat solvent in a stripper.

The ammonia solution containing sodium methyl sulfate is partially flashed and the vaporized ammonia is recondensed and recycled. The remaining slurry of sodium methyl sulfate is mixed with water and then steam stripped to recover ammonia. The sodium methyl sulfate solution is acidified and passed to a reboiler–hydrolyzer, where methanol is recovered as overhead and sodium sulfate—by neutralization—as bottoms. The methanol stream is recycled to a reactor where it is reacted with sulfuric acid to reform dimethyl sulfate.

Pyrolysis of Isobutylene (15). Isobutylene, $CH_2=C(CH_3)_2$, mixed with steam is passed through a tubular reactor where it is cracked. The effluent gases are rapidly quenched in a spray cooler (as in the propylene pyrolysis process). The gas mixture is then compressed and partially liquefied by cooling. A lean-gas mixture is removed as an overhead stream from a separator through which the compressed mixture had been passed. The liquid stream from the separator is sent to a distillation column from which allene and lighter hydrocarbons are removed as overhead, and methylacetylene and isobutylene as bottoms. They are separated in another distillation column. The isobutylene is flashed to remove polymer and returned to the isobutylene storage. The allene portion may be isomerized to an allene–methylacetylene mixture in a further step to increase the process yields.

Dehydrogenation of Propane by Sulfur (17). Propane is the preferred feed in this two-step process which first involves the reaction of the feed with sulfur at a temperature of approximately $1200°F$.

$$CH_3CH_2CH_3 + 2S \rightarrow CH_3C\equiv CH + 2H_2S$$

This is followed by a reconversion process in which the hydrogen sulfide produced by the oxidation with sulfur in the first step is partially oxidized to SO_2. The remaining H_2S is reacted with the SO_2, using the well-known Claus process, to produce elemental sulfur and water, thereby recovering sulfur for use in step one.

From High-Temperature Pyrolysis. Methylacetylene is produced via a pyrolysis process in Monsanto's plant in Chocolate Bayou near Alvin, Texas (18). The feed being cracked is essentially a wide-boiling mixture of naphtha and gas oil. The plant produces some thirty-one products including methylacetylene.

Methylacetylene may also be obtained as a by-product from the production of acetylene by partial combustion of hydrocarbons (Sachse process) (15), and from the production of butadiene by dehydrogenation of butenes (15). The same principal products are present regardless of the feedstock, but the relative proportions vary widely, depending on stock and pyrolysis conditions (eg temperature, pressure, contact time, catalyst employed, etc). References 19–28 furnish further details regarding the pyrolysis processes.

ISOMERIZATION OF ALLENE TO METHYLACETYLENE

As mentioned above, methylacetylene is usually produced with allene; the exact proportions are determined by the isomerization equilibrium of the two at the given temperature. It is desirable to have a method of converting the allene fraction to its isomer, thereby increasing the yield of methylacetylene from the given process or vice versa. Several patents have been issued on the subject; two (29,30) are discussed here.

Basically, the isomerization technique involves contacting the vaporized feedstock of allene with an activated catalyst at temperatures preferably in the range of 200 to 400°C. The isomerization is usually carried out at atmospheric pressure (or at pressures close to atmospheric).

The gaseous feed flows over the catalyst at space velocities ranging from about 50 to 1000 volumes of vapor (measured at 0°C and 1 atm per hour per volume of catalyst space); the higher the reaction temperature employed, the higher the space velocity.

Among the various catalysts which can be used are alumina, treated with silicon tetrafluoride, hydrogen fluoride, methyl iodide, ammonium bifluoride, hydrogen fluorosilicate, H_2SiF_6, and aluminum trifluoride.

As an example of the effectiveness of this technique, when alumina, treated with methyl iodide at a temperature of 580°C, was used to isomerize allene at a reaction temperature of 320°C (space velocity 165), 82.3% of the allene reacted, of which 88.8% formed methylacetylene giving a yield (ie moles of methylacetylene produced per mole of allene fed) of 73.1%.

PURIFICATION

In some instances, the desired methylacetylene product is found to occur in a mixture with various other C_3 and also C_4 hydrocarbons, and its separation from this mixture is difficult. The problem is believed to result from the changing relative volatility of methylacetylene with varying compositions of hydrocarbons of paraffin, olefin, and diolefin types, or perhaps it is due to the formation of azeotropes between the methylacetylene and one or more of the other hydrocarbons present.

Hill et al. (31) gave a discussion of vapor–liquid equilibria for C_3 hydrocarbons. This information has been applied to more complex systems and to the partial evaporation of synthetic mixtures containing methylacetylene, such as might be encountered in the removal of vapor from cylinders of liquefied material (32), but not to problems of purification.

Fractional distillation in the presence of propane removes substantially all the methylacetylene from such a mixture (33). This method takes advantage of the fact that propane increases the relative volatility of methylacetylene in such mixtures. A minimum-boiling azeotrope between methylacetylene and propane (and any other C_3 hydrocarbon present) is formed and taken as overhead from the distillation column. The components in this overhead (propane, methylacetylene, allene, and propylene) may then be further separated by other methods (eg liquid extraction, crystallization, etc).

The azeotrope formed between methylacetylene and propane boils at 140.3°F at 322.5 psia, as compared with 174.8°F for pure methylacetylene and 143.8°F for pure propane. The azeotrope contains 15.5 mole % of methylacetylene and 84.5 mole % of propane.

The use of dimethylformamide and similar solvents in extractive distillation systems also affords a procedure for avoiding azeotrope formation among the hydrocarbons boiling close to methylacetylene and allene in a pyrolysis effluent.

HANDLING INFORMATION

Explosive Limits in Air (34). The explosive limits of methylacetylene–allene gas mixtures (MAPP) are approximately 3.4–10.8% in air and 2.5–60% in oxygen. These values are much narrower than those for acetylene but about the same as those for propane and natural gas.

Shock Sensitivity (34). Because acetylene is unstable to shock, it might be expected that methylacetylene and allene would behave similarly. However, shock-sensitivity tests conducted at the U.S. Bureau of Mines indicate that these pure fuels and their mixtures are not subject to detonation. The tests were conducted by subjecting a tube filled with the fuel to the shock initiated by a No. 8 commercial detonator embedded in 100 g of tetryl.

Exothermic Decomposition (32,34–36). Methylacetylene and propadiene both have the property of liberating heat on decomposition. They are flammable in the absence of air when ignited by a high-temperature source. In a confined space the pressure developed by this type of reaction represents a substantial hazard, especially under pressures and when conducting reactions which are themselves exothermic.

Formation of Explosive Salts with Metals (34). Methylacetylene, like acetylene, in contact with copper can form explosive acetylides. Therefore no brazing or copper alloys containing more than 67% copper should be used either in containers or piping. From this standpoint, any equipment which is capable of handling acetylene is also satisfactory for use with methylacetylene–allene mixtures.

Vapor Toxicity. Methylacetylene and propadiene vapors are similar in toxicity to acetylene and propane. Although high concentrations of the vapor mixture can have an anesthetic effect, recovery on removal from the contaminated area is rapid and complete.

Shipping. The ICC classifies methylacetylene and propadiene as liquefied flammable gases. They can be shipped in cylinders or small container without dissolving in acetone or other diluents, as is necessary in the case of acetylene.

Uses

The possible uses for methylacetylene depend, naturally, upon its cost. However, it is not easy to fix a price for methylacetylene on the industrial scale, because of the wide variety of possible production methods. As a primary chemical for large-scale use, it can probably be produced for less than 10¢/lb. As a by-product it may be available at considerably lower cost from pyrolysis streams.

A stabilized mixture of methylacetylene and allene fuel gas, called MAPP (registered trademark of The Dow Chemical Company), gas was introduced to the metal-working industry in 1963 (37). It has been found to be less susceptible to spontaneous decomposition than either pure methylacetylene or pure propadiene, both of which themselves are somewhat easier to handle than pure acetylene. It has attained some use for cutting, brazing, welding, heating, and metallizing with a volume ratio of oxygen to MAPP gas of approximately 4 to 1. The applicability of methylacetylene, allene, and their mixtures in these fields stems from the fact that compounds with triple bonds or adjacent double bonds are thermodynamically unstable and evolve heat upon decomposition (34). Methylacetylene may find application as a high-energy fuel propellant for rocket engines (38–39) in view of its exothermic character.

The manufacture of methyl methacrylate using methylacetylene as the starting material has attracted attention as a new synthetic method which possibly could replace the acetone cyanohydrin process currently employed. See Vol. 1, p. 294 and Vol. 13, p. 335. Considerable research (40–42) is being undertaken in examining possible routes to methyl methacrylate starting with methylacetylene. The basic reaction involved uses nickel carbonyl as a catalyst for the carbonylation reaction:

$$CO + CH_3OH + CH{\equiv}CCH_3 \xrightarrow{Ni(CO)_4} CN_2{=}C(CH)COOCH_3$$

In view of the growing importance of photochemically initiated reactions in industry, the use of free-radical additions of thiols to allene and methylacetylene seems promising. Compounds of this type have possibilities as insecticides and as oxidation inhibitors in motor oils. Polymers containing sulfur atoms in the chain, which are more or less resistant to various hydrocarbon solvents, are also accessible by these reactions (11).

Bibliography

1. Technical Data Book, *Petroleum Refining*, American Petroleum Institute, Div. of Refining, Port City Press, Inc., Baltimore, Md., 1966.
2. R. W. Gallant, "Physical Properties of Hydrocarbons," Parts 3 and 4, *Hydrocarbon Process. Petrol. Refiner* **44** (9) and (10) (1965).
3. D. R. Stull, Edgar F. Westrum, Jr., and Gerard C. Sinke, *The Chemical Thermodynamics of Organic Compounds*, John Wiley & Sons, Inc., New York, 1969.
4. J. F. Cordes and H. Günzler, "Das Propin/Propadien-Gleichgewicht," *Chem. Ber.* **92**, 1055–1063 (1959).
5. Thomas F. Rutledge, *Acetylenes and Allenes—Addition, Cyclization and Polymerization Reactions*, Reinhold Book Co., New York, 1969.
6. Thomas F. Rutledge, *Acetylenic Compounds—Preparation and Substitution Reactions*, Reinhold Book Co., New York 1968.
7. H. G. Viehe, *Chemistry of Acetylenes*, Marcel Dekker, Inc., New York, 1969.
8. I. L. Kotlyarevskii, M. S. Shwartsberg, and L. B. Fisher, "Reactions of Acetylenic Compounds," *Isdat. Nauka, Novosibink* (*in Russian*) (1967).
9. K. Griesbaum *Angew. Chem. Intern. Ed. Engl.* **5** (11) 933–946 (1966).
10. *Chem. Rev.* **67**, 317 (1967).
11. Karl Griesbaum et al., "Cyclobutane Compounds III. The Ionic Addition of HCl, HBr, and HI to Allene and Methyl Acetylene," *J. Am. Chem. Soc.* **87**, 3151 (1965); see also *Angew. Chem. Intern. Ed. Engl.* **5**, 933 (1966) and **9**, 273 (1970).
12. G. D. Shier, *J. Organomet. Chem.* **10**, 15 (1967).

13. S. C. Lind and R. J. Livingston, "The Photochemical Polymerization of Methyl Acetylene and Allene," *J. Am. Chem. Soc.* **55**, 1036–1047 (1933).
14. J. Janak, "Chromatographic Semicroanalysis of Gases V. Analysis of Unsaturated C_2 and C_3 Hydrocarbons," *Chem. Listy* **47**, 1184–1189 (1953).
15. "Survey of Processes for the Production of Methyl Acetylene," Acetylene Chemicals Co., Corona, New York, Sept. 1952. (In reply to Dept. of the Navy, Bur. of Aeronautics.)
16. "Propylene Cracking," U.S. Pat. 3,200,076 (1966), J. Happel and C. J. Marsel.
17. "Production of Methyl Acetylene and Propylene," U.S. Pat. 3,344,203.
18. *Chem. Eng. Progr.* **65** (8), 53–58 (1969).
19. "Cracking of Olefins," U.S. Pat. 2,429,566 (1942), Francis O. Rice.
20. Belg. Pat. 612,415,(1962) J. Happel and C. J. Marsel (to National Lead Co.).
21. "Conversion of Propylene and Isobutylene to Allene and Methyl Acetylene," U.S. Pat. 2,925,-451 (1960), M. G. Hogsed (to E. I. du Pont de Nemours & Co., Inc.).
22. "Cracking of Isobutylene with Steam to Produce Substituted Acetylenes and Diolefins," U.S. Pat. 2,763,703 (1956), J. Happel and C. J. Marsel.
23. "Production of Methyl Acetylene and Allene," Brit. Pat. 1,113,004 (1966), to Chiyoda Kako Kensetsu Kabushiki Kaisha Corp.
24. "Catalytic Conversion of Isobutylene and Propylene to Allene and Methyl Acetylene Thereof," U.S. Pat. 3,198,848 (1965), J. Happel and C. J. Marsel (to National Lead Co.).
25. Karl Schugerl and John Happel, "High Temperature Pyrolysis of Isobutene," *Ind. Eng. Chem. Process Design Develop.* **8** (3) (1969) and references cited there.
26. Y. Sakakibara, "The Synthesis of Methylacetylene by the Pyrolysis of Propylene I, II, and IV," *Bull. Chem. Soc. Japan* **37** (9), 1262–1276 (1969); **42** (4), 1082–1089 (1969).
27. S. Kunichika et al., "Synthesis of Methylacetylene by the Pyrolysis of Propylene III—Effect of Catalysts on Product Yields," *Bull. Inst. Chem. Res. Kyoto Univ.* **43** (5) 469–479 (1965).
28. Fr. Pat. 1,389,109 (1965), J. Happel and C. J. Marsel (to National Lead Co.).
29. "Isomerization of Unsaturated Hydrocarbons," U.S. Pat. 2,594,706 (1952), M. L. Allan (to Imperial Chem. Ind. Ltd.).
30. "Isomerization of Allene to Methyl Acetylene," Can. Pat. 770,653 (1967), J. Happel, C. J. Marsel, and J. H. Blanck (to National Lead Co.).
31. A. B. Hill, R. H. McCormick, P. Barton, and M. R. Fenske, *Am. Inst. Chem. Engrs. J.* **8**, 681 (1962).
32. R. F. Huston, C. A. Burrios, and R. A. Holleman, *J. Chem. Eng. Data* **15**, 168 (1970).
33. "Separation of Methyl Acetylene From C_4 Hydrocarbons," U.S. Pat. 2,371,860 (1945), W. S. Walls and M. R. Dean.
34. J. F. Hembree et al., "A New Fuel Gas—Stabilized Methyl Acetylene-Propadiene," *Welding J.*, *N.Y.* **42** (5), 395–404 (1963), and references cited there.
35. D. R. Forshey et al., "Potential Hazards of Propargyl Halides and Allene," *Fire Technol.* **5** (2), 100–111 (1969), and references cited there.
36. J. M. Kuchta et al., "Flammability Characteristics of Methylacetylene, Propadiene (Allene), and Propylene Mixtures," *J. Chem. Eng. Data* **9**, 3 (July 1964).
37. R. D. Green, "Metalizing Developments Utilizing Stabilized Methyl Acetylene–Propadiene," *Welding J.*, *N. Y.*, **45** (12), 992–998 (1966).
38. G. D'Alelio, U.S. Pat. 3,362,860 (1968), to Dal Mon Reasearch Co.
39. G. D'Alelio, U.S. Pat. 3,375,235 (1968), to E. I. du Pont de Nemours & Co., Inc.
40. Y. Sakakibara, "The Synthesis of Methacrylic Esters by Carbonylation of Methyl Acetylene I. Methyl Methacrylate; Reaction Conditions and Products," *Bull. Chem. Soc. Japan* **37** (11), 1601–1609 (1964).
41. S. Kunichika, Y. Sakakibara, and T. Nakamura, "The Synthesis of Methacrylic Esters by Carboxylation Reaction of Methyl Acetylene II. Catalytic Synthesis of Methyl Methacrylate Using Nickel Carbonyl as Catalyst," *Paper 18th Ann. Meet. Chem. Soc. Japan, Osaka, 1965; Bull. Chem. Soc. Japan* **41**, 390 (1968).
42. "Carbonylation of Methylacetylene to Produce Methacrylic Compounds," U.S. Pat. 3,496,221 (1970), J. Happel et al (to National Lead Co.).

J. Happel and D. Walsh
New York University

MICROPLANTS

A newly discovered process or product must be carried through research, development, and into production as rapidly and as economically as possible. Timing is critical. The first company to the market place has a definite competitive advantage, and has the most latitude in establishing a price structure and in working with customers on special product development.

Research and development costs for a new process or a new product must be held to a minimum. They create a negative cash position for the project which must be repaid from future profits. Because of the considerable degree of business risk involved, corporations would prefer not to have a large research and development (R & D) expenditure on any single new process or product.

The largest expense item in the R & D budget is the pilot plant. Total investment in the construction and operation of a pilot plant may run as high as 25% of the cost of the production plant. Pilot plant operating costs average $1,000 per day. While most companies attempt to limit pilot plant operation to less than one year, some pilot plants operate several years, thereby running up sizable costs against the project.

The trend in the past two decades has been to hold R & D budgets in line by obtaining more technology at the bench-scale level and by reducing the scale and lifetime of the pilot plant. Good design information from bench-scale research can lead to less pilot plant operating time. The extreme limit of this trend, the direct scale-up from the bench-scale unit to the commercial plant, is happening with ever increasing frequency. The bench-scale pilot plant, microplant, or mini-plant is the key to controlling R & D costs and to increasing the scale-up factor.

Definition. A microplant is taken to be the smallest possible process system that will produce both representative product for evaluation and accurate data for the design of a production plant. The size of a microplant varies according to what is needed to produce representative product. Reaction vessels may range in size from a 6 in. length of capillary tubing to a 5 gal, stirred reactor. The capillary-sized reactor is used to study the reactions of low-viscosity fluids. The 5 gal, stirred tank is used to study slurry reactions carried out in a high-viscosity liquid.

Modern microplants are fully integrated and contain extensive automation. Integrated microplants are needed to produce representative product and to study systems response. Automation is necessary to ensure safe, reliable operation of complex microplants with a minimum of operating manpower. Automation is also necessary to obtain more and better data cheaper. To this end, at least one company has been grouping automated bench-scale units. See below.

The capital equipment cost for building a complex, automated microplant may run as high as $100,000 but is more likely to average $50,000. Operating costs will average $500 per day. (Compare $1,000 per day, as mentioned above for an old fashioned pilot plant.) Needless to say, all costs will be much lower if the microplant is entirely of glassware and is operated on a single shift.

Construction of Microplants

Housing. Microplants have been described as fully integrated plants that can be assembled and operated in the laboratory. They are constructed and operated indoors. The best data and most reliable operations are obtained when the building is heated, air conditioned, and humidity controlled. Relative humidity is a frequently overlooked process variable. A room height greater than 20 ft is rarely needed to house microplants. And except for safety or security reasons, a number of microplants can be housed in each room.

In a facility designed specifically to house microplants, Unistrut steel supporting racks are used to support the apparatus. The microplant can be disassembled at the end of its useful life and the rack can be used to support equipment for the next new microplant.

Construction. Construction and operation of a microplant are facilitated by the availability of utilities. Utility service lines are permanently attached to the back of the rack and valved at convenient locations. Recommended service lines are cold water, distilled or demineralized water, steam, compressed process air, instrument air hydrogen, high-purity nitrogen, liquid refrigerants, and vacuum.

Microplants are temporary plants at best and should have a maximum of flexibility built in. Equipment should be accessible from all sides so that changes and repairs can be made easily. Tubing, be it glass, copper, or stainless steel, should be fitted to facilitate disconnection. A little extra investment in flexibility during construction will pay big dividends during operation. No attempt should be made to conserve space in the microplant.

General-Purpose Equipment. Most of the equipment that goes into a microplant is of a general-purpose type. The equipment must have a broad enough operating range to handle all foreseeable conditions in the microplant. It will then have enough flexibility to be used in future microplants. A company that uses microplants extensively will build up a stock of versatile, miscellaneous, general purpose equipment such as pumps, flow meters, recorder-controllers, distillation columns, reactors, etc. The actual cash outlay for each microplant then becomes a successively lower percentage of the total cost. However, it takes considerable testing and searching to find high-quality equipment, rugged enough to survive use on successive microplants.

Portions of any new microplant can usually be assembled from equipment on hand. These portions of the microplant can be "debugged" and ready for operation by the time purchased equipment arrives. The time saving from this technique may amount to three to six months. However, the purchase and use of general-purpose equipment can present a real problem. Equipment should be purchased in a versatile material of construction. Pumps, for example, may be of stainless steel or of tantalum; reactors may be glass-lined and provided with powerful agitators. The net result might be that many equipment-related problems are overlooked. There is this natural tendency to overdesign the microplant. While it seldom causes any financial problem on the microscale, the scale-up of an overdesign may be disastrous in a commercial plant. Although overdesign of the microplant may assure better results, lower cost modifications should also be studied at the microplant scale before scale-up.

A decade ago the lack of bench-scale equipment seriously hampered the development of microplants. Many of the items had to be custom fabricated. Replacement parts were difficult to obtain. The whole advantage of microplants was negated by this problem. Today, a wide range of bench-scale equipment is available off-the-shelf for assembly of the microplant. There are dependable, low-volume pumps on the market. There are pneumatic control valves for low-flow ranges. The availability of this equipment has greatly encouraged the use of microplants.

Microplant Operation and Usage

Product Evaluation. The microplant is the smallest scale process system that will produce both a representative product for evaluation and accurate data for the design of a production plant. The product from the microplant must be representative of the product that will be delivered by the commercial plant when it is constructed. Care must be taken in the microplant not to lose product fractions that might drastically alter the character of the product.

The condition of the product must be known when the microplant is producing design data. So, during operation of the microplant, product samples are taken for chemical and physical testing. As test procedures have been improved, smaller and smaller samples have been needed for evaluation. Thus, the minimum size microplant needed to supply test quantities of product has been decreasing. No more than a few microliters of product are needed to characterize a low-molecular-weight sample via gas chromatography. Ten or more grams of a polymer are needed for a satisfactory characterization of a number of physical properties.

The principal disadvantage of a microplant is its inability to supply a product for market studies. It can supply a product to produce demonstration articles or for small laboratory trials, and as potential customers request additional quantities, the microplant can be operated continuously for one or two weeks to supply requests. But beyond these quantities, the microplant cannot meet the demand. However, the microplant might easily provide data early enough to allow the construction of a suitable semiworks operation to supply products for market testing.

Care must be exercised when the microplant is used to supply market-evaluation samples. The microplant is farther, time-wise, from the production plant than is the larger-scale pilot plant. A sample of the product in the hands of a competitor could enlighten him on the raw materials and production process used.

Recycle Streams. Microplants are important for the study of recycle processes. In the operation of a continuous reactor, a portion of the product stream may be split off, treated, and recycled back into the reactor. Or, a solid product may be dried and the recovered liquids recycled back into the process after treatment. These recycled fluids frequently contain contaminants that interfere with the process. The contaminants may be difficult to identify because they may be present in trace quantities and have structures similar to noncontaminants already in the system. The continuous microplant is operated until the contamination level reaches equilibrium. Then the full impact of the contaminant on the reaction can be evaluated.

Competitive Processes. When a newly discovered product is to be brought to full-scale production, the technically strong company will give consideration to a number of possible processes. Economic analysis will eliminate some of these. Preliminary laboratory experiments will eliminate others as unfeasible. Finally, all processes will have been eliminated except for, say, two or three which look equally attractive. Microplants can be constructed to study these two or three competitive processes, and the results will serve as the final basis of selection of the process.

Integrated Microplants. A fully integrated microplant is one that contains all of the steps in the purposed process from raw material treatment to product recovery and packaging. The steps in the microplant operate together in the same relationship as they will in the commercial plant. The research and development of new processes or new products is most conveniently accomplished in a fully integrated microplant and nothing else will serve to study system response.

Sometimes only a partially integrated microplant is used. This may be because a partially integrated microplant contains only those key steps in the process which must be improved or which will give scale-up problems. Partial integration allows the engineer to concentrate his efforts on the problem area. There is no unnecessary equipment upstream or downstream to distract his attention. When the engineer watches the partially integrated microplant in operation, he sees only the problem areas that need to be solved.

Partial integration creates a number of problems for the microplant engineer. More often than not, these problems are of such a magnitude that they must be solved by fully integrating the plant. A source of raw materials may be a serious problem to the partially integrated microplant. A special case is when the raw materials are available from an existing plant. Generally, the raw materials have to be prepared in the quality required. The raw materials may have to have a certain age, temperature, history, or degree of compaction that only a more fully integrated microplant can produce. The microplant must produce representative product for evaluation. If the partially integrated microplant consists of the reaction part of the process and not the finishing end, the chemical engineer is left with the problem of recovering a representative product. He has to improvise a makeshift system to capture a representative product. With a little more effort, he could produce a fully integrated finishing end on the microplant and obtain useful data along with representative product.

Disposal of a product from an integrated microplant is more meaningful. A specification product can be used for testing and evaluation and an off-spec fraction product allows a trial of proposed waste-disposal techniques. On the other hand, a partially integrated microplant may produce a partially finished product that has to be treated further for safety and disposal purposes.

Mathematical Model Simulation. Process simulation via mathematical modeling is a powerful process development tool. Microplant runs can be pretested with the simulation. Only the most productive runs need be made in the microplant. The simulation is unparalleled as a process scale-up tool. It is excellent for explaining and understanding the results of experimental runs. While most of the mathematical model can be devised from theoretical considerations, there are a number of empirical constants that must be evaluated from experimental data. The microplant provides an excellent means of evaluating these constants.

The mathematical models for various steps in the process are worked up in the early research stages. The models of the various steps are then fitted together to match the microplant design. Shortly after the microplant has been debugged and is operable, runs are made to evaluate the empirical constants in the model. Thereafter the model will be used to screen various sets of reaction conditions for microplant runs. Therefore, it is essential that the microplant and mathematical model behave similarly.

Process simulation has given chemical engineers confidence in large scale-up efforts. Scale-up of a process from the bench to a commercial plant is difficult. Only since 1965 have engineers accomplished successful scale-ups by factors as great as 20,000. These scale-ups have been made possible by process simulation. The pilot plant may no longer be necessary for scale-up.

Precise process control can mean the difference between a successful plant and a failure. Process-control systems can be designed with the aid of a process simulation and checked on the microplant. A wide variety of control techniques can be simulated mathematically. Here again the process simulation is an excellent screening tool. Each control system model can be used to control the simulated process. Once the optimum control scheme has been devised, it can be installed on the microplant and be thoroughly tested.

Automation. An integrated microplant is a complex structure. Many microplant operations depend on several other vessels. For example, the conditions within a reaction vessel will depend on feed rate and product take-off. However, the recycle rate and condition may be dependent on the operating conditions in a product separator vessel. In order for the operator to know if any one vessel is performing satisfactorily, he must know simultaneously the condition of several other process vessels. In fact, the best operation of the microplant requires detailed operating data from the entire plant. These data will consist of temperatures, pressures, flows, viscosities, and compositions.

A microplant operator cannot gather data and samples fast enough to prevent time-skew of the data. In the late 1950s and early 1960s, data loggers were used to record the outputs of various sensing devices. While the data loggers performed satisfactorily in this role, they were relatively inflexible and, as such, unsuitable for research and development.

Modern microplants require electronic computers for maximum utilization and flexibility. The microplant is equipped with electronic sensing devices to detect operating conditions. These devices are transducers, thermistors, load cells, strain gages, etc. The on-line digital computer has the capability to convert incoming analog data signals to digital signals. Conversion is almost instantaneous so that time-skew is minimized. Once a set of data signals has been read into the computer, the computer can be used to convert the volt and millivolt signals to usable temperature and pressure data. See also Instrumentation and control.

Most importantly, the computer not only enables the researcher to collect quality data but it also enables him to make the most effective use of the data. The computer can be used to interpret plant performance. Instead of estimating heat transfer from temperature and flow-rate data, the researcher can have the computer calculate and print out the instantaneous heat-transfer coefficient. Product costs can also be calculated from operating conditions. The microplant can be manipulated with a new level of dependent variable.

Mechanical equipment failures are by far the biggest problem associated with consistent successful pilot plant operations. The pilot plant engineer may spend 85% of his time solving equipment problems. In the microplant, increased sophistication of automated equipment has permitted leaving more operations unattended that formerly required special attention to safety precautions and equipment reliability. Simple automation techniques allow 24-hr operation with operator attention only during the daytime. Costs are reduced without affecting either flexibility of operation or the high quality of data produced.

Bibliography

C. D. Akerman, "Grouping Automated Units," *Chem. Eng. Progr.* **61** (1), 67–69 (June 1965).

"How to Beat the High Cost of Pilot Planting," *Chem. Week* 43–56 (June 7, 1958).

Anon., "Micropiloting" *I&EC* **57** (4), 61–63 (April 1965).

Anon., "Full-Blown Pilots Yielding to Microunits," *Chem. Eng. News* **43** 52–53 (December 18, 1967).

Anon., "Goodrich Opens Ohio Micropilot Plant," *Chem. Eng. News* **44** (November 25, 1968).

F. A. Biribauer et al. "Bench Scale Continuous Distillation Techniques," *Ind. Eng. Chem.* **49** 1673–1678 (October 1957).

E. L. Clark, "Economic Pros and Cons of Pilot Plants," *Chem. Eng.* **71,** 169–184 (April 13, 1964).

E. L. Clark, "How to Scale Up Pilot Plant Data and Equipment," *Chem. Eng.* **65,** 129–140 (October 6, 1958).

C. E. Ellis, "Unattended Pilot Plants," *Chem. Eng. Progr.* **64** (10), 50–53 (October 1968).

R. Fleming, "Making the Most of Bench-Scale Experimentation in Process Development," *I&EC* **51,** 48A–52A (November 1959).

E. G. Fochtman, "On the Subject of Pilot Plants," *Frontier* **29** (1) (Summer 1968).

D. E. Garrett, "Bench Scale Pilot Plant," *Chem. Eng. Progr.* **55** (9), 44–48 (September 1959).

M. O. Gernand, "Streamlined Data Gathering Systems," *Chem. Eng. Progr.* **61** (6), 62–66, 84–87 (June 1965).

L. C. Hardison and R. A. Lengemann, "Automate Your Pilot Plants," *Chem. Eng.* **71,** 129–132 (June 22, 1964).

D. P. Harrison et al, "An Automatic Precision Microreactor," *Ind. Eng. Chem.* **57,** 18–25 (January 1965).

E. J. Herbster and J. J. Nedwick, "A High Pressure Experimental Unit," *Chem. Eng. Progr.* **61** (6) 70–74 (June 1965).

W. M. Herring and S. E. Shields, "Development, The Automated Way," *Chem. Eng. Progr.* **61** (6), 94–98 (June 1965).

P. J. Horvath, "Case History of a Micropilot Plant," *Chem. Eng. Progr.* **61** (6), 88–93 (June 1965).

D. Hyman and W. B. Corson, "Computer Assisted Data Processing Cuts Costs," *Chem. Eng. Progr.* **61** (6), 99–102 (June 1965).

R. Katzen, "When is the Pilot Plant Necessary?," *Chem. Eng.* **75,** 95–98 (March 25, 1968).

P. Knapp, "Effective Techniques for a Multi-Product Pilot Plant," *Ind. Eng. Chem.* **54** (2), 58–61 (February 1962).

W. M. Miller, "Automatic Weight Balances," *Chem. Eng. Progr.* **61** (6), 75–79 (June 1965).

W. E. Morrow et al, "Scale Up by Advanced Methods," *Chem. Eng. Progr.* **61** (6), 57–61 (June 1965).

K. A. Muller et al, "Specialized Pilot Plant Equipment," *Chem. Eng. Progr.* **59** (6), 33–37 (June 1963).

C. H. Stockman and R. E. Lynn, "Equipment for Miniature Pilot Plants," *Ind. Eng. Chem.* **50,** 585–590 (April 1958).

ARTHUR T. SCHOOLEY
The B. F. Goodrich Co.

MICROWAVES

During the past 50 yr we have become accustomed to using electrical devices fed from dc or ac power supplies, usually with frequencies of 50–60 cps. However, these frequencies are not necessarily the most effective for applications of electrical power. It has long been known that energy elsewhere in the electromagnetic spectrum would be much more effective in certain applications. This article discusses the microwave region of the energy spectrum. It presents methods for utilizing microwave energy and applications that give it characteristics uniquely suited to numerous industrial processes.

Microwaves have been used for communications and military purposes (eg radar) for several decades. Early development of industrial applications began about 15 yr ago. Laboratory experiments using microwave frequencies were reported as long ago as 1912. Early work on the principles of radar and on the electromagnetic properties of materials form a solid base for today's microwave technology. It is only since the late 1960s, however, as high-power microwave sources have become available at reasonable cost, that there have been extensive industrial applications.

Some possible reasons for selecting microwave energy over more conventional sources include the following: uniform heating occurs throughout the material; process speed is increased; desirable physical and chemical effects are produced; chemical reactions are promoted by heat from microwaves; the energy source is not hot; floor space requirements are decreased; better and more rapid process control is achieved; the finished product quality is improved, often resulting in fewer rejects; and in certain cases selective heating occurs which may significantly increase efficiency and decrease operating cost.

Careful consideration must be given to the economic aspects of a microwave installation, because microwave energy is expensive compared with conventional heating methods. A complete economic evaluation including advantages resulting from the use of microwave energy is normally required to justify the capital investment in microwave equipment.

Only recently have techniques and equipment become sufficiently well developed to stimulate private investment in development of practical microwave applications. At present, requirements for industrial processes using microwaves are being established, and research and development on industrial microwave equipment is being actively pursued. Although much remains to be accomplished in adapting laboratory equipment to production hardware, technology has advanced to the stage at which more and more companies are investing in research to gain the benefits of microwave energy at an early date. The remaining tasks in realizing the economic potential of microwave energy are those of development of specific processes and microwave applicators for specific industries.

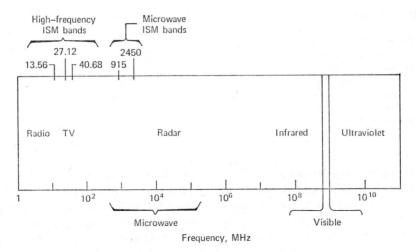

Fig. 1. The electromagnetic spectrum.

Frequency. The microwave region of the electromagnetic spectrum comprises frequencies ranging from about 300 MHz to 300 GHz (giga = 10^9), or a part of the electromagnetic spectrum between radio broadcasting and the visible region (see Fig. 1). The Federal Communications Commission, recognizing that electromagnetic radiation in the microwave region would be of importance in industrial applications, set aside certain frequencies designated as the industrial, scientific, and medical (ISM) bands (1). International agreements have been reached regarding ISM bands, but not all countries conform fully (2). Of particular interest for microwave applications are the ISM frequencies at 915 and 2450 MHz, as shown in Figure 1. These ISM frequencies in the microwave region are of interest today because large power tubes for converting dc to microwave energy have recently become available and have made practical applications possible at these frequencies. ISM bands at 5800 and 22125 MHz in the microwave region have also been allocated, but for these inexpensive high-power sources are not yet available. The current use for 5800 and 22125 MHz bands is in microwave instrumentation. The wavelength at 2450 MHz bands is about 12 cm, whereas 60 Hz household ac has a wavelength of 3000 miles. Other ISM bands also exist in the high-frequency range at 13.56 MHz (22 m), 27.12 MHz (11 m), and 40.68 MHz (7.4 m).

Microwave Power Sources

One of the most important elements of any microwave system is the source of energy. Although it is not possible to produce microwave energy directly from thermal or hydroelectric energy sources, many devices exist that convert dc to microwave frequencies. There are four basic types of devices: power-grid tubes, linear-beam tubes (such as traveling-wave tubes and klystrons), cross-field devices (such as magnetrons and amplitrons), and semiconductors. Linear-beam tubes and cross-field devices have been used most extensively in industrial applications at the ISM bands of 915 and 2450 MHz. Although progress is being made in the development of microwave semiconductors, it is not expected that they will be competitive in price with vacuum tubes in the immediate future (3).

In general, the range of tubes for industrial uses is as follows: At 2450 MHz, magnetrons have been used almost exclusively for power levels up to 5 kW, whereas at 30-

kW power levels, klystrons have been used exclusively. At 915 MHz, magnetrons operating at 30 and 50 kW have been used extensively.

Some examples of currently available large power tubes are shown in Table 1. Within today's technology, industrial klystron power tubes can operate at continuous power levels of up to 500 kW, some with efficiency in excess of 65%. The largest commercially available industrial microwave tubes are 500-kW klystrons. Over the past 10 yr, the average power generated by a single microwave tube has increased at least an order of magnitude. Tube life in some operating systems now exceeds 20,000 hr, and it is possible to buy small high-production 1-kW tubes for as little as $100. Tube costs can be expected to drop significantly in the next ten years in dollars per kilowatt as large tubes, such as the 250- and 500-kW klystrons, also come into higher production. Tube life is continuing to increase and should ultimately reach the point at which it is no longer a significant factor in the cost of operating a system. Continuing demand for increased power capacity will require the development of larger tubes. It appears that it will ultimately be feasible to build klystrons or hybrid devices that operate in the 1–3 GHz range at power levels approaching 10 MW (3).

Table 1. Large Industrial Microwave Power Tubes

Manufacturer	Average power, kW	Frequency, MHz	Tube type
Varian Associates	500	2450	klystron
Raytheon Co.	400	2450	amplitron
Varian Associates	250	2450	klystron
Varian Associates	100	2450	klystron
Raytheon Co.	50	915	magnetron
Varian Associates	30	2450	klystron
Varian Associates	30	915	magnetron
Associated Electrical Industries	30	915	magnetron
Philips	5	2450	magnetron
American Microwave Litton, Philips	2½	2450	magnetron

Since most microwave tubes have a finite life shorter than that of the other major components, initial tube cost per kWh and the mean time between failures have a definite effect on the operating cost of a system. Based on current costs, a microwave system using 30-kW tubes with a mean time between failure of 10,000 hours has a tube replacement cost of 1¢/kWh. A 30-kW system based on klystron tubes operates with an overall conversion efficiency of 50% from ac to microwave frequency. One can usually assume 80% or better coupling efficiency to the product. At 5 mill/kWh for ac power, the result is an overall operating cost of 2.25 cents/kWh of microwave power delivered to the product. As tube efficiency and life continue to increase, operating costs can be expected to decrease.

Microwave Power Transmission

Before considering the advantages of microwave power for industrial processes, we shall first examine the transmission of microwaves from the generator to the product.

Microwave energy is usually transmitted to an applicator through a waveguide or hollow pipe. In a waveguide, microwave currents exist within the first few thousandths of an inch depth of the inside surface. Waveguides may be either rectangular or circular and are made entirely of conductive material, such as aluminum or copper; or a nonconductive material with a thin conductive coating on its inner surface. The energy is fully contained within the waveguide, which operates at ground potential. Since there are no external currents on the waveguide, high power can be safely transmitted over long distances, either above or underground. A typical 2 × 4 in. rectangular waveguide for 2450 MHz is capable of carrying several megawatts of power. A 10 ft diameter waveguide can transmit power levels of up to 30,000 MW safely and economically (4).

Another means for microwave-power transmission is the coaxial cable. This has the advantage that the inner and outer conductors can be made flexible. Such flexible coaxial cables can handle over 1 kW at 915 MHz, but are severely limited in power handling ability at higher frequencies. Coaxial transmission lines are usually limited in application to lower frequencies and/or power and are used in low-power microwave instrumentation.

Microwave energy can be transmitted through a vacuum or dielectric material by use of a highly directive radiating antenna, such as a parabolic reflector. The energy transferred in this manner can be applied to a product, or used for communications, or converted to another form of energy, such as a direct current. Indeed, a small helicopter has been powered aloft in this manner (5).

Microwave Systems

Principles of Microwave Heating. Dielectrics can be divided into two groups, polar or nonpolar. A polar dielectric is one in which the molecule has an intrinsic dipole moment, whereas a nonpolar dielectric has not.

When an electric field is applied to a nonpolar dielectric it becomes polarized as a result of the dipole induced within the molecule by the relative movement of the electrons and the nucleus. Because this process has a very small interaction with the surrounding lattice there is very little loss associated with an alternating electric field. In other words, the absorption of microwave power is very small.

In polar substances, where each molecule possesses a dipole, the material becomes polarized by the potential rotation of each molecule so that it is aligned in the direction of the applied electric field. Because this involves a mechanical rotation of the complete molecule there is a strong coupling to the lattice. In general, this coupling causes the material to have a high dielectric constant ϵ' and a high loss factor ϵ'', and makes its dielectric properties depend on frequency and temperature. The variation of the complex dielectric constant ϵ with frequency can often be expressed in terms of a single relaxation time according to the formula:

$$\epsilon = \epsilon' - j\epsilon'' = \epsilon_p + \frac{\epsilon_s - \epsilon_p}{1 + j\omega\tau}$$

where $\epsilon_p = \epsilon$ for $\omega = \infty$, $\epsilon_s = \epsilon$ for $\omega = 0$, ω is the frequency in radians per second, τ is the relaxation time in seconds, and j is the square root of minus one (6). The parameter τ can vary over several orders of magnitude with temperature and composition and its value in any particular application will often control whether or not microwaves are useful in that application.

The advantage of microwave heating derives mainly from this direct interaction of a varying electric field with the material being heated. There is no heat per se in the microwave radiation. The radiation is converted into heat in the material itself and throughout its whole bulk. When microwave energy is used for the evaporation of polar solvents the conversion into heat takes place in direct proportion to the amount of solvent present. The rate of conversion of microwave energy to heat is given by:

$$P = 2.78 \times 10^{-11} fE^2 V_s \epsilon''$$

where P is in W, f is frequency in Hz, E is the electric field in V/m, V_s is the volume in m³ and ϵ'' is the dielectric loss factor (7).

As the radiation penetrates into a body being heated it is attenuated because of the heating effect that takes place. The depth D at which the electric field is attenuated to $1/e$ of its initial value is given by:

$$D = \lambda \sqrt{\epsilon'} / \pi \epsilon''$$

where λ is the free-space wavelength of the radiation (7).

Under certain circumstances it is possible to use microwaves for selectively heating one component of a mixture. For example, when a mixture of sand and water is subjected to microwave radiation, most of the energy will be dissipated in the water because it is polar and has a high dielectric loss factor, whereas very little will be dissipated in the nonpolar nonconducting sand.

One of the most important design factors in a microwave system is correct matching of the microwave energy with the product being heated. This procedure is similar in concept to the coating of lenses to increase their transmission. In the microwave case it is desirable to effect an optimum transfer of energy into the product, even though it may have a very high dielectric constant and would therefore normally reflect the greater part of the radiation. This matching can be achieved by techniques that will be discussed in the following section.

Microwave Applicators. Once microwave energy has been generated and is transmitted to the product, it must be applied efficiently and in a manner that will create the desired result. The device which applies microwave energy to the product is called an applicator.

These are some of the basic applicator types: (1) traveling wave; (2) resonant—multimode; (3) resonant—single mode; (4) slow wave; and (5) radiative. The choice of applicator type and geometry is determined by the geometry and microwave properties of the product.

In general, resonant structures will be needed where the loss factor of the product is relatively low. Traveling-wave structures are normally used where the microwave loss factor is intermediate or high. The slow-wave structure is usually applied in the low or intermediate loss range. The radiative type is used primarily for in-situ applications. Examples of various types of applicators are discussed below.

Applicators for Bulk Materials. A bulk material product is one whose dimensions are large compared with the length of microwave. In general, the applicator will be of the resonant-multimode type. That is, the resonator must be large to accommodate the product and thus will have many possible resonant modes. Usually a device resembling a rotating fan, called a "mode stirrer" is installed within the resonant cavity. Its purpose is to excite all of the possible modes equally on the time average. As the number of possible modes is very large, the time average field will be nearly uniform within the cavity.

The uniformity of the "stirred" fields will decrease with the size of the cavity (number of possible modes). However, the field intensity will increase with diminishing cavity dimensions, ultimately allowing only a single mode to exist. This, then is a single-mode resonant applicator where the field distribution is uniquely defined by the particular geometry of the applicator.

Two types of multimode bulk applicator are in general use, the batch and the conveyor types. A typical example of the batch type is the microwave oven used in home and institutional cooking. The conveyorized cavity is used for continuous processes, eg cooking, drying, and curing and presents the problem of microwave radiation from the entrance and exit. Microwave-absorbing water-filled "end traps" are often used to overcome this.

Applicators for Sheet Materials. Sheet materials, such as paper, textile, and plastics, can be treated with microwaves. The applicators are generally of the traveling-wave or slow-wave type. The simplest sheet applicator is a conventional waveguide with a slot cut in the center of each of the two broad walls. For narrow slots, this structure does not radiate appreciably.

Such slotted waveguides can be disposed transverse or parallel to the direction of motion of the sheet. If the transverse orientation is used and the end of the one guide is connected with the adjacent one on alternating sides, the applicator is commonly called a meander-line. In this case, the energy is introduced into the guide at one end of the applicator and passes in alternative directions through the waveguides containing the sheet, with the remaining energy being dissipated in a load at the opposite end of the applicator. Enough waveguide passes must be provided to ensure that most of the energy is dissipated in the sheet and that the effect of the decaying excitation in each pass adds up so that the total energy absorbed by the sheet is essentially uniform across its width.

Similar slotted waveguides can be disposed along the sheet, close together with the applicator tilted a few degrees from the direction of motion. Uniform application of energy can be achieved in this way when the guides are equally excited. Where the longitudinal extension of the slotted guides required to achieve essentially complete absorption of energy in the sheet is too long to be practical, a slow-wave structure can be employed. A slow-wave structure can take the form of a similar slotted guide with bars or plates equally spaced along its length. Ten or more times the alternation per unit length can be obtained from an appropriately designed system of this type.

Applicators for Liquids. One effective way of transmitting microwave energy into a liquid is by passing the liquid through a tube which crosses the waveguide at a narrow angle. The gradual transition into the liquid gives a transfer of energy with comparatively little reflection (8). Another useful method is to pass the liquid through a box at the end of a waveguide and match it using a quarter-wave transformer (9,10). These methods of matching do not give a very uniform distribution of heat across the containing tube, but in general this is not important as turbulence in flow effectively mixes the liquid. In addition, the flow of the liquid ensures that it passes through several different parts of the electric field, thereby producing a further averaging effect.

Applicators for Fibers and Extrusions. In this case the uniformity of the electric field is more important as there is no mixing effect to average out the heating. The most suitable applicators are waveguides operating in modes in which the electric field is longitudinally along the axis (11,12). Matching can be achieved either with a traveling-wave structure or with a resonant structure. The choice depends on whether the material has a high or low loss.

In order to increase the power dissipation in the case of low-loss dielectrics the most effective method is to use a resonant structure. We saw earlier that the power dissipation increases with increased electric field. A resonant structure will produce this increase in the electric field. A resonant cavity can be regarded as a transmission line with multiple reflections rather similar to a laser structure. Like the laser, a resonant cavity requires a partially reflecting barrier to contain the reflections but to allow the continual introduction of power from the generator. The biggest drawback to a cavity is that it is usually very sensitive to frequency. It then becomes a problem to make sure that the cavity and the tube are on the same frequency. There are several ways of surmounting this problem:

1. Special microwave elements can be designed to make sure that the oscillator follows the frequency of the cavity.

2. The cavity can be made a part of the oscillator circuit so that the cavity itself is the controlling element in the oscillator circuit.

3. Tuning elements can be introduced into the cavity so that the cavity may be continually tuned to correspond with the oscillation frequency of the generator.

4. The cavity can be broadbanded. This is achieved by making it possible for the cavity to resonate in a large number of modes, so that there is always one that corresponds with the frequency of the magnetron (multimode cavity). This effect is augmented by the use of mechanical mode stirrers in the cavity that cause a rapidly changing resonance pattern and also by the fact that most generators for heating usually oscillate over a band of frequencies rather than at a fixed frequency.

Applicators for Coated Cables. The considerations here are similar to those for fibers and extrusions, except that the presence of the metallic conductor introduces certain complications. A suitable applicator has to be designed so that the wire becomes a part of the transmission line. This is usually a coaxial cable. In this case heating also takes place by conduction losses in the metal wire, as well as by absorption by the dielectric.

Applicators for Plasma Generation. A plasma, or ionized gas induced by electrical discharge by microwaves or other energy, may have a wide range of characteristics depending upon gas pressure, flow rate, power input, excitation frequency, and geometry.

In general, the microwave electric-field vector should be parallel to the longest dimensions of the discharge vessel and the vessel should be as large as the applicator geometry will permit. This will reduce wall heating and electron, ion, and free-radical losses, thereby raising the efficiency of the process (13).

The microwave applicator is generally of the single-mode resonant type with adjustments for Q (coupling) and frequency (tuning). The adjustments enable a variety of plasma conditions to be easily ignited and maintained efficiently without unnecessary waste of microwave power (14). Multimode plasma applicators do not allow these critical adjustments. Indeed, they are often unstable, jumping from one mode to the next in a rapid and unpredictable manner.

Being normally restricted to single-mode resonant applicators, one, and usually two dimensions of the discharge vessel are limited by the excitation frequency, ie the dimensions are limited to a fraction of the excitation wavelength. These limits, at the common ISM frequencies, are approximately 1.5 in. at 2.45 GHz and 4 in. at 0.915 GHz. Higher-order single-mode applicators can somewhat alleviate these restrictions in specialized applications.

Discharges in the pressure range of 0.5–50 torr are easiest to initiate and maintain. At lower and higher pressures, special techniques are usually required, eg discharges at a pressure approaching one atmosphere are normally unstable and difficult to ignite. The introduction of a primary or secondary electron emitter, such as a small piece of ceramic maintained at 700–1500°C, will stabilize the plasma and ease the ignition problem.

Most plasma-chemistry work has been carried out using a continuous flow of gas, ie gas or gases are continuously entering and leaving the discharge. The entering gas(es) may be the reactant(s) while the exiting gas(es) (or solid(s)) may be the reaction products or free radicals to be reacted further downstream (13,15).

It has been shown (16) that the use of pulsed microwave power can greatly enhance the electrical efficiency (energy for dissociation divided by electrical energy consumed) of nitrogen-atom production in a microwave discharge. It can be inferred from this that substantially increased efficiencies in production of other atomic and free-radical species may be possible using pulsed microwave power. Indeed, an efficiency increase of nearly 20:1 has been observed in this work.

Instrumentation

Power Measurement. There are two basic methods of measuring microwave power. One is by calorimetric means, the other by rectification (17).

Calorimetric. This is a fundamental method of measuring power. Microwave power can be dissipated in a load and the rate of heat dissipation can be measured and is equal to the microwave power that is incident upon the load. Precautions must be taken to ensure that microwave power is not reflected from the load (ie the load is well matched) and that heat is not lost to the surroundings. This method for measuring high power is very time consuming but is absolute and can be made very accurate. It is normally used for the calibration of other measuring instruments.

There are also calorimetric methods of measuring low power. These are thermistor power meters and thermocouple power meters. They operate on the principle that power dissipated in a load will raise the temperature of that load. In a thermistor power meter the resistance of the thermistor will change as the result of this temperature increase and by measuring this change in resistance one can indirectly measure the power incident on the load. Modern thermistor power meters have several sophisticated circuits which enable this resistance change to be related accurately to an absolute-power level, and also that compensate for ambient changes in temperature. Thermocouple power meters also work by measuring the temperature increase caused by the dissipation of microwave power. In this case the temperature increase is measured by a thermocouple junction (in practice a very large number of thermocouple junctions connected in series to obtain a high output signal). The output voltage from the thermocouple junctions is directly proportional to the input microwave power and can be measured on a voltmeter. Thermocouple-junction power meters are usually slightly more expensive than thermistor power meters but the calibration of the thermocouple meter is usually more direct and because it gives a voltage output which is linearly connected with power it is especially useful in automated systems.

Detection. The method of power detection uses crystal diodes to rectify the microwave signal and relates the dc output to the power in the microwave signal. Diode detectors are simple and inexpensive but they have three major disadvantages. First, they are very sensitive to temperature and in most industrial applications precautions must be taken to maintain their temperature constant within a few degrees. Secondly, they depend critically on the modulation waveform of the microwave power. Since for most industrial applications no effort is made to maintain a pure continuous-wave (CW) signal, this can be a major problem. The detectors must be calibrated for the particular application in which they will be used so that allowance is made for the particular waveform in that application. Thirdly, the output from the detectors is nonlinear. In most cases each crystal must be individually calibrated whenever it is replaced.

Power Sampling Techniques. The crystals and power meters mentioned above are usually low power measuring tools. So that they can be used for measuring high power various sampling techniques are used. Specialized microwave components are made that will sample the power flowing down a waveguide and these devices can usually distinguish between the two possible directions of travel. In this way readings can be taken of the power that is transmitted to an applicator and the power that is reflected back from it.

The design of these components is a specialized task and the details are available in books on microwave techniques.

Frequency Measurement. *Wave Meters.* The most common method of measuring microwave frequencies is by the use of a wave meter (17). This is a resonant cavity that can be tuned over a band of frequencies, usually by some mechanical adjustment. The position of this adjustment can be calibrated against frequency. The wave meter is used in conjunction with a power-measuring device. The wave meter is tuned until a maximum absorption of power takes place and the resonant frequency of the cavity is measured, using the calibration. This should correspond to the frequency of the microwave radiation. This type of wave meter has the advantage that it is inexpensive and fairly simple to use. It is, however, not adaptable to any form of automatic measurement.

Counters. At present sophisticated electronic counters are available that effectively measure frequency by counting the number of cycles in a fixed period of time. The count is usually related to a crystal oscillator which is very stable and accurate. If necessary, the crystal frequency can be related to standard-frequency broadcasts, or even to ammonia maser time standards. These counters are usually very expensive, but their extreme accuracy, and the fact that they often have digital outputs compatible with computer control systems can be of overriding importance (17).

Measurement of Microwave Properties of Materials. In order to evaluate any microwave induced or augmented process, a detailed knowledge of the microwave properties of the treated materials is required. Information on the static dielectric properties of many materials (ϵ' and ϵ'') is available (17,18). However, new processes will often be dealing with new materials or mixtures with chemical changes on a dynamic basis. Thus means are required for obtaining not only static data, but also dynamic data on material subjected to a microwave field.

Static data may be obtained in several ways. One of the easiest of these is the use of perturbation technique in a resonant cavity of known field distribution. Here, a sample of material is inserted into the cavity. The change in resonant frequency and bandwidth of the resonance are measured to obtain ϵ' and ϵ'', respectively.

Almost no literature exists on dynamic measurements. One method which has been employed is the use of a fast responding (millisecond) scale and an optical pyrometer to examine a small sample (50–500 mg) when exposed to high-power microwave energy. The energy can be modulated or pulsed to simulate statically many applicator configurations. From the information so gained, an optimum applicator design can be made.

Measurements Employing Microwaves. As mentioned above, microwaves can be used for measuring such parameters as moisture content. This usually relies on the increase in electric loss that results from an increase in water content. The change in loss can be measured by a waveguide system or by a transmit-and-receive antenna (18).

Effective radiation temperature can also be measured by microwave means, similar in principle to the use of pyrometers for measuring the temperature of a furnace. Because the frequencies are much lower than those of infrared, and because the temperatures are lower, techniques similar to those used in radio astronomy are used. Such radiometers have been used for aerial survey and can give useful information about geological formations.

Applications of Microwave Energy

This section deals with the physical and chemical effects of microwaves on matter. It includes an exhaustive search of *Chemical Abstracts* up to 1969, with emphasis on significant references to the following subject areas:

1. Physical and chemical effects produced by microwave irradiation (excluding microwave plasmas).
2. Use of nonplasma microwave energy to promote chemical reactions.
3. Industrial applications of microwaves.

The literature on the application of microwave energy to organic and inorganic materials is extremely large; however, the vast majority of studies relate to the measurement of microwave spectra of organic molecules to determine structural parameters. Several thousand references to this subject occur in the literature, but this topic falls outside the scope of the present survey. There are also many references to the treatment of biological materials, particularly foods and forest products, and accounts of these subjects will be found elsewhere in this article.

Microwave energy possesses two distinct advantages over conventional methods of applying heat to chemical systems:

1. It heats uniformly throughout the system, as opposed to surface and conventional heating processes.
2. Microwave energy bulk-heats much faster to temperatures at which chemical reactions can occur.

Microwave heating possesses the following disadvantages:

1. It is much more expensive than conventional heat derived directly from fossil fuels or from electricity.
2. It is occasionally difficult to control input (eg a chemical mixture irradiated with microwaves may be overheated beyond the temperature at which it would nor-

mally start to react, thus resulting in an uncontrollable, almost explosive, reaction). This will occur when the loss factor has a positive temperature coefficient.

In circumstances in which differential heating is desired (eg in a mixture of unreactive, nonlossy matter which is to be bonded with a lossy polymer), microwaves are distinctly superior to conventional heating processes.

From the standpoint of practical use, microwaves will only heat matter that is lossy (ie microwave-absorptive). Monomer and polymer systems, for example, are not usually very lossy as they are fairly nonpolar or very poor conductors. They can be made so by mechanically mixing them with lossy, nonchemically reactive, nonpolymeric polar additives (eg water, alcohols, ketones, amides, etc).

General information has appeared on the application of microwaves in the nondestructive testing of materials (68–70). A useful book specially devoted to carrying out microwave measurements has also appeared (71).

WATER

As early as 1912 radio waves were employed in the detection and location of sheets of underground water. Sending and receiving instruments were placed in mineshafts 800 m deep, and 1200 m apart. By varying the wavelengths of the signals between 200 and 700 m, the interference minima (due to reflection of the waves from the overlying layer of ground water) were found (19).

The influence of temperature on the absorption of 3.15 cm microwaves by water of crystallization and adsorbed water has been studied (20). Adsorbed water retains its liquid character at temperatures as low as $-90°C$. To a first approximation, at room temperature, liquid water absorbs centimeter microwaves, and ice below $0°C$ absorbs kilometer waves. Microwaves are easily absorbed by free water at room temperature, but not readily below $0°C$. Water of crystallization does not significantly absorb microwave energy at any temperature (with the possible exception of the alums). It is significant, however, that adsorbed water absorbs microwave energy well, both above and below $0°C$. For example, water adsorbed on silica gel absorbs best at $-37°C$ and $-97°C$ (21% adsorbed H_2O). Similar behavior is observed in water adsorbed on starch. Water adsorbed on silica gel or alumina strongly absorbs 3.14 cm microwaves, and shows a steady desorption temperature curve as the temperature is raised through $0°C$ (21).

Since most systems to be heated by microwave absorption are heterogeneous, the dielectric properties of heterogeneous mixtures are of considerable importance, and especially the properties of mixtures containing water in either the "free" or "bound" (ie adsorbed) state. Measurements in the microwave region on agar agar and potato starch have shown that conductivity losses and losses due to the dipolar relaxation of water are important (22). The losses determine the amount of heat absorbed by the system. Together with the dielectric constant they determine the penetration depths (ie the depth in the material at which the microwave energy is attenuated to $1/e \sim 37\%$). Thus, when using microwaves in practical situations, an optimum frequency range must be found, which varies for different materials and/or applications.

The two methods of utilizing microwave energy are by direct resonance absorption, and by formation of plasmas (23). This section deals with the nonplasma aspects of microwaves. The water content of nonmetallic solids, liquids, and gases has been successfully monitored using microwaves. An approximately linear relationship exists between the water content and the attenuation of 2.8, 10.0, and 12.23 cm microwaves passing through concrete, bricks, coal, cereals, grains, etc (24). Microwave equipment has been developed for the continuous measurement of the moisture content of moving solids (eg on a conveyor belt) (25). A moisture-meter, using operating wavelengths of 1, 3, and 12 cm microwaves, has been developed and employed to determine the water content of plastic foams, asbestos, and cement (26). The use of centimeter-range microwaves lowers the error in measurement associated with the presence of salts in the moisture. A device for the continuous measurement of the moisture content of paper has recently been described (27). This consists of a microwave generator and deflector on one side, and a reflecting plate on the other side of the paper. The intensity of the reflected microwaves is inversely proportional to the moisture present. Microwave moisture meters are now employed to monitor the water content of "green" (ie unfired) ceramic ware (28,29,30). In general, the attenuator readings are proportional to the moisture content of a ceramic material at a given thickness, and to the thickness at a given moisture content. Ceramic ware with too high a water content can disintegrate during firing, and it has been past practice to place the ware in a drying chamber for a time longer than the minimum required to ensure an acceptable moisture content. The use of the microwave meter now allows continuous monitoring to be carried out on the ceramic ware, and indicates when it can be fired safely.

The amount of adsorbed and "free" water in hydrophilic fibers has also been studied using 3 cm microwaves (31). The amount of adsorbed water in Acrilan (Chemstrand Corporation) acrylic fiber, for example, was thus found to be approximately 1.5%. Two microwave cavities, one a reference, have been used to determine the amount of moisture in gases (32). Differences in the resonant frequency of the cavities (volume, 1.4–65 ml) were measured by a microwave detector. Water vapor (0–2%) in nitrogen could thus be determined with an accuracy better than 2%.

INORGANIC MATERIALS

If sufficient microwave energy is absorbed by an inorganic (or organic) material to raise its temperature to the point at which chemical bonds would normally be broken by conventional heat, then chemical reactions can occur according to the well-known laws of thermodynamics. Otherwise, the absorption of microwave energy does not result in the fission of chemical bonds, and chemical reactions do *not* occur. Physical changes of state can occur when inorganic or organic materials are irradiated with microwaves (eg crystallization, denaturation, flocculation, etc.).

The quasi-chemical action of microwaves was demonstrated as long ago as 1934 by Arkad'ev (33), who randomly placed pellets of copper and zinc on a filter paper moistened with phenolphthalein solution. Irradiation of the paper produced magenta-red spots under each copper pellet, due to the voltaic action induced by the microwaves. Irradiation with 4, 8, and 15 m microwaves increases the catalytic activity of colloidal copper toward hydrogen peroxide, the shorter wavelengths being the most effective (34). No specific change was observed on treating metallic colloids with 3.5 m microwaves; however, proteins were irreversibly denatured by the heat produced in the system (35).

Studies have recently been made on the microwave absorption characteristics of glasses (36). The absorption coefficients of glasses were measured using 0.5–2.0 mm microwaves emitted by a monochromatic source. A monotonic increase of the absorption coefficient with decreasing wavelength was observed. The absorption coefficients and refractive indexes with respect to 2 mm microwaves have also been measured for sodium chloride, cesium iodide, fused quartz, glass, polymethylmethacrylate, and polytetrafluoroethylene (37).

A novel application of microwaves to determine the rate of formation and composition of aluminum complexes has recently been described (38). The stoichiometric composition and kinetics of formation of donor-acceptor complexes in nonpolar solvents (usually hydrocarbons) have been investigated by following the changes in the transmittance curve of a microwave cavity in which the titration is carried out. The exact stoichiometry of each of several aluminum halide complexes with ethers and isopropyl alcohol was determined using this method. Titration curves were characterized by abrupt breaks which enabled accurate equivalence points (and therefore stoichiometry) to be obtained. The method has also been employed to study fast reactions, such as that which occurs between diethylzinc and an alcohol, and the isomerization of n-propyl bromide to isopropyl bromide, by studying their aluminum bromide adducts. This technique is of particular importance in organometallic and inorganic complex chemistry in nonpolar or slightly polar solvents (39,40).

ORGANIC MATERIALS

As early as 1933, de Pereira Forjaz (41) irradiated a 1:1 mixture of ethyl alcohol and acetic acid (containing water) with 1.256 m microwaves for several days at 25°C, and showed that the rate of ethyl acetate formation was increased over that for mixtures which had not been irradiated. A maximum increase over the normal amount of esterification was observed after two days' irradiation; thereafter the difference decreased. After two days' irradiation with microwaves (1.256 m), the acidity of olive oil was decreased 37.5%, of wine, 15.71%, and of vinegar, 5%.

The concentration of certain components in organic liquids has been measured by placing the mixture in a microwave cavity exposed to a vibration source of constant frequency (42). The intensity of the energy transmitted, reflected, or absorbed is measured as a resonance curve and then compared with calibration data for each of the components. In general, each component makes a linear contribution toward the resulting signal. By this method the concentration of cyclohexane in benzene, or of organic compounds with permanent dipoles, or of catalysts in monomer–polymer mixtures can be determined, or regulated.

Among numerous references illustrating the use of microwaves to produce physical, rather than chemical, effects on organic materials may be mentioned the microwave-induced crystallization of sucrose. Susich et al. (43), using a 100-watt generator producing microwaves of wavelength 12.5 cm, irradiated supersaturated solutions of sucrose-containing gelatin, in which crystallization is normally inhibited, and caused crystallization of radially arranged sucrose spherulites.

Microwave treatment of wheats of high amylase activity improved the pasting properties of the flours (44); however, flours in which the amylase had been inactivated by microwaves could no longer form gluten, and their water-absorption characteristics were considerably greater than those of the original flours. Severe microwave treatment of carbohydrates in flours resulted in products that gave extremely viscous pastes of little practical value.

Among other biochemical effects of microwaves their ability to denature ovalbumin (45) and hydrolyze serum proteins may be mentioned. The values obtained for polypeptide nitrogen in deproteinized human and horse blood serum agree within $\pm 1.5\%$. Thus, by using microwaves, the determination of α amino and polypeptide nitrogen in samples in clinical laboratories can be made in a single day (46).

Microwaves have found application in the technology of textile dyeing. For example, textiles treated with a reactive dye, containing a N-(4-halo(or hydroxy, mercapto, alkyl, or aryl)-6-halo-s-triazin-2-yl)-N-alkylamino group, and irradiated in a microwave field, give fabrics in which the dyes are satisfactorily bonded (47).

That organic matter may be disintegrated by the action of microwaves of wavelength 100 cm and above, depending on the density of the material, was recognized several decades ago. Indeed, a Swiss patent on this process was issued in 1943, in which hydrocarbons of high molecular weight were cracked to lower-molecular-weight compounds by incorporating a microwave emitter into the distillation unit (48). This process has also been employed for converting crude oils and shale oils into gasoline. It has been claimed in a Belgian patent that microwave irradiation of crude oils and shale oils causes them to undergo a process similar to thermal cracking, but at a lower temperature and in higher yields, to produce gasoline and other low-molecular-weight hydrocarbons (49). Coal and oil shales have been decomposed by microwaves to give products different from those produced by thermal pyrolysis. Since microwave energy is penetrating, essentially uniform heating is attained, and apparently uncracked volatile decomposition products leave without traversing the gradual temperature gradient which occurs in conventional pyrolyses. With a microwave input power level of 700 W, decomposition of coals was found to be immediate and complete, the major products being high-molecular-weight, orange, varnishlike resins, carbon black, and soft friable coke. Conventional light oil products do not form. Oil shales behave similarly, but require an induction period. Aliphatic materials, such as torbanites, are transparent to microwaves (50).

POLYMERIZATION REACTIONS

The use of microwave energy to effect polymerization has been described (51) and it has been shown that resins of the alkyd, phenolic, epoxy, and urethan type respond well to microwave treatment. In every case it is necessary to heat the monomer or oligomer with microwave energy to the temperature at which chemical reaction would normally occur before polymerization takes place. It is important to remember that it is immaterial whether microwave energy is absorbed by the monomer to be polymerized, or by some lossy component present in the system (eg water, alcohols, ketones, amides, etc), or by microwave-absorptive pigments such as carbon, or by particulate ferroelectric materials.

Polymeric sheets have been fused together by microwave heating. For most polymers, as the fusion temperature is approached, the relaxation frequency recedes from the region of radio frequencies and approaches microwave frequencies. The following polymeric sheet materials have been bonded using microwaves: poly(vinyl fluoride) (DuPont Tedlar film), poly(ethylene terephthalate), cellulose acetate butyrate, vinyl plastisol adhesive. Poly(vinyl fluoride) (Tedlar) sheets have been bonded at rates of 0.3–1.0 m/min, using 200 W microwave power at 2450 MHz. Vinyl plastisol adhesive on paper has been cured at 2450 MHz, and layers of glass cloth containing epoxy resin have been bonded to a substrate using the same microwave frequency in a multimode cavity.

Heavy-wall, glass-fiber filament reinforced epoxy pipe has been cured at the rate of 20 in./min, using 2450 MHz microwaves (52). The epoxy resin was a low-to-medium-molecular-weight oligomer derived from the reaction of "bisphenol-A" (see Vol. 1, p. 912) with epichlorohydrin (eg Shell Epon 828). In the system studied, the coreactant employed was 4,4'-diaminodiphenyl sulfone.

Layers of polystyrene sheets, approximately 3 mm in thickness, have been heated by microwaves (2450 MHz) in a multimode cavity to form a foam block about 15 cm thick. Although polystyrene is itself not very lossy, microwaves were absorbed into the system by placing microwave-absorptive vinyl acetate-impregnated paper between the sheets (53). Microwave-irradiated heat-shrinkable plastic films for encapsulation of food, electronic equipment, etc, have been described, but no chemical reactions are involved (54).

An important application of microwave power is the production of phenolic-resin-impregnated overlay papers for the plywood industry. It has been suggested that this is an area of high potential for processing bonded polymeric overlay with 2450 MHz microwaves (55–57).

It is possible to obtain essentially nonthermal curing provided a polymer system is sufficiently microwave-absorptive (58). By suitable choice of monomer or polymer structure, a resin can be made that possesses the required microwave properties when wet, and which cures to a low-loss dielectric when polymerized. Addition of inorganic (ie polar) salts to accelerate the microwave heating process has been employed in the polymerization of vinyl chloride–vinyl acetate copolymer (59). Rapid curing by the addition of lossy organic additives has been successful in the vulcanization of rubber (60). Microwave heating to effect the vulcanization of rubber tires has been used in Japan (61).

Cores for making inner wall portions of hollow metal casts have been made by mixing sand with thermosetting urea–formaldehyde, furfural, or phenol–formaldehyde resins (62). These cores are produced in a completely automatic, time-cycle controlled, compressed-air core blowing apparatus, equipped with a microwave cavity.

Considerable interest in the production of urethan polymers (qv) using microwave heat sources has resulted in the issue of three patents to General Motors Corporation (63–65); the subject has also been discussed by Rajan (66). Refrigerators have been insulated by strong, low-density, cellular-foamed polyurethan. The polymer has been both foamed and bonded into place by microwave treatment (63). A mixed diisocyanate (comprising 80% 2,4-tolylene diisocyanate and 20% 2,6-tolylene diisocyanate) and an aliphatic polyether are mixed with a curing agent consisting of an aliphatic polyether, a diamine (eg 2,2,4,4-tetramethylbutanediamine), a silicone surfactant, and the blowing (ie gas-generating) agent, trichlorofluoromethane. These components are discharged into the insulation chamber of the refrigerator, then microwave heating is applied, which results in concurrent polymerization and foaming. A very strong, low-density, closed-cell insulation material (permanently containing trichlorofluoromethane) is thus obtained. A similar procedure has been reported using a rotary electromagnetic stirrer with a microwave antenna for uniform distribution of heat energy throughout the space to be filled with foamed polymeric insulation material (64). Rigid and flexible cellular polyurethan foams have been prepared by microwave heating a tolylene diisocyanate–polyester–polyether mixture (65).

The economics of employing microwaves in polymer processes have been discussed by Will (67), who showed that the initially high equipment costs are offset by other technical and financial advantages that render this method of curing polymers economically feasible in certain applications (eg drying operations, uniform heating and curing, etc).

FOOD

Freeze Drying. This is a sublimation process removing water from frozen foods with minimum change in colors or flavors. Products so treated can be stored without refrigeration and require only rehydration prior to cooking and eating.

In conventional freeze-dry processes heat is supplied to the product to be dried through liquid-heated trays or platens in a vacuum chamber. As the product dries, the outer layer acts as an insulator and impedes the transfer of heat to the volume containing the remaining ice. In a microwave field, the ice interacts with the microwave radiation uniformly throughout the product, generates heat and sublimes more rapidly. In conventional processes drying times of up to 24 hr are not uncommon, whereas comparable drying can be accomplished with microwaves in 2.5–3 hr.

There are certain technical considerations in the freeze drying process. For example, ice at 0°C has a vapor pressure of 4.4 torr; if this pressure is exceeded the ice will melt. The saturated vapor pressure for foodstuffs generally falls below that for pure water. This is a critical consideration for microwave drying in that liquid water exhibits a substantially higher microwave loss factor than ice. Therefore, if the ice melts, a potential runaway condition prevails wherein much more heat is generated in the product than is desired and cooking would take place rather than freeze drying. This can be avoided by operating the freeze-dry chamber at a very low pressure to ensure that melting does not occur. Operation of the drying chamber at low pressures complicates the application of microwave energy. This comes about because the intensity of the electric field is limited by the vacuum voltage breakdown, a condition in which a glow discharge will occur. If the glow discharge is present the surface of the foodstuff being dried will be scorched. Because the voltage breakdown is much lower in a vacuum than it is in ambient air, this represents a potential limitation on the amount of power that can be introduced into the foodstuff and limits the rate at which the drying operation can proceed.

The power input is also limited by the upper temperature limit that the dried foodstuff can sustain without damage during the drying process. It has been established, for example, that the surface temperature of beef should not exceed 50°C, while that of pork should be limited to 40°C. Although once dried, the dry portion of the foodstuff is less lossy than that portion still containing ice, it will still abstract a certain limited amount of energy from the microwave field and experience a rise in internal temperature. It becomes necessary, as a practical matter, to be able to adjust the microwave field during the drying process to avoid both scorch and overheating.

Because it couples primarily with remaining ice, the utilization of applied microwave energy is more efficient than utilization of energy from conventional sources. It has been estimated that removal of one pound of water from a foodstuff under freeze-dry conditions would require approximately 372 Wh. This includes energy required to supply the heat of fusion and vaporization as well as whatever additional energy is acquired by the vapors.

For production quantities of freeze-dried foodstuffs, certain problems are encountered in the design of the microwave applicator. For cavities, such as microwave ovens, standing wave patterns are often encountered which complicate their use. Mode stirrers are helpful in overcoming this problem.

A promising approach for continuous processing is that of the tapered waveguide applicator. This allows uniform product heating to take place over almost the entire length of the applicator. At 915 MHz the foodstuff depth within the applicator can be approximately 2 in. with good uniformity of heating, top to bottom.

Finish Drying of Potato Chips. One of the largest commercial applications of microwave energy is the finish drying of potato chips. In this application practically all of the advantages of microwave heating are utilized without encountering any disadvantage.

There are two salient reasons for the application of microwaves to potato chip finish drying. These are the color and moisture content of the final cooked chip. In conventional high-temperature oil cooking of potato chips there is often encountered a very undesirable deep browning of the chip, reducing its consumer acceptance. This browning is a result of the Maillard reaction between reducing sugars and amino acids contained in the potato. Any glucose in the potato in excess of 0.2% leads to commercially unacceptable browning under conventional process conditions. Temperatures normally used in conventional processing are equal to or greater than 325°F. Microwaves, on the other hand, selectively remove the water without overheating the chip, the maximum temperature attained being approximately that of boiling water, or 212°F. At this lower temperature potatoes with glucose content as high as 1% have been processed without color generation. This absence of browning affords the manufacturer a much greater latitude in selecting and handling of potatoes and can save many thousands of dollars on an annual basis in acquiring potato supplies.

The actual finish operation as installed commercially uses microwaves in conjunction with hot air (190–220°F) to remove the moisture. Chips are cooked in oil until they reach a moisture content of 5–8%; then they are introduced into the microwave finish dryer. After a residence time of $2\frac{1}{4}$–4 min they are removed, graded and packaged. A 50 kW microwave unit operating at 915 MHz in conjunction with a hot air supply, will process up to 2000 lb/hr of high-quality chips from marginal potatoes to a final moisture content of 2–2.5%. This is a production rate increase of 5–10% over a comparable conventional unit.

Many other advantages to microwave cooking may be cited including the fact that the oil content of the finished chip can be more closely controlled than with conventional processing, leading to lower rancidity and longer product shelf-life. Finally, taste tests by independent laboratories have established that microwave processed chips are as acceptable, or better, than conventionally processed chips.

Heating Precooked Food. Microwave heating of prepared foods has recently demonstrated substantial institutional acceptance. Prepared foods cover those individual entrees or complete meals which are cooked by conventional methods and then chilled or frozen until ready for use. Microwave ovens are used to heat the cold food to serving temperature either in a central location or in portable 1–2 kW units that can be moved about to the final serving site (72). The nutritive and palatability factors of foods heated by microwaves compare favorably to those of foods heated by other means.

The use of microwave heating for precooked foods was pioneered by those mainly interested in improved hospital food service. It was quickly established that there was no special advantage in cooking food from the raw state with microwave energy (73). Studies, however, demonstrated that reduction in food costs and dietary staffs were possible by limiting food-preparation activity to a five-day-week operation with hot food being supplied as necessary to patients from a central storage facility (74).

Patient acceptance of microwave heated meals has been enthusiastic because food can be served hot rather than warm and because of its freshness and taste.

Microwave ovens have been and are being used in a number of other food-service areas including snack bars, passenger trains, ships and airplanes for quick heating of frozen foods. At present, there is limited use in domestic food service but future growth is foreseen.

Poultry Cooking. Preparation of chicken as a convenience food normally requires a precooking step utilizing water immersion or steam wherein the internal temperature of the meat is raised to approximately 185°F. This usually takes 30–60 min or more depending upon the size of the chicken piece. Following this precooking step the pieces are cooled, dipped in batter and then frozen. Preparation for consumption requires frying in hot fat or baking to brown the outside and to raise the internal temperature to 140°F (75).

The precooking step results in a weight loss of 20–30% when water or steam is used. It has been found that a combination of steam and microwave cooking reduces this loss substantially and decreases cooking time to 10–12 min (76,77). The steam in the combination process serves to prevent excessive dehydration of the bulk of the chicken as well as to maintain the surface temperature at 212°F.

Cooking times in the microwave process are dependent upon the mass of the chicken pieces. For this reason breast and thighs are separately treated from wings and legs. A plant has been installed using the steam-microwave combination which has a capacity of 2500 lb/hr of poultry parts. It operates at 2450 MHz and has a total power output of 130 kW.

FOREST PRODUCTS

Forest products consist of wood, its products, and their derivatives. These include lumber, paper, particleboard, pressed wood, veneers, plywood, laminated and prestressed structural members, and composites.

The areas in which microwave energy contributes to forest products are: drying; moisture leveling; resin-curing and glue-drying; laminate bonding; and composite bonding. The areas of the maximum activity in the utilization of microwaves have been drying and moisture leveling.

In lumber drying, microwaves offer a substantial time and usually quality advantage over thermal means because of the ability of microwave energy to create a negative thermal gradient from the interior of the product toward the exterior. Thus, the microwaves supply a thermal driving force toward the surface for moisture as well as the concentration gradient driving force, which is in contrast to the thermal force for conventional thermal means. Increased economy by reduced microwave power consumption may be achieved by the use of hot air to vaporize the water brought rapidly to the surface by the microwave interaction. Drying times for some woods have been reported to be reduced from months or years to hours or days (78).

Radiofrequencies (rf) have been long employed as a power source for wood drying with similar advantages to microwaves (79). However, to obtain the high drying rates observed with microwave energy, very high radio-frequency field strengths are required. These are conducive to arcing and charring of the wood in its drier portions. The much lower field strengths required for microwave drying eliminate this problem. Indeed for thin wood, such as veneer, which is not severely diffusion limited, a microwave-thermal system may operate on the in-line production basis, drying at the rate of a few hundred ft/min.

For moisture leveling, microwaves appear to offer great advantages over thermal means.   Thus we can say:

$$P_v = \epsilon_0 \omega \epsilon'' E^2 = K \epsilon'' E^2$$

where P_v is the power dissipated per unit volume. If it is assumed that the host (wood, paper, etc) to the moisture is constant in volume and lossless ($\epsilon_H'' = 0$), then ϵ'' for the mixture can be written, neglecting synergistic effects (ie nonlinear superposition of dielectric properties in a mixed dielectric), as:

$$\epsilon'' = K_1 p \epsilon''_{H_2O}$$

where K_1 is constant; p can be expressed as follows:

$$p = \frac{W_{H_2O}}{W_{H_2O} + W_{Host}}$$

and W indicates weight. Thus we obtain the following expression:

$$P_v = p K K_1 \epsilon''_{H_2O} E^2$$

Therefore, wetter regions will receive energy in proportion to their wetness, p. In this case, all regions of the product would simultaneously reach $p = 0$, which is called proportional leveling, a situation difficult to attain by thermal means.

The finite loss and synergistic effects (80,81) of the matrix of wood or paper with water make the above analysis somewhat simplified. However, careful control of temperature and chemical content of the product can greatly enhance the leveling effect of microwaves. On the other hand, nonideal temperature and chemical conditions can cause nonleveling; ie, the existing moisture variation is less uniform than the entering one.

In the area of resin curing and glue drying, many of the above arguments apply. When resin or glue can be made more microwave absorptive than the product being bonded, then microwaves can effectively cure or dry without appreciably heating the product and avoid its degradation (82).

Cure times of a few seconds for "finger joints," as used in laminated structural beams, have been observed with a cool product. At best, require rf techniques tens of seconds with high probability of arcing and/or wood charring. Similar reasoning can be applied to particle- and pressed-board production, but the restrictions of microwave geometry require careful consideration of applicator design.

Again, similar nonequilibrium heating using microwaves, can be applied to laminates such as plywood and synthetic paneling. When applying laminates, the desire is to set the glue or resin quickly without undue heat to the substrate. This may be done with microwaves, as in other cases, only if the bonding agent is substantially more absorptive to microwaves than the laminate material. Although certain of the existing adhesives have shown good microwave sensitivity, the chemistry associated with microwave loss of bonding agents will play a great role in the future of microwaves in the forest-products industry.

ELECTRON ACCELERATORS

Microwave frequencies from 500 to 10,000 MHz have been used to accelerate electrons and light ions (83). Lower frequencies have been used for heavy ions.

Electron energies, greater than 40 BeV, have been attained using a linear-microwave accelerator (Linac) although typical commercially available machines operate in the 1–10 MeV region. Circular crossed-field machines, such as the synchrotron and microtron, range in energy from 10 MeV to 10 BeV.

Uses of such machines cover a broad spectrum, including radiation chemistry; medical radiation therapy (eg cancer); particle physics research; sterilization; x-ray production; and crosslinking of plastics and resins.

Ionized Gases. The energy associated with microwave-region photons (approximately 1×10^{-5} electron volts) is insufficient to dissociate even the weakest chemical bond directly. However, an electron in the path of an electromagnetic wave is subject to an oscillating electric field from which it may abstract energy under the proper conditions.

In this regard it is instructive to compare the behavior of an electron in a dc field with that in an oscillating field. In a dc field an electron is accelerated until it suffers an elastic collision with a gas molecule, resulting in a change in direction of its motion. Because of the difference in mass of an electron and the gas molecule, the electron retains most of its kinetic energy when it rebounds after its collision. It is then accelerated further by interaction with the applied field and the acceleration is built up following successive collisions until finally the electron obtains sufficient energy to undergo an inelastic collision with a gas molecule. This results in gas ionization, free-radical formation or excitation.

The energy transferred to the electron is a function of the ratio of the electric field strength to the gas pressure, or E/P.

In an oscillating field several types of interaction with an electron can occur. If the frequency is small compared to the collision frequency of the electron, its motion will be identical with that displayed in a dc field. However, as the field frequency is increased or the gas pressure reduced a point is reached at which collisions no longer occur frequently enough to keep the electron drift current in phase with the field. The electron inertia causes an out-of-phase component of motion. As the pressure is reduced further or the frequency is increased a point is reached at which the electron merely oscillates out of phase with the field without acquiring energy from the field. Frequency choice for coupling energy into the electron is highly dependent upon gas pressure. For example, the collision frequency for electrons with hydrogen is $V = 4.85 \times 10^9\ P$/sec, where P is gas pressure in torr; at 20 torr pressure, $V = 10^{11}P$/sec. This represents a natural upper limit to the radiation-source frequency for efficient utilization of the applied electromagnetic waves to accelerate free electrons.

One advantage of microwave discharges over dc systems is that the former can create discharges in gases without electrodes being present in the gas. Therefore, with microwave discharges there is no electrode contamination or resulting plasma perturbation. It has been observed that at low microwave power levels (100 W, 2450 MHz) and low gas pressures (approximately 10 torr) the sensible gas temperature is 700°K whereas the electron temperature exceeds 10,000°K (84).

In the microwave discharge through a gas the electrons gain energy from the applied field and lose energy by elastic and inelastic collision with gas molecules and chamber walls. Ionization of gas molecules supplies new electrons while flow to the chamber walls represents the removal mechanism. Free radicals are produced within the gas at relatively low sensible temperatures when the ratio of the electron temperature to gas temperature is at least 10:1. There is an approximately linear relationship between this ratio and the ratio of the electric field strength to the gas pressure. Thus, it is desirable to maintain the electric-field strength in the microwave discharge as high as possible to allow operation at moderate gas pressures.

The average power imparted to a unit volume of gas in microwave discharge is:

$$\bar{P} = \frac{e^2 E^2 \, n}{2m} \frac{V}{V^2 + \omega^2}$$

where e = electronic charge, E = maximum field strength, n = electron concentration, m = electron mass, V = elastic collision frequency, and ω = applied field frequency.

Above electron concentrations of $10^9/cm^3$, at constant pressure, E is sensibly constant. At the electron concentrations and gas pressures usually encountered in microwave chemistry, the electron concentration in the plasma is directly proportional to the specific power at constant pressure. As the specific power level is reduced, a point is reached at which electrons are removed by the chamber walls at a rate greater than they are produced by the field and at that point the discharge ceases.

The maximum utilization of field energy in the production of free radicals occurs when no energy is used in generating excess electrons. It has been established that this occurs when the power level is just sufficient to accommodate the discharge.

It has been shown that microwave irradiation of the appropriate gases can provide atoms of hydrogen, nitrogen, oxygen, chlorine, bromine, and boron. Nitric oxide can be produced from air, the yield depending upon electric field strength, residence time and gas pressure.

Radical lifetimes in microwave discharges vary depending upon the free-radical type and system pressure. Usually, lifetimes range from 20 microseconds to a fraction of a second.

Ethylbenzene, styrene, and phenylacetylene have been synthesized from toluene in a microwave discharge (85). This was indicated as not being a free-radical reaction as no xylenes were observed in the products. On the other hand, dissociation of n-hexane in a microwave discharge yielded 25 specific compounds, and free radicals played a significant role in the breakdown and product-forming reactions (86).

Sulfur hexafluoride, disulfur decafluoride, and sulfur tetrafluoride have been decomposed in a microwave discharge. When these compounds were reacted with chlorine under discharge conditions they produced pentafluorosulfur chloride. Reaction with oxygen produced sulfur oxytetrafluoride and sulfuryl fluoride (87).

Boron trichloride yielded diboron tetrachloride under discharge conditions (88), and germanium tetrachloride gave digermanium hexachloride (89).

Several investigators have examined the reactions of CF_4 in microwave discharges. One group produced C_2F_6 but no C_2F_4 (90). Another succeeded in producing CF_2 radicals (91).

It has been found that ethylene, ethane, and methane yielded carbon and hydrogen when subjected to a microwave discharge. Acetylene and benzene were unaffected under the same conditions (92).

Attempts to produce hydrazine from ammonia have been practically unsuccessful because the hydrazine is destroyed as rapidly as it is formed (93).

The oxidation of hydrochloric acid to chlorine and water (Deacon reaction) has been successfully accomplished in a microwave discharge. One-pass conversions of up to 50% have been achieved at a gas temperature of 700°K (94).

The oxidation of sulfur dioxide to sulfur trioxide has been accomplished in a discharge at a temperature of 600°K (95).

In summation, microwave discharge in a gas is capable of producing a free-radical-rich plasma at lower sensible gas temperatures than are achieved by other electrical methods. Contamination of the gas stream from metal electrodes is avoided. A number of chemical reactions accomplished in microwave discharges have demonstrated the technical, but not economic, feasibility of the method.

The low pressure required to keep the gas temperature low and the relatively high cost of microwave power compared to dc power currently militate against commercial application of the technique.

MICROWAVE MOTORS

When microwaves are used for the transmission of power (see p. 565), the need arises for direct conversion of this electrical energy to mechanical energy. Some work has been directed toward utilization of microwave power for the operation of motors (96). Most progress has been made on the method that rectifies microwave energy and uses it to operate a dc motor. By appropriate techniques the conversion can be made reasonably efficient, although at the present time the development is not at a level to justify commercial exploitation.

Some work has been carried out on the direct conversion of microwave energy to mechanical energy. This is in effect a utilization of the radiation pressure. The biggest difficulty is increasing the efficiency of a motor to reasonable values.

Microwave Radiation Hazards

The effects of microwave radiation on human beings are as yet imperfectly understood. For many years it was assumed that any damage caused by exposure was due merely to the thermal effects of microwaves on living tissues. It was recognized that there is a connection between frequency, power density, and energy density, and the biochemical changes produced in various organs. Radiation standards were established about 1960, and it was generally agreed in the United States that the maximum possible exposure to microwaves should be set at a level of 10 mW/cm². Since 1960, however, work carried out in several parts of the world (particularly in Russia), on animals and humans, has shown that subtle nonthermal biochemical and enzymic damage can occur in living tissues exposed to considerably less intense microwave energy than the 10 mW/cm² "safe" level previously established. As some of the effects produced are biochemically irreversible, the whole subject of what constitutes a "safe" level of exposure to microwave energy remains obscure.

This subject is being actively investigated, and in a recent Symposium on the Biological Effects and Health Implications of Microwave Radiation (97) it was concluded that it would perhaps be advisable to consider lowering the U.S. -accepted 10 mW/cm² standard. It was suggested that whole-body exposure be limited to 10 mW/cm² for a whole working day; 100 μW/cm² for 2 hr daily; and 1 mW/cm² for 15–20 min/day.

As there remains a wide divergence of opinion among microwave experts, and until quantitative biological data become available, it must be concluded that exposure to microwave radiation above certain limits does present a very real danger to health. Consequently every precaution should be employed to protect users of microwave equipment from accidental exposure.

General information on exposure of animals and humans to various intensities of microwave irradiation has been reported by several investigators (98–100). The effect on the polynuclease activity and nucleic acid content of skin, liver, spleen, and small intestine when rats were irradiated with microwaves has been studied in the Ukraine (101). Ribonuclease and deoxyribonuclease were inactivated to varying degrees, ribonucleic acid concentration increased, and deoxyribonucleic acid decreased in all the organs examined. Female beagles exposed to 24,000 MHz at a power density of 20 mW/cm² for 33 and 66 hr per week over a 20-month period showed no difference from normal, including reproductive activity (102). There was, however, a slight increase in plasma cholesterol esters (with a decrease of free cholesterol), as well as a decrease in body weight equivalent to 1.8–3.5 g/exposure hour. The dogs showed no evidence of eye damage or other radiation effect.

The effect of microwave radiation on the blood in living animals and humans has been studied by several workers. Daily 1 hr irradiation of rabbits with waves of 10 mW/cm² intensity induced a rise in the blood histamine level during the first 2–4 weeks, but this index gradually returned to normal (103) Protein fractions and blood histamine levels were increased significantly in 65 adult humans who were exposed to microwaves of several wavelengths (cm and m) (103a). Microwave irradiation of 37 humans was shown to lower the chloride level, and increase the cholesterol level, as well as change the properties of blood protein slightly (103b,104).

It is well known that exposure of the eyes to microwave radiation can bring about irreversible biochemical changes, and result in cataract formation by protein denaturation. The insidious aspect of this subject is that cataracts can be induced as a cumulative effect of sub-threshold exposures. Irradiation of the eyes causes physicochemical and biochemical changes, including an early decrease in the ascorbic acid content of the lens and accumulation of water as opacities develop. It has been shown that microwaves produce a nonthermal effect on the lens, in addition to the usual thermal effect. Protection of the eyes from incident microwave radiation, even at subthreshold levels, is thus of the greatest importance (105).

The effect of microwaves on testicular tissue has been investigated in rats (106). Exposure of rat testes to microwaves (24,000 Mc, 1.5 cm wavelength) at a distance of 7.6 cm (power density, 0.25 W/cm²) for 5, 10, and 15 min resulted in minimal, moderate, and serious damage. Histological tests showed that serious (but not permanent) damage had occurred after the 10 min exposure; and that permanent damage had occurred as the result of the 15 min exposure. The delicate and complex chemistry occurring in the human reproductive system is undoubtedly affected in the same way. For this reason, all due care should be exercised by workers operating microwave equipment to avoid accidental exposure and possible involuntary sterilization.

In addition to the serious changes that can be induced in the chemistry of the eyes, blood, testes, etc, adverse changes can also be effected in the heart muscle proteins by microwave irradiation (107). Rabbits whose hearts had been exposed to microwaves (0.05–0.1 W/cm) for 20 min/day for 10 successive days showed an increased phosphorylase activity, and decreased myogen content of the heart muscles. Further information on the effect of microwave irradiation on vital organs and the central nervous system has been published in a recent booklet to which the reader is referred for details (108).

Economic Aspects

The technical advantages that microwave energy may have over more conventional energy forms must be justified on an economic basis. Because microwave energy is expensive, the decision to use microwaves for a process must be carefully made. It is generally desirable to combine microwave energy with, for example, hot air to increase the total energy in a system.

A large industrial production machine with its auxiliary equipment represents a substantial investment. Actually, the profit per ton of product is less important than the earning capacity per year. For this reason, three-shift operation, seven days per week, is becoming increasingly necessary in order to give sufficient margin over the break-even point to warrant investment. If the installation of microwave energy can increase productivity in a given operation, it should be given serious consideration.

An economic evaluation can be made by comparing the annual profit from an operation employing microwave energy to that from one using only conventional energy forms. Cost benefits, such as better and more rapid process control, improved product quality and fewer rejects are real, but are difficult to assess until experience is gained with a particular process (57). Decreasing reject-quality material in the initial stages of production can have a cumulative effect in later stages since less reject material is processed further with the associated expenditure of manpower and energy.

Operating costs for a microwave system include microwave-tube replacement, electrical power to the power supply, power to the auxiliary systems and maintenance (109). Tube replacement cost can be computed from the initial tube cost and tube life which are discussed above under Microwave power sources. Other factors affecting tube cost are quantity discounts and the possibility of rebuilding some tubes a given number of times at a cost per rebuild that is substantially less than the new tube cost. Maintenance costs per year for a three-shift operation should be about 3% of the capital cost for microwave equipment.

Savings in floor space may be important. The microwave power supply will require approximately a half square foot of net floor space per kilowatt and applicators need one square foot net per kilowatt. Comparable surrounding space will be requred for service, for an approximate total of three square feet per kilowatt.

The typical capital cost for a large industrial multikilowatt microwave system will range from $1000 to 2000 per kilowatt.

A cursory look can be taken at the profitability of employing microwave energy for industrial processes. For this, compare incremental operating revenues generated by using microwave energy with both (1) any incremental direct operating costs involved, and (2) the total incremental capital investment required divided by the expected years of useful economic life of the improved process equipment. A more realistic analysis requires discounting projected cash flow to take into consideration the time value of money (110).

Bibliography

1. *Frequency Allocations*, R. C. A. Frequency Bureau, New York, 1965.
2. E. C. Okress ed., *Microwave Power Engineering*, Academic Press, New York and London, 1968.
3. D. J. Goerz, *Industrial Microwaves Today*, Bechtel Laboratory Rept., Bechtel Corporation Belmont, Calif., 1969.
4. D. J. Goerz, K. R. Broome, and J. W. Hankin, *J. Microwave Power*, **3**, 47 (1968).
5. W. C. Brown and J. F. Mims, *J. Microwave Power*, **2**, 111 (1967).
6. F. Buckley and A. Maryott, "Tables of Dielectric Dispersion Data for Pure Liquids and Dilute Solutions," *Natl. Bur. Std. (U.S.) Circ.* **589** (Nov. 1958).

7. A. F. Harvey, *Microwave Engineering*, Academic Press, New York, 1963.

7a. Ref. 7, p. 976.

8. H. Püschner, *Heating with Microwaves*, Philips Technical Library, Springover Lake, 1966, p. 114.

9. R. Z. Gerlack, *Microwave J.*, **11**, 142 (1968).

10. R. Keitley, *J. Brit. Inst. Radio Engrs.*, **9**, 97 (1949).

11. Ref. 7, p. 977.

12. Ref. 8, p. 120.

13. R. F. Baddour and R. S. Timmons, *Applications of Plasmas to Chemical Processing*, MIT Press, Cambridge, Mass., 1967.

14. C. Fehsenfeld, K. M. Evenson, and H. P. Broida, *Rev. Sci. Instr.*, **36**, 29 (1965).

15. F. K. McTaggert, *Plasma Chemistry in Electrical Discharges*, Elsevier Publishing Co., New York, 1967.

16. W. J. Leidigh, "A Comparison of Nitrogen Atom Yields from a Microwave Discharge Using Pulsed and CW Power," *paper presented at the 1967 IMPI Symposium, Boston, October 1967.*

17. E. L. Ginzton, *Microwave Measurements*, McGraw-Hill Book Co., New York, 1957.

18. W. A. G. Voss, *J. Microwave Power*, **4**, 210 (1969).

19. H. Löwy and G. Leimboch, *Physik. Z.*, **13**, 397 (1912).

20. M. Freymann and R. Freymann, *Compt. Rend.*, **232**, 1096 (1951).

21. M. Freymann and R. Freymann, *J. Phys. Radium*, **15**, 165 (1954).

22. G. P. de Loor, *Dechema Monograph.*, **56**, 109 (1965).

23. E. J. Mezey, G. J. Falkenbach, and J. H. Oxley, *Battelle Tech. Rev.*, **14**, 3 (1965).

24. A. Watson, "Humidity Moisture," *Paper, Intern. Symp., Washington, D.C., 1963*, 4, 87 (Published 1965).

25. Ger. Pat., 1,231,926 (1967), C. W. E. Walker.

26. M. A. Berliner and V. A. Ivanov, Prib. Sist. Upr., **1967**, 14; *Chem. Abstr.*, **67**, 65864n (1967).

27. Ger. Pat., 1,238,243 (1967), C. W. E. Walker and E. J. Justus.

28. A. C. Allen, *Ceram. Ind.*, **83**, 62, 63, 656 (1964).

29. W. J. Steen and J. Watkins, *Trans. Intern. Ceram. Congr. 9th, Brussels, 1964*, p. 47.

30. S. I. Golota, Prib. Sist, Upr., **1967**, 15; *Chem. Abstr.*, **67**, 67298e (1967).

31. T. Baillie and J. L. Spencer-Smith, *J. Textile Inst. Trans.*, **57**, 130 (1966).

32. G. Johansson, "Humidity Moisture," *Paper, Intern. Symp. Washington, D.C. 1963*, **2**, 609 (Published 1965).

33. V. K. Arkad'ev, *Compt. Rend. Acad. Sci. U.R.S.S.*, **3**, 412 (1934); *Chem. Abstr.*, **29**, 2089 (1935).

34. G. Izar and P. Moretti, *Klin. Wochschr.*, **13**, 771 (1934).

35. E. Hasché and H. Leunig, *Strahlentherapie*, **52**, 179 (1935).

36. E. M. Dianov, N. A. Irisova, and V. N. Timofeev, *Fiz. Tverd. Tela*, **8**, 2643 (1966); *Chem. Abs.*, **66**, 15423 (1967).

37. E. M. Dianov and N. A. Irisova, *Zh. Prikl. Spektroskopii, Akad. Nauk Belorussk. SSR*, **5**, 251 (1966); *Chem. Abstr.*, **66**, 23915 (1967).

38. E. H. Adema and J. Schrama, *Anal. Chem.*, **37**, 229 (1965).

39. E. H. Adema, *Chem. Weekblad*, **61**, 353 (1965).

40. E. H. Adema, A. J. J. M. Teunissen, and M. J. J. Tholen, *Rec. Trav. Chim.*, **85**, 377 (1966).

41. A. de Pereira Forjaz, *Compt. Rend.*, **197**, 1124 (1933).

42. Neth. Pat. Appl. 6,414,967 (1966), (to Stamicarbon, N. V.).

43. G. Susich, A. O. King, and L. M. Dogliotti, *Science*, **130**, 567 (1959).

44. G. H. Edwards, *J. Sci. Food Agr.*, **15**, 108 (1964).

45. K. Higashi, M. Takeda, and H. Sassa, *Science (Japan)*, **18**, 467 (1948).

46. J. Gligorijevic, D. Pavlovic, and A. Jankovic-Zagorcic, *Acta Vet. (Belgrade)*, **11**, 3 (1961); *Chem. Abstr.*, **58**, 10499 (1963).

47. Brit. Pat., 1,022,651 (1966) (to CIBA Ltd.).

48. Swiss Pat. 227,117 (1943), B. de Vevey.

49. Belg. Pat. 481,314 (1948), A. Losange and A. Celen.
50. R. F. Cane, *Nature*, **209**, 197 (1966).
51. Ref. 2, p. 115.
52. N. H. Williams, *Curing Epoxy Resin Impregnated Pipe at 2450 Megahertz*, Technical Report, Varian Associates, Industrial Microwave Operation, San Carlos, California, March 21, 1967.
53. Ref. 2, p. 125.
54. Ref. 2, p. 323.
55. H. D. Warner, *J. Microwave Power*, **1**, 81 (1966).
56. N. H. Williams, *J. Microwave Power*, **1**, 173 (1966).
57. D. J. Goerz, Jr. and J. A. Jolly, *J. Microwave Power*, **2**, 87 (1967).
58. Ref. 2, p. 170.
59. U.S. Pat. 2,780,481 (1956), B. F. Day.
60. U.S. Pat. 2,604,665 (1956), G. P. Boxomworth and F. H. Mason.
61. Japan. Pat. 2,484 (1951), S. Mizuma.
62. Neth. Pat. App. 6,606,859 (Nov. 22, 1966), (to Litton Industries, Inc.). U.S. Pat. App., May 21, 1965.
63. U.S. Pat. 3,288,894 (1966), H. W. Deaton (to General Motors Corp.).
64. Brit. Pat., 1,032,219 (1966), G. B. Long (to General Motors Corp.).
65. U.S. Pat., 3,294,879 (1966), J. W. Jacobs (to General Motors Corp.).
66. R. Rajan, *J. Cellular Plastics*, August, 1968.
67. C. H. Will, *SPE Soc. Plastic Engs. J.*, **24**, 29 (1968).
68. W. G. Clark, Jr., *Mater. Design. Eng.*, **64**, 100 (1966).
69. S. Stuchly, *Pomiary, Automat., Kontr.*, **12**, 442 (1966).
70. W. W. Brandon, Jr., *NASA Accession No. N65-19787, Rept. No. AD 609982 (1964), 61pp.*
71. M. Sucher and J. Fox, *Handbook of Microwave Measurements*, John Wiley & Sons, Inc., New York, 1963, 3 Vols.
72. Ref. 2, Vol. 2, p. 80.
73. U. C. Hart, *Hosp. J. Am. Hosp. Assoc.*, **31**, 78 (1957).
74. A. C. Avery, *Hosp. J. Am. Hosp. Assoc.*, **34**, 72 (1960).
75. Ref. 2, Vol. 2, p. 85.
76. Anon, *Food Process Packaging*, **27**, 92 (1966).
77. Anon, *Broiler Ind.*, **29**, 58 (1966).
78. H. Resch, *Preliminary Technical Feasibility Study on the Use of Microwaves for the Drying of Redwood Lumber*, Serv. Rept. 35,01.55. Forest Products Lab., Univ. of Calif., Richmond, Calif., 1966.
79. D. G. Miller, "Radio Frequency Lumber Drying: Methods, Equipment and Costs," *Can. Forest Ind.*, **86** (6), 53–57 (June 1966).
80. W. J. Leidigh, E. W. Stephansen and W. J. Stolte, "Some Experimental and Analytical Aspects of Microwave Paper-Drying." *Paper, presented at 1969 IMPI Symposium, Edmonton, Can., May 1969.*
81. W. R. Tinga, "Multiphase Dielectric Theory—Applied to Cellulose Mixtures," Thesis, University of Alberta, Edmonton, Fall 1969.
82. G. Gruber, "Practical aspects of microwave veneer redrying," *J. Microwave Power* **2**, 37 (1967).
83. Ref. 2, Vol. 2, chap. 5.4.
84. R. F. Baddour and R. S. Timmins, eds., *The Application of Plasmas to Chemical Processing*, MIT Press, Cambridge, Mass., 1967.
85. A. Streitwieser, Jr., and H. R. Ward, *J. Am. Chem. Soc.*, **84**, 1065 (1962); **85**, 539 (1963).
86. A. D. Coates, *Report No. 1181 (AD 409436)*, Ballistic Research Laboratories, Md., 1962.
87. H. J. Emeléus and B. Tittle, *J. Chem. Soc. (London)* 1644 (1963).
88. U.S. Pat. 2,994,652 (1961), J. W. Frazer, R. T. Holzmann.
89. D. Shriver and W. L. Jolly, *J. Am. Chem. Soc.*, **80**, 6692 (1958).
90. E. J. Mezey et al., *Battelle Technical Review*, November, 1965.
91. N. Cohen and J. Heicklen, *TDR-469* (**9240-01**) **2**, Aerospace Corporation, Los Angles, Calif. December, 1965.

92. F. J. Vastola et al., *J. Appl. Chem.*, **14,** 69 (1964).

93. W. W. Cooper, S.B. Thesis, Dept. of Chemical Engineering, MIT, Cambridge, Mass., 1963.

94. W. W. Cooper, Sc.D. Thesis, Dept. of Chemical Engineering, MIT, Cambridge, Mass., 1966.

95. N. F. Brockmeier, Ph.D. Thesis, Dept. of Chemical Engineering, MIT, Cambridge, Mass., 1966.

96. W. C. Brown and J. R. Mims, *J. Microwave Power*, **2,** 111 (1967).

97. J. M. Osepchuk, *Microwave J.*, **12,** 36 (1969).

98. Ref. 7, Chap. 20.

99. G. M. Knauf, *Am. J. Public Health*, **50,** 364 (1960).

100. P. G. Rentos and E. J. Baier, *J. Chem. Educ.*, **44,** A541, A543-A544 (1967).

101. N. I. Kerova, *Biol. Deistivie Ul'trazvuka i Svekhvysokochastotnykh Elektromagnitn. Kolebanii, Akad. Nauk Ukr. SSR, Inst. Fiziol.*, **1964,** 108; *Chem. Abstr.*, **63,** 8842 (1965).

102. W. B. Deichmann, E. Bernal, F. Stephens, and K. Landeen, *J. Occupational Med.*, **5,** 418 (1963).

103. I. A. Gel'fon, *Tr. Lab. Elektromagnitn. Polei Radiochastot Inst. Gigieny Truda i Prof. Zabolevanii Akad. Med. Nauk SSSR*, **2,** 68 (1964); *Chem. Abstr.*, **65,** 12702g (1966).

103a. I. A. Gel'fon, *ibid.*, 133 (1964); *Chem. Abstr.*, **65,** 12702h (1966).

103b. N. K. Byalko and M. N. Sadchikova, *ibid.*, 137 (1964); *Chem. Abstr.*, **65,** 12703a (1966).

104. U. Vaher, *Vopr. Biofiz. i Mekhanizma Deistviya Ionizir. Radiatsii (Kiev: Zdorov'e) Sb., 1964,* 83; *Chem. Abstr.*, **64,** 9037e (1966).

105. R. L. Carpenter, *U.S. Dept. Comm., Office Tech. Serv., AD 275,840* (1962), 51 pp.

106. S. A. Gunn, T. C. Gould, and W. A. D. Anderson, *Lab. Invest.*, **10,** 301 (1961).

107. D. G. Grigor'yan, *Vop. Kurovotol., Fizioter. Lech. Fiz. Kul't.*, **32,** 13 (1967); *Chem. Abstr.*, **67,** 7998 y (1967).

108. W. Bergman, *The Effect of Microwaves on the Central Nervous System*, Ford Motor Co., Detroit, Michigan, 1966, 69 pp. (translated from German).

109. M. Disman, "An Economic Model for Microwave Heating Systems," *J. Microwave Power*, **1,** 33 (1966).

110. L. R. Damskey, J. W. Hankin and E. W. Stephansen, "Economic Modeling in the Paper Industry,' *J. Microwave Power*, **4,** 294 (1969).

ROY G. NEVILLE
DAVID J. GOERZ, JR.,
A. THEODORE STEWART, JR.,
JEROME W. HANKIN
JOHN D. A. DAY, AND
W. JARED LEIDIGH
Bechtel Corporation

N

NITRILES

The nitriles are organic cyanides containing a cyano radical, $-C\equiv N$, as the characteristic functional group. Propanenitrile was the first nitrile to be synthesized when Pelouze (1) in 1834 distilled potassium cyanide with ethyl barium sulfate. The cyano group, however, is usually derived from the corresponding carboxylic acid or ester (see also Amines (fatty), Vol. 2, page 128). Nitriles are therefore also known as carbonitriles, or acid nitriles. The carbon to nitrogen triple bond is highly polarized and contributes to the rather large dipole moment for nitriles. This results in association which causes nitriles to have higher boiling points than those expected on the basis of their molecular weights. The cyano group is similar in its behavior to the halogen atoms. The lower-molecular-weight nitriles (up to $C_{13}H_{27}CN$) are liquids having fairly pleasant odors. Acetonitrile is soluble in water, but this solubility rapidly decreases as the molecular weight of the nitrile increases. Nitriles have slightly toxic properties, but are only moderately hazardous as compared to hydrocyanic acid or to isomeric isonitriles.

In addition to being good solvents for organic materials and inorganic salts, there are a variety of uses for nitriles, which include the following: chemical intermediates; additives for improving jet fuels (2); lubricants (3,4); plasticizer (4); insect repellent (4); stabilizer for SO_3 (5); weed control (6); removal of CO_2 from natural gas (7); and electroplating additive (8), to mention a few.

Tables 1–3 give information on a number of commercially available nitriles.

Table 1. Physical Properties of Some Commercially Available Nitriles (26)[a]

Nitrile	Manu-facturer[b]	Approx 1969 bulk price, $/lb	Sp gr	Boiling point,[c] °C	Freezing point, °C	Flash point,[d] °C	Solubility in H₂O wt%	at °C	ICC label required
aceto	6,23,25	0.24	0.783_{20}^{20}	81.6	−45.7	9	miscible	20	Red
acrylo	1,5,10,16, 23,25	0.145	0.807_{20}^{20}	77.4	−83.6	1	7.08	20	Red
benzo	27	0.34	1.008_{20}^{20}	190.7	−12.75		1.00	100	none
n-butyro	6	0.54	0.795_{4}^{17}	117.9	−111.9				
3-cyanopyridine	19,21	1.24	solid	206.2	49.6	99	12.3	20	
glycolo	1	0.40	1.104^{19}	183	<−72.0		miscible		
iso-butyro	6,8	0.45	0.775_{4}^{15}	103.9	−71.5				
malono	3,14,17	3.75	1.049_{40}^{34}	233.4	30.5	130	sol		Class B poison

[a] Information also obtained from various Company bulletins.
[b] See Table 3.
[c] At 760 mm Hg.
[d] ASTM D-1310, Tag open-cup below 50°C; ASTM D-92, Cleveland open-cup above 50°C.

Table 2. Other Available Nitrile Intermediates (27)

Nitrile	Manufacturers[a]
adipo	5,16
allyl-*sec*-butylcyanoacetic acid, ethyl ester	24
allyl	14
3-anilinopropio	9
2-benzofuranaceto	6
1-benzyl-4-phenylisonipecoto	24
(*p*-bromophenyl) aceto	4
(*p*-chlorophenyl) aceto	12,20
coco	7
cottonseed oil	7
cyanoaceto	6,14,16,17
1-(2,5-dichlorophenyl)-3-triazenecarbo	9
(3,4-dimethoxyphenyl) aceto	15
3-dimethylaminopropio	1
diphenylaceto	15
ethoxymethylenemalono	14
3-ethoxypropio	1
3-(*N*-ethyl-*m*-toluidino) propio	5,6,9,11
gerano	13
hexadecyl	7
hydracrylo (ethylene cyanohydrin)	25
3-[*N*-(2-hydroxyethyl)anilino]propio	5,11
3-[*N*-(2-hydroxyethyl)anilino] propionitrile benzoate ester	5
lacto	16
lauro	2,7
mandelo	14
methacrylo	23
3-methoxypropio	5
2-methyllacto (acetone cyanohydrin)	1,22
oleo	2,7
phenylaceto	4,20,24,26
3,3'[(phenyl)imino]dipropio	5
3-*iso*-propoxypropio	1,5
stearo	7,18
tallow	3,7
tallow, hydrogenated	7
3,3'-thiodipropio	1

[a] See Table 3.

Nomenclature. Nitriles are often referred to as cyanides or cyano compounds, but are usually named from the acids they yield upon hydrolysis. They are named by dropping "-ic acid" from the common name of the acid and adding "-nitrile," eg benzoic acid becomes benzonitrile. In other cases "o" is added for euphony between the root and the ending, eg acetic acid becomes acetonitrile. In the IUPAC system they are named by adding "-nitrile" to the name of the parent hydrocarbon, eg acetonitrile becomes ethanenitrile. This compound can also be called methyl cyanide by a method which names the compound as a cyanide and then identifies the hydrocarbon group which is attached. Benzonitrile becomes phenyl cyanide by this system. One additional system names nitriles as cyano compounds and thus benzonitrile and acetonitrile become cyanobenzene and cyanomethane, respectively.

Table 3. Manufacturers of Nitriles

1. American Cyanamid Co.
2. Armour and Company
3. Ashland Oil & Refining Co., Inc.
4. Cowles Chemical Co., Benzoyl Products Div.
5. E. I. du Pont de Nemours & Co., Inc.
6. Eastman Kodak Co.
7. Eldorado Chemical Co.
8. Escambia Chemical Corp.
9. General Aniline & Film Corp.
10. B. F. Goodrich Co., Chemical Div.
11. Interchemical Corp., Color and Chemical Div.
12. Interchemical Corp., Organic Chemicals Dept.
13. Interchemical Flavors and Fragrances, Inc.
14. Kay-Fries Chemicals, Inc.
15. Eli Lilly and Co.
16. Monsanto Co., Organic Chemicals Div.
17. Balwin-Montrose Chemical Co., Inc., Montrose Chemical Div.
18. National Dairy Products Corp., Humko Products Chemical Div.
19. Warner-Lambert Pharmaceutical Co., Nepera Chemical Co.
20. Orbis Products Corp.
21. Reilly Tar & Chemical Corp.
22. Rohm and Haas Co.
23. Vistron Corp.
24. Sterling Drug, Inc., Sterling-Winthrop Research Inst.
25. Union Carbide Corp.
26. Universal Oil Products Co., UOP Chemical Co.
27. Velsicol Chemical Corp.

Preparation

Inorganic Cyanides and Alkyl Halides (9).   There are a number of different procedures for the preparation of nitriles. One of the oldest is the preparation from an inorganic cyanide and an alkyl halide in an aqueous alcohol solution.

$$RX + KCN \xrightarrow[\Delta]{aq\ ROH} RCN + KX$$

This method is good with primary alkyl halides. Phenylacetonitrile, an intermediate to phenylacetic acid, is prepared from benzyl chloride and NaCN in good yields by this method. With secondary alkyl halides, silver cyanide or cuprous cyanide (10) must be substituted for the alkali cyanides and yields are lower. Tertiary alkyl halides do not react.

Carboxylic Acids or Esters (11–13). Many variations exist in the procedure of making nitriles from carboxylic acids or esters which mainly include different dehydration catalysts, temperatures, and pressures. The process essentially involves the conversion of the acid or ester to the amide, using an excess of ammonia, which is then dehydrated to the nitrile.

$$RCOOH + NH_3 \xrightarrow[250-350°C]{Al_2O_3} RCN + 2 H_2O$$

$$RCOOR' + NH_3 \xrightarrow[250-350°C]{Al_2O_3} RCN + R'OH + H_2O$$

This process is easily adapted to continuous production and can be carried out in the vapor phase up to 450–500°C.

Ammoxidation. A modern modification of the above method is ammoxidation. In this process a hydrocarbon is oxidized to the acid in the presence of ammonia and a dehydration catalyst and the nitrile is produced directly without isolation of the acid. A good example (14) is the ammoxidation of o-xylene. The catalyst is 5% V_2O_5 on Al_2O_3/K_2SO_4.

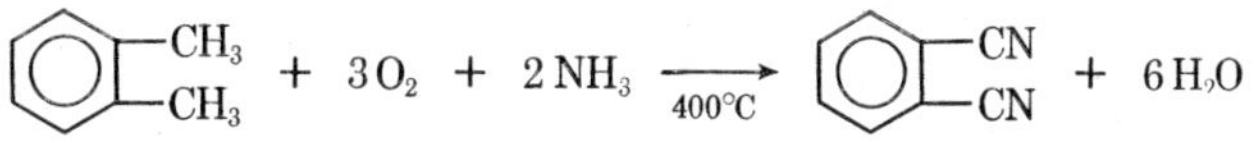

$$\text{(o-xylene, }CH_3, CH_3) + 3 O_2 + 2 NH_3 \xrightarrow{400°C} \text{(benzene, }CN, CN) + 6 H_2O$$

This method is widely used in the manufacture of aromatic nitriles and also of acrylonitrile (15). (See Acrylonitrile, Vol. 1, pp. 338–350.)

$$2 C_3H_6 + 2 NH_3 + 3 O_2 \rightarrow 2 CH_2\!\!=\!\!CHCN + 6 H_2O$$

Cyanoethylation (16). A variety of organic compounds having labile hydrogen atoms add readily to acrylonitrile in a Michael-type addition to form nitriles:

$$RH + CH_2\!\!=\!\!CHCN \xrightarrow{\text{base}} RCH_2CH_2CN$$

Reactions

Nitriles may be hydrolyzed either acidic or basic, as shown:

$$RCN + 2 H_2O \xrightarrow[\Delta]{H^+} RCOOH + NH_4^+ \qquad\qquad \text{acidic}$$

$$RCN + H_2O \xrightarrow[\Delta]{OH^-} RCOO^- + NH_3 \qquad\qquad \text{basic}$$

They may also be partially hydrolyzed with hydrogen peroxide in slightly basic solution, stopping at the amide stage (17).

$$RCN + 2 H_2O_2 \xrightarrow{40°C} RCONH_2 + H_2O + O_2$$

Nitriles can be reduced to primary amines with hydrogen using Raney nickel. Ammonia is helpful in inhibiting the formation of secondary amines.

$$RCN + 2 H_2 \xrightarrow[1500\ psi]{NH_3/Ni} RCH_2NH_2$$

Nitriles react readily with primary alcohols in dilute acid solution to form esters (18,19).

$$RCN + R'OH \xrightarrow[H_2O]{H^+} RCOOR' + NH_4^+$$

Many reagents condense with nitriles, giving a variety of condensation products. A few which reveal the functionality of the nitriles are shown below.

With hydrogen sulfide they form thioamides.

$$RCN + H_2S \rightarrow RCSNH_2$$

With hydroxylamine they form amidoximes.

$$RCN + H_2NOH \rightarrow RC(\!\!=\!\!NOH)NH_2$$

With acetylenes they form pyrimidines (20).

$$2\,RCN \;+\; HC\!\equiv\!CH \;\longrightarrow$$

With dienes they form pyridines (21,22).

$$RCN \;+\; \text{butadiene} \;\longrightarrow$$

With dicyandiamide they form guanimines (23).

$$RCN \;+\; H_2NC(\!=\!NH)NHCN \;\xrightarrow[ROH]{OH^-}$$

With Grignard reagent they form ketones (24).

$$RCN + R'MgX \rightarrow RR'CNMgX \xrightarrow[2\,HX]{H_2O} RCOR' + MgX_2 + NH_4X$$

With resorcinol they form ketones (25).

$$RCN + \;\;\; \xrightarrow[H_2O]{HCl} \;\;\; + \; NH_4Cl$$

With alkenes or secondary or tertiary alcohols in concentrated sulfuric acid (Ritter reaction) they form *N*-substituted amides.

$$RCN + (CH_3)_2C\!=\!CH_2 + (H_2O) \xrightarrow{H_2SO_4} RCONHC(CH_3)_3$$

Acetonitrile

Acetonitrile may be prepared by several methods, but one of the best is the vapor-phase ammonolysis of glacial acetic acid. The acid is vaporized, mixed with anhydrous ammonia, and the stream directed through a bed of silica gel or some other dehydration catalyst. The bed temperature may range from 150 to 500°C in this continuous reaction. The effluent gases contain acetonitrile, ammonia, and water and the product is recovered in 85–95% yields by azeotropic dehydration.

Acetonitrile is a water-white, low-boiling liquid with an etherlike odor and has good solvent properties. It undergoes the typical reactions of nitriles in regard to the CN group and has been used as a chemical intermediate for vitamin B_1, substituted pyrimidines, and pharmaceuticals. It also contains labile hydrogen atoms on the α carbon that give aldol-like condensations. In toxicity acetonitrile is comparable to acetic acid; it has the following LD_{50}'s (25a):

Single oral dose in rats: 2.46 gm/kg.

Single skin penetration in rabbits: 1.25 ml/kg.

Single inhalation by rats: 4,000 ppm killed 3 of 30, 8,000 ppm killed 10 of 30, 32,000 ppm killed 17 of 30.

Acrylonitrile

See Vol. 1, pp. 338–350.

Benzonitrile

This nitrile was first prepared in 1844 by the dry distillation of ammonium benzoate (28). There are many different laboratory methods of preparation, but the three most successful industrial methods are: (a) ammoxidation of toluene in which toluene is oxidized at elevated temperatures in the presence of ammonia using a dehydration catalyst; (b) catalytic ammonolysis of benzoic acid and subsequent dehydration; and (c) catalytic ammonolysis of toluene in the presence of a dehydrogenation catalyst. Good yields are obtained in all cases, but the first two methods give a purer product and higher conversions.

Benzonitrile is a high-boiling colorless liquid with an odor resembling benzaldehyde. The π electrons of the triple bond between carbon and nitrogen are highly polarizable and contribute to the large dipole moment, 4.08 D (29). It is, however, a neutral compound having neither basic or acidic properties. In addition to the properties given in Table 1, it has the following physical constants: Refractive index, n_D^{20} 1.5289; fire point, 75.0°C; viscosity at 100°F, 1.054 cSt; surface tension at 25°C, 34.7 dyn/cm.

Benzonitrile is completely miscible with many organic solvents and immiscible with water. The solubility at 25°C of a number of different resins and polymers is shown in Table 4.

Table 4. Solubility of Various Resins and Polymers in Benzonitrile (30)

Soluble	Partially soluble	Insoluble
poly(vinyl acetate)	cellulose acetate	polyethylene
poly(vinyl chloride)	nitrile rubber	nylon
chlorinated rubber	neoprene	poly(vinyl alcohol)
nitrocellulose		paraffin wax
polystyrene		carnauba wax
poly(methyl methacrylate)		
cellulose acetate–butyrate		
wood rosin		
gum arabic		
shellac		

Benzonitrile is most unusual in that it also dissolves many anhydrous inorganic salts and organometallics that are used as catalysts in numerous reactions (31). This property, in addition to the relatively low vapor pressure, stability, and polarity, suggests its use as a reaction solvent in many liquid-phase reactions and polymerizations. Table 5 lists the solubilities of some common catalysts.

Reactions. Benzonitrile undergoes the reactions typical for all nitriles and the following examples show the reactive characteristics of the CN group:

Benzonitrile is catalytically reduced to benzylamine in acetic acid using Pd–BaSO$_4$ (32). It may also be reduced with Raney nickel at 1000 psi. The presence of NH$_3$ inhibits the formation of dibenzylamine.

$$C_6H_5C{\equiv}N + 2\,H_2 \xrightarrow{\text{Raney Ni}} C_6H_5CH_2NH_2$$

Table 5. Solubility of Various Catalysts in Benzonitrile

Catalyst	Wt % soluble at °C	
	25	45
aluminum chloride	17	
arsenic trichloride	miscible	
bismuth trichloride	18	
cobalt chloride		0.6
cuprous chloride	3	9.8
ferric chloride	15	
mercuric acetate		2.4
mercuric chloride	1	14.1
mercuric bromide	1	13.5
silicon tetrachloride	miscible	
silver nitrate	50	
stannic chloride	5	
titanium tetrachloride	2	
zinc chloride	5	33.8
zirconium chloride	4	10.0

Hydrolysis of benzonitrile may be accomplished in either acid or base and can proceed stepwise.

$$C_6H_5CN \xrightarrow[H_2O]{H^+} C_6H_5CONH_2 \xrightarrow[H_2O]{H^+} C_6H_5COOH + NH_4^+$$

$$C_6H_5CN \xrightarrow[H_2O]{OH^-} C_6H_5CONH_2 \xrightarrow[H_2O]{OH^-} C_6H_5COO^- + NH_3$$

One of the most important condensation reactions of benzonitrile is the alkaline-catalyzed reaction with dicyandiamide to form benzoguanimine (23), an important intermediate for surface-coating resins for white baked finishes. See Amino resins and plastics.

$$C_6H_5CN + H_2NC(\!=\!\!NH)\!-\!\!NHCN \xrightarrow[OH^-]{ROH}$$

benzoguanimine

A trimer of benzonitrile may also be formed simply in the presence of chlorosulfonic acid (33).

$$3\ C_6H_5CN \xrightarrow{ClSO_3H}$$

Other reactions of benzonitrile include the usual substitution, or addition, to the aromatic ring.

Chlorine can be added to the ring using sunlight or aqueous chlorine (34).

$$C_6H_5CN + 3\ Cl_2 \xrightarrow{light} C_6H_5Cl_6CN$$

Substitution may also be accomplished using antimony pentachloride (35).

$$C_6H_5CN + 2 SbCl_5 \xrightarrow[\text{tube}]{\text{sealed}} C_6Cl_5CN + 5 HCl + 2 Sb$$

Substitution in the meta position predominates when fuming nitric acid is the nitrating agent in the presence of perchloric acid (36).

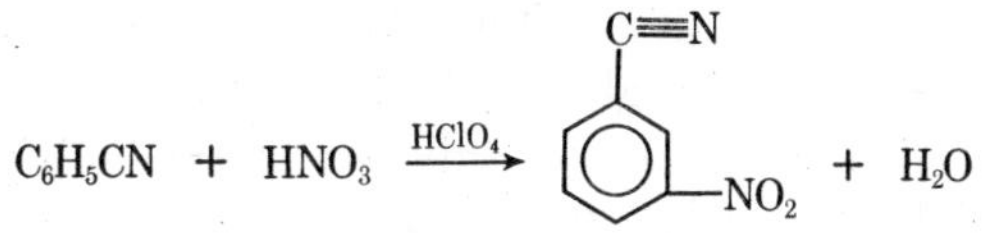

$$C_6H_5CN + HNO_3 \xrightarrow{HClO_4} \text{(structure)} + H_2O$$

Methyl or ethyl ether may be used with a Friedel-Crafts catalyst to alkylate benzonitrile (37).

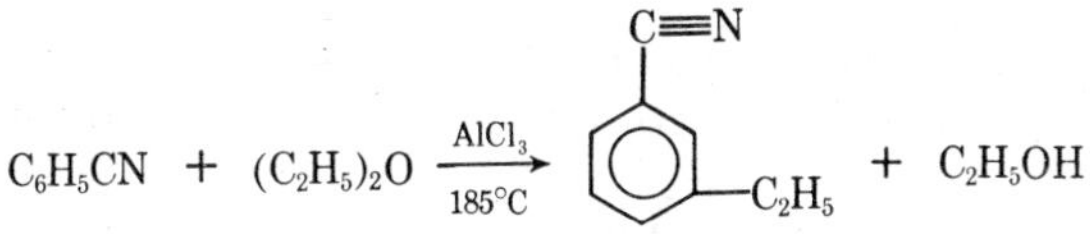

$$C_6H_5CN + (C_2H_5)_2O \xrightarrow[185°C]{AlCl_3} \text{(structure)} + C_2H_5OH$$

Assay. Analysis is by freezing point, as shown below ($K_f = 1.93$ mol %/°C):

Purity, mol %	Freezing point, °C
100.0	−12.75
99.6	−13.0
97.9	−14.0
96.1	−15.0

Shipping Regulations and Containers. There are no shipping regulations for benzonitrile. It is shipped in the following containers:

1. 55-gal nonreturnable lacquer-lined steel drums, 450 lb net, 500 lb gross.
2. Tank trucks, approx 32,000 lb net.
3. 8,000-gal tank cars, approx 68,000 lb net.

Handling Precautions. The physiological properties of benzonitrile have not been completely established. It may be toxic to some persons. Symptoms are headache, nausea, weakness, increased heart beat, and dizziness. There has been no indication of chronic toxic effects in handling and use where the normal precautions for handling organic chemicals have been observed. The following precautions are offered as suggestions:

1. Use good ventilation to minimize contact with benzonitrile vapors.
2. Avoid contact with skin or eyes. In case of contact with skin, wash with water and mild soap. In case of contact with the eyes immediately flush with large volumes of water for at least fifteen minutes and get medical attention.
3. Check exposed personnel for chronic toxic effects.
4. Follow rules of good personal hygiene regarding handling of any chemicals, such as shower and change of clothes each day after work.

Bulk Handling and Storage Facilities. Benzonitrile, while flammable, is not a difficult material to handle or store. To prevent discoloration, stainless steel, glass, fluorocarbon resins, or polyethylene can be used. Ordinary tanks, pumps, and fittings of these materials may be used. Storage should be adequately vented and so arranged that personnel are not exposed to the fumes.

Uses. In addition to having good solvent properties and having a commercial application as an intermediate for benzoguanimine, many other uses have been claimed, including the following:

Azeotropic agent for purification of naphthalene and its lower alkylated homologs from nonaromatic hydrocarbons (38). When benzonitrile is used in a nickel-plating bath, the deposited nickel is very bright and less brittle than usual (8). It has an antioxidant effect on benzaldehyde (39) and stabilizes liquid sulfur trioxide or oleum (5) (cf Vol 19, p. 473). Addition of benzonitrile to jet fuel causes a lowering of ignition temperature and smoother burning and makes the fuel nonexplosive (2).

n-Butyronitrile

n-Butyronitrile is a clear, colorless liquid at ambient temperature and has a sharp suffocating odor. Its physical properties (40) are listed in Table 6 (see also Table 1).

Table 6. Physical Properties of *n*-Butyronitrile

Property	Value
color, APHA	10
purity, by gas chromatography, %	99
distilling range, at 760 mm Hg	116–117.7
refractive index, n_D^{20}	1.3831
specific gravity, 20/20°C	0.7919
solubility at 25°C	
acetone	miscible
benzene	miscible
water, wt %	3.3
solubility of water in *n*-butyronitrile	trace

It is expected to find applications as an intermediate in the synthesis of industrial, specialty, and pharmaceutical chemical products.

n-Butyronitrile is available in 55-gal drums, tank-truck, and tank-car quantities.

Toxicity. *n*-Butyronitrile is an extremely toxic compound producing symptoms similar to those caused by other nitriles, such as isobutyronitrile. Results of screening studies by the Laboratory of Industrial Medicine, Eastman Kodak Company (40), show this compound to be extremely hazardous on oral ingestion, skin contact, or inhalation. For example, when a 10% solution of *n*-butyronitrile in corn oil was administered to rats orally in doses of 25–3200 mg/kg, it killed all animals given doses of 100 mg/kg or above. Intraperitoneal administration of the same material in similar doses killed all animals receiving 100 mg/kg and above, and one of the two animals receiving 50 mg/kg. In similar tests with mice, oral doses of 200 mg/kg and above of the same solution resulted in death, while intraperitoneal administration killed at 50 mg/kg.

The handling precautions and antidotes for *n*-butyronitrile as suggested on container labels should be observed.

Reactions. *n*-Butyronitrile undergoes the reactions typical of all nitriles, eg hydrolysis under either acidic or basic conditions to produce first *n*-butyramide and then butyric acid. A few additional reactions of interest are listed below:

1. With aldehydes to give N,N'-alkylidinebisbutyramide (41).

$$2\ CH_3CH_2CH_2CN\ +\ RCHO\ +\ H_2O\ \xrightarrow{H^+}\ \begin{array}{c} CH_3CH_2CH_2CONH \\ CH_3CH_2CH_2CONH \end{array}\!\Big\rangle CHR$$

2. With Grignard reagents to give ketones (42).

$$RMgX\ +\ CH_3CH_2CH_2CN\ \xrightarrow{(H_2O)}\ R\overset{\overset{\displaystyle O}{\|}}{-}C-CH_2CH_2CH_3$$

3. The CN group activates hydrogen atoms on the adjacent carbon, causing an aldol-like condensation (43).

$$CH_3CH_2CH_2CN\ +\ 2\ CH_3CN\ \xrightarrow{NaNH_2}\ CH_3CH_2CH_2-\overset{\overset{\displaystyle CH_2CN}{|}}{\underset{\underset{\displaystyle CH_2CN}{|}}{C}}-NH_2$$

3-Cyanopyridine

3-Cyanopyridine is a buff-colored solid at room temperature and may be prepared by the Sandmeyer reaction (44). It has the following structure:

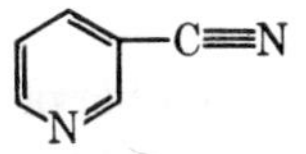

3-Cyanopyridine is used as an intermediate in the production of niacin and niacinamide (45). It is available in various commercial quantities.

For the physical properties of the pure compound, see Table 1. Its solubility in 100 g water at 20°C is 14 g. The typical properties of technical grade are listed below:

Property	Value
purity, %	98
freezing point, °C	48.5
vapor pressure at 100°C, mm Hg	21

Glycolonitrile

Glycolonitrile, $HOCH_2C\equiv N$, readily trimerizes when kept under anhydrous conditions at pH of 7 or higher. However, it may be prepared by reacting hydrogen cyanide with aqueous formaldehyde at 10°C by keeping the pH adjusted to 8–9 (46). See also Vol. 6, p. 671.

Isobutyronitrile

This reactive chemical intermediate is now available in commercial quantities. It has been prepared from the amide in 86% yield by dehydrating with phosphorous pentoxide and continuously distilling off the nitrile. It can also be made from isobutyraldehyde and ammonia using high temperatures and a copper catalyst on activated alumina. Table 7 lists properties and specifications of the technical grade (50).

Table 7. Properties and Specifications of Isobutyronitrile

	Value
property	
density, 30/40°C	0.7608
refractive index, n_D^{15}	1.3756
melting point, °C	−71.5
specifications	
color, APHA, ppm, max	20
boiling range, at 760 mm Hg, °C	100.5–105.5
specific gravity, 20/20°C	0.7700–0.7740
aldehydes,[a] % by wt, max	1.00
water, % by wt, max	0.50
methacrylonitrile, % by wt, max	2.00

[a] As C=O.

Isobutyronitrile is a water-white liquid which undergoes all of the typical reactions of the nitrile group, such as hydrolysis, reduction, and condensation. Oxidation of isobutyronitrile using molecular oxygen (47) produces methacrylonitrile.

$$2\ (CH_3)_2CHCN + O_2 \rightarrow 2\ CH_2{=}\underset{\underset{CH_3}{|}}{C}{-}CN + 2\ H_2O$$

Isobutyronitrile has been tested as an additive to gasoline (48) and as a catalyst for the polymerization of ethylene (49).

Toxicity (50). Isobutyronitrile is capable of being absorbed by the through skin and in full strength can cause systemic toxicity and death. Therefore, the handling precautions for isobutyronitrile as suggested on container labels should be observed.

Malononitrile

There are several U.S. patents (56) which describe the preparation of malononitrile, $CH_2(CN)_2$, starting with cyanoacetamide, $CH_2(CN)CONH_2$ (obtained via sodium chloroacetate and sodium cyanide). They claim various conditions, dehydration reagents, and inert solvents to obtain yields from 60 to 80%.

Malononitrile is a low-melting solid which polymerizes readily upon heating above 120°C or when in contact with alkaline materials (57). A stabilizer is recommended. Safe materials for storage and handling are glass, aluminum, and stainless steel.

It undergoes the typical nitrile reactions of hydrolysis and reduction. In addition, it has two labile hydrogen atoms which may be halogenated or condensed with various carbonyl compounds. One of the most important commercial reactions of malononitrile is the condensation with o-chlorobenzaldehyde to form o-chlorobenzalmalononitrile, $ClC_6H_5C{=}C(CN)_2$, a military and riot-control chemical agent (CS). It has vesicant properties and is a good tear gas. Its use has no lasting harmful effects if an individual is quickly removed from the contaminated area.

Malononitrile may also be used in the synthesis of vitamin B_1, has application as an oil-soluble polar additive to lubricating oils to suppress viscosity-index decrease (58), and is a valuable intermediate to new products employed in the plastics and agricultural-chemical industries (57).

Malononitrile is fairly toxic to humans (57). The LD_{50} (percutaneous) is 20–60 mg/kg (rabbits) and interperitoneal, 25 mg/kg (mice).

It is shipped in tin-lined containers according to ICC regulations for a "Class B Poison."

The physical properties of malononitrile are listed in Table 8.

Table 8. Physical Properties of Malononitrile (57)

Property	Value
boiling point, °C	223–224 (dec)
melting point, °C	31.6–32.4
specific gravity, 34/4°C	1.049
refractive index, n_D^{35}	1.4129
dielectric constant at 20°C	37.5–44.5
heat of combustion, cal/mole	395.1
heat of fusion, cal/mole	2400
dipole moment, at 25°C, D	3.56
surface tension at 37.5°C, dyne/cm	47.9
viscosity at 32.7°C, gm/(cm) (sec)	0.0285
cyroscopic constant[a]	4.89
flash point, °F	234
solubility[b]	
water	7.5
alcohol	2.5
benzene	15
$CHCl_3$	10
ether	5

[a] For 1 kg solvent.
[b] One part malononitrile in parts solvent.

Phthalonitriles

There are three isomeric phthalonitriles that may be prepared by ammoxidation (14) of xylenes. They may also be prepared by reacting hydrogen cyanide with benzonitrile over platinum oxide at 900–950°C, giving a mixture of isomeric nitriles (51). The mixture contains 10% ortho, 55% meta, and 35% para isomer. Their properties are listed in Table 9.

Table 9. Properties of the Phthalonitriles

Property	Value		
	ortho	meta	para
melting point, °C	138.3	161.5	224.6
boiling point, °C		sublimes	
flash point,[a] °C	164		
solubility[b] at 25°C			
acetone	27		
benzene	5		
nitrobenzene	12		
water	insol		

[a] Cleveland open-cup.
[b] gram per/100 g solvent.

Toxicity (52). Phthalonitrile was found to be moderately toxic orally and intravenously on the basis of single doses in animals. Approx acute LD_{50} oral toxicity in rats is 90 mg/kg; approx acute LD_{50} intravenous toxicity in mice is 30 mg/kg.   Prolonged or repeated contact with the skin and prolonged or repeated breathing of vapor should be avoided.

Uses.   *o*-Phthalonitrile is a most important intermediate for the production of phthalocyanine compounds (53) (See Vol. 15, p. 489).   Phthalocyanines are important to the pigment and dye industry, and have also been proposed for high-temperature-resistant lubricating greases (54) and as insecticides (55).

Bibliography

1. T. J. Pelouze, *Ann. Chem.* **10**, 249 (1833).
2. U.S. Pat. 2,983,099 (May 9, 1961), T. F. Doumani and C. S. Coe (to Union Oil Co.). *Chem. Abstr.* **55**, 26450b (1961).
3. Ger. Pat. 919,128 (Oct. 14, 1954), Hans Stephan (to Farbenfabriken Bayer A. G.).   *Chem. Abstr.* **52**, 13245a (1958).
4. Product Brochure, Armour Chemical Division, Chicago, Ill., Oct. 1952.
5. Ger Pat. 1,085,862 (July 28, 1960), Friedrich Wolf (to VEB Farbenfabrik Wolfen).   *Chem. Abstr.* **55**, 26390f (1961).
6. Brit. Pat. 862,863 (March 15, 1961), to N. V. Philips Gloeilampenfabricken.   *Chem. Abstr.* **55**, 13756h (1961).
7. U.S. Pat. 3,350,847 (Nov. 7, 1967), B. B. Woertz and O. C. Holbrook (to Union Oil Co.).   *Chem. Abstr.* **68**, 41982u (1968).
8. U.S. Pat. 2,524,010 (Sept. 26, 1950), A. H. DuRose and P. W. Moy (to Harshaw Chemical Co.). *Chem. Abstr.* **45**, 480g (1951).
9. H. E. Fierz-David and W. Kuster, *Helv. Chim. Acta.* **22**, 82 (1939).
10. S. Wawzonek and H. L. Hsu, *J. Am. Chem. Soc.* **68**, 2741 (1946).
11. U.S. Pat. 2,794,043 (May 28, 1957), J. E. Jansen and M. E. Roha (to B. F. Goodrich Co.). *Chem. Abstr.* **51**, 16514f (1957).
12. U.S. Pat. 2,493,637 (Jan. 3, 1950), W. D. Niederhauser (to Rohm and Haas Co.). *Chem. Abstr.* **44**, 2545f (1950).
13. U.S. Pat. 2,808,426 (Oct. 1, 1957), R. H. Potts and R. S. Smith (to Armour and Co.). *Chem. Abstr.* **52**, 2053f (1958).
14. Y. Ogata and K. Sakanishi, *Chem. Ind.* (*London*) **1966** (49), 2055–2056.   *Chem. Abstr.* **66**, 37604p (1967).
15. W. L. Faith, D. B. Keyes, and R. L. Clark, *Industrial Chemicals*, John Wiley & Sons, Inc., New York, 1965, p. 40.
16. R. Adams, *Organic Reactions*, Vol. 5, John Wiley & Sons, Inc., New York, 1949, p. 79.
17. L. McMaster and F. B. Langreck, *J. Am. Chem. Soc.* **39**, 103 (1917).
18. H. Beckurtz and R. Otton, *Chem. Ber.* **9**, 1590 (1876).
19. H. Szydlowsky and L. Spiegel, *Chem. Ber.* **51**, 297 (1918).
20. T. L. Cairns et al., *J. Am. Chem. Soc.* **74**, 3989 (1952).
21. G. J. Janz et al., *Ind. Eng. Chem.* **45**, 1343 (1953).
22. U.S. Pat. 2,549,651 (April 17, 1951), C. A. Weisgerber (to Hercules Powder Co.). *Chem. Abstr.* **45**, 8048e (1951).
23. J. K. Simons and M. R. Saxton, in C. C. Price, ed., *Organic Syntheses*, Vol. 33, John Wiley & Sons, Inc., New York, 1953, pp. 13–15.
24. T. S. Stevens et al., *J. Chem. Soc.* **1931**, 2568.
25. K. Hoesch, *Chem. Ber.* **48**, 1122 (1915).
25a. Acetonitrile, Tech. Bull., Union Carbide Corp., Industrial Medicine and Toxicology Dept., New York.
26. *Oil. Paint, Drug Reptr.* (Jan. 19, 1970).
27. U.S. Tariff Commission, *Synthetic Organic Chemicals, U.S. Production and Sales, 1967*, U.S. Govt. Printing Office, Washington, D. C., 1968.
28. H. Fehling, *Ann.* **49**, 92 (1844).
29. T. L. Brown, *J. Am. Chem. Soc.* **81**, 3233 (1959).
30. Data Bulletin CB-1, Socony Vacuum Co., Inc., July 1947.

31. Company Brochure 46100-1, Velsicol Chemical Corp., June 3, 1968.

32. K. W. Rosenmund et al., *Chem. Ber.* **56B**, 2260 (1923).

33. L. Rapoport and E. M. Smolin, "*s*-Triazines and Derivatives," Vol. 13 of A. Weissberger, ed., *The Chemistry of Heterocyclic Compounds*, Interscience Publishers, New York, 1959, p. 172.

34. T. Van der Linden, *Rec. Trav. Chim.* **53**, 45 (1934). *Chem. Abstr.* **28**, 4719 (1934).

35. V. Merz and W. Weith, *Chem. Ber.* **16**, 2885 (1883).

36. G. S. Hammond and K. J. Douglas, *J. Am. Chem. Soc.* **81**, 1184 (1959).

37. G. Baddeley, *J. Chem. Soc.* **1949** (Suppl. No. 1), S 229–230.

38. U.S. Pat. 2,551,912 (May 8, 1951), J. W. Teter (to Sinclair Refining Co.). *Chem. Abstr.* **45**, 8757f (1951).

39. C. Moureu et al., *Compt. Rend.* **183**, 685 (1926).

40. Technical Data Sheet No. N-111, Eastman Chemical Products, Nov. 1960.

41. E. E. Maget et al., *J. Am. Chem. Soc.* **73**, 1028 (1951).

42. C. R. Hauser et al., *J. Am. Chem. Soc.* **70**, 426 (1948).

43. U.S. Pat. 2,409,061 (Oct. 8, 1946), R. O. Norris (to Sinclair Refining Co.). *Chem. Abstr.* **41**, 1239d (1947).

44. A. Blinz and C. Roth, *Ann.* **487**, 127 (1931).

45. Product Information Bulletin, Form I-114, Reilly Tar and Chemical Corp., March 26, 1962.

46. Japan. Pat. 7,220 (Nov. 4, 1954), N. Fujiski and T. Takemoto (to Asahi Chem. Ind. Co.). *Chem. Abstr.* **50**, 4196g (1956).

47. U.S. Pat. 2,734,909 (Feb. 14, 1956), R. E. Gee, Jr., and H. J. Hagemeyer, Jr. (to Eastman Kodak Co.). *Chem. Abstr.* **50**, 16825i (1956).

48. U.S. Pat. 2,887,368 (May 19, 1959), J. P. Buckman (to Union Oil of Cal.). *Chem. Abstr.* **53**, 22888d (1959).

49. U.S. Pat. 2,765,297 (Oct. 2, 1956), R. G. Heiligmann and P. B. Stickney (to Borden Co.). *Chem. Abstr.* **51**, 4052a (1957).

50. Technical Data Report No. N-102, Eastman Chemical Products, Aug. 1957.

51. U.S. Pat. 2,758,129 (Aug. 7, 1956), N. L. Jennings (to Monsanto Chem. Co.). *Chem. Abstr.* **51**, 2856b (1957).

52. Product brochure, Allied Chemical & Dye Corp., 1956.

53. M. A. Dahlen, *Ind. Eng. Chem.* **31**, 839 (1939).

54. V. G. Fitzsimmons et al., *Ind. Eng. Chem.* **44**, 556 (1952).

55. M. C. Swingle et al., *Plant Quarantine*, E.T. No. E-548, U.S. Dept. Agr. Bur. Entomol., Washington, D.C., Sept. 1941; *Chem. Abstr.* **36**, 210 (1942).

56. U.S. Pat. 2,389,217 (Nov. 20, 1945), Alexander R. Surrey (to Winthrop Chemical Company); *Chem. Abstr.* **40**, 900[7] (1946). U.S. Pat. 2,459,128 (Jan. 11, 1949), Marvin J. Fabrenbach (to American Cyanamid Co.); *Chem. Abstr.* **43**, 3470b (1949). U.S. Pat. 2,802,857 (Aug. 13, 1957), George Kesslin and Leonard Nicholl (to Kay-Fries Chemicals, Inc.); *Chem. Abstr.* **51**, 17978f (1957). U.S. Pat. 2,799,697 (July 16, 1957), Emil J. Maxion (to Chase Chemical Co.); *Chem. Abstr.* **52**, 425c (1958).

57. Technical Data Brochure, Kay-Fries Chemicals, Inc., 1966.

58. U.S. Pat. 3,127,349 (March 31, 1964), Jack Rockett (to Esso Research and Engineering Co.); *Chem. Abstr.* **61**, 521c (1964).

R. W. INGWALSON
Velsicol Chemical Corp.

NITROGEN FIXATION

The world's population explosion and the scarcity of new arable land on the earth's surface encourage the continuing search for improved efficiency in the industrial fixation of atmospheric nitrogen on which all artificial fertilizers are based. Cheap hydrogen is essential, and in contrast to the earlier use of coal carbonization, and coke gasification with steam and air or oxygen, there are very few areas in the world where the currently used methods can be justified economically. Almost all modern plants utilize gaseous hydrocarbon feedstocks or the gasification of liquids, for the production of hydrogen to be used in ammonia synthesis. Developments in this area are briefly described here.

Processes by which microorganisms (either alone or in symbiotic association with certain plants) fix molecular nitrogen from the atmosphere converting it into nitrogenous cell constituents, have occupied the attention of chemists, biochemists, and biologists for many years. Not the least intriguing aspect of these biological processes is the contrast between the mild conditions under which they occur and the harshness of the temperature and pressure requirements of the process used in industry. Although the biological processes depend upon biochemical activation of the nitrogen molecule by metallo–enzyme systems present in microorganisms, it is only in recent years that such systems have been studied in cellfree extracts (1). As a result much new light has been shed on processes responsible for a high proportion of the combined nitrogen now in circulation on the earth. It has been estimated that the total nitrogen in circulation in the soil of the earth, including natural as well as synthetic, is about 100 million tons. Of this, the high-temperature industrial processes contribute about 20 million tons, so it can be seen that the natural sources exceed the synthetic by about 4 to 1. Recent developments in the continuing study of biological nitrogen fixation are reviewed here.

A completely different approach was started in about 1966, this time in synthetic chemistry, and from it have come a rapidly increasing number of laboratory processes for the fixation of nitrogen under extremely mild conditions of temperature and pressure. Although these discoveries have not arisen principally from studies of naturally occurring nitrogen-fixing enzyme systems (in fact they have their origins in observations of the behavior of Ziegler organometallic olefin-polymerization catalysts in the presence of nitrogen), nevertheless there are close anologies between fixation by transition metals (chemical) and by microorganisms (biochemical).

Industrial Processes

Current trends in industrial processes for nitrogen fixation have been summarized by Fowler of the Power-Gas Corporation Ltd. (2,2a). As already indicated, the problem of producing ammonia economically is largely that of producing cheap hydrogen. Two main types of process are used for the production of ammonia-synthesis gas and both are based on hydrocarbon feedstocks. The first is the partial oxidation process in which the hydrocarbon stream is reacted with oxygen and steam at a very high temperature. The proportion of oxygen present is adjusted so that the product gases contain large proportions of hydrogen and carbon monoxide. In the next stage of the process the carbon monoxide present is converted to carbon dioxide and hydrogen via the water-gas reaction, as follows:

$$CO + H_2O \rightarrow CO_2 + H_2 + 14,800 \text{ Btu/(lb)(mole)}$$

After absorption of the bulk of the CO_2 in some suitable liquor the residual methane, CO, and CO_2 are removed by scrubbing with liquid nitrogen. This condenses the impurities in the synthesis gas and the hydrogen:nitrogen ratio is adjusted to 3:1 preparatory to compression for ammonia synthesis.

The other industrial process now widely used for the production of hydrogen for ammonia synthesis is the steam–hydrocarbon reforming process. Unlike the non-catalytic partial oxidation process, steam reforming uses a nickel-containing catalyst, so that the first step is to desulfurize the naphtha stream. It is then mixed with super-heated steam and passed through alloy tubes filled with the reforming catalyst. These tubes are located in a furnace which supplies heat for the reaction and the composition of the product gases is determined by satisfying the equilibria for the following two reactions:

$$CH_4 + H_2O \rightarrow CO + 3 H_2 - 97,300 \text{ Btu/(lb)(mole)}$$

$$CO + H_2O \rightarrow CO_2 + H_2 + 14,800 \text{ Btu/(lb)(mole)}$$

In the second stage of reforming, air is added to the hot hydrogen-rich gas mixture which raises the temperature of the latter and thus enables the two reaction equilibria (see above) to be satisfied at a much higher temperature. The amount of air added at this stage is controlled so that, after the purification steps which follow, the hydrogen nitrogen ratio will be 3:1. Conversion of CO to CO_2 and removal of the latter follow as in the partial oxidation process. Remaining impurities are CO, CO_2, argon, and methane. Argon and methane are purged while the oxides of carbon are removed by methanation over a nickel catalyst, according to the following reactions:

$$CO + 3 H_2 \rightarrow CH_4 + H_2O$$

$$CO_2 + 4 H_2 \rightarrow CH_4 + 2 H_2O$$

Trends in the development of both processes may be summarized as follows: Severe though the conditions are for economic reduction of nitrogen on the industrial scale, the tendency is for them to become even more severe. High production pressures for synthesis gas give rise to lower compression costs (synthesis gas compressors are costly items), but lead to excessively high methane contents which can only be avoided by raising the temperature. Furthermore, the undecomposed steam from the reaction condenses then at a higher temperature and therefore more waste heat can be recovered, thereby improving the economics of the process.

A continuing trend is for the installation of larger production units. With a plant of larger capacity it is possible to use more economic synthesis-gas compressors. At production rates below 500–600 tons per day reciprocating compressors are normal, but above this level centrifugal compressors may be used. These compressors have a lower initial cost and, being more reliable, reduce plant down-time. They can also be run by direct drive from steam turbines.

Finally, as a third major trend, the tendency is for modern ammonia plants to be designed for maximum energy recovery. In particular, waste heat is now being recovered in a form in which it may be re-used. This is usually done by generating steam at high pressures and temperatures to drive the steam turbines for all the major prime movers in the plant. Modern ammonia plants are thus substantially independent of imported electrical energy because of their integrated steam- and power-recovery systems.

In addition to new developments in the major processes for the production of synthesis gas there have been some noteworthy improvements in the catalysts employed. The obvious attraction, as a feedstock for ammonia plants, of fairly cheap paraffinic naphtha arising from substantially increased crude-oil refining has led to a search for a catalyst by means of which such a feedstock (ie a liquid, bp 120–190°C) could be used in steam–hydrocarbon reforming processes.

A highly successful research program was carried out on this problem by Imperial Chemical Industries Ltd., drawing on their considerable technical and commercial experience in this field. This was described in a lecture by Hodgson of that company (3), who began by referring to the generalized reaction between steam and saturated hydrocarbons as follows:

$$C_nH_{2n+2} + n\,H_2O \rightarrow n\,CO + (2n + 1)H_2$$

Although apparently simple in practice this reaction poses quite a complex problem in the development of the catalyst. There are many possible competing reactions and the possibility of carbon deposition on the catalyst, which would destroy its activity, is always present. This was overcome when it was found that acid sites on the alumina catalyst support promoted carbon formation, but that alkali treatment made it possible for higher-molecular-weight naphthas to be processed at higher temperatures and with reduced quantities of excess steam.

About one thousand catalysts were tested in the ICI development program. A catalyst was ultimately found which could operate under pressures of 10 atm or more and this eliminated the first, and most expensive, stage of compression for ammonia synthesis. It was, therefore, not long before the early plants, reforming naphtha at atmospheric pressure, were replaced by plants operating under pressure. By 1964, only five years after the start-up of the first unit, all ICI ammonia production was based on naphtha.

In the overall process other catalysts, besides the one involved in the actual reforming step, had to be found, and their development constituted the most fundamental aspect of the whole program. Eight separate reaction stages, each requiring a different catalyst, include the vital removal of a variety of organic sulfur compounds from the naphtha, since these would otherwise poison the reforming catalyst.

The nickel catalyst employed in the secondary reformer fulfills a very similar function to the primary reforming catalyst. One problem which had to be overcome at this stage of the process was associated with the migration of silica. This is facilitated by the high temperatures and high partial pressures of hydrogen which are employed; the silica, which originates in either the catalyst support or the refractory lining, can migrate in the gas stream. This is redeposited in the colder sections of the plant and fouls heat-exchanger surfaces.

Reference has already been made above to the water-gas reaction in which CO is converted exothermically to CO_2, the residual CO being dependent on the equilibrium with excess steam present at the exit temperature of the shift converter. With the early catalysts, based on iron oxide, it was necessary to operate in the temperature range of 350 to 500°C, but a catalyst which would operate in a lower range was clearly desirable since this would enable a relatively low residual CO content to be obtained without the necessity for a step to remove CO_2 (to adjust the equilibrium). Such a catalyst, essentially a mixture of the oxides of zinc, copper, and chromium, was developed which operates successfully at temperatures in the range of 200 to 300°C. The use of this low-temperature shift-conversion catalyst has made possible a considerable simplification of this particular aspect of ammonia synthesis and in practice it is now carried out without interstage CO_2 removal.

The process and catalyst modifications just described have necessitated a number of improvements in the engineering design of ammonia-synthesis plants, as well as a search for new materials of construction to cope with the increasingly severe operating conditions. The modern reforming tube must be able to withstand internal pressures of 450 psi at temperatures of 950°C. In the early steam reformers the tubes were made from wrought alloys, but more recently they have been made by a centrifugal casting technique. This results in a coarse grain structure which has the effect of imparting a much better high-temperature strength to the alloy (chrome: nickel = 25:20). Reformer tubes are normally about 30 ft long and expand 5–6 in. from their cold to hot positions. Therefore, this movement has to be accommodated in the headers, which are made from a different alloy in order to cope with the complex expansion problems. The headers are usually made from wrought material containing 35% nickel.

Especially indicative of the efforts which have had to be put into engineering design is the likelihood that an increase in pressure from centrifugal compressors, from 150 atm to approx 350 atm, is now possible. A great deal depends upon the reliability and satisfactory performance of these machines since they represent a considerable capital investment, and when the compressor has to be shut down the whole plant is out of commission.

Optimization of the performance of an ammonia plant involves consideration of a number of important design parameters, the values of which must be carefully selected in regard to the cost of utilities and raw materials. Such parameters include operating pressure of the synthesis loop, concentration of inert gases in the synthesis loop, temperature profile in the converter, residual CO in the gas leaving the shift-conversion section, etc. Designers of ammonia plants are faced with the problem of optimizing these related parameters in order to secure the lowest possible ammonia-production costs. The problems are very complex and quantitative mathematical models are being designed for the whole system, so that computers may be brought to bear on their solution. The same principles and mathematical models are, of course, applicable to optimization in operation. However, the plant operator has to face the fact that the size of his equipment is fixed, and he must therefore optimize conditions to make the best use of the available raw materials and their quality at any given time of the day or year. His aim may be to obtain the maximum productive capacity, or alternatively to achieve the lowest production cost irrespective of capacity. There are now a number of ammonia plants in operation where the supervisory control function is carried out by an on-line computer. However, since the quality and availability of raw materials change and since plant efficiencies can vary, no final solution is possible for a given unit. For this reason more and more ammonia plants are relying on supervisory digital computers to optimize the plant performance continually.

On the whole the future situation seems to be that while there may be localized or temporary situations of overcapacity in the nitrogen-fixation industry it seems likely, in the long run, that more and more ammonia plants with increased capacity will have to be built. Mention has already been made of the economies to be achieved by the use of centrifugal compressors, which in turn means higher productive capacities, so that in the future ammonia-synthesis units capable of 1,000–2,000 tons per day will be used mostly. The search for catalysts effective in promoting ammonia synthesis at much lower temperatures will continue. (Although still very far from commercialization, the transition-metal systems capable of nitrogen fixation under mild conditions must be regarded as the ultimate in this context.) It follows from equilibria considerations that, if successful, this would be accompanied by synthesis at much lower pressure. If this could lead to the elimination of the synthesis gas compressor altogether the result would be a major, and dramatic, change in the nitrogen-fixation industry.

Biological Fixation—Enzymic Systems

While current developments in biological nitrogen fixation are almost entirely confined to investigation and directed toward elucidation of the mechanisms involved, their relevance toward potential commercial processes, particularly those having mild processing conditions as the objective, cannot be discounted. The study of cellfree, isolated enzyme systems, for example, by biologists and biochemists is likely to be particularly rewarding, and has already yielded valuable results of purely chemical interest. Further details of developments in this area follow.

Biological nitrogen fixation is effected by certain microorganisms which may be either free-living or occur in symbiotic association with higher plants. The former include aerobic, anaerobic, and photosynthetic bacteria, as well as blue-green algae, actinomycetes, yeasts, etc. Symbiotic associations, in which bacteria are incorporated into the root modules of certain plants, are found in members of the family Leguminosae, eg peas, clovers, and soya bean, in which the endophyte is a bacterium of the genus *Rhizobium* and in certain nonleguminous root-nodule-bearing angiosperms, such as alder, bog myrtle, etc.

FREE-LIVING ORGANISMS

Of the many organisms shown to fix nitrogen only a minute fraction have been investigated. Most of the work on cellfree extracts has been carried out with two free-living bacteria, namely the aerobic *Azotobacter vinelandii* and the anaerobic *Clostridium pasteurianum*.

The following techniques have been employed: Active cellfree extracts of *A. vinelandii* have been obtained either by ultrasonic or lysozyme (enzymic) disruption of cells in the medium in which they are grown (4). Successive high-speed centrifugations result in active particulate fractions sedimented between 25,000 and 144,000 G. Exposure of the extracts to ^{15}N or ^{13}N has confirmed fixation (5). Extraction of the nitrogen-fixing enzyme system from *C. pasteurianum* has been achieved (1,6) either by (a) crushing the frozen cells in a Hughes press and centrifugation to obtain an active cellfree extract, or (b) rapid dying (30–40°C) of a cell paste and extraction of the powder with 0.05 M phosphate buffer under hydrogen (pH 6.8), followed by high-speed centrifugation at 0°C.

Results of investigations with these and other microorganisms all lead to the same general conclusions, ie that nitrogen fixation by such isolated enzyme systems proceeds via the adsorption of the nitrogen molecule at an "active site" on the enzyme surface, and that it requires an energy source and the intervention of some reducing system to convert the bound nitrogen to ammonia. In general it may also be said that not all organisms make use of identical (only similar) enzyme systems, and that whereas related organisms appear to possess very similar systems, widely differing organisms do not.

It was also shown in another series of experiments that nitrogen fixation requires a supply of adenosine triphosphate (ATP) and an electron donor of low potential. For the latter sodium dithionite, $Na_2S_2O_4$, can be used experimentally while ferredoxin is known to be concerned in natural systems. One suggestion for the role of ATP (7) is that it activates the enzyme so that combination with nitrogen occurs, with subsequent use of the energy derived from ATP for sufficient activation of nitrogen to allow reduction to take place (8). In addition to nitrogen the systems just described are capable of reducing nitrous oxide, azide, acetylene, cyanide, methyl isocyanide, etc.

Purified cell extracts have now been separated into an iron–molybdenum protein fraction and an iron–protein fraction, neither of which functions by itself; they recombine spontaneously to yield an active nitrogen-fixing complex (9). Apparently only two protein components are required. The iron–protein fraction from one organism can effectively be combined with the iron–molybdenum fraction from related organisms, but no activity results if the two fractions are derived from unrelated organisms.

One of the most dramatic developments in the elucidation of the precise nature of the enzymic system involved took place at the experimental station of Du Pont in Wilmington. Burns, Holsten, and Hardy (10) prepared large quantities of the nitrogenase from *Azotobacter vinelandii*, separating from it a crude fraction of the iron–molybdenum protein. When they lowered the salt concentration the protein crystallized out in large regular crystals, quite pure and in yields of about half a gram.

With relatively large quantities of pure enzyme various new studies now become possible. Perhaps the most interesting is the likelihood that determination of the enzyme's three-dimensional structure by x-ray crystallography will be attempted. This should throw considerable light on the mechanism by which these biological iron–molybdenum catalysts function.

Blue-green Algae. As free-living organisms, the *Myxophyceae* or blue-green algae are also of great interest. Although certain species form associations with other organisms these cannot be regarded as nitrogen-fixing symbioses (cf the legume-Rhizobium association described above), since the algae are active on their own. Their distribution is world-wide and they are particularly abundant in the moist tropics. They are capable of living photoautrophically in an environment entirely free of combined nitrogen, and they are the only class of algae in which fixation of atmospheric nitrogen has been convincingly demonstrated. They are also unique in that photosynthesis and nitrogen fixation appear to occur not only in the same organism but in the same cell. In the past the inability to prepare pure cultures has inhibited the study of nitrogen fixation by these organisms, but this difficulty has been overcome in recent years by the use of such techniques as ultraviolet irradiation, treatment with antibiotics, etc (11–13).

Given suitable culture conditions, these algae can grow as rapidly on molecular nitrogen as they can on combined nitrogen. For optimum nitrogen fixation, the critical conditions are hydrogen-ion concentration, temperature, and light intensity. The latter depends on various factors, such as the density of the culture and the availability of carbon dioxide, but fixation is impaired if the intensity is too low or too high.

A noteworthy feature is that those species of algae which are active in nitrogen fixation all contain cells which, under the microscope, appear to be empty. These cells, which are called heterocysts, are formed by ordinary vegetative cells developing a thick wall and appearing to lose their contents. In some cases this is preceded by an increase in the size of the cell. The similarity of heterocysts to root nodules in symbiotic associations (see below) has led to the speculation that these abnormal cells may be, in fact, the site of nitrogen fixation. New evidence has been accumulating which suggests that their relationship to nitrogen fixation is coincidental.

As with free-living bacteria, systematic studies of the localization of active sites received a considerable impetus with the introduction of techniques for preparing cellfree extracts. Centrifugation of such extracts showed that maximum photosynthetic and nitrogen-fixing activity occurred together in the same fractions, and that these were characterized by the presence of the pigments chlorophyll and pyocyanin.

As mentioned earlier a number of facts concerning biochemical nitrogen fixation were established through investigations using cellfree extracts of free-living bacteria, such as *Clostridium pasteurianum*. ATP has been identified as the energy source while ferredoxin or some similar compound is involved in the electron transfer to the nitrogen-fixing system. Furthermore pyruvate, CH_3COCOO^-, has been found to be the main organic source of electrons for the ferredoxin reduction (7). Since, in *C. pasteurianum* pyruvate undergoes a phosphoroclastic type of cleavage, which results in the synthesis of ATP, it appears that pyruvate alone can supply both basic cofactor requirements of nitrogen fixation. These facts are summarized in Figure 1.

The involvement of pyruvate in nitrogen fixation is, however, not restricted to *C. pasteurianum* and has been demonstrated also for *Anabaena cylindrica* (15,16). However, in photosynthetic nitrogen-fixing organisms such as blue-green algae, the requirements of reducing power and ATP might also be met photochemically. In support of this possibility are reports of close relationships between photosynthesis and nitrogen fixation (17,18). Short-term experiments have shown that the main dependency of nitrogen fixation upon photosynthesis is for a supply of carbon skeletons to assimilate ammonia, the end product of nitrogen reduction (15), and it has therefore proved difficult to establish whether photochemically generated cofactors are also needed for nitrogen fixation. However, it is possible temporarily to break the dependency of nitrogen fixation on carbon skeletons, produced simultaneously by photosynthesis, by a prior period of nitrogen starvation. During this process, endogenous carbohydrate reserves build up and can be used as a carbon pool during subsequent nitrogen fixation. Under these conditions nitrogen fixation takes place in the absence of carbon dioxide in the light and in the dark (14).

Cox and Fay (19) reported to the Royal Society on a series of experiments in which the effect of light on nitrogen fixation by nitrogen-starved cells of *A. cylindrica* were studied. Their conclusion was that photochemically generated ATP was needed for nitrogen fixation in *A. cylindrica*. However, reducing power appeared to be associated with dark reactions concerned with the decarboxylation of pyruvate and to

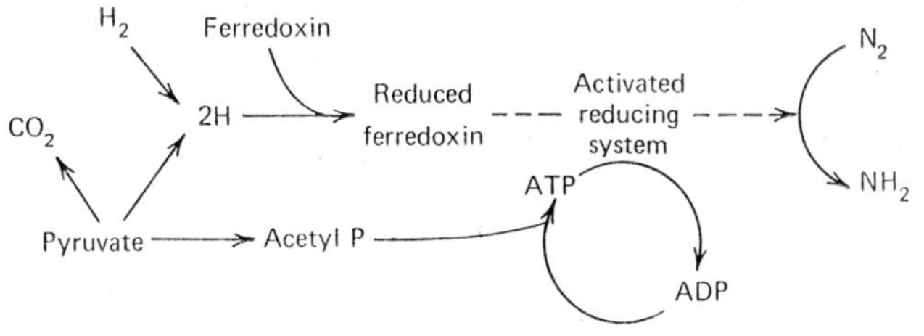

Fig. 1. Scheme of reactions suggested to be involved in nitrogen fixation (14).

be unconnected with photochemical action. The light requirement for the ATP supply suggests that either pyruvate phosphorylation is loosely coupled to nitrogen fixation or that pyruvate does not undergo a phosphoroclastic cleavage in blue-green algae.

No confirmation that heterocysts could be the sites of nitrogen fixation could be obtained although the conclusion that nitrogen fixation was independent of any photosynthetically generated reductant links up with the known inability of heterocysts to synthesize reducing power photochemically. Since heterocysts contain chlorophyll there is no reason why cyclic photophosphorylation should not occur in them, although this possibility has not been demonstrated experimentally.

SYMBIOTIC SYSTEMS

Notwithstanding the considerable amount of light which has been shed on biological nitrogen fixation through studies of free-living organisms, the fact remains that fixation by symbiotic root-nodule bacteria is the principal source of nitrogen replenishment in the biological environment. As already indicated, studies of symbiotic fixation systems have lagged behind those of the free-living nitrogen-fixing bacteria. There are several reasons for this; first, it is convenient for biochemists to use relatively easily grown mass-cultures of bacteria. Secondly, there are intrinsic difficulties in working with the nodule system, which is susceptible to inactivation at many points during preparation. In addition, the fact that the products of the reaction are freely soluble and not associated with any nodule components, delayed identification of the bacteroids as the nitrogen-fixing agents and led to hypotheses which have now been abandoned.

Once it was demonstrated that the active agents were bacteroids (symbiotic form of root-nodule bacteria) (20), use of the experience gained previously with *Clostridium* and *Azotobacter* resulted in many of the properties of the nodule nitrogen-fixing enzyme complex (nitrogenase) being elucidated. Cellfree extracts were again extensively studied, having been successfully obtained for the first time in 1967 by Koch (21). It had been known for some time that excised root nodules themselves actively fix nitrogen and in 1960 Bergersen proposed the following general theory for plant cells of this type: Fixation occurs within a membrane envelope which encloses the bacteroids and leghaemoglobin, a haemoprotein component in active nodules whose presence had been established previously. (It is now thought to be associated with oxygen transfer in nodules.) After nearly ten years Bergersen had further refined this theory for presentation to the Royal Society (22). The bacteroids in soybean root nodules were shown to develop, after a series of complex metabolic and

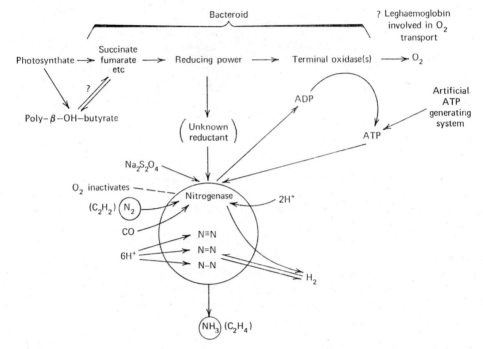

Fig. 2. Schematic representation of factors involved in nitrogen fixation in soybean nodules.

structural changes in bacteria, during the final stages of growth within membrane enclosed vesicles. Nitrogenase appears when these changes are complete.

In intact nodules the primary product of nitrogen fixation is ammonia, rapidly converted to α-amino compounds for use by the host plant. In cellfree extracts the process terminates with the formation of ammonia which is then released into the medium. Free oxygen is required for energy production in both the naturally occurring nodule systems and in cellfree extracts thereof. Oxygen also causes inactivation of the nitrogen-fixing system and exerts important kinetic influences on the reaction.

Reducing power and energy for the reduction of nitrogen to ammonia is provided by an unspecified photosynthetic product present in the nodules; in bacteroid suspensions substrates such as succinates are required. In cellfree extracts requirements for energy and reductant are met by ATP and sodium dithionite but the natural reductant has not yet been identified.

Figure 2 gives a schematic representation of the various factors affecting nitrogen fixation in nodules, bacteroid suspensions, and cellfree extracts. It is clear that there are many features common to the symbiotic system in legumes and the systems of free-living nitrogen-fixing bacteria already described.

Chemical Fixation

ORGANOMETALLIC SYSTEMS

Until 1966 the reduction of molecular nitrogen under the mild conditions of the enzymic nitrogen-fixing reaction was completely unparalleled by any nonenzymic reaction of the completely inert and thermodynamically stable nitrogen molecule.

Since then research groups in Moscow, Stanford, Toronto, and Sussex (Agricultural Research Council, ARC unit), to name only a few, have been studying the problem with increasing intensity.

In order to describe this now very fast-moving development recourse has been made to a survey which is largely chronological. As Chatt (ARC unit, Sussex) has said: "It is difficult to make any connected account except chronologically" (23). Furthermore, since interest has centered mainly on the investigations carried out by Vol'pin and his group in Moscow, and by van Tamelen and his in Stanford, it is the work of these schools which is being reviewed. However, many other teams all over the world, are beginning to make contributions in ever-increasing numbers to our knowledge of this field. Accounts of their work are to be found, in profusion, in the literature.

In an early paper, the Russians Vol'pin and Shur (24) began by comparing the drastic conditions of temperature and pressure needed to make molecular nitrogen react (an exception being the reaction with metallic lithium) with the facile fixation of nitrogen achieved by the enzyme systems of many microorganisms. The participation, in enzymic fixation, of enzymes containing transition elements (molybdenum, iron, etc) led these workers to consider the possibility that activation of nitrogen might be due to the formation of π-complexes with the enzyme metal, to be followed by further reduction to ammonia.

In order to test this theory Vol'pin and Shur studied the behavior of various transition-metal systems, capable of forming complexes with olefins, carbon monoxide, acetylene, and other unsaturated compounds, toward molecular nitrogen. It was found that a number of such systems, after reaction with a variety of reducing agents, such as aluminum and lithium alkyls, Grignard reagents, etc, were capable of fixing nitrogen at room temperature. In all cases, after decomposition of the reaction mixture with dilute acid followed by alkali, the main product of fixation was found to be ammonia.

Table 1 summarizes the results described in a whole series of early, classic papers (25–31) and illustrates the point that the ligands surrounding the transition metal appreciably influence its activity.

Thus, the dicyclopentadienyl compound, $(C_5H_5)_2TiCl_2$, in mixtures with organomagnesium and lithium compounds is much more active in nitrogen fixation than is $TiCl_4$, and is in fact the most effective of all the transition-metal compounds investigated in this series of experiments. The yield of ammonia amounted to 0.9–1.0 mole/mole of $(C_5H_5)_2TiCl_2$ at a nitrogen pressure of 150 atm. Such a system was also capable of fixing nitrogen at atmospheric pressure. On passing nitrogen through a mixture of the cyclopentadienyl compound with ethylmagnesium bromide in ether at room temperature and atmospheric pressure for 8 hr the amount of ammonia formed was 0.7 mole/mole $(C_5H_5)_2TiCl_2$.

The activity of transition metals in nitrogen fixation was also shown to be appreciably inhibited by the presence of complexing agents which compete with nitrogen, eg carbon monoxide, olefins, etc. This suggests that this type of reaction does in fact proceed via a transition-metal complex with nitrogen, of a type similar to those known to be formed with the inhibitory molecules just mentioned.

In the series of experiments just described the reactions under review could be considered to be no more than stoichiometric, and the next objective was to achieve some degree of catalysis in the reaction. This is claimed in a paper published by

Table 1. The Reaction of Nitrogen With Transition-Metal Compounds and Reducing Agents

Transition-metal compound	Reducing agent	Solvent	Nitrogen pressure, atm	Ammonia produced on hydrolysis, moles/mole of transition metal
$TiCl_4$	$Mg + I_2$	ether	90	1.30
$(C_5H_5)_2TiCl_2$	C_2H_5MgBr	ether	150	0.93
$(C_5H_5)_2TiCl_2$	LiC_6H_5	ether	100	0.65^b
$(C_5H_5)_2Ti(CH_3)_2$		ether	80^a	0.20
$TiCl_4$	$Al(i\text{-}Bu)_3$	heptane	150	0.25
$TiCl_4$	C_2H_5MgBr	ether	150	0.104
$VO(acac)_2$	$n\text{-}BuLi$	toluene	83	0.35
$CrCl_3$	C_2H_5MgBr	ether	150	0.20
$CrCl_3$	C_2H_5MgBr	ether	150	0.168
$MoCl_5$	C_2H_5MgBr	ether	150	0.075
WCl_6	C_2H_5MgBr	ether	150	0.147
$Mn(acac)_2$	$Al(i\text{-}Bu)_3$	toluene	100	0.09
$FeCl_3$	C_2H_5MgBr	ether	150	0.088
$CoCl_2$ $NiCl_2$ $PdCl_2$ $(C_6H_5P)_2PtCl_2$ Cu_2Cl_2	C_2H_5MgBr	ether	150	0.00

^{a} At 100°C; all other reactions carried out at room temperature.
^{b} Plus 0.15 moles $C_6H_5NH_2$.

Vol'pin and his colleagues in 1968 (32). Starting from the assumption that the non-catalytic character of the reactions examined hitherto might be due to the instability of the transition-metal compounds used, or to the formation of "strong nitride-like bonds," preventing regeneration of active transition-metal compounds, the effect of acids on the nitrogen-fixing systems was investigated. Since protic acids destroy such systems it was decided to study the catalytic fixation of nitrogen using aprotic acids.

Specifically, nitrogen reactions with a variety of systems consisting of aluminum, aluminum halides, and transition-metal compounds, such as $TiCl_4$, $Ti(OR)_4$, $ZrCl_4$, $MoCl_5$, WCl_6, etc, were observed, and it was found that by using such systems catalytic nitrogen fixation could, in fact, be achieved. Nitrogen was reduced by a mixture of $TiCl_4$, Al, and $AlBr_3$, at temperatures above 50°C, to form products with metal–nitrogen bonds which yielded ammonia on hydrolysis. The reaction proceeded in the absence or presence of added solvent. With increasing amounts of Al and $AlBr_3$ the ammonia yield increased up to 200 or more moles per mole of $TiCl_4$.

However, neither aluminum nor its mixture with $AlBr_3$ reacts with nitrogen, which indicates that $TiCl_4$ catalyzes the reduction of nitrogen with aluminum. Natta et al. (33) showed that, on heating titanium halides with a mixture of aluminum and aluminum halides in benzene, Ti(IV) is reduced to Ti(II) and the stable complex $C_6H_6 \cdot TiX_2 \cdot 2AlX_3$ is formed. This is probably the catalyst responsible for nitrogen fixation carried out in the presence of benzene. This appeared to be confirmed by the following experiment: If Al, $AlBr_3$, and a catalytic amount of the above complex (in which X = Cl) were heated together at 130°C with nitrogen the latter was reduced to give 115 moles of ammonia per mole of titanium complex. In the absence of Al and

AlBr$_3$ the complex reacted with nitrogen at this temperature to form a compound whose analysis indicated it to be C$_6$H$_6$(TiCl$_2$.2AlCl$_3$)$_3$N and which gave a stoichiometric yield of ammonia on hydrolysis.

Meanwhile a group at Stanford University, under the direction of van Tamelen, had been developing systems similar to those of the Russian chemists. In the beginning they did not have recourse to a final hydrolysis step in order to liberate ammonia from the bound nitrogen, but later the generation of ammonia was put on a continuous basis through repeated steps of fixation, reduction, and hydrolysis (using 2-propanol). The stages by which the Stanford team achieved these striking results can be summarized as follows:

Initially the claim was made (34) for "the direct formation of volatile ammonia, carried out at room temperature and under atmospheric pressure and brought about by the combined action of a low-valent organic titanium species and an electron source." Specifically, one equivalent of potassium metal was added to a suspension of dialkoxy titanium dichloride in "diglyme" (diethylene glycol dimethyl ether). During the disappearance of the potassium metal and the formation of divalent titanium, nitrogen was blown through the mixture. Ammonia was detectable in the exit gases 48 hr after the addition of the potassium and its evolution continued for several weeks. Thereafter the addition of further amounts of potassium metal produced more volatile ammonia. The yield of the latter was found to be on the order of 10–15% (based on titanium). When argon was substituted for nitrogen in this experiment no ammonia was produced, nor when one of the system's ingredients, ie alkali metal, or alkoxytitanium dichloride (formed from potassium alkoxide and titanium tetrachloride) was omitted. It was also found that reduction of dicyclopentadienyltitanium dichloride with sodium naphthalide (see Vol. 18, p. 436) in tetrahydrofuran (THF) or diglyme in a nitrogen atmosphere generated ammonia. Solutions of sodium naphthalide are very strong reducing agents and behave, to some extent, as solutions of electrons. The diglyme was regarded as the most likely source of hydrogen; yields of ammonia did not appear to be dependent on the moisture content of the system.

The next step was in fact a dual one; it was reported a year later (35) that the process had not only been made cyclic (catalytic) but effective in the reduction of atmospheric nitrogen to ammonia. The fixation agent used this time was obtained by reducing titanium tetraisopropoxide with sodium naphthalide in an ether solvent. The resulting solution absorbed nitrogen in an amount dependent on concentration, stirring rate, and solvent. After addition of a proton source (isopropyl alcohol) ammonia was liberated in 110% yield based on titanium. Addition of more sodium metal or sodium naphthalide regenerated the fixation agent and thus rendered the process cyclic. In this way yields in excess of 340% ammonia were produced in the course of five cycles, showing that the process is catalytic. The net cycle could be expressed as follows:

$$N_2 + 6\ (CH_3)_2CHOH + 6\ e^- \rightarrow 2\ NH_3 + 6\ (CH_3)_2CHO^-$$

In fixation experiments with air, the same general method was employed, but yields of fixed ammonia were substantially lower.

This process was further developed the following year, after it had been shown (36) that electrolytic reduction could replace reduction by sodium naphthalide. The electrolysis medium consisted of a solution of titanium tetraisopropoxide and aluminum chloride (molar ratio 1:1.5) in ethylene glycol dimethyl ether (glyme).

During electrolysis nitrogen gas was bubbled through the cell, usually a single-compartment type equipped with platinum electrodes. After running for 2 days at 90 V (initially at 50 mA), with a polarity change from time to time, the product was hydrolyzed and the ammonia detected by the Berthelot test was determined by titration (ca 10% yield, based on NH_3:Ti molar ratio). When the nitrogen was replaced by argon, no ammonia could be detected; a similar result was obtained when the titanium ester was absent. Although the yields in this experiment were only very modest the practical significance is obvious, revealing as it did, the interchangeability of chemical and electrolytic electron sources for reduction of bound nitrogen in the van Tamelen system. The aluminum chloride is considered to function primarily as an electrolyte and there were indications that no significant nitrogen reduction took place until the titanium had been reduced beyond the (III) state.

As stated above, the cyclic process first reported in 1968 was further developed in 1969 in a manner highlighting the vital role played by the titanium (II) species in a system involving a fixation-reduction-protonation sequence (37). One system described for the first time was extremely simple. The claim was made that it was the first recorded case of the detention, and subsequent reduction to ammonia, of a transition-metal compound made by direct reaction with nitrogen or other means. The literature since 1965 had contained many references to transition-metal compounds with N_2 ligands, but all these were of such stability that reduction (or oxidation) of the ligand was precluded. This was not the case in the experiment with dicyclopentadienyltitanium ("titanocene") described by van Tamelen and his colleagues. On dissolving in dry, oxygenfree benzene at 20–25°C the solution was exposed to a nitrogen atmosphere with stirring. During the course of three weeks nitrogen uptake was continuous, after which it ceased. Titanium(II) n-hexyloxide behaved similarly, but neither titanium(II) allyloxide nor benzyloxide was effective. The titanocene–nitrogen reaction was found to be reversible under the conditions described. After treatment of the titanium–nitrogen complex with excess sodium naphthalide, and subsequent hydrolysis, high yields of ammonia were produced. No ammonia was produced in the absence of either the sodium naphthalide or the titanium compound, and maximum yields were obtained when these reagents were present in a ratio of 6:1, reflecting the redox relationship required for the overall conversion of nitrogen to ammonia.

Summarizing the progress made up to this point toward a cyclic process for nitrogen fixation, in essentially anhydrous systems of this type, van Tamelen postulated the scheme illustrated in Figure 3. Yields of up to 65% were obtained in this cycle, much higher than those obtained at a single pass in the Haber process.

The cyclic operation depends on the ability of titanium(II) to fix nitrogen, as well as the regenerability of titanium(II) and reduction of the titanium-bound nitrogen. Both can be brought about by "NaNp" (sodium naphthalide), available from a naphthalene pool by periodic reaction with sodium metal. The overall net process can be expressed as follows:

$$N_2 + 6\,e^- + 6\,ROH \rightarrow 2\,NH_3 + 6\,RO^-$$

It is evident that this mode of nitrogen fixation—the first room-temperature, atmospheric pressure process to be operated in an overall catalytic fashion—differs from the original Vol'pin reaction (24) wherein transition-metal compounds are used in conjunction with alkyl Grignard reagents or metal hydrides as reducing species

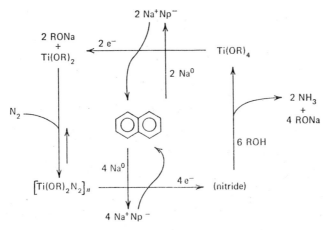

Fig. 3. Titanium(II) in molecular nitrogen fixation reduction.

and hydrogen sources (38). Finally, this cycle serves as a crude parallel or model for the biological nitrogen-fixation process, which in its simplest form probably involves the initial interaction of a lower-valent transition metal with nitrogen from the air, reduction of the coordinated nitrogen species, followed by protonation of the fixed reduced entity to give ammonia and regenerated lower-valent metal.

The catalytic effect of titanium in an electrochemical system was demonstrated (39) with an electrolysis cell equipped with an aluminum anode and a nichrome cathode. The contents of the cell, dissolved in glyme, $CH_3OCH_2CH_2OCH_3$, included titanium tetraisopropoxide (1.68 mM), naphthalene (7.6 mM), and aluminum isopropoxide (42 mM). The solution, while being stirred under nitrogen, was electrolyzed at 40 V until the conductance of the cell had greatly diminished (11 days). The solution was then treated with sodium hydroxide solution and heated in a water bath. Ammonia gas was produced in 610% yield based on an NH_3:Ti molar ratio.

No ammonia could be detected when titanium tetraisopropoxide was omitted or argon substituted for nitrogen. In the absence of naphthalene, ammonia was formed, but in decreased yield. There were indications of naphthalide formation due apparently to the naphthalene functioning as an electron carrier; naphthalide formed in this manner is oxidized back to naphthalene by titanium–nitrogen species.

The aluminum tetraisopropoxide, in addition to its function as an electrolyte, is believed to free the Ti(II)–nitrogen compound of reduced nitrogen so that it can fix more molecular nitrogen. The overall process is illustrated in Figure 4.

Toward the end of 1969 Stanford reported "the first case of substantial transition-metal catalyzed conversion of elemental nitrogen to any compound other than ammonia" (40). Again the system was basically the same one used by this group in previous experiments, ie a transition-metal alkoxide–radical-anion system together with a proton source. Specifically, on adding titanium(IV) tetraisopropoxide to a stirred THF solution of sodium naphthalide, under nitrogen at room temperature and atmospheric pressure, hydrazine and ammonia were liberated in proportion to the ratio of the fixing to the reducing agent.

Hydrazine was detected in hydrolyzates, after removal of ammonia, by the Feigl spot test (41) and by the isolation of the p-dimethylaminobenzaldehyde azine. It was determined quantitatively by a spectrophotometric method. The yield rose with

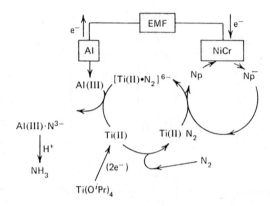

Fig. 4. Catalytic fixation of nitrogen by electrolytic reduction. (Lower-valent titanium may be monomeric or polymeric.)

decreasing Ti(IV):NaNp molar ratios to a maximum of 15–19% (based on Ti) at a Ti(IV):NaNp ratio of 1:5 to 1:6, while the $2NH_3 : N_2H_4$ ratio varied within the range of 3.3:1 to 5.0:1.

When various transition-metal halides were substituted for titanium(IV) tetra-isopropoxide no hydrazine could be detected as product. Equally it was not to be obtained by treatment of either of the complexes $(C_5H_5)_2Ti \cdot N_2$ (37) or $[Ru(NH_3)_5N_2{}^{2+}]$ (42) with water, alcohol, aqueous acid, aqueous base, or a 2–4 molar equivalent of NaNp in THF.

Two further observations permit a tentative interpretation of the hydrazine-ammonia synthesis sequence: (a) there is an increase (up to 22) in the $2NH_3 : N_2H_4$ ratio after a reaction mixture of the type described above is treated overnight with a large excess (12 equiv) of sodium naphthalide, and (b) if the fixation-reduction reaction is carried out in the presence of Al(III), presumed to permit facile reduction of nitrogen from the Ti(II)–N_2 complex to NH_3 (40), hydrazine cannot be detected in the product. Taken in conjunction with the evidence accumulated previously in Stanford the scheme in Figure 5 is postulated.

$$Ti(OR)_4 \xrightarrow{NaNp} [Ti(OR)_2]_x \xrightarrow{N_2} [Ti(OR)_2 \cdot N_2]_x \xrightarrow{4\,NaNp}$$

$$[Ti(OR)_2 \cdot N_2]_x{}^{4-} \xrightarrow{2\,NaNp} [Ti(OR)_2 \cdot N_2]_x{}^{6-}$$

$$\Big\downarrow 4H^+ \qquad\qquad\qquad\qquad \Big\downarrow 6H^+$$

$$N_2H_4 \qquad\qquad\qquad\qquad 2\,NH_3$$

Fig. 5. Conversion of molecular nitrogen to hydrazine.

NITROGEN COMPLEXES AND NITROGENASE MODELS

Notwithstanding the considerable significance, from a practical standpoint, of the cyclic processes devised by van Tamelen and his group, Chatt, at Sussex University (41a), considers them to be no more noteworthy than a simple nitriding effect; lithium wire, for example, can be induced to yield considerable quantities of Li_3N by reaction with nitrogen. It is also of interest to note that iron nitride has been isolated as an intermediate compound in high-pressure ammonia synthesis; it reacts rapidly with hydrogen.

$$N_2 + 3 H_2 \rightarrow 2 NH_3 \quad \text{very slow}$$
$$N_2 + 2 Fe \rightarrow 2 FeN$$
$$2 FeN + 3 H_2 \rightarrow 2 NH_3 + 2 Fe \quad \text{rapid}$$

However, it does not seem likely that this type of reaction could form the basis of nitrogen activation in the aqueous biological environment since, like the systems developed by the Stanford workers, it requires anhydrous conditions. The formation of stable transition-metal complexes with molecular nitrogen as a ligand is considered to be of far greater importance.

Such complexes have been sought for a long time by chemists holding the belief that nitrogenase was a metalloenzyme, and special attention was given to molybdenum compounds. When nitrogen complexes finally were isolated however, it was as the result of accidental discoveries although, in Chatt's view, this in no way reduces the likelihood of their ultimate employment in nitrogen-fixation processes using mild conditions.

In 1965, Allen and Sennoff (42), while attempting to prepare [Ru(NH₃)₆]Cl₂ by reacting ruthenium trichloride in aqueous solution with hydrazine, found that formation of the pentaaminenitrogen ruthenium ion (see above) accompanied the disproportionation of hydrazine into nitrogen and ammonia.

$$RuCl_3 \xrightarrow{H_2O,N_2H_4} [Ru(NH_3)_5N_2]^{2+}$$

It was further shown that this complex liberates all its N_2 ligand as N_2 gas on oxidation with ceric sulfate (43) and yields 6 moles NH_3 on reduction with sodium borohydride (44).

The next step forward, and it was a considerable advance, was the discovery that some nitrogen complexes can be formed rapidly using gaseous nitrogen. Working on polymerization catalysts Yamamoto et al. (45) found that an orange, crystalline nitrogen complex is formed when cobalt trisacetylacetonate, Co(acac)₃, reacts with diethylaluminum ethoxide in the presence of triphenylphosphine and nitrogen.

$$Co(acac)_3 + 3 AlEt_2(OEt) + 3 PPh_3 + N_2 \rightarrow Co(N_2)(PPh_3)_3$$

The product, air sensitive and difficult to purify, invariably contains at least 10% of CoH(N₂)(PPh₃)₃ and, when N₂ and H₂ are passed through the solution, this is the main product (46).

In the same year the direct replacement of a ligand by nitrogen was first demonstrated by Sacco and Rossi (47) who showed that the hydridic hydrogen in CoH₃(PPh₃)₃ could be replaced by nitrogen reversibly in ethanol.

$$CoH_3(PPh_3)_3 \underset{H_2}{\overset{N_2}{\rightleftharpoons}} CoH(N_2)(PPh_3)_3$$

This reversibility is interesting since hydrogen is a competitive inhibitor of natural nitrogen fixation. If the active site in nitrogenase is analogous to that in the cobalt complex then the inhibition of nitrogen fixation in the natural system by hydrogen would be explained. The cobalt complex shows other close analogies with the activity site in nitrogenase, eg it reacts with CO₂, acetylene, methyl isocyanide, and other known inhibitors of nitrogen fixation. However, reduction does not give NH₃ but leads to a reversal of the above reaction.

A further type of N_2 complex should be mentioned. Harrison and Taube in 1967 (43) prepared $[Ru(N_2)(NH_3)_5]^{2+}$ directly from N_2 as follows:

$$[Ru(NH_3)_5Cl]^{2+} \xrightarrow[\text{0.1M } H_2SO_4]{\text{Zn/Hg}} [Ru(NH_3)_5(H_2O)]^{2+}$$

$$\downarrow N_2$$

$$[Ru(NH_3)_5N_2]^{2+} \xleftarrow{\text{NH}_3 \text{ at pH9}} [\{Ru(NH_3)_5\}_2N_2]^{4+}$$

The intermediate dinuclear complex doubtless contains N_2 as a bridging group, and may be formulated as $[(NH_3)_5Ru-N{=}N-Ru(NH_3)_5]^{4+}$.

Stable N_2 complexes are comparatively rare but formation of unstable "ghosts" by the action of N_2 on transition-metal complexes, under strongly reducing conditions, appears to be widespread in the periodic table from Cr to Ni. They are often obtained as oils or impure solids, or seen as color changes on passing N_2 and argon or N_2 and H_2 through suitable solutions of transition-metal complexes.

The formation of N_2 complexes of cobalt described above offers the first known rapid reaction of N_2 in protic solvents under mild conditions. In Chatt's view this narrows the gap between the pure chemistry of nitrogen fixation and the biochemistry of the natural systems; thus, these cobalt complexes may be regarded as a model for the enzyme nitrogenase, which is believed to contain molybdenum and iron as essential elements. It is likely that one of these provides the active site, and considerations of electronic structure suggest that this is an iron atom in the low-spin ferrous state. Thus, the most likely nitrogen-fixation mechanism from the chemical standpoint is that the enzyme contains an iron atom in such an electronic state, determined by the nature of the protein ligand attached to it, and that it picks up nitrogen very easily, as in the preparation of the cobalt complex. The molybdenum is most likely to be concerned with the reducing activity of the enzyme, the reducing energy being produced by the hydrolysis of ATP which is an essential feature of nitrogen fixation.

Commercial Prospects

The mild conditions under which the cycle fixation, reduction, and hydrolysis (or alcoholysis) can be induced to occur in transition-metal complexes closely resemble those under which atmospheric nitrogen is fixed in nature. Microorganisms remove nitrogen from the air under very mild conditions and biochemical investigations, showing that certain transition metals—notably iron and molybdenum—are always present in the natural systems, have revealed a further resemblance. As yet however, the purely chemical systems cannot function without organic solvents whereas enzymic fixation invariably occurs under moist conditions. Of the three methods under consideration, however, it is the industrial process with its harsh conditions of temperature and pressure (300–600°C at several hundred atm) which is now beginning to look inelegant. A similar comparison between the established processes for low- and high-density polyethylene (using harsh and mild conditions, respectively) gives at least two different products, having different properties and uses. On the other hand the Haber process, with its resort to extremes of physical conditions, only produces ammonia, identical with that which for countless centuries has arisen at atmospheric pressures and temperatures in the roots of legumes or, much more recently, in the laboratories of Stanford and Moscow.

In the light of present-day knowledge it is of interest to recall Sir William Crooks' warning to the British Association at Bristol in 1898 that only the achievement of a successful route to the fixation of atmospheric nitrogen could prevent famine on a world-wide scale. Had the results now being achieved by Vol'pin, van Tamelen, Allen and Senoff, and the other investigators been available in 1898, the passage of an electric discharge through air (Birkland and Eyde), or the catalyzed hydrogenation of nitrogen at high temperatures and pressures (Haber), might not have been regarded as the most promising reactions on which to base commercial processes.

From the purely practical standpoint the isolation of a crystalline iron–molybdenum protein from nitrogenase (10), and the synthesis of a molybdenum–nitrogen complex, of some stability, from molecular nitrogen (48) must be regarded as significant developments capable of further exploitation. However, it may not be wholly desirable to bridge the gap between the crystalline metalloenzyme and the transition-metal complex. Attractive though they may be in terms of stability in the presence of moisture, and mildness of the environment generally, the biological processes described above hardly embody all the desiderata for chemical processes to be operated under mild conditions. They are, for a start, inefficient—indeed if they were more efficient excess ammonia would be produced and cause disturbance in the biological environment. Thus, without modification in the direction of improved efficiency, they do not constitute wholly admirable models for a commercially successful route.

This is not to say that the commercial prospects for such processes have not aroused a good deal of attention and comment. Many views have been expressed on the possibility that chemical fixation processes, based on organometallic catalysts bearing some resemblance to nitrogen-fixing enzymes, are now within reach.

Thus Henrici-Olivé and Olivé (49) ask the question whether the recent development of stable nitrogen complexes "can be expected to mean competition for the industrial processes for the production of ammonia," and then proceed to answer it as follows: "In view of the present price of NH_3, the answer to this must be no. However, the question as asked is wrongly phrased, since ammonia is only the industrial starting point for the chemistry of nitrogen. A more sensible question would be whether any competition is to be expected with the current processes for the production of amines, amides, nitriles, etc. In view of the outstanding progress that has been made in homogeneous catalysis on transition-metal complexes in the course of the last 10–20 years, this possibility must be taken very seriously."

Murray and Smith (50) in summarizing their review on the activation of molecular nitrogen, point out that nitrogen and hydrogen coordinate to a metal; that the change in reactivity of organic and inorganic substrates by coordination is a basic premise of organometallic chemistry; that hydrazine and ammonia complexes are well known and that now a diimide complex has been reported (51). From all this they conclude that the scene is now set for the discovery of the vital reaction—the catalytic production of ammonia from nitrogen and hydrogen at room temperature and atmospheric pressure (50). Other significant comments appearing in the technical press are as follows:

"In present processes (for ammonia synthesis) the reaction temperature is not our biggest problem. It's the high pressure. If we can get rid of those big compressors, we could have the capital investment in new ammonia facilities. But if we don't use the steam from the natural gas reformers (producing the hydrogen used) for power, management is going to have to put it to use somewhere else to maintain the economics of the cracking process" (52).

"Obviously much work needs to be done before it can be determined whether or not the van Tamelen compounds could be used in a commercial-scale process. For example, more needs to be known about the part played by the organic groups in the catalyst molecule. However, with about eight million tons of nitrogen being fixed as ammonia each year, much of it for eventual use as fertilizers, the stakes are big enough to give any breakthrough—and van Tamelen's certainly seems to be that—breathtaking possibilities" (53).

"It is too early to predict whether this technique could form the basis of a commercial process for fixing nitrogen but, by combining the electrolytic and chemical reduction of nitrogen into a single, catalytic process, van Tamelen and his co-workers have produced a system that could set a lot of people thinking" (54).

"They (du Pont workers) might then be able to discover how nature fixes nitrogen at room temperature and pressure whereas the chemical industry needs high temperatures and pressures to do it. The world market for nitrogenous fertilizers is enormous, and the company that first discovers how biological molybdenum-iron catalysts work, and then makes its own version, will gain a huge profit" (55).

Bibliography

1. J. E. Carnahan, L. E. Mortenson, H. F. Mower, and J. E. Castle, *Biochim. Biophys. Acta* **44**, 520 (1960).
2. *IUPAC Symp., "Modern Chemistry in Industry," Eastbourne, England, 1968.*
2a. R. Fowler, *Trends in the Nitrogen Fixation Industry,* in reference 2, p. 211.
3. M. A. E. Hodgson, *From Research to Production,* in reference 2, p. 49.
4. D. J. D. Nicholas and D. J. Fisher, *Nature* **186**, 735 (1960).
5. D. J. D. Nicholas, D. J. Silvester, and J. F. Fowler, *Nature* **189**, 634 (1961).
6. J. E. Carnahan, L. E. Mortenson, H. F. Mower, and J. E. Castle, *Biochim. Biophys. Acta* **38**, 188 (1960).
7. L. E. Mortenson, *Proc. Natl. Acad. Sci. U.S.* **52**, 272 (1964).
8. R. W. F. Hardy and A. J. D. D'Eustachio, *Biochim. Biophys. Res. Commun.* **15**, 314 (1964).
9. R. H. Burris, *Proc. Roy. Soc. (London) Ser. B* **172**, 345 (1969).
10. R. C. Burns, R. D. Holsten, and R. W. F. Hardy, *Biochim. Biophys. Res. Commun.* **39**, 90 (1970).
11. G. C. Gerloff, G. P. Fitzgerald, and F. Skoog, *Am. J. Botany* **37**, 216 (1950).
12. I. J. Pintner and L. Provasoli, *J. Gen. Microbiol.* **18**, 1 (1958).
13. W. D. P. Stewart, *Ann. Botany (London)* **26**, 439 (1962).
14. R. M. Cox, *Arch. Mikrobiol.* **56**, 193 (1967).
15. *Ibid.,* **53**, 263 (1966).
16. R. M. Cox and P. Fay, *Arch. Mikrobiol.* **58**, 357 (1967).
17. G. E. Fogg and Than-Tun, *Proc. Roy. Soc. (London) Ser. B.* **153**, 111 (1960).
18. P. Fay and G. E. Fogg, *Arch. Mikrobiol.* **42**, 310 (1962).
19. R. M. Cox and P. Fay, *Proc. Roy. Soc. (London) Ser. B.* **172**, 357 (1969).
20. F. J. Bergersen, *Proc. 9th Intern. Congr. Microbiol. Symp., Moscow, 1966,* p. 97.
21. B. Koch, H. J. Evans, and S. Russell, *Plant Physiol.* **42**, 466 (1967).
22. F. J. Bergersen, *Proc. Roy. Soc. (London) Ser. B.* **172**, 401 (1969).
23. J. Chatt, *Proc. Roy. Soc. (London) Ser. B.* **172**, 330 (1969).
24. M. E. Vol'pin and V. B. Shur, *Nature* **209**, 1236 (1966).
25. M. E. Vol'pin and V. B. Shur, *Dokl. Akad. Nauk. SSSR* **156**, 1102 (1964); *Chem. Abstr.* **61**, 8933a (1964).
26. M. Vol'pin et al., *Dokl. Akad. Nauk. SSSR* **164**, 861 (1965); *Chem. Abstr.* **63**, 15840b (1965)
27. M. E. Vol'pin et al., *Bull. Acad. Sci., USSR, Div. Chem. Sci. (English Transl.)* **1966**, 1033.
28. *Ibid.,* **1964**, 1644.
29. *Ibid.,* **1965**, 2196.
30. M. E. Vol'pin and V. B. Shur, *Vestn. Akad. Nauk. SSSR* **34** (1), 51 (1965).
31. M. E. Vol'pin and V. B. Shur, *Zh. Vses. Khim. Obshchestva im D. I. Mendeleeva* **12**, 31 (1967).
32. M. E. Vol'pin et al., *Chem. Commun.* **1968**, 1074.

33. G. Natta, G. Mazzanti, and G. Pregaglia, *Gaz. Chim. Ital.* **89**, 2065 (1959,
34. E. E. van Tamelen et al., *J. Am. Chem. Soc.* **89**, 5707 (1967).
35. *Ibid.*, **90**, 1677 (1968).
36. E. E. van Tamelen and B. Åkermark, *J. Am. Chem. Soc.* **90**, 4492 (1968).
37. E. E. van Tamelen et al., *J. Am. Chem. Soc.* **91**, 1551 (1969).
38. H. Brintzinger, *J. Am. Chem. Soc.* **88**, 4305, 4307 (1966).
39. E. E. van Tamelen and D. A. Seeley, *J. Am. Chem. Soc.* **91**, 5194 (1969).
40. E. E. van Tamelen, R. B. Fechter, and S. W. Schneller, *J. Am. Chem. Soc.* **91**, 7196 (1969).
41. F. Feigl, *"Spot Tests in Inorganic Analysis,"* Elsevier Publishing Co., New York, 1958, p. 240.
41a. J. Chatt, *Proc. Roy. Soc. (London) Ser. B* **172**, 328 (1969).
42. A. D. Allen and C. V. Senoff., *Chem. Commun.* **1965**, 621.
43. D. E. Harrison and H. Taube, *J. Am. Chem. Soc.* **89**, 5706 (1967).
44. A. D. Allen et al., *J. Am. Chem. Soc.* **89**, 5595 (1967).
45. A. Yamamoto et al., *Chem. Commun.* **1967**, 79.
46. J. H. Enemark et al., *Chem. Commun.* **1968**, 96.
47. A. Sacco and M. Rossi, *Chem. Commun.* **1967**, 316.
48. H. K. Tominari, Y. Uchida, and A. Misono, *Chem. Commun.* **1969**, 814.
49. G. Henrici-Olivé and S. Olivé, *Angew. Chem. Intern. Ed. Engl.* **8** (9), 650 (1969).
50. R. Murray and D. C. Smith, *Coordination Chem. Rev.* **3**, 465 (1968).
51. W. G. Hanstein, J. B. Lett, C. E. McKenna, and T. G. Traylor, *Proc. Natl. Acad. Sci. U.S.* **58**, 1314 (1967).
52. *Chem. Week* **100** (3), 65 (1967).
53. *New Scientist,* **1969**, p. 193.
54. *New Scientist,* **1969**, p. 327.
55. *New Scientist,* **1970**, p. 270.

R. H. STANLEY
Titanium Intermediates Ltd

NONLINEAR OPTICAL MATERIALS

The discovery of low-threshold, high-power lasers provides us with convenient sources of coherent, monochromatic radiation at optical frequencies. Such sources have important uses in micromachining, surgery, accurate distance measurement, information storage, spectroscopy, and communications. For these and many other future applications, it is necessary to manipulate the coherent light waves to achieve the desired effects. This manipulation may entail such processes as mixing, amplifying, detecting, limiting, modulating and frequency conversion. The most useful process is frequency conversion and the ability to generate coherent light at literally any visible frequency in addition to the useful laser frequencies in this range. All of these functions are most suitably performed at the present time in single crystals of nonlinear optical materials. Such materials are transparent to the frequencies of interest and interact with high-intensity light waves in a nonlinear manner which is described in more detail.

When an ordinary beam of light passes from air into a transparent material, the beam slows down. This is seen from a bending of the beam by an amount that depends on the ratio of the index of refraction of air to that for a transparent material. The actual interaction occurring is that between the oscillating electric field of the light beam and the electric charges in the atoms or molecules of the material. This results in oscillations of the electron cloud around the nuclei which, in turn, reradiate at the same frequency as the incoming field but delayed in time phase by 90°. The vector sum of these two fields is the resulting wave and it has a lower velocity than the incident wave. For light of normal intensity the magnitude of the oscillating electron-nucleus dipole varies linearly with magnitude of the electric field of the incoming light wave. However if the incident light source is intense, the excursion of the electron cloud is no longer small and the dipole moment varies nonlinearly with the magnitude of the driving field. Under these conditions, other frequencies are generated in addition to the incident light frequency. In nonlinear optical materials, the crystal structures do not possess a center of symmetry and consequently a distorted polarization wave is generated at electric-field intensities far below the breakdown field of the solid. This wave is composed of the fundamental frequency and its overtones (particularly the second harmonic) and a "direct current" or steady polarization component.

Second Harmonic Generation. The first nonlinear optical effect to be studied was the generation of second harmonic radiation. This experiment was performed by Franken and his associates at the University of Michigan in 1961 (1). They focused the red beam of a ruby laser onto a quartz crystal and observed a faint second harmonic in the ultraviolet. The conversion efficiency however was very low (one part in 10^8). Such a low efficiency was found to occur because of an interference effect. Since the refractive index varies with wavelength (called normal dispersion), the fundamental and harmonic light must travel at slightly different velocities. Consequently, the harmonic component interferes with the polarization wave from which it is produced. This interference is destructive at any distance greater than a distance called the coherence length which is of the order of a thousandth of a centimeter. Thus a long optical path was of no value in building up a huge amount of second harmonic signal.

Such interference phenomena have been overcome by generating the second harmonic in a doubly refracting material. Here, the two velocities of propagation in the crystal—one for waves polarized in one direction and one for waves polarized in the other direction—allow the speed of the harmonic to be matched to that of the fundamental. This technique made possible an increase in coherence length from a thousandth of a centimeter to more than a centimeter and has led to a millionfold increase in efficiency. Conversion efficiencies from red to blue light of up to 20% were first observed in crystals of ammonium dihydrogen phosphate (ADP) and potassium dihydrogen phosphate (KDP) (2). Subsequent work, which is discussed below, has uncovered materials with even larger nonlinear gains.

Parametric Oscillation and Amplification. The generation of a second harmonic is only a special case of the general situation in which two frequencies are mixed together to produce sum and difference frequencies. Second harmonic generation is a special case of sum-frequency generation. In difference mixing, a laser beam of frequency ω_L is placed through a nonlinear crystal together with radiation at a lower frequency ω_S (the subscript S refers to a signal). The presence of the lower frequency triggers the creation of additional radiation at ω_S, as well as at the difference frequency, $\omega_L - \omega_S$. The high frequency splits into two lower frequencies and, irrespective of the phase of ω_S, the phase of the difference frequency (usually referred to as the idler) can be adjusted so that power is transferred from ω_L to the two lower frequencies. This is accomplished by adjusting the birefringence of the crystal so that the polarization wave travels at the same velocity as the freely propagating idler wave. The idler wave also mixes with the laser (also called the pump) to produce a traveling polarization wave at the signal frequency, phased so that growth of the signal field also results.

This process is called parametric amplification. The first experimental parametric oscillator was constructed with lithium niobate, $LiNbO_3$ (3).

With the pump frequency fixed, any process which changes the refractive indexes at the signal, idler, or pump frequencies, tunes the oscillator. Tuning methods include temperature, angular variation of the extraordinary refractive indexes, and possibly pressure tuning by the photoelastic effect. Temperature or angular tuning may be used to tune over broad frequency ranges, and pressure or electric fields may be used for fine tuning.

The optical gain of nonlinear optical materials serves as a useful comparative standard for their performance. The gain is proportional to $|d|^2/n^3$ where d is the effective nonlinear coefficient and n is the refractive index. This figure of merit is shown in Figure 1 together with the transparency range for a number of nonlinear materials. Lithium niobate and barium sodium niobate, $Ba_2NaNb_5O_{15}$, have a very useful visible and infrared transparency range for presently available laser wavelengths and are the most widely used at this time. The phase equilibria and associated crystal-growth problems of these materials are discussed below. An understanding of these problems is essential if optical uniformity is to be achieved.

Electrooptic Modulation. We have seen that sum- and difference-frequency generation is accomplished in noncentrosymmetric materials with a birefringence which exceeds the normal dispersion of the refractive indexes. The position of the electrons in such crystals can be easily influenced by the internal electric field developed by the light passing through the material. However, the application of external electric fields can also alter the velocity of light (and refractive index) in nonlinear optical materials. In directions of zero birefringence or crystals with small natural birefringence this electrooptic effect predominates and offers a means of modulating light. Modulation involves the rapid variation of the amplitude, frequency, or phase of the carrier. Since changing the light velocity affects the phase of the wave, an electrooptic modulator is basically a phase modulator. It can be converted to an amplitude modulator (AM) by placing the crystal between crossed polarizers oriented at 45° to the incident electric field. The phase difference imparted by the electrooptic effect causes the incident-linearly polarized wave to become elliptically polarized so that the amplitude of light passing through the second polarizer becomes a function of the applied voltage. If the voltage is alternated between the two extreme values for 0 and 90° rotations of the polarization axis, one can pulse-code-modulate (PCM) the laser beam. Denton, Chen, and Kinsel have used lithium tantalate, $LiTaO_3$, as a broad-band modulator (4). The path length (and hence modulating effect) was doubled by means of a reflector at one end of the crystal. Also the small natural birefringence of lithium tantalate was cancelled by means of another birefringent crystal in the form of a wedge inserted in the beam. This modulator has been used in both a conventional AM mode and in a PCM mode. Lithium niobate has also been used successfully as a modulator and electrooptic switch when light is directed along the c-axis where the natural birefringence is zero.

There are many other techniques used to modulate laser light which do not involve nonlinear optical materials. However these other materials (for example gallium phosphide, GaP, diodes using electrooptic effects or yttrium iron garnet, $Y_3Fe_5O_{12}$, using magnetooptic effects) have more limited usefulness because of optical absorption in important regions of the visible spectrum.

Pyroelectric Detection of Radiation. Nonlinear optical materials exhibit some

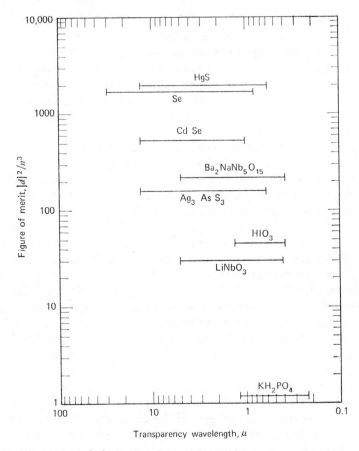

Fig. 1. Transparency and $|d^2|/n^3$ of some phase matchable nonlinear optical materials (43).

interesting interactions between stress, temperature, and electric fields.   One such effect is the generation of electric charge by a change in temperature.   This is called the pyroelectric effect and the electric current, i, is directly proportional to the time rate of change of polarization, P, as follows:

$$i \sim \frac{dP}{dT}\frac{dT}{dt}$$

where T and t are temperature and time respectively.   This effect was extensively studied (5) in triglycine sulfate, $(NH_2CH_2COOH)_3 \cdot H_2SO_4$.   The pyroelectric coefficients become quite large in the vicinity of the ferroelectric–paraelectric transition (the Curie temperature).   In materials where the increase in electrical conductivity is not large in this same temperature region, the pyroelectric effect may be used to detect electromagnetic radiation as a result of the heating effect produced in the crystal by that radiation.   Nonlinear materials with Curie temperatures just above room temperature are particularly useful for detecting infrared radiation.   Glass (6) has constructed highly efficient room-temperature detectors from crystals of barium strontium niobate, Ba_x-$Sr_{1-x}Nb_2O_6$ ($0.2 \leq x \leq 0.8$).   There are many other factors which enter into the efficiency of detection with respect to the crystal thickness, electrode configuration, optical reflection losses and the method of crystal mounting (to minimize the piezoelectric signal which is also generated).

Evolution of Nonlinear Optical Materials

A comprehensive materials search program was undertaken after the discovery of Franken and Ward. At the outset, there were few property measurements which could be simply performed to help in this search. However, the intuitive approach was to find a connection between the known properties (such as the refractive index and birefringence) and the expected magnitude of its nonlinear optical properties. This approach was based upon the fact that the velocity of light in any medium depends on the distribution of electrons in the medium. Consequently materials with a large polarizability were of interest. Two classes of materials were studied: one with a large electronic polarizability where atoms possess many loosely held electrons (elements with high atomic numbers and nearly closed electron shells), and the other with large ionic polarizability where a permanent molecular dipole moment exists in the crystal (piezoelectric and ferroelectric materials with complex anionic groups). In addition, only crystal structures lacking a center of symmetry were of interest. A rather simple experiment used to check for the absence of a center of symmetry is the Giebe-Scheibe test (7) which searches for piezoelectric coupling. This test works well on ceramics as well as crystals. Another useful test for single or polycrystalline specimens is the powder technique developed by Kurtz (8) which measures the (integrated) intensity of the generated second harmonic from a ruby laser relative to a quartz standard. This test checks for acentricity as well as relative ease of phase matching. The measurement of the halfwave retardation voltage in crystals gives a measure of the electrooptic effects. This is the applied voltage for a standard crystal, light and field configuration which will cause light to emerge from the crystal one-half wavelength behind (or ahead of) the position of the light in the absence of a field. Halfwave voltages are inversely proportional to both the electrooptic constants and the index of refraction. All materials must have transmission windows in the wavelength regions of interest.

In addition to these tests, there are some empirical and theoretical rules which are useful in searching for new nonlinear optical materials. The original correlation is the Miller delta rule (9) which showed that the nonlinear optical susceptibility, d, is related to the linear optical susceptibilty, χ (where $4\pi\chi = n^2 - 1$, and n is the index of refraction) by as follows:

$$d = \chi^3 \Delta$$

where Δ is constant to within a factor of ± 2 for most inorganic crystals. Wemple and DiDomenico (10) have related the Miller delta to the spontaneous polarization and packing fraction of oxygen octahedra on the basis of a band-structure model. These results show that the tetragonal distorted (C_{4v}) systems are better than trigonally distorted (C_{3v}) systems and that the d coefficient increases with decreasing principal quantum number of the cationic constituent in the oxygen octahedra. Thus in systems with Ti, Nb and Ta, the titanates would be expected to be more nonlinear. The polarizations needed to compute Δ may be estimated for displacive oxide ferroelectrics from the Curie temperature by an empirical relationship given by Abrahams (11).

Most acentric materials are of little or no practical value, either because of their small nonlinear optical effects, or because crystals of high quality cannot be prepared. When a given compound appears to be of potential nonlinear interest on the basis of the tests described and on a theoretical basis, the next task is to prepare large single crystals. The most appropriate exploratory growth technique is that of pulling crystals from their congruent melts. Difficulty in producing large uniform crystals by pulling indicates that a given system possesses undesirable phase equilibria and may not be worth further consideration. Some of these aspects are considered below.

There is a materials preparation technique being developed which avoids the problems encountered when growing large crystals. In this method, polycrystalline ceramic powders are reacted at high pressures and temperatures in the solid state. The resulting ceramic specimen has almost the maximum density expected for crystals and is optically transparent over centimeter distances. The material currently used most, lead zirconate-titanate, $PbZrO_3$–$PbTiO_3$ (12), is used for switching and beam deflection purposes by either applying an external biasing field (the electrooptic effect) or by partially switching the ferroelectric polarization. However more sophisticated harmonic generation or mixing experiments have not been performed with such specimens.

Crystals grown from their melts are single crystals in most respects. However the electric dipoles are not uniformly aligned throughout the crystal but rather are oriented similarly in small regions called domains. For optical applications, the crystals must be single-domain. This is accomplished by cooling the crystal through the Curie temperature while simultaneously applying a dc electric field. This process is called poling. Recent work has indicated that many nonlinear materials require the incorporation of protons at the electrode surfaces to be successfully poled (13). These protons raise the resistivity of the crystal by several orders of magnitude and thus ensure that a reasonably large electric field can be maintained across the crystal.

The first materials widely used for nonlinear optics were ammonium dihydrogen phosphate (ADP) and its potassium counterpart (KDP). These crystals are the only ones with transparency in the ultraviolet, as well as the visible. These materials are phase matched by angular tuning primarily. Temperature tuning is not possible with these crystals because they are grown from aqueous solution and tend to decompose at elevated temperatures. Hard optical coatings are also difficult to obtain for the same reasons.

Materials with Large Ionic Polarizability. Lithium niobate was first grown as large single crystals by Ballman (14) in 1966 and is the most widely used oscillator material at this time because of its useful visible and infrared transparency range as well as its tuning versatility (both temperature and angle). The melting point is about 1240°C and the Curie temperature is in the neighborhood of 1170°C. The properties of lithium niobate (Curie temperature, birefringence and phase matching temperature) were shown by Bergman et al. (15) to vary with the composition of the melt from which the crystals were pulled. Subsequently, Lerner et al. (16) showed that lithium niobate existed over a solid solution range of 48.0–50.0 mole % Li_2O at room temperature. Furthermore the congruently melting composition was located in this range rather than at the stoichiometric (50% Li_2O) composition. This was confirmed by Peterson and Carruthers (17) in an NMR study that showed that all pulled crystals were lithium-deficient. More refined phase equilibria investigations by Carruthers et al. (18) located the congruently melting composition at 48.6% Li_2O.

Crystals grown at this composition were shown independently by Nash et al. (19) and Byer et al. (20) to be extremely uniform in composition as expected. Birefringence variations of less than 2.5×10^{-6} per cm due to nonstoichiometric composition changes are routinely obtained from congruent melts. In addition phase matching temperature variations have been reduced to the theoretical limit ($0.72°C/cm$ for $\lambda = 1.08 \mu$) in these crystals.

Crystals produced at congruently melting compositions may not always possess desirable properties even though these properties may be spatially uniform. In the case of lithium niobate, laser damage was shown to occur in crystals operating below 170°C (21). Above this temperature the damage could be annealed out. Thus crystals grown from melts containing excess Li_2O which possessed phase-matching temperatures (at 1.06μ) in excess of 170°C were required. However such crystals were found to be very nonuniform because, at noncongruent compositions, normal freezing compositional variations and striations due to interface growth fluctuations become problems. The damage susceptibility of lithium niobate stimulated a search for new nonlinear materials by Van Uitert and co-workers at Bell Telephone Laboratories (22,23) and by IBM workers (24,25). These workers discovered that ferroelectrics with the tetragonal wolfram bronze-type structure were more resistant to laser damage and possessed larger nonlinear optical coefficients. The most useful material in this class is barium sodium niobate, $Ba_2NaNb_5O_{15}$, from which the first continuous-wave optical parametric oscillator was constructed (26). Phase equilibria investigations in this system also show that the congruently melting and stoichiometric compositions are not the same (27). The Curie temperature was found to be in the neighborhood of 570°C and a tetragonal-to-orthorhombic twinning transformation occurs near 260°C, both temperatures being dependent on the stoichiometry. The lattice distortions existing during the ferroelectric transition were found to be a major factor in the susceptibility of barium sodium niobate to cracking (28). The cracking tendency increases dramatically in the presence of stoichiometric composition variations in the crystal (29).

The utility of lithium niobate has been increased greatly by the addition of magnesium oxide to the congruent Li/Nb ratio (30). The phase-matching temperature is raised to well above the damage-anneal temperature by such additions and the spatial uniformity is maintained for additions of up to at least a few percent.

Lithium tantalate, which is isostructural with lithium niobate, was first grown as large crystals by Ballman (31). This material possesses a very low natural birefringence and large electrooptic coefficients and thus is very useful as for electrooptic modulation (4). It has also been shown that lithium tantalate is a better piezoelectric material than crystalline quartz and that a zero temperature coefficient orientation exists so that it may replace quartz in many applications (32). The high-temperature phase equilibria and defect structure resemble those of lithium niobate (33) although there are some important differences (34).

Barium strontium niobate is another tetragonal wolfram bronze-type material discovered independently by Francombe (35) and Ismailzade (36). The first large crystals were grown by Ballman and Brown over a wide range of melt compositions (37). This material has a Curie temperature just above room temperature and has been shown by Glass to possess interesting pyroelectric properties (6). The phase equilibria in this system have been reported by Carruthers and Grasso (38) and the congruently melting composition has been located.

Materials with Large Electronic Polarizability. The search for materials with high electronic polarizability has recently focused on iodates. The IO_3 group contains an unshared pair of electrons which contribute to this polarizability and in addition create noncentrosymmetric structures (39). The M^{1+} iodates are of particular interest based on second harmonic generation experiments on powders. Crystals have been grown from aqueous solution and are sufficiently large and optically uniform to be used as simple frequency doublers although the spectral windows are somewhat narrower than those of the niobates or tantalates.

There is some interest in oscillation further in the infrared $(1-10\ \mu)$ than the above materials can be used. Proustite (Ag_3AsS_3) and cadmium selenide (CdSe) are two materials which have been used (40,41,42). Proustite has been used for mixing experiments but not as an oscillator. A substantial effort is underway in many laboratories to search for more suitable materials in this wavelength region.

Bibliography

1. P. A. Franken, A. E. Hill, C. W. Peters, and G. Weinreich, *Phys. Rev. Letters* **7**, 118 (1961).
2. J. A. Giordmaine, "The Interaction of Light with Light," *Sci. Am.* June, 1964; R. W. Terhune, "Nonlinear Optics," *Internat. Sci. Tech.*, Aug., 1964.
3. J. A. Giordmaine and R. C. Miller, *Phys. Rev. Letters* **14**, 973 (1965).
4. R. T. Denton, F. S. Chen, and T. S. Kinsel, *J. Appl. Phys.* **38**, 1611 (1967).
5. A. G. Chynoweth, *J. Appl. Phys.* **27**, 78 (1956).
6. A. M. Glass, *J. Appl. Phys.* **40**, 4699 (1969).
7. E. Giebe and A. Scheibe, *Z. Physik* **33**, 760 (1925).
8. S. K. Kurtz and T. T. Perry, *J. Appl. Phys.* **39**, 3798 (1968).
9. R. C. Miller, *Appl. Phys. Letters* **5**, 17 (1964).
10. S. H. Wemple and M. DiDomenico, Jr., *J. Appl. Phys.* **40**, 720, 735 (1969).
11. S. C. Abrahams, S. K. Kurtz, and P. B. Jamieson, *Phys. Rev.* **172**, 551 (1968).
12. C. E. Land and P. D. Thatcher, *Western Electric Engineer*, p. 13, Jan. 1970.
13. L. C. Bobb, I. Lefkowitz, and L. Muldower, *Solid State Commun.* **7**, 937 (1969).
14. A. A. Ballman, *J. Am. Ceram. Soc.* **48**, 112 (1965).
15. J. G. Bergman, A. Ashkin, A. A. Ballman, J. M. Dziedzic, H. J. Levinstein, and R. G. Smith, *Appl. Phys. Letters* **12**, 92 (1968).
16. P. Lerner, C. Legras, and J. D. Dumas, *J. Cryst. Growth*, **3,4**, 231 (1968).
17. G. E. Peterson and J. R. Carruthers, *J. Solid State Chem.* **1**, 98 (1969).
18. J. R. Carruthers, G. E. Peterson, P. M. Bridenbaugh, and M. Grasso, *J. Appl. Phys.* **42**, 1846 (1970).
19. F. R. Nash, G. D. Boyd, M. Sargent IIIrd., and P. M. Bridenbaugh, *J. Appl. Phys.* **41**, 2564 (1970).
20. R. L. Byer, J. F. Young, and R. S. Feigelson, *J. Appl. Phys.* **41**, 2320 (1970).
21. A. Ashkin, G. D. Boyd, J. M. Dziedzic, R. G. Smith, A. A. Ballman, H. J. Levinstein, and K. Nassau, *Appl. Phys. Letters* **12**, 186 (1968).
22. J. E. Geusic, H. J. Levinstein, J. J. Rubin, S. Singh, and L. G. Van Uitert, *Appl. Phys. Letters* **11**, 269 (1967) and Erratum.
23. L. G. Van Uitert, S. Singh, H. J. Levinstein, J. E. Geusic, and W. A. Bonner, *Appl. Phys. Letters* **11**, 161 (1967).
24. E. A. Giess, G. Burns, D. F. O'Kane, and A. W. Smith, *Appl. Phys. Letters* **11**, 233 (1967).
25. G. Burns, E. A. Giess, D. F. O'Kane, B. A. Scott, and A. W. Smith, *J. Appl. Phys.* **40**, 901 (1969).
26. R. G. Smith, J. E. Geusic, H. J. Levinstein, J. J. Rubin, S. Singh, and L. G. Van Uitert, *Appl. Phys. Letters* **12**, 308 (1968).
27. J. R. Carruthers and M. Grasso, *Mater. Res. Bull.* **4**, 413 (1969).
28. A. A. Ballman, J. R. Carruthers, and H. M. O'Bryan, Jr., *J. Cryst. Growth* **6**, 184 (1970).

29. W. A. Bonner, J. R. Carruthers, and H. M. O'Bryan, Jr., *Mater. Res. Bull.* **5**, 243 (1970).
30. P. M. Bridenbaugh, J. R. Carruthers, J. M. Dziedzic, and F. R. Nash, *Appl. Phys. Letters* **17**, 104 (1970).
31. A. A. Ballman, H. J. Levinstein, C. D. Capio, and H. Brown, *J. Am. Ceram. Soc.* **50**, 657 (1967).
32. A. W. Warner and A. A. Ballman, *Proc. IEEE* **55**, 450 (1967).
33. R. L. Barns and J. R. Carruthers, to be published, *J. Appl. Cryst.*
34. G. E. Peterson, J. R. Carruthers, and A. Carnevale, *J. Chem. Phys.* **53**, 2436 (1970).
35. M. H. Francombe, *Acta Cryst.* **13**, 131 (1960).
36. I. G. Ismailzade, *Kristallograf.* **5**, 268 (1960).
37. A. A. Ballman and H. Brown, *J. Cryst. Growth* **1**, 311 (1966).
38. J. R. Carruthers and M. Grasso, *J. Electrochem. Soc.* **117**, 1426 (1970).
39. S. K. Kurtz, J. G. Bergman, Jr., and T. T. Perry, *Bull. Am. Phys. Soc.* **13**, 388 (1968); J. G. Bergman, Jr., G. D. Boyd, A. Ashkin, and S. K. Kurtz, *J. Appl. Phys.* **40**, 2860 (1969).
40. W. Bardsley, P. H. Davies, M. V. Hobden, K. F. Hulme, O. Jones, W. Pomeroy, and J. Warner, *Opto-Electronics*, **1**, 29 (1969).
41. K. F. Hulme, O. Jones, P. H. Davies, and M. V. Hobden, *Appl. Phys. Letters* **10**, 133 (1967).
42. C. K. N. Patel, *Phys. Rev. Letters* **16**, 613 (1966).
43. S. E. Harris, *Proc. IEEE* **57**, 2096 (1969).

General References

P. A. Franken and J. F. Ward, "Optical Harmonics and Nonlinear Phenomena," *Rev. Mod. Phys.* **35**, 23 (1963).
D. F. Nelson, "The Modulation of Laser Light," *Sci. Am.* June 1968, p. 17.
J. G. Bergman and S. K. Kurtz, "Nonlinear Optical Materials," *Mater. Sci. Eng.* **5**, 235 (1970).
R. A. Laudise, "The Search for Nonlinear Optical Materials for Laser Communications," *Bell Laboratories Record*, January 1968, p. 3.
R. A. Laudise, "Optical and Nonlinear Optical Materials," *Proc. of the Chania Conference on Electronic Materials, Chania, Greece, 1970*, to be published.

J. R. CARRUTHERS
Bell Telephone Laboratories

O

OLEFINS

The olefins discussed here are the monoolefins, C_nH_{2n}. Except for the two lowest members of the series, ethylene and propylene, they may be either linear or branched. Although some branched olefins are used in fair volume in the chemical industry, the linear olefins are by far the more significant. Of these the alpha olefins, rather than those having the double bond in an internal location, are of particular interest. (It may be noted that the term "alpha olefins" is often used to refer specifically to linear alpha olefins.)

In physical properties, olefins run the entire gamut from compounds which are gaseous under normal pressure and temperature (C_2–C_4) to liquids (C_5– about C_{19}) and solids (about C_{20} and above). For selected physical properties of the C_2–C_{20} linear olefins and the C_5 and C_6 isomers, see Vol. 14, pp. 315–316.

In their general properties, olefins strike a happy medium between high reactivity on the one hand, and stability and relative safety of storage and handling on the other. Olefins undergo virtually all of the commercially important chemical reactions such as oxidation, hydrogenation, polymerization, amination, hydration, halogenation, alkylation, hydroformylation, etc. This diversity permits the manufacture of a variety of more complex organic chemicals. The chemical reactivity centers around the double bond, one reason why the location of this bond in the molecule is important. Olefin reactivity, although much greater than that of the paraffins, is more easily controlled than that of the more unsaturated compounds, such as diolefins and acetylenes, thereby reducing the chance of runaway reactions and the formation of undesired by-products. In their toxicity and flammability, olefins are comparable to the paraffins. Gradual peroxide formation upon storage of liquid olefins exposed to air can readily be inhibited (see Vol. 14, pp. 320–321).

Perhaps the most prominent reason for the industrial significance of olefins is their relatively low cost and abundant availability from petroleum. Olefins as a group, particularly ethylene and propylene, are the key building blocks of the modern organic chemical industry. This is especially true of the aliphatic sector, although many tonnage cyclic compounds, such as styrene, cumene, and benzenoid surfactants, also require olefins for their manufacture.

The olefins field can be conveniently divided into two major groupings: the lower or gaseous products (C_2–C_4) and the higher olefins (C_{6+}). In between these two are the C_5 olefins which form, in many respects, a class by themselves, and which are discussed separately.

The end-use spectra, logistics, and derivation of the two major groupings differ in several economically significant respects.

1. The gaseous olefins find application in a broad and diversified number of fields, which include both the chemical and petroleum industries. By contrast, the higher olefins have a narrow and specialized end-use pattern, essentially confined to the chemical industry, in which two applications predominate: as intermediates for detergents and plasticizers.

2. Due to their physical state, downstream conversion of the gaseous olefins tends to be raw material-oriented. Production and subsequent transformation of higher olefins, on the other hand, are not so closely linked geographically, except where they are manufactured in a dilute state, which requires considerable recycling. Recent developments in transportation and storage of gaseous products, including pipeline grids and cryogenic techniques, have introduced a greater degree of flexibility into the logistics of gaseous olefins.

3. The gaseous olefins are either obtained as a by-product of petroleum refining operations or are made intentionally in olefin plants. By contrast, the higher olefins are made exclusively in plants designed for that specific purpose.

The gaseous olefins are by far the more important and versatile. In terms of tonnage, they are an order of magnitude above the others, even apart from their refinery uses. In the U.S., for instance, about 28 billion lb of gaseous olefins was produced for chemical purposes in 1969, according to the U.S. Tariff Commission, compared with only about 1.5 billion lb of higher olefins, or a ratio of greater than 18:1. While comparable figures for the rest of the world are not readily available, the ratio is, if anything, greater still.

Olefins are not found as such in nature but can be produced industrially from naturally occurring hydrocarbons by cracking or dehydrogenation. Many of the higher olefins are synthesized from the gaseous olefins, although some are also produced from selected petroleum fractions. Both lower and higher olefins can also be made from the corresponding alcohols by dehydration. This is still being done in certain special situations, notably for high-purity long-chain alpha olefins, but it is not a major source of tonnage products. Ethylene has also been recovered from coke-oven gas, a derivation which has virtually ceased to have commercial significance. In addition, there are numerous laboratory preparations to produce ethylene and other olefins (1).

It is theoretically possible to convert an olefin into other olefins of higher and lower molecular weight by disproportionation, a technology pioneered by Phillips and British Petroleum. Thus far its only commercial application is the Shawinigan Chemicals plant in Canada which converts propylene into ethylene and butenes. Other uses of olefin disproportionation that have been proposed include the synthesis of detergent range linear olefins (2) and of "isoamylene" by disproportionation of isobutylene and propylene, or of isobutylene and 2-butene (3).

The Gaseous Olefins

The gaseous or lower olefins include ethylene, propylene and four isomeric butylenes: α-butylene (1-butene), β-butylene (2-butene), cis and trans, and isobutylene (methylpropene). Their physical and chemical properties have been discussed under Ethylene, Propylene, and Butylenes; see also Ethylene in this volume.

Chemistry and technology of the monoolefins have most recently been comprehensively covered by Professor Friedrich Asinger (4), and that of ethylene by a group of some thirty international authorities (5). The similarities and complex interrelationships among the various individual gaseous olefins suggest that they can be discussed in a more meaningful way as a group rather than separately.

The first olefin to be used chemically on an industrial scale was propylene which was hydrated with sulfuric acid to yield isopropyl alcohol in a plant constructed at Bayway by Standard Oil Company of New Jersey in 1920. Soon thereafter this plant also started using butylenes to synthesize secondary butyl alcohol for solvents. Ethylene did not find tonnage use as a chemical raw material until several years later when Union Carbide erected an ethylene oxide and derivatives plant at Charleston, West Virginia, followed shortly by a synthetic ethyl alcohol plant at the same location.

The ensuing period was one of intense technological development, with new derivatives boosting first one and then another of the olefins into prominence. This was particularly true in the case of ethylene and propylene, for which a steady stream of commercial applications was developed. The butylenes, by comparison, have thus far found primary use in only a few compounds, largely butadiene for synthetic rubber, polybutylenes and solvents (2-butanol and methyl ethyl ketone). Since World War II, growth in the ethylene family has conclusively outpaced that of propylene, which, in turn, has exceeded the butylenes.

Today the significance of the individual gaseous olefins as chemical raw materials is in reverse order of their carbon chain length, since the lowest member, ethylene, is the product most in demand. For example, in 1969, the quantity of ethylene produced in the U.S. for chemical use was more than double that of propylene (16.4 billion lb vs 7.2 billion lb), and propylene twice that of butylenes (about 3 billion lb). This ranking of chemical usage generally holds for the rest of the Free World, as shown in Table 1.

Two factors suggest that future growth patterns of olefin demand will be less spectacular than in the past, although still at rates well above those foreseeable for conventional petroleum products. In the first place, many of the leading derivatives have now reached the status of "mature" products. In the second, much of the initial growth has gone at the expense of natural products and acetylene, but this displacement has just about run its course. For example, propylene has, at the expense of acetylene, now captured virtually the entire market as a raw material for acrylonitrile. In some cases, this trend is being reversed. For instance, replacement of soap by synthetic detergents was a major factor in the demand for propylene in earlier years. More recently propylene-based detergents themselves have been losing out to other materials, such as paraffins, because of biodegradable shortcomings.

Similarly, ethylene is today a major source of synthetic alcohols, and it has made significant inroads in poly(vinyl chloride) (PVC) and acetaldehyde manufacture heretofore dominated by acetylene. As an intermediate to butanols and 2-ethylhexanol, acetaldehyde must, in its turn, face increasing competition from the oxonation of propylene. Isobutylene is a potential competitor for propylene as a raw material for isoprene. A first commercial plant using the isobutylene route is reportedly in operation in Russia (7).

Industry projections suggest that ethylene will continue to be the leading olefin both within and without the U.S. In certain regions, the ethylene-propylene gap may

Table 1. Projected Development of Ethylene and Propylene Demand for Chemical Manufacture in the Free World for 1970–1980 (6), million metric tons

Countries	1970		1975		1980	
	Ethylene	Propylene	Ethylene	Propylene	Ethylene	Propylene
U.S.	7.0	4.1	11.0	5.8	16.0	7.8
W. Europe	5.1	2.4	8.7	3.6	13.2	4.9
Japan	2.3	1.1	4.3	2.0	6.6	3.4
other	1.1	0.1	3.0	0.3	7.2	0.6
total Free World	15.5	7.7	27.0	11.7	43.0	16.7

even widen; see Table 1 which presents data prepared at The Lummus Co. Other sources differ somewhat in the tonnages projected, but are in general agreement with the trends indicated by the data. The ratio in which the demand for olefins evolves bears significantly on the economics of their manufacture.

REFINING ENVIRONMENT AND OLEFIN ECONOMICS

The economics of gaseous olefins, including the availability of particular feedstocks, are closely linked to the petroleum refining and natural gas environment of a country. Olefins are in great demand not only as chemical building blocks but also for the manufacture of polymer gasoline and motor fuel alkylate as well. Quality considerations and the relative availability of olefins compared to isobutane have led to an increasing switch from polymer gasoline to alkylate, at least in the U.S.

Refinery demand for olefins is greatest in such gasoline-oriented economies as the U.S. It is less significant, or almost nonexistent, in Europe and Japan, where the markets are preponderantly for the heavier parts of the crude oil barrel. For technical and economic reasons, the refiner's preference for individual olefins is in approximately inverse order to that of the chemical demand. At the end of 1966, for instance, about 44% of the U.S. motor alkylate was based on butene and 56% on a mixed butene-propylene feed (8). Some C_5 olefins are used as alkylate feedstock; however, the quantities involved are small. Only a small amount of propylene as such, and virtually no ethylene, was used in gasoline alkylates. The first major ethylene alkylate plant at Norco, La., however, was announced by Shell (1970). A shift to lead-free gasoline would stimulate the overall demand of the refiner for olefins and could conceivably also bring ethylene alkylation more prominently into the picture.

The complementary nature of chemical and refinery demand for the individual olefins in gasoline-oriented economies is subject to qualification. There may be a greater degree of flexibility in the refinery to substitute the one olefin for the other than exists in the chemical plant. Also, a refiner can use olefins in a relatively dilute form, such as propane–propylene, butane–butylene, or mixed streams. By comparison, the chemical company for most purposes requires a raw material in much higher concentration and purity.

Olefin purity requirements are greatest for polymer-grade material. For commercial specifications of polymer-grade ethylene, see Vol. 8, p. 521; for polymer-grade propylene, see Vol. 16, p. 590. Specifications for commercial grades of butylenes, such as required for production of butyl rubber and poly-1-butene, are presented in Table 2.

The degree to which a refiner is oriented towards gasoline is a significant factor in determining not only his role as an olefin consumer, but also as a producer. The re-

Table 2. Specifications and Analyses of Butylenes (9)

	α-Butylene (1-butene)	β-Butylene (2-butene)[b]	Isobutylene[a]	
	Specifications			
1-butene (liq vol)	99% min			
2-butene (liq vol)		95% min		
water, ppm	25 max	100 max		
	Typical analyses (liq vol)		*Specifications*	
1-butene	99.30%	0.3%	⎫ 0.8% max	
2-butene, trans	0.01%	⎫ 97.6%[b]	⎬	
2-butene, cis	0.00%	⎭	⎭	
isobutylene	0.30%	0.0%	99.0% min	
normal butane	0.32%	1.5%	⎫ 0.5% max	
isobutane	0.05%		⎬	
butadiene	0.02%	0.6%	⎭	
pentane		0.0%		
propane and propylene			0.5% max	
total	100.00%	100.00%		
water, ppm	15	30	100 max	
sulfur, ppm	3	5	10 max	

[a] Suitable for manufacture of butyl rubber.
[b] Approximately a 50–50 mixture of cis and trans isomers.

fining environment likewise determines which refinery streams can be most economically made available as petrochemical feedstocks. Where gasoline is the main product, the complementary nature of chemical and refining operations is largely in their demand for the individual olefins. By comparison, in fuel-oil oriented economies, the two industries complement one another on the feedstock end.

European and Japanese refineries, because of their different product slates, practice less cracking than their U.S. counterparts. For instance, as of Jan. 1, 1970 for every 100 bbl/day of crude distillation capacity, the U.S. refiner had, on average, about 47 bbl/day catalytic cracking capacity, but his European colleague only 5.5 bbl/day. Also, because of different product slates cracking in Europe is less severe than in the U.S. The effect of severity on gas formation is illustrated in Table 3, which gives some typical yields for the fluid catalytic cracking of a paraffinic gas oil (650–1020°F). As catalytic cracking accounts for the great bulk of a refiner's economically recoverable olefins, more and deeper cracking thus combine to give the U.S. refinery about 15 times as much propylene for an equivalent crude oil throughput as in Europe (0.6 lb/100 bbl vs 0.04 lb.).

Petroleum refining remains a major source of gaseous olefins in gasoline-oriented economies, but the days that refining alone could satisfy chemical demand, particularly for ethylene, are long since past. These requirements are now produced intentionally by the steamcracking of a wide range of gaseous and liquid hydrocarbons. In the U.S., with its vast and growing natural-gas industry, ethane and propane are particularly economical feedstocks to supplement refinery gases under most circumstances. Liquid feedstocks are costly because of their relatively high alternative use value as gasoline or other energy products. Moreover, they pose the problem of finding profitable outlets for a much greater variety of by-products than in the case of

Table 3. Fluid Catalytic Cracking of Gas Oils;
Effect of Cracking Severity on Distribution of Product Yield (10), Wt% of Fresh Feed

	High severity, 90% conversion, (optimum selectivity to gasoline, typical of U.S.)	Low severity, 67% conversion, (optimum selectivity to middle distillate, typical of Europe)
C₂ and lighter	3.0	1.8
propane	1.5	0.6
propylene	4.1	2.3
isobutane	5.1	2.8
n-butane	0.9	0.5
butylenes	7.5	3.4
debutanized naphtha	59.6	38.3
light gas oil	7.2	39.3
heavy gas oil	3.5	3.5
coke	7.6	7.5
total	100.0	100.0

ethane or propane, as shown in Table 4. For companies having such outlets, however, liquids can be more desirable feedstocks than liquefied petroleum gas (qv) (LPG) despite their higher initial price. Thus, in the U.S., several companies, including Monsanto at Chocolate Bayou and Texas City, Texas; Dow at Bay City, Michigan; Enjay at Baton Rouge, La.; and Carbide at Taft, La. and in Puerto Rico make olefins from liquids. Furthermore, plants under construction (1970) to use liquid feedstocks include Corco-PPG in Puerto Rico and Shell at Deer Park, Texas.

A switch to lead-free gasoline may call for a reevaluation of the economics of LPG versus liquid feedstocks. One consequence of such a switch is that low-octane fractions would become increasingly undesirable gasoline components, but might therefore become more readily available at economic prices for steamcracking operations. Cracking of liquid feedstocks might also find wider application in the U.S., at

Table 4. Yield Patterns for Steamcracking of Various Feedstocks,
High Severity Operations (11), Wt%[a]

Products	Feedstock					
	Ethane	Propane	n-Butane	Full-range naphtha	Light gas oil	Heavy gas oil
off-gas	16.1	30.0	25.1	17.2	11.3	10.0
ethylene (polymer grade)	76.3	42.0	40.0	31.2	26.3	23.4
propylene (chemical grade)	2.9	16.2	20.9	16.1	15.1	14.3
C₄ fraction						
butadiene	1.3	3.2	2.9	4.5	4.0	4.0
butylenes	0.6	1.4	6.9	4.5	4.9	4.4
C₅–400°F	2.8	6.0	3.7	22.0	15.2	13.8
400°F +		1.2	0.5	4.5	23.2	30.1
total	100.0	100.0	100.0	100.0	100.0	100.0

[a] In all cases based on recycle cracking of ethane produced in pyrolysis; for propane feed propane is recycle cracked as well.

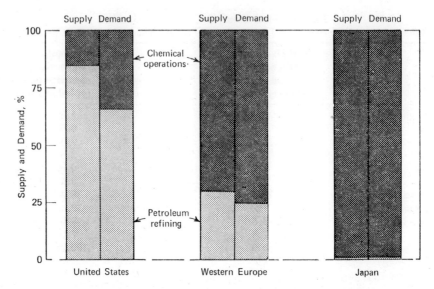

Fig. 1.   Regional Supply and Use Profiles of Propylene—1970.

least by the large chemical and oil companies, should there be a major liberalization of the Oil Import Program.

Europe and Japan do not have abundant LPG, the notable exception being the Lacq gas field in southern France. The recent gas finds in Holland and the North Sea, while prolific, contain little C_2 and higher. Thus, the chemical industry abroad has resorted to refinery by-products, and notably naphtha, for its feedstocks. Naphtha became a distress product in Europe when the export of surpluses to the U.S. was severely restricted by the U.S. Mandatory Oil Import Program.

The effect of refinery environment on olefin supply and demand profiles is illustrated for propylene in Table 5 and Figure 1. In the U.S., the refiner dominates both

Table 5.   Regional Supply and Use Profiles of Propylene, 1970 (12)

	Total supply or total demand, %		
	U.S.	W. Europe	Japan
supply			
petroleum refining	85	30	negligible
steamcrackers	15	70	95+
total supply	100	100	100
use			
petroleum refining	66	25	negligible
chemicals	34	75	nearly 100
total use	100	100	100

as a supplier and a consumer which provides a flywheel effect in that relatively major swings in the chemical sector can be accommodated with comparative ease. On the other hand, even minor changes in refinery product demand or technology will have a greatly leveraged impact on chemical propylene. The situation in Japan is in almost every respect the opposite of that in the U.S.; Europe is somewhat between these two extremes.

In a nongasoline-oriented environment the minor role of the refiner as an olefin source and, worse still, the lack of a refinery sponge to absorb possible surpluses, set unique parameters for the economics of olefin manufacture. A further complication is that in such an environment this manufacture is preponderantly based on liquid feedstocks with an attendant variety of coproducts and by-products.

Plant size is obviously also a significant cost factor. The following empirical formula (13) has been suggested as an approximation of ethylene cost for naphtha steamcrackers in the range of 200,000–500,000 tons ethylene/yr.

$$C_T = C_1 + C_2 \left(\frac{Q_1}{Q_2}\right)^{0.9} + C_3 \left(\frac{Q_1}{Q_2}\right)^{0.15} + C_4 \left(\frac{Q_1}{Q_2}\right)^{0.6}$$

in which: Q_1 = reference capacity;

Q_2 = required capacity;

C_1 = the difference between the raw-material cost and the value of the by-products or net raw-material cost, per unit of ethylene;

C_2 = labor cost including operating, maintenance, and overhead factors, per unit of ethylene;

C_3 = utility and chemicals cost, per unit of ethylene;

C_4 = capital cost based upon ten-year depreciation plus 5% fixed charges giving 15% per year based on total investment cost of the plant, per unit of ethylene;

C_T = net production cost at capacity Q_2, per unit of ethylene.

However, as modern plants are mostly of comparable size, in the 400,000–500,000 ton/yr range, C_1, the net raw-material cost, stands out as the principal competitive variable.

Under such circumstances, the ability to attune the output of ethylene and other cracked products to a specific end-use pattern, by process flexibility or otherwise, becomes a major competitive factor and may overshadow mere feedstock cost. The propylene-to-ethylene ratio is particularly important in this context, and lends added interest to the possible use of such supplemental feedstocks as ethane and propane to adjust imbalances in this ratio. The importation of ethane and other liquefied gases in cryogenic form from producing areas such as North Africa and the Persian Gulf could be potentially important for Europe and elsewhere, especially if this movement were combined with LNG.

For some time, the trend in steamcracker design was towards increasingly higher severities to reduce the propylene-to-ethylene ratio. More recently, however, there is evidence of a reversal of this tendency. In Europe, for example, this production ratio from new plants reached an all-time low of 0.46 in 1968–1969 (14), but is expected to rise to 0.52 by 1972-73, see Table 6. Individual plants, including some recently announced, are designed for an even higher ratio. For instance, the one announced by BASF for Ludwigshafen will have an annual design capacity of 300,000 metric tons of propylene and 400,000 tons of ethylene, or a ratio of 0.75. The plant projected by Shell for England will be capable of making annually 300,000 tons of propylene and 450,000 tons of ethylene, a ratio of 0.67. Another interesting feature of this latter plant, which is based upon the Stone & Webster USC (ultraselective cracking) process, is that it is designed to provide maximum flexibility both in the range of feed-stocks used and in the operating conditions (16). Even more extreme than the two

Table 6. Propylene:Ethylene Production Ratios in Western Europe (17)

For units coming on-stream, year	Ratio
pre–1960	0.73
1960–61	0.77
1962–63	0.63
1964–65	0.57
1966–67	0.58
1968–69	0.46
1970–71	0.54
1972–73	0.52

steamcrackers mentioned is the project of Grampian Chemical in Invergordon, Scotland, which contemplates making more propylene than ethylene (350,000 and 300,000 metric tons/yr, respectively, or a ratio of 1.17).

Such high propylene-to-ethylene ratios as the above are clearly at variance with demand projections for Western Europe as a whole which rather suggest a fairly constant level of about 0.5 over the next decade (15). These deviations from the regional average are indicative of the vast differences in individual company situations and optimization of operations. They also suggest that the days when propylene in Europe could be regarded as a mere by-product of ethylene manufacture are drawing to a close. There are signs that steamcrackers are being increasingly regarded as olefin plants, in which each product has its own cost, rather than as mere ethylene plants

These changes in costing philosophy will logically lead to modifications in the value relationships between ethylene and propylene and such other products as butadiene and benzene. Even at the status quo, the economics of olefin manufacture in such nongasoline-oriented environments as Europe or Japan are so complex as to defy meaningful generalized comparisons with the situation in the U.S. The subject is the source of considerable debate and controversy surrounding the impact of the U.S. Oil Import Program on the chemical industry.

One view (18) is that, lacking modification of this system, ethylene made in the U.S. from U.S. liquids will cost approximately the same as ethylene made in Europe from European liquids. Both are higher than the present cost of producing ethylene in the U.S. from LPG or LRG (liquefied refinery gas, similar in composition to LPG but obtained from petroleum refineries rather than from natural gas). The author expects, however, that increased LPG/LRG prices will make the cost of ethylene via liquids in the U.S. the appropriate basis for cost comparison in the future. He further concludes that, when coproduct propylene and butadiene are also considered, the cost of the standard mix (defined as the ratios in which these products will be required in the U.S. in 1980) would be higher for U.S. than European conditions unless feedstocks can be imported into the U.S. free of tariffs and quotas.

Whatever the validity of such generalized regional comparisons, both in the U.S. and overseas the economics of olefin manufacture depend to a large extent on the degree of integration between refining and chemical operations. A judicious combination of the two permits optimum use of crude oil and intermediates in each sector. For instance, deisopentanizing and deisohexanizing can improve the octane value of the gasoline pool and, at the same time, provide a premium petrochemical feedstock, as compared to an untreated virgin naphtha feed.   The question of how best to optimize both the energy and chemical feedstock requirements from a variety of crude oils is gaining increased attention, particularly as the volume of chemical products and the scale of process operations are growing year by year (19).

CHANGING TECHNOLOGY

While steamcracking remains the preponderant process for ethylene manufacture worldwide and naphtha is the preferred feed abroad, several attempts have been made to overcome the inherent limitations in terms of product mix and raw materials.

Work at Stone & Webster Co. (20) on the pyrolysis of pure hydrocarbons indicates that olefin formation and yields can be predicted with a fair degree of accuracy by assuming a free-radical reaction mechanism.   The principle of the regenerative furnace utilized in the Wulff and Koppers-Hasche processes is aimed at simultaneous production of ethylene and acetylene, described in Vol. 8, p. 508.   Several Wulff plants have been built, but have been plagued with numerous operational problems, including tar separation and removal, heat-exchanger fouling, boiler plant malfunction, plant corrosion due to solvents, compressor corrosion, low furnace-refractory life and combustion efficiency, and product purity.   These difficulties in the British Oxygen plant in Northern Ireland appear to have been largely overcome (21).

Another route to ethylene and acetylene is the Hoechst high-temperature pyrolysis (HTP) process.   Here, a suitable feedstock, preferably light virgin naphtha (boiling range 250-280°F), is subjected in a combustion-chamber reactor system to high temperatures (2500-3000°C) and short residence time (0.002–0.003 sec).   The energy is produced by combustion with oxygen of fuel gases from cracking.   The cracked gases are quenched to about 200–300°C, with cracked oil manufactured in the process.   It is claimed that acetylene and ethylene may be produced in ratios varying all the way from 70/30 to 30/70, an acetylene/ethylene ratio of 40/60 being optimum from thermodynamic and economic considerations.   An overall acetylene plus ethylene yield of up to 54% by weight (based on naphtha feed) is claimed.   The first full-scale plant using the Hoechst HTP process was started in 1960 (22).

Modification of steamcracker technology to use heavier feedstocks, notably gas oils, is described under Ethylene in this volume.   Other routes using even heavier feeds, or the whole crude, have been investigated (23).   They generally involve cracking with a heat carrier to supply considerable quantities of heat; eg, 300–500 kcal/kg crude oil.   The Japanese have developed a process to produce ethylene and propylene from crude oil utilizing a bed of inorganic oxide particles which act as a catalyst as well as a heat-transfer medium.   The process of Ube Industries claims high yields; eg, 34% ethylene and 7.8% propylene at 1615°F and 28% ethylene and 12% propylene at 1545°F (24).

C_5 Olefins

The C_5 monoolefins, C_5H_{10}, can be referred to by the general term *pentylenes*, since the *total* number of carbon atoms is five.   The name *pentenes* is in the I.U.P.A.C. system, and refers to five carbon atoms in the *longest straight chain;* it is therefore only applicable to the straight-chain pentylenes.   The names of the individual pentylenes are as follows:

1-pentene
$CH_2=CHCH_2CH_2CH_3$

2-methyl-1-butene
$CH_2=CCH_2CH_3$
$\qquad\ \ |$
$\qquad\ \ CH_3$

2-pentene
$CH_3CH=CHCH_2CH_3$

(cis and trans forms)

3-methyl-1-butene
$CH_2=CHCHCH_3$
$\qquad\quad\ |$
$\qquad\quad\ CH_3$

2-methyl-2-butene
$CH_3C=CHCH_3$
$\quad\ \ |$
$\quad\ \ CH_3$

In the petroleum industry it has been customary to use the word "amylenes" for the pentylenes, although this word is not recommended by either the A.C.S. or the I.U.P.A.C.

It is often necessary to refer to the straight-chain pentylenes and the branched pentylenes; convenient names for these groups are *pentenes* (straight chain) and *methylbutenes* (branched).

The principal commercial significance of the pentylenes is for the methylbutenes, which yield isoprene upon dehydrogenation. Isoprene can be polymerized to poly-isoprene, the synthetic "natural" rubber. It is also used in small amounts (2–3%) in the polymerization of isobutylene to butyl rubber. While numerous routes to isoprene have been proposed (see Vol. 12, pp. 73–78), thus far only two, dehydrogenation of methylbutene and demethanization of propylene dimer, have reached commercial realization in the Free World. Another, the IFP process, which produces isoprene via

Table 7. Existing and Projected Isoprene Plants

Company	Location	Capacity (lb/yr $\times 10^6$)	Process
operating			
Goodrich-Gulf	Port Neches, Tex.	120	methylbutene dehydrogenation
Shell	Marietta, Ohio	80	methylbutene dehydrogenation
Enjay	Baton Rouge, La.	10 }	by-product from high-temperature cracking
	Baytown, Tex.	10 }	
Goodyear	Beaumont, Tex.	132	propylene dimerization and demethanization
Shell[a]	Pernis, Neth.	na (145 PI)	methylbutene dehydrogenation
USSR	na	90	isobutylene–formaldehyde
		90	methylbutene dehydrogenation
projected			
Rhône-Alpes[a]	Feyzin, France	na (130 PI) postponed	isobutylene–formaldehyde
ANIC[a]	Ravenna, Italy	na (45 PI)	acetylene–acetone
Japan Geon	Mitzushima, Japan	88	methylbutene dehydrogenation
Japan			
Polyisoprene	Kashima	66	na
Erdoelchemie	Cologne, Germany	175	extraction from steam cracker C_5 streams

[a] Capacity for isoprene monomer not available (na). PI figures shown in parentheses are for size of polyisoprene plant.

the catalytic reaction of isobutylene and formaldehyde, has reportedly been licensed and is in commercial use in the USSR (25). The existing and projected isoprene plants are listed in Table 7.

Methylbutenes are contained in the C_5 fraction from thermal and catalytic cracking operations. However, the total volume of recoverable methylbutenes that may be obtained from a single catalytic cracking unit or steam cracker may not be adequate for one large isoprene plant. One recently announced unit, that of Erdoelchemie in Germany, is predicated on the extraction of isoprene from the C_5 streams collected from steam crackers within a wide geographic radius. Various processes have been proposed to overcome the methylbutenes bottleneck by the dehydrogenation of isopentane to isoprene, either directly or via methylbutene. These are similar to the commercial routes whereby n-butane is dehydrogenated to butenes and/or butadiene. However, the C_5 version has not yet found industrial application. The same applies to the production of methylbutene by the disproportionation of isobutylene with propylene or with 2-butene.

An unusual route to 2-methyl-1-butene is described in Dutch Pat. Appl. 6,606,883, May 18, 1966, Halcon International. The process involves the oxidation of isopentane into its hydroperoxide, 2-methyl-2-hydroperoxybutane, which is catalytically reacted with propylene to yield propylene oxide and *tert*-amyl alcohol. The latter is readily dehydrated to 2-methyl-1-butene. This technology is similar to that employed in a plant in the U.S. by Oxirane Chemical Company except that in the U.S. isobutane instead of isopentane is the hydroperoxide former. Plans for a first plant to produce methylbutene in the Benelux appear to have been shelved in favor of one which operates on isobutane.

The Higher Olefins

The commercially important reactions of the higher olefins are discussed in some detail in Vol. 14, pp. 313–335. By far their most significant use is in the production of detergent and plasticizer intermediates, notably alkylbenzenes and alcohols by the oxo process (qv). The great bulk of the olefins heretofore consumed in these applications were branched-chain compounds made by the polymerization or copolymerization of propylene and butylenes. Demand for linear olefins as raw materials for biodegradable detergents, however, received strong stimulus as the "hard" branched-chain materials came under increasing attack. Internal olefins are acceptable for producing linear alkylbenzene and oxo alcohols, although alpha olefins are usually preferred for the latter, at least when conventional hydroformylation catalysts are employed. New oxo catalysts, however, such as those modified with trialkylphosphines, permit conversion of internal olefins to terminal alcohols (26). Nevertheless, there will remain applications in which alpha olefins are the preferred raw material. One patent (27), describes a method by which internal olefins can be isomerized to alpha olefins by treatment with trialkylboron.

Until the search for petrochemical processes to make low-cost alpha olefins in bulk was stimulated by water pollution considerations, such materials were produced only in small volume by the dehydration of fatty alcohols from natural fats and oils. Priced as specialty chemicals in the $0.34–1.00/lb range, their total U.S. market was estimated to be a mere three million pounds per year (28). The availability of alpha olefins at chemical commodity prices has aroused considerable interest among potential producers and consumers alike.

Because much of the alpha olefin technology is still in the development and market testing stages, it is hazardous to venture a guess at this point as to the probable volume uses of tomorrow. The Stanford Research Institute (29) discusses those application areas most frequently mentioned as potential outlets for alpha olefins. Company literature (30) suggests that, in addition to such obvious outlets as linear alkylbenzene, secondary alkyl sulfate, such as Teepol (Shell Oil Co.), and oxo alcohol feedstocks, their most significant potential is for conversion to alpha olefin sulfonates, a detergent intermediate. These alpha olefin sulfonates are claimed to be highly biodegradable and equivalent in detergency to linear alkylate sulfonate (31). Materials of this kind are commercially produced in the U.S. by Stepan Chemical Company, and by a detergent manufacturer in Japan. Other possible applications for alpha olefins include conversion to specialty surfactant intermediates, such as epoxides (offered by Union Carbide), amines, bromides, synthetic acids, plastics (as copolymers with ethylene and/or propylene, or with acrylonitrile (32) or styrene (33), or as high-molecular weight-homopolymers), and synthetic lubricants. Alpha olefins can also be used in place of alcohols for the direct esterification of phthalic acid, but this leads to secondary substitution. Accordingly, it provides the same type of ester which would be obtained from a secondary alcohol rather than the commercially preferred product made by esterification with a primary alcohol (33a).

Industry efforts to manufacture alpha olefins petrochemically have taken a number of directions. Some have pursued the cracking of paraffin wax, others investigated routes to manufacture straight-chain olefins from the corresponding straight-chain paraffin by catalytic or oxidative dehydrogenation, or by chlorination and subsequent dehydrochlorination. Still others have chosen oligomerization or telomerization of ethylene with aluminum alkyls.

Mention should also be made of an attempt directed at making "relatively" linear monoolefins of C_8 to C_{16} chain length by two successive dimerization steps of a gaseous olefin, such as propylene (34). The resulting product contains 90–95% by weight of straight-chain olefins or branched olefins having only a single branch. While this route may avoid excessive chain branching, it does not appear to be suitable to produce linear alpha olefins of high purity.

Insufficient information prevents a comparison of the relative economics of the different routes to alpha olefins. Moreover, further process improvements can be expected, since research continues unabated, witness the many patents on the subject issued each year. The ultimate choice of which way to go is likely to differ from company to company, depending upon such factors as available feedstocks, outlets for the product spectrum, tie-in with other operations (eg, alkylation, alcohols), desired olefin purity, etc. The major inherent differences between the present processes are the quality and the carbon-number distribution of the olefin product. These are summarized in Table 8.

Alpha olefins are presently available in commercial quantities only from plants using wax cracking or ethylene growth reactions. Catalytic dehydrogenation and chlorination–dehydrochlorination of n-paraffins are also practiced on a commercial scale, but only in conjunction with detergent alkylate production. In these operations the linear olefins are not extracted as such. Oxidative dehydrogenation has reached commercial importance for the manufacture of dienes (notably, butadiene) rather than of long-chain length monoolefins.

The following companies are listed by the U.S. Tariff Commission as producers of alpha olefins in 1969:

Table 8. Summary of C_6–C_{20} Linear Olefin Processes

Process	Raw materials	Product range	Product quality	Impurities	Comments
ethylene chain growth, conventional one-step; eg, Gulf	ethylene	C_6–C_{20}, even carbon numbers only	95+% linear alpha	vinylidene olefins,[a] internal olefins, paraffins	in commercial operation
ethylene chain growth, modified two-step; eg, Ethyl	ethylene	selective, even carbon numbers only	95+% linear alpha	vinylidene olefins, internal olefins, paraffins	capable of peaking olefin product in the desired C number range, first commercial plant under construction
ethylene oligomerization, one-step; eg, Esso	ethylene	C_6–C_{20}, even carbon numbers only	95+%[b] linear alpha	vinylidene olefins	experimental stage
wax cracking	linear paraffin wax	C_6–C_{20}, mixed even and odd carbon numbers	90% linear alpha	paraffins, aromatics, internal olefins, branched olefins, diolefins	in commercial operation
chlorination–dehydrochlorination	selected linear paraffin, chlorine	selective (same as paraffin feed), even and/or odd carbon numbers	random internal	diolefins, paraffins	produces HCl by-product. In commercial operation
catalytic dehydrogenation	selected linear paraffin	selective (same as paraffin feed), even and/or odd carbon numbers	random internal	diolefins, aromatics, paraffins	olefin used as a dilute stream for linear alkyl benzene production; first commercial plant to use olefin–paraffin separation process now being constructed

[a] Containing the grouping $C=C\underset{R'}{\overset{R}{\diagup}}$

[b] However, purities of 99% or better have been achieved in some runs.

Molecular weight range	Company
C_6–C_7	Gulf, Goodyear, Phillips, Chevron
C_8–C_{10}	Gulf, Chevron
C_{11}–C_{15}	Enjay, Gulf, Chevron
all others	Texas Eastman, Gulf, Sinclair-Koppers, Chevron, Getty

Gulf produces alpha olefins via the ethylene growth process, while the Chevron and Enjay products are made by wax cracking. The basis for the inclusion of some of the other companies, however, is not clear. The Sinclair-Koppers entry may be related to their production of neohexene, CH_2=$CHC(CH_3)_3$, or heptylenes. The Goodyear product is believed to be 2-methyl-1-pentene (a branched alpha olefin made by dimerization of propylene), which is a precursor to isoprene. Phillips offers a number of high-purity specialty olefins, including 1-hexene. The nature of the alpha olefins produced by Texas Eastman and Getty are unknown.

The salient features of the various alpha-olefin processes are discussed below: wax cracking, (p. 646); oligomerization of ethylene; (p. 648); chlorination-dehydrochlorination of paraffins, (p. 653); catalytic dehydrogenation of paraffins, (p. 653).

WAX CRACKING

Paraffin wax can be thermally cracked to produce a broad range of even and odd numbered olefins. Starting with a linear wax, as much as 85–90% linear alpha olefins can be obtained. The product contains internal olefins, branched olefins, diolefins, aromatics, and paraffins as impurities. The kinetics of wax cracking have been studied by Worrell (35).

Process Variables. Conversion: The amount of fresh wax cracked per furnace pass affects both the yield and purity of the olefins produced. While it is evident that highest purity products may be achieved by "once-through" cracking, thus avoiding recycle of heavy, partially cracked wax, it is equally evident that such an operation would be expensive. Thus, in practice, wax cracking is a recycle operation in which only a certain amount of fresh wax is converted per furnace pass. A variety of conversion rates have been investigated (36), but commercially conversions of 20–40% have been found to be most practical. There is some evidence to show that the aromatics and naphthenes (alicyclics) content of the cracked olefins increases rapidly as conversion exceeds 40%.

Purity of olefin fractions is also dependent on the partial pressure obtained in the furnace. Thus, higher partial pressures, while favoring the liquid-to-gas ratio, tend to produce greater cyclic and diolefinic contaminants in the final product. There are, however, economic disadvantages in reducing the partial pressure to the extent that these side reactions are minimized, and normally wax cracking is carried out in the pressure range of 2–4 atm abs (37–40) with enough dilution steam to maintain a hydrocarbon partial pressure of 0.6–2.0 atm abs (40).

Cracking temperature is normally in the 500–600°C range and at a residence time of between 2.5 and 10.0 sec (41). Higher temperatures tend to increase gas production without improving olefin quality.

Experiments describing the kinetics of thermal cracking of waxes have determined an overall reaction order of 1.3. (42)

Typical Olefin Yields. The yield of C_6–C_{20} liquid olefins under optimum cracking conditions is in the range 55–65% weight on wax (41). This is to some extent dependent on the amount of wax discarded as a liquid residue between evaporator and cracking stages of the process; the residue yield is dependent on feedstock quality and may vary from less than 5% weight for higher-purity waxes to up to 20% weight for lower-quality feedstocks.

Considerable work has been carried out on separation of this residue, particularly from the vapor phase feed to the cracking section, by use of a cyclone separator at the outlet of the evaporating unit (43). The yield of the lowest-molecular-weight olefins in the liquid olefin product is about twice that of the highest-molecular-weight olefins. A typical distribution of the C_6–C_{20} olefin product is:

C_6–C_{10} (plasticizer range)   30–55 wt%
C_{11}–C_{15} (detergent range)   30–40 wt%
C_{16}–C_{20} 5–30 wt%

It will be noted that, for every detergent-range carbon chain length, at least an equal quantity of plasticizer-range material is obtained. In addition to the normal and branched olefins produced, paraffins, naphthenes, diolefins, and aromatics are present in the cracked product (44, 45). The gas product (C_1–C_5) is highly unsaturated and contains about 25 wt% ethylene and 18 wt% propylene.

Feedstocks. Slack waxes (see Petroleum waxes) were initially the main source of wax-cracking feedstocks (41). In the later years, the demand for such feedstocks and for higher-quality products was met by using various raffinates obtained by solvent extraction (eg, furfural) of catalytically cracked cycle oils (46) and other distillates. More recently, feedstocks containing a high percentage of n-paraffins (80 wt%) are obtained by more selective processes; eg, urea extraction of waxy distillates.

The purity of product olefins is largely dependent on wax purity (37,39,40,45, 47–49) but the latter can only be achieved at fairly high processing costs. Likewise expensive would be the purification of the product by using the approach described in U.S. Pat 3,291,853 (50). According to this, alpha olefins (C_5 and higher) may be separated from a cracked hydrocarbon stream by reacting with a dialkylaluminum hydride which is recycled.

A Montecatini patent (51) claims that linear olefins of good purity can be obtained by the steamcracking of heavy petroleum fractions of virtually any composition by selective urea adducting of the linear-chain olefins and their separation from the cracked product. Yields are low, however. In one example, 7.30 wt% of the feed of a C_{10}–C_{14} fraction was obtained containing 27% n-olefins. The ultimate C_{10}–C_{14} n-olefin yield calculated was thus 1.97% on feed.

Location of Existing Wax-Cracking Units

Company	Location	Wax intake, tons/yr
Shell Chemical Co.	Holland	300,000
Shell Chemical Co.	England	50,000
Shell Chemical Co.	France	150,000
Chevron	California	50,000
Humble Oil	Louisiana	small

The composition and typical inspections of Chevron's cracked-wax alpha olefins (covering the C_6–C_{20} range) are presented in Vol. 14, p. 329. A slightly revised set of data has been prepared by the company (see Table 9) which covers the same carbon range but groups the olefins into different fractions.

Table 9. Typical Alpha Olefins Inspections (52)

Property	C_6–C_9	C_{10}	C_{11}–C_{14}	C_{15}–C_{18}	C_{18}–C_{20}	C_{15}–C_{20}
straight-chain mono alpha olefins, wt %	89	90	89	91	86	88
diolefins, wt %	4	5	6	8	4	5
paraffins, wt %	3	2	1	2	9	5
color, Saybolt[a]	+18	+17	+14	+7	<−16	−12
density, g/ml	0.713	0.751	0.770	0.783	0.797	0.787
flash point, TOC, °F	<30	103	162	260	330	280
pour point, °F			−20	+40	+70	+55
bromine no., g/100 g	165	118	98	73	57	67
water content, ppm	130	130	130	80	40	50
sulfur content, ppm	5	8	10	15	15	15
carbon no. distribution, wt %						
C_5	2					
C_6	39					
C_7	24					
C_8	17					
C_9	16	4				
C_{10}	2	95	1			
C_{11}		1	27			
C_{12}			24			
C_{13}			24			
C_{14}			23	1		1
C_{15}			1	29		17
C_{16}				28		18
C_{17}				27	1	17
C_{18}				14	23	17
C_{19}				1	37	15
C_{20}					30	12
C_{21}					9	3
av. mol. wt.	100	140	174	228	269	244

[a] Appearance, clear and bright and free of sediment.

OLIGOMERIZATION OF ETHYLENE

The reaction whereby long-chain olefins are prepared from ethylene is variously referred to in the literature as oligomerization, telomerization, and polymerization. Oligomerization denotes a combination of a relatively few, three or four, building blocks. The term polymerization generally implies higher-molecular-weight products. Telomerization refers to the use of a "telomer," ie an end stopper such as aluminum alkyl, which plays a major part in the synthesis of alpha olefins from ethylene in some, but not all, processes. The term oligomerization is used here to refer to the ethylene-based routes to C_6–C_{20} alpha olefins, as distinguished from the higher-molecular-weight products such as polyethylene.

In contradistinction to the products of wax cracking, which contain both even and odd numbered carbon-chain olefins, those resulting from ethylene oligomerization include only the even carbon members. They are produced from ethylene and aluminum alkyls by the following basic reactions (al = $1/_3$ Al):

Chain growth:

$$\text{alC}_n + \overset{|}{\underset{|}{\text{C}}}=\overset{|}{\underset{|}{\text{C}}} \rightarrow \text{al}-\overset{|}{\underset{|}{\text{C}}}-\overset{|}{\underset{|}{\text{C}}}-\text{C}_n \qquad (1)$$

Displacement:

$$\text{al}-\overset{|}{\underset{|}{\text{C}}}-\overset{|}{\underset{|}{\text{C}}}-\text{C}_n \rightarrow \text{alH} + \overset{|}{\text{C}}=\overset{|}{\underset{|}{\text{C}}}-\text{C}_n \qquad (2)$$

$$\text{al}-\text{H} + \overset{|}{\text{C}}=\overset{|}{\underset{|}{\text{C}}} \rightarrow \text{al}-\overset{|}{\underset{|}{\text{C}}}-\overset{|}{\underset{|}{\text{C}}} \qquad (3)$$

These reactions are among the several practical applications of "Ziegler chemistry," so named in honor of Professor Dr. Karl Ziegler, who, with his co-workers, pioneered the aluminum alkyl chemistry at the Max Planck Institut in Mülheim, Germany. This fundamental work is discussed more fully in Vol. 1, pp. 560–563 and Vol. 14, pp. 323–330.

The aluminum alkyls can be made directly from aluminum, hydrogen and olefins (53). The aluminum can be activated by the presence of a halide of titanium, zirconium, niobium, vanadium, scandium, uranium or hafnium, as described in U.S. Pat. 3,382,269 (54).

The chain growth and displacement reactions can be carried out simultaneously or in two separate steps (55). Reactions 1 and 2 are rate controlling, reaction 3 being very rapid at even modest ethylene pressures. Reaction 1 is favored by high ethylene pressure, and reaction 2 is favored by high temperature or by the use of catalysts.

Typical reaction conditions are:

One-step process:

    350–550°F
    2000–4000 psig (56)

Two-step process:

reaction 1:	200–250°F
	1500–3000 psig
reaction (thermal displacement) 2:	500–600°F
	100–300 psig

When the one-step process is used, only a catalytic amount of aluminum alkyl is employed, with several chain-growth displacement sequences occurring on each aluminum bond during each pass through the reactor. The aluminum alkyl can be destroyed after the reaction without undue economic penalty to facilitate separations and avoid by-products during olefin recovery.

In the two-step process, each aluminum bond produces one mole of olefin on each pass through the chain growth plus displacement reactors. Large quantities of aluminum alkyls are thus required, and aluminum alkyls must be recycled for the process to be economical. Laboratory experiments to separate alpha olefins from aluminum triethyl are described by Ziegler (56). Since triethylaluminum has approximately the same boiling point as dodecene, separation of triethylaluminum from C_4-C_{20} olefins is not a simple procedure. By-product reactions between olefins and aluminum alkyls further complicate the olefin recovery. No single approach to this separation is universally accepted. Several methods, including complexing of the aluminum alkyl and displacement or transalkylation with higher olefins, have been explored, as is apparent from the work of Ziegler et al. and from several later patents discussed below.

The olefin-product distribution from the two-step process is markedly different from that of the single-step process. The olefin-product distribution from the latter is predicted by the equation:

$$N_{C_{n+2}} = QN_{C_n}$$

where: N_{C_n} = moles of olefin, carbon number n

$N_{C_{n+2}}$ = moles of olefin, carbon number $n + 2$

Q = a constant dependent on reaction conditions, typically 0.4–0.7

The olefin product from the two-step process generally follows a Poisson distribution:

$$X_i = \frac{n^i e^{-n}}{i!}$$

where: n = average moles of ethylene reacted per al-C bond

X_i = mole fraction of chains containing i moles added ethylene

In practice, the product deviates slightly from the Poisson distribution since some displacement occurs during the chain growth reaction.

Typical olefin distributions in wt % are as follows:

	One-step		Two-step	
	low mw	high mw	low mw	high mw
C_4	33	14	9	2
C_6–C_{10}	52	40	66	28
C_{12}–C_{14}	10	18	20	35
C_{16}–C_{18}	3	12	4	22
C_{20+}	2	16	1	13

As seen from the above data, the two-step process makes a significant improvement with respect to peaking the product in a desired carbon-number range, but still produces a fairly broad distribution of products. This is particularly true if the desired products are detergent range, which are usually more valuable than plasticizer range.

Gulf, who has a 110 million lb/yr plant at Cedar Bayou, Texas, is currently the sole commercial producer of alpha olefins from ethylene. The composition and physical properties of individual alpha olefins from 1-hexene to 1-eicosene are shown in Vol. 14, p. 330. Gulf also offers a C_{22}–C_{28} and a C_{30+} alpha-olefin fraction, with the properties shown in Table 10.

Ethyl Corp. is presently producing and market testing pilot-plant quantities of surfactant-range alpha olefins derived from ethylene chain growth. A commercial plant with an estimated 110 million lb/yr capacity is under construction in the Houston Ship Channel, and is expected to be on-stream in early 1971. This will give Ethyl a total Ziegler chain-growth capacity of approximately 500 million lb/yr, including alpha olefins sold as such and those converted to alcohols, acids, and other aliphatics (57).

Continental Oil Company could be a potential entrant in the alpha olefin field.

Table 10. Gulf Alpha Olefins, C_{22+} (58)

	$C_{22}-C_{28}$ Fraction	C_{30+} Fraction
composition (sales specifications)		
carbon no., wt % distribution		
C_{20} and lower, max[a]	7.5%	
$C_{22}-C_{28}$, min[a]	85.0%	
C_{30} and higher, max[a]	7.5%	
C_{28} and lower, max[b]		28%
C_{30} and higher, min[c]		72%
color, saybolt	+20 to +30	0 min
appearance	clear and bright	clear and bright
physical properties (typical analyses)		
melting point, °F	106.5	160
viscosity, SUs at 210°F		52.4
viscosity, cSt at 210°F		8.0
flash, COC, °F		510
olefin type, %		
$RCH{=}CH_2$	59.1	
$RCH{=}CHR$ (trans)	2.1	
$RCH{=}CHR$ (cis)	11.3	
$R_2C{=}CH_2$	18.0	
$R_2C{=}CHR$	9.5	

[a] Gulf Research Method 2006. [b] Gulf Research Method 1030. [c] ASTM Method D-127.

The Company did much of the pioneering work in reducing the Ziegler chemistry to practice, and was the first to commercialize it for the production of linear primary alcohols, tradenamed Alfol alcohols. It does not, however, use this technology to manufacture alpha olefins, nor has it thus far announced any plans along these lines.

Gulf employs a one-step and Ethyl a two-step approach in their alpha-olefin plants. The Ethyl process is further modified to produce a nonstatistical distribution of products. The major advantages claimed for the Ethyl process are its ability to produce a selective range of products with little sacrifice in the alpha-olefin quality of ethylene chain growth olefins. Processes to accomplish this peaking are suggested by several issued patents, as is the olefin-aluminum alkyl separation. It is not known, however, whether any of these, or some as yet undisclosed approach, will be adopted in commercial practice.

A one-step process different to that referred to above is described in U.S. Pat. 3,441,630 (59), and in a paper by Langer (60). The process involves the catalytic polymerization of ethylene to even numbered linear olefins in the C_4-C_{50} range with a high alpha content (close to 100% in the $C_{12}-C_{20}$ fraction), over a soluble catalyst obtained by mixing a reducible transition metal halide such as $TiCl_4$ with an aluminum alkyl compound. The polymerization takes place at low temperatures (preferably in the range of $-30°C$ to $+10°C$, at moderate pressures (about 100–500 psia) and in a polar solvent. The pressure of ethylene is critical with respect to the selectivity to linear alpha olefins. With a suitable catalyst, and at an ethylene pressure of 250 psia, 99% linear alpha olefins in the C_{12-20} fraction was obtained in 2 hr. Raising the ethylene pressure to 500 psia yielded 100% C_{12-20} linear alpha olefins in ½ hr.

Recent process improvements have reportedly been made by Esso which raise the polymerization temperature to eliminate the need for refrigeration, avoid the restriction to polar solvents, and raise the preferred pressures somewhat.

Among the efforts to facilitate separation of olefins from mixtures with aluminum alkyls in ethylene oligomerization processes are those using a complexing agent (61).

U.S. Pat. 3,308,143 (62) claims the use of a compound R_nMX such as tetramethylammonium chloride as an effective complexing agent, in which R represents an alkyl, M an element of the group consisting of nitrogen, arsenic, phosphorus, sulfur, selenium and telurium, and X is a halogen.

U.S. Pat. 3,406,187 (63) claims the complexing with alkali metal azides.

U.S. Pat. 3,352,894 (64) recommends as a suitable complexing agent polymers such as poly p-methoxystyrene or polyethylene oxide, which have Lewis base groups containing atoms selected from the group oxygen, sulfur, selenium, nitrogen, phosphorus and arsenic.

Another method of separation is claimed in U.S. Pat. 3,309,416 (65), which suggests oxidizing the aluminum trialkyl to the trialkoxide, followed by hydrolysis to the alcohol. The alpha olefin is then separated from the alcohol by distillation.

A number of patents have been issued which deal with methods of conducting the displacement of the desired alpha olefins subsequent to the growth step as follows:

U.S. Pat. 2,978,523 (66) suggests that the reversal of the displacement reaction (as well as the undesired isomerization of alpha olefins) can be inhibited by conducting the displacement in the presence of a reduction catalyst (nickel, cobalt, palladium, and certain iron compounds) and an acetylenic alcohol such as propargyl alcohol, butynediol, etc.

According to U.S. Pat. 3,317,625 (67), reverse displacement and olefin isomerization are also minimized by presaturating the aluminum trialkyl with the displacing olefins prior to introducing the aluminum trialkyls to the displacement reactor.

A selective displacement of the lower olefins from the aluminum alkyl growth product can be achieved by reacting the latter in the atomized state in the absence of a catalyst, and recovering the displaced olefin as product. The percentage of the lower mole weight olefins displaced is greater than of the higher mole weight compounds. This approach is described in U.S. Pat. 3,210,435 (68).

U.S. Pat. 3,395,166 (69) describes a method of displacing olefins by transalkylating trialkylaluminum compounds with gaseous alpha olefins (C_2–C_4) in a continuous thin liquid film.

A method of preventing decomposition of aluminum alkyls at the displacement temperature is described in U.S. Pat. 3,358,050 (70). The patent concerns the maintenance of liquid phase conditions in the displacement reactor by utilizing as a diluent a hydrocarbon fraction generated within the process itself.

Among the several approaches designed to overcome the limitations of the statistical distribution of the alpha-olefin products and to improve the yield of desired fractions are U.S. Pats. 3,391,175 and 3,391,219 (71). Both involve the separation of the mixed alpha olefins from a catalytic polymerization into a low-boiling fraction consisting of the lower olefins and a higher-boiling fraction. The lower than desired olefins are either recycled to the polymerization step or used in a displacement whereby those which are remote from the desired range are preferably recycled to the catalytic polymerization step and those which are close are transferred to a chain growth section.

Typical results mentioned in the first of the two patents are yields of 80 wt %

of C_{12}–C_{16} alpha olefins compared with only about 50% in this range when ethylene is used in the displacement.

In several patents issued to Continental Oil, U.S. Pat. 3,423,444 (72) and U.S. Pat. 3,445,494 (73), an upward shifting of the Poisson distribution curve is achieved by alkylation of dialkylaluminum hydride with low-molecular-weight olefins recycled from the displacement section. In one example cited, reacting up to C_{10} olefins with alkylaluminum hydride, followed by the growth reaction, yielded 87 wt % in the C_{12}–C_{16} olefin range. In a variation on the second of these two patents, U.S. Pat. 3,458,594 (74), alteration of the product distribution is achieved by displacing the growth reaction product with low-molecular-weight olefins obtained by reverse displacement of selected aluminum trialkyls.

CHLORINATION-DEHYDROCHLORINATION OF PARAFFINS

Linear olefins can be produced by chlorination of linear paraffins followed by dehydrochlorination. Hydrogen chloride is a significant by-product. No selectivity is obtained by this approach, and the double bond is randomly located in the chain. Thus products from this process are preponderantly internal olefins. They contain diolefins as the main impurity. The chlorination step is typically carried to about 20% conversion to avoid large quantities of dichloroparaffins, which are converted to diolefins upon dehydrochlorination. A large paraffin recycle is thus required.

Chlorinated paraffins can be separated from paraffins by distillation when a narrow range of paraffins is used. The process could thus serve to make relatively pure linear olefins. However, such separation is not generally economic, and no olefins from this source are currently offered for sale as such. The chlorinated paraffins are rather dehydrochlorinated without prior separation and the olefin-containing stream used as feed to a subsequent conversion unit such as alkylation, from which the paraffins are recycled to the chlorination step.

U.S. Pat. 3,277,205 (75) describes the dehydrochlorination of alkyl monochlorides over solid acidic catalysts under conditions minimizing isomerization to undesired branched and cyclic compounds by maintaining a partial pressure of an inert gas, such as nitrogen, in the reactor.

U.S. Pat. 3,402,216 (76) claims photochlorinating saturated acyclic hydrocarbons and dehydrochlorination of the monochlorinated hydrocarbons, followed by recovery of the selected monoolefins and recycle of the remaining monoolefins to extinction through isomerization to convert them to the desired monoolefin.

The chlorination-dehydrochlorination technique has been particularly explored to make detergent-range linear olefins. As far as is known, Chemische Werke Huels in Germany is the sole commercial user of this technique. Its plant at Marl is estimated to have a capacity of 60,000 tons alkylate/yr, or slightly less in terms of olefin. Most other producers of linear alkylate are believed to convert the appropriate chloroparaffin directly into alkylate; ie, without intermediate conversion to the corresponding linear olefin. There is some speculation, however, that the large Shell plant in Geismar, La. will use a chlorination-dehydrochlorination route to make oxo feedstocks, but no details are available.

CATALYTIC DEHYDROGENATION OF PARAFFINS

Under appropriate conditions, paraffins can be catalytically dehydrogenated to the corresponding olefins without major disturbance of the carbon chain. Thus, linear paraffins would yield linear olefins of the same carbon length.   As in the chlorination-dehydrochlorination process, the location of the double bond along the carbon chain is random, and the product is essentially a random internal olefin.   Dehydrogenation conversions must be kept low, typically 10–15%, to avoid serious by-product formation (diolefins, aromatics, cracking products).   In practice, the product from dehydrogenation is about 10% olefin and 90% paraffin.

Thus far, the only commercial application of dehydrogenation as a route to olefins has been where olefins can be recovered from unreacted paraffins through chemical reaction; specifically, by alkylation of benzene.   The alkylbenzene can then be separated by conventional distillation and the paraffin recycled to the dehydrogenation step.

Two such combination units, using a dehydrogenation step licensed by Universal Oil Products (UOP), have recently been completed, one in Japan and another in Spain.   The former, with a capacity of 34,000 metric tons/yr, is owned by Nippon Petroleum Detergent Company Ltd. at Kawasaki.   The second is the unit of Petroquímica Española, a joint venture of Continental Oil Company (U.S.) and Cia. Española Petróleos, S.A. at Algeciras, designed for 50,000 metric tons (110 million lb) linear alkylate per year.   In the U.S., Monsanto is also believed to be employing a paraffin dehydrogenation route to produce 200 million lb/yr of linear alkylate in its complex at Chocolate Bayou, Texas.

UOP has recently advertised an adsorption extraction process, the Olex process, for the separation of n-paraffins and olefins ranging up to C_{18} from mixed streams such as those derived from n-paraffin dehydrogenation (77).   A first plant combining UOP's paraffin dehydrogenation process, the Pacol process, with its Olex selective extraction route is presently under construction for Mitsubishi at Yokkaichi, Japan, and was due on-stream in late 1970.   The Pacol-Olex combination when feeding on linear paraffins is reported (78) to produce a stream analyzing about 94 wt % linear olefins, more than 96% of which are monoolefins, at over 90% yields, with a recycle of the unreacted paraffins.

The work of UOP and Monsanto on paraffin dehydrogenation is reflected in the following recent patents: U.S. Pat. 3,248,451 (79) and U.S. Pat. 3,356,757 (80) suggest the dehydrogenation of long-chain saturated hydrocarbons over a cobalt–molybdate catalyst supported on alumina.   Conversion of n-dodecane to dodecene ranged from 3.3 to 9.4% per pass, depending upon temperature (485–600°C) and contact time (2–5 sec).

Another Monsanto patent, U.S. Pat. 3,315,008 (81), refers to the dehydrogenation of saturated hydrocarbons in the presence of hydrogen over a noble-metal catalyst.   Per-pass conversions to dodecene of 10–13.8% are obtained.

U.S. Pat. 3,391,218 (82) describes the dehydrogenation over Group VIII noble-metal catalysts in the presence of hydrogen and about 0.5–2.0 mole aromatic hydrocarbons per mole paraffin.   The addition of benzene is found to raise per-pass conversion and selectivity to the desired monoolefin (in one case, from about 10.7% and 93.3% selectivity to 11.5% and 96.6% selectivity).   Activity and selectivity of the catalyst are also better maintained.

UOP finds in U.S. Pat. 3,360,586 (83), that the addition of water (400–3000 ppm) and minor quantities of sulfur (50–150 ppm) protects conversion activity and stabilizes the catalyst.   U.S. Pat. 3,383,431 (84) describes the preparation of a catalyst suitable for dehydrogenation of butanes, pentanes, and hexane by treating a Group VIII metal with a metal subfluoride such as aluminum monofluoride.

A combination process whereby linear paraffins in the C_{10}–C_{15} range are converted to the corresponding linear monoolefins in the presence of a nonacidic dehydrogenation catalyst, followed by monoalkylation of benzene and recovery of the resulting bio-degradable detergent intermediate, is described in U.S. Pat. 3,432, 567 (85).

According to U.S. Pat. 3,448,165 (86), C_{10}–C_{18} paraffins can be dehydrogenated with a once-through conversion of 15–20% by passing at relatively high space velocities (liquid hourly space velocity LHSV of at least 12.0) through a fixed-bed catalyst of arsenic-attenuated platinum on lithiated alumina in the temperature range of 400–600°C.

One problem encountered in paraffin dehydrogenation is the formation of diolefins (75% of which are conjugated) which, at high conversion, can represent up to 30% by weight of the total olefinic product. A method of separating the desired monoolefin product from the diolefins is described in U.S. Pat. 3,459,822 (87), which calls for condensing the conjugated dienes with a dienophilic compound, preferably ethylene, and separating the adduct from the monoolefins.

Ethyl Corp. has also extensively investigated, but never commercialized, paraffin dehydrogenation. The company rather appears to have abandoned this route as a source for linear olefins in favor of ethylene chain growth. U.S. Pat. 3,433,852 (88) claims the dehydrogenation of long-chain saturated hydrocarbons over a calcium-nickel-phosphate-chromia catalyst complex. Conversions per pass (12–22 %) vary inversely with olefin selectivity. With the catalyst bed at 501°C and at a LHSV of 1.0, dodecane yielded about 22.5% of a product consisting of 40% olefins, 40% aromatics and 20% cracking products. Changing operating conditions to 450°C at LHSV of 0.4 dropped conversion to 9.8% but raised the olefin content of the product to 77% and reduced that of the aromatics and cracked products to 6 and 17%, respectively.

An earlier Ethyl patent, U.S. Pat. 3,322,849 (89), claims a dehydrogenation catalyst consisting of a mixture of chromium oxide, cupric oxide and manganese dioxide.

Bibliography

1. S. A. Miller ed., *Ethylene and its Industrial Derivatives*, Ernest Benn Ltd., London, 1969.
2. U.S. Pat. 3,296,330 (Jan. 3, 1967), F. Sherk (to Phillips Co.).
3. R. Banks and R. Regier, "Synthesis of Isoamylene via Olefin Disproportionation," a paper presented to the American Chemical Society, Feb. 1970.
4. F. Asinger, *Chemie und Technologie der Monolefine*, Akademie-Verlag, Berlin, 1969.
5. S. A. Miller, *op. cit.*
6. J. G. Freiling et al., "Commercial Implications of Trends in Cracker Technology," a paper presented to the European Petrochemical Assoc., Knokke, Belgium, Oct. 1968.
7. *Chemical Economics Handbook*, Stanford Research Institute, p. 525.5620E.
8. *Oil and Gas J.*, May 20, 1968, p. 132.
9. Data supplied by Petro-Tex Chemical Corporation.
10. *Oil and Gas J.*, Dec. 22, 1969, p. 52.
11. J. G. Freiling et al., *op. cit.*
12. N. E. Ockerbloom et al., "Outlook for Propylene in Western Europe, Japan, and United States," a paper presented to the European Petrochemical Assoc. meeting, Wiesbaden, Germany, Sept. 29, 1969.
13. R. G. Minet et al., "Technical Aspects of Ethylene Plant Design," *Het Ingenieursblad*, No. 11, 1968.
14. C. Wickham-Jones, "The Market for Propylene in W. Europe," paper presented to the Society of Chemical Industry, London, Nov. 1969.
15. *Chemical Age*, Jan. 16, 1970, p. 6.
16. N. E. Ockerbloom, *op. cit.*

17. C. Wickham-Jones, *op. cit.*

18. R. B. Stobaugh, Jr., "The U.S. Oil Import Program and Petrochemical Industry," a report prepared for the U.S. Govt. Cabinet Task Force, Dec. 1969.

19. D. F. Beavon et al., "Chemical Production and Fuel Refineries," *Chem. Eng. Prog.* **65,** July, 1969.

20. S. Zdonik et al., "Ethylene Worldwide," *Oil and Gas J.,* Aug. 21, 1967, p. 86; Sept. 11, 1967, p. 98; Oct. 16, 1967, p. 112.

21. "BOC Overcomes Wulff Plant Limitations," *European Chemical News,* March 6, 1970, p. 34.

22. H. K. Kamptner et al., "HTP; After Five Years," *Hydrocarbon Processing,* **45,** (4), April 1966, pp. 187–193.

23. A. Steinhofer, "Make Petrochemicals From Crude Oil," *Hydrocarbon Processing,* **44,** Aug 1965, p. 134.

24. *Chemical Engineering,* Jan. 26, 1970, p. 39.

25. *Chemical Economics Handbook,* Stanford Research Institute, p. 525.5620E.

26. U.S. Pat. 3,239,567 (March 8, 1966), L. Slaugh et al. (to Shell Oil).

27. U.S. Pat. 3,173,967 (March 16, 1965), H. C. Brown.

28. *Chemical & Engineering News,* Feb. 18, 1963, p. 34.

29. K. E. McCaleb, "Linear Alpha Olefins," in *Chemical Economics Handbook,* Stanford Research Institute, 1966.

30. "Chevron Alpha Olefins, New Products for New Profits," Technical Bulletin, Chevron Chemical Co.

31. D. M. Marquis, *Hydrocarbon Processing,* **47** (3), p. 109.

32. *Chemical Engineering,* July 8, 1963, p. 73.

33. *Modern Plastics,* Dec. 1965, p. 190.

34. U.S. Pat. 3,409,703 (Nov. 5, 1968), R. M. Engelbrecht et al. (to Monsanto).

35. G. R. Worrell et al., "Kinetics of Wax Cracking for Alpha-Olefin Production," *Ind. Eng. Chem.,* **16,** Jan. 1969, pp. 89–95.

36. A. G. Guillemin, "Dempster," "Preparation of Concentrated Olefins from Petrolatum," Proceedings of Third World Petroleum Congress, Sect. IV, The Hague, pp. 184–190.

37. "Process for Producing α-Olefins," California Research Corp.; Brit. Pat. 843,385 (Sept. 14, 1960).

38. T. V. Gerasicheva and Y. A. Botnikov, "Thermal Cracking of Paraffin to Prepare Raw Materials for Detergents," *Tr. Vses. Nauc.-Issled. Inst. po Pererabotke Nefti,* **9,** 15–21, 1963.

39. U.S. Pat. 2,945,076 (Jul 12, 1960), W. A. Pardee and F. Chapel (to Gulf Oil Co.).

40. U.S. Pat. 2,172,228 (Sept. 5, 1939), A. J. Van Peski (to Shell Oil Co.).

41. B. Paulis, "Cracking *n*-Paraffins," *European Chemical News, Paraffins Supplement,* Dec. 2, 1966, pp. 33–36.

42. S. G. Woinski, "Process Design & Development 1," *Ind. Eng. Chem.,* Oct. 1968, pp. 529–538.

43. Brit. Pat. 722,114 (April 10, 1957), (to Bataafse Petroleum Maatschappij N. V.).

44. A. M. Brodskii et al., "Production of Higher α-Olefins by High-Speed Contact Cracking of Paraffinic Petroleum Products," *Neftekhimiya* **4, 6,** 880–887, 1964.

45. U.S. Pat. 2,736,685 (Feb. 28, 1956), H. L. Wilson, et al. (to Esso).

46. J. Phillips, "Refine Waxes for Suitable Properties," *Petrol. Refiner* **38,** Sept. 1959, pp. 193–198.

47. Brit. Pat. 884,634 (Dec. 13, 1961), (to Esso Research & Engineering Co.).

48. R. A. Franz, "The Production of Alpha Olefins," *Petrochemicals and Petroleum Refining,* Chemical Engineering Progress Symposium Series 34, **57,** 1961.

49. Brit. Pat. 783,469 (Sept. 25, 1957), (to Bataafse Petroleum N. V. Maatschappij).

50. U.S. Pat. 3,291,853 (Dec. 13, 1966), G. Feighner et al. (to Continental Oil).

51. U.S. Pat. 3,444,261 (May 13, 1969), Gianguido Caprioli et al. (to Montecatini).

52. "Chevron Alpha Olefins, New Products for New Profits," Technical Bulletin, Chevron Chemical Co, 1968.

53. K. Ziegler, *Liebigs Annalen der Chemie,* March 1960, vol. 629, pp. 1–13.

54. U.S. Pat. 3,382,269 (May 7, 1968), B. J. Williams et al. (to Continental Oil).

55. K. Ziegler et al., "Metallorganische Synthese Höherer-Aliphatischer Verbindungen aus Niedrigen Olefinen in Praxis und Theorie," *Angewandte Chemie* **72,** (22), 1960, pp. 829–835; K. Zosel, "Über zwei wesentliche Verbesserungen der Aluminumorganischen Synthese," *Brennstoff-Chemie* **41,** (11), Nov. 23, 1960, pp. 321–325.

56. U.S. Pat. 3,310,600 (March 21, 1967), K. Ziegler et al.: French Pat. 1,338,062 (Oct. 25, 1962), H. Fernald et al. (to Gulf Research); K. Ziegler et al., *Liebigs Annalen der Chemie*, March 1960, vol. 629, pp. 190–197.

57. J. Gubitosi, "Plasticizer Industry's Integration and Trend to Premium Grades Highlighted by Monsanto Move," *Oil, Paint and Drug Reporter*, Feb. 9, 1970.

58. "Normal Alpha Olefins from Gulf," Technical Bulletin, Gulf Oil Corp., 1969.

59. U.S. Pat. 3,441,630 (April 29, 1969), A. W. Langer, Jr., et al. (to Esso Research).

60. A. W. Langer, Jr., "Linear Alpha Olefins by Catalytic Oligomerization of Ethylene," a paper presented at the 159th National Meeting of the American Chemical Society, Houston, Texas, Feb. 1970.

61. U.S. Pat. 3,206,522 (Sept. 14, 1965), R. L. Poe et al. (to Continental Oil); U.S. Pat. 3,278,262 (Oct. 11, 1966), R. L. Poe (to Continental Oil).

62. U.S. Pat. 3,308,143 (March 7, 1967), R. L. Poe et al. (to Continental Oil).

63. U.S. Pat. 3,406,187 (Oct. 15, 1968), W. R. Kroll.

64. U.S. Pat. 3,352,894 (Nov. 14, 1967), D. L. Crain et al. (to Phillips Petroleum).

65. U.S. Pat. 3,309,416 (May 14, 1967), R. L. Poe et al. (to Continental Oil).

66. U.S. Pat. 2,978,523 (April 4, 1961), D. M. Coyne et al. (to Continental Oil).

67. U.S. Pat. 3,317,625 (May 2, 1967), W. B. Carter (to Continental Oil).

68. U.S. Pat. 3,210,435 (Oct. 1965), E. F. Kennedy et al. (to Continental Oil).

69. U.S. Pat. 3,395,166 (July 30, 1968), R. T. Johnson (to Chevron Research).

70. U.S. Pat. 3,358,050 (Dec. 12, 1967), J.A. Acciarri (to Continental Oil).

71. U.S. Pat. 3,391,175 and 3,391,219 (July 2, 1968), W. T. Davis et al. (to Ethyl Corp.).

72. U.S. Pat. 3,423,444 (Jan. 21, 1969), M. T. Atwood (to Continental Oil).

73. U.S. Pat. 3,445,494 (May 20, 1969), J. A. Acciarri (to Continental Oil).

74. U.S. Pat. 3,458,594 (July 29, 1969), L. D. Boyer (to Continental Oil).

75. U.S. Pat. 3,277,205 (Oct. 4, 1966), M. F. Hughes (to Chevron).

76. U.S. Pat. 3,402,216 (Sept. 17, 1968), T. Hutson, Jr., (to Phillips Petroleum).

77. *European Chemical News*, August 15, 1969, p. 22.

78. D. B. Broughton and R. C. Berg, "Two Processes Team Up to Make Linear Monoolefins," *Chemical Engineering*, Jan. 26, 1970, p. 86.

79. U.S. Pat. 3,248,451 (April 26, 1966), L. J. Hughes (to Monsanto).

80. U.S. Pat. 3,356,757 (Dec. 5, 1967), J. Roth (to Monsanto).

81. U.S. Pat. 3,315,008 (April 18, 1967), J. Abell, Jr. (to Monsanto).

82. U.S. Pat. 3,391,218 (July 2, 1968), H. S. Bloch (to Universal Oil Products).

83. U.S. Pat. 3,360,586 (Dec. 26, 1967), H. S. Bloch (to Universal Oil Products).

84. U.S. Pat. 3,383,431 (May 14, 1968), N. Fishel (to Universal Oil Products).

85. U.S. Pat. 3,432,567 (March 11, 1969), E. K. Jones (to Universal Oil Products).

86. U.S. Pat. 3,448,165 (June 1969), H. S. Bloch (to Universal Oil Products).

87. U.S. Pat. 3,459,822 (Aug. 5, 1969), H. S. Bloch (to Universal Oil Products).

88. U.S. Pat. 3,433,852 (March 18, 1969), K. A. Keblis (to Ethyl Corp.).

89. U.S. Pat. 3,322,849 (May 30, 1967), J. M. McEuen (to Ethyl Corp.).

H. K. NIEUWENHUIS,
M. GARFINKEL, AND
D. ARKIN
Chemical Projects Associates Inc.

OXYGEN GENERATION SYSTEMS

This article discusses devices for the generation of oxygen, for breathing, in such systems as submarines, aircraft, spaceships, bomb shelters, and breathing apparatus. Convenience and reliability, rather than low cost, are desired, and above all the systems must have "storageability"; even compressed cylinders of oxygen are not reliable, long term, unless they are routinely inspected and, if necessary, recharged. Electrolysis of water requires electric power, and is not adaptable to portable, personal use. It has been used to some extent on submarines and spacecraft, but disposal of the hydrogen may present a problem.

This discussion is limited to systems based on chlorates or perchlorates, and on peroxides and superoxides.

Chlorates and Perchlorates

The chlorates and perchlorates of lithium, sodium, and potassium evolve oxygen when heated, and these salts have been compounded with a fuel to form a coherent shape, called a chlorate candle, which will produce oxygen by a continuing reaction. Components of the overall composition include the oxygen-producing material, the fuel, a material to hold back traces of chlorine which are produced, and generally an inert binder. Once the reaction is started, oxygen is released from the hot salt by thermal decomposition. A portion of that oxygen is then used to react with the fuel to produce more heat which in turn produces more oxygen, etc.

These materials were known before World War II, the Germans using chlorate candles in the 1920s. Both the Japanese and the Germans experimented with these sources of oxygen supply for high-altitude flight in World War II. The British and Americans also investigated applications of chlorate candles and they are presently standard items on submarines of both countries. Recent work has resulted in application of emergency oxygen uses on American aircraft (1).

Relevant properties of the chlorates are shown in Table 1, together with other data for comparison. It will be seen that the oxygen density is higher than for liquid oxygen.

Sodium chlorate is generally used. Lithium and potassium chlorates and perchlorates are not used because their decomposition takes place above the melting points, making the candle hard to contain because of a long molten zone which runs from the reaction area. Lithium chlorate is also hard to dry. However a lithium perchlorate candle (2) of very high oxygen-storage density has been described.

Table 1. Chlorates and Perchlorates as Sources for Oxygen

Substance	Mp, °C	Decomposition, at °C[a]	Oxygen density		
			lb O_2/lb	lb O_2/ft³ [b]	g O_2/liter[b]
$LiClO_3$	129	270	0.53	87	139
$NaClO_3$	261	478	0.45	70	112
$KClO_3$	357	400	0.39	57	93
$LiClO_4$	247	410	0.60	91	146
$NaClO_4$	471	482	0.52	82	131
$KClO_4$	585	(400)	0.46	73	117
liquid oxygen			1.0	71	114
7500 psi O_2			1.0	36	57.5

[a] Without catalyst.   [b] Based on crystal densities.

Chlorate candles are perfectly stable on storage; they have been stored for as long as 20 years, even uncontained, and then operated successfully with no loss of oxygen output. Thus, for emergency uses, they are most attractive (3). Another characteristic is the ability to continue to produce oxygen under pressure, making it possible to pressurize cylinders if desired.

Equipment. A candle apparatus consists generally of the components shown in Figure 1. The candle mass has in it a cone, of material high in iron, which is used to initiate the reaction. It is in turn started by a flash powder train or electric wire. Shown is a spring-actuated hammer firing a percussion cap into the cone area.

An outer jacket is furnished to collect the oxygen. It contains a relief valve and a gas exit port. The candle is wrapped in insulation and placed within this jacket. A gas-conditioning filter can be added and arrangements provided to prevent vibration and shock damage to the candle (4).

A fuel is used to generate heat by oxidation, using some of the oxygen released by the thermal decomposition of chlorate. Powdered elements such as Fe, B, Al, Co, etc, have been tried with varying degrees of success. Iron is universally used in commercial applications. Thermal analysis of the heat of decomposition vs heat required to bring $NaClO_3$ to the decomposition point shows a 25% deficit to keep the reaction self-sustaining. Hence, some fuel is needed to produce a packaged, satisfactorily operating candle.

Generalized reactions are:

$$2\ NaClO_3 + heat \rightarrow 2\ NaCl + 3\ O_2\ (major)$$

$$4\ Fe + O_2 \rightarrow 2\ Fe_xO_y + heat\ (major)$$

$$4\ NaClO_3 \rightarrow 2\ Na_2O + 2\ Cl_2 + 5\ O_2\ (minor)$$

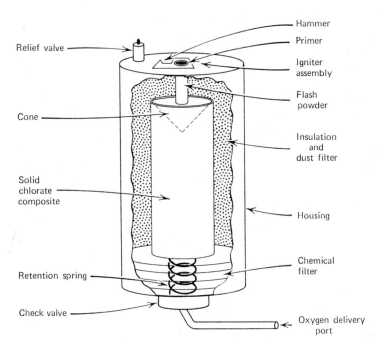

Fig. 1. Cutaway view of generator housing.

An interesting point is the incomplete combustion of the iron (3). The Fe_xO_y shown is taken as a median between FeO, Fe_3O_4, and Fe_2O_3.

During evolution of oxygen, a bleach odor is generally evolved. This is attributed to chlorine-containing compounds such as ClO_2 or elemental chlorine, although for convenience gas analyses of candle oxygen list this component as Cl_2. Barium peroxide, BaO_2, is used to retain the major portion of this material, forming $BaCl_2$. Coincidentally, some oxygen is evolved as follows:

$$BaO_2 + Cl_2 \rightarrow BaCl_2 + O_2$$

Between 2 and 5% BaO_2 by weight is used.

Glass fiber, asbestos fibers, or steel wool are used as a binder to hold the candles together. Structural integrity is improved; the burning zone is reinforced so that the ash and unused portion stay together; the ash is more coherent; and there is evidence of enhancement of reaction by the binders. Asbestos is rarely used because it catalyses the evolution of chlorine, and glass fiber is generally used. Steel wool can be used both as the fuel and binder, but it makes a hotter burning candle. Binder composition is 4–7 wt %.

Work has been performed on adding catalysts to help decomposition of the chlorate. Acidic oxides (oxides of V, U, W, B, P) seem to enhance chlorine evolution and hence are not desirable. Basic oxides (oxides of Co, Mn, Ni, Fe, Cu) catalyze the decomposition reaction. The aim here is not to speed decomposition, but to lower the decomposition temperature. Less fuel is needed and a lower operational temperature results.

An investigation was made (5) of a number of basic oxides as catalysts. Of those tested, cobalt metal was found to lower the decomposition temperature of pure $NaClO_3$ from 478 to 280°C. The metal serves both as a fuel and as a catalyst. A suggested composition is (in wt %): $NaClO_4$, 90; Co, 4; glass fiber, 6; as compared with $NaClO_4$, 86; Fe, 4; glass fiber, 6; and BaO_2, 4. Initiation of reaction was 270°C, compared to 370°C for the iron-fueled candle. $Co(OH)_2$ produces more pronounced effects and also holds back chlorine. MnO_2 and Al_2O_3 had little effect on reducing decomposition temperature.

Oxygen Purity. Impurities formed are "chlorine," CO, CO_2, H_2O, simple organics. All of these can be minimized by high-purity ingredients, control of moisture, or gas conditioning.

Candles are generally made from as-received chlorate and BaO_2. All other materials are degreased by "burning off" at 800°F. This includes steel wool and glass fiber. Iron powders are preferably hydrogen reduced.

Carbon in iron (or from inadequate degreasing) can form CO and CO_2. Carbon particles can appear in the sodium chlorate, the source being the graphite anodes used in its production. Barium peroxide contains carbonate as an impurity.

Water in the candles is suspect as a controlling factor in the evolution of Cl_2 and ClO_2 (6,7). First, HCl can be produced by hydrolysis of chlorides present as trace impurities in the chlorate. Then the HCl can react with the chlorate, producing either Cl_2, or CO_2, or any combination thereof, according to the equations:

$$NaClO_3 + 6\, HCl \rightarrow NaCl + 3\, H_2O + 3\, Cl_2$$

$$5\, NaClO_3 + 6\, HCl \rightarrow 5\, NaCl + 6\, ClO_2 + 3\, H_2O$$

It is possible that chlorite, or hypochlorite, is also produced.

Table 2. Impurity Levels in O_2 from Chlorate Candles

Impurity	Unfiltered, ppm	Filtered, ppm
H_2O	1000	unchanged
CO	5–25	1
CO_2	50–400	5
Cl_2	2–10	0.2
hydrocarbon	2	1

Hydrocarbon impurities can be introduced by contamination of the outer surface of the candle. Candles have been shaved to reduce such contaminants.

Purity of oxygen from candles varies widely but generally is in the range shown in Table 2. Also shown are impurity levels attained with gas filtration. A particulate filter is always used. Chemicals employed are Hopcalite (oxidizes CO to CO_2), molecular sieves (remove chlorine compounds), and basic materials such as sodalime (CO_2, chlorine compounds). The ultimate purity is well within required limits for continuous oxygen use. In some applications, a total of all impurities (other than H_2O and N_2) of <1 ppm can be attained.

Gas purity is also a function of overall candle packaging—not just composition. A hotter burning unit generates more impurities.

Candle Fabrication. All ingredients must be grease free—burned off as mentioned. Preferably the candle materials ($NaClO_3$ and BaO_2) should also be dry for oxygen of highest purity.

The oxygen-generator mass is made by mixing the ingredients and then pressing or casting. Care must be taken to assure homogenous mixing or reaction rates will vary throughout the candle mass. Shape can be varied as desired, especially with the casting process. With pressing the shape is limited to some extent, although hydrostatic pressing provides considerable freedom. All other factors being equal, the rate of oxygen evolution is directly proportional to the cross-sectional area of the unit.

Casting is performed by heating the ingredients to just above the melting point of the sodium chlorate. It is necessary that the materials which have not become molten remain in suspension to produce a homogeneous composition throughout the cast candle. Molds of desired shape are used and the slurry is poured into the mold when a homogeneous mixture is achieved. Depending upon the length/diameter ratio of the mold, some settling of iron may take place. For this reason, certain items may be cast on their side rather than upright. Cast items are characterized by a high density and maximum resistance to breakage.

Pressing can be performed in a variety of ways: (1) wet pressing of a damp mix at room temperature; (2) hot pressing; (3) pressing with finely divided materials; and (4) hydrostatic pressing.

For a length-to-diameter ratio of approximately 2:1, wet pressing is satisfactory. Those units which have been used by the Navy are approximately 7 in. in diameter by approximately 12 in. long, and have been produced by pressing a composition with approximately 1.5% water to pressures of about 4,000 psi. They are then dried to approximately 0.5% moisture and packaged for shipment.

Hot pressing has been investigated and has been used especially for smaller shapes. No moisture is used in the mixture for hot pressing and generally the materials are more finely divided than with cold pressing. The mixture and the molds are heated to approximately 400°F and pressed as required.

Hot pressing can sometimes be circumvented by room-temperature pressing of very finely divided materials (300-mesh particle size), but the mechanical integrity of the candles is poor. This process can be considered for low-cost production for special applications.

Hydrostatic pressing is particularly advantageous in producing non-right circular cylinders and shapes with varying diameters. Pressures from 15,000 to 30,000 psi are used.

In any pressing technique gradations of density along the length of the candle will produce differences in burning rates. In fact, too much pressure and too high a degree of densification can result in the candle not functioning at all. This is only one of the factors which enter into the production of an acceptable unit.

Reaction can be initiated by several means, all of which depend upon the delivery of heat at a relatively high temperature to a starting cone. Cartridge-actuated and electrical match units are the most used. The heat generated by the starting device initiates the reaction in a "cone," which is a button of material of composition similar to the main body of the candle but higher in fuel content (30% Fe vs 4–8%). Thus, more heat per unit volume is generated, along with some oxygen, although its primary function is to provide sufficient heat to initiate reaction of the candle mass.

The cones are generally pressed, cast compositions being too difficult to light. Pressure is considerably lower than used for the candle to preclude too high a densification. Incorporation of the cones into candles can be done before pressing or casting, the cone then being held in place by the resulting bond. Alternatively, a cavity can be pressed into the candle shape, the cone materials added to the cavity and then pressed into place. The bond formed in the latter method is weak but is generally sufficient for most purposes.

Operational Characteristics. The reaction is exothermic, and handling the heat release is a function of design of the total unit into which the candle is incorporated. Because of the low heat content of the gas, the gas exit temperature is normally under about 200°F. Since some of the heat is taken up within the candle shape by specific heat or even heat of fusion of the sodium chloride which is formed by the reaction, the candle mass will continue to evolve heat after the reaction is finished. The heat release is to some extent a function of the fuel content, but averages 100 Btu/ft^3 O$_2$ for 4–8% Fe compositions.

Oxygen release rate is directly proportional to the cross-sectional area of the candle and also depends on the linear burn rate. However, lower fuel contents decrease the burning rate slightly, about 2% Fe being a lower limit for reliable room temperature operation. Low temperature starts require at least 3.5% Fe. A factor in burn rates is the direction of gas flow. If the hot oxygen flows over the unburned portion of the candle, up to 15% rate increases can be produced.

Higher operating pressures will increase the oxygen release rate. Varying data have been reported on this point, but a rule of thumb is that the burn time is halved for each 500-lb pressure rise. The ultimate pressure that can be reached by a confined candle is at least 20,000 psi.

Uses. The early use for chlorate candles in aircraft at the beginning of World War II never became operational because of poor experience with the overall systems. In the late 1940s and early 1950s, a unit was constructed and demonstrated to a commercial airline for first-aid oxygen administration to passengers. However oxygen in cylinders was also available, and there was such a vast background of experience with it, that the project was not pursued further.

A major use then appeared in the incorporation of a 10-liter cast chlorate candle in the "quick start" canister, filled with potassium superoxide and used in a self-contained breathing apparatus: the candle supplies oxygen rapidly until the superoxide becomes fully activated. Hundreds of thousands of such canisters have been used. Large candles, delivering 120 ft^3 in 45 min, then began to be used for long-duration submergence of submarines. These candles were used in a "furnace" which was sized to accept two candles, the one igniting the other and delivering oxygen for 120 men for $1\frac{1}{2}$ hr.

A number of special uses have arisen in such areas as oxygen for fuel cells, for long-term unattended service (8). Here candles are fired successively on demand by the pressure sensor in the oxygen accumulator. Considerable work was done in incorporating chlorate candles into a back pack for use in the Apollo moon missions (9).

The newest large-scale use that is beginning to appear is oxygen supply in event of decompression in passenger aircraft (10). This application is nearly ideal because it fulfills the requirement of no maintenance, no oxygen leakage, high reliability and extremely long storage life (20 years minimum).

In projecting uses for candles, the characteristics to be considered are: volumetric oxygen density nearly equal to that of liquid oxygen; extremely high pressure can be developed; high oxygen purity; long storage life with no leakage; preprogrammed oxygen delivery; heat release. General parameters are given in Table 3.

Table 3. Chlorate Oxygen Generator Parameters

Parameter	Value
average composition	80–85% NaClO$_3$; 3–10% Fe; 4% BaO$_2$; rest binder
O$_2$ available, wt %	40% maximum
specific gravity of mixture	2.3–2.5
average reaction rate through shape, in./min	0.25
heat evolution, cal/g	200
reaction zone temperature, °F	1000
shape of chlorate unit	unlimited
starting method	hot wire, Bouchon cap
cone material	up to 30% Fe; 60% NaClO$_3$; remainder binder and BaO$_2$
time before O$_2$ evolved, sec	up to 1
gas purity, %	99.99+

Peroxides and Superoxides

Chlorate candles do only one thing—produce oxygen. Another class of compounds, the peroxides and superoxides, produce oxygen and also absorb carbon dioxide.

A man on a normal diet, for every volume of oxygen that he breathes will exhale 0.82 volume of carbon dioxide. This gives a *respiratory coefficient*, RQ, of 0.82. It will be seen that it is desirable for a device to be used in a closed system to mirror this RQ, absorbing 0.82 volume of carbon dioxide and liberating 1.0 volume oxygen.

It may be noted that even complete recovery of oxygen from the carbon dioxide exhaled is not sufficient for long-term habitability. There is an 18% deficit of oxygen, which will result in deterioration of the system. Thus, long-term space flight requires additional oxygen, usually supplied by electrolysis of water.

Table 4 (11) gives the relevant properties of the peroxides of lithium and sodium, and the superoxides of sodium, potassium, and calcium. See also Peroxides. It may be noted that potassium peroxide is difficult to prepare (see Vol. 14, p. 749). Lithium superoxide is too unstable to be considered. The ozonides, MO_3, of the alkali metals contain a very high percentage of oxygen, but they are only stable below room temperature.

Table 4. Peroxides and Superoxides

Substance	lb O_2/lb	lb CO_2/lb[a]	RQ	Unstable above, °C	Mp, °C
Li_2O_2	0.35	0.96	1.94	315	315
Na_2O_2	0.21	0.56	1.94	311–400	596
NaO_2	0.43	0.40	0.67	100	forms series of solid solutions; reaches Na_2O_2 at 250
KO_2	0.34	0.31	0.67	145–425	440
$Ca(O_2)_2$	0.46	0.42	0.67	200 estd	?

[a] To form carbonate.

Peroxides. With water present, carbon dioxide will react with evolution of oxygen. The steps have been postulated (12) as follows:

$$Li_2O_2 + 2 H_2O \rightarrow 2 LiOH + H_2O_2$$

$$2 LiOH + CO_2 \rightarrow Li_2CO_3 + H_2O$$

$$H_2O_2 \rightarrow H_2O + \tfrac{1}{2} O_2$$

$$Li_2O_2 + CO_2 \rightarrow Li_2CO_3 + \tfrac{1}{2} O_2$$

Because of the delay in decomposition of the peroxide, the oxygen evolution lags the carbon dioxide sorption. A catalyst is required to obtain total decomposition of the peroxides; 2% nickel sulfate is often used. The temperature of the bed is stated to be the controlling variable, 400°F being required to produce the best decomposition rates (13).

The above described reaction mechanism for lithium peroxide, Li_2O_2, holds also for sodium peroxide. Both carbon dioxide and moisture are required to generate oxygen. Sodium peroxide has been used extensively in breathing apparatus.

All the peroxides are colorless and diamagnetic, when pure. Traces of the superoxide in technical-grade sodium peroxide impart a yellow color. Sealed storage containers are required to prevent reaction with atmospheric carbon dioxide and water vapor.

Superoxides. The superoxides are colored and are paramagnetic: KO_2 is yellow, NaO_2 is orange-yellow, and $Ca(O_2)_2$ is red.

In their uses as oxygen suppliers and carbon dioxide scrubbers, they are "demand chemicals," that is, they react to the load imposed by generating more oxygen as more water is introduced. Reactions during use are, first, a reaction with water to liberate oxygen and then a reaction with carbon dioxide as follows:

$$2 MO_2 + H_2O \rightarrow 2 MOH + \tfrac{3}{2} O_2$$

$$2 MOH + CO_2 \rightarrow M_2CO_3 + H_2O$$

$$2 MOH + 2 CO_2 \rightarrow 2 MHCO_3$$

Some moisture must be present to promote the reactions. Dry carbon dioxide does not react with the superoxides. One mole of MO_2 gives $\frac{3}{2}$ moles oxygen, and then absorbs one mole of carbon dioxide to form carbonate, or two to form bicarbonate. Thus if only carbonate is formed, an RQ of 0.67 is reached; if only bicarbonate is formed, an RQ of 1.33 results. The required stoichiometry for an RQ of 0.82 is:

$$2\, MO_2 + 1.23\, CO_2 + 0.23\, H_2O \rightarrow 0.77\, M_2CO_3 + 0.46\, MHCO_3 + \tfrac{3}{2}\, O_2$$

By control of the moisture content of the inlet gas and of the temperature of the bed, some control over the ratio of carbonate to bicarbonate can be obtained.

Potassium superoxide, KO_2, is most used of the Group I metals. It is produced by spraying the molten metal into dry air. The superoxide is formed as a fine yellow powder which is processed to the desired size. Copper oxychloride is added to make a material more active at low temperature.

Sodium superoxide is produced from an open-pore sodium peroxide which is produced by spraying liquid sodium into dry air. Oxygen at 2000 psi and 400°C is used to oxidize the peroxide to the superoxide. The material can then be pressed and regranulated as required.

Calcium superoxide, $Ca(O_2)_2$, has been produced in up to 60% purity by careful dehydration of $CaO_2 \cdot 2H_2O_2$. It is of interest for breathing apparatus because it is less sensitive to water and because calcium hydroxide has a higher melting point than the hydroxides of potassium or sodium.

Analysis. Analysis of the peroxides and superoxides, fresh or spent, is done by adding the material to water. About 0.1% permanganate is used in the water to decompose the peroxide ion which otherwise forms. The evolved oxygen is measured volumetrically. If the material is spent, the base strength is titrated to a phenolphthalein end point, further acidified and the carbon dioxide is determined volumetrically.

APPLICATIONS OF PEROXIDES AND SUPEROXIDES

The peroxides, and also the superoxides, must be hermetically sealed for storage. The superoxides especially are strong oxidizing agents and should be kept away from grease, oil, and organic materials.

Peroxides. It will be seen from the equations above that the peroxides give high absorption of carbon dioxide, with some evolution of oxygen. In general, sodium peroxide is more widely used than lithium peroxide. Breathing apparatus using peroxides is often supplied also with bottled oxygen, since the peroxides are not very weight-efficient for oxygen.

Superoxides. These are used in breathing applications requiring no auxiliary source of oxygen. Sodium superoxide is about ten times as expensive as potassium superoxide, because high-temperature, high-pressure autoclaves are required for its production (although if the demand became much greater, the cost would be reduced). Calcium peroxide is still in the experimental stage. Thus, potassium peroxide has been most used.

Self-contained portable breathing apparatus are used by fire departments, damage control teams, and in general work in unbreathable atmospheres. Here the wearer uses a canister containing the chemical, a breathing bag, and a mask. The chemical is packaged as 2–4-mesh granules with glass fiber filters to hold back any dust. About three breaths are required to start the chemical reaction and deliver oxygen. Alternatively, a small chlorate candle can be used to deliver oxygen immediately.

In personal breathing apparatus, efficiency is generally about 70% in oxygen utilization of the chemical because of excessive water vapor generated at high work rates. At low work rates, efficiency is as high as 95%. It is in the ability to match the work rate that the superoxides are valuable. If a candle were used it would be necessary to size it for the maximum work rate—wasting oxygen at other times. The same canister of KO_2 will sustain a man at hard work for an hour, or last 7 hours if the man is resting.

Various physical forms can be used: granules of various sizes, densities, and porosities, or plates pressed from powder. Granules are produced by pressing the "fluff" or powdery KO_2, grinding, and screening. Plates are made by pressing the fluff to a coherent stage but not so dense as to impede penetration of the gases (14).

In air-conditioning closed spaces, a wider latitude in design features can be exercised (15,16). Blowers are used to pass room or cabin air through arrays of granules or plates. Efficiencies are high in this service, generally 95% or better oxygen utilization. The limiting factor is generally the decreased rate of absorption of carbon dioxide. An auxiliary small CO_2 sorption canister has been used. Control of moisture entering the KO_2 canister extends the life of the chemical also, and helps control the RQ to the desired 0.82.

Generally the systems are used dry, but a system has been built to react the superoxide with water and absorb CO_2 in the resultant KOH solution. Here the RQ is fixed at 0.67.

An unusual application is to use KO_2 in a closed-cycle diesel system. Oxygen is supplied and CO_2 removed in a KO_2 bed, through which the exhaust is cycled back to the engine. Undersea and non-atmospheric operations are then possible.

The superoxides compare successfully with a combination of liquid oxygen or gaseous oxygen systems and a CO_2 scrubber such as LiOH. Heat release is somewhat less and the volume required is roughly equivalent to the LiOH alone.

Bibliography

1. E. B. Thompson, Jr., "An Investigation of the Chemical Formulation of Solid Chemical Oxygen Generators for Aircraft Emergency Oxygen Supply," *AFFDL-TM-70-4-FEFE*, Flight Dynamics Laboratory, Wright-Patterson Air Force Base, Ohio, September, 1970.
2. U.S. Pat. 3,174,936 (March 1965), P. R. Gustafson and R. R. Miller (to U. S. Government).
3. W. H. Schecter, R. R. Miller, R. M. Bovard, C. B. Jackson, and J. R. Pappenheimer, *Ind. Eng. Chem.* **42**, 2348 (1950).
4. V. Hwoschinsky, "Solid State Oxygen Development Program," *Safe Engineering* **4** (2), 21 (1970).
5. W. J. O'Reilly et al., "Development of Sodium Chlorate Candles for the Storage and Supply of Oxygen for Space Exploration Applications," *Rept. No. 69-4695*, Air Research Corp., Los Angeles, Calif., July, 1969.
6. H. Nagate, K. Kusomoto, and N. Karel Makai, *J. Ind. Explosives Soc. Japan* **27**, 99 (1966).
7. P. R. Gustafson, S. H. Smith, Jr., and R. R. Miller, "Chlorate Candle Fabrication by Hot Pressing," *NRL Rept. 5732*, *AP No. 272580*, Naval Research Laboratory, Washington, D.C., January, 1962.
8. J. W. Mausteller and M. J. McGoff, MSA Research Corp., unpublished data, 1968.
9. R. N. Prince, T. L. Illes, and W. J. O'Reilly, "Development of the Portable Environmental Control System," *Conference on Portable Life Support Systems, NASA-Ames Research Center, Moffett Field, California, April 1969.*
10. Anonymous, *New Scientist* **27**, 628 (1970).
11. "Exploratory Study of Potassium and Sodium Superoxides for Oxygen Control in Manned Space Vehicles" *Contract No. NASW-90*, MSA Research Corp., Evans City, Pa., March, 1962.

12. M. M. Markowitz and E. W. Dezmelyk, "A Study of the Application of Lithium Chemicals to Air Regeneration Techniques in Manned Sealed Environments," *AMRL-TDR-64-1*, Wright-Patterson Air Force Base, Ohio, February, 1964.
13. K. J, Dressler, and R. N. Prince, "Lithium Peroxide for Portable Life Support System Atmospheric Regeneration," *Conf. on Portable Life Support Systems, NASA-Ames Research Center Moffet Field, Calif., April 1969.*
14. J. W. Mausteller, M. J. McGoff, D. A. Keating, and K. Weiswurn, "Superoxide Atmosphere Control System for Manned Space Assemblies," *36th Aerospace Medical Association Meeting,* New York, April, 1965.
15. J. Presti, H. Waalman, and A. Petrocelli, "Superoxide Life Support System for Submersibles," *Undersea Technology* **8** (6), 20 (1967).
16. H. M. David, "Superoxides Developed to Supply Astronauts' Air," *Missiles, and Rockets,* **9** (15), 30 (1961).

J. W. MAUSTELLER
MSA Research Corporation

P

PHENOLIC FIBERS

Development of a textile fiber which neither burns nor melts in a flame has become an increasingly important requirement. Testimony before a U.S. Congressional Committee has indicated that a quarter of a million people in the United States are injured each year in clothing fires and many thousands more from other fabric-related fires. As a consequence, the legislative controls which are being enacted to upgrade flame resistance of fabric materials have provided scientists with a major challenge.

The section on Fire resistant textiles under Textile technology in this volume describes two approaches to this problem: the development of fire-resistant treatments for conventional textiles, and the development of new, remarkably heat-resistant fibers. But this article is devoted to a somewhat different approach, the development of a fiber which, although not exceptionally resistant to high temperatures, has inherent flame-resisting properties.

To be useful for flame protection a fabric should neither melt nor burn in a flame and yet display comfort and wear features commonly associated with fibers used in wearing apparel. To achieve these requirements a fiber should give a high char yield, show minimal shrinkage, and not produce flammable or poisonous volatiles. Presumably a highly crosslinked aromatic structure would tend to resist melting in a flame and form a stable char. However, development of such a fiber could present formidable problems which would more than overshadow any potential gains. For example a crosslinked resin cannot be drawn directly into a filament. Furthermore, a highly crosslinked fiber might be expected to display unsatisfactory stress-strain properties for use in textiles. The fact that until now highly crosslinked organic fibers have not been developed or reported in the literature, was additional evidence arguing against this approach.   An extensive research effort was conducted at the Carborundum R & D laboratories which has led to the successful development of a crosslinked phenolic fiber (1–3).

This fiber known as Kynol possesses outstanding flame-resistance combined with good mechanical properties.   Its current price (1971) is $5.00/lb for crimped staple; if demand develops, it is believed that the price could be reduced to a level competitive with other synthetic fibers.

Properties of Kynol Fibers

Mechanical Properties.   As might be expected for a crosslinked fiber, the stress-strain values depend significantly upon fiber diameter (Table 1).   Typical stress-strain curves are shown in Figure 1.

Table 1.   Dependance of Stress-Strain Properties of Kynol Upon Fiber Diameter

Diameter	Denier	Tenacity, g/den	Elongation, %	Modulus, g/den
9–10	0.7–0.9	2.7	45	60
12–13	1.3–1.5	2.3	36	53
15–16	2.0–2.3	2.0	30	50
17–25	2.6–5.5	1.6	15	45

Table 2.   Fracture Work of Kynol and Conventional Fibers

Fiber	Denier	Diameter, micron	Work to break, (g)(cm)/(den)(cm)[a]
Kynol	1.1	11	0.83
Kynol	1.1–2.0	11–15	0.66
Kynol	2.0–2.3	15–16	0.53
Kynol	2.3–2.6	16–17	0.39
Kynol	2.6–5.5	17–25	0.21
rayon	3.0	18	0.3
acetate	3.2	19	0.22
polyester	3.3	19	1.0
acrylic	2.6	16	0.5
nylon 66	3.4	19	1.7
Nomex[b]	3.4	19	0.9
cotton	1.3	12	0.2
wool	6.3	26	0.3
molded phenolic resin			0.01

[a] Calculated from the area underneath average stress-strain curve.

[b] Du Pont aromatic polyamide fiber.   See Fire resistant textiles under Textile technology in this volume.

Also, because of the amorphous structure, the distribution of the individual stress-strain data is slightly broader than that of conventional synthetic fibers.   Generally, small diameter fibers are stronger and exhibit a greater break elongation than larger diameter fibers.   The stress-strain behavior depends slightly upon the strain rate; the break elongation decreases as the strain rate increases from 100 to 2000%/min. The tenacity appears to be highest when fibers are tested at strain rates from 20 to

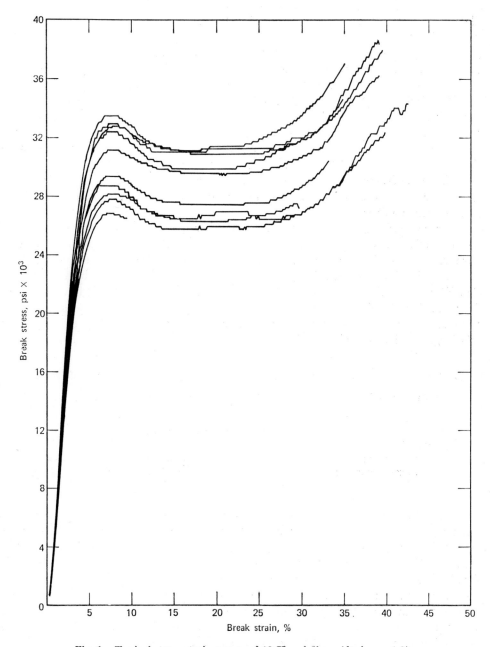

Fig. 1. Typical stress-strain curves of 10 Kynol fibers (denier $\approx$ 1.8).

100%. The work necessary to break Kynol filaments, as measured by the area underneath the stress-strain curve, depends strongly upon the fiber diameter. Small diameter filaments require a substantially larger amount of work to break than most of the conventional textile fibers (Table 2).

Properly treated Kynol filaments assume a strong birefringence indicating molecular orientation. Although crystalline regions are still absent, the treated filaments possess an average tenacity of 3–4 g/den, ie, over 50% higher than the values of the untreated fiber.

A crimp is easily incorporated by treating the fiber in a stuffer-box system in the presence of steam or water. Small diameter fibers (~1.5 denier) can endure severe crimping without any apparent loss of strength and elongation.

Kynol fibers possess an ellipsoid cross section. The average ratio of the small to the long axis is 0.9. A small fraction of fibers have a more elliptical cross section with the axis ratio as low as 0.6. The stress-strain behavior of the fibers does not appear to be affected by the shape of the cross section. Fibers with trilobal, ribbon- or Y-shaped cross sections can also be made.

Flame Resistance. The flame resistance of Kynol is unique in that it not only resists burning in a flame but also has a thermal insulating character superior to that of any available fiber.

For comparison the flame resistance of other available fibers has been broken down into five categories as shown in Table 3. Practically all of the organic fibers will burn in a flame with considerable evolution of smoke. Wool, Nomex, and treated cotton tend to be self-extinguishing when removed from the flame. Fibers made from PTFE or glass will not burn but will melt in a flame. Only carbon and boron nitride fibers display the desired features of nonburning and nonmelting; however, these fibers are inorganic, and along with glass fiber find limited use in textiles due to their relatively low elongation.

Table 3. Flame Resistance of Commercially Available Fibers

Behavior in a flame	Fiber
melts, burns	nylon, polyester, acrylic, olefin
chars, burns	cotton, rayon
chars, self-extinguishes	wool, Nomex, treated cotton
melts, nonburning	polytetrafluoroethylene (PTFE), glass
nonmelting, nonburning	carbon, boron nitride

Kynol fibers have been tested under a variety of flames including an oxyacetylene torch and shown to be nonmelting and nonburning. The fibers carbonize showing excellent shape retention with little evolution of smoke or noxious gases. In a test exposure to the flame of a Meker burner, cloth derived from an aromatic polyamide shrinks and begins to burn within several seconds; Kynol fabric did not burn or melt, but carbonized and retained considerable strength after one minute. Even under the stringent conditions of an oxyacetylene torch where temperatures may reach 2500°C a Kynol batt shows excellent resistance. The surface of the batt forms a layer of carbon fibers which insulates the next layer as well as providing an effective black-body surface for radiating away heat.

The relatively low shrinkage of the fiber (<15%) can be attributed to the presence of stable crosslinks during carbonization as well as the high char yield. The intrinsic flammability of Kynol fibers when measured in terms of the oxygen index, or limiting oxygen index (LOI) is also superior to that of other organic fibers (Table 4).

The LOI describes the minimum volume fraction of oxygen in nitrogen necessary to sustain candle-like burning. See under Fire resistant textiles in Textile technology in this volume.

Table 4. Limiting Oxygen Index of Textile Fibers

Fabric	Weight, oz/yd²	LOI
Kynol	6.5	0.36
Kynol	4.5	0.35
Verel	6.5	0.33
Dynel	6.5	0.267[a]
Nomex	8.0	0.28
nylon	6.5	0.201[a]
polyester	6.5	0.206[a]
Acrylan	6.5	0.182[a]
rayon	6.5	0.197[a]
cotton, 65% rh	6.5	0.21
cotton, 40% rh	6.5	0.20
cotton, dried at 110°C/30 min	6.5	0.18
wool	7.0	0.252[a]

[a] Data from Giuliana C. Tesoro and Charles H. Meiser, Jr. (4).

Kynol fibers can impart flame resistance to other fibers, though the exact behavior of blends is not always predictable. In fact depending on the ingredients in the blend, the physical structure of the blend, and the nature of the test, almost contradictory results can be obtained.

As might be expected, blended fabrics reacted differently in the flame. With a 50:50 cotton/Kynol blend the cotton initially burned rapidly in the flame but the combined cotton/Kynol char still displayed flexibility and strength, and continued to function as a flame barrier. A Kynol/aromatic polyamide blend burned in the flame but was self-extinguishing when the flame was removed. A blended fabric of polyester/Kynol burned more vigorously than the pure polyester fabric. This behavior should be expected since the Kynol fibers provide a grid which prevents the polyester from melting and shrinking away from the flame.

Comparatively thin layers of Kynol fibers in the form of either a cloth, felt, or paper provide effective protection to a burnable substrate such as a cellulosic.

Thermal and Chemical Resistance of Kynol. Phenolic fibers display very good stability at high temperatures in an inert environment. A weight loss of about 3% occurs when fibers are exposed for 1000 hr at 250°C, and weight losses amount to 15 and 19% when the fibers are treated 100 hr at 350 and 400°C, respectively.

It is important to emphasize that Kynol is not a high-temperature fiber and in fact tends to degrade slowly in air at 200°C. Even at 150°C a slight oxidative instability has been detected which indicates that this temperature represents the upper limit in air for long-term use. The fibers display no net weight change in air after 1000 hr aging at 150°C, but the weight loss is substantial when fibers are exposed to temperatures above 200°C.

The corrosion resistant properties of Kynol fibers are summarized in Table 5.

Textile Properties. Because of the presence of hydrophilic phenolic hydroxyl groups, Kynol fibers display a higher moisture regain than is commonly observed in conventional synthetic organic fibers. As shown in Table 6 the moisture regain is dependent on the fiber diameter, ie, it increases with increasing surface area. At a denier of 1.0 the fibers display a moisture regain of 8.4% which is comparable to cotton. This factor contributes substantially to the excellent comfort characteristics which have been observed in wearing Kynol apparel. Kynol fibers exhibit considerable

Table 5. Corrosion Resistance of Kynol Fibers

Environment	Resistance	
	1 week at 25°C	1 week at 100°C
acids		
HCl, H₃PO₄	excellent	excellent
HF, H₂SO₄		
dilute HNO₃	excellent	good
conc HNO₃	poor	poor
bases		
NH₃	excellent	excellent
dilute NaOH, KOH	excellent	good
50% NaOH, KOH	fair	poor
organic solvents	excellent	excellent

Table 6. Kynol Moisture Regain

Relative humidity, %	Moisture regain, %		
	4 denier	2 denier	1 denier
40	2.3	3.6	5.5
65	4.2	6.0	8.4
100	15	18	22

resistance to wrinkling, and provide a soft and pleasant touch to the skin. The "feel" of the fibers can be influenced by changing the diameter and the shape of the cross-sectional area.

The fibers possess a natural gold color which can range from a light gold to a deep copper tone. Dyeing can be accomplished relatively easily by using cationic or dispersion dyes in an organic solvent dyeing process. The colors into which natural fibers can be dyed are limited to intense or darker hues. When Kynol fibers are exposed to weathering, a "reverse" fading can be observed, ie, the intensity of the natural color increases slowly while the hue shifts from gold to red brown. Some deterioration in elongation occurs after a three-month outdoor exposure (in full sun) in fibers located on the surface. Fibers underneath the surface retained their initial elongation fully. Kynol fiber can be bleached by a chemical process into essentially white fibers which display excellent lightfastness. The bleached fiber can be dyed into any of the pastel shades. Bleaching and dyeing has little or no effect on the mechanical or flame properties of the fiber. In fact, bleaching imparts a greater oxidative stability to the Kynol fibers.

Fabrication and Uses for Kynol

Kynol fibers are available as crimped and uncrimped staple fibers as well as blown fibers. The crimped staple can be converted into spun yarn on cotton or worsted systems. Staple or blown fibers can be made into nonwovens using a card or an air layup system. The nonwovens can be bonded with a resin such as phenolic, urea, or melamine formaldehyde to produce battings with bulk densities ranging from 0.3 to 3.0 lb/ft³. They can also be needled into felts of greater bulk density. The fibers when chopped into short lengths (1/16 to 1/2 inch) can be fabricated into paper. Kynol fabrics should find broad applications among industrial and military workers who must work with hazardous chemicals and flammable materials. The combined corrosion and flame resistance of Kynol fabrics seems ideally suited for protecting industrial personnel. Also, as opposed to practically all other fibers, Kynol shows little tendency to shrink even in very hot flames and would provide protection against burns resulting from shrinkage or melting of fabrics in a fire. The relatively high moisture regain of Kynol fibers suggests good comfort characteristics combined with an inherently good hand. The wrinkle resistance of Kynol fabrics is another advantage.

There is a real need for improved flame-resistant fibers for use as drapery, bedding, slip covers, carpeting, and wall covers, particularly in aircraft and institutions such as hospitals, rest homes, motels, hotels, and theaters. The excellent flame resistance of Kynol combined with its very low smoke evolution would be ideally suited for use in enclosed areas where smoke inhalation presents as serious a hazard as the actual flames. It seems reasonable to expect that curtains made from Kynol could also act as flame barriers preventing the spread of flames to adjacent areas.

In the form of batting, Kynol provides a number of advantages over conventional glass insulation. For example, felts of Kynol are resilient and can be compressed to one tenth the original volume, while glass batting suffers considerable damage when compressed to less than one half its original volume. The fact that Kynol fibers possess a density of 1.25 g/cm³ versus 2.56 g/cm³ for glass suggests a real advantage where weight is at a premium such as in aircraft. The irritating characteristic observed in handling of glass fiber has not been observed with Kynol. The thermal conductivity of Kynol is significantly lower than that of glass fiber.

The excellent corrosion resistance of Kynol suggests many uses in filtration of highly corrosive liquids. Use of Kynol in filtration of hot oils and strong acids has been successfully tested. A paper made from Kynol can be used to filter hot 85% phosphoric acid repeatedly. A glass filter paper exposed to the same conditions is rapidly attacked by the hot phosphoric acid. Fabric filtration of hot corrosive gases containing particulate matter represents another area of use for Kynol fibers; however, the temperature of the gases should not exceed 150°C if air is present.

Bibliography

1. J. Economy, L. C. Wohrer, and F. J. Frechette, "Kynol—A New Flame Resistant Fiber," *39th Ann. Meet., Textile Research Inst., New York, April 11, 1969.*
2. L. C. Wohrer, F. J. Frechette, and J. Economy, "Aerospace Applications for Kynol Fibers," *Proc. Natl. SAMPE Tech. Conf., Aircraft Structures and Materials Application,* Vol. 1, 1969, p. 83.
3. L. C. Wohrer, F. J. Frechette, and J. Economy, "Textile Properties of Kynol Fibers," *41st Ann. Meet., Textile Research Inst., New York, March 10, 1971, p. 37.*
4. Giuliana C. Tesoro and Charles H. Meiser, Jr., "Some Effects of Chemical Composition on The Flammability Behavior of Textiles," *39th Ann. Meet., Textile Research Inst., New York, April 11, 1969.*

James Economy
and Luis C. Wohrer
The Carborundum Company

PHOSGENE

Phosgene (carbonyl chloride, carbon oxychloride), $COCl_2$, when pure, is a colorless, low-boiling liquid, first prepared by John Davy (brother of Sir Humphry Davy) in 1812 by the action of light on a mixture of carbon monoxide and chlorine. The name phosgene, derived from two Greek words meaning "light" and "to produce," was inspired by the method of synthesis (1).

In the last twenty years this compound, which at one time was primarily known as a chemical warfare agent, has assumed considerable importance as a chemical intermediate. It is used extensively in the preparation of isocyanates (qv) leading to polyurethans (see Urethan polymers) and in the preparation of another important group of polymers, the polycarbonates (qv).

Physical and Chemical Properties

The physical properties of phosgene are listed in Table 1. It is a colorless gas at ordinary temperature and pressure. It is shipped as a liquefied gas under pressure and/or refrigeration. It is classified as a "Class A" poison. Due to impurities it may at times be lightly colored, usually pale yellow to green. Phosgene has a characteristic odor which warns of its presence, but the gas has the ability to condition the sense of smell so that the characteristic odor can be detected only briefly at the time of initial exposure. At low concentration (from 0.5 ppm) in air the odor has been described as pleasant, similar to new-mown hay or cut green corn. At high concentration the characteristic odor may be strong, stifling, and unpleasant. Following exposure to low concentrations the taste of tobacco smoke is quite often unpleasant.

In general, phosgene is soluble in aromatic and aliphatic hydrocarbons, chlorinated hydrocarbons and organic acids and esters. It is easily removed by heating or air blowing, but due to its toxicity, great care must be taken to control its presence in the the atmosphere.

The structure is planar and the interatomic distances are C—O $= 1.28 \times 10^{-8}$ cm (3) and C—Cl $= 1.68 \times 10^{-8}$ cm. The angle Cl—C—Cl is 117°. For spectral properties, see the following references: infrared (6,7), ultraviolet (8), and Raman (6,9).

Reactions. Due to its high degree of reactivity, phosgene interacts with many classes of inorganic, as well as organic reagents.

Phosgene forms chlorides with metals in the general order of their reactivity. Sodium reacts at ordinary temperatures but zinc requires warming.

Oxides and sulfides of metals react with phosgene at elevated temperatures to give the chlorides, often in a very pure state. The reaction of cadmium sulfide is a good method for preparing carbonyl sulfide (carbon oxysulfide), COS. For the reaction of phosgene with calcium see reference 10, magnesium (11,12), tin (13,14) and zinc oxide (15). Of particular interest has been the study of the reaction of titanium oxide with phosgene (16,17) and the chlorination of oxides of interest in the nuclear field, especially uranium oxide (18), plutonium oxide (19), and thorium oxide (20).

Phosphates and silicates of metals often react with phosgene at elevated temperatures to give the metal chloride and phosphorus oxychloride or silicon dioxide. The reaction with ferric phosphate at 300–350°C has been proposed as a method to prepare phosphorus oxychloride, $POCl_3$.

Table 1. Physical Properties of Phosgene (2,3)

Property	Value
melting point, °K	145.37
	142.09
	139.19
boiling point, °C	7.48
density, d_4^t	$1.435 - 2.377 \times 10^{-3}t - 0.7 \times 10^{-6}T'^2$
surface tension, dyn/cm	
at 16.7°C	20.1
at 34.5°C	17.6
at 46.1°C	15.9
crit temperature, °C	182
crit pressure, atm	56
crit density, g/ml	0.52
latent heat of vaporization at 7.5°C, cal/mole	
observed	5832 ± 6
calcd	5825
heat capacity of liquid at bp, cal/(°C) (mol)	24.09
heat of formation, kcal/mole	
from elements, ΔH_f^0	52.1
from CO and Cl_2	25.8
entropy change,[a] ΔS, 0–280.66°K, cal/(°C) (mole)	
calorimetric measurements	66.63
molecular data	68.26
coefficient of expansion at 0°C, per °C	0.001226

equilibrium dissociation[b] to CO + Cl_2	°C	%	°C	%
	101	0.45	503	67
	208	0.83	553	80
	309	5.61	603	91
	400	21.26	800	100

vapor pressure	
between 215 and 281°K	$\log_{10}Pcm = -1690.3/T + 9.68020 -$
	$7.8981 \times 10^{-3}T + 5.5847 \times 10^{-6}t^2$
between −15 and 23°C	$\log_{10}Pmm = 7.5595 - 1326/(283 + T)$

[a] The discrepancy in the entropy values, as calculated from calorimetric measurements and from molecular data, is interpreted as due to random orientation of the planar triangular carbonyl chloride molecule in the solid at low temperatures. The maximum value for this effect would be 2.18 cal/(°C)(mole). In confirmation, phosgene has been observed to have an abnormal expansion below its melting point.

[b] For further dissociation data, see references 4 and 5

Anhydrous aluminum chloride forms a variety of complexes with phosgene, such as $Al_2Cl_6 \cdot 5COCl_2$ at lower temperatures, $Al_2Cl_6 \cdot 3COCl_2$ at 30°C, and $Al_2Cl_6 \cdot COCl_2$ above 55°C. Aluminum bromide yields carboxy bromide, $COBr_2$, and aluminum chlorobromide, $AlCl_2Br$. Antimony trifluoride with phosgene and chlorine yields carbonyl fluoride (21). With sodium fluoride and HCN, phosgene yields carbonyl fluorocyanide and carbonyl fluoride (22).

$$AlBr_3 + COCl_2 \rightarrow COBr_2 + AlCl_2Br$$

$$SbF_3 + COCl_2 + Cl_2 \rightarrow COF_2 \text{ (80–85\% yield)}$$

$$NaF + HCN + COCl_2 \rightarrow COFCN + COF_2$$

Ammonia reacts very vigorously with phosgene in solution. The products are urea, biuret, ammelide (polymer of urea), cyanuric acid, and sometimes cyamelide (polymer of cyanic acid). The secondary products probably arise through the very reactive intermediate carbamyl chloride, NH_2COCl.

Primary amines react violently with phosgene. The moderated reaction by dilution with solvent, etc, gives the symmetrical disubstituted ureas. The reaction may also be modified to give carbamyl chlorides, which on heating decompose to the isocyanates.

$$RNH_2 + COCl_2 \rightarrow RNHCOCl + HCl$$

$$RNHCOCl \rightarrow RNCO + HCl$$

Carbamyl chlorides are very active intermediates and react with alcohols to give urethans, $RNHCOOR'$, and with amines to give unsymmetrical disubstituted ureas. They may serve as the acid chloride in the Friedel-Crafts reaction.

Secondary amines react to give the expected tetrasubstituted ureas. The intermediate carbamyl chlorides are more stable thermally than those derived from the primary amines. Mono- or unsymmetrically disubstituted hydrazines react with phosgene to give the corresponding derivatives of carbohydrazide, $NH_2NHCONHNH_2$. By-product HCl reacts with the starting material to form an amine hydrochloride. This can be avoided by working above the decomposition point of the amine hydrochloride, either in a high-boiling solvent or in the vapor phase (23).

The tertiary amines do not give the same reactions as the mono- and diamines because of the absence of hydrogen on the nitrogen. However, trimethylamine reacts by a complex mechanism, as follows:

$$(CH_3)_3N + COCl_2 \xrightarrow{60-70°C} (CH_3)_2NCOCl + (CH_3)_4NCl + CH_3Cl$$

Tertiary amines undergo the Friedel-Crafts reaction with phosgene in the presence of anhydrous aluminum chloride.

Michler's ketone, $((CH_3)_2NC_6H_4)_2CO$ (see Vol. 20, p. 679 and Vol. 12, p. 132) and other valuable dye intermediates are produced by this reaction.

The reactions of phosgene with piperazine and triethylamine have also been investigated (24–26).

Diamines react with phosgene, the typical reaction being that with o-phenylene-diamine to give 2(3H)-benzimidazolones.

The reaction of phosgene with hydrazine derivatives is of interest (27), yielding $(H_2NNH)_2CO$ and some $(H_2NNHCONH)_2$.

Much attention has been focused on the reaction of substituted ureas and thioureas with phosgene. Using 1,3-disubstituted ureas, a number of isocyanates and sulfonyl isocyanates have been prepared which are otherwise difficult to synthesize (28,29).

$$RSO_2NHCONHR' + COCl_2 \rightarrow RSO_2NCO + R'NCO + 2 HCl$$

1,3-disubstituted thioureas on the other hand can be readily converted to carbodiimides which then can add phosgene (30).

$$RNHCSNHR + COCl_2 \rightarrow RN{=}C{=}NR \xrightarrow{COCl_2} RN\underset{\underset{Cl}{\overset{|}{C}}{=}N{=}R}{\overset{\overset{\overset{O}{\parallel}}{C}}{\diagup}}\diagdown Cl$$

The reaction of phosgene with aliphatic alcohols or glycols gives the expected product, either the chloroformic (chlorocarbonic) esters, ClCOOR, or the carbonic diesters, R_2CO_3, depending on the proportions of the reactants. As in the case of the reaction with amines, the successful vapor-phase reaction has been described (31).

The reaction with glycols or with dihydroxy aromatics is particularly important since it leads to the formation of polycarbonates, a new and highly useful group of polymers (see Polycarbonates). The reaction of phosgene with alkylene sulfides (32), imines (33) or epoxides (34) results in ring opening and addition of phosgene.

Phosgene reacts with paraffins to form acid chlorides by a free-radical process (35).

$$RH + (COCl_2)_2 \rightarrow RCOCl + CO + HCl$$

$$RH + COCl_2 \rightarrow RCOCl + HCl$$

With aromatic hydrocarbons in the presence of a Friedel-Crafts catalyst aroyl chlorides are formed which yield acids on hydrolysis (36).

$$C_6H_6 + COCl_2 \xrightarrow[HCl]{AlCl_3,} C_6H_5COCl \xrightarrow{H_2O} C_6H_5COOH$$

However, the reaction does not generally stop at the formation of the aroyl chloride, which readily reacts with excess aromatic hydrocarbon to give the corresponding ketone (36).

$$C_6H_5COCl + C_6H_6 \xrightarrow[HCl]{AlCl_3,} C_6H_5COC_6H_5$$

The reaction of phosgene with amino acids to form the chloroformate derivatives has been used for their isolation and purification (37–39).

While $POCl_3$ is the preferred reagent in the Vilsmeir aldehyde synthesis, phosgene may be employed, and its role, as well as the intermediates formed, has been studied extensively (40,41).

Phosgene may be formed at elevated temperature by oxidation of chlorinated solvents (42).

Manufacture

Depending on the quantity needed and the availability of the raw material, a large number of variations of the basic process are being practiced. Continuous processing and a high degree of automation is in order with phosgene being purified, condensed, and stored as required. Due to its toxicity, careful and extensive safety procedures are being employed in plant design and operation.

The manufacture of phosgene consists of the following steps: (a) preparation and purification of carbon monoxide; (b) preparation and purification of chlorine; (c) metering and mixing of reactants; (d) reaction of mixed gases over activated charcoal;

and (e) purification and condensation of phosgene. Great care must be taken to recover all traces of the highly toxic phosgene.

Carbon monoxide may be manufactured according to standard processes by the reduction of carbon dioxide over coal or by controlled oxidation of hydrocarbon fuels.

A carbon monoxide process must be chosen which yields a gas of the highest possible purity. Noncondensable impurities are particularly objectionable since they make the recovery of phosgene more difficult. Water, hydrogen, and hydrocarbons must be removed from the starting gas since hydrochloric acid might be formed in the converter. Other impurities might poison the catalyst. Sulfides must be excluded since they produce sulfur chlorides which are usually very undesirable impurities

The chlorine must be just as dry and pure as the carbon monoxide to avoid corrosion of the equipment and decomposition of phosgene by water, as well as other impurities.

Good activated charcoal having a high adsorptive capacity is suitable for use as a catalyst without treatment with metallic salt or other substances. If starting materials of high purity are employed, excellent and economic catalyst efficiency can normally be obtained.

Converters employed are relatively simple tubular heat exchangers. Since the reaction is rapid and exothermic, efficient heat removal is important to avoid decomposition of phosgene into its starting materials which takes place at 300°C.

General engineering recommendations to control hazards include the use of outdoor installations or extensive ventilation where phosgene has to be employed indoors. Ventilation should be sufficient to keep general concentrations of phosgene in the air below 0.1 ppm, even though liquid phosgene is released. Safety in handling phosgene depends to a great extent on the effectiveness of employee education, proper safety instrumentation, intelligent supervision, and the use of safe equipment. Plant design should include proper facilities for neutralization. Water-fog equipment should also be available for emergencies (43). The fact that phosgene is 3.4 times as heavy as air and settles readily in low places must be considered.

Storage and Handling

All phosgene containers require "Poison A" labels. Phosgene is transported in steel cylinders conforming to rigid specifications. These specifications provide special hydrostatic tests at 800 psi and extension rings to protect the valves. Phosgene is shipped in cylinders of 150 and 2000 lb. Careful testing for leaks is required after filling.

Since phosgene reacts with water, great care must be taken to prevent contamination with traces of water since this could lead to the development of pressure by hydrogen chloride and carbon dioxide. Phosgene should never be stored with traces of water in any quantity (43).

Detection and Analysis

Phosgene in air and in mixture with other gases can be detected by a variety of methods. It is claimed that trace quantities to a limit of 0.05 μg/liter of air can be detected by uv spectroscopy (44).

Gas chromatography has also been used extensively. Concentrations of phosgene as low as 4 parts per billion were measured in air and in presence of HCl by electron-capture gas chromatography (45).

For higher concentration, colorimetric methods using a variety of aromatic amines have been employed extensively. An automated phosgene analyzer is available (46).

Liquid phosgene is assayed by the iodometric method of Rush and Danner (47), using the following reaction (the released iodine is titrated with sodium thiosulfate):

$$COCl_2 + 2 NaCl \rightarrow CO + I_2 + 2 NaCl$$

One manufacturer gives the following specifications and standards:

Assay	Percent
$COCl_2$, min	99.0
Cl_2(free), max	0.1
HCl, max	0.2

Health and Safety Factors

The physiological effects of phosgene are observed at about the following concentrations in air: odor perceptible, 0.0044 mg/liter; irritation of eyes, nose, and throat, 0.044 mg/liter; estimated lethal concentration for man, 0.11 mg/liter for 30 min. The maximum safe concentration for working exposure has been set at 0.1 ppm (0.0004 mg/liter).

Breathing phosgene causes pulmonary edema which may often have a delayed onset. Proper first aid is vital. Exposed persons must be removed immediately from the contaminated area. Care must be taken to protect the rescue workers by a self-contained breathing apparatus. Injured persons should not be allowed any physical activity. If breathing has stopped, start artificial respiration by any effective means known to the rescuer. Send for a physician. When breathing is present or has been restored oxygen should be administered, but only by someone familiar with the operation of an oxygen inhalation apparatus and having approval of a physician to administer such treatment. Oxygen should be given as long as necessary to maintain normal color of the skin. The patient should be kept comfortably warm but not hot. Any person exposed to phosgene should be kept quiet and not permitted to walk, but should be carried by stretcher to medical care. Further treatment should be directed by a physician but do not delay treatment for lung irritation.

Treatment by the physician may include the use of oxygen. In most exposures, administration of 100% oxygen at atmospheric pressures has been found to be adequate. This is best accomplished by use of a face mask having a reservoir bag of the nonrebreathing type. Inhalation of 100% oxygen should not exceed one hour of continuous treatment. After each hour, therapy should be interrupted for one-half hour. It may be reinstituted as the clinical condition indicates (43).

Outstanding success has been claimed (43a) for the treatment of phosgene poisoning with hexamethylenetetramine (methenamine, urotropine). It is administered intravenously in a 20% solution (one 5-ml capsule with 15 ml sterile water) injected over a 5-min period.

Some authorities believe that superior results in the relief of symptoms are obtained when exposures to lung irritants are treated with oxygen under an exhalation pressure not exceeding 4 cm water. These same authorities believe that breathing oxygen under pressure is also useful as an aid in the prevention of the pulmonary edema which may occur after breathing an irritant chemical. Masks providing for such exhalation pressures are available. Persons exposed to phosgene, but having no symptoms, may benefit from breathing oxygen under 4-cm exhalation pressure for one hour as a preventive measure against pulmonary edema (43).

In the event of an exposure causing symptoms, the patient may be treated with oxygen under 4-cm exhalation pressure for several hours. Treatment should be continued until the symptoms subside or other clinical indications for interruption appear (43).

Pulmonary edema has been treated successfully by the administration of oxygen through intermittent positive-pressure breathing equipment (IPPB). In addition to providing oxygen under positive pressure, this equipment has the value of allowing simultaneous administration of aerosolized bronchodilators and/or foam suppressants as the clinical conditions of the patient may indicate. Prolonged bronchospasm may suggest the need for parenteral administration of corticosteroids (43).

Pneumonia is a frequent complication of pulmonary edema and the patient should be closely watched for evidence of bacterial infection. Should this occur, appropriate antibiotic therapy should be instituted without delay (43). Other treatment is symptomatic and no specific antidotes are known (43).

Waste Disposal. Because of its low boiling point and high toxicity, phosgene should never be allowed to enter drains or sewers. If recycle of phosgene is not feasible, phosgene waste can be handled most effectively through caustic scrubbing in packed columns. Other scrubbing liquids can also be used but sodium hydroxide has the distinct advantage of low cost and resistance to freezing in winter.

Direct reaction of phosgene with water alone presents a distinct risk because it is very difficult to get the necessary intimate mixing of the gas and the water. Burning of phosgene is not recommended (43).

Applications and Economic Aspects

Phosgene is an important and widely used chemical intermediate. Its historic employment as a war gas in World War I is of no significance today. It is easy and cheap to manufacture, but it can no longer be considered as an effective chemical warfare agent, especially in light of the de-emphasis of lethal agents and the predominance of aerial warfare.

Phosgene in cylinders (depending upon quantity) is priced at 19–25¢/lb in 1970. For large contracts on the order of a million lb/yr a contract price as low as 15 ¢/lb may be possible. However, when phosgene is required in large quantity, it is usually manufactured on site with economics geared primarily to chlorine costs. In many operations employing phosgene, the chlorine is recovered as hydrogen chloride and disposal, preferably sale, may become an important economic factor.

Phosgene can be employed in a variety of metal-recovery operations such as the recovery of platinum (48), uranium (49,50), plutonium (51), and niobium (52). Phosgene has been proposed for the manufacture of aluminum chloride (53), beryllium chloride (54), and boron trichloride (55). Phosgene has been patented as a stabilizer for liquid SO_3, either by itself or in combination with thionyl chloride (56,57).

Possibly the most significant industrial use of phosgene today is in the large-volume manufacture of isocyanates (qv) which are the raw materials for polyurethans (see Urethan polymers).

Phosgene is also used in the production of chloroformates (chlorocarbonates, see Vol. 4, p. 386), which in turn are intermediates in a variety of fields, such as ore-flotation agents, perfumery, herbicides, and insecticides, and especially the preparation of pharmaceuticals (58). Chloroalkyl chlorocarbonates have been manufactured as intermediates for pharmaceuticals and pesticides (64).

Phosgene is also used in the manufacture of carbonic esters (see Vol. 4, p. 390), (59–61). These carbonates are used as organic intermediates for pharmaceuticals and agricultural chemicals, as photoengraving assist agents, and as specialty solvents. They can also lead to peroxydicarbonates, which are useful as polymerization catalysts and bleaching agents (62). Carbonates are also used for the manufacture of "prodrugs"; these are carbonate diesters of drugs containing an OH group. They have properties differing from the parent drug, but revert to it with the desired pharmacological effects after hydrolysis in the body.

Phosgene has been suggested as a starting material for manufacture of carbon tetrachloride (65–68) and other chlorinated hydrocarbons (69–71).

A number of pesticides have been patented based on the reaction of a thiol or dithiol with phosgene to form chlorothiolformates (72,73).

The preparation of aromatic acids using phosgene has been described (74), including a detailed process for the manufacture of terephthalic acid from toluene and phosgene (75).

An important direct use of phosgene is in the preparation of polymers. Polycarbonates (qv) are the most significant and commercially valuable group. However, the use of phosgene has been described for other polymer systems such as fiber-forming polymeric polyketones (76) and polyureas (77–79).

Phosgene may also be employed for the modification of polymers such as asphalt, bitumen, and tar (80), starch (81), and lignin (82). Phosgene has been suggested to improve the effectiveness and to ensure prolonged action of insulin (83,84) and to prepare ion-exchange resins from poly(vinyl alcohol) (85) and polystyrene (86,87). The use of phosgene has also been patented to improve the dyeability of polyolefin fibers (88).

With rapidly increasing markets, especially for isocyanates and polycarbonates, manufacture and on-site use of phosgene should continue to increase significantly.

Bibliography

1. A. J. Shake, *The Development of Modern Chemistry*, Harper & Row, New York, 1964, p. 165.
2. W. F. Giauque and L. B. Ott, *J. Am. Chem. Soc.* **82**, 2689–2695 (1960).
3. R. W. Gallant, *Hydrocarbon Process.* **47**, 141 (July 1968).
4. H. J. Ingleson, *J. Chem. Soc.* **1927**, 2244–2254.
5. D. N. Seshadri, D. S. Viswanath, and N. R. Kuloor, *J. Indian Inst. Sci.* **50** (3), 151–160 (1968).
6. A. H. Nielsen, T. G. Burke, P. J. H. Woltz, and E. A. Jones, *J. Chem. Phys.* **20**, 596–604 (1952).
7. R. H. Pierson, A. N. Fletcher, and E. St. Clair Gantz, *Anal. Chem.* **28**, 1218 (1956).
8. V. Henri and O. R. Howell, *Proc. Roy. Soc. (London) Ser. A* **128**, 190 (1930).
9. R. Anathakrishnan, *Proc. Indian Acad. Sci. Sect. A* **5**, 285 (1937).
10. A. N. Ketov, V. V. Pechkovskri, and L. P. Kostin, *Issled. Obl. Khim. Tekhnol. Mineral's Solei Okislov, Akad. Nauk SSR, Sb. Statei* **1965** 202–207; *Chem. Abstr.* **65**, 1753a (1966).
11. A. N. Ketov, V. V. Pechkovskri, and L. P. Kostin, *Izv. Vysshikh Uchebn. Zavedenii, Tsvetn. Met.* **7** (2), 94–98 (1964); *Chem. Abstr.* **61**, 3894h (1964).
12. A. N. Ketov, V. V. Pechkovskri, and L. P. Kostin, *Zh. Neorgan. Khim.* **9** (2), 467–469 (1964); *Chem. Abstr.* **60**, 11601h (1964).
13. Yu. P. Kuznetsov, E. S. Petrov, and A. I. Vakhrusheva, *Izv. Sibirsk. Otd. Akad. Nauk SSR, Ser. Khim. Nauk* **1969** (2) 63; *Chem. Abstr.* **71**, 18414p (1969).
14. *Ibid.* **1969** (3), 60–65; *Chem. Abstr.* **71**, 116862c (1969).
15. A. N. Ketov, V. V. Pechkovskii, and L. P. Kostin, *Sb. Nauchn. Tr. Permsk. Politekhn. Inst.* **1963** (14), 3–6; *Chem. Abstr.* **62**, 3642e (1965).

16. A. N. Ketov, V. V. Pechkovskii, and I. M. Kolesov, *Izv. Vysshikh. Uchebn. Zavedenii, Khim. i Khim. Tekhnol.* **9** (4), 570–573; *Chem. Abstr.* **66,** 592761k (1967).

17. A. N. Ketov and I. M. Kolesov, *Sb. Nauchn. Tr., Permsk. Politckhn. Inst.* **18,** 42–47 (1965); *Chem. Abstr.* **66,** 7991 (1967).

18. D. Naumann, *Kernenegie* **5** (2), 118–119 (1962).

19. R. J. Sorenson, *U.S. At. Energy Comm.* **1963** (HW-79141), 22.

20. D. T. Peterson and D. J. Sundquist, *U.S. At. Energy Comm.* **1964** (IS-917), 30.

21. R. Hazeldine and H. Iserson, *J. Am. Chem. Soc.* **79,** 5801 (1957).

22. C. W. Tullock and D. D. Coffman, *J. Org. Chem.* **25,** 2016 (1960).

23. R. J. Slocombe, Edgar E. Hardy, J. H. Saunders, and R. L. Jenkins, *J. Am. Chem. Soc.* **72,** 1888–1891 (1950).

24. H. Morren and R. Denayer, *Bull. Soc. Chim. Belges* **58,** 103–111 (1949).

25. Yu. A. Strepikheev, T. G. Perlova, and L. A. Zhivechkova, *Zh. Org. Khim.* **4** (11), 1891–1893 (1968); *Chem. Abstr.* **70,** 28207s (1969).

26. Yu. A. Strepikheev and T. G. Perlova, *Zh. Vses. Khim. Obshchestva* **14** (5), 588–589 (1969); *Chem. Abstr.* **72,** 54705p (1970).

27. O. Glemser, H. Weber, and H. Duyster, *Z. Anorg. Allgem. Chem.* **286,** 205–210 (1956).

28. H. Ulrich and A. A. R. Savigh, *Angew. Chem.* **78** (16), 761–769 (1966).

29. H. Eilingfeld, G. Neubauer, M. Seefelder, and H. Weidinger, *Chem. Ber.* **97** (5), 1232–1245 (1964).

30. H. Ulrich and A. A. R. Savigh, *J. Org. Chem.* **28,** 1427–1429 (1963).

31. J. H. Saunders, R. J. Slocombe, and Edgar E. Hardy, *J. Am. Chem. Soc.* **73,** 3797 (1951).

32. G. Yu. Epshtein, I. A. Usov, and S. Z. Ivin, *Zh. Obshch. Khim.* **34** (6), 1948–1950 (1964); *Chem. Abstr.* **61,** 8178c (1964).

33. H. Bestian, J. Heyna, A. Bauer, G. Ehlers, B. Hirsekorn, T. Jacobs, W. Noll, W. Weibezahn, and F. Romer, *Ann.* **566,** 210–244 (1950).

34. J. Idris Jones, *J. Chem. Soc.* **1957,** 2735–2743.

35. M. S. Kharasch and H. C. Brown, *J. Amer. Chem. Soc.* **64,** 320 (1942).

36. George A. Olah and Judith A. Olah, "Acid Syntheses," in George A. Olah, ed., *Friedel-Crafts and Related Reactions,* Vol. III, *Acylation and Related Reactions,* Part 2, John Wiley & Sons, Inc., New York, 1964, pp. 1257–1258.

37. Th. Wieland and H. Bernhard, *Ann.* **527,** 190–194 (1951).

38. G. Losse and W. Goedicke, *Chem. Ber.* **100** (10), 3314–3318 (1967).

39. Rodney D. Hamilton and Donald J. Lyman, *J. Org. Chem.* **34** (1), 243–244 (1969).

40. Gerard Martin and Mme. Maryvonn Martin, *Bull. Soc. Chim. France* **1963** (8–9), 637–646.

41. H. H. Bosshard and H. Zollinger, *Helv. Chim. Acta* **42,** 1659–1671 (1959).

42. L. W. Spolyar, R. N. Harger, J. P. Keppler, and H. E. Bumsted, *Arch. Ind. Hyg. Occupational Med.* **4,** 156–160 (1951).

43. *Chemical Safety Data Sheet SD-95,* Manufacturing Chemists' Assoc., Washington, D.C., July 1967.

43a. "Case History No. 1658," *Accident Case Histories,* Manufacturing Chemists' Ass., Washington, D.C., Aug. 1970.

44. W. B. Crummett and J. D. MeLean, *Anal. Chem.* **37** (3), 424–425 (1965).

45. L. J. Priestley, Jr., F. E. Critchfield, N. H. Ketcham, and J. D. Cavender, *Anal. Chem.* **37** (1), 70–71 (1965).

46. B. W. Thomas, *Oil Gas J.* **63** (24), 119, 121–124 (1965).

47. C. A. Rush and C. E. Danner, *Anal. Chem.* **20,** 644 (1948).

48. Ger. Pat. 1,077,642 (March 17, 1960), George R. Bond, Jr. (to Houdry Process Corp).

49. U.S. Pat. 2,890,099 (June 6, 1959), Harrison B. Rhodes, Wm. F. Pesold, and Jack M. Hirshon (to U.S. Atomic Energy Commission).

50. Fr. Pat. 1,472,438 (March 18, 1965), to Atomic Energy Research Inst.

51. H. L. Brandt, *AEC Accession No. 42455, Rpt. No. HW-83235, CFSTI, 20,* Washington, D.C., 1964.

52. U.S. Pat. 3,212,847 (Oct. 19, 1965), Bernard J. Lerner (to Dominium Gulf Company).

53. J. Hille and W. Dürrwächter, *Angew. Chem.* **72,** 850–855 (1960).

54. U.S. Pat. 3,146,065 (Aug. 25, 1964), Ricardo O. Bach (to Beryllium Metals and Chemical Corp.).

55. R. K. Pearson, T. W. Platt, J. C. Renforth, R. J. Shreve, N. J. Sheetz, L. L. Lewis, and L. J. Edwards, *U.S. At. Energy Comm.* **1957,** CCC-1024-TR-234.

56. U.S. Pat. 3,042,490 (July 3, 1960), Thomas W. Saults and Joseph J. Wimberly (to Tennessee Corp).
57. Brit. Pat. 975,318 (Nov. 18, 1964), Ralph V. Riley, Thomas F. Eden, and Wm. D. Hopkinson (to Stavely Iron & Chemicals Co., Ltd.).
58. U.S. Pat. 3,152,167 (Oct. 6, 1964), Meyer Sletzinger (to Merck & Co., Inc.).
59. Brit. Pat. 841,654 (July 20, 1960), to Farbenfabriken Bayer A.G.
60. Ger. Pat. 887,650 (Aug. 24, 1953), Rudolf Reuber and Hellmuth Reinshagen (to Farbwerke Hoechst).
61. Ger. Pat. 1,181,205 (Nov. 12, 1964), Heinrich Pelster and Ernst Muehlbauer (to Farbenfabriken Bayer A.G.).
62. U.S. Pat. 2,517,964 (Aug. 8, 1950), Wm. E. Bissinger (to Pittsburgh Plate Glass Co.).
63. Joseph V. Swintosky, H. J. Adams, H. C. Caldwell, L. W. Ditteret, Th. Ellison, and D. E. Rivard, *J. Pharm. Sci.* **55** (9), 992 (1966).
64. Ger. Pat. 1,179,922 (Oct. 22, 1964), Hans Grassner and Fritz Stolp (to Badische Anilin & Soda Fabrik A.G.).
65. U.S. Pat. 2,892,875 (June 30, 1959), Frederick E. Kung (to Columbia Southern Chemical Corp.).
66. U.S. Pat. 3,069,481 (Dec. 18, 1962), Robert N. Haszeldine, Hyman Iserson, and Francis E. Lawlor (to Pennsalt Chemical Corp.).
67. R. N. Haszeldine and H. Iserson, *J. Am. Chem. Soc.* **79**, 5801–5804 (1957).
68. O. Glemser, J. Schroeder, K. Kleine-Weischede, Boris Meyer, G. Peuschel, H. Fleugel, and D. Velde, *Angew. Chem.* **75** (18), 823–825 (1963).
69. Ger. Pat. 1,188,570 (Mar. 11, 1965), Willi Ziegenbein and K. Heinz Hornung (to Chemische Werke Huels A.G.).
70. U.S. Pat. 3,406,212 (Oct. 15, 1968), Karl O. Christie and Attila E. Pavlath (to Stauffer Chemical Co.).
71. Ger. Pat. 1,133,716 (July 26, 1962), Dieter Ludsteck, Gerald Neubauer, Heinrich Pasedach, and Matthias Seefelder (to Badische Anilin & Soda Fabrik A.G.).
72. U.S. Pat. 3,277,143 (Oct. 4, 1966), Harry Tilles (to Stauffer Chemical Co.).
73. U.S. Pat. 3,093,537 (June 11, 1963) Harry Tilles.
74. U.S. Pat. 2,552,591 (May 15, 1951), Walter H. C. Rueggeberg, Russel K. Frantz and Abram Ginsburg.
75. F. Runge, H. Reinhard, and G. Kühnhanss, *Chem. Tech. Berlin*, **8**, 644–649 (1956).
76. Ger. Pat. 1,148,073 (May 2, 1963), Rolf Moroni and Eugen Dumont (to Collo-Rheincollodium Koeln G.m.b.H.).
77. Brit. Pat. 815,168 (June 17, 1959), to E. I. du Pont de Nemours & Co., Inc.
78. Swiss Pat. 322,061 (July 15, 1957), Robert Neher.
79. U.S. Pat. 3,412,072 (Nov. 19, 1968), Constantine J. Bouboulis and Isidor Kirshenbaum (to Esso Research & Engineering Co.).
80. F. J. Nellensteyn and J. E. W. van den Driessen Mareeuw, *Chem. Weekblad* **48**, 158–160 (1952).
81. U.S. Pat. 3,376,287 (April 2, 1968), Wadym Jarowenko and Morton W. Rutenberg (to National Starch and Chemical Corp.).
82. U.S.S.R. Pat. 214,307 (Mar. 20, 1968), L. N. Mozheiko, V. Jaunzems, and V. N. Sergeeva (to Institute of Wood Pulp Chemistry).
83. G. Mohnike, G. Schnuchel, L. Kupffer, and W. Langenbeck, *Z. Physiol. Chem.* **294**, 12–29 (1953).
84. Ger. (East) Pat. 10,002 (June 30, 1955), Wolfgang Langenbeck, Gunther Schnuchel, and Gerhard Mohnike.
85. Hitoshi Senda and Ryohei Oda, *J. Chem. Soc. Japan. Ind. Chem. Sect.* **56**, 534–536 (1953).
86. Brit. Pat. 1,095,746 (Dec. 20, 1967), Friedrich Wolf and Karola Frederich (to VEB Farbenfabrik Wolfen).
87. Ger. (East) Pat. 57,703 (Sept. 5, 1967), Friedrich Wolf and Karola Frederich.
88. Brit. Pat. 881,981 (Nov. 8, 1961), to Montecatini Società Generale per l'Industria Mineraria Chimica.

EDGAR E. HARDY
Monsanto Research Corp.

PICKLING OF STEEL

The reaction of steel surfaces with oxygen forms oxides of iron. During the hot rolling or working of steel, the surfaces of the metal react with air to form oxides of iron that are called mill scale and are combinations of FeO, Fe_3O_4, and Fe_2O_3. In order to further process the steel, the oxide scale must be removed because it interferes with drawing, cold working, plating, or painting. Of the several processes used to remove the scale from steel surfaces, pickling is by far the most universally used. The term "pickling" refers to the process of dissolving the oxides with acids and the term originated in the eighteenth century from the fact that sheets of steel were descaled by soaking them in vats of vinegar. The solutions used to descale steel are referred to as pickle liquors.

Nature of Mill Scale. The scale that forms on steel during the hot working consists of three layers (1), ie an outer layer of ferric oxide or hematite (Fe_2O_3), a middle layer of ferroferric oxide or magnetite (triiron tetroxide, Fe_3O_4, ferrosoferric oxide), and an inner layer of ferrous oxide or wustite (FeO) next to the base steel. Studies by Dahl and Lueg (2) revealed that the scale layers build up irregularly and show many cracks and pores. The total thickness of each layer depends upon the conditions of hot working, ie the temperature, the time at temperature, and the access of the air to the steel surface while it is hot. The mechanism of scale formation is generally considered to be one of oxidation of the outermost iron surface to $Fe(III)$ ions and the diffusion of iron atoms outward (3). Ferrous oxide is only stable at temperatures above 1040°F. The cooling conditions influence the distribution of the various oxide phases (4,5). With slow cooling, ferrous oxide decomposes into ferroferric oxide and iron at temperatures below 1040°F. It will be shown below that the rate of pickling depends upon the distribution of the oxide layers. The solubility of the oxides in acids varies greatly. Ferrous oxide is the most soluble, followed by ferroferric oxide and ferric oxide, which is the least soluble. For fast pickling, it is desirable that the scale be mostly ferrous oxide with only minimal amounts of ferric and ferroferric oxides. This is accomplished by low final rolling temperatures and rapid cooling rates.

Chemistry of Pickling. Sulfuric acid has traditionally been the pickling medium for descaling steel. The reason for this preponderance is economics and suitable materials of construction. Since 1963, hydrochloric acid pickling has been replacing sulfuric acid pickling at an ever increasing rate. The reasons for this are: (1) the availability of low-cost by-product hydrochloric acid from chlorination processes in the chemical industry; (2) the steeply rising cost of sulfuric acid; (3) the faster speed of pickling by hydrochloric acid; and (4) the greater ease with which spent pickle liquor from hydrochloric acid pickling can be disposed of or regenerated.

The chemical reactions in the pickling of steel with sulfuric acid are:

$$FeO + H_2SO_4 = FeSO_4 + H_2O \tag{1}$$

$$Fe_2O_3 + 3\,H_2SO_4 = Fe_2(SO_4)_3 + 3\,H_2O \tag{2}$$

$$Fe + H_2SO_4 = FeSO_4 + H_2 \tag{3}$$

$$Fe + Fe_2(SO_4)_3 = 3\,FeSO_4 \tag{4}$$

$$Fe_2(SO_4)_3 + H_2 = 2\,FeSO_4 + H_2SO_4 \tag{5}$$

Ferric and ferroferric oxide are slow to dissolve in sulfuric acid. Ferrous oxide and iron, however, are quick to dissolve. In the pickling of steel with sulfuric acid, the reactions given in equations 1 and 3 predominate. In order for sulfuric acid to remove mill scale from hot-rolled steel, the acid must penetrate the outer scale through pores and cracks and attack the more readily soluble ferrous oxide layer next to the iron. It is only practical to pickle with sulfuric acid when there are numerous cracks in the mill scale through which the acid can seep and undermine the outer scale while attacking the base metal and the ferrous oxide. The reaction of the acid with metallic iron generates hydrogen gas. The gas exerts a pressure on the outer scale and essentially pops it off. This in turn exposes more iron and ferrous oxide to the action of the acid. The mill scale on coils and sheets of steel is often deliberately cracked to speed the pickling action. This is done by flexing the steel by passing it over small diameter rolls or by cold-rolling it lightly on a temper mill. (This is not without its disadvantage, however, as the cold-working increases the hardness of the steel.) The higher oxides of iron dissolve slowly in the acid. Only small amounts of ferric ions are ever found in pickle liquor because of reactions given in equations 4 and 5. Inhibitors are often used to reduce the loss of metal by slowing the reaction represented by equation 3, the attack of the acid on the base metal. In the case of sulfuric acid, this use of inhibitor also tends to slow the pickling rate by reducing the hydrogen formation and retarding some of the undermining reactions (see Vol. 6, p. 321).

The chemical reactions involved in pickling of steel with hydrochloric acid are similar to those which occur when sulfuric acid is used.

$$FeO + 2\,HCl = FeCl_2 + H_2O \tag{6}$$

$$Fe_2O_3 + 6\,HCl = 2\,FeCl_3 + 3\,H_2O \tag{7}$$

$$Fe + 2\,HCl = FeCl_2 + H_2 \tag{8}$$

$$2\,FeCl_3 + H_2 = 2\,FeCl_2 + 2\,HCl \tag{9}$$

$$2\,FeCl_3 + Fe = 3\,FeCl_2 \tag{10}$$

Winterbottom and Reed (6) found that the mechanism of hydrochloric acid pickling at room temperature is similar to that of sulfuric acid—the rapid dissolution of the underlying ferrous oxide to undermine the slow dissolving mill scale. At higher temperatures (170–200°F) it has been found (7) that the dissolution rate of iron oxide in 10% acid is eight times as fast in hydrochloric acid as it is in sulfuric acid and it is thirty times as fast in 15% acid. The fundamental nature of the pickling of steel with hydrochloric acid at elevated temperatures is thus one of dissolution of the scale as opposed to its undermining by attack on the inner layers (8).

The attack of hydrochloric acid on the base metal (equ. 8) is much slower (8) than it is with sulfuric acid (equ. 3). Nevertheless, it has been found highly beneficial to use inhibitors in hydrochloric acid pickle liquors to retard the iron dissolution and reduce the waste of free acid.

Because of the more rapid dissolution rate of the mill scale with hydrochloric acid, much higher pickling rates are possible—even at lower temperatures than those used with sulfuric acid. The mechanism of pickling with hydrochloric acid has made scale breaking unnecessary (8). Table 1 compares the average time required to pickle eight different carbon steels in hydrochloric acid with the time required to pickle the same eight steels in sulfuric acid. It will be noted that the effect of cracking the scale is one of reducing the sulfuric acid pickling time by one half, whereas there is only a negligible effect on the hydrochloric acid pickling time.

Much lower acid concentrations can be used when pickling with hydrochloric acid because of the high reaction rates. Common practice is to use only 10% hydrochloric

Table 1. Pickling Time to Descale Carbon Steel[a] (8), sec

Pickling conditions			Without temper mill scale breaker	With temper mill scale breaker
Acid, g/liter	Fe, g/liter	Temp, °F		
H_2SO_4, 280	10	200	37	18
HCl, 100	10	175	23	23
HCl, 100	10	200	17	14

[a] Average of eight steels.

acid in contrast to 25% sulfuric acid. Spent pickle liquor from sulfuric acid baths often contains 7% free acid whereas it is uncommon to dispose of hydrochloric acid pickle liquor containing more than 1% free acid.

As pickling proceeds, the bath becomes more concentrated in ferrous chloride but there is essentially no reduction in the pickling rate because of this increase. High concentrations of iron salts can thus be tolerated in hydrochloric acid pickle liquor and in practice this occurs. Iron concentrations of 10–15% are common. As explained below, the buildup of iron sulfate in sulfuric acid pickling baths cannot be tolerated to the extent that the buildup of iron chloride is tolerated in hydrochloric acid pickle liquors.

Continuous Sulfuric Acid Pickling

The mill scale from hot-rolled steel coils is continuously removed in long, horizontal pickling lines. The rate of pickling is affected by the thickness and composition of the scale and its porosity. The rate of attack of sulfuric acid is dependent on the temperature, acid concentration, agitation, ferrous sulfate concentration, and inhibitor concentration. Marked increases are possible by increasing the temperature; more modest increases are possible by increasing the concentration of the acid. The solution rate of iron in sulfuric acid is about 100 times greater at 200°F than it is at room temperature. The rate of acid attack at 25% acid concentration is about double of that at a 12% concentration. The strongest concentration used in continuous pickling lines is about 25%.

Some modern continuous pickling lines operate at speeds as high as 800 ft/min, but with those using sulfuric acid, speeds of 300–400 ft/min are more likely. The continuous pickling lines consist of several (3–5) acid tanks, each about 80 ft long, plus the associated equipment needed to uncoil the hot-rolled steel, weld the coils together, and either flex them or roll them to crack the mill scale before pickling. After pickling, there is the equipment to rinse, dry, oil, and recoil the pickled steel.

The pickle liquor flows countercurrently to the direction of travel of the strip through the line. The individual pickle tanks are connected so that the pickle liquor can flow from one tank to the next. In the steel industry, this process is referred to as "cascading." Fresh acid is added continuously to the last pickling tank to maintain the acid concentration in this tank at about 20 wt % H_2SO_4. Inhibitors are almost always added to the acid to prevent excessive metal loss during line stoppages. If it were possible in practice to run the line continuously, there would be no need for inhibitors; unfortunately, this is not the case. Each succeeding tank is maintained at a lower concentration merely by consumption of the acid by the pickling process. The concentration in the first tank is generally down to 7% free acid when it is dumped.

Acid additions are made to the last tank on the basis of about 35–50 lb of pure acid per ton of steel pickled.

As pickling proceeds, the concentration of ferrous sulfate builds up in the bath and exerts an inhibiting effect on the pickling. This is most pronounced in pickle liquors weak in acid. Martin (9) has shown that 15% ferrous sulfate as heptahydrate in 25% sulfuric acid has only a negligible effect on the pickling rate, but that the same iron content in a pickle liquor containing only 8% acid exerts a five-fold retardation on the pickling rate. Consequently, the acid concentration in the first tank (most dilute acid) cannot be allowed to fall much below 7% or it will not pickle. The result is a waste of acid in the effluent from the first tank which may contain as much as 25% of salt (ferrous chloride). Fresh acid and water additions are made to the last tank and these additions help to keep the concentration of iron salts down. A comprehensive explanation of cascade pickling is given by Stuck and Abrams (10).

The typical conditions for the continuous cascade pickling of carbon steel with sulfuric acid are compared with those of hydrochloric acid in Table 2.

Table 2. Typical Pickling Conditions for Continuous Pickling of Steel

Conditions	Tank 1	Tank 2	Tank 3	Tank 4	Acid consumption
H_2SO_4, %	7	11	15	20	40 lb H_2SO_4 per
$FeSO_4$, %	13	13	9	4	ton of steel
temperature, °F	200	200	210	210	
HCl, %	0.2	3	5	10	12 lb HCl
$FeCl_2$, %	25	20	20	15	per ton of steel
temperature, °F	200	190	180	170	

Insufficient pickling may occur when the hot-rolled steel has not had enough time in the pickle liquor to lose its adherent mill scale. This condition is possible when the temperature or acid concentration is too low, the line speed too high, or the iron salt concentration in the last tank is too high. The thickness and composition of the oxide scale can also play a role in underpickling, especially if the mill scale is tight and has not been sufficiently cracked in the scale breaker.

Line stoppages often cause overpickling by allowing the steel to remain in the acid too long. Overpickling results in excessive metal loss, high acid consumption rates, and pitting of the steel. Inhibitors will reduce overpickling. Without inhibitors, even short delays will appreciably reduce the thickness of the steel.

Continuous Hydrochloric Acid Pickling

Many continuous sulfuric acid pickling lines have been converted to use hydrochloric acid with only minimal changes. Because hydrochloric acid is highly volatile, the pickle tank covers must be tight and the fume exhaust and scrubbing system must be in good repair. It is common to use lead for equipment such as steam jets in pickling with sulfuric acid, but lead is attacked by hydrochloric acid and must be replaced with materials resistant to this acid. Plastics such as the polyfluorocarbons have been found suitable.

It has been found that much faster line speeds can be attained with hydrochloric acid. A line speed of 900 ft/min has been attained in one commercial pickling line

(11). The pickled product is cleaner, whiter, and in many cases softer because cold working the steel to break the scale is not necessary.

The last pickle tank is maintained at an acid concentration of about 10% HCl and at a temperature of about 170°F. Inhibitors are added to hydrochloric acid pickle tanks for the same reason that they are added to sulfuric acid tanks, ie to reduce metal loss during times when the line is stopped and the strip is allowed to remain in the pickle liquor. As the pickle liquor flows back through the line it becomes more dilute in free acid. The spent pickle liquor in the first tank is generally less than 0.5% HCl when it is discarded. No attention is paid to the buildup of iron chloride in any of the tanks because the salt exerts only a negligible influence on the pickling rate. The typical conditions for the cascade pickling of carbon steel with hydrochloric acid are given in Table 2.

Since the early 1960s the economics which once favored sulfuric acid have been reversed and hydrochloric acid is now favored. In addition to the direct savings involved, the ease with which spent pickle liquor from hydrochloric acid pickling can be handled has influenced many management decisions to convert sulfuric acid pickling lines to hydrochloric acid. One consequence of the conversion is a potential reduction in water pollution because the spent pickle liquor is only weakly acid and its ferrous chloride content is amenable to a pyrohydrolysis conversion back to hydrochloric acid (see p. 692). This makes possible a closed-loop operation, under which no disposal of spent pickle liquor is necessary.

Tower Pickling with Hydrochloric Acid

The first continuous pickling lines utilizing hydrochloric acid were of the tower type. The first tower pickler in the United States started operating in 1964 (12). The entry and exit portions of the line are conventional in nature and the same as those on horizontal picklers. The heart of the pickler is two towers about 85 ft high. The hot-rolled strip passes through the towers between pickling sprays. The sprays which come from holes drilled in plastic spray pipes allow the pickle liquor to run onto the strip. From the towers the strip travels through wringer rolls into a rinse section, then into a neutralizing section, and then through a final rinse to the dryer.

The pickling solution is about 12% hydrochloric acid and 13% ferrous chloride, and is maintained at a temperature of about 160°F. There is no need for an inhibitor as the spray of pickle liquor automatically stops when a line stoppage occurs. The pickle liquor is pumped through the sprays onto the strip and runs down the strip into a bottom tank where it is then pumped back to a storage tank. A portion of the pickle liquor is bled from the storage tank and replaced with fresh hydrochloric acid in a controlled manner to maintain the pickle liquor at the desired acid concentration.

An important part of one tower hydrochloric acid pickler in the United States is an acid reclamation plant (13) which operates independently of the pickling line. It takes spent pickle liquor from the storage tank and returns hydrochloric acid, generating high-purity iron oxide in the process (14) (see below). This total regeneration is not only an economy move, but it is a solution to the waste disposal problem. There is no waste disposal stream from this pickling line.

Batch Pickling

Hot-worked bars, rods, wire, and cut sheets are pickled by dipping them into vats of hot dilute acid—sometimes into hydrochloric acid but most often into sulfuric acid.

Some arrangement is required to separate the pieces to be pickled so that the acid has easy access to all surfaces of the work. Sheets are placed in a nearly vertical position on acid-resistant racks, and pins are inserted between every few sheets to facilitate the pickling of all surfaces. Agitation can effectively increase the pickling rate and is accomplished by either agitating the work to be pickled or by recirculating the pickle liquor. Several arrangements to accomplish this are explained in reference 15.

The action by which sulfuric acid removes the mill scale is for the most part mechanical because of the low solubility of the oxides in sulfuric acid. The acid penetrates the mill scale and reacts with the ferrous oxide and iron as explained above. This loosens and detaches the scale from the surface of the metal; the scale sinks to the bottom of the pickle tank where it accumulates and must be removed at frequent intervals. The ferrous sulfate formed by the pickling action builds up continuously in the pickle liquor as fresh acid additions are made to the bath. The pickling action is eventually stifled by the inhibiting action of the salt. At this point the spent acid bath must be replaced.

There is a wide latitude in pickling conditions at many installations where it is done. Different kinds of steel pickle at different rates, and the hot-working conditions under which the mill scale was formed also exert an influence on the pickling rate. The temperature of the bath may vary from 140 to 210°F, the concentration of the sulfuric acid may range from 4 to 25%, and the time of pickling may be as short as a few minutes to as long as an hour. Inhibitors are generally added to the pickle bath to prevent excess loss of base metal.

Inorganic halides, particularly sodium chloride, are often added to batch picklers. They were once thought to accelerate the pickling action but are now known to act as inhibitors (16,17). They are relatively ineffective as inhibitors because such high concentrations are needed to be as effective as low concentrations of commercially available inhibitors.

Stainless Steel Pickling

The stainless steels are those iron-base alloys which are characterized by their high resistance to corrosion. The high corrosion resistance is primarily imparted to the steels by their chromium content, but many other elements are also added to increase this corrosion resistance and to impart other valuable engineering properties. At the present time, there are over thirty different types of stainless steels which are considered standard or popular grades and a considerable number of other grades which are commercially available for specialized applications. Each grade of stainless steel has its own characteristics, but most of them can be separated into two broad classifications, ie the straight chromium grades and the chromium–nickle grades.

Each grade of stainless steel reacts differently to hot-working, depending upon its chemical composition. The resulting mill-scale composition is consequently different for each grade. The pickling operation to remove the mill scale from the stainless steel surface must then of necessity be varied according to the type of stainless steel being processed. The type of acid used, the concentrations needed and the required time of immersion must all be adjusted to the grade of stainless steel.

As the number and percentage of alloying elements in stainless steels are increased to make them more resistant to corrosion, the scale produced and the base metal itself become increasingly resistant to acid attack and thus more difficult to pickle. Stainless steels are more resistant to attack by the pickling solutions than the mill scale, and the undermining action responsible for the removal of mill scale from carbon steel is no longer applicable. The scale itself must be dissolved, but complete dissolution of the scale would often require an intolerably long time. In practice, the scale is attacked and disintegrated so that it is easily removed from the surface.

In the production of stainless steels, the heavy, thick scale that is formed during the hot-rolling or forging operations is extremely difficult to pickle off. In normal production facilities, the steel is often either subjected to shot-blasting, which knocks the heavy scale off the surface, or to immersion in a bath of fused sodium hydroxide or sodium hydride to reduce the scale. In either case, the subsequent pickling operation does not then require an excessively long time.

Sulfuric, hydrochloric, nitric, and hydrofluoric acids are all commonly used in the pickling of stainless steels. Combinations of these acids are often favored, as is the practice of pickling in successive baths of different compositions. Combinations of nitric and hydrofluoric acids are often preferred because the resulting pickled steel is stainfree and pleasing in appearance. The rate of pickling of mixtures of nitric and hydrofluoric acids is also faster than the rate in other acids. Sulfuric acid is particularly slow; its appeal is its ease of handling. For particular details on the best practices of pickling the various grades of stainless steel, reference should be made to manuals or texts on the stainless steels or the pickling processes (15,18–20,23).

In the cold working of stainless steels, the metal is rapidly work-hardened and must often be softened by intermediate annealing. Straight chromium grades can be annealed at temperatures in the range of 1500°F, but chromium–nickel grades must be annealed at temperatures as high as 2100°F. The annealing is commonly done in air and results in a scale formation on the surface. The chromium–nickel grades come out of the anneal with a heavy oxide which requires a strong acid solution such as nitric–hydrofluoric to remove it. The straight chromium grades often emerge from the anneal with only a dark heat tint due to the low annealing temperature. The thin oxide on the chromium grades can be pickled electrolytically in a nitric acid bath in one to two minutes. The steel to be pickled is made the anode. The bath may be a dilute solution of only about 2% nitric acid. Current densities of 75–200 A/ft^2 are suitable. Nitric acid alone, without an electrical assist, does not attack stainless steels, but the electrical current oxidizes the base metal and undermines the scale in a manner not unlike the attack of sulfuric acid in the pickling of carbon steel. In the case of stainless steels, however, the gas which is generated in the electrolytic pickling action is oxygen rather than hydrogen. Chromium–nickel grades of stainless steels are also sometimes pickled electrolytically to loosen the scale before it is finally pickled in strong acids.

Some of the annealing temperatures and typical acid pickling solutions that can be used in the treatment of stainless steels are listed in Table 3. The pickling solutions listed are more apt to be used in batch picklers than in continuous strand annealing and pickling lines.

The trend in the steel industry in the last decade has been to do more and more intermediate and final annealing in a protective atmosphere to prevent the formation of mill scale. This is accomplished most often in dry hydrogen or cracked ammonia, but some installations utilize a high vacuum. No pickling is necessary after such "bright" annealing. The cost of installing the expensive bright annealing equipment has been justified by a brighter, more corrosion resistant surface on the stainless steel and the elimination of the costly problem of disposing of the spent pickle liquors.

Table 3. Typical Annealing and Pickling Conditions for Stainless Steels

Type of stainless steel	Full anneal, °F	Pickling treatment	
		Solution	Temperature, °F
501, 502	1525–1550 slow cool to 1100	8–12% H_2SO_4	150–170
403, 410, 416^a	1550–1650 slow cool to 1100	8–12% H_2SO_4 6–10% H_2SO_4 + 6–10% HCl 10% HNO_3 + 1% HF	150–170 130–140 120–130
420	1550–1650 furnace cool to 1100	same as above	
430	1500–1550 furnace cool to 1100	same as above	
440	1550–1650 furnace cool to 1200	same as above	
446	1500–1600 air cool	same as above	
302, 316, 317, 321 347, 302B, 303	1850–2050 water quench	20% HCl 10% HNO_3 + 2% HF	120–130 120–130
309, 310	2000–2100 water quench	same as above	

^{a} Do not use 10% HNO_3 + 1% HF solution on 416.

Pollution Control

In the past, spent pickle liquors of all types have frequently been discharged into adjacent water bodies. It has become increasingly apparent that this disposal method may not be in the best interest of the community as it often interferes with the water usage by others. It is thus considered a water pollutant, and great efforts have been expended to control the waste streams from pickling operations.

The tonnage of steel products that require pickling has increased rapidly (21). By 1950, the net production of carbon steels in the United States was 97 million tons, of which 21% was pickled. It is difficult to estimate the volume of spent pickle liquor, but it was probably in excess of 600 million gallons in 1952. It may be over a billion gallons today and its disposal is a major concern in the control of pollution in the steel industry.

Great strides have been made by the steel industry in recent years in reducing the pollution of water by pickle liquor. This has been accomplished in a variety of ways by the expenditure of many man hours and millions of dollars. The pickling operations themselves have become more efficient, resulting in a reduction in the volume of spent pickle liquor leaving the pickling plants. Much of the highly acid, spent pickle liquor is now neutralized and sent to a lagoon where the precipitated solids are allowed to settle out; this permits an essentially clear stream of water to be decanted. Some pickle liquors are pumped into deep wells, and this method of disposal may well increase in the future now that geologists have approved of this disposal method.

There have been a great many schemes proposed for regenerating sulfuric acid from spent pickle liquor or for recovering other useful products from the waste solution. A quick survey of the literature will disclose a wealth of such proposals. From all of them, however, no practical benefit has accrued to the steel industry. From a study of all the schemes proposed to convert spent sulfuric acid pickle liquor into useful products, it will be concluded that at the present time the necessary disposal of waste pickle liquor will be a loss and further advances in technology are needed. One reason for this is that the tremendous volume of liquor to be treated and the variations in its quality in the many plants producing it demands that a successful process should be adaptable to a number of different technological and economic situations (22).   A second reason is that the difficulty of separating iron from process streams requires expensive equipment and processing techniques.   Most of the proposals base their appeal upon high-priced by-products obtained, which represent attractive processing credits. However, there is no demand for these products in the huge quantities generated, and this makes these credits unrealistic.

The disposal of spent pickle liquor from hydrochloric acid does not pose as great a problem as does that from sulfuric acid.   The acidity of the spent pickle liquor is low and rarely exceeds 0.5%.   There are useful ways to utilize the ferrous chloride from hydrochloric acid pickling wastes; one particularly attractive method is to use it in the secondary treatment of sewage.   The city of Detroit, Michigan, is the first major city to take advantage of the availability of the large quantities of cheap ferrous chloride for this purpose.

Another advantage of hydrochloric acid pickling, and one that will play an important role in influencing the trend to this acid in the pickling of steel, is that the spent pickle liquor can be economically regenerated if the operation is performed on a large enough scale.   A full regeneration plant was first built and put into operation in the United States in 1964 in Gadsden, Alabama.   The regeneration plant operates essentially in reverse of the pickling operation, turning ferrous chloride and water into iron oxide and hydrochloric acid.

The spent pickle liquor is filtered and pumped through sprays into the top of gas-fired, cylindrical roasters.   The descending fine droplets of pickle liquor are heated by the rising swirl of combustion gases from tangentially mounted burners in the bottom. Free hydrogen chloride and water are rapidly evaporated.   The ferrous chloride is then converted into ferric oxide and hydrogen chloride.   The pyrohydrolysis reaction is:

$$4\,FeCl_2 + 4\,H_2O + O_2 \rightleftharpoons 2\,Fe_2O_3 + 8\,HCl \qquad (11)$$

Oxygen comes from the excess air to the gas burners.   The conversion of ferrous chloride to the oxide exceeds 99%.   The gaseous products are taken overhead and the iron oxide drops to the bottom.   The overhead is passed through a cyclone to remove entrained iron oxide and passes to an absorber for recovery of the hydrogen chloride as hydrochloric acid.

The disposal of pickle liquors from the pickling of stainless steels is a lesser pollution problem to the steel industry because of the smaller volumes of spent pickle liquor generated.   Bright annealing has greatly helped the reduction of the quantities of pickle liquor that must be treated.   The handling of the pickle liquor must be more carefully controlled, however, because high fluoride and chromium contents cannot be tolerated in waste streams leaving the plants.   Even small amounts cannot be discharged into nearby streams.   It must be treated to remove the toxic elements or disposed of in such a manner as to avoid seepage into ground waters.   Several processes are under consideration for recovering the valuable metal content of spent pickle liquors from the descaling of stainless steels.

Health and Safety

Concentrated acids used in pickling can cause severe burns if they are allowed to come into contact with the skin.   Normal safety precautions must be taken by workers in pickling areas.   Fumes from hydrochloric acid pickle tanks can be extremely irritating if the acid is allowed to accumulate in the pickle room.   It is imperative that an exhaust system be installed over hydrochloric acid tanks to remove the fumes. Although sulfuric acid is not volatile and does not fume, the hydrogen that is generated in the bath from the pickling action will carry fine droplets of sulfuric acid into the pickling room. Small concentrations of the acid in the air will cause a choking sensation to be experienced by the workers. Primarily for this reason, a fume exhaust system is required for sulfuric acid tanks. The fine droplets of sulfuric acid are also corrosive to metals and must not be allowed in the pickling room atmosphere for this reason also.

Both nitric and hydrofluoric acids used in the pickling of stainless steels give off irritating and toxic fumes, but the health and safety problems are minimized because of the relatively lower temperatures used in the pickling process. Hydrogen fluoride is given off from hydrofluoric acid pickling tanks and is considered dangerous only if the concentration is high enough to be extremely irritating. The brown fumes of nitrogen dioxide which is evolved from nitric acid baths are easily visible and are toxic in high concentrations. Exhaust systems are required for both acids since high concentrations of nitrogen dioxide can be formed in a few minutes and even low concentrations of hydrogen fluoride are irritating.

Bibliography

1. L. B. Pfeil, *J. Iron Steel Inst.* (*London*) **119,** 501 (1929).
2. W. Dahl and W. Lueg, *Stahl Eisen* **77,** 845 (1957).
3. J. O. Edstrom and G. Bitsianes, *Trans. AIME* **203,** 760 (1955).
4. P. Funke and E. Wend, *Stahl Eisen* **89,** 101 (1969).
5. S. Garber, *Nature* **183,** 1388 (1959).
6. A. B. Winterbottom and J. P. Reed, *J. Iron Steel Inst.* (*London*) **124,** 159 (1932).
7. *Continuous Pickling of Hot Rolled Steel Sheet with Hydrochloric Acid,* The Dow Chemical Co., Midland, Mich., 1964.
8. R. M. Hudson and C. J. Waring, *Sheet Metal Ind.* **44,** 542 (1967).
9. E. D. Martin, "Continuous Strip Pickling," *Yearbook Am. Iron Steel Inst.* **1948,** 602.
10. W. H. Stuck and J. H. Abrams, "Continuous Cascade Pickling," *Yearbook Am. Iron Steel Inst.* **1951,** 135.
11. R. S. Miltenberger, "The Use of Hydrochloric Acid in Continuous Pickling Facilities," *Yearbook Am. Iron Steel Inst.,* **1965,** 241.
12. J. R. Lowey, "Hydrochloric Acid Pickling," *Yearbook Am. Iron Steel Inst.* **1965,** 253.
13. D. E. Poole, "Republic's Continuous Reclamation of Hydrochloric Acid Pickling at Gadsden, Ala.," *Am. Iron Steel Inst., Birmingham Regional Technical Meeting, Dec. 9, 1964.*
14. C. M. Brown, "High Purity Iron Oxide from Spent Hydrochloric Acid Pickle Liquor," in T. R. Ingraham, ed., *Continuous Processing and Process Control; Proceedings of a Symposium, Metallurgical Society Conference, Philadelphia, Pa., Dec. 5–8, 1966,* Vol. 49, Gordon & Breach, New York, 1968.
15. H. E. McGannon, ed., *The Making, Shaping and Treating of Steel,* 8th ed., United States Steel, Pittsburgh, Penn., 1964.
16. K. F. Hager and M. Rosenthal, *Corrosion* **6,** 344 (1950).
17. R. M. Hudson and C. J. Waring, *Mater. Protect.* **6,** 52 (1967).
18. E. Gregory and E. N. Simons, *Stainless and Heat-Resisting Steels,* Hutchison and Co. Ltd., London, 1946.
19. *Republic Enduro Stainless Steels,* Republic Steel Corp., Cleveland, O., 1951.
20. J. H. G. Monypenny, *Stainless Iron and Steel,* Vol. 1, Chapman and Hall Ltd., London, 1951.
21. *Disposal of Spent Sulfate Pickling Solution,* Steel Industry Action Committee of Ohio River Valley Water Sanitation Commission, 1952.
22. J. M. Roblin and E. G. Bobalek, "Recovery of Waste Pickle Liquor Values Using Liquid–Liquid Extraction," *Am. Chem. Soc. Meeting, Atlantic City, N.J., Sept. 11, 1962.*
23. *Metals Handbook,* Vol. 2, 8th ed., Am. Soc. Metals, Metals Park, Ohio, 1964.

EDWIN P. KAWASAKI
Republic Steel Corporation

PIPELINE HEATING

Many liquids, eg water and aqueous solutions, sulfur, also benzene, freeze at moderate temperatures. If transported in pipes, they must be kept heated to prevent freezing. Sufficient heat is sometimes added by increasing the temperature before the fluid enters the cold length of pipe to make up for heat losses during transit; but this is not always possible.

Also, some materials must be kept in the vapor state by supplying heat to maintain a temperature above the dew point, thus preventing condensation. For example, gaseous hydrochloric acid with water vapor and air may be piped in a steel pipe if the pipe is always maintained at a temperature above the condensing point of water in this system. Gaseous HCl does not attack steel; it is only corrosive if it condenses with water on the inside of the pipe. Other vapors may also be superheated above the boiling point to prevent condensation.

Transport pipes for some fluids must be kept at a temperature above the ambient, sometimes as high or higher than 400–500°F, to prevent a change of phase, ie liquid to solid, or vapor to liquid. Heat must be supplied to balance that lost to the surroundings.

Of much more industrial importance is the piping of those fluids which have high viscosities at ambient temperatures and must be heated to permit reasonable flow. Besides petroleum oils, crudes or residues, commercial fluids transported by pipe include molasses, other food syrups or melts (such as butter, oils and fats, chocolate, etc), strong sulfuric acid, tar, bitumen, some synthetic resins, and numerous other chemicals.

Low-sulfur fuel oils for electric-power generation often have to be heated to a temperature at which they flow, ie the pour point. They may have high viscosities at usual temperatures, thus substantial heating is necessary to give sufficient fluidity for pumping, especially at low ambient temperatures. Often the wax, high in amount in many low-sulfur oils, crystallizes slowly against the pipe wall until flow is completely blocked. Of particular importance is the demand in metropolitan areas for minimum SO_2 pollution from stack gases of power plants, thus requiring the use of fuel oils which are difficult to handle. At least one utility company has spent millions of dollars in providing heat for its network of interstation oil lines, necessitated by the use of low-sulfur oils (1).

A bigger problem is the transport of crude oil from the arctic regions of Alaska, Canada, Russia, and within a few years probably Greenland, to refineries and consuming areas in more hospitable climates. It is estimated (2) that $6 billion ($6 \times 10^9$) will be spent in Canada alone to bring south the crude oil which stores the solar energy released there in the warmer climate of millions of years ago. Pipes up to 8 ft in diam will be used and the cost of transport will add greatly to the large cost of production of the crudes under such cryogenic conditions, where even steel loses its strength. To make it possible for man to live and work in such an environment, water and sewer lines must also be heated.

Energy for Heating vs Energy for Pumping. The balancing of the energy required for heating and that required for pumping is always of major engineering and economic interest. In long-distance pipelines, the pipe friction develops so much heat from the mechanical energy of the pumps that, in a well-insulated pipe, the temperature may be maintained as much as 60–100°F above the ambient. When little or no heat energy is supplied to a pipeline the oil viscosity may remain high and the energy for pumping is also high.

As heat energy is added, the temperature goes up, the viscosity goes down, and so does the energy required for pumping. The total energy requirements at any given velocity or throughput in the pipeline may be determined readily by adding the pumping or hydraulic energy requirement to that for thermal energy; then the minimum is noted of the curve of total energy costs against temperature maintained in the pipeline at a given throughput. These minimum total power costs are determined for various different velocities or throughputs of the pipeline; again a minimum point may be noted in a curve so plotted. This will be the low point of a valley in a three-dimensional surface of a plot of total energy costs, temperature, and throughput for a given pipeline.

However, for the optimum design and pipe size for a given required throughput one must also consider the energy and other operating costs and the total capital costs for lines of different sizes, which can accommodate the desired throughput. The low point can best be found with a computer.

Heating with Thermal Energy

Terminal Heating. In many industrial piping installations and in oil transport, oil which would not flow at the ambient temperature is preheated to a high temperature before it enters a pipeline so as to receive as much sensible heat as will be lost by the pipe through its insulation to the surroundings. The oil is then pumped through the line to another storage vessel where it is preheated again and the process repeated. Obviously, the temperature of the first oil through may drop, before it reaches the end, to a temperature which is undesirably (or impossibly) low. A slug of low-viscosity hot oil or naphtha may be pumped through the pipeline first, often in the reverse direction, to preheat the line. It is then pumped in again after handling the oil to be transported, to fill the pipeline so it will remain there for start-up after a cold shutdown. The procedure is only slightly more sophisticated than the Indian method of cooking a stew in a goatskin bag by dropping in stones taken from a hot fire.

In this method, the preheating of both oils in the tanks at the terminals necessarily requires very much more heat input than is required if applied uniformly along the pipeline. There is usually no danger of overheating a petroleum crude, but a naphtha must be kept below its bubble point. The system is wasteful of pipeline capacity and subject to risk of shutdown with unpumpable oil. It is used if nothing else is available—as the Indian also had to do his cooking because he had no metal pot.

This system cannot be used with vegetable or other food oils, which could not be mixed with another oil stream at start-up and cut-off points, and could not stand overheating. It could not be used with molten sulfur, most aqueous solutions, and many other liquids.

Heating Fluids. The elementary way to thaw a frozen pipe or prevent one from freezing is to apply a torch or other form of direct fire. In some countries of Latin America, small streams of oil are diverted at intervals along the length of an oil pipeline. This oil is burned under the pipe itself in a direct firing; less clumsy methods are needed. The next simplest system is to place a jacket around the pipe and to circulate a hot fluid in the annular space, usually an oil. Other high-boiling liquids are used including melted waxes and even melts of metals or salts. Jacketed systems have been used in chemical plants for over 50 years and a complete line of sizes of jacketed pipes, fittings, valves, and pumps is available, some at very high cost, for use in the confines of a plant area. Extruded aluminum pipe is available in a range of sizes with two channels either equal or unequal, on either side of an interior wall. The larger channel is for process liquid, the smaller one for the heating fluid.   The sensible heat of the hot fluid is usually quickly dissipated, in some hundreds of feet at most.

Steam is most often used as the heating fluid (3,4) and since its latent heat is many times as much per pound as the available sensible heat of any fluid, a relatively small channel is required.   Thus, a small steam pipe "traces" the larger pipe carrying the process liquid.   Installations up to some miles have been built with steam headers paralleling the transport lines to supply steam at intervals which traces many small pipes or tubes bound to the main pipe and enclosed within an extra large insulation.

The disadvantages of freezing steam lines, condensate lines, steam traps, and the difficulty of maintenance, have ruled these out, except for uses in or near plants (5,6). Even within battery limits, steam tracers are being superseded because of their high initial and maintenance costs, and also considerably higher costs for energy, as will be noted below (7).

Conventional Electrical Systems of Heating Pipelines

Resistance of Pipe Wall to ac.   Direct heating by using resistance or impedance of the metal is one of the several systems of electrical heating that have been employed to heat short steel pipelines, always with nonaqueous and nonconducting fluids (8). The pipe must be completely insulated electrically from all other pipes, steel supports and other structures, pumps, the surroundings in general, and especially the ground. Flanges, bolts, and nuts must be electrically insulated between each short length of pipe on different circuits.   The low resistance of the pipeline requires very low voltage for reasonable lengths; high voltages for long lengths are unsafe.   The usual design is for 50 V and a high-voltage line is installed to carry the ac overhead and parallel to the pipeline.   A step-down transformer is required for each short section which is separately heated and controlled as a unit.   Even with the greatest care in insulation, the heavy current presents a potential arcing hazard if an electrical short does develop from the massive conductor to a grounded steel structure or otherwise.   No grounding is possible to remove static generated by the flowing liquid or by lightning, or to permit a sacrificial cathodic-protection system

The pipe is uniformly heated and high inputs of heat are possible.   The efficiency of the heat input is about 75% of the power used (8); the power factor is low, 45–75%.

Induction Heating.   Eddy currents produced in a steel pipe by a coil of wire carrying ac around the pipeline produce induction heating due to electrical losses within the steel pipe.   The efficiency of heat from electric power is very low and the power factor may be only 25% for small pipes, up to 75% for large pipes.   Induction heating is very expensive to install and to operate, except for very special purposes, and has never been suggested for long-distance lines.

Individual Resistors.   The electrical system of heating used by far most often carries a resistance heater cable in a sheath for electrical insulation and mechanical protection, which is supported as close as possible to the outside of the pipe by wires or clips and cement with heat-transfer properties.

Again, as with impedance heating and induction heating, the high-voltage power-transmission line must be built parallel to the pipeline for many taps off to the multiple pipe-heating circuits.

External resistance heating depends on many small, separate resistors, usually each on a separate circuit.   They are insulated in sheaths which are banded or clamped against the wall of the pipe.   Mineral insulated (MI) cables are copper tubes encasing two bare resistance wires joined at the far end and filled with a powdered refractory insulator, eg magnesium oxide. If the resistance heater becomes loosened and pulls away from the clamps, the heat which it develops does not pass to the pipe, the temperature of the resistor rises rapidly, and it burns out. There is also some danger of hot spots, particularly when no fluid is flowing. An application of a heat-conducting cement around the resistors and under the thermal insulation tends to minimize these difficulties and, in the case of explosive atmospheres, these dangers.

Heating by separate electric resistors is a highly developed industry supplying engineering equipment and installation (9). Single projects have involved more than 2,500 individual circuits with all accessory switch gear, controls, etc, for each, to heat a pipeline over 250,000 ft long. Essentially, this system is for relatively short installations, but it can be expanded by many multiples of these short lengths with corresponding multiple complications and multiple costs.

Skin Effect

Skin effect is an electromagnetic phenomenon of ac flow to be discussed later, which concentrates the ac flow toward the surface of conductors. It is particularly important with ferromagnetic conductors. In this application an insulated wire runs through a steel tube and is connected to it at the far end. An ac supply is connected to both the wire and the tube at the near end. The magnetic field of the ac is set up between the wire acting as one leg of the circuit and the steel tube acting as the return leg. Because the steel tube is ferromagnetic, the penetration of the magnetic field is hindered. The resulting crowding of the current toward the inner surface of the tube causes an effective increase in resistance of this as the return leg, as well as shielding the outside of the tube from electromagnetic fields inside of the pipe.

Some aspects of this phenomenon have been utilized in Japan by several engineering companies in installations of systems for supplying heat to oil pipelines up to 15 or 20 miles long, and from 4 to 32 in. in diam (10,11). As many as six parallel 1-in. heat tubes were welded, spot or continuously, to the outside of a 32-in. pipeline (with 2 in. of insulation) to keep it at 122°F, with 32°F ambient temperature. This 8300 ft long pipeline used 1500 V–60 cycle ac. Another parallel design of an isolated or separate heat-tube is on the axis of the oil-pipe. In both cases, the heat given up by the line loss of the insulated electric wire must pass from the wire through the insulation, through the air space in the heat-tube, and through the heat-tube wall to the oil inside.

In those heat-tubes which are either applied with heat-transfer cement or welded (tack or continuously) on the outside, the cross section of the outer wall of the oil-pipe and of the heat-tube is two circles in contact, tangent at one point. The heat-tube is parallel to the axis of the pipe. The heat generated by the heat-tube passes through the air space and the welding bead or heat-transfer cement and then through the pipe wall to the oil adjacent to that element of the pipe.

As compared to later and improved systems using the skin effect, these heating tubes are rather separate or isolated from the oil-pipe. The temperature of the heat-tube must not be more than a few degrees higher than that of the oil-pipe to prevent expansion which would crack the weld. Thus, energy inputs for these separate or isolated heat-tubes are limited. The standard thermal insulation around the main pipeline also covers the heat-tube to minimize heat losses. This insulation was applied in specially cut pieces around the one to a half dozen small heat-tubes built out as appendages on the surfaces of the oil-pipe.

The pipeline was well grounded and it was noted that it could be buried in the ground or in water without leakage or loss of the high voltage employed, or any danger to persons from shock, or as a fire hazard in handling flammable fluids in hazardous areas. Thermostatic control allowed maintenance of the desired temperature without overheating of liquid or use of more heat than required.

THEORY OF THE SKIN EFFECT

Skin effect and *shielding* are terms indicating the inherent inability of magnetic fields of alternating currents to penetrate the metallic surface of a conductor, thus causing a nonuniform distribution of current within the conductor. With power circuits, this is usually detrimental because of the increase of resistance and less than optimal use of the cross section of the conductor material. In heater applications, the nonuniform distribution of current may be made to increase the resistance, while it shields the surroundings from the fields and practically eliminates current flow on an outer surface.

Skin and skin effect are not absolute terms. The ac tends to flow near the inner surface of the wall of a tube which has an inside ac conductor insulated therefrom and carrying one leg of a circuit which is returned by the steel tube, herein called a "heat-tube." The density of the current falls off rapidly in the tube wall according to an exponential function of the distance from the inner surface.

A magnetic field surrounds the central wire carrying the ac and extends for some distance. However, there is no term in the mathematical relation for the skin effect and the skin depth referring to the distance between the conductors, since the skin phenomena depend only on the properties of the metals and the ac frequency. Thus, it has been found possible to use larger heat-tubes in much improved designs and arrangements, compared with the original isolated ones. Tubes up to 2 in. or even larger may be used advantageously and, of more importance, even a much larger tube, the transport pipe itself, may be used as its own heat-tube, without any tracer tube.

The skin effect phenomena may be illustrated by an isolated coaxial conductor pair with cross section (shown in Fig. 1). The ac is flowing in one direction in the axial conductor which is surrounded by its block insulation, and in the other direction in the tube wall, the two representing the two legs of the circuit, since the conductor is connected to the inside surface of the tube at the far end. Produced concomitantly is a magnetic field, as shown by the typical circular field line.

The current is nonuniformly distributed in the conductors if they are of substantial size. Most of the current crowds toward the inner surface of the outer conductor and the outer surface of the inner conductor, as indicated by the (+) signs in the outer surface of the inner copper conductor wire and the inside surface of the outer steel conductor tube.

A major effect of the redistribution of the current is the increase of the effective value of resistance above what it would be for a uniform distribution as it occurs with dc flow, or in small conductors with ac. The physical justification is that the resistive dissipation in an elementary volume is proportional to the square of the current density. This dissipation integrated over the conductor cross section is least for a uniform distribution.

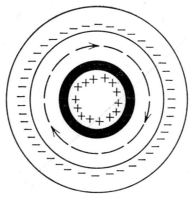

Fig. 1. Diagram of skin effect in conductor wire on axis of heat-tube as shown by the crowding of current densities on near surfaces of conductors due to magnetic field.

Accompanying this redistribution of current is a decrease of magnetic field as the outer conductor is penetrated from its inside surface and the inner conductor is penetrated from its outside surface. For the isolated conductor pair, the magnetic field at the outside surface of the outer conductor is practically zero. The axial electric field of the drop of ac current flowing also decreases in a similar way as the metal is penetrated by the field, except that the electric field on the outside of the outer conductor is extremely small but finite, although simultaneously there is a great decrease in the effective voltage from the inside to an extremely small voltage on the outside wall of the tube.

For large pipes with 60 cycle ac the penetration of the field into the conductor and the current flow are quite important. The intensity of the circular magnetic field at the inner surface is determined by the current I, flowing, in the conductor. At any point in the steel wall at a distance, x, from the inner surface, the intensity of the electric field in the axial direction may be called E, and the current density J (in A/m^2), while the corresponding values at the inner surface are E_0 and J_0, respectively. Since all the quantities are sinusoidal functions of time, their root-mean-square values (rms) are used.

The wall thickness may be regarded as infinite for steel if it is more than about 0.16 in. thick, as will be shown below, and the relation may be formulated as follows:

$$J/J_0 = e^{-x}/\delta \tag{1}$$

If ρ is the resistivity, μ the relative permeability and f the frequency in cps, then δ, the depth of penetration, is the following:

$$\delta = \frac{1000}{2\pi} \sqrt{\frac{10\rho}{\mu f}} \tag{2}$$

The function δ is defined as the distance inside the metal at which the current density decays to $e^{-1} = 0.368$ of its surface value. Let W be the actual thickness of the tube wall; for $W = 4\delta$, the current density would decrease to 0.018 of the value at the inner surface and, from a practical standpoint, making the wall thickness equal to 4δ is virtually equivalent to making the wall thickness infinite.

For an infinitely thick tube, the ratios of the circumferentially directed magnetic field, H, the current density J, and the axial voltage, E, to their respective counter-

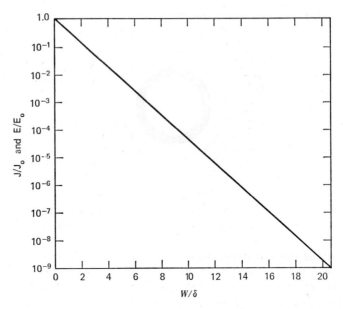

Fig. 2. Ratio of current densities and voltages on the outside surface to those on the inside surface of the tubes of different wall thickness plotted logarithmically against the normal value of the ratio of the wall thickness to the skin thickness.

parts on the inner surface, all follow the exponential dependence of equation 1, as indicated in Figure 2. Here, on semilogarithmic coordinates, is the ratio of the voltage drop, E, along the outer tube surface to the inner surface plotted against the ratio of the wall thickness to the skin depth, δ. On the same plot is the ratio of the current density flowing, J, outside to inside, also the ratio of the magnetic-field intensity, H, outside to inside. If the thickness of the tube is 16 times that of the skin for the particular material, these ratios are all 1×10^{-7}. The part of the curve below $W/\delta = 4$ has a somewhat more complicated mathematical relation which would make little difference in practice.

The depth of penetration is a characteristic of the metal used, being dependent on the resistivity, ρ in ohm-m, the relative permeability, μ, (dimensionless), and the frequency, f, in cps.

Again, where the wall thickness of a large pipe is at least four times the skin depth, the effective resistance, r, per unit length of the outer tube of Figure 1 is approximated closely by the following relationship:

$$r = \frac{R_s}{\pi \, (D - 2\,W)} \tag{3}$$

where D is the outside diameter and R_s is the surface resistivity given as follows:

$$R_s = 2\,\pi\sqrt{f\mu\rho} \times 10^{-7} \text{ ohms} \tag{4}$$

For a 60-cycle ac and ρ given in units of 10^{-1} ohm-cm, the depth of penetration, δ, and surface resistivity, R_s, are given as follows:

$$\delta = 0.649 \sqrt{\frac{\rho}{\mu}} \text{ cm} \tag{5}$$

$$R_s = 1.54 \sqrt{\mu\rho} \text{ microhms} \tag{6}$$

It is interesting to note here that the effective resistance is proportional to the square root of the resistivity of the metal, rather than being directly proportional.

Commercial steels have permeabilities and resistivities which vary with impurities and other factors; but they may be assumed to have an effective skin thickness of about 1 mm or 0.04 in.

Since the pipe has a finite thickness, there is always a very small axial voltage drop per unit length appearing on the outside wall. Figure 2 shows this to be very much smaller than the inside voltage drop, ie by a factor of $\frac{1}{50}$ if the pipe is 4δ thick; $\frac{1}{150}$ if 5δ thick; $\frac{1}{200,000}$ if 10δ thick, which would be about $\frac{1}{2}$ in. thick of ordinary steel, or 1 billionth if about 1 in. thick. In any commercially useful thickness of steel pipe, this voltage drop of the pipe per mile, whether grounded or not, becomes immeasurably small. Thus, if the voltage drop on the inner surface is 250 V per mile of length, and the pipe wall is about 0.2 in. thick, the outside voltage drop would be about 2 V per mile; if about $\frac{1}{2}$ in. thick, it would be about 0.5 V per mile; if about $\frac{1}{2}$ in., less than 0.002 V per mile; if 1 in. thick, about one one-millionth V per mile.

The current flow induced by such small voltage gradients in surrounding earth, or even in seawater, would be negligible. In any case, when heat is to be supplied to oil pipelines, they would usually be lagged with thermal insulation, which would provide a yet higher electrically insulating environment. Pipelines above the surface are normally grounded at reasonable distances, to dissipate static caused by the flow of the oil or by lightning discharge. Pipelines in corrosive surroundings may have the conventional sacrificial cathodic protection system without interference from the skin effect heating.

Elements of the Heat-Tube

The heat-tube may be of a metal with special electrical properties, but these metals are expensive, while mild steel is always available and cheapest. It may have a shape other than cylindrical and, preferably, it may be an integral part of the oil-pipe. The electric conductor for the one side of the ac circuit may be a copper or aluminum wire or cable. It is always connected to the inside of the tube at the far end. Its near end and the near end of the tube are connected to the source of ac.

The line loss developed in the electric wire gives all of its heat to the heat-tube and hence to the oil-pipe and the oil therein. A much smaller wire size may be used than is usually specified for a given amperage. The standard tables tend to balance a larger size with smaller losses against the smaller size and larger line losses. But here all heat developed in the conductor, is used as line losses. Relatively inexpensive steel wire may also be used, but consideration must then be given to its skin effect. The electric wire usually has a somewhat higher temperature, ie 1–5°F, than that of the heat-tube. This is negligible in specifying insulation materials. If the fluid does not conduct electricity it may be in contact with the surfaces of both the electrical conductor and the heat-tube, thus minimizing the temperature rise in the electrical conductor and eliminating other thermal resistances.

Insulation for the electric wire may be of any suitable material which maintains its physical, electrical, and chemical characteristics at the temperature of the heat-tube, which is never more than a degree or two higher than that of the oil-pipe. The cheapest materials may usually be used. Poly(vinyl chloride) is satisfactory up to about 180°F; polyethylene up to about 215°F. Silicone-resin materials to be used from 350–400°F are available; teflon at temperatures to 500°F or above.

Methods of connecting these electrical conductors are conventional and safe, even in hazardous atmospheres. Valves and fittings may be heated by a simple modification of the system.

Heat-Tube and Oil-Pipe with Common Wall. Oil-pipes are made most often of mild carbon steel which develops the skin effect. The separate or isolated round heat-tube is shown in Figure 3, lower left. However, a better system mechanically, economically, and thermally (heat transfer) uses a part of the wall of the steel oil-pipe as a part of the heat-tube.

A heat-tube may be made in place with a U-shaped cross section, as shown in Figure 3, upper right. A strip of steel is preformed as a U-shaped trough and welded along two elements of the oil-pipe. Thus, the wall between the two elements is an effective part of the heat-tube and carries part of the ac, its skin resistance to the ac giving heat directly. The steel added to the pipeline weighs less than a circular isolated tube, shown at the lower left, for the same internal perimeter (Fig. 3). As always, the conductor wire is electrically connected at the far end to the inside of the tube.

A standard angle iron may be used instead as the shape for the applied part of the heat-tube as shown in the upper left of Figure 3. It is also welded along two elements of the pipe. As much as 40% of the heat-tube may thus be made up of the oil-pipe surface to perform a dual service. Heat transfer is aided greatly when the pipe wall is used as an actual conducting and heat-generating part of the heat-tube.

In Figure 3, as in the other figures, the heat-tube may be shown quite out of scale with the oil-pipe for purposes of illustration and several quite different heat-tubes may be shown on the same oil-pipe merely to indicate the differences in construction, rather than an actual use of multiple heat-tubes.

Heat-Tube Integrally Welded into the Pipe Wall. A preferred design is shown in Figure 4, taking advantage of using the heat-tube itself, integrally welded in as part of the oil-pipe wall, particularly in pipes larger than 24 in. Skelp (strip metal) is formed into a cylindrical shape and the slit left between the adjacent edges is filled with the heat-tube. Standard pipe-making equipment welds these common elements of the oil-pipe and the heat-tube, as shown in Figure 4 upper left, so that the heat-tube does not project into the pipe.

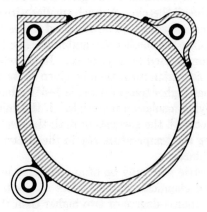

Fig. 3.   Cross section of heat-tubes on outside surfaces of oil-pipes.

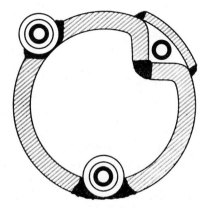

Fig. 4. Heat-tubes built into the wall of the oil-pipe.

The lower heat-tube of Figure 4 is supported during welding so that its outer element is flush with the outer surface of the oil-pipe. The weld bead fills the spaces to give a surface which may be finished as a true cylinder, if desired. Much of the heat-tube is actually inside the oil-pipe; thus, there is excellent thermal relationship with the pipe and immediate contact with the oil, in addition to the application of insulation being simplified.

Still another construction, Figure 4 upper right, forms two sides of an internal "V" during the pressing of the skelp. The closing weld is along the bottom of the "V," which is covered with a steel strip welded along its edges to complete the heat-tube for enclosing the insulated wire.

Pipes over 30 in. in diam may be made by pressing strips of skelp in dies 40 to 60 ft long to form semicircular troughs. Two of these are made into pipes by welding two seams, the opposite elements of the finished cylinder. A heat-tube may be welded in each of the two cracks in the same operation.

In oil pipelines as large as 32 in., as many as six small isolated heat-tubes, externally applied but not a part of the pipe wall, have been used under moderate conditions. Even more would be necessary to give a good distribution of heat to the oil-pipe and the oil, under severe conditions. The improved heat transfer of heat-tubes integrally welded into the wall of the pipe make such a large number unnecessary for any oil-pipe of any size used in practice. However, three such tubes, with a Y connection at the far end, may carry the three phases from an alternator or transformer. Each of the three pieces of skelp might then make up 120° of the pipe wall for a very large pipe.

The choice of heat-tube size, wire size and type, also insulation type and thickness, depends on several considerations of design and construction of the complete assembly. If the tube is filled with oil rather than empty, the pulling of the electrical cable through it is easier, the electrical insulation will be better, and the heat conductivity to the pipe from line losses will be better, leading to a lower temperature of the conductor. A 1½-in. steel pipe may be used for carrying a very heavy conductor cable. Standard wall thicknesses and inside diameters are shown below. Wall thickness should not be less than half the pipe wall.

Required voltage is reduced somewhat with a larger conductor wire, at increased wire cost; conversely reducing the wire size increases the voltage but reduces its cost.

Schedule	Wall Thickness, in.	Inside Diam, in.	Outside Diam, in.
40	0.145	1.610	1.900
80	0.200	1.500	1.900
160	0.281	1.338	1.900
xx	0.400	1.10	1.900

Since all the heat of the normal line loss of the copper or aluminum conductor wire is immediately utilized, this is not as important as in the usual parallel electrical transmission line which carries the current in separate wires outside on its own supports.

Helical Heat-Tubes. For heavy crudes and some other viscous oils, sufficient heat transfer from one parallel heat-tube is not obtained before the adjacent oil is overheated while oil elsewhere in the pipe is cold. An overheated crude is not injured, but additional energy is used for the overheating and for pumping the unheated oil of higher viscosity nearby. With food oils even a slight overheat may be objectionable.

With high Reynolds numbers, turbulent motions give a uniform temperature. However, there is always a streamline flow adjacent to the pipe wall. The extension inwardly of this layer of viscous oil, and particularly the build-up of wax crystallized out of some crudes, reduces the effective capacity of the pipeline appreciably, unless excess heat is applied. This is a particular difficulty in the start-up of an oil-pipe filled with viscous oil, now thoroughly chilled. Also, there may always be some relatively stagnant oil near the bottom of an oil-pipe if it is heated only at the top.

A multiplicity of parallel heat-tubes minimizes these disadvantages and the distance which heat must be transferred around the pipe wall and through the fluid to obtain a more or less uniform minimum temperature. Even so, with as many as six isolated heat-tubes distributed around a 48-in. pipeline, the oil flowing next the inner wall may be over 12 in. away from a heat-tube; part of the oil may never be adequately heated and will be in viscous flow. If there is adequate heat input to heat all of the oil, some oil is heated to a higher temperature than necessary, thus wasting electric power.

Fluid friction in the oil-pipe may be minimized, however, while heating uniformly all oil flowing immediately adjacent to the pipe wall and in pipes of the largest possible commercial size, many miles in length. This is done by winding the heat-tube helically around the oil-pipe. Unexpectedly, rather than flowing the length along the element, the ac flows the much longer spiral path of the heat-tube even though it is an integral part of the pipe wall.

Thus, using the pipe wall itself as the conductor-resistor with the skin effect, in a heat-tube which includes some part of the surface of the oil-pipe, the ac may be made to flow several times as far as the shortest possible distance, an element.

If the helix of the heat-tube has a pitch (distance along the pipe for one complete turn) equal to the diameter, D, the heat-tube length per turn is about $3.3D$; its total length is thus about 3.3 times the pipeline length. Even greater ratios are possible.

Using this helical heat-tube, any given angle of the peripheral arc of the pipe— and especially the oil which flows past it—receives throughout the length the same amount of heat as every other equal arc. This gives lower heat costs and lower pumping costs.

Most of the friction to fluid flow is in the slip of the oil layers immediately adjacent the pipe wall; thus, a uniform heating of the oil next to the wall reduces the friction considerably, even if the oil in the center of the pipeline is still cold.

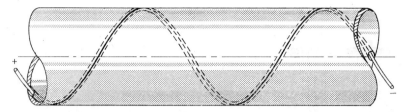

Fig. 5. Helical heat-tube similar in cross section to Figure 4, bottom, with heat-tube flush with outside of oil-pipe.

The oil-pipe shown in Figure 5 has a spirally wound heat-tube which may be applied in any one of several ways to its wall, preferably as shown in Figure 3, upper right and left, and Figure 4. Oil flowing near the surface crosses all of the paths of the turns of the helix of the heat-tube and thus is uniformly heated all around; its viscosity is reduced and it flows with a minimum of friction. Since it is uniformly heated around the tube, all of the interior oil, cold at start-up, flows as a cylinder or "plug" surrounded by this uniformly less viscous layer, which "greases" the flow of the inner plug of cold oil. Even before the bulk of the oil in the center is heated, the amount of oil pumped for a given pressure drop of the pipeline is not substantially less. This system gives the lowest total energy for heating and pumping.

For fixed heating and pumping costs a spiral heat-tube has greater flow capacity than parallel heat-tubes on the surface, because of the reduction of the viscosity of the oil where it slips past the inner wall. The cross flow of oil past the heat-tube allows a very high heat flux to be used effectively, particularly when using heat-tubes as in Figure 3, upper left and right, and Figure 4. The two edges of the trough-shaped or angle-shaped heat-tubes of Figure 3 may be welded spirally against the pipe wall in the shop or in the field. The slight continuous distorting of the trough or angle in winding the spiral is almost automatic as it is softened with the heat applied in the welding.

In the production of spiral pipe by welding a ribbon of skelp around a mandrel, a heat-tube, shown in Figure 5, may be wound between the two adjoining edges of the skelp being welded; this is done in building the heat-tube into the wall of a pipe along the element. This may be the least expensive method for making long lengths of oil-pipe with a heat-tube built integrally into the wall for supplying the large heat losses under arctic conditions.

Spiral heat-tubes may be placed on a double or triple thread helix by any of these methods, as it may be necessary or advantageous to secure the desired heat effect simultaneously and three such heat-tubes, each with one phase, allow a three-phase alternator to be balanced.

The Oil-Pipe Itself as a Heat-Tube

Electric Wire on Axis of Pipe. The heat-tube may actually be the oil pipe itself, as shown in Figure 6. If the pipeline carries oil or other liquid which does not conduct the ac, the conductor wire need not be insulated if it is always kept away from the pipe, although insulation would generally be used as a safeguard. The wire contacts the fluid and the heat it develops goes directly to the oil without having to pass through the wall of the heat-tube. The skin resistance of the pipe wall now heats its inner surface and minimizes the friction. This design is preferable for long oil-pipes of large diameter.

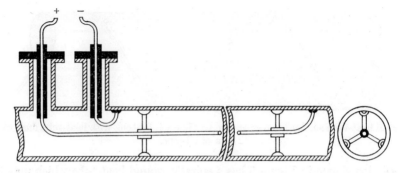

Fig. 6.   Oil-pipe as heat-tube.

In Figure 6, the electric wire is carried on the pipe's axis and is not insulated except for the connection through the branch, which has the tubular insulator and flange insulator. Suspenders made of polyethylene or other material support the wire along its length from hooks welded on the inside wall. The other connection to the ac is made at a point near the end where the electric wire enters. Here again, a branch allows a tubular insulator and a flange insulator to carry the wire outside the tube to the other (−) terminal.

The axial conductor may also be of steel, but if it is a bar more than about ⅛ in. in diam, the skin effect greatly reduces its effective cross-sectional area for ac conduction. Also, any steel tube with a wall thicker than the depth of penetration, or about 0.04 in. thick, has steel which is not conducting. A strip about twice as thick as the penetration depth may be used. A steel shape, tube, or cable may have advantages of tensile strength in pulling, or rigidity in support; or if it is of large surface per unit length, it has an increased rate of heat dissipation.

Electric Wire Not on Axis of Oil-Pipe—The Proximity Effect.   The effective resistance of the heat-tube, now the pipe itself, may be greatly increased over that of the skin effect as described, by making the magnetic field nonuniform. In the heating of the oil-pipeline the insulated conductor wire may be fixed, not on the axis, but on the bottom of the pipeline, as shown by the lower conductor in the cross section of Figure

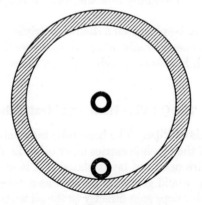

Fig. 7.   Cross section of oil-pipe as heat-tube. The insulated conductor wire may be axial as in Figure 6, or at any position in between the axis and the bottom, or at the closest possible point to the pipe wall.

7. A coaxially placed conductor, as in Figure 1, has a circularly uniform magnetic field and shows no proximity effect. The proximity effect of the ac conductor, when moved from its axial position, becomes important due to the nonuniform circular variation of the magnetic field which causes the current flow due to the skin effect to vary in intensity around the periphery of the heat-tube. However, it is possible to calculate and design for this proximity effect and it then makes no difference in subsequent operation of the pipe as its own heat-tube.

When the conductor wire is on the axis of the heat-tube, the concentration of the field, its degree of penetration of the wall of the heat-tube, and the distribution of the density of current flow in the heat-tube, are all uniform all around and the effective resistance can be calculated based on the electrical properties of the particular steel used. The resistance varies with the position of the wire and it is least when the wire is along the axis. The center of the conductor is assumed to be small compared with the diameter of the pipe. Taking the radius of the pipe as equal to 1, the conductor may be at a distance, y, from the wall and thus $(1-y)$ is the distance from the center. An integration for all points of the inner perimeter results in a value for the effective equivalent resistance, R_o, of the heat-tube leg of the circuit for the particular position of the wire. The effective equivalent resistance is given in Table 1 in terms of R_e/R_o, where R_o is the resistance when the wire is at the center ($y = 1$).

Table 1. Effective Equivalent Resistance as a Function of y

Distance from wall, y	Distance from center, $1 - y$	R_o/R_o
1	0	1.0
0.9	0.1	1.02
0.8	0.2	1.08
0.7	0.3	1.2
0.6	0.4	1.38
0.5	0.5	1.67
0.4	0.6	2.12
0.3	0.7	2.91
0.2	0.8	4.56
0.1	0.9	9.57
0.05	0.95	19.6
0.04	0.96	25.0
0.01	0.99	98.8
0.001	0.999	999.4
0.00	1.00	infinite

The same figures are plotted logarithmically in Figure 8. The curve approaches the 45° line as an asymptote from below and the equation is as follows:

$$\frac{R_e}{R_o} = \frac{1 + (1 - y)^2}{1 - (1 - y)^2}$$

The nearness to the surface is limited by the size of the wire and thus the outer radius of the insulation enclosing the wire when it touches the inner surface of the pipe. The change in the resistance of the conductor wire, if of copper, may be neglected.

Changing the size of the copper conductor changes its resistance, but not that of the heat-tube surface (skin effect). Proper design locates the wire to give the desired

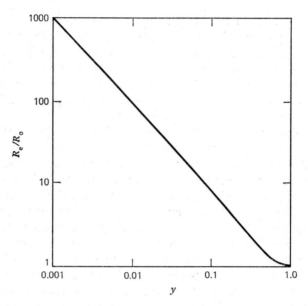

Fig. 8. Logarithmic plot of the ratio of the resistance at the outer surface, R_e to that at the inner surface, R_o, of an oil pipe used as its own heat-tube against the distance, y, of an insulated conductor from the inner surface.

effective resistance. For example, in a 48-in. pipe, with the conductor lying on the bottom, the eccentricity may be made as much as 0.96 or more of the radius, and R_e/R_o may be 15–25. For this 48-in. pipe, when the conductor wire is on the axis, the "skin" with an assumed thickness based on the particular steel may be 0.04 in. and represents an effective electrical conductor of steel having a cross section of about 6 in.^{2}, ie a very low resistance. However, when the conductor wire is laid on the bottom of the pipe, the effective cross section of the heat-tube as a conductor may be divided by 15 to 25 to equal an effective cross section of only about 0.25–0.4 in.^{2} of steel conductor.

The use of the oil-transport pipe as its own heat-tube thus becomes quite practical despite the large apparent cross section of the effective "skin." Moreover, depending on the internal voltage drop per foot which is desired, the effective resistance of the wall of the pipeline may be varied within a range of as much as 25 times or more by moving the conductor wire from along the axis to the bottom of the pipe.

With the electric conductor on the bottom of the pipe instead of on the axis, the percent of the current flow near the bottom, and thus of the heat given off, increases greatly because of the wire and the heat it produces, also because of the much greater concentration of ac flow in the lower section of the skin of the pipe itself. Usually this is advantageous, particularly when heating up after a shutdown. However, there is some current flow, and hence some heat dissipation, throughout the entire perimeter of the skin.

The flow of oil in practice increases somewhat faster than the square of the diameter, while the heat losses to be made up by electric heating increase approximately with the circumference, hence the diameter. Of course, the effective size of the conductor formed by the skin also increases directly with the circumference; but in pipes up to 8 ft in diam, as presently suggested, the effective cross section of the skin as return conductor becomes very large. The proximity effect reduces this. However, the diameter of a copper conductor becomes smaller in relation to that of the pipe and with a larger pipe, its center can approach the pipe wall closer; thus, the increased relative resistance due to the proximity effect which is possible may be greater as the size of the pipe increases.

As always, an advantage of this system is that, by supplying heat directly to the oil-pipe wall, as well as to a conductor directly contacted by the oil, a more uniform distribution of the heat is possible.

Another advantage is that the conductor contacts the oil directly to increase the heat-transfer efficiency greatly, since heat from the "line loss" of the electric wire does not have to be transferred through a heat-tube to add to that which must be dissipated from its surface.

Here, as in other uses of the heat-tube principle, oil-pipes are grounded frequently throughout their length following standard pipeline practice. They may also have the usual cathodic system for cathodic protection without reference in either case to the major ac current on the inner skin.

Varying the Effective Skin Depth—Frequencies Other than 60 cps

In long-distance oil transport, alternators may be installed only or principally for heating the pipeline. If several or more are required in a major installation of hundreds of miles of 3–8 ft pipe, this might warrant the consideration of special machinery designed to deliver ac of frequency other than 60 cps. The thickness of the effective skin depends on the steel, but may be taken as 0.04 in. for 60 cycles. It is inversely proportional to the square root of the number of cycles of the ac; thus, it follows that increasing from 60 cycles by 16 times to 960 would reduce the skin depth or effective conductor cross section to one fourth, or about 0.01 in. Reducing the number of cycles from 60 to 15 or one fourth, would increase the skin depth and hence the effective cross section by the square root of 4 or 2. A number of cycles from 10 to over 1000 may be used. In large installations, the costs may be less using special alternators; but usually special alternators are not necessary in the adjustment of the effective skin thickness and hence resistance.

By varying the design by changing (a) the eccentricity of the conductor wire, and also (b) the number of cycles of the ac wide latitude in establishing the optimum resistance, and hence the required voltage, is possible in the design of a major installation, eg those where distance between power supplies may be 40 miles or more.

Energy Costs

The electrical energy input by the improved heat-tubes integrally built into the pipe wall, as shown in Figures 3 and 4, or using the pipe wall as the heat-tube, is practically 100% available as heat to the oil or the pipe. This is higher than for an isolated heat-tube attached to the outer surface and much higher than resistors entirely surrounded by electrical insulation and nearly surrounded by thermal insulation.

An excellent analysis of the relation between the energy costs for steam tracing and for electric tracing by conventional resistors has been made by Decker (7). The temperature to be maintained was 40°F to prevent freezing. Under conditions of the lowest normal annual temperature of −10°F (Chicago) the conclusion was as follows: "On a line traced to prevent freezing manually controlled or uncontrolled, steam will expend over 700% more energy to maintain the temperature than will electric tracing.

With flow in the pipe, the heat wasted by steam can be even greater since the flowing material acts as a heat sink. It is quite possible that a steam tracer will expend energy at its maximum rate under conditions that would not require any heat. Steam tracing is more efficiently used on lines requiring a temperature approaching that of the tracing steam." Also: "The maximum economical temperature for electric tracing increases with an increase in the percent of flow time and with an increase in the rate of flow." These calculations do not include the large additional losses of steam due to the heat in the condensate—almost 25% of that in saturated steam above the pertinent temperature—nor of the major "line losses" of heat in the steam and condensate lines.

The costs for energy used in these careful analyses were \$0.59 per million Btu in steam and \$1.00 per million Btu in electricity (3.43 mils/kWh). Since the efficiency of electric heat utilization is always better with skin effect heat-tubes than with external small resistors, these values may be used safely. Particularly in long-distance pipe lines, the heat input from the mechanical energy supplied by the pump is considerable, and should be subtracted in determining the thermal energy to be supplied by electric heat.

Combination of Methods of Varying Pipe-Wall Resistance

The pipe wall heats itself as its own electrical conductor-resistor while simultaneously almost completely insulating electrically the surroundings from the ac employed. The effective resistance of a steel pipe thus may be increased 10 to 30 times by the skin effect, also by another factor of 20–50 times by the selective use of the proximity effect, and then by at least another 16 times through varying the frequency of the ac. The insulation effect through the pipe wall goes up accordingly. Pipes themselves, even 8 ft in diam as now planned, may through the multiplication of these effects thus become self-insulating resistance elements of quite variable thermal output to keep themselves and the oil warm at a relatively low voltage drop under even the severest arctic conditions.

Advantages of Skin-Effect Pipe Heating

The heating of pipelines transporting many materials from melted chocolate to residual oils, in lengths of less than 1000 ft up to 20 miles, and in sizes from 4 to 30 in. in diam, has demonstrated (11) major advantages of skin-effect heating compared to other systems, including economy of installation, low operating costs, efficiency of heat utilization, no overhead power-transmission lines, safety, uniformity of heating, dependability, simplicity, minimum maintenance (if any) and repair, and also immediate accessibility of parts. The further application of electromagnetic-field theory to pipe heating, so that a part or all of the wall of the pipe becomes the heat-tube, accentuates each of these advantages many times. Thus, the only addition needed in either a new or existing pipeline may be the laying of a single insulated wire in its bottom, to heat miles of its length, with the pipe wall serving as its own electrical resistor and its own electrical insulation. The electrical power input is utilized 100% as heat.

By combining these effects, the electrical insulation effectiveness of the steel increases exponentially with thickness. This insulation of steel may be so effective that a 1-in. thick pipe has a voltage drop on the outside only one-billionth of that on the inside, or a drop per mile of possibly one-millionth of a volt. As is standard practice, the pipe may be grounded periodically; it may be buried or submerged in water; and cathodic protection systems are operated as standard practice.

Bibliography

NOTE: Patents and patent applications in countries throughout the world cover skin heating of steel by ac in all aspects, as described above, and numerous others.

1. M. C. Smith and A. A. Salerno, "Engineering for Low Sulfur Fuels," *Combustion* **41,** 6 (May 1970).
2. G. K. Korbacher and J. T. McGrath, *North Slope Pipelines*, privately circulated report, Univ. of Toronto, Nov. 1970.
3. F. S. Chapman and F. A. Holland, "Keeping Piping Hot—by Heating," *Chem. Eng.* **73,** 133 (Jan. 17, 1966).
4. F. F. House, "Pipe Tracing and Insulation," *Chem. Eng.* **76,** 243 (June 17, 1968).
5. C. H. Butz, "When is Electricity Cheaper than Steam for Pipe Tracing?" *Chem. Eng.* **75,** 230 (Oct. 10, 1966).
6. W. H. Holstein, Jr., "What it Costs to Steam and Electrically Trace Pipelines," *Chem. Eng. Progress* **62,** 107 (March 1966).
7. R. L. Dekker, "Electric vs Steam Energy for Pipeline Tracing," *IEEE Trans.* **IGA-6** (5) 517, (1970).
8. R. M. Yurkanin and E. O. Claussen, "Impedance Heating—How it Works, What it Costs," *Chem. Eng.* **75,** 182 (Aug. 12, 1968).
9. J. E. Bilbro and J. E. Leavines, "Electric Heat Tracing—State of the Art," *IEEE Trans.* **IGA-5** (4) 476 (1969).
10. M. Ando and D. F. Othmer, "Heating Pipelines with Electrical Skin Current," *Chem. Eng.* **77,** 154 (March 9, 1970).
11. D. F. Othmer, "Pipeline Heating with Skin Electric Current Tracing," *Power* **113,** 89 (June 1969).

D. F. OTHMER AND J. W. E. GRIEMSMANN
Polytechnic Institute of Brooklyn

POLLUTION

Pollution has become increasingly more important in recent years, not only because people are more sensitive on this subject, but also because the amount of pollution has increased markedly. Pollution represents a health hazard and a deterioration in the quality and beauty of our surroundings. It is one of the undesired consequences of our rising production, our modern civilization, our increased utilization of natural resources and our rising population.

The discussion of this subject is presented in several sections, Water Pollution (p. 713) including Thermal Pollution (p. 721), Sludge Handling, Treatment and Disposal (p. 725), Air Pollution (p. 730), and Treatment of Solid Wastes (p. 737).

Although treated separately, these several types are closely interrelated. For example, the cleaning of exhaust gases from furnaces yields fly ash, which in turn results in a slurry or solid waste disposal problem. The burying of solid wastes in a landfill can result in the pollution of ground water. Solid waste, when burned, can create air pollution. Therefore, a *systems approach* that considers all types of liquid, solid, or gaseous pollutants on any specific pollution source, such as a plant, is becoming increasingly more prevalent.

The treatment of pollution has been progressing on a broad front. There have been recent drastic changes in the technology for detecting, isolating, and treating pollutants and, sometimes, recovering valuable materials. Not only have the quality standards (to which pollution emissions or waste disposals have to conform) been tightened and made more difficult to attain, but legislation, regulations, and enforcement at the local, state, and federal levels have become much more specific and stringent, and the costs of treatment have accordingly risen sharply. Federal sponsorship of research and development has accelerated the advance of technology of new treatment processes, instruments, and equipment.

All manufacturing and processing plants, municipal waste treatment installations, present and new industrial establishments, and transportation systems now have to conform to these tighter controls. Although pollution treatment for a typical new industrial plant had averaged 1–4% of total initial capital expenditures not long ago, they now amount to perhaps 3–15% of this initial cost. Costs of sewage treatment to meet the advanced quality standards may mean the tripling or quadrupling of plant costs. With these increased costs in mind, it becomes more urgent and important to optimize and select from various alternatives those pollution treatment processes and systems which not only conform to present regulations or result in a minimum of initial and operating costs, but also which will be capable of being upgraded as quality standards are being further tightened and as the total quantity or quality of polluted material to be treated changes during the life of the installation.

Experience with unusual chemicals, such as pesticides, detergents, disinfectants, and certain pharmaceutical preparations has shown that the ecology, various animals, plants, and in fact the environment can be changed. The long term effects of prolonged exposure to small dosages of pollutants are still largely unknown. With thousands of new chemical compounds now being synthesized every year, the ecology faces new potential modifications and this leaves a great deal of research yet to be done.

This discussion is quite general and is aimed to give an overview of the problems. For more specific discussion the reader is encouraged to seek data from the references and from qualified specialists in the field. See also Wastes, industrial and Water, where similar problems are discussed. This article does not, in general, give details of the equipment used in the various operations; however illustrations of similar hardware appear in such articles as Adsorption; Centrifugal separation; Drying; Dust; Electrostatic precipitation; Filtration; Flotation; Gas cleaning; Gravity concentration; Sedimentation; Sewage; and Wastes, industrial.

The systems approach includes the following steps:

1. Determination or identification of all the present and potential future sources and types of wastes. For example, in a typical industrial plant there are usually several different polluted water sources (sanitary wastes, batch residues, floor drains, wash water, process water, cooling water, etc), several gaseous wastes (boiler, furnaces, process ventilation, blow-off, odors, etc) and perhaps also some solid wastes (ashes, excess materials or residues).

2. Determination of applicable quality standards, inspection obligations, reporting requirements, and pollution regulations; local, state and federal authorities who have to approve plans and specifications or conduct official inspections or tests, and likely applicable future changes in quality standards, enforcement proceedings, or laws.

3. Determination of the raw materials and the characteristics of each of the wastes (composition, toxicity, solids content, pH, particle count, organic content, flow, flow variation with time, temperature, odor, composition variation with time, etc). Relatively simply measurements (such as a weir, orifice, samples analysis) will often give considerable detailed information. This can require extensive on-

sight measurements and an analysis program of several months; this can include a number of flow and material balances.

4. Determination of existing facilities (sewer map of the plant, ultimate disposal sites for solid or liquid wastes, details of presently existing process or waste treatment plant, etc).

5. Examination of the process itself to determine possible modifications in the process or the raw materials aimed at reducing or eliminating pollutants or the recovery of valuable products. For example, the waste water from chlor-alkali processes with mercury electrodes has always been a major source of toxic mercury pollution; however, by improved housekeeping (less spills, more careful handling) and some minor process or plumbing changes, the amount of mercury in the waste water effluent can be reduced by 80–95%.

This should include an evaluation of potential methods for recycling or reusing the water wastes or hot gases in the process or in an adjacent facility (watering of lawns), segregation of wastes and their separate treatment, substitution of new materials or chemical additives, and reduction of the waste flows.

6. Examination and evaluation of alternative methods of treating the wastes. In addition to evaluating the costs of alternative waste treatment processes, this may include an examination of possible process improvements, such as mixing an acidic and an alkaline waste water to achieve neutralization, the addition of fly ash from a furnace to the sludge to improve solid–liquid separation with a filter or centrifuge, combining several sludges prior to dewatering, combustion of organics to create heat, segregation of waste streams and their separate treatment, use of a minimum of different types of chemical additives for coagulation and flocculation, or alternative equipment or unit processes, and consideration of future plant growth.

In some cases it will be necessary to develop new waste treatment processes or equipment, which usually are tested in the laboratory and sometimes in a pilot plant.

7. Selection of the preferred treatment method, its orderly implementation, the preparation of plans, drawings and specifications, approval by the proper authorities, manufacture of process equipment, construction of a treatment facility.

8. Start-up of the treatment facility, determination of its actual performance (and comparison with the planned performances), and, if necessary, changes and improvements to the waste treatment process or facility. This includes the training of operators, the development of orderly monitoring, maintenance, service and process improvement programs and often an inspection or review by appropriate Government authorities.

Water Pollution

Water is mankind's most serious resource problem. Although water covers 70% of the earth's surface, only 0.63% of this resource is available for general use. Water is essential for life as we know it. No life can long exist without the presence of some water. Use of water increases as our population and industry grow. With increased use, pollution of the available water supply becomes more of an economic burden to society.

As a liquid, nothing compares with water, as it dissolves most substances, quenches thirst, washes clothes, puts out fires, cooks food, and carries our waste away, just to name a few common usages.

There are three major demands for water: personal, agricultural, and industrial. As of 1970, residential or municipal demands for water constituted only about 7% of the total United States fresh water consumption. Agriculture accounted for 39%, with the remaining 54% used by ever expanding industry. Industrial use therefore constitutes the greatest demand and also the greatest area of increased demand. By 1980, industry will require 428 billion gallons of water daily or 68% of the total U.S. demand.

With nearly all uses of water, the quality is reduced. That is, with use, pollutants are added. These pollutants may be dissolved material both organic and inorganic, particulate material both organic and inorganic, and absorbed gases. When the concentration of these pollutants increases to levels which render the water unfit for further use or unfit to be returned to the environment, treatment is necessary to reduce or completely remove the objectionable pollutants. In general, methods now used to remove the pollutants include gravity sedimentation, flotation, granular media filtration, biological oxidation, activated carbon adsorption, and chemical precipitation.

Pollutants can be of two types, particulates and solubles, which are discussed separately below.

REMOVAL OF PARTICULATES

Particulates, or solid particles suspended in water, are considered pollutants if they (a) can be seen; (b) decay and cause a depletion of oxygen present in water; (c) settle in receiving water, smothering bottom plant and animal life; (d) remain in suspension and inhibit the penetration of sunlight; (e) cause bad tastes or odors; (f) can cause disease (eg, typhoid bacteria); (g) are radioactive; (h) are toxic to living organisms (eg, pesticides).

Particulates are either organic or inorganic. Organic particulates are especially troublesome since they have a doubly negative effect on the environment. Not only are they associated with limiting sunlight penetration, smothering bottom plant and animal life and forming sludge banks, but their natural decay depletes the water of dissolved oxygen and the entire biota system is upset, resulting in fish kill, odor, and an absence of all the pleasant environmental sights normally associated with a healthy receiving water such as a stream, river, or lake.

Inorganic particulates such as sands, silts and clay cause many of the problems stated above in receiving waters, but they do not decay, and therefore have a less deleterious effect on the water environment.

Sources of organic particulates in our water resources are numerous. Approximately 70% of the particulates associated with municipal waste are organic in nature. The food processing industry (eg, canneries, meat producing, sugar, etc) is a major source of organic particulates. The washing, rinsing, cooking, and cleaning of a modern food processing plant require large quantities of water which serves to carry away the waste produced.

Sources of inorganic particulates include mining, metal processing, and natural erosion. Most wastewaters contain both organic and inorganic particulates. The best known example is that of municipal wastewaters.

Water is considered polluted when it contains only a relatively small concentration of either organic or inorganic particles. Consider that the average municipal wastewater contains about 250 mg/liter of particulates and a pollutant load of about 500 mg/liter (particulate and soluble), yet it is normally considered grossly polluted. Considering *all* of the dissolved and particulate material in sewage, it is more than 99.9% pure H_2O. The above is given to illustrate that only a relatively small concentration of pollutants results in what is normally considered grossly polluted conditions.

The size of particulates associated with wastewaters ranges from tree trunks to very fine colloids. The specific gravity of particulates ranges from less than 1.0 (floatables) to 3.0 or more (grit). Obviously, removal of particulates with such a wide range of size, specific gravity and other characteristics, requires different treatment approaches.

Large debris, which might damage equipment downstream, may be removed by a bar screen. In some cases, as when the waste stream contains rags, a comminutor may be used to reduce the material to an acceptable size for the subsequent processes.

Grit, being mainly sand, is relatively easy to remove. Because its specific gravity is 2.5 times that of water, methods of removal employing centrifugal action, such as cyclones, have been successfully used. A more conventional approach is to provide a basin having a relatively short detention time sufficient to settle the grit but not large organic particulates. An effort is made to limit the amount of organics removed with the grit since organic-free grit requires no further treatment prior to final disposal in a land fill. The removal of grit is very important because of its deleterious abrasive effect on pumps and other subsequent treatment equipment.

Gravity Sedimentation. The oldest and yet most commonly employed method of particulate removal is gravity sedimentation. This method involves the use of a tank to detain the waste flow for a sufficient period of time to allow settling of particulates. Unfortunately particulates associated with wastes do not all settle at the same rate; in fact, some settle so slowly that they can be considered in permanent suspension. Therefore, the degree of removal will depend on the size and specific gravity of the particulates.

Two to three hours detention time is used for the design of gravity settling basins. For municipal wastes, between 40 to 60% of the particulates are removed by this treatment method. This represents a significant particulate reduction by a simple and inexpensive method of treatment.

The fraction of particulates that are not removed by gravity settling in two to three hours of detention time can often be chemically conditioned so that an additional fraction can be removed. Chemical coagulants such as alum have been used to improve removal greatly. The coagulant acts on the particulates in such a way as to allow agglomeration of the particles. The addition of a coagulant to municipal wastes has been demonstrated to improve removal to such an extent that after two-to-three hours gravity settling, more than 90% removal of particulates is achieved.

Flotation. Often, floatable particulates and oils are present in wastewaters and must be removed. The same particulate characteristics that govern the rate of gravity settling, govern the rate of flotation, ie specific gravity and particle size. The lower the specific gravity and the larger the size of the floatable particulates, the more rapid is the flotation process. Very small particles with specific gravity close to 1.0 float very slowly. Removal of easily floatable particulates and oil is accomplished in the same way that readily settleable particulates are removed, that is, by detention in a tank for two or three hours. Sedimentation and flotation can therefore be achieved in the same basin, the floatable material being removed at the top and the settleable material at the bottom. Chemicals such as alum (aluminum sulfate, see Vol. 2, p. 58) and acids have been used to condition fine colloidal suspensions or oil emulsions for more complete removal of floatables and oils. The addition of alum or acid to a waste stream containing emulsified or finely dispersed oily material causes the oily material to agglomerate and float more rapidly.

The use of dissolved gases (dissolved gas flotation process) has been employed to achieve very high removal of floatable particulates and oils. This treatment method consists of forming very fine gas bubbles which become attached to the particulates, thereby causing them to rise or float.

Granular Media Filtration. Filtration through granular media has been used to remove particulates from water for millenia. A contemporary granular media filter consists of a layer of sand, coal, or any other suitable granular substance through whose pores the liquid is passed. It retains particulates by mechanical screening, gravity sedimentation, and adsorption.

An ideal granular media filter would consist of one in which the size of void volume decreased uniformly in the direction of flow. In reality the media depth and particle size employed depend on the size and concentration of particulates to be filtered and the rate of liquid flow through the filter. Normally, granular media filtration is not used where more than 100 mg/liter of particulates are to be removed because gravity sedimentation is then more economical. In most treatment facilities, filtration is employed following gravity sedimentation. In this case only very fine particulates are removed by the filter. In most wastewaters there are fine particulates that are not amenable to filtration because they pass through a filter. To remove these, a coagulant (such as alum) is added to condition them and render them filterable.

With chemical conditioning, this treatment method can achieve particulate removal to a residual concentration of less than 1.0 mg/liter. Therefore, granular media filtration is a very effective method of removing essentially all particulates from a wastewater or polluted stream.

REMOVAL OF SOLUBLES

Solubles in water are considered pollutants if they (a) can be tasted, have an offending odor, or can be observed; (b) decay and deplete the water of oxygen; (c) precipitate from solution causing scaling; (d) cause corrosion; (e) are radioactive; (f) are toxic to living organisms (eg, pesticides). Soluble pollutants can be either organic or inorganic. Organics in the soluble form are not only associated with taste, odor and staining, but also can serve as a source of food for microorganisms thus contributing to the depletion of dissolved oxygen from the receiving water; this can cause a drastic change in the flora and fauna. Fish kills and the evolution of smelly gases often indicate the effect of uncontrolled release of organic pollutants.

Removal of soluble organics is conventionally achieved by controlling the natural processes of nature. One of these natural treatment methods is described in detail below.

Activated Sludge. This natural treatment process consists of intimately contacting the three basic reactants, food (organic material), oxygen, and microorganisms in a reactor (aeration basin) to achieve removal of organics (conversion of the organics to carbon dioxide, water, and additional microorganisms) followed by liquid-solids separation (clarification). In order to maintain a desirable maximum popula-

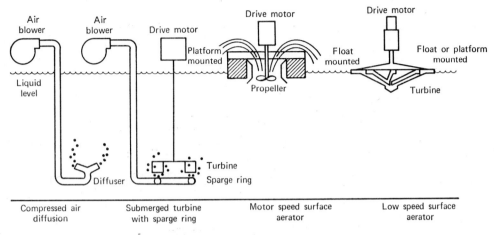

Fig. 1. Oxygenation and mixing devices.

tion of microorganisms in the reactor, a portion of the microorganisms removed in the liquids-solids separation step are returned to the reactor. Since oxygenation and mixing are normally provided by the same unit operation and are necessary to achieve good treatment results, an efficient device to achieve both is desirable. Several methods are presently used to accomplish both oxygenation and mixing. They are listed below and shown in Figure 1.

Compressed air diffusion (bubbling of air from bottom of basin).

Submerged turbine with sparge ring (same as above, plus a submerged impeller to achieve better dispersion and distribution of bubbles).

Motor speed surface aerators (high speed direct drive impeller at water surface, mixing air into surface of the water).

Low speed surface aerators (usually the most efficient device; low rpm impeller mixing air and water).

Figure 2 shows flowsheets of the activated sludge treatment process. There have been many modifications of the basic or conventional flowsheet shown to achieve improved treatment results. A list of some of the modifications tried is shown on Figure 2 and included below:

Conventional activated sludge (plug flow)

stepped aeration activated sludge

tapered aeration activated sludge

contact stabilization activated sludge

completely mixed activated sludge

These modifications have been effective steps in the improvement of the basic treatment process. After considerable experience with the activated sludge treatment process, it was recognized that it should not be designed any differently than other chemical processes, that is, the reactants should be completely mixed to achieve maximum treatment efficiency. This idea of a "completely mixed" reactor was the direction in which the above modification appeared to be heading, but was quite a departure from the original "plug flow" concept.

The "completely mixed" concept offers the following advantages over the "plug flow" concept:

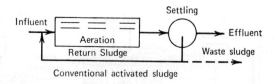

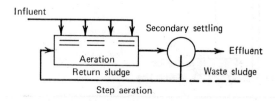

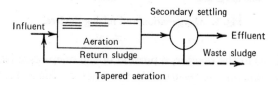

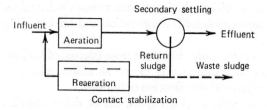

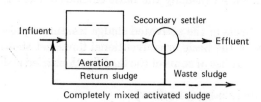

Fig. 2. Flowsheets of the various activated sludge treatment methods. The distribution of aeration equipment is depicted by the lines in the aeration basin. For example,

$$\equiv = \text{—}$$

means that one-half of the aeration equipment is located in the first one-third of the basin.

1. Complete use of the reactor for dilution of shock organic loads, toxic material, or temperature changes.
2. Uniform organic loading of the process resulting in stable operation.
3. Efficient removal of pollutants.
4. Effective use of oxygenation, mixing, and basin facilities.

The activated sludge treatment process is best designed on the basis of organic loading to the microorganisms. This loading is expressed as a unit weight of organic material (food) to a unit weight of microorganisms (sludge) per unit of time. It is referred to as the F/M food-to-microorganism ratio. The unit of measurement for the F/M ratio is BOD_5 (5-day biological oxygen demand; see Vol. 2, p. 700), MLSS (mixed liquor suspended solids), and days. The BOD_5 is expressed in mg/liter representing the amount of oxygen required by living organisms engaged in the utilization and stabilization of the biodegradable organic material present in a wastewater. It is a bioassay-type test requiring five days of incubation at 20°C. The value of BOD_5 observed in most municipal wastewaters ranges from 100 to 500 mg/liter with an av value of 250 mg/liter.

The MLSS represents the microorganism population present in the reactor and is also expressed in terms of mg/liter. The MLSS measurement is the suspended solids present in the reactor and not a definite indication of viable microorganisms. Obviously a true value of the F/M ratio would have to include only the viable microorganisms, but no simple method is presently available for such a direct viable organism measurement. Since MLSS is very simple and can be done with reasonable accuracy, it has been generally accepted as the basis for activated sludge design. Listed below is the expected activated sludge treatment efficiency based on the F/M ratio.

F/M Ratio	% BOD_5 Removal
0.1	95
0.5	90
1.0	80
2.0	70

The lower the F/M ratio, the greater is removal efficiency for the *soluble* BOD_5. As this table indicates, activated sludge treatment of organics in wastewater is very efficient. Normally, the F/M ratio used ranges from 0.2 to 0.5, meaning that in excess of 90% of the soluble biodegradable organic material will be removed by this treatment process.

Other process conditions which must be controlled to achieve consistent removal results are listed below:

1. Control of toxic substances, such as arsenic, dissolved copper.
2. Control of pH.
3. Control of temperature.
4. Presence of required nutrients, nitrogen, phosphorus, etc.
5. Effective mixing and utilization of full basin.
6. Introduction and dispersion of air (oxygen).
7. Efficient removal of pollutants.

Since any natural (biological) process requires that biocides be removed or reduced in concentration to a non-toxic level, controls must be included in the process design to limit their presence or effect. Likewise, all natural processes are greatly affected by low or high pH conditions, low or high temperature conditions, and by the presence of nutrients. All bacteria require nitrogen and phosphorus, and the removal of N and P (as explained in a subsequent section) can be helpful in preventing the growth of bacteria and algae in receiving waters and in improving their clarity and taste. Complete use of the aeration basin is necessary for dilution of shock organic loads, temperature changes, or toxic materials. Several other natural treatment processes involving the use of microorganisms are presently used to remove organics from wastewaters. They include, trickling filters, oxidation ponds and anaerobic digestion. These are described in the article Water, sewage.

All of these natural or biological treatment processes have been in use for years. One of the inherent problems with the natural methods of wastewater treatment is that environmental conditions (toxic materials, pH, temperature, etc) have such a great effect on the results achieved. The process to be discussed next avoids the unreliability of the natural processes.

Adsorption by Activated Carbon. It has been established for a number of years that activated carbon was very effective in the removal of soluble organic material from a liquid stream. Activated carbon has been used typically to remove color in the sugar manufacturing processes and tastes and odor from drinking or potable water. With the present and possible future demands for ever higher quality effluents from wastewater treatment, activated carbon adsorption appears to be the only method capable of consistently producing the desired results. The process is basically very simple, requiring only that the liquid be in contact with activated carbon for a sufficient time period to allow adsorption to occur.

Activated carbon is commercially available in two forms: powdered and granular (see Vol. 4, p. 149). Powdered activated carbon (minus 325 mesh) has been used to a limited extent in the removal of taste and odor from water supplies and industrial application. Use of the powdered activated carbon in municipal waste treatment is limited because an inexpensive and efficient method of regeneration has not yet been developed. If the regeneration problem can be solved, the use of powdered activated carbon should increase since its cost is about one-third the cost of granular activated carbon and it is easy to apply. It can easily be fed to meet variable demand by forming a slurry and using a metering pump.

Granular activated carbon has found widespread use in industry, and water and wastewater treatment. It is regenerated in a multiple hearth furnace at temperatures between 1600 and 1800°F. The cost of regeneration ranges from two to three cents per pound with an average makeup of lost activated carbon of 5%.

Chemical Precipitation. Soluble inorganic pollutants present a problem that is not solved by liquid-solids separation, biological oxidation, or adsorption processes. It may be noted that the concentration level that constitutes pollution varies widely with different salts. A high concentration (250 mg/liter or more) of chloride is not harmful to living organisms, whereas even a low concentration (3 mg/liter) of heavy metals such as copper, zinc, etc, can be fatal to bacteria, fish, algae, or humans. Removal of these polluting ions can be relatively easy or extremely difficult. Calcium, magnesium, most heavy metals and phosphorus can be removed by simple chemical precipitation, but chlorides, sulfates and some other salts require more exotic treatment methods such as reverse osmosis, distillation, and electrodialysis.

Since municipal and industrial wastewaters do not normally contain appreciable concentrations of those salts that are most difficult to remove, and since most receiving-water or reuse-water quality requirements do not at present call for their removal, only chemical precipitation of phosphorus and heavy metal ions will be discussed in detail.

Lime $(Ca(OH)_2)$ "alum" (aluminum sulfate, see Vol. 2, p. 58) and ferric salts have been used successfully for the removal of phosphorus by precipitation. Addition of lime to wastewater to increase pH and cause the precipitation of heavy metals in the hydroxide form has been employed successfully. Lime softening of water for the removal of calcium and magnesium carbonate has also been employed extensively and successfully. Therefore, removal of the most common inorganic soluble pollutants is neither difficult or expensive.

The efficiency of removal of soluble inorganics by chemical precipitation depends on the chemical used and the solubility of the precipitate. Very low concentrations of phosphorus (less than 1 mg/liter as P), and heavy metals (less than 1 mg/liter for most) are possible with this method of treatment. Reduction of hardness by chemical precipitation in wastewater appears to be inhibited to some degree, even with excess lime (more than required for complete softening). The phosphorus and organics appear to have an inhibiting effect on the softening reaction.

Bibliography

J. W. Hassler, *Activated Carbon*, Chemical Publishing Company, Inc., New York, 1963.

R. E. McKinney, *Microbiology for Sanitary Engineers*, McGraw-Hill Book Company, Inc., New York, 1962.

E. Nordell, *Water Treatment for Industrial and Other Uses*, Reinhold Publishing Corporation, 2nd ed., New York, 1961.

F. P. Sebastian, "Water Reclamation and Reuse," *Water and Wastes Engineering* 46 (Nov. 1970).

Thermal Pollution

Causes and Effects (1). Waste heat is a pollutant equally dangerous to our waters as the more material forms of water pollution discussed previously. The addition of heat to water not only causes physical and chemical changes, but it can adversely affect naturally occurring aquatic life and cause harm to plants, fish, algae, or bacteria.

Most of the heat created by thermal machinery as used by residential installations and industries must be wasted or rejected and therefore absorbed; this includes the heat rejected by condensers of nuclear-powered or fossil-fuel-fired boiler plants, by many chemical operations, cooling of gasoline or diesel engines, cooling of electrical power equipment, cooling coils from refrigeration and air conditioning systems, or various power generators and industrial heat exchangers. Unfortunately, the thermal cycle of all heat engines is such that the majority of the created energy has to be rejected to a medium at a temperature lower than the maximum temperature of the heat engine.

The raising of the temperature of water diminishes the solubility of oxygen and thus can cause dissolved oxygen to come out of solution. Thus, the addition of heat to natural waters such as rivers, causes a decrease in the oxygen which is available for oxidation of organic waste material, for breathing by aquatic plant life or aquatic animals such as shrimp or fish. The temperature limits at which fish can reproduce are narrow; eg, trout cannot normally reproduce in water above 55°F. If organic nutrient materials are available in the water, then an increase in water temperature causes a more rapid multiplication of bacteria and accelerated growth for other forms of aquatic life, thereby rapidly depleting the already limited or decreased dissolved oxygen supply. This accelerated consumption of the already diminished oxygen supplies thus contributes to more rapid die-off of aerobic or oxygen-consuming species and a more likely occurrence of septic conditions (creation of gases and odors). Even if ample oxygen would be available, many aquatic species are unable to survive in hot water (say, average temperature of 90–100°F).

There have been many notable instances where hot water discharged from large power plants has caused regions of estuaries, ocean bays, reservoirs, rivers or lakes to become devoid of normal aquatic life or where a lack of oxygen has caused undesirable chemical or biological reactions (smell, color, formation of gases) of already present pollutants or impurities, which would otherwise have been oxidized. The only effective way to minimize thermal pollution is to limit the heat energy which is allowed to be discharged to the water.

Some 80% of all cooling water is used by power plants for the generation of electricity. The problem of thermal pollution is becoming more serious, because of the rapid increase in power generation (the electrical energy consumed in the U.S. is predicted to double every 7 to 10 years), the increasing use of nuclear power plants (which reject more heat per kW output than fossil-fueled power plants) and the decreasing availability of natural waters for cooling.

Waste heat can be rejected by (1) heating water, (2) evaporating water, (3) transfer of heat to the air, or (4) a combination of these. In some cases, the process itself can be changed to reduce the quantity of heat rejected, eg, by increasing the efficiency of the power plant and thus converting more energy into useful work.

Heat Dissipation Methods to Water. Cooling water from a river, lake, pond, estuary, or the ocean is used regularly in heat exchangers. Where ample water supplies are available to limit the temperature rise of the cooling water to 10 or 20°F, and to permit the use of river water for dilution, water cooling by a heat exchanger is generally preferred. For higher heat loads, the excess energy is generally transferred to the air as described below.

A stratification of layers of different temperature can occur in reservoirs, cooling ponds, lakes or estuaries, where hot water is discharged. Decomposing organic or vegetable matter and man-made pollutants deplete the oxygen from these lower layers (which are relatively richer in oxygen); with little prospect of regenerating the oxygen or diffusing oxygen from the warm upper layers, harm is caused to the aquatic life.

Special provisions such as plates and baffles are often needed to prevent the hot discharge waters from being recirculated into the inlet to the heat exchanger. Excess heat loads of some large plants can be handled by temporarily storing hot water discharge in a basin or reservoir until the plant heat output diminishes, when it can be safely discharged into the receiving waters.

Heat Dissipation to the Air. There are two basic methods: (1) direct air cooling (eg, air-cooled internal combustion engines or forced draft heat exchangers) and (2) an interim transfer of the heat to a liquid coolant with a subsequent transfer of heat to air, or evaporation of this coolant into the air. This latter method is generally used and it includes the following:

1. In *spray ponds* simple water jets or sprays throw liquid droplets into the air above the surface of a large body of water; some of the water of each droplet is evaporated, thus cooling the remainder of the droplet, which falls back to the pond. These spray ponds are simple devices, require usually a relatively large amount of land, need relatively little pumping power, and sometimes have large losses of water due to winds.

2. *Cooling towers* are accepted for most of the industrial and utility cooling tasks (1,2). Cooling towers utilize either natural or mechanically induced draft. A *natural-draft tower* (Figure 1) is a very large chimney, where the warm air, diluted with water vapor, rises to the top (1). Heavier, cool air enters around the base of the tower. The water to be cooled (which has been used as the cooling water in the process) is dis-

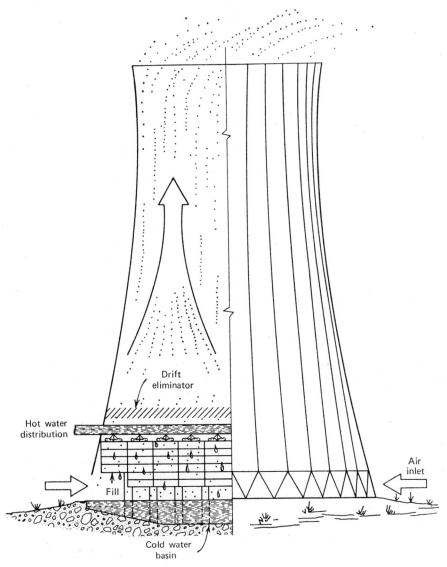

Fig. 1. Natural draft tower.

tributed over the packing and flows countercurrent to the air. The performance of these towers is sensitive to wind. A *forced-draft tower* or *mechanical-draft tower* (Figure 2) uses one or more electrically driven fans to move large quantities of air through the unit, countercurrent to the water. The use of baffled fences or drift eliminators allows the catching and return of much of the entrainment, thus often minimizing drift losses to 0.2%.

The effectiveness of a cooling tower on a spray pond depends on the moisture already in the air. For a given heat dissipation, geographic regions with warm, humid air require larger cooling towers than those with relatively dry or relatively cool air. A decrease in wet bulb air temperature from say 80 to 68°F could in many cases permit a doubling of the cooling capacity of a given tower.

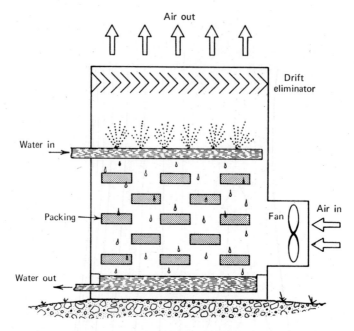

Fig. 2. Forced draft tower.

The water used in cooling towers often is treated to (1) maintain pH between 6.0 and 7.0 for minimizing corrosion, (2) reduce the content of carbonates and bicarbonates to minimize scale deposits, (3) add an algaecide or fungicide (usually chlorine, but often other chemicals), and (4) add a chromate to prevent biological surface attack of the wood used in the construction of the cooling tower (3). With certain water supplies a more complex treatment is required.

Natural-draft towers are quite popular in European power plants where the highest loads occur in the winter when the available cooling air is cold and thus able to absorb a lot of waste heat. In many parts of the United States the maximum power loads occur in the summer (largely due to air conditioning), when the air available for cooling is hot, very humid, and thus not able to absorb much heat; this is one of the principal reasons why natural-draft cooling towers have not been widely accepted in the U.S. Also, some mistakes that were made with early installations of this kind in the U.S. have caused them to receive a bad reputation, which they probably do not deserve.

Some of the problems inherent in cooling towers are concerned with freezing in the tower in cold weather, with formation of ice deposits on roads or buildings downwind of the tower, or with wind causing the humid outlet air to be partly recirculated into the inlet, thus reducing the capacity of the cooling air to absorb water vapor.

Bibliography

1. *Industrial Waste Guide on Thermal Pollution*, Revised Edition, Pacific Northwest Water Laboratory, Federal Water Pollution Control Administration, U.S. Department of Interior, Corvallis, Oregon, 1968.
2. "Cooling Towers," *Power*, S-1 to S-16 (March 1963).
3. F. L. Parker and P. A. Krankel, *Thermal Pollution: Status of the Art*, Department of Environmental and Water Resources Engineering, Vanderbilt University, Nashville, Tennessee, 1969.

Sludge Handling, Treatment, and Disposal

Almost all wet pollution control or wastewater treatment processes separate the waste into at least two separate streams: (1) an effluent or clear liquor, which has relatively few impurities or suspended solids, and (2) a smaller flow of concentrated wastes or sludge, which has a relatively high proportion of suspended solids.   This section deals with the handling, treatment, and dewatering of sludges and the ultimate disposal of the sludge solids.   This not only applies to sludges from water or wastewater treatment, but also to sludges from air pollution scrubbers or industrial processing wastes.   In the treatment of municipal or industrial wastes, the process steps in the treatment of sludges are usually the more expensive portions of the overall treatment.

Sludge may be defined as a semiliquid waste having a total solids concentration of at least 2500 ppm.   Sludges are obtained from wastewater containing impurities by processes such as liquid-solid separation (such as sedimentation clarification), a chemical reaction, (eg, coagulation) or a biological process.   Usually, sludges can be made to flow, can be pumped, and exhibit thixotropic characteristics.   They are often jelly-like and colloidal materials having a gray, brown, black, or other color.   They are difficult to handle or move, keep from emitting odors, transport, or de-water.   Municipal sewage sludges and mineral processing sludges usually contain abrasive solid material.

Sludges vary in moisture content from 99%, which is typical for alum sludges from water treatment plants, to perhaps 40–50% water, which is typical for chemical plant sludges, clay products, or evaporated black liquor wastes in pulp and paper mills. The characteristics of a sludge depend on the quantity and type of suspended and dissolved materials.   The handling characteristics are concerned with the ability to move a sludge by conveyor or shovel; many sludges are too liquid to be thus transported and are therefore moved by pump.   The odor, biodegradability, settleability, filterability, pH, color, turbidity, are all important properties affecting the treatment of sludges.   Sludges are derived from many different sources.   They contain the wastes from sewage treatment, industrial processing, mineral ore processing, backwash from granular media filters, food processing, pulp and paper wastes, petroleum refining, etc. Most sludges are aqueous, but there are also sludges based on alcohols, ethers, or other liquids that are used in chemical processing.

The selection of the optimum handling, treatment, or disposal method will depend on such factors as the characteristics and composition of the sludge, the local climate, the capital and operating costs of alternative methods, the availability and the location of ultimate disposal sites, the amount of waste, the type of plant from which the waste is to be taken, the size of the required equipment, local pollution regulations, the opportunity to recover by-products, and the experience of the key people involved.   The majority of municipal and industrial sludges can be treated satisfactorily by most of the processes listed in this article.   There are some sludges which can only be treated effectively by one or two of these processes.

Handling and Transportation.   There are three types of transportation of sludges: (1) in-plant movement from one unit process to another usually over very short distances; (2) movement to an ultimate disposal site (this may involve travel for many miles); and (3) movement from one plant to another.   For example, a city with multiple sewage treatment plants can obtain a cost advantage by centralizing sludge treatment and dewatering.   Because sludges are neither a true liquid nor a true solid, they do not obey the simple physical laws applicable to Newtonian liquids or Hookean solids, and the design of sludge handling and transport equipment is thus often empirical.

Storage of sludges may be temporary, such as in holding tanks or lagoons; for example, these are used to permit a steady flow of sludge to subsequent unit processes. Alternative storage facilities may be permanent, such as the disposal of radioactive sludges in sealed containers.

Sludge storage is usually accomplished in tanks or containers; but well-dried non-odorous or stabilized sludges, which can be handled with a shovel, can be stored in piles on the ground.   Trucking or rail transportation are preferred methods for long-distance hauling.   Movement by boat or barge is used for ocean disposal.   Conveyors are suitable only for well-dried sludge.

TREATMENT PROCESSES

The objectives of treating sludge are: (1) to dispose of a waste, safely and at low cost, from a location or from a plant where it normally cannot be accumulated; (2) to reduce the weight and volume of material to be disposed, usually by removing water; (3) to decompose organic materials into a form which is sterile and stable; (4) in some cases to recover by-products.

Sludge contains water in at least four different ways: (1) chemically combined water, such as the water of hydration; (2) colloidally held or "bound" water; (3) physically trapped or confined water (such as inside living cell walls or in hollow fibers); and (4) water of dilution or entrained water.   By using dewatering techniques some of all of these forms of water can be removed.   Mechanical separation (eg, gravity thickening) will only remove water in the last category, while heat and pressure can also remove some of the water in categories 1, 2, and 3.   Combustion can remove all the water.

There are several concentration processes whereby additional water is removed from the sludge and the percentage of suspended solids is increased.   These include thickening, filtration, centrifuging, and drying.   The principal merit of increased concentrations is that it usually reduces the size of equipment and the costs of subsequent unit processes, such as the disposal of the solids.

Gravity Thickening.   This is one of the simplest and most common methods of concentration, but it does not work with all sludges.   Because this process really only removes entrained water, the concentration that can be achieved is limited.   Basically, thickening is achieved in a large sedimentation tank of liquid, the flow velocity is greatly reduced, and the suspended solids have an opportunity to sink to the bottom; there, the sludge is compacted or compressed, and settled before being removed in a concentrated form.   A gentle stirring or slow agitation assists the dewatering and the settling and removal of the sludge.

The addition of a small amount of chemicals (eg, lime or polymers for coagulation) or the use of inert weighting additives (eg, flyash) can improve the performance of many thickeners, ie, increase the solid concentration in the sludge; but cost is also increased.   Typically, thickeners are used as a pretreatment, ahead of a filter.

Flotation Thickening.   This process uses tiny air bubbles, which attach themselves to small suspended solid particles and float them to the surface; this forms a concentrated float layer which can be skimmed off or removed. One of the methods of generating small bubbles is to use dissolved air flotation, where air is put into solution at elevated pressure (40–60 psi) and subsequently released in an open flotation tank. Flotation is particularly effective if the sludge contains dispersed oils or greases, or is gelatinous in nature, or contains solids whose specific gravity is close to that of the liquid, such as organic matter in water.

Centrifugation. Of the various types of centrifuges, the horizontal solid bowl cylindrical-conical type centrifuge is most commonly used for sewage sludge concentration, and is also used to classify and separate industrial sludges in the coal, potash, or synthetic fiber industries. This dewatering process is simple, makes use of a compact, totally enclosed machine (this controls odors), and costs are moderate.

Additions of small amounts of chemical flocculating agents (eg, certain polymers) will increase the recovery of solids, lower the dryness of the cake, and flocculate and thus assist in removing the fine solid particles. Solid bowl centrifuges are particularly suitable for sludges where the suspended solid particles are of a density which is sufficiently different from that of the liquid and where there are relatively large particles (above 200 mesh) of noncolloidal solids, such as with synthetic plastics. They are not always satisfactory for very fine particles.

Vacuum Filters. The rotary-drum vacuum filter (see Vol. 9, p. 278) is generally applicable to a wide variety of municipal or industrial sludges. Filter media include: woven and felted cloths, woven plastics, steel mesh or tightly wound adjacent coil springs. The use of chemicals (eg, lime and ferric chloride) improves the cake yield or dryness. The type and quality of the filter medium is important in the performance and life of the unit. The use of a pre-coat, such as a layer of diatomaceous earth, on the filter cloth improves the ability to handle small particles and improves the effluent quality; however, the flow per unit area is diminished.

Pressure Filters. By using a positive, high, water pressure (40–300 psi) and passing a sludge through a filter medium, it is possible to dewater many different sludges. A filter cake forms on the medium and it must be periodically removed. It permits a higher pressure difference across the filter medium than the maximum of 14.7 psi available with vacuum filters. There are many different designs including leaf types (frame and plate filters) and automatically operated units, which minimize the manual labor needed for removing the filter cake and cleaning the filter medium. Precoats can also be very effective with this type of filter.

Drying. The simplest and lowest cost form of sludge drying is by open (or covered), shallow, sand beds or lagoons, a method often used with sewage sludges and industrial sludges. Dewatering is accomplished by natural evaporation and natural drainage of water. This method is particularly suitable for small installations, warm and dry climates, sludges relatively free of grease or oil, which would otherwise clog the sand, and locations with a relatively permeable subsoil. The dried sludge cake is usually removed by scrapers, tractors, conveyors or other mechanical means and taken to landfill sites. Dewatering is normally accomplished in 2 to 30 days, depending on the sludge, weather and soil conditions. It has the disadvantages of requiring large areas, causing a potential nuisance, problems with inclement weather, and costly sludge removal operations.

The application of heat will accelerate the process of drying. Industrial sludges, where a valuable product can be recovered, use various types of mechanical dryers.

Screening. The use of vibrating multiple screens is a simple, low power process requiring small sized equipment. It is often used in conjunction with a filter or another dewatering device.

Composting. Certain organic sludges lend themselves to a natural biological treatment at somewhat elevated temperatures (120 to 180°F) by aerobic thermophilic bacteria to yield a relatively stable humus that can be used as a soil conditioner. This soil conditioner is usually not as rich in nutrients as fertilizers, but it has some nutrients and is effective as a mechanism for retaining moisture in the soil. This treatment method has been controversial because of its failure to compete economically with chemical fertilizers. However, it does create a stable and sterile material which can be spread safely on land surfaces and does not require an earth cover, as used in landfill. Composting garbage or municipal refuse has not generally been successful, because of the sensitivity of the process to biologically toxic materials, the problems of separating metals and glass from the sludge, and the cost of the process. However, the compost treatment of organic or sewage sludges has been successful in small-scale units.

Combustion. Incineration of sludges has been a practice for many years. It reduces the volume of wastes to be handled and thoroughly sterilizes the solids; however, it is relatively expensive and may cause air pollution problems. A variety of different furnaces and techniques are used, such as the multiple-hearth furnace (see Vol. 21, p. 639), and the fluidized-bed furnace (see Fluidization).

Chemical Conditioning. This is really a technique for augmenting or improving the performance of other sludge treatment methods, such as centrifugation, gravity thickening, vacuum filtration, etc. The addition of small amounts of chemicals thus improves the effectiveness, but increases the costs.

Heat Treatment. Certain sludges are much easier to dewater by centrifuges or filters once the sludge has been heated to between approximately 200 and 500°F. This is accomplished by a pressure cooking process whereby the sludge is heated in a pressure vessel by direct heating or injection of steam and held there for a short period. Heat exchangers are used to conserve thermal energy. A flow diagram of the Porteous process, which is one of the several heat treatment processes, is shown in Figure 1; here steam is used as the source of heat (1). Once the sludge has been conditioned by a heat treatment, it is easily handled and dewatered at low cost by subsequent filters or centrifuges without the use of chemical aids. By introducing air or oxygen into the pressure vessel, the heat treatment process can be augmented by a wet oxidation reaction, which will oxidize to various degrees some of the organic matter; however, it causes some problems of corrosion and scale formation.

Digestion. In the majority of existing U.S. sewage plants, sludges have been treated by digestion, an anaerobic biological wet treatment process in a confined airtight vessel. The rate of digestion is dependent on proper bacterial seeding, pH, character of the sludge, temperature, and degree of mixing. During the process, the microorganisms digest organic material creating gases (eg, methane, ammonia, or H_2S), and organic materials such as fatty acids and alcohols. The gases can be used for generating power and sludge volume is reduced. The digested sludge can be further dewatered and the material is generally stable. Newer plants generally do not use this process, partly because of operating problems, the difficulties of handling the resulting sludges, associated odors, and the problems in further treating the material.

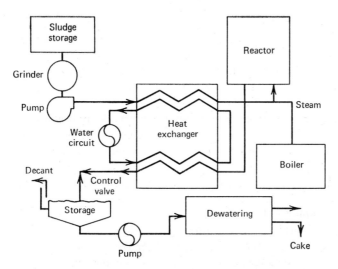

Fig. 1. The Porteous process permits a pressure cooking treatment of sewage sludges; it allows easy dewatering without the need for chemical additives.

By-product Recovery. In some industrial sludges valuable by-products can be recovered by a variety of different processes. For example, in the meat industry sludges contain lard, tallow, or grease that can be recovered after flotation or a cooking process, and can be used for making soap. Potato processing waters contain organic material and peelings which are suitable for animal feed and starch; it can be concentrated into a useable filter cake. Corn processing wastewater involves materials which are suitable for animal feed, oil production, corn syrup, and starch. Fibers and fillers are recovered in the paper and textile industry usually by filtration or sedimentation. The principal pollution load from a distillery is stillage, the residual grain mash from distillation columns; this material is recovered for use as animal feed and as a byproduct for conversion to chemical products. Pharmaceutical houses recover bacterial mold from fermentation processes for antibiotics by drying the cake from vacuum filters or evaporating spent broth. A certain nickel wire plating facility made plating wastewaters alkaline with soda ash, precipitating nickel as a carbonate, and then separated and dried the sludge to recover the nickel. The electrical machinery industry (circuit boards, switches, relays, vacuum tubes, etc) recovers silver and gold by solvent or precipitation processes.

ULTIMATE DISPOSAL

The disposal of sludge waste material must be done in such a manner that it does not interfere with the intended use of the environment. There are ultimately only three basic ways in which pollutants can be disposed: (*1*) in the air (as oxidized products such as CO_2 or H_2O); (*2*) on land; or (*3*) in the ocean. With the exception of water, there are no sludge materials that should be disposed in large quantities into fresh waters such as rivers or lakes. Only materials which cannot be economically recovered and reused need to be disposed of in the manner described below.

Land Spreading. This is one of the oldest and least expensive methods for the disposal of organic or inert sludges such as sewage or paper mill sludges. The fertilizer value of these sludges is usually very low when compared to commercial fertilizers. The sludge is usually sprayed from a tank truck or fed through special nozzles. Porous soil allows natural oxidation and biological degradation of these wastes. Some form of treatment (eg, digestion or drying) is necessary before sludge spreading, to minimize odors and sterilize the material. Sludges containing soluble salts or toxic materials are not suitable for this method of disposal.

Land Disposal.   Landfill is probably the most widely used method of disposal for solid and semisolid (sludge) wastes today. The wastes can be placed in prepared land excavations and covered with soil to prevent odors, prevent access to rodents and other vermin and assure compaction. In another method of landfill, the wastes can be placed and compacted into abandoned mines; however, this is usually more expensive.

Ocean Dumping.   The only really acceptable disposal sites for nontoxic salts in solution (eg, chlorides, sulfates, nitrates, etc) are the ocean or the salt lakes. Concentrated sludge from water purification, water treatment by reverse osmosis, or the backwash from ion exchange processes fall into this category.

Dilution.   The dilution of sludge wastes with water and the disposal to fresh waters is still practiced in many areas today. However, recent pollution control regulation is aimed to make this method of disposal a rare occurrence and other more expensive but more acceptable disposal methods will have to be used instead.

Bibliography

R. Sherwood and J. Phillips, "Heat Treatment Process Improves Economics of Sludge Handling and Disposal," *Water and Wastes Engineering*, 42–43 (Nov. 1970).

R. S. Burd, "A Study of Sludge Handling and Disposal," *Water Pollution Control Research Series Publication No. WP-20-4*, U.S. Department of Interior, Washington, D.C., May 1968.

"Waste Disposal From Water and Wastewater Treatment Processes," *Proceedings, Tenth Sanitary Engineering Conference*, Department of Civil Engineering, University of Illinois, Urbana, Illinois, 1968.

W. W. Eckenfelder, Jr., *Water Quality for Practicing Engineers*, Barnes & Noble, Inc., New York, 1970.

J. M. Coulson and F. J. Richardson, "Unit Operations," *Chemical Engineering*, Vol. 2, 2nd ed., Pergamon Press, Inc., New York, 1968 (contains chapters on Filtration, Centrifuges, Sedimentation and Thickening, Fluidization, Pneumatic and Hydraulic Conveying, Drying, etc).

Air Pollution

Air is essential to the life of plants, animals, and men. The average person inhales 35 pounds of air per day, which is six times as much as he consumes in food and drink.

Polluted air has been estimated to cost the United States at least $12 billion per year in ruined vegetation, flowers, or crops; corrosion, discoloration or peeling of paints and surface finishes; extra costs of cleaning houses, offices, clothing, and drapes; rusting of iron; tarnishing of silver; cracking of tires; deterioration of fabrics of nylon and other fibers; and blocking out of natural sunlight, thus causing extra lighting bills and reduced growth of crops. Air pollution is responsible for shortening human lives and is a major factor in emphysema (progressive breakdown of air sacs in the lungs), bronchitis, and lung cancer; it is believed to contribute to common colds, pneumonia, and bronchial asthma.

Sources.   Some of the principal sources of air pollution are shown in Table 1. The largest sources are the motor vehicles; they contribute through exhaust gases, crankcase blow-by, carburetor leakage, and gas tank venting. Most of the electrical power generating plants in the United States (more than 90%) burn coal and oil

Table 1. U.S. Air Pollution Emissions, 1965[a]

| Source | Pollutants, million tons/yr | | | | | | Percent of total |
	Carbon monoxide	Sulfur Oxides	Hydro-carbons	Nitrogen oxides	Particles	Total	
automobiles	66	1	12	6	1	86	60
industry	2	9	4	2	6	23	17
electric power plants	1	12	1	3	3	20	14
space heating	2	3	1	1	1	8	6
refuse disposal	1	1	1	1	1	5	3
total	72	26	19	13	12	142	

[a] From "The Sources of Air Pollution and Their Control," *Public Health Service Publication No 1548*, Government Printing Office, Washington, D.C., 1966.

which contain substantial portions of sulfur. Industrial factories create special air pollutants, the exact nature of which varies with each industry and each local plant. Space heaters and refuse disposal contribute another significant portion of the air pollution. Natural sources like dust storms, pollen, forest fires or volcanos now only contribute a minor portion. However, natural sources for hydrocarbon and other organic vapors from plants, such as fragrances from fir trees or flowers, decaying vegetation, or dead animals, can be significant.

The control of automobile emission is perhaps the most urgent problem in alleviating air pollution. Automobile exhaust in the United States contributes about 60% of the carbon monoxide, perhaps 20% of the sulfur oxides, some 35% of the nitrogen oxides, and 52% of the man-made hydrocarbons. These values have recently been decreasing, thanks due to more attention to pollution control. The use of exhaust-gas catalysts, venting of the crankcase into the inlet manifold, and the use of lean combustion mixture ratios are steps that diminish this pollution. Internal combustion engines can be designed or tuned to minimize exhaust gas pollution; however, these engines will be more expensive and possibly less efficient. See also Automobile Exhaust control and Fuel cells, in this volume.

The use of lead in gasoline has for many years been effective in improving the anti-knock and detonation characteristics and thus improving the efficiency of engines. The quantity of hydrocarbon exhaust emissions is increased when deposits of lead accumulate in the combustion chamber. In automobiles equipped for catalytic oxidation of carbon monoxide and hydrocarbons in the exhaust gases, lead also appears to interfere with the catalysis. The long-term effects of lead on plants, animals and humans are believed to be detrimental, but there is controversy about the damaging dosages. The production of lead-free gasoline with an octane number equivalent to that of gasoline with lead-alkyl additives can only be achieved at a fairly substantial increase in cost.

In addition to the basic emissions of gaseous pollutants, mists, and particles into the air, there are chemical reactions of these pollutants in the air which produce other irritating and harmful pollutants. For example, with the action of ultraviolet radiation from the sun (under the influence of nitrogen oxides which act as catalysts), it is possible to make ozonides out of certain hydrocarbon impurities in the atmosphere and thus form the aggressive ingredients of what is known as "smog." Radioactive pollutants are also found in the air; they present special technical problems which are not discussed here.

Table 2. Typical Air Pollutants

Air pollutant	Typical sources	Typical effects
sulfur dioxide	combustion of coal, oil (power generating plants) smelting of ores (primary metals) paper manufacture by sulfite process, petroleum refining, sulfuric acid plants, coke ovens	sensory and respiratory irritation; damage to vegetation, corrosion of metal, textiles, paint; possible adverse effect on health
carbon monoxide	automobile exhausts fuming of metal oxides incomplete combustion in furnaces or incinerators; jet engine exhaust	reduction of oxygen carrying capacity of blood; toxic
carbon dioxide	automobile exhausts combustion of organic matter jet engine exhausts	toxic in large concentrations. With moisture it forms an acid
aldehydes	thermal decomposition of fats, oils, glycerol, mostly in food processing	very irritating, choking odor; not immediately dangerous to life; becomes intolerable quickly
nitrogen oxides	hight-temperature combustion causes reaction with nitrogen in air; metal cleaning; fertilizers; nitric acid; explosives manufacture	irritating gas affecting lungs; corrosion; damage to vegetation
chlorine	by-product of electrolysis and chemical processing; bleaching of cotton, flour, pulp	toxic; attacks respiratory tract, mucous membranes, eyes; strong oxidizing agent, bleaching of plant foliage, corrodes metals, discolors paints
hydrogen cyanide	possible product from certain processes in metal plating, dyestuffs	poisonous gas; affects nerve cells
hydrogen sulfide	can result from certain processes of petroleum-refining chemicals with sulfur content, mining, kraft mills, coke ovens	highly toxic material, strong odor, irritating to eyes, nose, lungs; darkens exterior of paints, corrodes and tarnishes metals
organic odors	slaughtering and rendering of animals; tanning of animal hides; canning, coffee roasting, beer brewing, etc	objectionable odors
suspended particles	most combustion processes; gravel pits, open mines; dust; ore processing and beneficiation; concrete and cement manufacture blast furnaces, open-hearth furnaces, other metal furnaces	causes soiling, dust, dirt reduces visibility causes dryness in mouth, nose
hydrocarbons	petroleum refinery effluents gasoline tank ventilation chemical process vapors pharmaceutical process vapors synthetic rubber manufacture asphalt paving smoke	hydrocarbons in air can be oxidized to become "smog"; irritation to eyes, respiratory system, certain particulate organic compounds are believed to cause lung cancer
lead particles and lead compounds	exhausts from automotive engines which burn leaded gasolines; some industrial wastes	may have long term toxic effects
hydrogen chloride	production of chlorine and chlorine compounds, ore extraction processes, burning of chlorinated compounds, coal	irritates eyes and respiratory system, erosion of teeth, damage to vegetation, corrosion of metals

Pollutants. The pollutants in the air (see Tables 2 and 3) are of the following types:

1. *Particulates.* These are solid or liquid particles varying in size from approximately 1000 microns to 0.001 micron. These include particles from dust, cements, coal, bacteria, carbon black ores, etc. The larger particles settle out (by gravity) relatively easily; however, small particles will stay suspended for a long time as aerosols. Particles suspended in the air can grow by condensation, absorb and adsorb vapors and gases, collide with other particles and thus coagulate into larger particles, disperse over wide geographical areas, and absorb and scatter light.

2. *Gaseous impurities.* This includes gases not normally present in air; they arise from industrial sources, from chemical combustion devices such as automobile engines, power plants, furnaces or incinerators, and from natural sources such as hydrocarbon emissions from forests or plants. Gaseous industrial pollutants include SO_2, SO_3, NO, NO_2, N_2O_4, N_2O, H_2S, HCN, Cl_2, HCl, F_2, HF, various hydrocarbons and organic compounds containing Cl, S, and P. Combustion reaction gases include CO_2, CO, SO_2, and various hydrocarbons.

Odors are usually gaseous pollutants (eg, H_2S) or liquid mists, such as organic compounds. The human nose, which is a very sensitive odor detector, is not very reliable or quantitative. Masking of odors can be obtained by releasing a counter-irritant or another odorous chemical which masks or neutralizes the objectionable odor, so that it can no longer be sensed directly. See Odor control.

Abatement or Control Devices. The techniques for minimizing air pollution include the following:

1. *Modifications in the raw materials or the process.* Sometimes it is possible to use a different manufacturing process, or a different raw material, to reduce air pollution. An example is the treatment of oil prior to combustion to remove sulfur compounds. See Hydroforming under Hydroprocesses.

2. *Removal of particulates.* In the articles Dust, Engineering and Gas cleaning, data are given on particulate matter and mists, ranges of particle sizes for different pollutants, and ranges of effectiveness for different specialty equipment. Table 4 gives data on several types of equipment used for the removal of particles. As can be seen, different equipment is effective at different particle sizes and different values of dust loading, and requires more or less pressure drop and power.

Cleaning of Gaseous Impurities. There are a large number of different processes for the removal of gaseous impurities, each suitable for specific applications, concentrations, and performance requirements (see also Gas cleaning). For example, there are perhaps a dozen different experimental processes for removing sulfur dioxide; the discussion below gives the general principles used in the removal of most types of gaseous impurities.

A great many gaseous pollutants can be destroyed or rendered harmless by *combustion*. This includes odors, most organic materials, and also inorganic substances such as NH_3, H_2S, and HCN. If the pollutant gas contains combustible material and oxygen, and is already hot (400–1000°F), then a *catalytic bed* can be effective in accelerating the combustion reaction. The most commonly used catalysts are from the platinum family, usually deposited as a thin coating on an alloy substrata base. Catalyst poisoning (eg, heavy metals or phosphates or arsenic) on the coating of the catalyst (eg, certain oxides) must be avoided.

Thermal incineration is accomplished at higher temperatures (1200–1600°F) by

Table 3. Sources of Air Pollution

Pollutant and source		Percent
sulfur dioxide (1966)[a]		
burning of coal		58
combustion of petroleum products		20
smelting of ores		12
refinery operations		5
other		5
total		100
hydrocarbons (1968)[b]		
transportation		51.9
motor vehicles, gasoline engines	47.5	
motor vehicles, diesel engines	1.2	
aircraft	1.0	
railroads	1.0	
vessels	0.2	
fuels handling and non-highway use	1.0	
stationary combustion sources		2.2
industrial processes		14.4
solid waste disposal		5.0
forest fires		6.9
agricultural burning		5.3
solvent evaporation		9.7
other		4.6
total		100
carbon monoxide (1968)[c]		
transportation		62.8
motor vehicles	58.2	
aircraft	2.4	
vessels	0.3	
railroads	0.1	
other non-highway use of fuels	1.8	
stationary source		1.9
industrial processes		11.0
solid waste disposal		7.7
miscellaneous		16.6
man-made	9.5	
forest fires	7.1	
total		100

adding fuel and air to the polluted gas and burning them in a separate combustion chamber. A typical device, called an after-burner, can often be installed directly in the smoke stack or the furnace. For the destruction of certain pesticides and complex odorous organics, combustion temperatures between 1600 and 2000°F are needed.

Adsorption is the collection of gas or vapor molecules on the surface of a solid absorbent material such as activated carbon. Typical examples are exhaust gases from drycleaning operations or solvents from chemical processes. This is generally an expensive process unless the pollutant is sufficiently valuable to recover. Adsorption works best with relatively dilute gas or vapor impurities. The adsorbing material can usually be regenerated and reused; for example, heat can cause activated carbon to give up the adsorbed material.

Wet scrubbers are not only able to remove particulates, but are also very effective in absorbing and thus removing many gaseous pollutants.

Table 3 (*continued*)

Pollutant and source	Percent
nitrogen oxide (1968)[d]	
motor vehicles	35
railroads	2
vessels	1.5
other transportation	2
stationary fuel combustion	48.4
forest fires	5.8
open burning of solid wastes	2
other	2.3
total	100
particulates (1966) (NAPCA AP-51)[e]	
power generation	26.1
incinerators, refuse burning	8.7
space heating	8.7
mobile sources (vehicles)	4.3
industrial emissions	52.2
total	100

Data taken from the following publications by the National Air Pollution Control Administration, U.S. Dept. of Health, Education, and Welfare, Public Health Service, Environmental Health Service, Washington, D.C.

[a] *NAPCA AP-50*, "Air Quality Criteria for Sulphur Oxides," 2nd printing, April, 1970.

[b] *NAPCA AP 64*, "Air Quality Criteria for Hydrocarbons," March 1970.

[c] *NAPCA AP 62*, "Air Quality Criteria for Carbon Monoxide," March 1970.

[d] *NAPCA AP 67*, "Control Techniques for Nitrogen Oxide Emissions," March 1970.

[e] *NAPCA AP 51*, "Air Quality Criteria for Particulate Matter," 2nd printing, April 1970.

A gas–gas reaction can be used to create solid material, which is subsequently removed. For example, SO_2 can react with H_2S to form solid elemental sulfur.

Gas–solid reactions can be used. For example, hot lime (CaO) or dolomite (calcium and magnesium oxide) particles can react in a fluidized bed to capture SO_2 and form $CaSO_3$ particles. This is the basis for the so-called limestone process for sulfur dioxide removal.

Catalytic reactions. A catalyst can be used, for example to promote the oxidation of SO_2 into SO_3, which can readily be combined with water in a scrubber; in this process fly ash must be removed, for it would plug the vanadium oxide catalyst.

Table 5 summarizes several of the processes currently under development for removal of SO_2 emissions in typical power plants. There are at this time no completely satisfactory processes available and proven on a full-scale, long-term installation; however, active current efforts will soon permit the installation of proven equipment for this purpose. There are processes currently under development other than those listed in Table 5. It is too early to forecast which of these processes will be successful in the several types of plants (high or low sulfur fuel, large or small plant, new plant or retrofit).

Bibliography

A. C. Stern *Air Pollution*, 2nd ed., Academic Press, New York; Volume I: "Air Pollution and Its Effects," 1968; Volume II: "Analysis, Monitoring Surveying," 1968; Volume III: "Sources of Air Pollution and Their Control," 1970.

Cleaning our Environment; The Chemical Basis for Action," a report of the American Chemical Society, Washington, D.C., 1969.

Table 4. Comparison of Devices for Particulate Removal

Equipment type	Air velocity, ft/min	Pressure loss (inches water)	Typical dust load, grains/ft³	Power cost, kW/1000 cfm	Particle size	Remarks
gravity settling chamber	25–100	0.2–0.5	10	0.1	only effective for 100μ or larger	requires large space
cyclones or mechanical collectors	2000–4500	0.5–5.0	0.1–100	0.2–1.0	mostly for 5μ or larger; good above 20μ	compact, dry units
low-energy scrubber	200–1000	0.1–2.0	0.1–10	0.2–1.5	5μ or larger	corrosion problem; good for hot gas; slurry handling
high-energy scrubber	3000–20,000	4–40	0.1–1	1–8	80–90% at 1μ 99% at 5μ or larger	same as for high energy
filter or bag	3–25	2–5	0.1–30	0.5–1.2	99% at 1μ 99.9% at 5μ+	can handle difficult dust maximum temperature, 500°F
electrostatic precipitator	200–500	0.2–0.7	0.1–1	0.2–0.6	80–99% up to 50μ	efficiency is sensitive to variations in dust, moisture, gas; cannot handle explosive gases

Table 5. Methods of Controlling SO$_2$ Emissions from Stationary Combustion Sources

change fuel	switch to a fuel with lower sulfur content
change energy source	use hydro-electric or nuclear energy
desulfurize the fuel	
coal	use coal cleaning technique which includes crushing and flotation; some 25 to 50% of sulfur can be readily removed
fuel oil	catalytic treatment with hydrogen removes sulfur from oil; cost of fuel is increased by \$0.04 to \$0.12 per million Btu
remove sulfur oxides from flue gas; typical treatments under development include the following:	all require special process equipment, usually heat exchangers, scrubbers, fans, reactors, etc
limestone	limestone reacts with SO$_2$ and can be removed
alkalized alumina sorption	SO$_2$ is sorbed onto a solid metal oxide; the oxide can be regenerated and sulfur can be recovered
catalytic oxidation	SO$_2$ is catalytically oxidized to SO$_3$, scrubbed and recovered as condensed dilute sulfuric acid
caustic scrubbing	wet scrubber with caustic additive to water
increase combustion efficiency	reduces amount of fuel burned

Air Pollution Manual, Parts I and II, American Industrial Hygiene Association, Detroit, Michigan, 1968.

"Control Techniques for Sulphur Oxide Pollutants," *Publication No. AP 52, January, 1969*, National Air Pollution Control Administration, U.S. Dept. of Health, Education and Welfare, Washington, D.C.

J. A. Danielson, ed., "Air Pollution Engineering Manual," *Public Health Service Publication No. 999-AP-40*, U.S. Government Printing Office, 1969-0-368-923.

"Control Techniques for Particulate Air Pollutants," *Publication No. AP 51, January, 1969*, National Air Pollution Control Administration.

"Control Techniques for Carbon Monoxide, Nitrogen Oxide, and Hydrocarbon Emissions from Mobile Sources," *Publication No. AP 66, March, 1970*, National Air Pollution Control Administration.

"Air Quality Criteria," *National Air Pollution Control Administration, Publication Nos. AP 49, 50, 62, 63 and 64, January, 1969 and March, 1970*.

"Abatement of Sulfur Oxide Emissions from Stationary Combustion Sources," National Research Council, Committee on Pollution Abatement and Control, National Academy of Sciences, Washington, D.C., 1970.

Solid Wastes

In 1969 an average of 5½ pounds of solid wastes per person per day was collected in the United States. The range in daily per capita waste production is higher in urban areas than in rural areas and was from 2.5 to 7.5 pounds, with a nationwide total of about 200 million tons per year. In 1980 some 235 million inhabitants are expected to generate about 8 pounds per person, per day, or 340 million tons per year. This essentially includes only municipal wastes.

Solid wastes can be categorized in various ways. Table 1 shows a listing by major source groupings. They can also be categorized by inorganic content (metals, glass and noncombustibles), and organic content (essentially combustible), such as toxic and nontoxic materials, by density, by chemical constituents, as soluble and non-soluble substances, or as special hazard wastes (explosive, radioactive, pathological).

Table 1. Types of Solid Wastes

Category	U.S. total,[a] million tons/yr	Typical ingredients	Typical disposal operation
municipal refuse (household, commercial, and street wastes)	200	tree and shrub cuttings, dirt, cardboard boxes, paper, bricks, construction and demolition rubble, tin cans, garbage, street sweepings, rubber goods, rags, glass, metal parts, wood pieces, furniture, packaging materials, plastics, bathtubs, TV's and radios, ash, sewage sludge cakes, wire	storage (garbage cans), collection (trucks), compaction, landfill, composting, incineration, salvage, dumping or burial, pyrolysis
junked automobiles and scrap machinery	15	upholstery, batteries, electric motors, radiators, engine blocks, frames, glass, tires (30% reclaimed), tractors, lathes, other machinery	stripping and recovery, incineration, baling, compacting shredding, smelters
industrial wastes	110	many different products (with varying physical and chemical properties); some are toxic; plastics, powders, slurries, sheets, containers, metals, ash	special dumps, collection, separation and recovery, incineration and wasteheat utilization
mining and ore processing wastes	1100	various oxides, silicates, red mud, clays, slimes, sand, rocks, slag, ore residues, cinder, ash, clinkers, dross	dumps, ponds, mounds
animal wastes	1500	chicken droppings, hog manure, feathers, hoofs, bones, dairy wastes, cattle wastes, skins, carcasses	incineration, landfills, dumps, biological treatment, natural decay
agricultural wastes	550	fruit and vegetable canning residues, cuttings, corn stalks, nut shells, rice hulls, trees, crop insecticides, bark, leaves, residues, dead trees	incineration, pyrolysis, biological deterioration, composting, natural decay

[a] Estimates by Public Health Service.

The effects of poorly managed solid wastes include the following: (1) unpleasant sight, aesthetic problem; (2) an associated air or water pollution problem (fumes, odors, ash, smoke, contaminated ground water, etc); (3) if dumped, prevention of the use of land for other purposes; (4) breeding of flies, maggots, mosquitoes, rats, or other rodents, etc, many of which are carriers of disease; (5) attraction of dogs, birds, and other scavengers (the problem of bears being attracted to garbage dumps has become severe in our National Parks); (6) safety hazard to children, animals.

Several of the typical disposal operations are briefly described below and the reader is referred to the bibliography for more details.

Collection and Transportation. With municipal refuse, this operation accounts for at least 75% of the waste disposal cost. Typical costs are $15.00 to $30.00 per ton. It includes packaging in plastic bags, special garbage or refuse trucks, which have a built-in compaction device, or occasional rail transport to remote sites.

Dumping. Although outlawed in many cities and states, this method of disposal is still used by many small communities. Here refuse is simply dumped in a place near town. It often catches or is set afire, causing smoke, odor, and fumes.

Landfill. Here refuse is dumped at a prepared site and compacted. The waste should be covered with at least six inches of earth or dirt at the end of each day. If compacted to a depth of 10 feet, a typical city of 100,000 people requires 17 acres of landfill each year. If not properly planned and designed, there can be problems with ground water contamination, generation of methane gas, sinking of the land, and underground fires.

Composting. This is a conversion of garbage and other solid wastes by bacterial action, which sterilizes the waste and causes a reduction in weight and volume by oxidation of organic materials. Unfortunately, the bacteria have no effect on most plastics, rubber, and all metals or glasses. The product is a soil mulch or conditioner and not a fertilizer unless fortified by chemicals. Many garbage or refuse compost plants in the U.S. have not been economically successful and have been closed.

Compaction. Municipal refuse has a typical density of 5 lb/ft^3. The object of compaction (by mechanical piston action or by shredding) is to increase this density and to reduce the volume of trash that has to be handled.

Incineration. The combustion of organics results in the evaporation of contained water and the generation of CO_2, H_2O, and some CO. It substantially reduces the volume of many wastes, yields a sterile, stable, odor-free ash or clinker residue, and can yield usable heat. Old incinerators are basically simple fire boxes with or without grates; they usually cause odors and smoke, and often combustibles remain in the ash. Modern incinerators have an integral air pollution control system to remove flyash, odors, and minimize the emission of noxious gases. There is a large variety of different incinerator designs and types, with various degrees of automation, different insulation or wall cooling methods, design geometries, various afterburner devices and grate configuration. The solid residues (ash and clinkers) require a separate handling system and are usually disposed of by landfill; other end uses are being investigated (eg, manufacture of bricks, road topping material, recovery of metals, etc). Compared to other methods, incinerators are expensive to install and maintain and require skilled operators. However, it is a disposal method that is gaining considerable acceptance.

Junked Automobiles. Automobile wreckers process about 80% of all junked vehicles. The remainder are generally abandoned or scavenged. The wrecker typically removes useful parts, such as batteries for their lead, radiators or electric motors for their copper, or engine blocks for their cast iron. The remaining hulk (1000–1500 lbs) is often burned (to clean out combustibles) and then converted to metal scrap by special baling, shearing, or shredding machines. Open burning of car hulks is being outlawed in an increasing number of communities.

Industrial Wastes. There is a large variety of different solid waste materials ranging from scrap metals to plastics, to specialty chemicals, packaging materials, pharmaceutical excess, wood wastes such as sawdust, food processing wastes such as fruit pits or nut shells, ashes, cuttings, etc. The most common operations are again dumping and incineration. Emphasis is on economic recovery of valuable by-products.

Mine Wastes. This includes rock from mines, mill tailings, ore processing plant rejects, smelter slags, and other solid wastes. Most have no known economic value. Some present difficult disposal problems, such as the slime residues from phosphate mining, red mud from bauxite processing, or fine dusts, which are readily picked up by winds.

Agricultural and Animal Wastes. Although these are large amounts when compared to other sources of solid wastes, they usually occur mostly in nonurban areas, are often less noticeable and troublesome. The increasing legislative attention to these wastes will require more sophisticated and more costly processing.

Recovery.   Although solid wastes contain a large number of valuable ingredients, which could be separated, salvaged, and reused (or burned to generate energy), the recovery of these materials or this energy has in most cases not been economically feasible. The processing of industrial wastes, however, has been leading the trend toward recovery of valuable products. As more technology for separation and recovery becomes available, more solid wastes will be subjected to a salvage process.

Combination Treatment with Liquid Wastes.   In many cases the solid wastes are mixed with liquid (usually water) and treated by conventional liquid waste methods as described separately. Examples are kitchen garbage disposal units which grind up solids and put them into a sewer system, or flotation treatment of ground ore particles.

Commercial Refuse Disposal.   This includes refuse from hotels, shopping centers, stores, restaurants, markets or hospitals. Recent legislation is increasingly requiring the disposal (usually by incineration or haul-away) at the source or in the building.

Bibliography

Municipal Refuse Disposal, 2nd ed., American Public Works Association, Chicago, 1966.

Solid Waste Management, RRJ Publishing Corp., New York (monthly journal).

R. C. Corey, *Principles and Practices of Incineration*, Interscience Publishers, a division of John Wiley & Sons, Inc., New York, 1969.

Solid Waste Management, National Association of Counties Research Foundation, Washington, D.C. (10 separate brochures).

Automobile Disposal, A National Problem: Case Studies of Factors That Influence the Accumulation of Automobile Scrap, Bureau of Mines, U.S. Department of the Interior, 1967.

T. J. Sorg and H. L. Hickman, "Sanitary Landfill Facts," *Publication Number 1792*, U.S. Public Health Service Solid Wastes Program, U.S. Government Printing Office, 1968.

Cleaning Our Environment; The Chemical Basis for Action, American Chemical Society, Washington, D.C. 1969.

"Comprehensive Studies of Solid Waste Management," *Public Health Service Publication No. 2039*, U.S. Department of Health, Education and Welfare, 1970.

J. De Marco, D. J. Keller, J. Leckman and J. L. Newton, "Incinerator Guidelines," *Public Health Service Publication No. 2012*, U.S. Department of HEW, Bureau of Solid Waste Management, 1969.

F. P. Sebastian and P. J. Cardinal, Jr., "Solid Waste Disposal," *Chemical Engineering*, Deskbook Issue, October 14, 1968, pp. 112–117.

G. P. Sutton and
G. Shell (Water pollution)
Envirotech Corp.

POLY(HYDROXYBENZOIC ACID)

The search for polymers with useful properties at temperatures of 200–400°C arose from the needs of the aerospace industries. Initially in the early 1950s emphasis was placed on inorganic polymers on the assumption that the higher bond energies available with hetero atoms in polymer backbones would lead to improved thermal stabilities. However, in many of the elements, the ionic character of the bonds, and the availability of bonding orbitals provide low-energy pathways for various degradation reactions such as (1) oxidative degradation; (2) nucleophilic or electrophilic attack; and (3) reorganization-type reactions. By the late 1950s emphasis had shifted to the use of highly stable aromatic or heterocyclic rings in the backbone. This work culminated in the development of polybenzimidazoles and a family of aromatic polyimides as commercially available materials. (See Polyimides in this volume.) During that time considerable work was also carried out on the synthesis of aromatic polyesters. A whole range of polymers and copolymers, based on combinations of terephthalic acid and isophthalic acid with hydroquinones and 1,3-benzenediol, were prepared and evaluated (1–3). However, none of these polymers provided any particular advantages for high-temperature use. The polymers of m- and p-hydroxybenzoic acid were also examined during this period, but the meta polymer was shown to melt at 185–205°C and the p-hydroxybenzoic acid polymer was reported to be intractable and decomposed at 350°C (4).

Very recently work carried out at the Carborundum R & D laboratories has shown that p-hydroxybenzoic acid polymer is tractable and stable in air at temperatures up to 400–500°C (5).

Apparently in earlier investigations preparation of this polymer was complicated by the ease with which the monomer can decarboxylate as well as difficulties in obtaining higher molecular weights (6). The development of a linear p-hydroxybenzoic acid polymer appears to provide a major breakthrough for the field of high-temperature polymers since for the first time a polymer is available which displays long-term stability in air at temperatures of over 325°C and can be fabricated by rapid forming methods. In addition this polymer possesses an inherent self-lubricating character combined with the highest reported elastic modulus, thermal conductivity, electrical insulating character, and solvent resistance of any available polymer.

The polymer is known commercially as Ekonol (Carborundum Company) brand of oxybenzoyl polyester. Pilot plant facilities have been constructed (1971) to produce Ekonol powder, and as these facilities are scaled up it is believed that the cost of the powder will drop to below $5/lb.

Preparation of Hydroxybenzoic Acid Polymers

It is instructive to compare the synthetic routes for the various hydroxybenzoic acid polymers since they are all prepared in a similar manner and differ structurally only in the ortho, meta, and para configurations. Work on preparation of this group of polymers goes back as far as 1910 when Fischer prepared a tetramer from p-hydroxybenzoic acid (7). In 1919 a polymer of o-hydroxybenzoic acid was obtained by heating acetylsalicylic acid above 200°C (8).

Direct preparation of hydroxybenzoic acid polymers by self-condensation is very difficult since the phenolic hydroxyl is relatively inert to direct esterification with the carboxylic acid. On heating such systems some polymer residues may be obtained but decarboxylation also occurs at an increasingly rapid rate at temperatures over 150°C. Several possibilities exist for getting around this problem. For example, the acetoxy derivatives of all three hydroxybenzoic acids appear to polymerize by an ester interchange reaction with elimination of acetic acid.

Another route involves the preparation of the acyl chloride of the hydroxybenzoic acid followed by a condensation reaction splitting out hydrogen chloride (9).

This route is complicated by the fact that the acyl chloride tends to react with the hydroxyl groups of the unreacted hydroxybenzoic acid. Thus in the reaction of p-hydroxybenzoic acid with thionyl chloride only dimers and trimers could be obtained. Even in the acetoxy route there is a tendency for the carboxylic acid unit to decarboxylate. Presumably blocking of the carboxylic acid would protect against decarboxylation and yet permit polymerization to proceed to high molecular weights. It is essentially this type of approach which has been used successfully for the preparation of Ekonol.

Properties of Ekonol

The Ekonol polymer is insoluble in all organic solvents, even at their boiling points, although there is a slight tendency to swell when heated at 325°C in chlorinated biphenyls for 24 hr. Ekonol is not affected by dilute inorganic acids and bases; however the polymer is attacked by hot concentrated sulfuric acid and hot concentrated sodium hydroxide.

Ekonol is not attacked by concentrated phosphoric acid, trifluoroacetic acid, or pyridine. The hydrolytic stability of the polymer is excellent. For example the polymer was boiled in water for 100 hr without loss of properties. The polymer shows excellent stability to anhydrous reagents such as HCl and ammonia.

End group analysis was used to indicate a number-average molecular weight of between 8000–12,000. Ekonol is a linear highly crystalline polymer as evidenced by its x-ray diffraction pattern, which, except for changes due to thermal expansion, remains unchanged up to temperatures of 330°C.

Changes in the structure of the polymer with weight loss in air at 425°C have been studied by x-ray powder analyses. It was found that up to a weight loss of 11%, a significant degree of order is still evident.

The polymer does not melt below a temperature of 550°C where it decomposes rapidly. A molded piece appeared to adhere to a surface heated to 600°C suggesting either melting or degradation. The weight loss in air under isothermal conditions is shown in Table 1.

Table 1. Isothermal Heat Stability of Ekonol in Air

Temperature, °F	Rate of weight loss, %/hr
600	0.06
650	0.1
750	0.5
800	1.4
850	3.0

The isothermal properties reported here are on powder samples (particle size averaged 75-100μ). Much lower weight losses are usually observed on fabricated pieces due to the lower surface area.

Fabrication. Ekonol is unique with respect to fabrication of polymers in that it is formed below its melting point. Compression sintering of Ekonol has been extensively investigated. It was found that for good sintering, temperatures of 420°C and pressures greater than 5000 psi were required. Sintering times vary from a few minutes to an hour, depending on the thickness of the sample. The size and number of voids is sharply decreased as the sintering temperature is increased. Fabricated pieces of Ekonol can be ground to a powder and remolded, indicating that no degradation or crosslinking has occurred during compression sintering. The incorporation of fine fillers in the compression sintered pieces generally leads to an improvement in the mechanical properties of the formed material. This may be attributed to a reduction in thermal stresses during fabrication. However incorporation of fillers of large particle size, especially at high volume concentration, leads to a decrease in the mechanical properties of the molded pieces because of the difficulty in getting the polyester to flow and wet the fillers.

It was observed that compression sintered polyester pieces could be hammered and bent at elevated temperatures in a manner similar to hot forming of certain metals. High-energy rate forging and plasma spraying have both been investigated. Both methods depend on imparting a high-energy impulse which permits flow of the polymer.

The high-energy rate forge (HERF) provides a versatile technique for rapid forming of Ekonol shapes. Samples can be fabricated at forming cycles of 6–10 sec. A preform is heated to 155–260°C and then subjected to HERF. The energy generated during the forging is sufficient to produce flow and apparent fusion of the material. The result is a highly fused piece (density 1.50 g/cm^3) containing no apparent microporosity.

In plasma spraying, a plasma of helium or argon is first produced by passing the gas through a carbon arc, the temperature then being maintained by induction heating. The polyester of the proper particle size is then introduced into the plasma and the combination of heat and pressure on impaction is sufficient to produce a coherent coating. The temperatures in the plasma are over 3000°C, however the contact time of the polymer is short enough so that no degradation occurs. The resulting coatings can be made virtually pinhole-free by burnishing the surfaces. Such coatings are highly resistant to penetration of corrosive media. A variety of fillers can be sprayed together with the polymer. Since the substrate temperature may be as low as 50°C, coatings can be sprayed onto many materials including metals, ceramics and plastics. Coatings from 0.5 to 200 mils thick can be produced by this technique.

Properties of Fabricated Ekonol. Perhaps the greatest interest in Ekonol lies

Table 2. Mechanical Properties (Room Temperature) of Unfilled Engineering Plastics

Property	Ekonol	Polyaryl-sulfones (10)	Poly-imides (11)	Polyfluoro-carbon (12)
density, g/cm³	1.44	1.36	1.40	2.13
flexural strength, psi	10,700	17,200	11,800–14,000	
elastic modulus, psi × 10⁶	1.03	0.39	0.46	0.09
compressive strength, psi	38,500	17,900	24,000	1000
machinability	excellent		fair	good

Table 3. Thermal Properties of High-Temperature Engineering Plastics

Property	Ekonol	Polyaryl-sulfones (10)	Poly-imides (11)	Polyfluoro-carbons (12)
thermal conductivity, cal/(sec)(cm²)(°C/cm) × 10⁻⁴	18.0	6.0	6.0	6.0
coefficient of thermal expansion, °F × 10⁻⁵	2.8	2.6	2.4	5.5
weight loss in air				
at 260°C, %/2000 hr	1		1	0
at 400°C, %/hr	1		1	decomp

Table 4. Comparison of Electrical Properties of High-Temperature Engineering Plastics

Property	Ekonol	Polyaryl-sulfones (10)	Poly-imides (11)	Polyfluoro-carbon (12)
dielectric strength, vol/mil, thickness 0.125 in.	660	300	430	620
dielectric constant	3.8	3.9	3.6	2.1
dissipation factor × 10⁻⁴	1.98	30	34	3.0
volume resistivity, ohm-cm	10^{15}	10^{13}	10^{16}–10^{17}	10^{18}
water absorption				
at room temp, %/24 hr	0.02	0.22	0.30	0.01
at 100°C, %/100 hr	0.40			

in its excellent combination of properties. Tables 2, 3, and 4 compare the mechanical, thermal, and electrical properties of other high-temperature engineering plastics with compressed, sintered samples of Ekonol.

The flexural strength of Ekonol compares well with those of most polyimides but is lower than the polysulfones; however, it keeps up well at high temperatures, even up to 300°C. The elastic modulus is markedly higher than any of the high-temperature engineering plastics. The high stiffness and compressive strength contribute to its excellent load-carrying capacity. Resistance to creep or cold flow coupled with a self-lubricating character suggests a major advance over existing materials of construction for self-lubricating bearings.

Ekonol has the highest thermal conductivity of any plastic material. This is important for applications such as self-lubricating bearings where localized heating and degradation can be detrimental to the long-term performance of the material. Also, the high thermal conductivity contributes to the excellent machinability by minimizing localized charring. The reasons for this high thermal conductivity are not clear but are probably related to the high degree of crystallinity of the polymer.

Most of the electrical properties of Ekonol compare favorably with those of the other high-temperature engineering plastics.

The exceptional dielectric properties of Ekonol provides a major advance in the field of electrical insulating materials. Of particular interest for high-temperature application is the combination of high dielectric strength, low dissipation factor, high thermal conductivity, and long-term thermal resistance up to 325°C. Areas of possible application include high-temperature circuit boards, machinable insulation components, and encapsulation of diodes, transistors, and integrated circuits.

The coefficients of friction of the various engineering plastics are compared in Table 5.

Table 5. Coefficient of Friction of High-Temperature Engineering Plastics

Material	Coefficient of friction (static)
Ekonol	0.10–0.16
polyimides (11)	0.25–1.2
polyfluorocarbons (12)	0.05–0.08

As can be seen in Table 5 Ekonol appears to display a self-lubricating character.

The Effect of Fillers. The role of fillers in fabricated forms of Ekonol is extremely important since the properties are strongly influenced by the nature of the filler. Addition of lubricants such as graphite, polyfluorocarbons, MoS_2, and BN fibers greatly enhance the self-lubricating properties of the polymer. Use of chopped BN fibers not only enhances the self-lubricating properties of the composite but also provides reinforcing. Table 6 compares PV values of filled Ekonol and other materials.

Table 6. Comparison of Bearing Materials

Material	Limiting PV value[a]
polyfluorocarbon	1,000
nylon	3,000
Ekonol	8,000
glass-filled polyfluorocarbon	20,000
porous bronze	40,000
Ekonol with 30% polyfluorocarbon	60,000

[a] Product of the applied load, in psi, and the surface velocity, in ft/sec.

The electrical properties of Ekonol can be controlled over a wide range by use of various fillers. Thus, incorporation of $BaTiO_3$ results in significantly higher dielectric properties which might be of interest for radio frequency transmission lines. The resistive character of Ekonol can be controlled by incorporation of graphite, and addition of SiC is of interest for voltage-sensitive resistors. With the addition of fine metal powders, properties such as thermal conductivity can be improved.

Bibliography

1. W. M. Eareckson, III, *J. Polymer Sci.* **40,** 399 (1959).
2. U.S. Pat. 3,036,990 (May 29, 1962), S. W. Kanter and F. F. Holub (to General Electric Co.).
3. U.S. Pat. 3,160,604 (Dec. 8, 1964), F. F. Holub and S. W. Kanter (to General Electric Co.).
4. R. Gilkey and J. R. Caldwell, *J. Polymer Sci.* **2,** 198 (1959); U.S. Pat. 2,600,376 (June 17, 1952), J. R. Caldwell (to Eastman Kodak Co.).

5. J. Economy, B. E. Nowak, and S. G. Cottis, *Polymer Preprints* **2** (1), 332 (1970); J. Economy, B. E. Nowak, and S. G. Cottis, *SAMPE J.* **6** (6), 21 (1970).
6. For leading references see Beilstein's *Handbuch der Organischen Chemie*, 4th ed., Vol. 10, Julius Springer Verlag, Berlin, 1927, pp. 148–151, 151–154.
7. E. Fischer and K. Freundenberg, *Justus Liebigs Ann. Chem.* **372**, 32 (1910).
8. R. Anschutz, *Ber. Deut. Chem. Ges.* **52B**, 1815 (1919).
9. T. Kametani and K. Fukumoto, *Yakugaku Zasshi* **80**, 1188 (1960).
10. H. A. Vogel, *Polyarylsulfones: Synthesis and Properties*, 3M Co., Central Research Laboratories, St. Paul, Minnesota; *Astrel 360 Plastic*, Y-1APF (59-5)K, 3M Co., St. Paul, Minnesota.
11. *Vespel Polyimide Resins*, A-60614 5-68, E. I. du Pont de Nemours and Co., Inc., Wilmington, Delaware; *Meldin Polyimides*, HCG 7310 10 M, Dixon Corp., Bristol, Rhode Island, Feb. 1967.
12. *Teflon Fluorocarbon Resins*, A-40844, E. I. du Pont de Nemours and Co., Inc., Wilmington, Delaware.

J. Economy and S. G. Cottis
The Carborundum Company

POLYIMIDES

Wholly aromatic polyimides have attained considerable importance since their disclosure in 1955 by Edwards (1). The aromatic polyimides are of interest primarily because of their great thermal stability, particularly in air; indeed, they are among the most thermally stable organic polymers known. In addition, aromatic polyimides have outstanding dielectric and mechanical properties at high temperatures, and outstanding resistance to ionizing radiation and to solvent attack. A substantial amount of research on aromatic polyimides has been done in the 1960s, mostly directed toward the development of films, coatings, varnishes, and laminating resins, ie toward those products which are in general best suited for taking advantage of the high-temperature dielectric properties of polyimides. The high glass-transition temperature of the polyimides also recommends them for use as structural adhesives and as the matrix resin of composites which are to be used at elevated temperatures. Applications of the foregoing types have already reached the commercial stage in a number of products, ie Kapton (registered trademark E. I. duPont de Nemours & Co., Inc.) film (known experimentally as H-film), Pyre-ML (registered trademark E. I. duPont de Nemours & Co., Inc.) wire enamel, and the Skybond (registered trademark Monsanto Co.) 700 series of laminating varnishes and enamels. Shaped objects from Vespel (registered trademark E. I. duPont de Nemours & Co., Inc.) molding resins also have been introduced by the duPont Company and polyimide foams and precursor powders have been announced by Monsanto Company. Several excellent experimental fibers of the polyimide class have been reported but no plans to commercialize any of these have been announced. Modified polyimides appear to have an important role in the development of the polyimides; eg Amoco's amide–imides, because of their relatively low price, are achieving a significant place in the marketing of polyimide resins.

Despite the fact that aliphatic–aromatic polyimides have been known for as long as the wholly aromatic polyimides, they have received relatively little attention, owing no doubt to the fact that the wholly aromatic polyimides appear to have considerably greater commercial potential as a consequence of their greater thermal stability. Nevertheless, an aliphatic–aromatic polyimide molding resin, Poly X, apparently is being market tested by the Raychem Corporation for molded parts and wire insulation (2).

Of considerable potential interest are the polyimides based on bis-maleimides (and their Diels-Alder condensation products). These are aliphatic in type and consequently do not have high thermooxidative stability in comparison with the wholly aromatic polyimides. The ease of processing and crosslinking the bis-maleimide monomers, however, recommends these special polyimides for certain applications where the maximum in stability is not required.

Although the markets for polyimide products have been slow to develop, the potential appears to be large, ie about 25 million lb/yr (3,4). However, one estimate (2) predicts a meteoric rise in consumption of polyimides beginning in 1970, rising to 50 million lb/yr by 1972 or 1973. It is certain that the dollar volume will be great at any rate because these products sell for about $2/lb for the polyamide–imides to about $30/lb for Kapton film. The 1970 prices for polyimide adhesives and varnishes, on a dry basis, are about $5–6/lb and could be considerably cheaper when a higher production volume is reached.

Syntheses

Wholly aromatic polyimides are derived from aromatic dianhydrides and aromatic diamines (AA–BB polyimides) or from aromatic compounds containing both an amine and an anhydride group (A–B polyimides). The polymers are not fusible and are soluble only in strong acids, such as fuming nitric acid. The highly intractable nature of these polyimides has precluded both their direct synthesis (with but very few exceptions) and their direct fabrication to useful articles. The recent successes in the synthesis of linear, wholly aromatic polyimides and in their manufacture have been due to (a) the discovery that polyimides can be prepared stepwise by way of a soluble polyamic acid precursor that can be fabricated, and (b) to the fact that high-molecular-weight polyamic acid precursors can be prepared by low-temperature solution-polycondensation techniques (5–13). Films, fibers, flexible coatings, and the like are made from the polyamic acid which is then readily converted to the polyimide.

In addition to aromatic polyimides of the AB and AA–BB types, other more complex polyimides have been prepared, synthesized for example, by condensation of a simple dianhydride with a diamine containing preformed heterocycle, amide, or ester units.

The other important types of polyimides achieve their high molecular weight by thermal means. Thus, crosslinked aromatic polyimide resins are prepared by heating a mixture of monomers; aliphatic polyimides generally are prepared in a melt; addition polymerizations in bulk are brought about by thermal means for certain bis-imide monomers or for short blocks of polyimides capped with unsaturated groups. Each type is discussed below.

WHOLLY AROMATIC POLYIMIDES

Simple AA–BB Polyimides. Soluble polyamic acids (also called poly-o-carboxy-aromatic amides or aromatic polyamide acids) are produced by low-temperature polycondensation of aromatic dianhydrides with diamines in polar solvents, eg dimethylformamide, dimethylacetamide, dimethyl sulfoxide, N-methyl-2-pyrrolidone, or m-cresol. For optimum polymerization, a temperature of around 50°C should not be exceeded. It has been reported (14), however, that m-cresol solutions of polyamic acids can be heated safely to 125–160°C. Attainment of high molecular weight depends on extremely pure monomers, rigorous exclusion of moisture, solvent used, and the maintenance of a low to moderate polymerization temperature. Polyamic acids do show some variation in solubility with variation in structure, but apparently solubility is adequate in all cases for the preparation of a high-molecular-weight polymer useful for fabrication.

Synthesis of a polyamic acid and conversion to the corresponding polyimide are shown below.

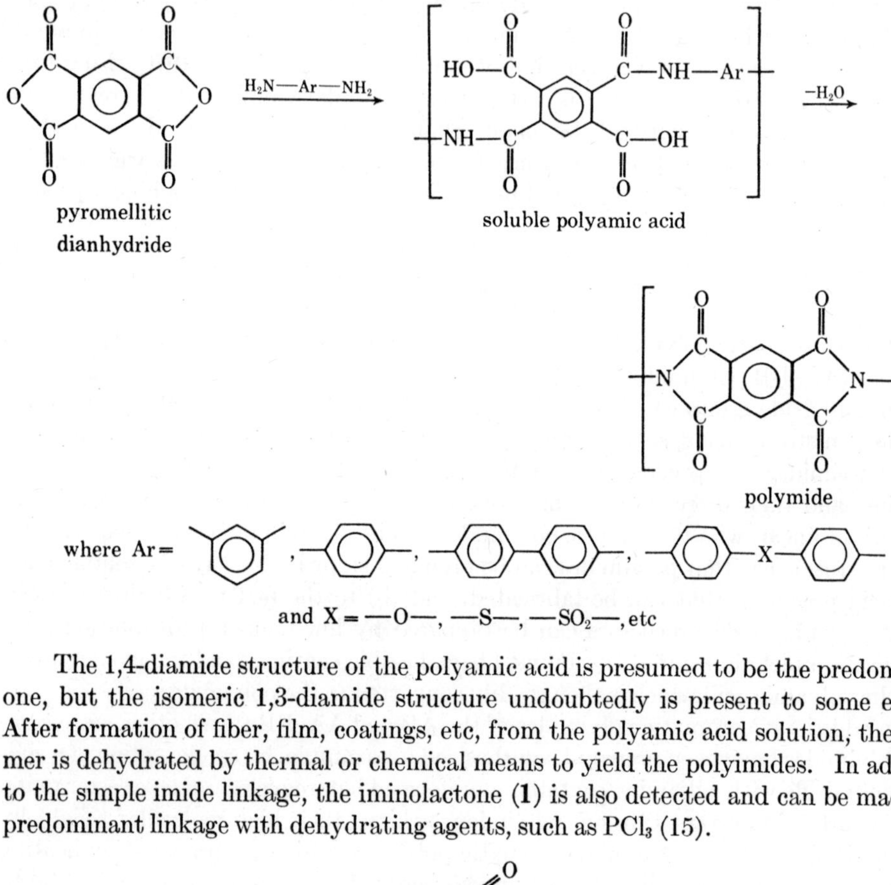

pyromellitic
dianhydride

soluble polyamic acid

polymide

where Ar =

and X = —O—, —S—, —SO$_2$—, etc

The 1,4-diamide structure of the polyamic acid is presumed to be the predominant one, but the isomeric 1,3-diamide structure undoubtedly is present to some extent. After formation of fiber, film, coatings, etc, from the polyamic acid solution, the polymer is dehydrated by thermal or chemical means to yield the polyimides. In addition to the simple imide linkage, the iminolactone (1) is also detected and can be made the predominant linkage with dehydrating agents, such as PCl$_3$ (15).

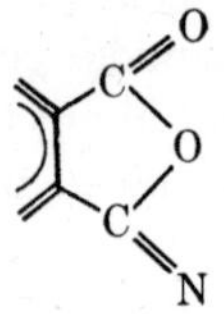

(1)

The polyamic acid derived from pyromellitic dianhydride and bis(4-aminophenyl) ether has been characterized thoroughly (16). It is reported (17) to be unstable in solution and to degrade slowly upon aging. The cause, apparently, is the water formed by the unwanted reaction of some amic acid groups to form imide groups; the water so produced presumably brings about hydrolysis of some of the amide groups linking the units of the polymer chain. Similar reactions have been shown for monomeric carboxyamides (18). Bower and Frost (6) reported that the amide groups of the polymer chain undergo an interchange with amine and anhydride end groups, making stoichiometric equivalence most important. Although addition of excess diamine or dianhydride can cause rapid lowering of the viscosity, recovery can be effected by the introduction of an equivalent of the complementary reactant (6). Salts of polyamic acids, unlike the acid polymers themselves, are quite resistant to hydrolysis, and films can be cast from aqueous solutions of such polyamic acid salts (19).

The only dianhydride of importance (as of 1970) other than pyromellitic dianhydride for the preparation of polyimides is 3,4,3′,4′-benzophenonetetracarboxylic dianhydride (**2**).

(2)

The products derived from this dianhydride and aromatic diamines are reported to be crosslinked (20) and patents have been issued which state that copolyimides containing benzophenone moieties indeed crosslink more readily. Crosslinking is thought to occur through the reaction of the carbonyl bridge (21) with amine groups (22); hydrazine and dihydrazides have been mentioned as crosslinking agents (23). Copolymers from diamines and mixtures of dianhydrides containing at least 20 mole% of (**2**) are claimed (24) to yield films with mechanical properties superior to those of polyimide homopolymers.

When polyamic acids are heated above 150°C, conversion to the polyimide is rapid; heating in the range of 300°C, however, is necessary for complete conversion. It has been pointed out (7) that polyimides high in imide content, eg polyimides derived from *m*- or *p*-phenylenediamine and pyromellitic dianhydride, are more apt to be brittle when heated at 150°C for only an hour or two than are polymers of lower imide content. Toughness and flexibility of films high in imide content can be improved markedly by heating the partially converted films to a temperature of about 300°C for a few minutes (6). The good flexibility of polyamic acids films can probably be attributed to the high order that exists in these polymers. On the other hand, the poor flexibility of polyamic acid films after heating to temperatures too low to effect complete cyclodehydration (150–225°C) can probably be ascribed to disorder introduced into the polymer, ie to the random occurrence of amic acid and imide groups. Good flexibility of the film is achieved once more when order has been restored upon conversion of the remaining amic acid groups to imide groups by heating the film to 300°C or higher. Incorporation of some linkages which are well known to provide high flexibility in polymers, such as —O— and —S—, results in films which are fairly flexible during conversion from polyamic acid to polyimide.

In addition to thermal processes for conversion of polyamic acids to polyimides, low-temperature chemical processes employing dehydrating agents such as acetic anhydride in pyridine (25) also cause conversion to the imide structure. In practice room temperature is usually employed.

Polyimides can also be prepared from the reaction of dianhydrides with diisocyanates or indirectly by the condensation of diamines with diester–diacid chlorides, diacid–diesters (1) or tetraesters. The reaction of a diester–diacid and a diamine is particularly attractive for use in making laminating resins because varnishes of high percent solids but low viscosity can be obtained (20,26). Advancement of the resin occurs as the volatiles (solvent and condensation by-products, ie alcohol and water) are expelled; when one of the starting materials is benzophenonetetracarboxylic dianhydride or one of its derivatives, crosslinking can be effected during the molding of the laminate.

Simple A–B Polyimides. Jones (5) has pointed out that probably the first recorded synthesis of a polyimide was made by Bogert and Renshaw (27), who observed that heating 4-aminophthalic anhydride or dimethyl 4-aminophthalate yielded an insoluble, infusible gray material, which they called "a polymolecular imide"; this product was not characterized further. A solid-state polymerization of 4-aminophthalic anhydride can be carried out to yield a polyamic acid (3) which can then be

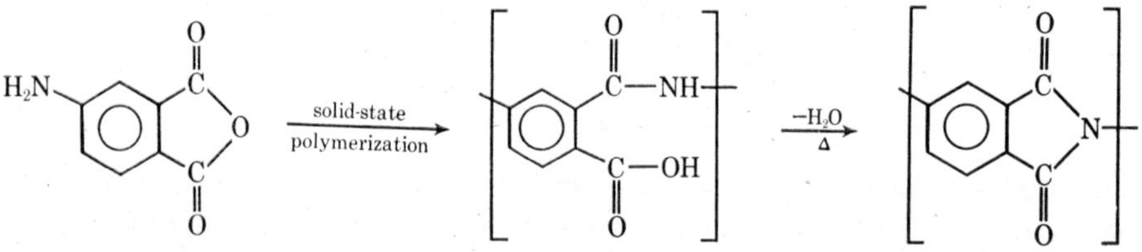

(3)

dissolved in dimethylformamide, dimethylacetamide, or dimethyl sulfoxide, and cast into film (cf solution polymerization of the AA–BB type above). This film can be converted to the polyimide by thermal or chemical dehydration in the same manner as AA–BB polyamic acids. Some details of the polycondensation of 4-aminophthalic anhydride were reported at duPont (28); A–B-type polyimides from a polyamide ester have been claimed (29).

Most polyimides of the A–B type, in addition to being difficult to prepare, possess rather poor mechanical properties; they are quite brittle in general compared with polyimides of the AA–BB type. However, the use of flexibilizing groups, eg —O—, reportedly yields nonbrittle films of the A–B type polyimides.

Heterocycle–Imide Copolymers. An ordered heterocycle–imide copolymer (8,30,31) is produced when a diamine containing a heterocyclic unit is polymerized with a dianhydride followed by cyclodehydration of the intermediate polyamic acid, the same as in the case of other AA–BB polyimides.

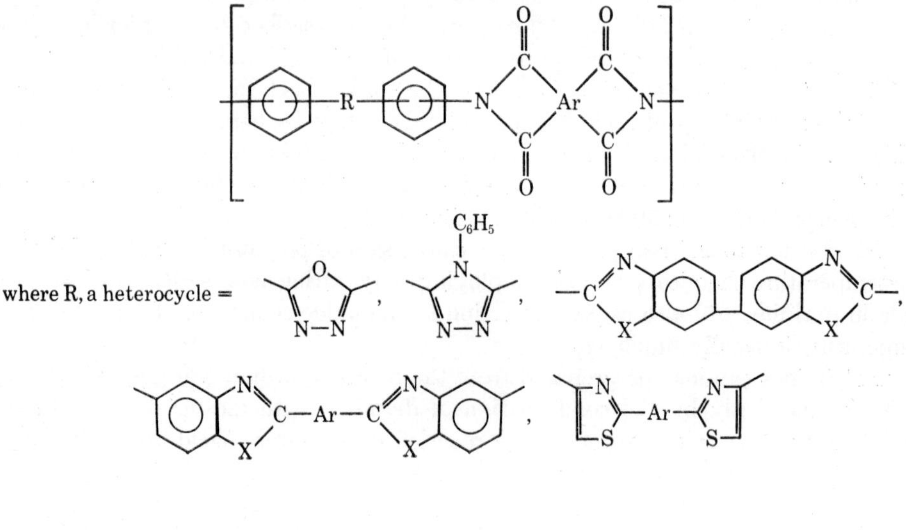

where R, a heterocycle =

$$X = -NH, -O-, -S-$$

and Ar =

Heterocycle copolymers in which the units are less ordered than in the preceding polymers have also been prepared (32).

Polyamide–Imides. These copolymers can be prepared by the reaction of dian-

hydrides with diamines containing preformed amide groups (6,33,34) or by the reaction of trimellitic anhydride acid chloride with diamines (33–35).

The parenthesis means that the moiety shown may appear this way or in the reverse manner.

Another method is the reaction of a diamine with a dianhydride containing a preformed amide group. A low-molecular-weight aromatic polyamide with amine end groups can be reacted with an aromatic dianhydride to yield a polyamide–imide (34).

Polyester–Imides. These copolymers have been prepared by the reaction of diamines containing preformed ester linkages with a simple dianhydride (6), by the reaction of a diamine or a diisocyanate with a dianhydride containing a preformed ester group and by the reaction of diols with diacids containing preformed imide groups.

Miscellaneous Aromatic Polyimides. A novel polyimide (4) devoid of hydrogen has been reported to be highly resistant to air oxidation (38); however, no physical properties, such as retention of weight or strength and elongation after heat-aging in air, were measured to support the claim of lack of oxidative degradation at elevated temperatures.

(4)

ALIPHATIC–AROMATIC POLYIMIDES

Both melt and low-temperature solution polycondensation have been used to prepare aliphatic–aromatic polyimides; the early work was concerned only with meltable polyimides which can be shaped from the melt. Use of solution-polymerization techniques for obtaining these polyimides indirectly via soluble polyamide acid precursors is a more recent development.

The early syntheses of aliphatic–aromatic polyimides were based on fusion of salts of aliphatic diamines and aromatic tetraacids or their derivatives, such as the diacid–diesters (1,39,40).

where R = alkyl and R′ = alkylene

Polymers of high molecular weight can be prepared by the fusion method; inherent viscosities up to 1.7 dl/g (0.5% solution in *m*-cresol) have been reported (1).

In order to obtain such high-molecular-weight polymers by this and related procedures (39,40), the resultant polymer has to be meltable. Consequently, when the polyimide is based on pyromellitic dianhydride, only straight-chain aliphatic diamines containing nine carbons or more, or seven when branched (40), can be utilized for preparing high-molecular-weight polymers. Polypyromellitimides from diamines containing fewer than seven carbon atoms in the chain degrade at or below their melting points, the polyimide from hexamethylenediamine being borderline in this respect. Polypyromellitimides derived from diamines having very long chains, such as 2,11-diaminododecane, $H_2N-C_{12}H_{24}-NH_2$, and 2,17-diaminoeicosadecane, $H_2N-C_{20}H_{40}-NH_2$, melt below 300°C; the polypyromellitimide of 4,4-dimethylheptamethylenediamine has a melting point of 320°C.

Polypyromellitimides derived from diamines containing both aliphatic segments and arylene rings have also been reported (7,38). If the aliphatic linkage is short, the melting point of the derived polyimide is quite high and consequently some of these polymers cannot be prepared by melt condensation. As the length of the aliphatic segments is increased, the melting point decreases. Inclusion of aliphatic or heteroatomic units in the dianhydride also leads to polyimides having lower melting or softening points.

POLYIMIDES VIA ADDITION POLYMERIZATION

Polyimides may be prepared which make use of polyaddition reactions for chain extension. Because of the aliphatic-type linkages employed to make polyaddition possible, polymers of this type are not as thermally stable as the wholly aromatic polyimides. However, in general, processing is simpler for this class of polymer. The simplest case is illustrated by the bis-maleimides which may be polymerized by heat alone (41) or by free-radical catalysts (41).

$$\text{(bis-maleimide structure)} \xrightarrow[\Delta]{\text{free-radical catalyst or}} \text{cross linked resin}$$

Polymers of this type were mentioned in 1948 in a patent describing the preparation of the bis-maleimide monomers (42). Diels-Alder adducts of the bis-maleimides, eg bis-norborneneimides (the cyclopentadiene adducts), may also be used to prepare crosslinked polyimides (41).

An epoxy–imide resin has been described (43) which, it is claimed, has properties intermediate between those of the epoxy and aromatic polyimides.

$$\text{(epoxy-imide structure)} \xrightarrow[\text{a diepoxide}]{\Delta \text{ with or without}} \text{epoxy-imide resin}$$

The addition of a diamine to a bis-maleimide has long been known to give a polymer (5) (44).

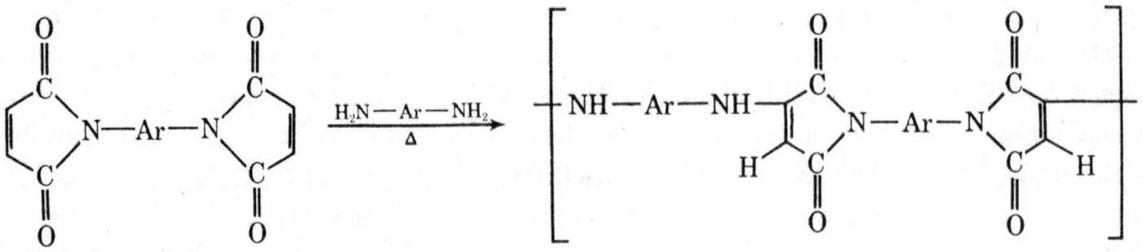

(5)

A mixture of (5) and a bis-maleimide may be prepared and subsequently used for the preparation of a crosslinked polyimide (45). Rhône-Poulenc's M-33A (crosslinked molding resin) and M-33B (soluble polymer for varnishes) appear to be based on such reactions.

Increased thermal stability can be obtained if preformed imide linkages are used (46) in a modified bis-maleimide, as shown below.

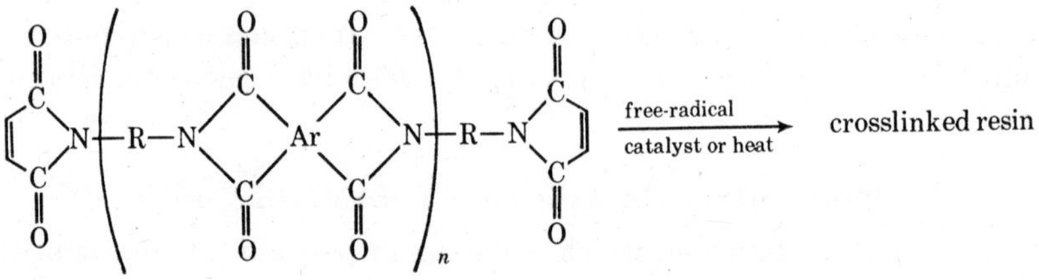

(6)

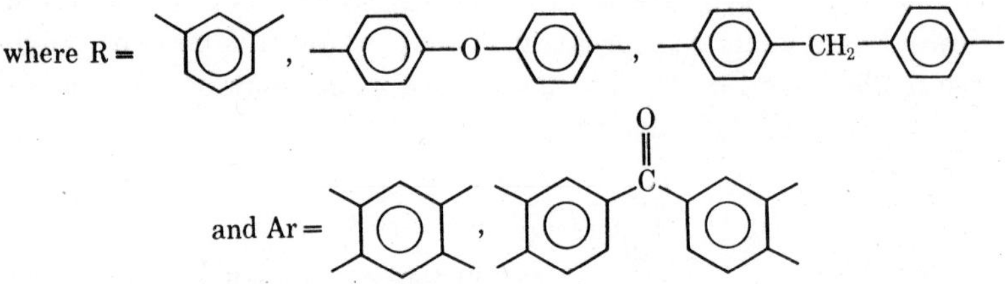

where R =

and Ar =

The relatively low-molecular-weight block (6) can be polymerized thermally or by means of free-radical catalysts (46). However, a more widely applicable reaction has been described (47–49). It makes use of the reaction of the cyclopentadiene adduct of maleic anhydride, an aromatic diamine, and an aromatic dianhydride, to yield an end-capped polyamic acid block which can be converted by heat treatment to a cross-linked polyimide, as shown in Scheme 1.

Use of the norbornylene group in Scheme 1 is significant because ring closure to the imide group can be effected by heat (50), whereas the maleamic acid of aromatic diamines must be ring closed to the imide by use of an anhydride plus catalyst, eg sodium acetate (42). Furthermore, it is well known that the norbornylene group is not polymerized at as low a threshold temperature as is the maleimide group. Hence, solvent can be driven off and the imidization (loss of water from the amic acid groups) can be carried to completion thermally without further polymerization (in this case, crosslinking) until the molding temperature is reached. Ciba-Geigy's P13N, produced under license from TRW, Inc., for varnish (48), molding resins (47), and adhesives (49) would appear to be based on such reactions (see Scheme 1).

Numerous reports on homopolymers and copolymers of maleimide and N-substituted maleimides have been published. One of the more interesting concerns N-sub-

Scheme 1

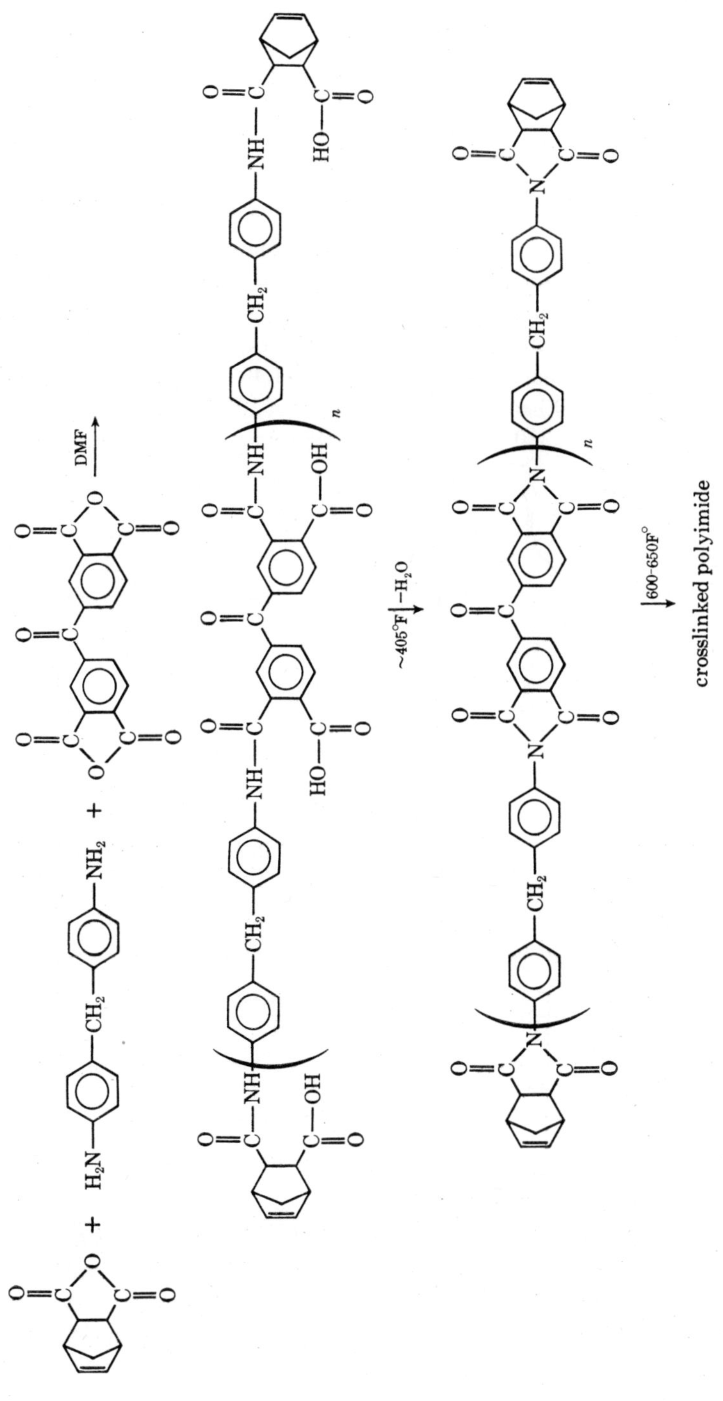

stituted maleimides with distinct melting points; a fiber was prepared from poly-N-n-butyl maleimide (**7**), mp 270°C (51).

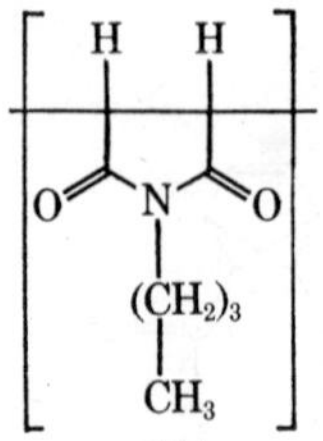

(**7**)

POLYIMIDES VIA DIELS-ALDER POLYMERIZATION

In view of the ease of polymerization of bis-maleimides on heating, it is somewhat surprising that these monomers may be heated with a second monomer to high temperatures to afford linear polymers via Diels-Alder polymerization (52,53). One of these polymers (**8**) can be prepared in solution at 260°C from 2,5-dimethyl-3,4-diphenylcyclopentadieneone dimer and N,N'-4,4'-(3,3'-dimethylbiphenyl)-bis-maleimide (54); the polymer has a reduced viscosity of 1.61 dl/g. Strong, tough film having excellent thermal ($T_g > 360°C$) and electrical properties has been reported (55).

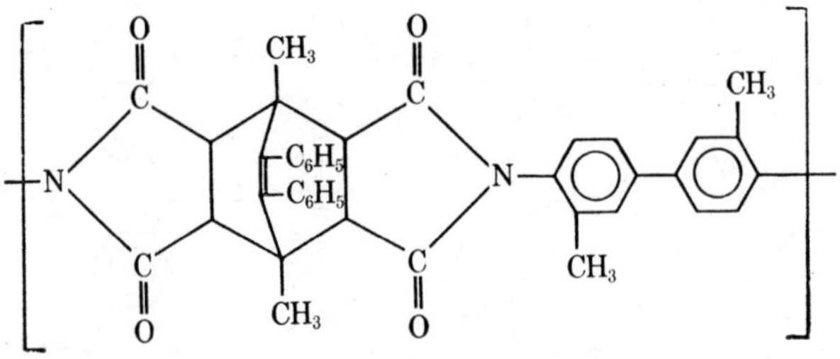

(**8**)

Properties

Very little has been reported concerning aliphatic–aromatic polyimides or wholly aromatic polyimides derived from dianhydrides other than pyromellitic dianhydride. Interest concentrates on the polypyromellitimide derived from bis(4-aminophenyl) ether, ie poly N,N-(p,p'-oxydiphenylene) pyromellitimide (**9**). It forms the basis of

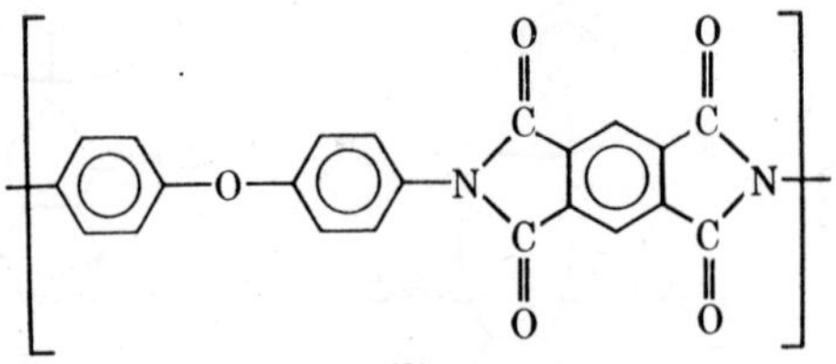

(**9**)

several commercially available products, including Kapton film (known as H-film while in the development stage). The polypyromellitimide of bis(4-aminophenyl) ether (ie Kapton) has been studied extensively, and much of the property data given below have been obtained on that material and are typical of those to be expected from polyimides in general.

FILMS OF WHOLLY AROMATIC POLYIMIDES

Thermal Properties.   Wholly aromatic polyimides, unlike wholly aromatic polyamides, show remarkably little variation in properties with changes in structure, as can be seen in the case of the polypyromellitimides listed in Table 1.   A number of polypyromellitimides, such as those derived from m- and p-phenylene diamine, bis(4-aminophenyl) ether etc, show no evidence of softening below their zero-strength temperatures of 750–800°C.   However, major changes of structure do lead to products of lower softening temperatures.   For example, incorporation of the highly flexible ether linkage in both the diamine and dianhydride yields a thermoplastic polymer which can be shaped while molten.

Table 1. Properties of Polypyromellitimides (7)

Diamine component	Solubility	Crystallinity	Zero-strength temp,[a] °C	Thermal stability in air[b] 275°C	Thermal stability in air[b] 300°C
(m-phenylene)	amorphous in conc H$_2$SO$_4$; crystalline insol	crystallizable	900	1 yr	>1 mo
(p-phenylene)	amorphous in conc H$_2$SO$_4$; crystalline insol	crystallizes readily	900	1 yr	
(biphenylene)	fuming HNO$_3$	highly crystalline	>900		1 mo
(—CH$_2$—)	conc H$_2$SO$_4$	slightly crystalline	900		7–10 days
(—C(CH$_3$)$_2$—)	conc H$_2$SO$_4$	crystallizable with difficulty	580		15–20 days
(—S—)	fuming HNO$_3$	crystallizable	800	10–12 mo[c]	6 weeks
(—O—)	fuming HNO$_3$	crystallizable	850	>1 yr	>1 mo
(—SO$_2$—)	conc H$_2$SO$_4$				>1 mo
(—SO$_2$—)	conc H$_2$SO$_4$				>1 mo

[a] "That temperature at which a film supports a load of 20 lb/in.^{2} of film cross-sectional area for no more nor less than 5 ± 0.5 sec" (25).
[b] As measured by retention of film creasability.
[c] Estimated.

Some wholly aromatic polyimides which do not melt in the conventional sense do, however, exhibit an incipient melt transition in the range of 550–570°C; this is also the temperature at which weight loss starts when the polymer is gradually heated in an inert atmosphere. (See Fig. 1.) Furthermore, 570°C is the temperature at which a typical polyimide, the polypyromellitimide of bis(4-aminophenyl) ether, shows a maximum in its rate of decomposition upon slow heating (see Fig. 1).

Resistance to thermal degradation is undoubtedly the most outstanding property of polyimides, and, accordingly, the thermal stability of these polymers has been studied extensively. Sroog and co-workers (7) reported that the polypyromellitimides derived from m-phenylenediamine, benzidine, and bis(4-aminophenyl) ether lost only

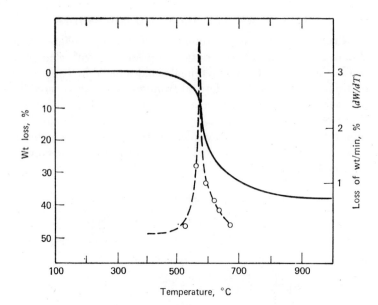

Fig. 1. Thermogravimetric curves for the polypyromellitimide of bis(4-aminophenyl) ether (**7**). LEGEND: —— the weight loss in helium at a heating rate of 3°C/min (18); --- the corresponding differential weight-loss curve.

1–1.5% of their original weight in a helium atmosphere upon heating up to 500°C at a rate of 3°C/min. The isothermal weight loss of the polypyromellitimide of bis(4-aminophenyl) ether in a helium atmosphere was only 1.5% after 15 hr at 450°C, and 7% after 15 hr at 500°C; weight loss in vacuum was also only slight.

Although the thermal stability of polyimides in air (thermoöxidative stability) is greater than that of most thermally stable polymers, it is nevertheless much poorer than the thermal stability in inert atmosphere or in vacuum. For example, the poly-pyromellitimide of bis(4-aminophenyl) ether lost less than 3 wt% after 12 hr at 450°C in helium, and the same amount in less than 1 hr in air at the same temperature. But after 12 hr in air at 450°C the weight loss was 40% in contrast to the 3 wt% loss in helium.

Of more significance than the weight loss at extreme temperatures as a measure of thermal stability, is the retention of film toughness (as measured by retention of creasability) after heat-aging in air (see Table 1). The thermal stability of H-film in air as measured by a related test, ie the retention of film flexibility, was found (7) to be at 400°C, 1 day; 300°C, 1 month; 275°C, 1 yr; and 250°C, 10 yr (extrapolated).

Ordered heterocycle–imide copolymers (8,30–32) offer a balance of physical properties not observed for the simple wholly aromatic polyimides, yet their thermal stability is quite high (see Table 2), except in those cases where the rupture of the heterocyclic ring occurs at a temperature lower than that causing rupture of the imide system.

The use of amide or ester linkages in the backbone of a wholly aromatic polyimide leads to polymers of lower softening and decomposition temperatures than those found for simple wholly aromatic polyimides; in fact, some polyester–imides have distinct melting points (56). Resistance to thermal aging is much poorer in the case of the polyamide–imides. In many respects, aromatic polyimide esters and aromatic poly-

Table 2. Thermal Properties of Ordered Heterocycle–Imide Copolymers

Structure	Melt-transition temp,[a] T_m, °C	Decomposition temp,[b] °C	Reference
	520	525	30
	450	510	30
	565	550	30
	575	575	30
	580	565	31
	615		31
	560	560	31

[a] Determined by means of programmed differential thermal analysis (DTA) in nitrogen.
[b] Determined by means of programmed thermogravimetric analysis (TGA) in nitrogen.

imide–amides behave more like aromatic polyamides and aromatic polyesters. The degree of thermal stability, a property of prime consideration, is more a function of the thermal stability of the aromatic amide and ester linkages than of the imide linkage.

Solubility. Wholly aromatic polyimides are insoluble in organic solvents. Fuming nitric acid, however, is apparently a general solvent for polyimides (7); many are also soluble in concentrated sulfuric acid. Unfortunately, both of these acids degrade the polymers, severly limiting their usefulness. Inorganic compounds, such as antimony and arsenic trichlorides, are also employed as solvents (57) and are useful for viscosity determinations because they apparently do not degrade polyimides.

Mechanical Properties. Wholly aromatic polyimides have useful mechanical properties over an exceptionally wide range of temperatures (see Table 3); for film of the polypyromellitimide of bis(4-aminophenyl) ether this range is reported (7) to be from −269 to over 800°C. Film of this polyimide has been shown by conventional testing to have measurable tensile strength up to temperatures of 500°C; both tensile strength and tensile modulus, however, tend to fall off at an increasing rate past 300°C.

Table 3. Tensile Properties of H-Film (60)

Property	Value
tensile strength,[a] psi	
at 25°C	25,000
200°C	17,000
300°C	10,000
500°C	4,000
elongation, %	
at 25°C	70
200°C	90
300°C	120
500°C	60
tensile modulus, psi	
at 25°C	400,000
200°C	260,000
300°C	200,000
500°C	40,000

[a] The film retained flexibility down to 4°K.

Although shear-modulus studies indicate neither a glass-transition temperature (T_g) nor a softening range for film of the polypyromellitimide of bis(4-aminophenyl) ether at temperatures up to 500°C, measurement of the electrical dissipation factor at 1 kc does indicate a glass-transition temperature at 385°C (58). (Internal friction studies indicate a transition beginning at about 280°C (59).) In contrast, the polybenzophenoneimides of bis(4-aminophenyl) ether and m-phenylenediamine have shear-modulus T_g's of 355 and 340°C, respectively (58). (Values approx 50°C higher were obtained on samples annealed at 250°C for 20 hr in vacuum.) The data clearly indicate that the carbonyl group of the benzophenone dianhydride introduces flexibility into the polymer chain.

Electrical Properties. Wholly aromatic polyimides have an outstanding high dielectric strength, a high volume resistivity and a low dissipation factor (see Table 4); moreover, the dielectric strength is essentially the same over the range 23 to 200°C. Even after heat-aging at 300°C for 8 weeks an 80% retention of the original dielectric strength is shown by film of the polypyromellitimide of bis(4-aminophenyl) ether; the volume resistivity actually increases after a short heat-aging period, then stays at a high level on further heat-aging.

Films of polyimides for motors and transformers and coatings for magnet wire are finding wide commercial use. In general, polyimides appear to have better po-

Table 4. Electrical Properties of Polypyromellitimide Films, 1–2 mil (7)

Property	Temperature, °C		
	23	150	200
dielectric constant, 1000 Hz	3.1–3.7 (3.5)[a]	2.9–3.1	2.8–3.2
dissipation factor, 1000 Hz	0.0013–0.002 (0.002)[a]	0.006–0.0014	0.0005–0.0010
volume resistivity at 23°C, 50% rh, Ω-cm	10^{17}–5 × 10^{18} (10^{18})[a]	>10^{15}	10^{14}–10^{15}
dielectric strength, V/mil	4550–6900 (7000)[a]		4600–5900

[a] For H-film use; see reference 61.

tential in electrical insulation applications than do aromatic polyamides, especially at elevated temperatures. The electrical properties of the polyamide–imides, however, are claimed to be excellent (34).

Crystallinity, Density, and Color. Although the thermal properties of the wholly aromatic polyimides are much alike, considerable differences are found in their color and tendency to crystallize. All the polyimides are colored materials and the color can be correlated with the diamine component (7); polypyromellitimides of bis(4-aminophenyl) ether, bis(4-aminophenyl) sulfide, and bis(4-aminophenyl) sulfone are yellow, deep red, and nearly colorless, respectively. To a lesser degree than the structure, the conditions of the synthesis also affects the color.

Many polyimides can be crystallized readily. The pyromellitimide of p-phenylenediamine is crystalline when prepared (7), but high-temperature annealing appears to be required to crystallize polyimides derived from less symmetrical diamines such as m-phenylenediamine. Hot-drawing of films of ordered heterocycle–imide copolymers was found to induce good orientation and moderate crystallinity (30).

The densities of films of six different aromatic polypyromellitimides were found to vary over a range of only 0.02 g/cm³, eg 1.41–1.43 g/cm³ (7). This is all the more striking considering the variation in the structure of the diamine used, ie p-phenylene, m-phenylene, bis(4-aminophenyl) ether, and bis(p-aminophenyl) sulfone. The slight variations in density reported cannot be correlated with structure.

Resistance to Change by Chemical Agents, uv, and Ionizing Radiation. Pyromellitimides exhibit good resistance to degradation by chemical agents. Hydrolytic resistance of these polymers is fair to good depending on whether basic or acidic conditions are employed. The quantitative determination of chemical resistance of a polyimide in the form of fiber is shown in Table 5; it seems reasonable to expect that a film, because of a smaller ratio of surface to volume, would show even better resistance to attack by chemicals. The hydrolytic stability of the polyimides in boiling water ranges from poor to outstanding, depending on the structure. Films of polypyromellitimides derived from m- and p-phenylenediamine, for example, are embrittled after a week or less in boiling water whereas films of polypyromellitimides derived from bis(4-aminophenyl) ether and bis(4-aminophenyl) sulfide retained toughness after a year and after three months, respectively (7).

Polyimides are susceptible to degradation by ultraviolet radiation, but possibly to a lesser degree than polyamides; nevertheless, if used in direct sunlight polyimide fibers, films, or coatings would probably require the addition of light stabilizers.

Table 5. Chemical Resistance of a Polyimide Fiber at 100°C (62)

Chemical agent	Concentration, %	Time, hr	Loss of tenacity, %
acids			
sulfuric	10	260	52
hydrochloric	10	260	71
hydrofluoric	10	150	36
bases			
sodium hydroxide	0.4	4	57
miscellaneous			
water	100	1400	4[a]
sodium hypochlorite	0.5	150	37
dimethylacetamide at bp, 166°C	100		0[b]

[a] Shrinkage, 0.25%.

[b] Shrinkage, 2%.

The resistance of aromatic polyimides to degradation by high-energy radiation is indeed outstanding. The degradative effect of exposure to over 10,000 megarads in a Van de Graaff generator on the polypyromellitimide of bis(4-aminophenyl)methane is considerably less than that for polyethylene terephthalate or polystyrene after only 600 megarads (see Table 6). The resistance of Kapton film to degradation by thermal neutrons in comparison with polyethylene terephthalate, polystyrene, and polyethylene is shown in Tables 6 and 7, which show the effect of radiation on polypyromellitimide films.

Table 6. Effect of Radiation on Polypyromellitimide Film, Exposure Van de Graaff 2 MeV

Polymer film	Thickness, mils	Passes	Dose, megarads	Remarks
polyimide from bis(4-amino-phenyl)methane	2.0	8000	10,000	retains toughness, good electrical properties
poly(ethylene terephthalate)	2.0–3.0	200	240	creasable
	2.03–3.0	500	600	brittle, yellow
	3.0			brittle, yellow
polystyrene	1.2	500	600	yellow, extremely brittle
polyethylene (branched)	6–10	200	240	very weak, sticky gum

Table 7. Effect of Radiation on Polypyromellitimide Film, Thermal Neutron Degradation

Polymer film	Thickness, mils	Exposure, days	Temperature, °C	Flux, 10^{13} neutrons/ (cm²)(sec)	Remarks
polyimide from bis(4-amino-phenyl) ether	2–2.7	40	50–75	0.4	slightly darkened, brittle in spots
		40	175	0.5	darkened, rough
		80	175	0.5	darkened, brittle
poly(ethylene terephthalate)	3.0	10	50–75	0.4	failed
	3.0	20	175	0.5	yellow, brittle
polystyrene	1.2	10	50–75	0.4	yellow, very brittle
polyethylene (branched)	3.0	10	50–75	0.4	sticky, rubbery
	3.0	40	50–75	0.4	brown varnish

Behavior on Ignition and Pyrolysis. Films of wholly aromatic polyimides burn only when in direct contact with an open flame, ie they are self-extinguishing. Studies of the gaseous pyrolytic decomposition products of the polypyromellitimide of bis(4-aminophenyl) ether under vacuum indicate that the composition of these gaseous by-products under constant vacuum (63) differs from that found when the system is closed off after evacuation but before pyrolysis (61). The principal products in both experiments, however, are carbon dioxide and carbon monoxide (61,63). Some solid and liquid components also include amines, phenols, and phthalimides. The residue obtained upon vacuum pyrolysis of the film at temperatures from 620–850°C is reported to be semiconducting (63).

FIBERS OF AROMATIC POLYIMIDES

As a consequence of molecular orientation and crystallization which can be imparted by drawing, fibers represent the most stable form for a given polymer. On the other hand, because of the large surface area presented by fibers, the adverse effects of oxidation and attack by irradiation or chemicals are maximized. Thus, the properties of polyimide fibers under a variety of conditions faithfully reflect the potential of polyimides.

Few simple polyimides have been spun to fiber, and very little has been reported concerning their properties, especially at elevated temperatures and after heat, ie aging. Several heterocycle–imide fibers have also been reported (32,64,65) and there seems to be considerable potential for the use of polyimide fibers in very harsh environments, as indicated by the thermal, electrical, and mechanical properties of polyimide films. (See Table 5 for resistance of a polyimide fiber to hydrolysis.)

Spinning and Fiber Tensile Properties. Polyimide fibers have been spun from solutions of their polyamic acid precursors by both dry- and wet-spinning techniques. The dry-spinning process would appear to be the preferred process, at least for the polypyromellitimide of bis(4-aminophenyl) ether; this process, however, may be limited to those polymers which are nonbrittle during the transition from polyamic acid to polyimide. In the dry-spinning process, fibers were prepared by spinning a solution of the polyamic acid into a gaseous medium at a temperature below 65°C, and then converting the fiber to polyimide at temperatures above 200°C. Wet spinning was accomplished by spinning a solution of a polyamic acid (containing an amine base such as pyridine as a dehydration catalyst) into a bath of acetic anhydride at room temperature, collecting and drying the fibers. The best wet-spun fibers were obtained using high draw ratios during spinning; fiber properties were improved by heating (ie annealing) at elevated temperatures.

Tensile properties for some of the best examples of the few simple polyimide fibers reported are given in Table 8. Tenacities have been low or only moderately high for wet-spun fibers and elongations have been medium to low; initial moduli of wholly aromatic polyimide fibers are high compared to the moduli of several conventional fibers, eg nylon.

Fibers from ordered heterocycle–imide copolymers (see Table 9) have good strength and exceptionally high initial moduli. The properties of the best fiber from a simple aromatic polyimide are given in Table 9.

Thermal Stability of Fibers. The data available on wholly aromatic polyimide fibers, as in the case of polyimide films, reflect the fact that these fibers have been

Table 8. Tensile Properties of Polypyromellitimide Fibers

Diamine	Inherent viscosity,[a] dl/g	Den[b]	Tenacity, g/den	Elongation, %	Initial modulus, g/den	Reference
m-phenylene						
wet spun	1.94		1.3	45	30	25
			2.2[c]	22[c]	43[c]	
bis(4-aminophenyl) ether						
wet spun	1.13	3.6	4.5	8.4	65	25
dry spun	2.03	3.4	5.6	17	56	66
4,4'-diaminophenylmethane						
wet spun	1.40		3.4[d]	26[d]	65[d]	25
bis(4-aminophenyl) sulfide						
wet spun	1.20		2.2	39	29	25
dry spun	1.63		5.7	14.5	53	66

[a] A portion of the viscous solution of polyamic acid was diluted with dimethylacetamide to 0.5% and the inherent viscosity determined at 30°C.

[b] Weight in gram of 9000 m of fiber.

[c] The improved properties given for wet spun fiber were produced by increasing the rate of takeup from 32 ft/min (1.7 draw ratio) to 70 ft/min (2.2 draw ratio).

[d] Tensile properties of the corresponding polyamic acid fiber are 1.1, 6.5, and 44, respectively (9).

Table 9. Properties of Fibers of the Polyimide Class, Expressed in $T/E/M_i$[a] at °C

Number[b]	21	100	200	300	400	500	Reference
1	5.2/6.1/110	4.0/5.8/91	3.1/4.2/105	2.1/6.0/44	1.4/3.7/58	0.8/1.4/31	64
2	6.3/9.7/122	4.5/8.7/86	3.2/8.5/67	1.4/9.7/45	0.7/7.8/11	0.4/3.1	64
3	3.9/19.1/100	2.9/12.4/65	1.8/14.4/56	1.0/18.0/42			64
4	4.8/5.1/168	4.4/5.7/154	3.5/8.8/146	2.3/10.2/80	1.6/6.8/57	1.7/4.2/67	65
5	6.4/5.8/203			2.0/14.9/65	1.5/15.7/32		65
6	5.2/4.0/148			2.0/5.0/63	1.1/3.6/32		65
7	4.7/19.3/57	3.6/18.4/44	2.9/25.9/40	1.8/22.6/28	1.7/31.5/15	0.6/6.9	65
8[c]	6.9/13.0/72	5.5 58	4.3 47	3.0			62

[a] $T/E/M_i$ = tenacity, g/den; elongation, %; initial modulus, g/den.

[b] See Table 9a for key.

[c] $T/E/M_i$ of highest strength fiber of this structure reported (66) = 8.6/11.9/75.

developed chiefly for applications where heat resistance is important. The properties of these fibers provide ample evidence of the potential importance of polyimide fibers.

Properties at Elevated Temperatures. The strength at elevated temperatures for fibers of the polyimide class is remarkable and is not surpassed by any other type of fiber based on an organic polymer. Although the strength of these fibers drops with increasing temperature (see Table 8), the strength even at 300–500°C in air is nevertheless greater in some instances than that for some textile fibers at room temperature. The dry-heat shrinkage in air for a polyimide fiber has been reported (62) to be nil at 300°C and only 2% at 400°C. The zero-strength temperature (in the range of 550 to 570°C) for most of these fibers is higher than that for aluminum.

Properties after Prolonged Aging at Elevated Temperatures. The heat-aging of fibers of the polyimide class indicates that these materials, for the most part, perform well under oxidative conditions for extended periods of time (see Fig. 2). The rapid drop of tenacity toward the end of the heat-aging experiments points up the hazard in

Table 9a. Key to Table 9

No.	Polymer

ordered heterocycle–imide copolymers

1

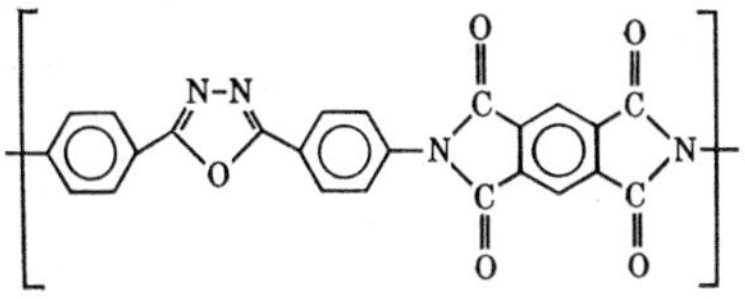

2

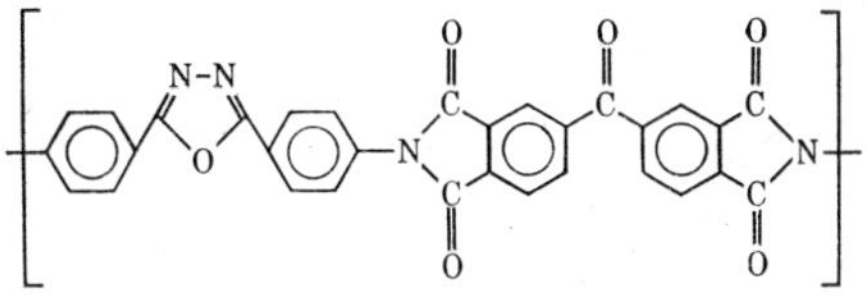

3

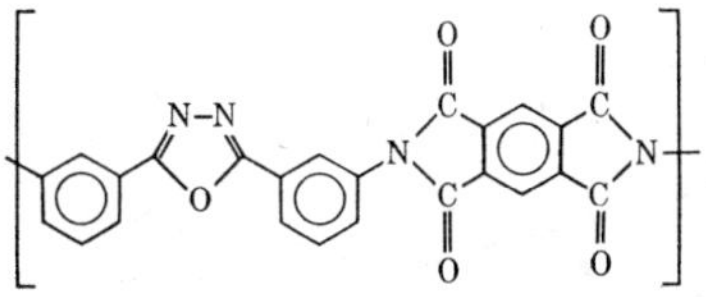

4

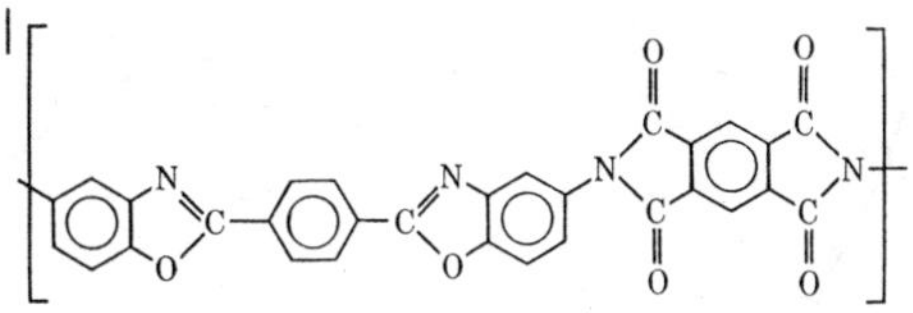

5

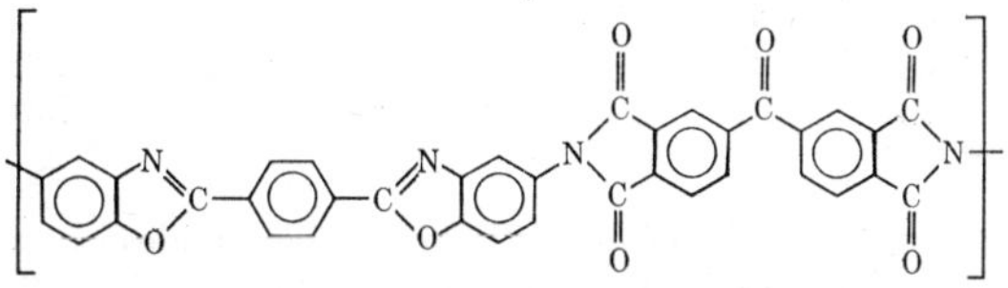

6

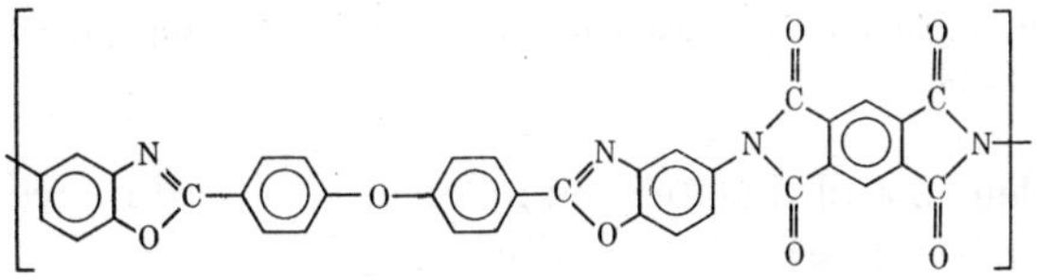

7

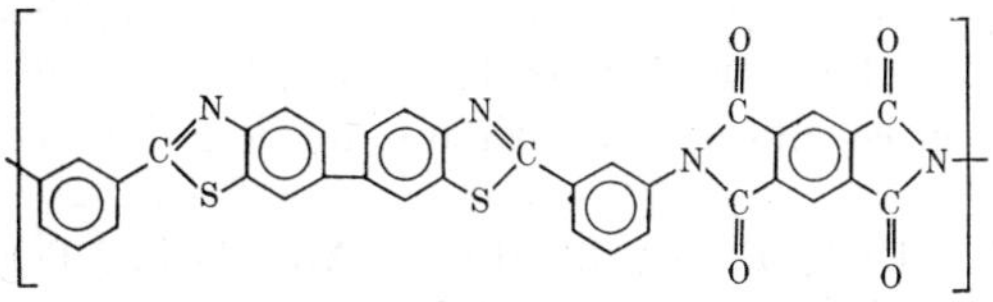

simple aromatic polyimide

8

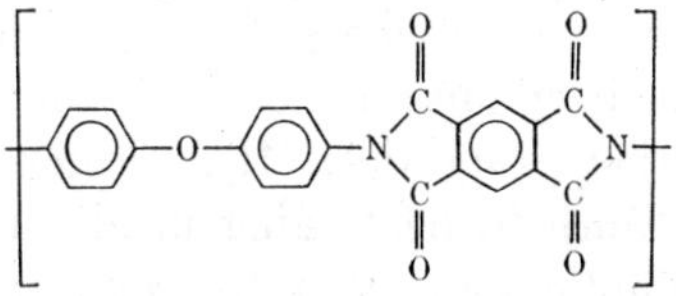

extrapolating heat-aging data. The endurance of the fibers is highly dependent on the use temperature. Thus, fiber which retains >80% of its original strength after 7 weeks at 300°C in air, is reduced in strength to <10% of its original strength at 350°C in air after 5 days. On the other hand, at about 250°C in air (the melting point of fibers such

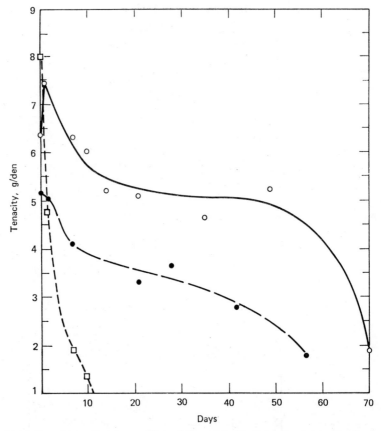

Fig. 2. Retention of tenacity of some fibers of the polyimide class after heat-aging in air at 300°C. LEGEND: –□--□– polypyromellitimide of bis-(4-aminophenyl) ether (7); –●–●– polypyromellitimide of 2,5-bis-(p-aminophenyl)-1,3,4-oxadiazole; –O–O– polybenzophenoneimide of 2,2'-p-phenylene-bis-(5-aminobenzoxazole).

as poly(ethylene terephthalate) and nylon 66), the endurance of polyimide fibers might be expected to be remarkable—possibly for many years.

The failure of most thermally resistant fibers upon heat-aging is caused by the loss of extensibility (elongation), ie embrittlement. For polyimide fibers, this is very likely the result of crosslinking rather than reduction of molecular weight.

PROPERTIES OF ALIPHATIC–AROMATIC POLYIMIDES

Information on the properties of aliphatic–aromatic polyimides is meager; no systematic study of any property of polymers of this type has been reported. But, not unexpectedly, more data have been obtained on their thermal properties, particularly thermal stability, than on other properties. It is primarily with respect to thermal properties, particularly resistance to heat-aging in air or thermoöxidative stability, that the incorporation of aliphatic segments into aromatic polyimides has its greatest effect. Powdered polyimides derived from aliphatic diamines begin to lose weight at 200–300°C even in an inert atmosphere, whereas aromatic polyimides show less than 1.5% weight loss upon heating to 500°C. Even the single aliphatic carbon in the back-bone repeat unit of the polypyromellitimides derived from such diamines as bis(4-

aminophenyl)methane and 2,2-bis(4-aminophenyl)propane has a detrimental effect with regard to thermal stability as determined by the degree of weight loss at elevated temperatures (7).

The stability of aliphatic–aromatic polyimides upon heat-aging in air is very poor compared with that of wholly aromatic polyimides. At 175°C the heat-aging stability of films of the polypyromellitimides of nonamethylenediamine, 4,4-dimethylhepta-methylenediamine, and 3-methylheptamethylenediamine was reported to be on the order of one day as measured by retention of film creasability (1). As in the case of weight loss at elevated temperatures, even a single aliphatic carbon in the polymer repeat unit results in a marked lowering of thermoöxidative stability. Thus, films of the polypyromellitimides of bis(4-aminophenyl)methane and of 2,2-bis(4-aminophenyl)-propane remained creasable for only 7–10 days and 15–20 days, respectively, after heating at 300°C in air, whereas wholly aromatic polypyromellitimides retained their creasability for more than a month in the same test (7).

The glass-transition temperature, T_g, for aliphatic polyimides is much lower than that of the aromatic polyimides. T_g values for the polypyromellitimides of nonameth-ylenediamine, 4,4-dimethylheptamethylenediamine, and 3-methylheptamethylene-diamine range from 110–135°C (1). Heat-distortion temperatures are also consider-ably lower than those of wholly aromatic polyimides. For example, the polyimide from tetramethylenediamine and 2,2-bis(3,4-dicarboxyphenyl)propane has a heat-distortion temperature of only 177°C (40), as compared with a heat-distortion tempera-ture greater than 300°C for the polypyromellitimide of bis(4-aminophenyl) ether (7).

Densities for only a few aliphatic–aromatic polyimides have been reported. These range from 1.30 to 1.36, and indicate that, in general, they are considerably lower than those for wholly aromatic polyimides.

Aliphatic–aromatic polyimides, unlike wholly aromatic polyimides, can be dis-solved in organic solvents such as m-cresol to permit solution characterization (40). Presumably, the solvents for aromatic polyimides, such as concentrated sulfuric or fuming nitric acid, antimony and arsenic trichlorides or a mixture of these salts, also are solvents for aliphatic–aromatic polyimides.

Almost nothing has been reported about the mechanical properties of the aliphatic–aromatic polyimides. The tenacity and elongation of the polyimide film derived from tetramethylenediamine and the dianhydride of 2,2-bis(3,4-dicarboxyphenyl)propane are 14,000 psi and 10%, respectively (40). Both values were considerably lower than the tenacity, 24,000 psi, and elongation, 65%, reported for a wholly aromatic poly-imide, the polypyromellitimide of bis (4-aminophenyl) ether (61). These differences, however, may only reflect a presumably more perfect nature of the solution-cast film of the wholly aromatic polyimide; film of the aliphatic–aromatic polyimide was pre-pared by hot-pressing.

Uses

Polyimides are mainly employed for the following uses: laminating varnishes, structural adhesives, wire enamels, coatings, films, foams, and molding powders. Several excellent fibers have been reported (62,64,65) but despite their great promise commercialization of polyimide fibers does not seem likely in the near future.

Varnishes. Polyimide varnishes are important for the preparation of laminated structures (eg panels), filament winding, gel coating of various composites, and coating of electrical components covered by an enamel. Laminated (10–14 plies) parts include printed circuit boards, honeycomb core, radomes, and structural parts for high-performance aircraft. Polyimides are also important for use as the binding agent for diamond grinding wheels; the life of the grinding wheels is greatly prolonged by use of the thermally stable resin.

Ideally, a good laminating varnish should possess suitable tack, and should set under heat (or upon contact with a catalyst) to a rigid, preferably crosslinked resin without evolution of volatiles which would create voids. (Most epoxy resins, for example, meet all of these requirements; however, the epoxies are limited in thermal stability.) In present practice (1970) polyimide varnishes are prepared from precursors having little or no tack, particularly after B-staging. Also, volatiles, both condensation by-products and solvent, must be expelled before or during the molding operation. If the B-staged (ie insoluble but still fusible) impregnating resin on fiber or fabric is heated until essentially no volatiles remain, then a very high laminating temperature and pressure must be used. If a resin-impregnated fiber or fabric having a relatively high volatile content is employed, the temperature and pressure may accordingly be reduced, but at the expense of creating voids in the laminate. Frequently, a postcuring operation is required to expel volatiles from the composite.

Although solutions of certain of the polyamic acid precursors may be used as laminating varnishes, the solids content must necessarily be kept low ($\leq 25\%$) because of the high viscosity of these solutions. Because it is desirable to use solutions of high-percent solids (60–90%), it is more common practice to use solutions of monomers (20,26) rather than polymers, or, alternatively, to use low-molecular-weight polymers; solutions of this sort are only moderately viscous. The polyimide resin increases in molecular weight during B-staging and molding. Suitable solvents for the varnishes are alcohols, glycols, cresol, and amide-type solvents, eg dimethylformamide (DMF), dimethylacetamide (DMAc), or N-methylpyrrolidone (NMP).

Varnishes yielding wholly aromatic polyimides include the duPont PI series and the Skybond series (700–703, 708, and 709) which are sold for application to glass cloth or fiber and to graphite or boron reinforcing fibers. In general, the duPont Company has chosen the route of supplying glass fiber (roving) or fabric which has been impregnated with varnish and B-staged to yield a "prepreg" which is ready for laminating; the prepregs are marketed under the name Pyralin.

Special "low flow" varnishes can be heated rapidly to expel solvent without losing viscosity and have been offered by Monsanto Company as Skybond 709 and by the duPont Company as PI-4707.

Amoco's polyamide–imide resins are AI-10 and AI-11; these can be obtained as varnishes in N-methyl-2-pyrrolidone. Westinghouse manufactures impregnated glass cloth for laminates containing the Aramidyl amide–imide resin.

The two following polyimide varnishes cure by means of addition polymerization (and therefore are not wholly aromatic): (1) Rhône-Poulenc's M-33 and Gemon, produced by General Electric under license from Rhône-Poulenc; and (2) P13N, produced by Ciba-Geigy, Ltd., under license from TRW, Inc.

The M-33B resin is sold as a yellow powder which may be dissolved to high-percent solids ($\sim 60\%$) in DMF or NMP. P13N varnish is sold as a 40%-solids solution (DMF) of a polyamic acid which is used for impregnating roving or cloth. The amic acid groups of the P13N resin imidize with loss of water during evolution of the solvent from the prepreg. Both the M-33B and P13N resins are cured during molding after volatiles have been expelled; consequently, it is possible to obtain laminates having a relatively low void content with these resins. However, because of the relatively large proportion of aliphatic groups present in these resins, the thermooxidative stability in air for M-33B and P13N resins is not as good as that of the wholly aromatic polyimides; the P13N resin might reasonably be expected to have better stability than the M-33B resin because P13N contains blocks of wholly aromatic imide joined by a relatively small number of aliphatic units whereas M-33B has a high proportion of aliphatic segments, derived from addition polymerization.

Enamels. In general the enamels differ from the varnishes in that they are solutions of polymer (amic acid) having a relatively low solids content ($\sim$25%). However, excellent enamels can be made from solutions of monomers when benzophenonediester–diacid is used as one of the starting materials. The resins employed in enamels usually form free-standing films. For highly flexible coatings, most enamels of the polyimide class are based on the diamine bis(4-aminophenyl) ether. It is well known that an —O— bridge imparts flexibility to polyimide films, particularly during cure when most polyimide precursors become quite brittle in the transition from polyamic acid to polyimide.

Because the coatings on electrical wires must be smooth, bubble- and blisterfree, and capable of being flexed without cracking for better windability, the polyimide precursors must be applied as very thin coatings and freed of solvent and by-product water at such a rate as not to produce bubbles in the coatings. It is common practice to use multiple dips to build up the coating to the desired thickness. The preferred solvents for the enamels are dimethylformamide, dimethylacetamide, N-methyl-2-pyrrolidone, and cresol. The latter is claimed to be an excellent solvent for both the polyamic acid precursors of the polyimides and for varnish-type precursors of the polyimides as well. Cresol is cheaper than the amide-type solvents and wire-coaters are experienced in its use with phenolic resins. Mixtures of amide-type solvents with cheaper diluents (including some nonsolvents) are also frequently employed.

The commercially important polyimide enamels are the following: duPont's Pyre-ML and Monsanto's Skybond 704 and 7W, the only wholly aromatic polyimides offered (in 1970) for Class-220 magnet wire; Amoco's AI wire enamel, a polyamide–imide, also for Class-220 magnet wire; and General Electric's Imidex-E wire enamel, a polyester–imide for Class-200 magnet wire. Some mixed aliphatic–aromatic polyester–imide enamels have also been prepared.

Applications for the polyimide enamel coatings are the following: stator-wound induction motors, hermetic motors, dry-type transformers, dc field coils and armatures, universal armatures and fields, random-wound coils and solenoids. In addition to wire-coating operations, glass or metal panels may be coated to provide insulation.

Adhesives. Good adhesives usually form a gel or hard film, each of which has good cohesive strength and can attach firmly to the materials to be bonded together. Adhesives are usually derived from polymers which wet the materials to be bonded quite well; the polyimide compositions which seem to make the best adhesives are at least partially film forming. Ideally, a good adhesive should possess a degree of tack which enables the surfaces to adhere on contact or with pressure, and to resist separation thereafter. Polyimide adhesives, however, have little tack and must be heat-cured to effect bonding.

Because the polyimide precursors must be B-staged to eliminate volatiles and because an adhesive bond is weakened by voids if the volatiles cannot escape, most adhesives are sold as the B-staged resin (containing 15–20% volatiles) supported on a reinforcing fiber (eg glass) carrier.   To match the thermal coefficients of the resin-to-metal or metal-to-composite, especially when the joints formed are to be subjected to thermal aging, it is common practice to use a metal filler, eg aluminum powder.   Additives, such as arsenic compounds, are frequently used in polyimide adhesives to complex impurities (such as iron which might be present in aluminum or titanium sheeting) which catalyze oxidation of the organic resin.   One of the principal suppliers of polyimide adhesives is the Bloomingdale Department of American Cyanamid Company, which supplies FM-34 adhesive film on glass fiber.   The duPont Company also supplies a formulated adhesive, PI-5505 (a B-staged polyimide on glass scrim).

The polyamide–imides are supplied either as an impregnated glass cloth or as a varnish to be formulated with aluminum powder (#120).   Westinghouse supplies AI-133 adhesive for steel and BI-1 for titanium;   their polyamide–imide resin, Aramidyl, is also supplied on glass cloth (AI-131):   Amoco's AI-10 and AI-11 polymers (AI-1032 and -1137 varnishes) may be formulated with aluminum powder for structural adhesives.

Molding Powders.   Polyimide powders are of two types: those which are injection moldable and those which must be shaped under high heat and very high pressure, ie employing the powder-metallurgical technique of sintering.   The fusible polyimides are of the aliphatic–aromatic type; such products are offered by American Cyanamid (XPI-182) and Raychem Corporation (Poly X).

The duPont Company apparently has chosen to sell molded parts (under the trade name Vespel) rather than to sell the molding powders; two types of Vespel parts are offered, one is formulated to provide low frictional performance (through added graphite, fluorocarbon resin or molybdenum sulfide) and the other (unmodified resin) is used in friction devices.   Vespel products are made for parts to be used at high temperatures, eg jet-engine components, nonlubricated seals and bearings, cryogenic bearings, heavy-duty brakes, and clutches.   Meldin PI, PI-30X and PI-15Y have been offered by the Dixon Corporation in sheets, rods, tubes, and fabricated parts.   Polyimide parts in some applications can be compared to fluorocarbon resin parts; however, the former are much stiffer at 550°F than the latter are at room temperature.

Amoco has offered polyamide–imide molding powders with good mechanical properties but not as good as the high-temperature properties of the wholly aromatic polyimides.

A molding powder, presumably based on an aromatic diamine and maleic anhydride (and hence a "polyimide," but not as the term is generally applied), is offered by Rhône-Poulenc as M-33A.   Foreign patents assigned to TRW, Inc., indicate that molding powders can be obtained from a short aromatic polyimide block capped by norbornylene–imide groups which crosslink during molding (46).   Both of these resins might be expected to perform less well under severe thermal conditions than wholly aromatic polyimides.

Foamed Plastics.   Both the Monsanto and duPont companies have sampled polyimide foams (67–71) for potential use in thermal and sound insulation, in strengthening applications, and, to a lesser degree, in padding.   Slab polyimide foams are nonflammable and generate little, if any, smoke and toxic fumes.   A flame applied to these materials only produces a char and slow degradation, whereas almost all other organic foams burn unless compounded with fire retardants.   The chief advantage of the polyimide-type foam over the latter types, is that the latter are only moderately self-extinguishing and generate large amounts of smoke and toxic fumes.   The polyimide foams are of two types, a slab foam and a cured-in-place syntactic foam.   The flexible slabs can be prepared with densities in the range of 0.5 to 1.5 lb/ft^3; the high-density, 6–35 lb/ft^3, syntactic foam contains, in addition to the high-density polyimide resin, a low-density filler, eg glass microballoons.   Foaming of the resin may be brought about by one of the following methods: foaming due to expansion of volatiles; introduction of gases into an incipient polymer gel; expansion of gases such as those used for the foaming of polyurethans; and liberation of carbon dioxide from the reaction of a diisocyanate with a dianhydride to yield a polyimide.

Precursor powders for foams are also available from Monsanto Company; the series of RI-7271 powders are designated -01, -06, -12, -18 (by means of which the approximate density in lb/ft^3 of the resulting foam is indicated).

Films.   The polyimide films, as exemplified by duPont's Kapton Type H, have excellent electrical properties, ie equivalent to polyester film, but with a much higher thermal cut-through temperature, ie 900 vs 480°F, and they can operate at a much higher use temperature (400–500°F) than polyester film (300°F).   The polyamide-imide and polyester–imide films exhibit thermal-electrical behavior intermediate between those of aromatic polyimides and polyesters.   Because of the lower density of the polyimide films compared to the densities of inorganic insulators, weight savings, critical in the aerospace industry, may be effected.   The higher electrical efficiency of the polyimide films permits an increase in the horsepower of electrical motors at the same weight level or permits a designer to obtain the same horsepower from a lighter weight motor.   Typical applications include wire and cable wrap, formed coil wrap, motor-slot liners, magnet wire, transformers, capacitors, and magnetic and pressure-sensitive tapes.   A fluorocarbon resin coated (one side) film, Kapton Type F, is sold for heat-sealable fabrication purposes.   Printed circuits on polyimide films have attracted some attention because it is possible to solder on these films without melting them.   Also, it is possible to etch the polyimide films with hydrazine; thus, printed circuits can be formed from the etched film (74).

Bibliography

1. U.S. Pat. 2,710,853 (1955), W. M. Edwards and I. M. Robinson (to E. I. duPont de Nemours & Co., Inc.).
2. *Plastic Focus* **1** (12), 1 (1969).
3. *Chem. Eng. News* **43**, 24 (1965).
4. *Oil, Paint, Drug Reptr.* 39 (Feb. 1967).
5. J. I. Jones, F. W. Ochynski, and F. A. Rackley, *Chem. Ind.* (*London*) **1962**, 1686.
6. G. M. Bower and L. W. Frost, *J. Polymer Sci. A* **1**, 3135 (1963).
7. C. E. Scroog, A. L. Endrey, S. V. Ambramo, C. E. Berr, W. M. Edwards, and K. L. Oliver, *J. Polymer Sci. A* **3**, 1373 (1965).
8. J. Preston and W. B. Black, *J. Polymer Sci. B* **3**, 845 (1965).
9. U.S. Pat. 3,179,614 (1965), W. M. Edwards (to duPont).
10. U.S. Pats. 3,179,630 and 3,179,631 (1965), A. L. Endrey (to duPont).
11. U.S. Pat. 3,179,632 (1965), W. R. Hendrix (to duPont).
12. U.S. Pat. 3,179,633 (1965), A. L. Endrey (to duPont).
13. U.S. Pat. 3,179,634 (1965), W. M. Edwards (to duPont).
14. U.S. Pat. 3,277,043 (1966), F. F. Holub (to General Electric Co.).
15. R. A. Dine-Hart and W. W. Wright, *J. Appl. Polymer Sci.* **11**, 609 (1967).
16. M. L. Wallach, *J. Polymer Sci. A-2* **5**, 653 (1967).
17. L. W. Frost and I. Kesse, *J. Appl. Polymer Sci.* **8**, 1039 (1964).
18. M. L. Bender, Y. L. Chow, and F. Chloupek, *J. Am. Chem. Soc.* **80**, 5380 (1958).

19. R. J. W. Reynolds and J. D. Seddon, *J. Polymer Sci. C* **23** (1), 45 (1968).

20. U.S. Pat. 3,190,856 (1965), E. Lavin, A. H. Markhart, and R. E. Kass (to Shawinigan Resins Corp.).

21. U.S. Pat. 3,492,270 (1970), D. J. Parish (to duPont).

22. U.S. Pat. 3,416,994 (1968), J. R. Chalmers and C. Victorius (to duPont).

23. U.S. Pat. 3,436,372 (1969), E. F. Hoegger (to duPont).

24. U.S. Pat. 3,264,250 (1966), W. G. Gall (to duPont).

25. Brit. Pat. 903,271 (1962), to duPont.

26. U.S. Pat. 3,347,808 (1967), E. Lavin, A. H. Markhart, and R. E. Kass (to Monsanto Co.).

27. M. T. Bogert and R. R. Renshaw, *J. Am. Chem. Soc.* **30**, 1135 (1908).

28. F. F. Rogers, Jr., and A. G. Kirk, *Paper Am. Chem. Soc., Southeastern Regional Meeting, Richmond, Va., Nov. 5–8, 1969.* See also U.S. Pat. 3,450,678 (1969), F. F. Rogers (to duPont).

29. U.S. Pat. 3,414,546 (1968), J. H. Werntz (to duPont).

30. J. Preston and W. B. Black, *J. Polymer Sci. A-1* **5**, 2429 (1967).

31. J. Preston, W. F. DeWinter and W. B. Black, *J. Polymer Sci. A-1* **7**, 283 (1969).

32. J. Preston, W. DeWinter, W. B. Black, and W. L. Hofferbert, Jr., *J. Polymer Sci. A-1* **7**, 3027 (1969).

33. U.S. Pat. 3,049,518 (1962), C. W. Stevens (to duPont).

34. U.S. Pat. 3,179,635 (1965), L. W. Frost and G. M. Bower (to Westinghouse Electric Corp.).

35. U.S. Pat. 3,260,691 (1966), E. Lavin, A. H. Markhart, and J. O. Santer (to Monsanto Co.).

36. Fr. Pat. 1,386,617 (1965), to Standard Oil Co.

37. U.S. Pat. 3,440,215 (1969), F. F. Holub (to General Electric Co.).

38. S. S. Hirsch, *J. Polymer Sci. A-1* **7**, 15 (1969).

39. U.S. Pats. 2,880,230 and 2,900,369 (1959), W. M. Edwards and I. M. Robinson (to duPont).

40. U.S. Pat. 2,731,447 (1956), W. F. Gresham and M. A. Naylor, Jr., (to duPont).

41. U.S. Pat. 3,380,964 (1968), F. Grundschober and J. Sambeth (to Rhodiaceto).

42. U.S. Pat. 2,444,536 (1948), N. E. Searle (to duPont).

43. U.S. Pats. 3,369,055 (1968) and 3,481,822 and 3,481,823 (1969), J. O. Salyer and O. Glasgow (to Monsanto Research Corp.).

44. P. Kovacic and R. W. Hein, *J. Am. Chem. Soc.* **81**, 1187 (1959); see also T. V. Sheremeteva, G. N. Larina, M. G. Zhenevskaya, and V. A. Gusinskaya, *J. Polymer Sci. C* **16**, 1631 (1967).

45. Fr. Pat. 1,555,564 (1969), to Rhône-Poulenc S.A.; see also Belg. Pat. 718,016 (1969) and Dutch Pat. 68,09559 (1969), to Rhône-Poulenc, S.A.

46. Dutch Pat. 68,18601 (1969), to TRW, Inc.; see also Fr. Pat. 1,537,135 (1969), to Rhone-Poulenc S.A.

47. Fr. Pat. 1,581,983 (1969), to TRW, Inc.; see also Dutch Pat. 68,13940 (1969), to TRW, Inc.

48. Fr. Pat. 1,572,798 (1969), to TRW, Inc.; see also Dutch Pat. 68,09244 (1969), assigned to TRW, Inc.

49. Dutch Pats. 68,09665 and 69,01939 (1969), to TRW, Inc.

50. P. O. Tawney, R. H. Snyder, R. P. Conger, K. A. Leibbrand, C. H. Stiteler, and A. R. Williams, *J. Org. Chem.* **26**, 15 (1961).

51. R. C. P. Cubbon, *Polymer* **6**, 419 (1965).

52. J. K. Stille and L. Plummer, *J. Org. Chem.* **26**, 4026 (1961).

53. J. K. Stille and T. Anyos, *J. Polymer Sci. A* **2**, 1487 (1964); *J. Polymer Sci. A* **3**, 2397 (1965).

54. E. A. Kraiman, in J. R. Elliot, ed., *Macromolecular Syntheses*, Vol. II, John Wiley & Sons, Inc., New York, 1966, p. 145.

55. U.S. Pats. 2,890,206 and 2,890,207 (1959), E. A. Kraiman (to Union Carbide Corp.); see also U.S. Pats. 2,890,207 (1959); 2,971,944 (1961); and 3,074,915 (1963).

56. D. F. Loncrini, *J. Polymer Sci. A-1* **4**, 1531 (1966).

57. H. A. Szymanski, W. Collins, and A. Bluemle, *J. Polymer Sci. B* **3**, 81 (1965); see also, *Appl. Spectry*, **19** (4), 137 (1965).

58. S. L. Cooper, A. D. Mair and A. V. Tobolsky, *Textile Res. J.* **35** (12), 1110 (1965).

59. G. A. Bernier and D. E. Kline, *J. Appl. Polymer Sci.* **12**, 593 (1968).

60. W. E. Tatum, L. E. Amborski, C. W. Gerow, J. F. Heacock, and R. S. Mallouk, *Paper Elec. Insulation Conf., Chicago, Ill., Sept. 17, 1963.*

61. J. F. Heacock and C. E. Berr, *SPE (Soc. Plastics Engrs.) Trans.* **5**, 105 (1965).

62. R. S. Irwin and W. Sweeney, *J. Polymer Sci. C* **19**, 41 (1967).

63. S. D. Bruck, *ASC Polymer Preprints* **5** (1), 148 (1964).

64. J. Preston and W. B. Black, *J. Appl. Polymer Sci.* **9**, 107 (1969).

65. J. Preston, W. B. Black, and W. DeWinter, *J. Appl. Polymer Sci.* **9**, 145 (1969).

66. U.S. Pat. 3,415,782 (1968), R. S. Irwin (to duPont).

67. U.S. Pat. 3,249,561 (1966), R. W. Hendrix (to duPont).

68. U.S. Pat. 3,310,506 (1967), L. E. Amborski and W. P. Weisenberger (to duPont).

69. I. Serlin, A. H. Markhardt, and E. Lavin, *Soc. Plastics Engrs., 25th Ann. Tech. Conf. Washington, D.C., 1970, Sect. 19-A*, p. 2. See also U.S. Pat. 3,483,144 (1969), to Monsanto Co.

70. Fr. Pats. 1,540,432 and 1,540,433 (1968), to Monsanto Co.

71. W. J. Farrissey, J. S. Rose, and P. S. Carleton, *ACS Polymer Preprints* **9** (2), 1581 (1968).

72, J. I. Jones, *J. Polymer Sci. C* **22** (2), 773 (1969).

General References

N. A. Adrova, M. I. Bessonov, L. A. Laius, and A. P. Rudakov, *Polyimides—A New Class of Thermally Stable Polymers*, Technomic Publishing Co., Stanford, Calif., 1970.

C. E. Skroog, "Polyimides," in N. Bikales, ed., *Encyclopedia of Polymer Science and Technology*, Vol. 11, Interscience Publishers, a div. of John Wiley & Sons, Inc., New York, 1969, pp. 247–272.

J. Preston and W. B. Black, "Wholly Aromatic and Aliphatic-Aromatic Polyimides," in H. F. Mark, S. M. Atlas, and E. Cernia, eds., *Man-Made Fibers, Science and Technology*, Vol. 2, Wiley-Interscience, New York, 1968.

J. PRESTON
Chemstrand Research Center, Inc.
Monsanto Company

POLYMERS OF HIGHER OLEFINS

The polymerization of 1-olefins to crystalline polymers using catalysts obtained by the reaction of transition-metal compounds with organometallic compounds of elements in the first three groups of the periodic table was demonstrated between 1954 and 1956, primarily by Ziegler et al. in Germany (1) and by Natta and co-workers in Italy (2,3). These important discoveries were exploited rapidly and commercial production of Ziegler polythene (an expression current in the United Kingdom for polyethylene) and of isotactic polypropylene was started by 1957 both in Europe and in the United States. The pace of development has been so rapid that world consumption of high-density polythene exceeded 680,000 tons in 1965, while that of polypropylene was over 300,000 tons and it was estimated that substantially more than 1 million tons of each were going to be consumed in 1970 (4). However, although many other 1-olefins have been polymerized to crystalline polymers, only two, poly-1-butene and poly-4-methyl-1-pentene, have been exploited commercially and in both cases the scale of manufacture has been small. There are two main reasons for this limitation in commercial interest. The first is that for general use as a thermoplastic material a crystalline polyolefin should have a melting point approximately in the range of 100 to 280°C (see Fig. 1). Secondly, successful exploitation requires that the parent olefin be available at relatively low cost. The lower limitation on melting point arises because if the melting point is below 100°C the mechanical properties of the polymer will not be maintained under normal conditions of use, while the upper limit of ca 280°C applies because polyolefin chains decompose thermally at 300–330°C (5) and these materials require temperatures at least 50°C higher than their melting points for easy melt fabrication.

Data relating the melting points of crystalline polyolefins to their molecular structures are given in Figure 1 and Scheme 1. With linear polyethylene the polymer chain

Scheme 1

Melting Points for Isotactic Polymers of Branched-Chain 1-Olefins (9), °C

branched in the 3 position

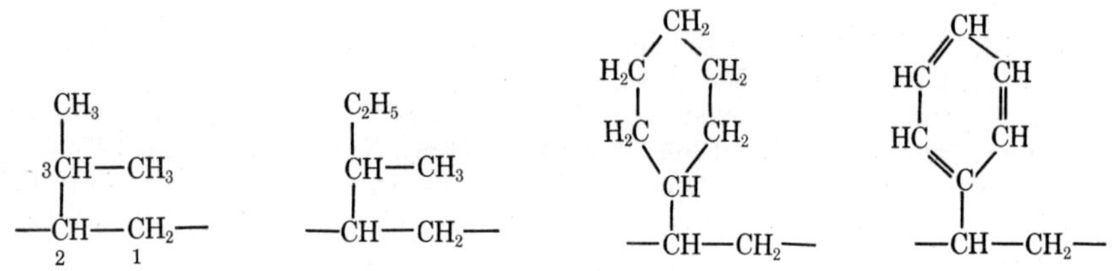

310	>350	372	250

branched in the 4 position

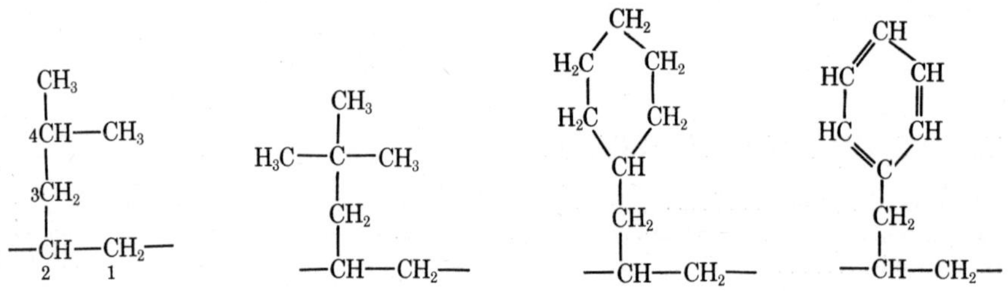

245	>380	230	230

branched in the 5 position

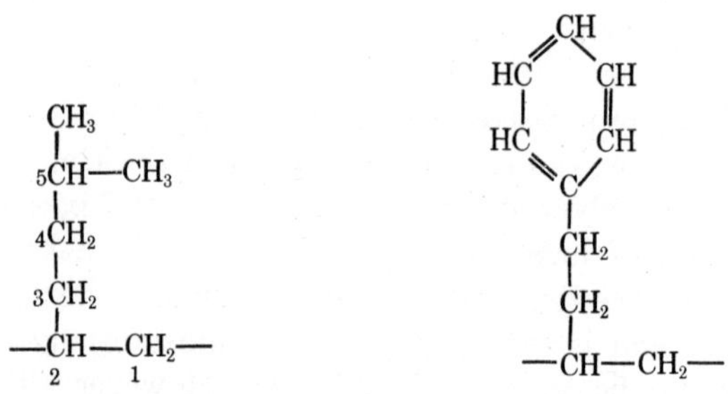

110	160

contains no structural irregularities which would inhibit crystallization, and in the crystalline phase the polymer repeat units adopt a planar zig-zag conformation. The chains of all other linear, head-to-tail poly-1-olefins possess a potential element of stereoirregularity, because if as a simplification the main chain is considered as a planar zig-zag, then the side chains can be positioned on either one side or the other of the zig-zag and if this occurs at random along the chain crystallization is prevented. However, the polymers under discussion have isotactic structures in which the side groups are all positioned on one side of the chain (see Vol. 14, p. 283) and this stereo-

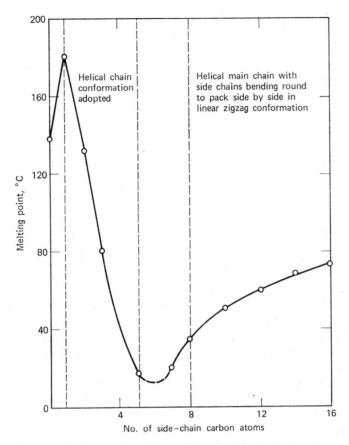

Fig. 1. Melting point vs number of side-chain carbon atoms for isotactic polymers of unbranched olefins.

regularity makes crystallization possible.   In the actual polymer crystals the steric requirements of the side chains prevent crystallization in a planar zig-zag conformation and instead the polymer chains adopt a helical conformation (6).   A composite conformation is found in the crystals of isotactic polyolefins with linear side chains containing eight or more carbon atoms, and here the main chains are helical but the side chains bend round to pack side by side in a planar zig-zag conformation (7).   There is a maximum and a minimum in the curve of melting point vs the number of side-chain carbon atoms for polymers of linear 1-olefins (see Fig. 1) and these correlate with the changes in chain conformation.   The drop in melting point from polypropylene to poly-1-heptene occurs as the longer more flexible side chains lead to less densely packed crystal structures, while the melting point increases from poly-1-decene onward as the side chains become able to pack more perfectly side by side as their length increases. The isotactic branched-chain 1-olefin polymers, shown in Scheme 1, adopt helical conformations in the crystalline phase and their melting points increase with increasing bulk of the side chains, due to reduced chain flexibility.   As might be expected, the melting points of polymers with side chains containing a given bulky group decrease as these groups are spaced further away from the main chain by interposition of methylene groups.

The melting point data presented in Figure 1 and Scheme 1 (not exhaustive, especially Scheme 1) indicate that only a small proportion of the known crystalline poly-1-olefins are likely to be useful as thermoplastics and application of the second criterion, ie monomer availability, leads to a short list of five: polyethylene, polypropylene, poly-1-butene, poly-4-methyl-1-pentene, and polystyrene. Isotactic polystyrene is at present excluded as this polymer crystallizes slowly from the melt (8) so that conventional melt-fabricated samples are of low crystallinity and offer no significant improvement in mechanical properties over ordinary atactic polystyrene. Of the remaining four, polyethylene and polypropylene are manufactured on a large scale and the small-scale manufacture of isotactic polymers of 1-butene and of 4-methyl-1-pentene has also been started.

Polymers of 1-Butene

MANUFACTURE OF ISOTACTIC POLY-1-BUTENE

Catalyst Systems. Isotactic poly-1-butene is produced by a range of catalysts based on the discoveries of Ziegler and Natta. In general, catalysts suitable for isotactic polypropylene can be used also for butene. Many ethylene polymerization catalysts are either inactive (eg cyclopentadienyltitanium derivatives and aluminum alkyls) or tend to isomerize 1-butene to 2-butene (eg $CrCl_3 + Al(C_2H_5)_3$). The most useful catalysts are restricted to those based on titanium and vanadium and of these the violet, crystalline modifications (α or δ) of $TiCl_3$ give the highest yields of isotactic polymer.

The catalyst systems used in manufacture have not been revealed but patent and other publications describe systems using a slurry of catalyst in inert hydrocarbon diluents saturated with butene to about atmospheric pressure. The aluminum alkyl is dissolved in the diluent. A convenient recipe (10) describes the use of a liter of a paraffin diluent (boiling range 180–220°C), stirred in anhydrous, airfree conditions. The diluent is saturated with butene at 35°C, and 72 m moles of diethylaluminum chloride and 18 m moles of the catalyst, $TiCl_3$, are added. The catalyst becomes dispersed in growing polymer, all but a small proportion of which remains insoluble in the diluent. After 2½ hr the temperature is raised to 50°C when the polymerization can proceed more rapidly, the slurry remaining particulate. Without this initial lower-temperature stage the polymer particles absorb the diluent more and the slurry deteriorates to a viscous mass with loss of heat control. The ultimate yield depends on how easily the slurry is stirred and whether polymerization is stopped before the rapid increase of viscosity due to the retention of the diluent held in the interstices between touching particles and the absorption by swelling polymer. The stage at which this happens depends, among other things, on the structure of the catalyst particles and so on its preparation. The shape and structure of polymer are closely related to the shape and structure of the catalyst. In the example presented (10) after 4 more hours a yield of 231 g of polymer was obtained.

The catalyst residues must be removed before fabrication. The various methods used for polypropylene can apply here. The catalyst and aluminum alkyl are destroyed by reaction with compounds such as an alcohol, acetylacetone, or water. The polymer can be dissolved in a hydrocarbon (eg heptane at 80°C) to facilitate catalyst removal, washed with water (11) and a complexing reagent, eg oxalic acid, or washed as a hydrocarbon slurry with water (12).

Suitable catalysts can be prepared by reduction of $TiCl_4$ with aluminum alkyls or aluminum metal. Aluminum-reduced $TiCl_4$ in activated form is marketed by Stauffer Chemical Co. as "AA" material. Other investigators have carried out polymerizations in bulk (13) or in the gas phase (14). Polymerization of 1-butene in a C_4 cut purified from butadiene is applied commercially (14a). A measure of the stereospecificity of the catalyst is provided by fractionation of the resulting polymer in a series of solvents, as shown in Table 1.

Table 1. Poly-1-butene Made with α $TiCl_3$ and $(C_2H_5)_3Al$ at 75°C (15)

Solvent, at boiling point	Extracted, %	Intrinsic viscosity,[a] dl/g	Type
acetone	5.5		amorphous
ether	19.0	0.28	amorphous
pentane	3.2	0.35	weakly crystalline
residue	72.4	2.09	highly crystalline

[a] In tetrahydronaphthalene at 135°C.

This criterion must be applied with caution as solubility of polymer is encouraged both by steric irregularities in the polymer chain and by low molecular weight. Hence the term "atactic" is not strictly a suitable term for soluble polybutene which contains a range of steric structures and can be induced to crystallize to a small extent on annealing. Nevertheless, using the insolubility in boiling ether as a rough indication of the tacticity a comparison of various catalyst systems can be made. A few results are given in Table 2.

Table 2. Variation of Poly-1-butene Tacticity with Catalyst and Aluminum Alkyl (16)

| Catalyst | Insoluble in boiling ether, % | | | |
	$Al(C_2H_5)_3$	$Al(C_3H_7)_3$	$Al(C_4H_9)_3$	$Al(C_{16}H_{33})_3$
$TiCl_3$	65	75	67.7	55
$TiCl_4$	51.5	36.8	47.3	35.7
VCl_3	48.7			
VCl_4	27.8			

Various other factors can affect the tacticity of the product, such as aging of the catalyst, addition of pyridine to the catalyst system, and the ration of aluminum alkyl to catalyst; these and other variables have been discussed by Rubin (17). Poly-1-butene of highest steric purity (98% insoluble in boiling ether) can be made using $(C_2H_5)_2$ AlI as activator (18), though comparable results have been claimed with $(C_2H_5)_2AlCl$ and $TiCl_3$ (10).

Poly-1-butene can be obtained from 2-butenes using catalysts that isomerize, as well as promote Ziegler-Natta polymerization (19), but these processes are not important commercially.

Kinetics. Like propylene and ethylene, 1-butene polymerization with $TiCl_3$ and aluminum alkyls can exhibit a rate-growth period during which the catalyst is disrupted to expose active sites. After this period the rate is proportional to monomer and catalyst concentrations if the ratio of aluminum to titanium is kept constant.

The overall activation energy for the system $TiCl_3$ (Stauffer HA)–$(C_2H_5)_3Al$ is 10 kcal/mole (20). A comparison of mean rates of polymerization using a single batch of $TiCl_3$ (Stauffer AA) is given in Table 3.

Table 3. Rates of Polymerization of 1-Butene Compared with Ethylene and Propylene (21)

Monomer	Temperature, °C	Al compound	Rate[a]
1-butene	50	$Al(C_2H_5)_3$	160
propylene	50	$Al(C_2H_5)_3$	285
ethylene	50	$Al(C_2H_5)_3$	770
1-butene	60	$Al(C_2H_5)_2Cl$	75
propylene	60	$Al(C_2H_5)_2Cl$	105
ethylene	60	$Al(C_2H_5)_2Cl$	250

[a] Rate calculated as moles of monomer polymerized per mole $TiCl_3$ per hour per atmosphere partial pressure of monomer, the rate being the mean value over the first hour of polymerization.

Rates decrease as the polymerization proceeds. The extent depends on the catalyst system, temperature, etc, and can be ascribed to various causes, such as inhibition by a by-product, $(C_2H_5)AlCl_2$, from the activating alkyl (21) or reduction of the catalyst (generally observed with $(C_2H_5)_3Al$). For polymerization with Et_2AlCl at 60°C (see Table 3) a figure of 10^{-3} mole active centers per mole of $TiCl_3$ has been measured (21), showing that relatively little of the $TiCl_3$ is available for catalysis. The molecular weight of poly-1-butene can be reduced by adding hydrogen (by analogy (22) with propylene) or zinc alkyls (23) to the polymerization. In some cases the ratio of aluminum alkyl to titanium compound affects the molecular weight (24).

Syndiotactic Poly-1-butene. Polymerization producing syndiotactic poly-1-butene has been reported, but no proof of the structure was given (25). Copolymerization with propylene using catalysts known to be syndiospecific for propylene (VCl_4 and $(C_2H_5)_2AlCl$ at −78°C) can yield a syndiotactic copolymer capable of crystallizing if the 1-butene content is less than 30% (26).

PROPERTIES OF ISOTACTIC POLY-1-BUTENE

Polymorphism. Three crystalline modifications of poly-1-butene can be isolated in almost pure forms. Type II is usually first formed from the melt and converts to Type I at a rate depending on a variety of factors, such as molecular weight, tacticity, temperature, pressure, and mechanical shock. This effect is illustrated in Figure 2 wherein the change effected at different temperatures of storage after molding is shown. Initially the rate of change is fastest at about 40°C, but the most rapid conversion to about 95% Type I is obtained at about room temperature. The thermodynamic driving force increases as the temperature is lowered, but at temperatures below about 20°C the rate of conversion decreases, due to the reduced thermal mobility of the polymer chains. Type II is unstable below 100°C with respect to Type I, which may be the only thermodynamically stable form of poly-1-butene (21).

The transformation of Type II to Type I has a marked effect on the physical properties at room temperature. The density, rigidity, and strength increase (27). The change can be followed by dilatometry, x-ray diffraction (28), the relative intensities of absorption bands at 925 cm^{-1} (Type I) and 900 cm^{-1} (Type II) in the infrared spectrum, and by the Raman spectrum (29).

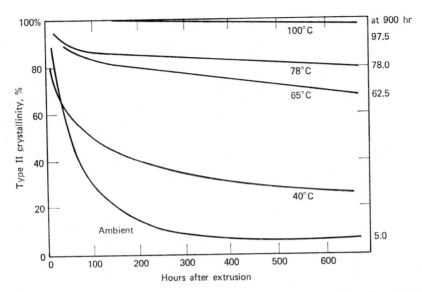

Fig. 2. The transformation from Type II to Type I of poly-1-butene (unoriented "Bu-Tuf" (petro-Tex) poly-1-butene extruded at 250°C and quenched to the temperature indicated). Data obtained at ICI Plastics Division.

A low-melting modification I' of Type I can be obtained by polymerization in *n*-heptane at −20°C (30) or by polymerization in absence of a liquid diluent (gas phase) (14). Type III and I' modifications can be formed by precipitation from solution at specific temperatures (31). These types are of minor importance.

Some properties of various polymorphs of poly-1-butene are given in Table 4.

Table 4. Polymorphism in Poly-1-butene (17)

Type	Final melting point, °C	Type	Unit-cell parameters, Å a	b	c	Helix form[a], X_Y	Crystal density, g/cc	Preparation
I	136	rhombohedral	17.7		6.5	3_1	0.95	transformation of Type II between −20°C and +80°C
I'	95–109							(a) very slow heating of Type III above mp (b) gas to solid-phase polymerization (c) polymerization in heptane below −20°C
II	124	tetragonal	14.85		20.6 ~76	11_3 or 29_8 or 40_{11}	0.90	normal form on crystallizing from melt
III	109	orthorhombic?	12.49	8.96	7.6	10_3		precipitation from solution[b]
		amorphous					0.85–0.86	

[a] X Monomer units are found in Y turns of the helix.   [b] Eg, amyl acetate.

The usual methods for measurement of approximate degrees of crystallinity can be employed for poly-1-butene, such as x-ray diffraction and density measurement (28), but it must be remembered that none are absolute as no polymer is a simple two-phase system. Poly-1-butene has the additional complication of different crystal phases of different density.

About 5 days storage at room temperature are required in the manufacture of poly-1-butene to allow the transformation from Type I to Type II to be effectively completed. The density of moldings increases from about 0.88 to 0.91 or 0.92 g/cm³. Poly-1-butene has a maximum (final) melting point a little lower than high-density polyethylene, but the softening point is higher. The comparison with other commercial crystalline polyolefins is shown in Table 5.

Table 5. Comparison of Melting (32) and Softening (33) Points

Polymer	Final melting point, °C	Softening point,[a] °C
polyethylene		
low density	~113	80–90
high density	142	117–124
polypropylene	180	148–153
poly-1-butene, Type I	136	120–126

[a] British Standards, BS 1493.

Morphology. Crystallization from the melt normally gives rise to spherulites, as is usually the case with polymers. The spherulite sizes can range up to 100 μ but large spherulites require particular crystallization conditions. The mean size can be reduced to a few microns or less by copolymerizing with a little propylene or other comonomers (39).

Solution Properties and Molecular Weight. Atactic poly-1-butene is soluble in many solvents, including hydrocarbons and diethyl ether which dissolve some poorly crystalline polymer containing stereoblocks, ie short runs of isotactic separated by atactic sequences in the same molecule. Isotactic polymer dissolves above room temperature in hydrocarbons (ie n-heptane, benzene, and tetradecahydronaphthalene) and in chlorinated solvents (ie 1-chloronaphthalene and chloroform) and tends to precipitate out on cooling. Phase separations can occur (39°C reported for toluene, 70°C for nonane, etc).

Polymerized isotactic poly-1-butene is a polydisperse material containing chains of a wide range in length. The ratio of weight-average to number-average molecular weight, M_W/M_N, is commonly quoted as a measure of the broadness in molecular-weight distributions (some authors prefer $(M_W/M_N)-1$). Values in the range of 7 to 13, similar to polypropylene, have been found (34,35). The polymer can be fractionated at about 60°C by addition of a nonsolvent, eg ethanol, to effect partial precipitation from a ligroin solution, filtering, redissolving the precipitate, and repeating the cycle (36,37). The fractions are recovered from the filtrates by excess precipitant. Alternatively, the polymer can be studied by gel-permeation chromatography, wherein the polymer is eluted from a gel by a solvent (35,38). For meaningful results it is essential to use an antioxidant, such as 4-methyl-2,6-ditertiarybutylphenol.

The molecular weight of polybutene in solution can be measured by light scattering ($\overline{M}_W$), by osmometry or, for atactic polymer with a mean degree of polymerization up to about 100, by end-group analysis using infrared spectroscopy ($\bar{M}_N$). Fractions of polymer with narrow molecular-weight distributions have been used to relate the two molecular-weight averages to the solution viscosity of the polymer by the Mark Houwink expression $(\eta) = KM^a$, where (η) is the intrinsic viscosity (35,37). (See Vol. 16, p. 248.)

Under ideal conditions the tacticity of the polymer should not influence the molecular-weight determination. This state of affairs seems to hold for ethylcyclohexane as solvent at 70°C; constants $K = 7.34 \times 10^{-5}$ and a = 0.80 have been measured for both atactic (ether-soluble) and isotactic polymers. Kriegbaum (36) and Stivala (37) used light scattering to measure the molecular weight of fractionated polymer. In perfect fractionation $\bar{M}_N = \bar{M}_W$ for each fraction. In the present case fractions retain some dispersity, and the constants given refer to the $\bar{M}_W$ values. For commercial polymers the $\bar{M}_W$ values, obtained using light scattering measurements (37), are found to be 20–30% lower than $\bar{M}_W$ due to the broader molecular-weight distribution.

Melt Flow. Isotactic poly-1-butene has the important characteristic that samples of a given solution or melt viscosity have a much higher molecular weight than corresponding samples of polypropylene or polyethylene. This is attributable among other reasons to the flexibility of the side chains. This means that higher-molecular-weight material can easily be fabricated on machines designed for polypropylene and polyethylene (33). The viscosity data are compared in Table 6.

Table 6. Comparison of Viscosity and Molecular-Weight Data of Polyolefins

Polymer	Reduced[a] solution viscosity, dl/g	Light scattering, $\bar{M}_W$	Melt index[b]
poly-1-butene	2	7.7×10^5	20.0
poly-1-butene	6	30.0×10^5	0.3
polypropylene	2	2.2×10^5	10.0
polypropylene	6	7.3×10^5	0.5
polyethylene	1.2	0.4×10^5	35.0
polyethylene	4.0	1.8×10^5	0.3

[a] Measured in decahydronaphthalene at a concentration of 0.1 g/100 cm³ at 135°C.
[b] ASTM 1238; 5 kg, 190°C.

Physical Properties of Molded Polymer. The outstanding properties of poly-1-butene, which are specially valuable commercially for uses up to about 85°C, are toughness, excellent resistance to creep rupture, and very good resistance to environmental stress cracking. The polymer also can be filled with up to 25% carbon black without losing valuable properties. It shares most of the characteristics of polyethylene and polypropylene by way of chemical inertness, dielectric properties, etc. A summary of physical properties is given in Table 7.

The stress-strain curve in an Instron tester at room temperature shows a behavior peculiar to poly-1-butene which is connected with its unusually high molecular weight (see Fig. 3). The initial maximum found with polyethylene and polypropylene is absent. The sample does not neck and cold draw, but reorganization of the polymer occurs allowing a slow buildup of stress to final rupture. The tensile stress is low at room temperature and falls as the temperature is increased. Low-pressure polyethylene, however, loses its tensile strength more rapidly as the temperature is raised so

Table 7. Physical Properties[a] of Compression-Molded Specimens of Poly-1-butene

Property	Test method	Value
crystalline melting point, °C	polarizing microscope	124–130[b]
softening point, °C	BS 1493	120–126
Vicat, $\frac{1}{10}$	ASTM D 1525–65T	107[c]
Vicat, full		113–118[c]
density, g/cm³	D 1505–63T	0.91–0.92[b]
tensile "yield,"[d] psi	D 638–66T[e]	2200[f], 2850[b]
tensile strength, psi		4200[f], 5000[b]
elongation at break, %		360[f], 250[b]
modulus of elasticity, 100 sec, psi	flexural test	70,000–130,000[c]
ball hardness, 60 sec, psi	VDE 0302	5400[b]
Shore hardness, D scale	ASTM D 1706–61	65[b]
impact strength, Izod	D 256–56	no break[f]
brittle point, °C	D 746–57T	−10 to −30[c]
environmental stress-cracking resistance[g]	D 1693–60T	no failures in 2000 hr[f]
dielectric constant, 10^3–10^6 Hz	D 150–65T	2.2–2.5[b]
dissipation factor, 10^3–10^6 Hz		0.0007[b]
thermal conductivity, kcal/m h °C	DIN 52612	0.2[b]
coefficient of linear thermal expansion, °C⁻¹	ASTM D 696	1.5×10^{-4} [b]
specific heat capacity at 20°C, cal/(g)(deg C)	see reference 41	0.474

[a] Measured at 23°C on samples aged for ten days, unless otherwise stated.

[b] Vestolen BT1711, produced by Chemische Werke Huels.

[c] ICI measurement.

[d] Since poly-1-butene shows no initial maximum in the stress–strain curve at 23°C these values cannot be precise. They represent the approximate stress at the point of inflection in the stress–strain curve. See also reference 40.

[e] Die C, 20 in./min.

[f] Mobil "Polybutylene."

[g] At 50°C, melt index 0.4 and 20.

Table 8. Elongations of Ziegler-Natta Polyolefins Under Continuous Load,[a] %

Polymer	Time, hr				
	0	1	10	50	500
poly-1-butene	8	10	11	11	13
polypropylene[b]	1.5	7	11	50	700
polyethylene[b]	4	50	700		

[a] Stress of 2140 psi at 23°C (34).

[b] The numerical values for these polymers can vary considerably depending on the grade of polymer, copolymerization, fabrication etc. The behavior of poly-1-butene nevertheless remains outstanding.

that above 75°C poly-1-butene is relatively stronger. At −30°C the polymer behaves in a brittle fashion.

Poly-1-butene also shows exceptional creep behavior. After an initial extension of 8% very little further elongation occurs on applying a load continuously. Poly-1-butene proves to be superior to polypropylene and polyethylene in this respect, as is seen from Table 8.

The resistance to creep is particularly useful in pipe application. Figure 4 shows the relation of hoop stress to duration of pressure. For 20 and 40°C no nonductile failure was observed after five years in these tests performed by Huels.

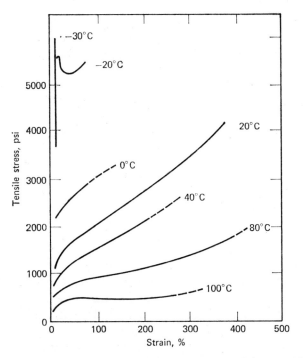

Fig. 3. The effect of temperature on tensile properties; rate of straining = 18 in./min on samples with nominal gage length of 1½ in.

Poly-1-butene is the softest of all polyolefins in the ball hardness test, equal to polyethylene in Shore hardness and better in scratch resistance. In surface gloss and transparency it resembles polypropylene.

The flexibility lies in between that of high- and low-density polyethylene. The toughness is greater than that of polypropylene and above 0°C greater than that of high-density polyethylene. The lowest temperature at which the material can be used, where toughness is required, is in the region of the glass-transition temperature, ie the temperature below which the amorphous phase behaves more like glass than a rubber. The temperature at which this occurs depends on the method of measurement. At high frequencies (NMR line narrowing, dielectric absorption at 3200 Hz) the amorphous phase behaves as a glass at relatively high temperatures (about +10°C). At very long time scales (dilatometry) low temperatures, −25 to −45°C, are reported for transitions in the amorphous phase. Dynamic mechanical tests and impact tests suggest temperatures in the region of −20 ± 10°C.

The exceptional resistance to environmental stress cracking is connected with the high molecular weight and the low crystallinity. This feature coupled with the good creep resistance recommends the use of poly-1-butene for pipes.

Electrical properties are comparable with polypropylene and polyethylene. The nonpolar nature coupled with good chemical resistance makes poly-1-butene suitable for electric cables.

The specific heat of poly-1-butene has been measured from 20 to 310°K and thermodynamic properties derived (41).

Film Properties. The permeability of poly-1-butene is similar to low-density polyethylene, ie reasonably resistant to water and oxygen. Blown film is more

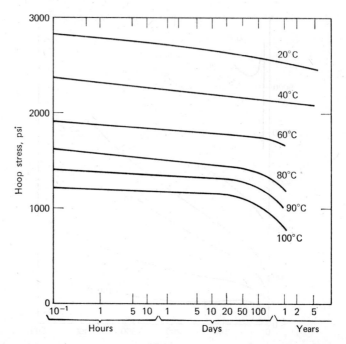

Fig. 4. Time to failure of pipes (Chemische Werke Huels, Vestolen BT 1711).

sensitive to extrusion condition and care must be taken to avoid orientation. The films toughness can be seen from the properties given in Table 9 which are superior to polyethylene films.

Flat films produced via chilled rolls or water batch cooling are highly oriented in the machine direction and are easily torn in this direction.

The tough, highly transparent poly-1-butene films can be used in shrink-wrap applications. Good seals are easily made and are durable in aging in the cold. The film can be shrunk at moderately low temperatures and is somewhat superior in toughness to poly(vinyl chloride) films.

Copolymerization of 1-butene with preferably 0.1–0.2 mole % ethylene has been claimed to improve the tear and impact strengths of films and lower the low-temperature brittle point significantly without serious loss of other properties (43).

Chemical Properties. Poly-1-butene is not attacked by acids and alkalis though it is affected by oxidizing agents, such as concentrated nitric acid. Polar solvents (acetone, ethanol, or ethylene) and oils cause no loss in strength. It is resistant to soaps and detergents up to 90°C. Aliphatic hydrocarbons can cause swelling and aromatic hydrocarbons tend to dissolve the polymers. Use has been made of this property for solution welding moldings (33). Chlorinated solvents are extensively absorbed.

Poly-1-butene is susceptible to oxidative degradation like polypropylene which also contains tertiary hydrogen atoms that facilitate peroxide formation. Heat and ultraviolet irradiation accelerate this process, leading to free-radical products on breakdown of peroxides, chain scission, and unsaturation. The polymer ultimately loses its strength. Inhibition of degradation is essentially the same as for polypropylene.

Peroxidation in air is accelerated by pressure and by using solvents to dissolve or

Table 9.   Physical Properties of Poly-1-butene Film[a] (42)

Property	Value	ASTM test method
tensile yield, psi		
at 23°C	2200	D 882–69
at 70°C	1310	D 882–69
tensile fail, psi		
at 23°C	4000	D 882–69
at 70°C	3300	D 882–69
elongation, %		
at 23°C	340	D 882–69
at 70°C	170	D 882–69
permeability		
water vapor, at 25°C, g mil/(day)(100 in.^{2})	28	
oxygen, ml(STP)/(day)(atm)(mil)	6730	
CO_2 ml(STP)/(day)(atm)(mil)	3860	
impact and tear		
Elmendorf test, 4 mil gage	810	D 1922
dart drop, 60 in. drop,		
2 mil gage	910	D 1709
4 mil gage	550	

[a] Mobil's polybutylene was used.

swell the polymer at 60 to 135°C or solvents such as cumene which are easily peroxidized to assist the process.   Peroxides may also be added.   Up to 4% oxygen can be introduced, mainly on the surface and in the amorphous regions, but some degradation also occurs (44).   Peroxidized polymer can be used to initiate graft polymerization.   This has been used to obtain a coating composition using atactic poly-1-butene and styrene (45).   Poly-1-butene can be modified by chlorination, bromination, or chlorosulfonation, which introduces —SO$_2$Cl groups together with —Cl.   Vulcanizable elastomeric materials can be made by carrying the treatment far enough to render the polymer substantially amorphous.

Thermal degradation can be used as a means of lowering the molecular weight of the polymer (46).   Generally, a narrowing of the molecular-weight distribution occurs due to chain scission being statistically more likely to occur with longer molecules. Pyrolysis above 500°C yields mostly n-butane, straight-chain C_7 and 3-methyl-5-ethyl substituted C_9 hydrocarbons.   Poly-1-butene can be crosslinked by γ-rays (47).

Filled Poly-1-butene.   Poly-1-butene can be mill blended with appreciable proportions of carbon black before deterioration of properties results (27).   There is an increase in stiffness, brittleness, and melt viscosity (decrease in melt index) with some loss in tensile strength.   Changes in properties are shown in Table 10.

Table 10.   The Effect of Carbon Black on Poly-1-butene

Property	Carbon black, %		
	0	3	23
flexural modulus, psi	26,000	26,000	75,000
impact strength, Izod, (ft)(lb)/in.	no break	no break	2.2
low-temperature brittleness, °C	−25	−25	−5
melt index, g/10 min	0.5	0.5	0.1
tensile strength, psi	3,800	3,800	2,600

Table 11. Copolymerization of 1-Butene with 1-Olefins (28)

Comonomer	Lowest crystallinity (annealed)		Crystalline phases (modified)	Modification of lattice dimensions	Effect on crystalline melting point	Type of poly-1-butene produced	
	% Crystallinity	Comonomer, %[a]				Type	Comonomer, %
ethylene (PE)	~10	62	PB I, PE	no measurable effect[b]	PB I decreases	I	
propylene (PP)	35	75	PB I, PP α[c]	PB I decreases	both decrease	I	10–20
1-pentene	39	51	only PB I	PB I increases	both decrease	I	~50
1-hexene	0	69	mostly PB I	PB I increases	both decrease		
1-octene	0	48	PB I, PB II	PB I increases	both decrease		
1-nonene					melting over a wide range of temperature		
3-methyl-1-butene (P$_3$MB)	50	15	(PB I), PB II P$_3$MB	PB II increases	PB II increases, P$_3$MB decreases	II	8–15
4-methyl-1-pentene (P$_4$MP)	30–35	11–14	PB II, P$_4$MP	PB II increases, P$_4$MP decreases	PB II increases, P$_4$MP both decrease	II	1–7
4,4-dimethyl-1-pentene (P$_{44}$DMP)	30	50	PB II, P$_{44}$DMP	no measurable effect[b]	PB II decreases, P$_{44}$DMP too high to measure	II	5

[a] Mole % of comonomer used in polymerization to obtain the crystallinity quoted in the 2nd column.
[b] Considerable phase separation occurs in these cases. Few comonomer units enter into the poly-1-butene lattice.
[c] Refers to the α crystalline form of polypropylene.

COPOLYMERS

Only copolymers containing a major proportion of butene units are discussed.

The type of Ziegler catalyst employed plays an important role. Soluble, homogeneous catalysts, ie those giving atactic or low-stereoregularity homopolymers, such as VCl_3 and $(C_2H_5)_3Al$, tend to give copolymers with a random distribution of monomer units (48).

Syndiotactic polypropylene is obtained with catalysts, such as VCl_4, with $(C_2H_5)_2$-AlCl and methyl phenyl ether at $-78°C$. These catalysts give—in poor yields—copolymers with ethylene or propylene wherein the butene units tend to alternate with the other monomer (26), and as mentioned earlier, there is a tendency to form a syndiotactic copolymer.

Insoluble catalysts, highly stereospecific in homopolymerizations, give heterogeneous products which probably arise from a tendency to form polymer molecules of different chemical composition, ie from molecules relatively rich in 1-butene to those containing more of the comonomer. This occurs even when supplies of both monomers are maintained in nearly fixed ratios. There is also probably a tendency to form blocks, ie a given molecule may contain a long butene-rich section, followed by a more random section or one rich in the other comonomer. If the sizes of the copolymer units are not very different from that of the butene units then the copolymer can enter the poly-1-butene crystal lattice, ie cocrystallize. The proportion of comonomer units that can be accommodated depends upon the actual difference in size. 1-Pentene units form a cocrystallizing system over the whole composition range, but propylene and 3-methyl-1-butene units increasingly disrupt the crystal lattice as the proportion rises. Phase separation incorporating butene-rich and comonomer-rich polymer molecules progressively increases. The net effect is a loss of crystallinity, crystal-phase separation and, generally, a lowering of the melting point in the middle composition range. Copolymerization of 1-butene, notably with 4,4-dimethyl-1-pentene, results in fairly marked phase separation into the homopolymers. The incorporation of other monomer units into the poly-1-butene lattice can result in changes of the lattice dimensions and in helical conformation. For a discussion of isomorphism, isodimorphism and cocrystallization in polymers, see references 28, 28a, 49, and 49a. Using a particular catalyst and conditions of polymerization a series of copolymers were obtained whose characteristics are described qualitatively in Table 11 (for details see references 28 and 28a).

Copolymerization generally causes a loss in stiffness. The products may ultimately become rubbery or even greasy (presumably associated with a low molecular weight). The transformation of Type II to Type I forms can be accelerated by copolymerization with 1-pentene, propylene, or ethylene (39). Direct crystallization to Type I from the melt can be achieved using the approximate percentages of comonomer in the last column of Table 11. Copolymerization with the branched olefins 3-methyl-1-butene, 4-methyl-1-pentene, and 4,4-dimethyl-1-pentene can retard the transformation or, when sufficient comonomer is present, even stabilize Type II (50). A copolymer with 4-methyl-1-pentene has reasonable transparency with a resistance to shock. Data for this material are presented in Table 12.

POLY-1-BUTENE PLANT CAPACITY

In 1965 Petro-Tex Chemical Corp., Houston, Texas, announced the operation of a pilot plant producing poly-1-butene under the trade mark Bu-Tuf (27). Petro-Tex

Table 12. Comparison of Poly-1-butene With a Copolymer
Containing 18% 4-Methyl-1-pentene

	Aging time, hr			
	Poly-1-butene		Copolymer	
Property	1	48	1	48
density, g/cm³	0.884	0.913	0.863	0.864
tensile strength, psi	4700	3900	4100	4250
elongation at break, %	254	283	655	730
elastic modulus, psi	17,000	56,000	25,000	22,500
resistance to shock and tension, psi	27,000	7100	26,000	21,000

has now discontinued production. The interest of Chemische Werke Huels A.G., Marl, West Germany, in poly-1-butene was also evident in 1965 (33,34). Huels has proceeded to a plant with a capacity of 12,000 ton/yr on stream in 1970. The polymer is being offered under the trade mark Vestolen BT 1711, primarily intended for the production of pipes. The development price is approx 35¢/lb. Mobil Chemical Co., New York, is offering (1970) semitechnical quantities of polybutylene for evaluation, covering a range of melt indexes from 0.4 to 20.0. Mobil has a particular interest in film, including shrink film, and in rotational molding, with applications in the packaging area (42).

FABRICATION AND USES

Poly-1-butene is available as a freeflowing, white powder or compounded with stabilizers, pigments, fillers, etc, into granules. The polymer can be injection molded in equipment used for polypropylene and polyethylene at temperatures in the range of 200 to 290°C. There is less shrinkage in the mold and an overall shrinkage of 1.5–3% is obtained. A longer cooling time is needed owing to the lower thermal conductivity compared with polyethylene and polypropylene. Freshly molded articles are comparatively soft and harden on aging, increasing in density and tensile strength (Type II transforming to Type I). The material may be shaped while still predominantly Type II and set by aging. For manufacturing pipe, extrusion temperatures in the range of 150 to 185°C with a single screw extruder are preferred. Pipes should be aged for five days before coiling. Pipe fittings with supporting conical inserts can be used for jointing and the pipe enlarged after heating in a glycol bath at 120 to 130°C. Pipes may also be joined by heated-tool welding.

In application poly-1-butene has to compete with well-established polymers from ethylene and propylene. The more expensive monomer and perhaps the peculiar difficulty of the aging process of several days have tended to delay its exploitation. It is now finding its way as an addition to the polyolefins range for uses which exploit its advantages in specialist areas. Some of these areas, notably in pipe and packaging films, could develop into high-tonnage markets if the extra price of the monomer is justifiable.

The good stress-crack resistance and creep properties are made use of in pipe manufacture and the polymer shows a weight advantage over polyethylene for the same strength. The low-temperature brittle point is low enough to envisage the laying of pipes uncovered to the weather, provided stabilization to ultraviolet is adequate. Hot-water pipes can be used up to 70°C (rated for continuous stress up to 400 psi) or even 80°C under stress, but development of this application in the domestic area at least is likely to be slow (52).

The employment of poly-1-butene for balanced blown films is recommended by the high toughness as measured by the tensile strength and the various tests for local damage, such as tear resistance and drop-dart tests. Applications include disposable refuse sacks, particularly where rupture could be a marked danger as with the disposal of germ-laden hospital refuse, industrial sacks, drum and sack liners, where toughness and moisture barrier are of prime importance, and food applications as in boil-in-the-bag foods.

Orientation in films produced by unidirectional draw which produces a tear weakness in one direction can be used in easily opened tear packages and in heat-sensitive tapes. Adjustment of the draw ratio can be used for shrink-film applications. The transparency is sufficient to form a puncture-resistant window on display boxes and food packages.

The low molded-in stress coupled with stress-crack resistance and a high melt index gives poly-1-butene a place in rotationally molded containers, particularly for applications where corrosiveness or other considerations make polyethylene unsuitable. These include fertilizers, batteries, and meat tanks.

Polymers of 4-Methyl-1-Pentene

MANUFACTURE OF 4-METHYL-1-PENTENE

So far as is known, the only commercial process used for the large-scale manufacture of 4-methyl-1-pentene is the alkali-metal-catalyzed dimerization of propylene. This process has been in operation since 1967 in a 2,000 ton/yr plant at Grangemouth, Scotland, by B.P. Chemicals Ltd. (53,54) and monomer from this plant has been supplied to Imperial Chemical Industries Ltd. for the manufacture of TPX methylpentene polymers. There is a wide scientific and patent literature concerning this type of process and the basic chemistry has been summarized by Wilkes (55) of the Chevron Research Co.

Propylene is dimerized to 4-methyl-1-pentene in 70–80% yield on contact with potassium (or rubidium, or cesium) at temperatures in the region of 150°C. Sodium is not an effective catalyst; it gives lower rates of dimerization and products containing only small amounts of 4-methyl-1-pentene. It is known that reaction occurs via the allyl carbanion (**1**) (formed in a preliminary reaction between potassium and propylene giving propane as a by-product) which adds across the double bond in propylene (equ. 1) to give the 4-methylpentenyl carbanion (**2**).

$$
CH_3\overset{|}{C}HCH_2CH=CH_2 + K^{\oplus}(\overline{CH_2\!-\!CH\!-\!CH_2})^{\ominus} \xrightarrow{CH_2=CHCH_3} K^{\oplus}\overset{\ominus}{C}H_2\overset{\overset{\displaystyle CH_3}{|}}{C}HCH_2CH=CH_2 \quad \tag{1}
$$

(**1**)   (**2**)

The carbanion (**2**) is not stabilized by delocalization of charge over an adjacent double bond and is therefore more strongly basic than the stabilized carbanion (**1**). Thus (**2**) abstracts a proton from propylene forming 4-methyl-1-pentene and regenerating the allyl carbanion so that the sequence can be repeated. Addition across propylene in the opposite direction occurs to a small extent so that 1-hexene is formed by the analogous reaction sequence (equ. 2). Under normal conditions there is little tendency for hexenyl anions to add across propylene so that trimers amount to less than 1% of the total product.

Thus, the primary reaction product is almost entirely a simple mixture of 4-methyl-1-pentene and 1-hexene. However, secondary products arise from double-bond isomerization of these olefins to give mixtures of internal hexenes (equ. 3). If isomerization were allowed to proceed to thermodynamic equilibrium the final product would contain less than 1% of 4-methyl-1-pentene.

$$
CH_3CH_2CH_2CH_2CH{=}CH_2 + K^{\oplus}(\overset{\frown}{CH_2{-}CH{-}CH_2})
\underset{\overset{\displaystyle CH_2=CHCH_3}{\longleftarrow}}{\overset{\displaystyle CH_2=CHCH_3}{\longrightarrow}}
K^{\oplus}(CH_3{-}\overset{\ominus}{CH}{-}CH_2{-}CH{=}CH_2) \qquad (2)
$$

$$
\underset{CH_3}{\overset{|}{C}}H_3CHCH_2CH{=}CH_2 + (\overset{\frown}{CH_2{-}CH{-}CH_2})K^{\oplus} \longrightarrow (CH_3{-}\underset{CH_3}{\overset{|}{C}}H{-}CH_2{-}\overset{\ominus}{CH}{-}CH_2)K^{\oplus}
$$

$$
\qquad (3)
$$

$$
CH_3CHCH{=}CHCH_3 + (\overset{\frown}{CH_2{-}CH{-}CH_2})K^{\oplus}
\underset{\overset{\displaystyle CH_2=CHCH_3}{\longleftarrow}}{}
$$

Isomerization is minimized by controlling the reaction temperature and catalyst contact time, and by using nonporous catalyst supports, eg quartz or potassium carbonate, which avoids trapping the terminal olefins inside catalyst pores where they would isomerize. Under favorable conditions the product contains up to 80% 4-methyl-1-pentene, ca 5% of 1-hexene, and ca 15% of internal hexenes. Separation of >95% pure 4-methyl-1-pentene from this mixture is difficult and requires highly efficient fractional distillation.

Two types of continuous process have been described in some detail; the first operated by B.P. Chemical (54) employs a fixed-bed catalyst and the second, developed by Chevron Research Co. (55), uses a slurried catalyst. In the fixed-bed process fresh propylene plus recycle propylene is preheated and then passed through a reaction section containing the catalyst. Two types of catalyst have been described in this context (53), one being based on lamellar complexes of potassium with graphite (56) (see Vol. 4, p. 311) and the other obtained by dispersing metallic sodium on anhydrous potassium carbonate at 400°C in an inert atmosphere (57). The second system would appear to offer marked economic advantage as it uses sodium rather than potassium, but provides the catalytic activity normally associated with potassium. It is known (58) that sodium reacts on heating with certain potassium salts to give metallic potassium and it is believed (57) that the sodium on potassium carbonate catalyst contains highly dispersed potassium. A batch reaction with this catalyst conducted at 1700 psig and 160°C for 24 hr gave a 95% conversion of propylene to a mixture of hexenes with the following composition (57):

Olefin	Percent	Olefin	Percent
4-methyl-1-pentene	74.8	2-methyl-2-pentene	1.2
4-methyl-2-pentene	17.7	1-, 2-, and	
2-methyl-1-pentene	4.1	3-hexenes	2.2

Details of the product from the fixed-bed reactor are not available, but it is known (54) that the selectivity for 4-methyl-1-pentene, based on propylene converted, is in the 80–90% range at a constant conversion in excess of 30% per pass over the complete operational life of the catalyst. The product from the reactor is passed first to a stripping column operating under pressure to remove propylene overhead for recycle, the bottoms from this column being passed to a second column which removes any C_4 and C_5 products. Finally, the hexenes are passed to a "superfractionator" column from which 4-methyl-1-pentene of the purity indicated in Table 13 separates overhead. Table 13 gives the analysis of the B.P. Chemical product.

Table 13. Typical Analysis of B.P. Chemical 4-Methyl-1-pentene

Component	Wt %
lighter than C_6	0.1
4-methyl-1-pentene	97.4
cis-4-methyl-2-pentene	0.9
trans-4-methyl-2-pentene	1.5
1-hexene	0.1

In the slurried-catalyst process developed by Chevron (55) dried propylene is fed to a reactor containing a stabilized dispersion of potassium on a finely divided calcium or magnesium silicate support (59) in a high-boiling hydrocarbon. A specific advantage over fixed-bed reactors (55), is the relatively simple heat removal from the highly exothermic dimerization reaction. The reactor is maintained at 140–150°C and 40–60 atm pressure. Propylene is fed at a rate sufficient to strip out the dimerization products at 5–15% conversion of the propylene. The product passes directly to a fractionation column operating under pressure where propylene is stripped out for recycle, and crude hexenes, containing ca 80% 4-methyl-1-pentene, are separated as bottoms. This crude material could then be purified by means similar to that used in the B.P. Chemical process.

POLYMERIZATION OF 4-METHYL-1-PENTENE

Homopolymerization. The polymerization of 4-methyl-1-pentene with Ziegler-Natta catalysts in inert hydrocarbon diluents, eg cyclohexane (60), heptane (61), and commercial saturated aliphatic hydrocarbon fractions (17) or in the bulk monomer (18), has been described frequently since the first report by Natta et al. in 1955 (2). A typical polymerization product contains a mixture of the required crystalline isotactic polymer, almost insoluble in warm aliphatic hydrocarbons, with a largely amorphous atactic polymer dissolved by the diluent. The relative proportions in which these two products are formed depend on several factors, but especially on the type of transition-metal-halide catalyst plus organometallic activator used, and on the temperature of polymerization, high temperatures favoring the formation of soluble polymer. Preferred catalyst-activator systems are those based on the violet forms of titanium trichloride (see Vol. 14, p. 292) activated by diethyl aluminum chloride. The use of such systems in the 20–80°C temperature range gives products containing only 2–5% of soluble polymer, whereas violet titanium trichloride activated with aluminum trialkyls gives ca 20% of solubles. Catalysts made directly from titanium tetrachloride and organoaluminum compounds can give 40% of the unwanted atactic material (60,63).

In the preferred systems the diluent dissolves the monomer, the activator and the atactic product, but not the violet titanium trichloride or any significant amount of the isotactic polymer. Thus, monomer polymerizes at the titanium trichloride–liquid interface and isotactic polymer precipitates out on the TiCl₃ crystals, forming a slurry of catalyst–polymer particles in the diluent.

The kinetics of polymerization with TiCl₃–AlEt₂Cl systems are similar to those described for propylene polymerization (see Vol. 14, p. 292), the rate being first order with respect to monomer and TiCl₃ (63). A retardation period in which the rate increased up to a steady level, which was then maintained from 3 to ca 20% conversion of the total monomer present, has been observed in bulk polymerizations catalyzed with TiCl₃ AA grade (Stauffer Chemical Co.). At higher conversions the rate decreased, owing either to inactivation of the catalyst or to the onset of a situation where diffusion of monomer through the catalyst polymer particles to the active sites becomes (63) rate determining. The activation energy for 4-methyl-1-pentene polymerization (in bulk) is 15 kcal/mole (63), a little higher than that generally reported for propylene polymerization (see Vol. 14, p. 297). 4-Methyl-1-pentene is less rapidly polymerized than 1-hexene or propylene (65); under comparable conditions (purple TiCl₃ catalyst, activated by ClEt₂Al in a paraffinic diluent at 60°C) the relative initial rates of polymerization for propylene and 1-hexene are, respectively, 1.8 and 2.4 times that for 4-methyl-1-pentene (66).

Control of polymer molecular weight to give products which are suitable for melt fabrication can be obtained by increasing the temperature of polymerization (61,63, 64), by using a mixture of aluminum and zinc alkyls as the activator (61), or by conducting the polymerization in the presence of hydrogen (62). Alternatively, Campbell (67) has described a technique for cracking the polymer in vacuo at 270–280°C which reduces the molecular weight smoothly without altering the polymer's structure and in this way he obtained a product suitable for laboratory characterization as fiber.

To isolate the isotactic polymer, the slurry of catalyst–polymer particles in diluent is treated with reagents which kill the catalyst (an alcohol is usually employed for this purpose) and solubilize the catalyst residues so that they can be washed out, polymer being separated from the wash liquors by filtration or centrifugation. Finally, residual liquor held in the polymer particles is removed by steam distillation and/or drying. Full realization of the remarkable optical transparency shown by certain 4-methyl-1-pentene polymers depends on an almost complete removal of catalyst residues, as the presence of these in molded samples of polymer gives the moldings a hazy appearance. The importance of removing residues to obtain products of high transparency is illustrated in Table 14. These data (64) show that simple treatments using aqueous washing (as used in polypropylene manufacture) are inadequate and that more complex systems involving washing with hydrocarbons or with alcohols are required. As in many processes, one stage is very dependent on another, and it has been shown (64) that the correct choice of catalyst system, in order to obtain easily processable polymer slurries, is vital for efficient catalyst removal.

Copolymerization with Linear 1-Olefins. Mixtures of 4-methyl-1-pentene with various linear 1-olefins have been polymerized under conditions comparable to those used for the homopolymer, but the composition of the copolymers resulting has not always been determined. It cannot be assumed that copolymers obtained by simple copolymerization of the mixed monomers contain repeat units derived from these monomers in the same proportion as was present in the monomer mixture, because

Table 14. Removal of Catalyst Residues from Slurries of Polymers[a] (64)

Reagents	Wash liquor	Catalyst residues in washed polymer			Haze,[c] %
		Ash,[b] %	Ti, ppm	Al, ppm	
acetylacetone–2-propanol	light petroleum	0.01	<10	<10	<5.0
2-propanol	light petroleum	0.05	58		17.6
2-propanol	water	0.05	62		20.0
2-propanol	2-propanol	<0.01	<10	<10	2.5
3,5,5-trimethyl hexanol	light petroleum	0.01	<10	<10	8.0
1-butanol	light petroleum	0.01	10	10	6.5
1-butanol	water	0.04	53		18.0
2-methyl-1-propanol	2-methyl-1-propanol	<0.01	<10	<10	3.5
methanol	methanol	<0.01	<10	<10	2.5

[a] Polymer prepared in light petroleum (bp 60–80°C) using a TiCl₃–ClEt₂Al system (3 m moles TiCl₃ per 100 g polymer) and treated under nitrogen with the reagent at 60°C for 1 hr and at room temperature overnight before washing.

[b] Residue after ignition.

[c] Measured by ASTM D 1003–61 on ⅛-in. compression moldings quenched from 265°C.

the relative monomer-reactivity ratios, r_1 and r_2, may well be different. Atarashi (65) has measured (by an infrared technique) compositions of the polymers obtained from mixtures of 1-hexene (monomer 1) and 4-methyl-1-pentene (monomer 2) using an Et₂AlCl–TiCl₃ (AA grade, Stauffer Chemical Co.) catalyst system in heptane as diluent at 50°C. Reactivity ratios, $r_1 = 5.4$ and $r_2 = 0.62$, were calculated from these data which show that copolymers of 1-hexene and 4-methyl-1-pentene are richer in 1-hexene units than the monomer mixtures from which they are made. Thus, unless simple copolymerizations are taken to completion the products are richer in 1-hexene units. However, the copolymers obtained by complete polymerization of monomer mixtures are not homogeneous in composition, the product at the start of the copolymerization being richer in 1-hexene units than that formed at the end, due to preferential consumption of 1-hexene in the monomer mixture. Copolymers of approximately constant composition can be obtained by terminating the copolymerization at low monomer conversions, or by feeding the more reactive monomer continuously to the system at such a rate that the relative concentrations of both monomers remain constant. Techniques such as these have been used to prepare copolymers of 4-methyl-1-pentene with propylene (minor amounts), 1-butene (64,68), 1-pentene, 1-hexene, 1-octene, 1-decene, and 1-octadecene (64,69).

Isolation of the copolymers is essentially similar to that described for the homopolymer and again the efficiency of catalyst removal depends on obtaining mobile slurries of the polymer-catalyst particles in the polymerization medium. This becomes more difficult as the weight proportion of linear side chains is increased, but Clark and Palmer report (64) that using a "favored" TiCl₃ catalyst (activated with Et₂AlCl) stable slurries of copolymers containing up to ca 13 mole % 1-pentene or 1-hexene, ca 8 mole % 1-octene, and ca 5 mole % 1-decene could be prepared in a hot diluent. With the same catalyst bulk copolymerization to low conversions at 20°C gave good slurries of copolymers containing up to ca 20 mole % 1-butene, 1-pentene, and 1-hexene. The proportions of repeat units derived from 1-butene, 1-pentene, 1-hexene, 1-octene, 1-decene, and 1-octadecene in 4-methyl-1-pentene copolymers have been determined (64) by measurements of the infrared absorption due to the *n*-alkyl branches at 13.1, 13.58, 13.76, 13.84, 13.87, and 13.88 μ respectively.

ISOMERIZATION-POLYMERIZATION OF CERTAIN PROPYLENE DIMERS

Dimerization of propylene by catalysts based on complex nickel salts (eg nickel acetylacetonate) and aluminum alkyl chlorides (eg Et_2AlCl) provides a very efficient route to a mixture of hexenes from which a fraction consisting essentially of 4-methyl-1-pentene and 4-methyl-2-pentene (*cis*- and *trans*-) is separated easily by fractional distillation (70,71). Work carried out at the Institut Français du Petrole has shown that such a fraction can be employed for the synthesis of 4-methyl-1-pentene polymers using a composite catalyst system in which one component effects isomerization of 4-methyl-2-pentenes to 4-methyl-1-pentene while the second component catalyzes stereospecific polymerization of the 1-olefin. The essential feature of this system is kinetic control of the isomerization reactions so as to convert 4-methyl-2-pentenes to 4-methyl-1-pentene which is then polymerized. Thermodynamic equilibrium conditions are avoided because they give the most stable isomers, 2-methyl-1-pentene and 2-methyl-2-pentene, with only traces of 4-methyl-1-pentene. Study of the isomerization of 4-methyl-1-pentene and of the cis- and the trans- isomers of 4-methyl-2-pentene (19,72) showed that with small concentrations of nickel salts activated by aluminum alkyl chlorides the equilibria 1, 2, and 6 were established very rapidly but equilibria 3, 4, and 5 quite slowly, as shown in Scheme 2.

Scheme 2.

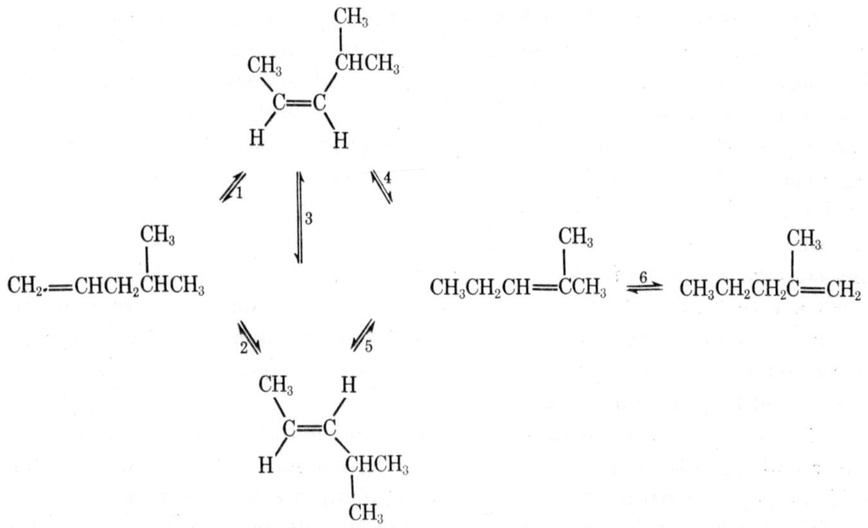

Thus, when *cis* 4-methyl-2-pentene (400 mmoles) was treated at 25°C with a composite catalyst (purple $TiCl_3$, 0.89 mmoles; nickel acetylacetonate, 0.028 mmoles; Et_2AlCl, 2.8 mmoles) 4-methyl-1-pentene was formed almost immediately and the concentration of this olefin in the system ranged from 4% after 30 min to 1% after 24 hr. 4-Methyl-1-pentene was removed from the system as polymer and the conversion of 4-methyl-1-pentene to poly-4-methyl-1-pentene was 15–20% during 24 hr. However, more than 15% of the 4-methyl-2-pentene was lost during this period by conversion to methyl-2-pentenes. Although the isomerization–polymerization process employs a potentially cheap mixture of propylene dimers as the monomer, it appears so far not to have been used for the production of 4-methyl-1-pentene polymers on a commercial scale.

PROPERTIES OF 4-METHYL-1-PENTENE POLYMERS

Structure, Crystallinity, and Transition Temperatures of the Homopolymer.
As is usual with crystalline polymers, massive samples of isotactic poly-4-methyl-1-pentene contain both crystalline and amorphous regions. Samples fabricated from the melt by normal techniques are ca 40% crystalline, but the crystallinity of annealed specimens can be as high as 65% (73). The crystalline melting point is 245°C (73). Polymer chains in crystalline regions adopt a helical conformation the repeat distance along the chain axis being 13.85 Å corresponding to 7 monomer repeat units and 2 twists of the helix. Thus, the poly-4-methyl-1-pentene helix (7_2) is less tightly coiled than the polypropylene helix (3_1) (see Fig. 5), due to the greater bulk of the isopropyl group, as compared with the methyl side groups. The unit cell has tetragonal symmetry, each cell has four polymer chains passing through it and the cell dimensions (measured on single crystals) are a = b = 18.6 Å and c = 13.8 Å (74). The density of partially crystalline polymer is 0.830–0.834 at 20°C, depending on the specimen's thermal history, but the crystal density is 0.828 at 20°C (75). Thus, at room temperature the density of the crystalline polymer is very close to that of the amorphous material, but because the coefficient of expansion for the amorphous polymer is greater that that for the crystalline the normal positive volume change on melting is observed. Griffith and Ranby's (75) dilatometric studies showed that, as with other polymers, the rate of crystallization depends on the degree of supercooling, the half-time of crystallization being 480 min at 236°C but only 0.5 min at 220°C. Single crystals of poly-4-methyl-1-pentene have been prepared from dilute solutions and the morphology of these crystals has been studied (74,76).

The glass transition temperature, T_g, of poly-4-methyl-1-pentene has been measured by dilatometry (75) and values in the range of 18 to 29°C obtained. Measurement of T_g via determination of heat capacity at different temperatures gave a value of 32°C (77) and dynamic mechanical measurements showed a normal glass-transition peak at 40°C (1 Hz) (61). Dilatometric, x-ray (79), and dynamic mechanical (79) measurements show the presence of a higher order transition between T_g and T_m at 125–130°C; this has been ascribed (78) to transverse chain-segment motion, but is more likely to involve a change in crystal form (80).

Structure, Crystallinity, and Transition Temperatures of Copolymers With Minor Proportions of Linear 1-Olefins. The copolymerization of 4-methyl-1-pentene with minor proportions of 1-olefins catalyzed by purple $TiCl_3$–Et_2AlCl systems and conducted so as to maintain the relative monomer concentrations constant throughout the reaction gives crystalline products which are structurally complex (64,49a). There is a marked tendency in these systems for the more reactive linear 1-olefins to homopolymerize so that the products made using ethylene or propylene as comonomer show marked separation of a microscopically dispersed phase of slightly modified polyethylene or polypropylene. This phase increases with increasing comonomer content. However, this effect was not detected in the copolymeric products with 1-hexene, 1-octene, 1-decene, or 1-octadecene as comonomer. When the comonomer does react to give chains containing substantial proportions of comonomer units (as is known to

Isotactic
polypropylene

Isotactic poly-
4-methyl-1-pentene

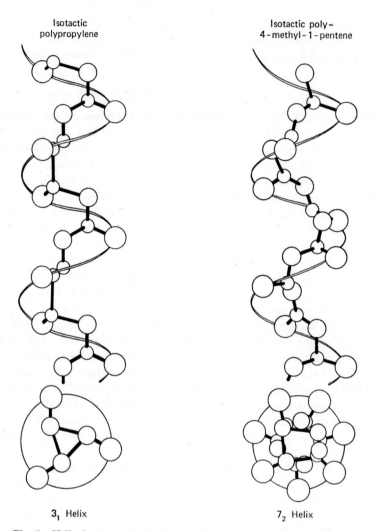

3₁ Helix

7₂ Helix

Fig. 5. Helical structures of polypropylene and poly-4-methyl-1-pentene.

occur with 1-butene, 1-pentene, 1-hexene, 1-octene, 1-decene, and 1-octadecene) there is
clear evidence that the chains comprising the product from a single copolymer preparation have a wide range of comonomer contents and are block copolymerized to different
extents. Cocrystallization in the poly-4-methyl-1-pentene crystal form occurs in these
copolymers to an extent depending on the comonomer unit. This is important technologically as it leads to products of relatively high crystallinity with useful mechanical
properties. The cocrystallization is most perfect in the 1-hexene copolymers where
crystallographic studies (28a,49a) have shown that 1-hexene chain units readily replace
4-methyl-1-pentene units in the crystal lattice with no disturbance in the 7_2 helix and no
change in the unit cell dimensions. With other linear 1-olefin copolymers cocrystallization occurs to a smaller extent, some being detectable with copolymers containing
1-butene or 1-decene but none with those containing propylene or 1-octadecene. There
is a contraction in the lateral unit-cell dimensions (tetragonal α-axis spacing) with the
1-butene and 1-pentene copolymers and an expansion with copolymers containing
1-octene or 1-decene (copolymers containing 10 mole % 1-butene, 1-pentene, 1-hex-

ene, 1-octene, and 1-decene have the α-axis spacings of 18.5, 18.5, 18.6, 18.7, and 18.9 Å, respectively, as compared with 18.6 Å for the homopolymer of 4-methyl-1-pentene). These changes in the α-spacing increase as the proportion of comonomer in the copolymer is increased. It appears that 1-octadecene units cannot be incorporated in the poly-4-methyl-1-pentene lattice (α-axis spacing for these copolymers is 18.6 Å), which is not surprising in view of the large difference in the side-chain dimensions, and it is believed that with these copolymers the 1-octadecene chain units must be incorporated entirely in the amorphous regions.

The crystallinities and final melting points for annealed specimens of these copolymers are shown in Tables 15 and 16. For a given comonomer there is a progressive decrease in crystallinity and melting point with increasing comonomer content and there is a steady decrease in these properties as the length of the comonomer side chain is increased beyond that of 1-hexene. The relatively high final melting point found for copolymers of much reduced crystallinity (eg a melting point of 225°C for a 5% 1-octadecene copolymer which is only 25% crystalline) is due to the substantial degree of block copolymerization which occurs in these systems. In general, the final melting points of all the copolymers are not much below that of 4-methyl-1-pentene homopolymer and this valuable effect is due largely to the block-copolymerized structures of these polymers.

The glass-transition temperatures of the copolymers are below that of the homopolymer and this reduction in T_g increases with increasing length of the comonomer side chain so that a 15–20°C reduction in T_g is obtained by copolymerization with 18 mole % 1-hexene or with 5 mole % 1-decene (69). In general, copolymerization increases toughness but decreases rigidity and tensile strength. Test data for a series of reputedly random linear 1-olefin copolymers are given in Table 17.

Table 15. Crystallinities for Copolymers of 4-Methyl-1-pentene With Linear 1-Olefins[a,b]

Comonomer concentration, %	Crystallinity, %, of copolymer with					
	1-butene	1-pentene	1-hexene	1-octene	1-decene	1-octadecene
0	65	65	65	65	65	65
5	~60		60	50	46	25
10	~54	~60	57	42	33	
20	~45	~55	53	28		

[a] Data obtained from references 28a, 49a, and 64.

[b] Samples cooled slowly from 240°C, except for 1-butene copolymers which were cooled from 250°C.

Table 16. Final Melting Points for Copolymers of 4-Methyl-1-pentene With Linear 1-Olefins[a,b]

Comonomer concentration, %	Melting point, °C, of Copolymer with					
	1-butene	1-pentene	1-hexene	1-octene	1-decene	1-octadecene
0	245	245	245	245	245	245
5			238	234	229	225
10	~240	240	235	225	219	
20	235	235	228	210[c]		

[a] Data obtained from references 28a, 49a, and 64.

[b] Samples cooled slowly from 240°C, except for 1-butene copolymers which were cooled from 250°C.

[c] Extrapolated.

Table 17. Selected Properties for "Random" Copolymers of 4-Methyl-1-pentene With 1-Hexene and 1-Decene (54)

Copolymer, mole %	Tensile yield strength, at °C, psi		Flexural modulus at 20°C, psi $\times 10^{-5}$	Izod notched impact strength at 20°C, (ft)(lb)/(in.)
	20	100		
none	4100	1000	2.46	1.4
1-hexene				
6.3	3300	900	1.03	1.0
12.0	1900	700	0.4	>10.0
1-decene				
5.4	2900	900	0.9	0.8
6.7	1900	700	0.5	6.6

Transparency of 4-Methyl-1-pentene Polymers. Certain crystalline polymers of 4-methyl-1-pentene show a high degree of optical transparency (62,64). Bulk samples of other crystalline polyolefins, eg polythene or polypropylene, are heterogeneous on the micron scale where they can be seen to contain both crystalline and amorphous regions. These regions normally do not have the same refractive index so that light is scattered on passing between them. Furthermore, the crystalline regions consist of spherulitic aggregates of radially orientated crystallites and as these crystallites are anisotropic the spherulites scatter light. In most crystalline polyolefins light scattering by these mechanisms would be such as to make crystallized specimens opaque in thick section, even if the specimens were completely free of voids. The transparency shown by 4-methyl-1-pentene polymers is due to the coincidence of two factors, ie the very near equality of density in the crystalline and amorphous phases and the low anisotropy of the polymer chain leading to spherulites of very low birefringence. Ziegler catalyst residues left in the polymer scatter light significantly, unless the concentration of these materials is low, so that careful removal of catalyst residues is essential to realize the full transparency of 4-methyl-1-pentent polymers. However, even when this is done the transparency can be spoiled if the samples are molded in such a way as to introduce interspherulitic voids. Thus, samples which are quenched from the melt are relatively free from microvoids and are of good transparency, but samples cooled slowly from the melt are heavily voided and have optical transmissions which are much lower (see Table 18). It is considered that quenching is beneficial because it reduces the crystallization temperature and thus minimizes the volume change on crystallization (because the densities of the crystalline and amorphous regions become more nearly equal at lower temperatures) which causes the voiding. Copolymerization with certain linear 1-olefins gives copolymers with optical properties which are better than those of the homopolymer and this improvement is due to the lower degree of voiding on crystallization shown by the copolymers. It is likely that this improvement is due to the considerable reduction in crystallization temperature caused by copolymerization. The temperatures when the start of crystallization was observed (64) (in samples cooled from the melt at 8°C/minute) were 225, 214, 198, and 197° C for polymers containing no comonomer, 9 mole % 1-hexene, 4.5 mole % 1-decene, and 3 mole % 1-octadecene, respectively. In the case of copolymers with 1-butene the improvement in transparency due to reduction in crystallization temperature is vitiated at comonomer levels greater than about 11 mole % due to the separation of a dispersed phase consist-

Table 18. Optical Properties of 4-Methyl-1-pentene Polymers (64)

Comonomer, mole %	Optical transmission for ⅛-in. compression moldings, %	
	Quenched from 265°C	Cooled from 300°C
none	80	20
1-butene		
11	95	72
17	62	59
1-pentene		
13	95	58
17	93	79
1-hexene		
13	89	55
18	96	66
1-octene		
5.5	87	69
8.5	91	85
1-decene		
3	93	>81
5	87	

ing essentially of poly-1-butene. Data on the transparency of 4-methyl-1-pentene polymers are given in Table 18 (64). It is seen that copolymerization can give polymer samples which even on slow cooling have relatively high transparencies which approach that of the quenched samples. This effect is important technologically as it reduces the extent to which transparency depends on the process used to prepare the samples.

A further improvement in the transparency of 4-methyl-1-pentene polymers may be obtained by using special nucleation procedures to control the polymers crystalline texture (81). These procedures provide substantially increased concentrations of nuclei in the melt from which crystallites can grow on cooling. The concentration of spherulites in the crystallized specimen is therefore increased and the average spherulite size correspondingly reduced. It has been found that incorporation of less than 1% of a finely dispersed polyolefin, having a melting point substantially higher than that of the 4-methyl-1-pentene polymer, provides crystallites of the dispersed polyolefins which survive in the melt to act as nuclei on cooling. This gives a molded product of outstandingly fine texture in which the average spherulite size is less than 5 μ, as compared with greater than 50 μ for polymers not nucleated artificially. Reduction in crystallite size leads to a reduction in the incidence of interspherulite voiding and hence to an increase in transparency. This striking effect, which is shown by the homopolymer and by copolymers of 4-methyl-1-pentene with linear 1-olefins, is illustrated in Tables 19 and 20 for moldings quenched from the melt, while an even larger effect is found for moldings that have been cooled slowly (see Table 20). It is seen from Table 20 that certain nucleated copolymer compositions provide moldings with optical transmissions up to 97% even when these moldings have been cooled slowly from the melt. Samples were quenched from the melt; the reduction in spherulite size was achieved by progressive nucleation with poly-4,4-dimethyl-1-pentene.

Polyolefins suitable as nucleating agents are the isotactic polymers of 3-methyl-1-butene, 3-methyl-1-pentene, or 4,4-dimethyl-1-butene which have crystalline melting points of 310, <350, and <350°C, respectively. These olefins are polymerized much more slowly than 4-methyl-1-pentene so that when a mixture of 4-methyl-1-pentene

Table 19. Optical Transmission of 4-Methyl-1-pentene Polymers as a Function of Spherulite Size (81)

Spherulite size, μ			Optical transmission, %
Max	Mean	Min	
100	50	<1	69
15	10	<1	86
<1	<1	<1	96

Table 20. Optical Transmission of 4-Methyl-1-pentene–1-Olefin Copolymers as a Function of Spherulite Size (81)

Comonomer, wt % used	Mean spherulite size, μ	Optical transmission, %	
		Quenched molding	Slow-cooled molding
none	>25[a]	84	20
	<2[b]	95	88
1-pentene, 2	>25[a]	87	64
	<2[b]	95	91
1-hexene, 2	>25[a]	80	38
	<2[b]	98	93
1-hexene, 2	>25[a]	87	72
	<2[b]	98	96
1-octene, 2	>25[a]	79	25
	<2[b]	98	96
1-decene, 2	>25[a]	90	47
	<2[b]	98	97

[a] Samples not nucleated.
[b] Samples nucleated with poly-3-methyl-1-pentene.

with one of them is polymerized the 4-methyl-1-pentene reacts first leaving the other olefin to be polymerized virtually by itself and thus give a fine dispersion of the nucleating polymer on the particles of 4-methyl-1-pentene polymer. Alternatively, a concentrated dispersion of the nucleating polymer in a 4-methyl-1-pentene polymer may be made in a preliminary stage by contacting the catalyst system with a small amount of the mixed monomers under conditions such that all reactant concentrations are high. In this way a suspension of catalyst–polymer particles may be prepared which can be used subsequently under normal polymerization conditions to prepare nucleated 4-methyl-1-pentene polymers.

TPX METHYL PENTENE POLYMER

The isotactic homopolymer of 4-methyl-1-pentene has technical defects, such as brittleness and inadequate transparency, which have prevented its commercial application. However, copolymerization with minor proportions of other 1-olefins, together with the addition of suitable oxidation and melt stabilizer systems, has led to the development of a commercially significant range of plastics materials. These materials were first launched commercially in the United Kingdom in 1965 by Imperial Chemical Industries Ltd. under the trade mark TPX. They were introduced in the United States in 1966 and in seventeen other countries during 1967. Following production on a semi-technical scale, a 2,000-tons/yr unit was commissioned at Wilton, Yorkshire, by June

1968 and TPX is available in most of the principal plastics markets of the world.   TPX is available in two basic forms, one being transparent and the other opaque white.

Physical Properties (73,82,83).   TPX exhibits some of the basic properties of a polyolefin, but in addition it possesses four distinctive features, ie very low relative density, excellent optical properties, a high softening point, and outstanding electrical properties, which give it a special role in plastics technology.   Some physical properties are presented in Table 21.

Table 21.   Physical Properties, at 20°C, of TPX Methylpentene Polymers[a]

Property	Test method	Typical value
relative density	ASTM D1505–67T	0.83
direct transmission factor, %		90
refractive index, n_D^{20}		1.465
tensile strength at yield, psi[b]		4000
elongation at break, %		15
tensile modulus, psi[c]		210,000
Rockwell hardness	ASTM D785–65	L 67–74
water absorption[d]	ASTM D570–63	0.01

[a] Grade RT-18; for test method, see reference 29.
[b] Rate of strain, 50%/min.
[c] Strain 0.2%, 100-sec value.
[d] Immersion, 24 hr.

The deformational behavior of TPX at 20°C as a function of time is given by the tensile-creep curves at three stress levels in Figure 6 which also includes curves for comparison (at one level of stress) with high-density (HD) polythene and polypropylene homopolymer.   Corresponding isochronous stress–strain curves are given in Figure 7.   The glass-transition temperature of TPX lies in the range of 30–50°C so that its deformational properties are very time dependent and sensitive to slight variations in temperature when tested near this range, as shown in Figure 8.   Under load for long periods, TPX fails in an essentially ductile manner, the failure being preceded by crazing or voiding.   Some data comparing these aspects of the TPX behavior with that of polypropylene are given in Figure 9.   The impact strength of various polymers is compared in Table 22.   Thus, TPX is tougher than most other transparent plastics, such as polystyrene or acrylic, but inferior to the "Engineering" plastics like nylon or acetal (aldehyde–ethylene oxide) copolymer.   (See Acetal resins.)   There is no abrupt decrease in impact strength below 20°C.

The effect of temperature change on the rigidity of TPX, as compared with high-density polythene and polypropylene, is illustrated by the 100-sec tensile-creep modu-

Table 22.   Impact Strength of Various Polymers, Measured by the Izod Test (ASTM D 256-56), ft-lb/in.notch

Polymer	Impact strength
TPX	0.8
poly(methyl methacrylate)	0.4
styrene–acrylonitrile copolymer	0.35–0.5
polystyrene	0.25–0.4
nylon 66	1.0
aldehyde–ethylene oxide copolymer	1.2–1.4

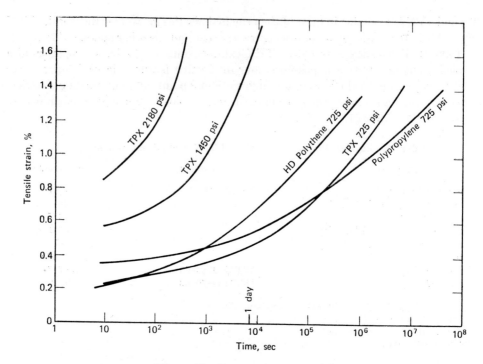

Fig. 6. Tensile-creep curves at 20°C.

lus (at 0.2% strain) vs temperature curves given in Figure 8. Initially TPX suffers a more rapid drop in modulus, but at higher temperatures it becomes superior in this respect to high-density polythene and polypropylene. Typical values for other thermal properties of TPX polymers are shown in Table 23.

The electrical properties of TPX polymer are at least as good as those of polytetrafluoroethylene and the best cable-grade polythene. In the frequency range of 10 kHz to 250 MHz those of TPX are superior. Test data are given in Table 24 and it should also be noted that the low permittivity remains essentially constant over a wide temperature range.

Chemical Properties (77,82,83). Like polythene and polypropylene, TPX polymers are highly resistant to inorganic environments, being appreciably affected only by strong oxidizing agents. In the presence of certain materials, such as surfactants, environmental stress cracking can occur, and tests with the Lander apparatus (84) indicate that TPX is more resistant to failure than molding grades of low-

Table 23. Thermal Properties of TPX Polymers

Property	Test method	Typical value
crystalline melting point, °C		240
Vicat softening point, °C		180
coefficient of expansion, (deg C)$^{-1}$	ASTM D696–44	1.2×10^{-4}
thermal conductivity, cal/(cm)(sec)(deg C)	B.S. 874A	4×10^{-4}
specific heat, cal/(g)(deg C)	ASTM C351–61	0.52
flammability, in./min	ASTM D635–63	1.0
mold shrinkage, in./in.		0.015–0.030

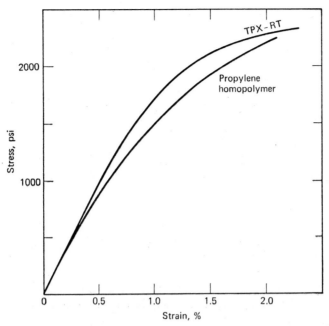

Fig. 7. Isochronous (100 sec) stress vs strain curves at 20°C for polypropylene and TPX-RT.

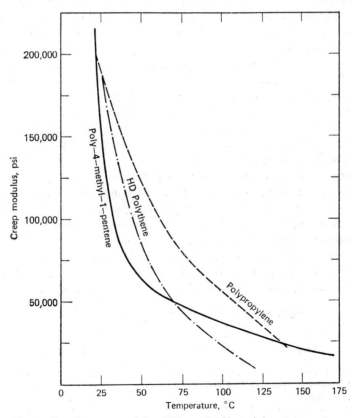

Fig. 8. Tensile-creep modulus (100 sec, 0.2% strain) vs temperature.

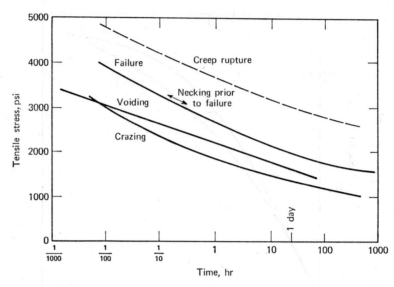

Fig. 9. Creep-rupture stress in tension vs time to failure at 20°C. LEGEND: — — — propylene homopolymer; ——— poly-4-methyl-1-pentene.

density polythene but less resistant than the best bottle-blowing grades. TPX polymer shows good resistance to many organic chemicals, although some are absorbed with consequent loss in bulk properties, and again stress cracking can also occur. The polymer's permeability to gases and water vapor is considerably higher than that of other crystalline polyolefins. Further data are presented in Table 25.

TPX polymer is stabilized against oxidative breakdown so that its useful life ranges from about a day at 200°C to a year at 130°C. The useful life varies according to the stabilizer concentration in the particular grade employed so that the above figures give only a very general guide. The polymer can be sterilized by electron and γ radiation without discoloration or embrittlement if the appropriate grade is used. But at present it cannot be recommended for extended use exposed to out-of-doors levels of ultraviolet irradiation, except when colored black.

Processing and Applications. The present grades are suited principally for fabrication by injection molding, extrusion, bottle blowing, and extrusion-melt coating. They process easily on conventional equipment, the operation being characterized by a high melting temperature, a narrow melting range, and a low melt viscosity. For comparative data (spiral flow vs temperature and melt viscosity vs shear stress) on the processing properties of TPX see references 82 and 83. Processing temperatures are generally in the temperature range of 270 to 300°C. Extruded sheet in thicknesses up to $\frac{1}{16}$ in. can be vacuum formed easily after preheating at ca 200°C.

Table 24. Electrical Test Data TPX Grade RT-18

Property	Test method	Typical value
permittivity at 20°C over frequency range 10^2–10^6 Hz	ASTM D150–655	2.12
loss angle over frequency range 10^2–10^6 Hz, micro radians	ASTM D150	<100
volume resistivity, ohm-cm	ASTM D257–66	>10^{16}
dielectric strength on $\frac{1}{8}$-in. sheet, V/0.001 in.	ASTM D149–64	700

Table 25. Chemical Properties of TPX Polymer

Property	Value
equilibrium water content (immersed)	
at 20°C	<0.05%
at 60°C	<0.05%
gas permeabilities, cm³(STP) cm/cm² cmHg × 10⁹	
oxygen	2.7
nitrogen	0.7
water vapor permeability at 38°C and 90% rh for 0.001 in. thickness, g/(m²)(24 hr)	95–110
resistance to	
mineral acids	
dil	excellent
conc	excellent[a]
alkalis	excellent
alcohols	excellent
ketones	fair–good
aromatic hydrocarbons	poor
chlorinated hydrocarbons	poor
detergent solutions	may show stress cracking
greases and oils	excellent

[a] Slightly attacked by concentrated oxidizing acids.

The five following general areas of application can be identified at present: lighting, eg for high-tensity internal fittings; electrical, eg electronic components and high-frequency coaxial connectors; medical, eg hospital ware, medical syringes, tubing, and connectors; packaging, eg containers for prepacked foods and as a coating (resistant to food at cooking temperatures) for paper board; and applications demanding clarity with chemical resistance, eg laboratory ware, sight glasses, waste traps, and catch pots.

Bibliography

1. K. Ziegler, E. Holzkamp, H. Breil, and H. Martin, *Angew. Chem.* **67**, 541 (1955).
2. G. Natta, *Atti. Accad. Naz. Lincei Mem. Classe Sci. Fis. Mat. Nat. Sez. II* **4** (8), 61 (1955).
3. G. Natta, P. Pino, P. Corradini, F. Danusso, G. Mazzanti, E. Mantica, and G. Moraglio, *J. Am. Chem. Soc.* **77**, 1708 (1955).
4. S. F. Pearce and L. M. Smith, *Paper 546, Chem. Marketing Res. Assoc. Meet., New York, May 1966.*
5. H. V. Boenig, *Polyolefines—Structure and Properties,* Elsevier Publishing Co., Amsterdam, 1966, p. 234.
6. G. Natta, P. Corradini, and I. W. Bassi, *Nuovo Cimento Suppl.,* **15**, 52 (1960).
7. A. Turner-Jones, *Makromol. Chem.* **71**, 1 (1964).
8. G. Mazzanti, *Chem. Ind. (London)* **1969**, 1208.
9. J. A. Faucher and F. P. Reding, *High Polymers* **20**, 691 (1965).
10. Brit. Pat. 940,145 (Oct. 23, 1963), K. J. Clark (to Imperial Chemical Industries, Ltd.).
11. Brit. Pat. 1,153,781 (May 29, 1969), to Petro-Tex Chemical Corp.
12. Fr. Pat. 1,468,240 (Feb. 24, 1965), to Chemische Werke Huels.
13. Brit. Pat. 909,081 (Oct. 24, 1962), to Montecatini Co. and K. Ziegler. (Ital. Appl. Febr. 24, 1958.)
14. J. P. Rakus and C. D. Mason, *J. Polymer Sci.* **B4**, 467–468 (1966).
14a. *Brit. Chem. Eng.* **15** (9), 1115 (1970).
15. G. Natta, P. Pino, and G. Mazzanti, *Chim. Ind. (Milan)* **37**, 927–932 (1955); *Gazz. Chim. Ital.* **87**, 528–548 (1957).

16. U.S. Pat. 3,197,452 (July 27, 1965), G. Natta, P. Pino, and G. Mazzanti (to Montecatini S.p.A.).
17. I. D. Rubin, *Poly(1-butene). Its Preparation and Properties*, Macdonald & Co., Technical and Scientific, London, 1969.
18. G. Natta, I. Pasquon, A. Zambelli, and G. Gatti, *J. Polymer Sci.* **51**, 387–398 (1961).
19. G. Lefebvre and Y. Chauvin, *World Petrol. Congr. Proc. 7th, 1967* **5**, 343–350 (1968); *Chem. Abstr.* **71**, 50574b, 1969.
20. G. Natta, A. Zambelli, I. Pasquon, and G. M. Giongo, *Chim. Ind. (Milan)* **48**, 1298–1306 (1966).
21. H. Schnecko, W. Lintz, and W. Kern, *J. Polymer Sci. A-1* **5**, 205–214 (1967).
22. G. Natta, *J. Polymer Sci.* **34**, 21–48 (1959).
23. G. Natta, I. Pasquon, and L. Giuffrè, *Chim. Ind. (Milan)* **43**, 871–874 (1961).
24. A. I. Medalia, A. Orzechowski, J. A. Trinchera, and J. P. Morley, *J. Polymer Sci.* **41**, 241–263 (1959).
25. U.S. Pat. 3,278,512 (Oct. 11, 1966), D. D. Emrick and R. Zorska (to Standard Oil Co., Ohio).
26. A. Zambelli, A. Léty, C. Tosv, and I. Pasquon, *Makromol. Chem.* **115**, 73–88 (1968).
27. T. Reed, *Plastics Technol.* **12**, 38–39, (Febr. 1966).
28. A. Turner-Jones, *Polymer* **7**, 23–59 (1966).
28a. A. Turner-Jones, *J. Polymer Sci.* **B3**, 591–600 (1965).
29. G. Goldback, G. Peitscher, *J. Polymer Sci.* **B6**, 783–788 (1968).
    S. W. Cornell, J. L. Koenig, *J. Polymer Sci. A-2* **7**, 1965–1982 (1969).
30. J. Boor, Jr., and E. A. Youngman, *J. Polymer Sci.* **B2**, 903–907 (1964).
31. R. L. Miller and V. F. Holland, *J. Polymer Sci.* **B2**, 519–521 (1964).
32. J. Brandrup and E. H. Immergut, eds., *Polymer Handbook*, Interscience Publishers, a div. of John Wiley & Sons, Inc., New York, 1966.
33. J. Plenikowski, *Kunststoffe* **55**, 431–437 (1965).
34. J. Plenikowski and O. Hahmann, *Chem. Ing. Tech.* **38** (10), 1063–1076 (1966).
35. W. Ring and W. Holtrup, *Makromol. Chem.* **103**, 83–90 (1967).
36. W. R. Krigbaum, J. E. Kurz, and P. Smith, *J. Phys. Chem.* **65**, 1984–1991 (1961).
37. S. S. Stivala, R. J. Valles, and D. W. Levi, *J. Appl. Polymer Sci.* **7**, 97–102 (1963).
38. J. Cazes, *J. Chem. Educ.* **47**, A505–514 (1970).
39. Brit. Pat. 1,084,953 (filed Jan. 31, 1964), K. J. Clark and A. Turner-Jones (to Imperial Chemical Industries Ltd.).
40. J. P. Rakus, C. D. Mason, and R. J. Schaffhauser, *J. Polymer Sci.* **B7**, 591–595 (1969).
41. F. S. Dainton, D. M. Evans, F. E. Hoare, and T. P. Melia, *Polymer* **3**, 286–296 (1962).
    R. W. Warfield and M. C. Petree, *J. Polymer Sci. A-2* **5**, 791–794 (1967).
42. C. R. Lindegren, *Polymer Eng. Sci.* **10**, 163–169 (1970).
43. Brit. Pat. 1,150,637 (April 30, 1969), to Petro-Tex Chemical Corp.
44. E. Beati, F. Severini, and S. Toffano, *J. Polymer Sci.* **51**, 455–462 (1961).
    L. Dulog, E. Radlmann, and W. Kern, *Makromol. Chem.* **60**, 1–17 (1963).
45. D. Pagani, E. Beati, and F. Severini, *Chim. Ind. (Milan)* **46**, 393–396 (1964).
46. U.S. Pat. 3,198,779 (Aug. 3, 1965), R. J. Kray and J. P. Rakus (to Allied Chemical Corp.).
47. J. E. Mark and P. J. Flory, *J. Am. Chem. Soc.* **87**, 1423–1429 (1965).
48. G. Mazzanti, A. Valvassori, G. Sartori, and G. Pajaro, *Chim. Ind. (Milan)* **42**, 468–474 (1960).
49. G. Natta, *Makromol. Chem.* **35**, 94–131 (1960).
49a. A. Turner-Jones, *Polymer* **6**, 249 (1965).
50. Brit. Pat. 1,013,885 (filed Jan. 17, 1963) K. J. Clark, R. P. Palmer, and A. Turner-Jones (to Imperial Chemical Industries, Ltd.).
51. Belg. Pat. 650,899 (Jan. 25, 1965), to Farbwerke Hoechst, A.G.
52. A. H. Willbourn, "Polymers in High Performance Applications," *Plastics Inst. and Soc. Plastics Engrs., Joint Meet. London, June, 1969*, pp. 37–51.
53. *New Scientist* **1968** (June 13) 564.
54. J. K. Hambling and R. P. Northcott, *Rubber Plastics Age* **49**, 224 (March 1968).
55. J. B. Wilkes, *World Petrol. Congr. Proc. 7th, 1967* **5**, 299–309 (1968).
56. Brit. Pat. 912,824 (Dec. 12, 1962), J. K. Hambling (to British Petroleum Co.).
57. Brit. Pat. 933,253 (Aug. 8, 1963), G. W. Alderson and J. K. Hambling (to British Petroleum Co.).

58. U.S. Pat. 2,968,681 (Jan. 17, 1961), G. L. O'Connor, H. E. Fritz, and M. A. Eccles (to Union Carbide Corp.).
59. U.S. Pat. 3,251,895 (May 17, 1966), J. B. Wilkes (to Chevron Research Co.).
60. T. W. Campbell and A. C. Haven, *J. Appl. Polymer Sci.* **1,** 78 (1959).
61. W. A. Hewett and F. E. Weir, *J. Polymer Sci. A* **1,** 1239 (1963).
62. Brit. Pat. 942,297 (Nov. 20, 1963), K. J. Clark (to Imperial Chemical Industries Ltd.).
63. J. Ehrig, J. J. Godfrey, and G. S. Krishnamurthy, "Elastomer Stereospecific Polymerisation," *Advan. Chem. Ser.* **52** (9), 105 (1966).
64. K. J. Clark and R. P. Palmer, *The Chemistry of Polymerisation Processes*, Monograph No. 20, Soc. Chem. Ind., London, 1966, p. 82.
65. Yuji Atarashi, *Kogyo Kagaku Zasshi* **68,** 2487 (1969).
66. A. D. Caunt, personal communication,
67. Tod W. Campbell, *J. Appl. Polymer Sci.* **5,** 184 (1961).
68. Brit. Pat. 1,014,886 (Dec. 31, 1965), K. J. Clark and M. E. B. Jones (to Imperial Chemical Industries Ltd.).
69. Brit. Pat. 1,001,801 (Aug. 18, 1965), K. J. Clark (to Imperial Chemical Industries Ltd.).
70. Fr. Pat. 1,540,270 (Sept. 27, 1968), Y. Chauvin, G. Lefebvre, and M. Uchino (to Institut Français du Petrole).
71. Fr. Pat. 1,540,271 (Sep. 27, 1968), Y. Chauvin and G. Lefebvre (to Institut Français du Petrole).
72. Y. Chauvin, N. Phang, N. Guichard-Loudet, and G. Lefebvre, *Bull. Soc. Chim. France* **10,** 3223 (1966).
73. R. M. Ogorkiewicz, ed., *Engineering Properties of Thermoplastics*, Wiley-Interscience, London, 1970, Chap. 9.
74. F. C. Frank, A. Keller, and A. O'Connor, *Phil. Mag.* **4,** 200 (1959).
75. J. H. Griffith and B. G. Ränby, *J. Polymer Sci.* **44,** 369 (1960).
76. A. E. Woodward, *Polymer* **5,** 293 (1964).
77. F. E. Karasy, H. E. Bair, and J. M. O'Reilly, *Polymer* **8,** 547 (1967).
78. B. G. Ränby, H. Brumberger, and K. S. Chan, *J. Polymer Sci.* **58,** 545 (1962).
79. R. W. Penn, *J. Polymer Sci. A-2* **4,** 559 (1966).
80. Y. Tanda, N. Kawasaki, K. Imada, and M. Takayanagi, *Rept. Progr. Polymer Phys. Japan* **9,** 165–168 (1966).
81. Brit. Pat. 1,085,914 (Oct. 4, 1967), K. J. Clark (to Imperial Chemical Industries Ltd.).
82. B. S. Dyer, *Plastics* **33,** 1145 (1968).
83. M. R. Day, *Plastics Polymers* **36,** 101 (April 1968).
84. L. L. Lander, *SPE (Soc. Plastics Engrs.) J.* **16,** 1329 (1960).

A. D. Caunt and J. B. Rose
Imperial Chemical Industries Ltd.

POLYPROPYLENE FIBER

Polypropylene fiber is an olefin or, more properly, a polyolefin fiber manufactured from isotactic polypropylene, which in the form of fine and medium denier filament accounts for most of the olefin used in fibers. Aside from polypropylene, a small amount of polyethylene is also converted into heavy fiber, ie "monofilament," for fishnet, rope, and cordage, or spun into fine fiber to be used in nonwoven disposable fabrics. Other isotactic polyolefins, such as poly(3-methyl-1-butene) or poly(4-methyl-1-pentene) yield fibers of considerably higher softening point than either polyethylene or polypropylene. They are not being used in fiber at present, primarily because they do not have a combination of properties that is useful. Unlike the other synthetic fibers the use of polypropylene as a plastic overshadows its use as a fiber, with approx 800 million lb going into plastics vs 250 million lb into fibers in 1969.

Historical. Natta's discovery of stereospecific polymerization employing the organometallic Ziegler catalyst systems led directly to the crystalline, highly isotactic fiber-forming polypropylene which we know. Atactic polypropylene is a rubbery material which is wholly unusable for the formation of fibers. Details of structure and polymerization have been discussed elsewhere, both in this encyclopedia (see Polypropylene under Olefin polymers) and in reference books (1,1a,1b) so that the discussion of these topics here is only in relation to the fiber.

Development of polypropylene as a plastic and as a fiber was pioneered by Montecatini starting in 1957–1959 and many patents in this area are held by this company (2). By 1960 and 1961, limited commercial quantities of the fiber were offered by a number of producers in both North America and Europe. Once polypropylene was introduced, the combination of excellent physical and chemical properties coupled with potentially low price generated tremendous interest in the fiber and predictions of large markets were made (3,3a). It has, however, not grown as rapidly as expected, but long-term predictions for its growth are still optimistic, based on potential new end uses. The actual place which polypropylene will take in the use spectrum of synthetic fibers and how large a fraction of the total market it will command, cannot be predicted. Aside from monofilament uses in webbing, cordage, and the like, by far the largest current market for polypropylene fiber has been in carpets, both as a pile yarn and as backing; in addition, upholstery is a rapidly growing market. This topic will be discussed in detail under Economic aspects.

Polymer Properties

A man-made fiber is actually a very special fabricated form of a polymer, one which has a very great length-to-diameter ratio and has been crystallized and oriented to a lesser or greater extent in order to organize its molecular units for achieving specific properties.

This means that strength, elongation, stiffness, resiliency, hand, and other properties affecting the use of the fiber polymer can be greatly influenced by the nature of its crystallites, the degree of orientation of the fiber structure, and how completely this structure has been "set." Some understanding of the polymer structure is, therefore, essential to an understanding of the fiber structure and how it responds to applied stresses and environments.

The polypropylene commonly used in melt-spinning fiber is a purified ("fiber-grade") linear homopolymer, which is partially crystalline and highly isotactic. Purification of a fiber-grade polymer is largely a matter of reducing contaminants and jelled particles to a minimum. This purification is necessary because in fiber spinning the polymer melt must be extruded through small holes at a high rate and with a large draw-down. Any plugging of spinneret holes or change in the rheology of the melt would thus be fatal to the efficiency of the process. Filter packs are used to further strain out impurities in the melt stream. If, however, impurities clog the filter packs too rapidly, excessive backpressure necessitates frequent pack changes, which is highly undesirable.

Molecular linearity in a polymer is essential in producing high-strength fine filaments. The use of copolymers, usually with other olefin monomers, for fiber production has been mentioned (4) but is not in widespread use, since modulus and strength are reduced in the copolymer.

Some improvement in the abrasion resistance of the fiber is brought about by either copolymerization with ethylene or addition of polyethylene, both in amounts less than 5% (5). These presumably "flexibilize" the polypropylene and enable it to absorb energy without mechanical failure.

Crystallinity and Isotacticity. These two properties of polypropylene and polymers in general are related, but not identical. An isotactic polypropylene polymer is a polymer whose monomeric units (propylene) are asymmetric, ordered in such a manner that when passing along a single polymer chain from one monomeric unit to the subsequent one, the unit configuration is repeated. "Isotactic" is an adjective from the Greek, meaning "placed in the same order." The stereoregularity of the isotactic structure allows it to crystallize, but all of the isotactic structure does not necessarily crystallize. As an example, crystallinity of polypropylene fibers is estimated at about 60% and in highly annealed samples possibly up to 75%. Commercial fiber-grade polymer, however, is at least 95% isotactic, as determined by its content of heptane-insoluble material.

Although there are at least four known crystalline forms of polypropylene, only two, the α or monoclinic, and the smectic or paracrystalline, are of concern in fibers (see Vol. 14, p. 285). The smectic form, which is considered to have a low degree of lateral order (6), forms on rapid quenching of the molten filaments after extrusion, but changes to the stable α form on heating. Crystallinity and orientation are the two major structural factors determining fiber properties which can be manipulated. Hence, they are of great importance and are discussed in detail in the section on fiber properties. In general, the degree of crystallinity affects the size, shape, and degree of perfection of the crystallites and these, in turn, control the physical properties. The calculated density of the monoclinic unit cell of polypropylene is 0.936, representing 100% crystallinity, whereas that of the completely amorphous atactic variety is 0.85. From the actual measured density, therefore, one may calculate the degree of crystallinity.

Physical Properties of the Polymer.   Some of the pertinent physical properties of polypropylene, which relate to its fiber properties, are listed in Table 1 along with comparable values for nylon 66, poly(hexamethylene adipamide), which is another melt-spun fiber whose base polymer is also a plastic.   It is to be noted that the molecular weight of the nylon is less than a tenth that of the polypropylene.   This is a reflection of the strong intermolecular forces, mainly hydrogen bonding, operating in the polyamide to hold it together.   In the polyolefins these polar interactions are lacking. Although the mechanical properties of bulk polypropylene are inferior to those of the nylon, once the polypropylene is converted into fiber and oriented, its comparison with the nylon becomes much more favorable.

Table 1.   Physical Properties of Polypropylene and Nylon 66

Property	Polypropylene	Nylon 66
molecular weight[a]	120,000–420,000	10,000–25,000
melting point, °C	165–175	245–255
specific gravity	0.90	1.14
tensile strength, psi	5,000	10,500
tensile modulus, psi	190,000	300,000
flexural modulus, psi	190,000	400,000
heat-distortion temperature, °C		
264-psi stress	46	85
66-psi stress	102	213
water absorption, 1/8 in. in 24 hr, %	0.01	1.5
impact strength,		
1/2 in. notched Izod, ft-lb/in.	1.5	1.5

[a] From intrinsic viscosity.

Chemical Properties.   The nonpolar paraffinic nature of polypropylene determines its chemical reactions as well as its physical properties.   These may be characterized in general as inertness and insolubility.   The polymer is relatively unaffected by nonoxidizing acids, bases, salts, and polar solvents.   Oxidizing acids, such as nitric and sulfuric, attack it, particularly at elevated temperatures.   There is no known solvent for polypropylene at room temperature.   Polar solvents, such as ketones, alcohols, nitriles, etc, have little effect even at higher temperatures.   It is, however, soluble in some aromatic hydrocarbons and some chlorohydrocarbons at elevated temperatures. For example, to measure its intrinsic viscosity solutions in tetrahydronaphthalene or decahydronaphthalene at 135°C can be used.   It should be remembered that these properties are for the stereoregular crystalline polypropylene only; atactic polypropylene is more soluble.   Details on solubilities and the effects of various reagents on the fiber are listed in a number of sources (7).

Heat Stability.   The heat degradation of most polymers can be broken into two parts: one purely thermal and proceeding in the absence of oxygen or any other reactive atmosphere, and the other oxidative, involving the thermally accelerated oxidation of the substrate.   In the extrusion process both conditions prevail with oxidation occurring as the polymer melts prior to being purged of air.   The melt is then degassed as it travels down the extruder barrel, conditions becoming essentially anaerobic, allowing only purely thermal degradation to take place.   Thermooxidation can also occur during subsequent processing of the fiber, as in heat setting, drying or curing, and in actual service.

The thermal cleavage of polypropylene is a pyrolysis involving random scission of the molecular chains, the mechanism of which has been reviewed in detail (8). There are no stabilizers known for this type of degradation, since a direct cleavage of carbon–carbon bonds in the backbone of polymer is prominently involved (9). What is done in practice, therefore is to minimize this type of breakdown by using the lowest melt temperature compatible with the demands of the particular process and the need to build the desired properties into the extruded fiber. Usually, the degradation during extrusion, as measured by the decrease in intrinsic viscosity, does not become severe until temperatures above 285°C are reached. Above 315°C the drop in intrinsic viscosity is quite rapid (10). Compensation for the breakdown can, of course, be made by starting with a resin of intrinsic viscosity higher than is desired in the final fiber.

Oxidative degradation of hydrocarbon polymers is a familiar phenomenon in rubber technology and antioxidants similar to those used in rubber have been very successfully applied to polypropylene. It is almost certainly true, in fact, that without these antioxidants or some other method for retarding the oxidation, polypropylene, with its vulnerable tertiary hydrogen atoms, would not have become a commercial product. The accepted mechanism for autoxidation of polypropylene involves a chain in which a single independently initiated free radical can generate many others via reaction with oxygen to form hydroperoxides (8,11), as shown below (PH = Polymer):

Initiation

$$PH \longrightarrow P\cdot$$
$$P\cdot + O_2 \longrightarrow POO\cdot$$

Propagation

$$POO\cdot + PH \longrightarrow POOH + P\cdot \text{ (etc)}$$

By deactivating the initiator species the antioxidant functions at quite low concentrations, usually on the order of 0.1%.

Although the alkylated secondary amines, such as N-phenyl-2-naphthylamine, used in rubber stabilization are effective in polypropylene, they are not used in fiber because they discolor during extrusion. Highly hindered alkylated phenols, shown in

Scheme 1

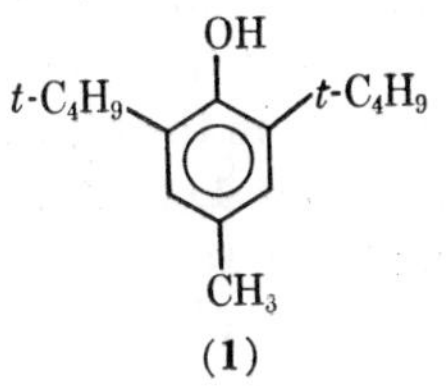

(1)

2,6-di-*tert*-butyl-4-methylphenol

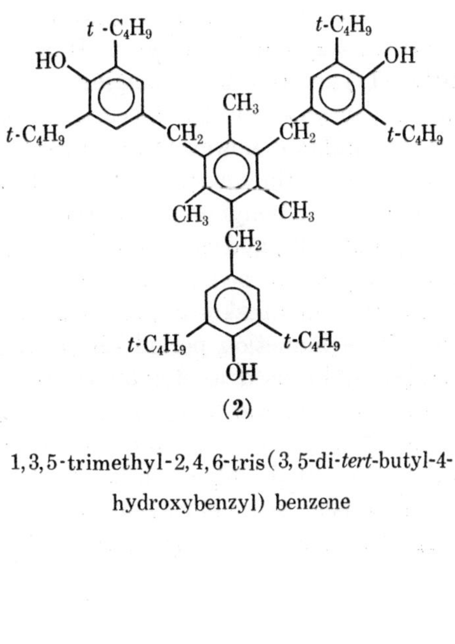

(2)

1,3,5-trimethyl-2,4,6-tris(3,5-di-*tert*-butyl-4-hydroxybenzyl) benzene

Scheme 1, are almost universally used. Those of lower molecular weight (**1**) are too volatile at the usual fiber-spinning temperatures, so that polynuclear higher-molecular-weight materials, as exemplified by (**2**), have been developed. In addition to the free phenols, their phosphate esters have also proven effective. Sulfur-linked, rather than methylene-linked phenols are also used, but caution in their selection is necessary, since some sulfur compounds can actually promote the breakdown of the polymer (12).

The hindered phenols react with the initiator fragments via hydrogen transfer to form an inactive species and a stable free radical which is incapable of further chain propagation.

$$P\cdot + \underset{\text{antioxidant}}{A\text{--}H} \longrightarrow PH + \underset{\substack{\text{stable free} \\ \text{radical}}}{A\cdot}$$

Since presumably some initiator does escape to react with oxygen, another type of stabilizer, a peroxide decomposer, is frequently used in combination with the hindered phenol. By converting any peroxides formed to inactive products, these stabilizers, usually sulfur compounds, likewise prevent further chain propagation. Long-chain alkyl esters of thiodipropionic acid, $S(CH_2CH_2COOR)_2$, are used almost exclusively for this purpose and it has been stated that these two classes of antioxidants act synergistically (13,14).

Although the present antioxidant systems protect the polypropylene through fiber spinning and for many subsequent uses, they are not capable of furnishing complete protection for all the uses desired. The greatest need is for antioxidants resistant to laundering and drycleaning. The combination of alkaline bleaching plus the oxidative action of bleaches during home and commercial laundering can apparently completely destroy the antioxidants in the fiber. Research is active in this area and polypropylene manufacturers have produced resins with laundry-resistant antioxidants (15). The oxidation of polypropylene is also catalyzed by traces of copper (16), although this effect can be inhibited by copper complexing agents. Yellowing of the fiber from atmospheric oxides of nitrogen, called "gas fading," can be traced to the phenolic antioxidants, but this effect has been reduced in the latest systems.

Light Stability. Deterioration by sunlight seriously hampers the use of a fiber and polypropylene is quite sensitive to photodegradation. This problem is similar to that of thermal oxidation, ie commercialization of the fiber had to wait until the development of satisfactory light stabilizers. It is generally agreed that the photodegradation is oxidative (11) and that the damaging wavelengths are those in the ultraviolet region which are not screened out by the earth's atmosphere (ie 3,000–4,000 Å). Since polypropylene is paraffinic, however, and thus should be completely transparent to light of these wave lengths, the question arises as to how the initiating photons are absorbed. Small amounts of carbonyl present in the unaged polymer are now considered to be the sensitizing groups (17) and since these build up during the course of the photooxidation, the reaction appears to be autocatalytic.

In this type of breakdown, there is an induction period during the buildup of carbonyl. This induction period disappears when an absorbing material, like the vinylpyridine units used as dye-binding sites, which is capable of transferring the energy, is present in the polypropylene. Figure 1 shows the loss of strength after exposure to a sunlamp-blacklamp (uv exposure unit).

Stabilization of the fiber can be effected by any of the three following different classes of materials: screening agents, including some pigments; ultraviolet absorbers; and energy-transfer agents. In practice, combinations of these are frequently used.

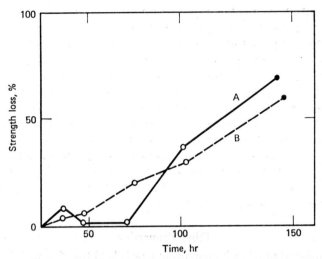

Fig. 1. Degradation of polypropylene fiber by exposure to a fluorescent sunlamp-blacklamp (a device giving visible plus uv, designed to be similar to sunlight). LEGEND ——A, without vinylpyridine polymer; - - - - B, containing 2.9% vinylpyridine polymer.

Carbon black as a screen makes probably the most efficient protective agent, but this, of course, limits the product to black fibers. Pigments are widely used in melt-coloring polypropylene and some do afford a degree of protection. There is a wide variation in the light stability of pigmented fibers and care must therefore be exercised in the selection of the pigments.

UV absorbers (see Ultraviolet absorbers) are frequently employed and, although many types have been mentioned in the literature, only two are widely used. The first and older type are the derivatives of 2,4-dihydroxybenzophenone in which the 4-hydroxy group has been aklylated to promote compatibility with the base polymer. A newer class is the benzotriazoles, which apparently function best in conjunction with the thiodipropionate peroxide decomposers. Both types are highly efficient protective agents and function by absorbing the radiation and dissipating the energy as heat.

The newest light stabilizers are the nickel chelates (3), usually of hindered phenols (11). These compounds, unlike other ultraviolet absorbers such as hydroxybenzophenone and benzotriazole types, do not have a strong absorption in the 3,000–4,000 Å region. They do have the property of quenching fluorescence and it is believed that they work by deactivating the excited states which are part of the degradation chain (19). Due to the nickel, however, such stabilizers usually impart a greenish cast to the fiber.

$$t\text{-}C_8H_{17} \quad\quad S \longrightarrow Ni \longleftarrow NH_2 \text{---} C_4H_9\text{-}n$$

$$t\text{-}C_8H_{17}$$

(**3**)

[2,2'-thiobis(4-tert-octylphenolato)]-*n*-

butylamine nickel

As mentioned above combinations of stabilizers are frequently used. The benzotriazoles are thus usually combined with the thiodipropionates. Outstanding light stabilities have been obtained when a hydroxybenzophenone is used in conjunction with a nickel chelate. A new phosphite antioxidant used with a hydroxybenzophenone has also been successful (20). It is thus obvious that there are many interactions which can occur with these combinations, which is not surprising in the light of the previous discussion of heat stabilization, since it is believed that the propagation mechanisms for both thermal and photooxidation are similar, but not identical (11,21).

The state of the art in light stabilization can be summed up as being similar to that in heat stabilization. Some very good systems have been developed, but better ones are needed. It would be highly desirable, for instance, to be able to achieve the stability levels obtainable from combinations of nickel chelate and hydroxybenzophenone without the attendant green color in the fiber.

Fiber Properties

As was mentioned previously, polypropylene is held together mainly by crystalline forces and this is the most important overall factor influencing mechanical properties and, in turn, their temperature response. After a description of the microscopic fiber properties, the relationship of structural parameters to properties is discussed.

Mechanical Properties. The tenacity and elongation of polypropylene multifilament fiber varies with production conditions, crystallinity and molecular weight of the polymer. In general, the tenacity and elongation are engineered to suit the end use. A tenacity of 1.5–7.0 g/den and an elongation at break of 15–80% encompass the normal ranges for staple and filament fibers. (The denier of a fiber or yarn is the weight in grams of 9,000 m.) Yarns for carpets, which are a major use for polypropylene, require high resiliency and for this purpose lower strengths and higher elongations are used. Polypropylene has a higher bending modulus than nylon but lower than polyester. Its flex resistance is excellent, so much so that it is superior to any other known fiber in this respect (22,22a).

The elastic properties of the fiber, as well as the other mechanical properties, can be controlled by processing conditions. For example, a truly elastomeric polypropylene fiber can be produced by orienting some crystals perpendicular to the fiber axis and then "crosslinking" from fiber to fiber with axially oriented crystallites. This is done by annealing undrawn, essentially unoriented, fiber at temperatures of 130–150°C to produce a fiber with 85–90% recovery after 25% elongation.

The creep (deformation under constant load) of a fiber such as polypropylene is good but not equal to that of other carpet fibers, such as nylon. Polypropylene undergoes cold flow of up to 0.5% of its original length when subjected to a load of 1.5 g/den for 16 hr at room temperature.

Abrasion Resistance and Friction. The factors influencing abrasion (23–25) are varied, interrelated, and dependent on the type of abrasion; eg yarn-to-yarn or yarn-to-nonfibrous material. Abrasion is a result of deformation due to compression, tension, bending, shear, and cutting. A high elastic energy is the main factor in combatting abrasion damage. In yarn-to-yarn abrasion of polypropylene multifilament yarn, maximum abrasion resistance has been obtained using materials of high molecular weight, low tenacity, and high elongation, made from undrawn fiber with low orientation. Annealing of low-molecular-weight yarn, which increases crystallinity, also increases abrasion resistance.

The mechanism of abrasion is believed to be surface fragmentation or peeling initiated at imperfections in the fiber crystallite. Surface finishes can improve the abrasion resistance dramatically by lowering the coefficient of filament-to-filament friction. See below under Spin finishes (p. 825).

Thermal Properties. The physical properties of polypropylene, as with all fibers, are a function of temperature. The low heat-distortion temperature of polypropylene is linked to the low melting point and represents an important restriction on the possible applications for this fiber. A more practical way of measuring the temperature limit of service for a fiber is the *stick temperature*, which represents the temperature at which the fiber softens and sticks to a hot metal surface, such as a household iron. For polypropylene this temperature is about 150°C. Since most household and commercial irons run at this temperature or higher, this means that polypropylene fabrics are essentially unironable. Blends of 20% polypropylene with cotton, however, can be ironed (26). It has been recommended that the processing temperature for the finishing of carpets not exceed 127°C (260°F) (27). Table 2 lists the thermal sensitivity of various fibers (28,28a).

Table 2. Thermal Sensitivity of Various Fibers

| Fiber | Temperature, °C | | |
	Soften	Melt	Decompose
polypropylene	145–150	165	
polyethylene			
low density	90–95	115	
high density	120–125	135	
polyester	235	250	
acrylic	235	250	
rayon			180
acetate	200	230	
nylon 6	205	220	
wool			135
silk			150
cotton			150
glass	735		

Polypropylene is the best insulator of all the natural and synthetic fibers on the market, since it has the lowest thermal conductivity. Table 3 lists the thermal conductivity of several commercial fibers. Polypropylene is currently the best fiber for thermal clothing, shoes, sleeping bags, and other insulating fabrics (29).

Table 3. Thermal Conductivity of Commercial Fibers

Fiber	Thermal conductivity[a]
polypropylene	6.0
poly(vinyl chloride)	6.4
wool	7.3
cellulose acetate	8.6
viscose rayon	11.0
cotton	17.0

[a] Expressed as ratio to thermal conductivity of air.

Flammability. It has been recognized that flammability is a very important property of fibers and plastics because of consumer and government concern for safety. Flame resistance is of prime importance to fiber producers since the end products normally become consumer items. Polypropylene, being a hydrocarbon, burns in the absence of flame retardants. In common with other thermoplastic fibers, when exposed to a flame, it shrinks, melts, and draws away from the flame without igniting. It is thus more difficult to ignite than some of the nonthermoplastic fibers. Table 4 compares the burning characteristics of polypropylene with those of other fibers (29a).

Table 4. Burning Characteristics of Polypropylene Compared with Those of Other Fibers

Fiber	Before touching flame	In flame	After leaving flame
nylon	melts before touching flame	melts and burns	does not readily support combustion
polyester	melts before touching flame	melts and burns	burns readily
Dynel[a]	shrinks away from flame and melts	melts and burns slowly	does not support combustion
acrylic	melts and ignites before reaching flame	melts and burns rapidly	burns readily with sputtering
polypropylene	shrinks rapidly from flame, curls, and melts	melts and ignites with difficulty	burns slowly

[a] Dynel (Union Carbide Corp.) is a copolymer of acrylonitrile and vinyl chloride.

Moisture Effects. The affinity of textile fibers for water is a property which has been misunderstood in discussions of fabric comfort, "breathability," and the like. It has generally been felt that the so-called "hydrophobic" fibers, a term which usually includes polyamides, polyesters, and polyolefins, are uncomfortable to the wearer, in that they are unduly warm and do not allow proper removal of body perspiration. There exists considerable disagreement in this matter, however, especially since the standard moisture regain (moisture uptake at 70°F and 65% rh) of the hydrophobic fibers ranges from essentially zero for the unmodified polyolefins to 0.4% for the polyesters to 4% for the polyamides (30). See Table 5. In some fabric construction polypropylene is beneficial in regard to body comfort and the fiber has been recommended for use in hosiery and undergarments because of its claimed ability to wick body moisture along the filament surface to the outside (31).

Table 5. Moisture Regain of Various Fibers at 70°F and 65% (29b)

Fiber	Moisture regain, %	Fiber	Moisture regain, %
polypropylene	0	polyester	0.4–0.8
acetate	6.5	polyethylene	
cotton, raw	8.5	high density	0
nylon	4–5	wool	16.0

Specific Gravity. The low specific gravity is an important property insofar as textile uses for the fiber are concerned. In applications where the textile serves in a covering or decorative rather than a strength function, the greater coverage per lb of a fiber should make it more economical. Such items include most apparel fabrics, draperies, carpets, upholstery fabrics, and other materials. The covering ability per lb of common fibers is compared to that of polypropylene in Table 6. These data show a very significant advantage for polypropylene over the other fibers. Comparisons based on density alone, however, can be misleading. Other factors, such as yarn and fabric constructions, have a great deal of influence on the covering ability of the final product and can, in fact, be great enough to mask the natural advantage in potential covering power. In any case, this difference represents a level which could be attained, and claims have been made that this has been achieved, at least in the laboratory (26).

Table 6. Relative Covering Power of Textile Fibers

Fiber	Specific gravity	Ratio to polypropylene	Relative covering power[a]
polypropylene	0.91	1.0	100
nylon	1.14	1.25	80
acrylic	1.18	1.30	77
dynel	1.30	1.42	70
acetate	1.32	1.45	68
wool	1.34	1.47	67
polyester	1.38	1.52	66
viscose rayon	1.52	1.67	60
cotton	1.55	1.70	58
saran[b]	1.72	1.89	52
glass	2.54	2.79	35

[a] Ratio of specific volume (1/sp gr) to that of polypropylene $\times$ 100.

[b] See Vol. 21, p. 275.

Mildew Resistance. Polypropylene fiber is extremely resistant to mildew and does not support the growth of microorganisms and fungi. Occasionally, finishes or impurities on the fiber surface allow some growth of fungi but this does not affect the strength of the fiber.

Insect Resistance. Polypropylene per se is not digestible by insects such as moths, etc, therefore, the yarn is not subject to insect attack.

Parameters Determining Fiber Properties (32–34)

The molecular units in linear crystalline polymers, such as polypropylene, develop major asymmetries and orientations when converted into fiber. In particular orientation, which involves both crystalline and less-ordered areas, can produce vast changes in the properties of fibers, especially in the mechanical properties. Modern technology of producing synthetic fibers is based to a large extent on this subject, but since much of the knowledge about orientation is pragmatic, research in this area is very active.

In relation to the process of converting bulk polymer to fiber, the conditions used for melt spinning, quenching, drawing, and annealing affect not only the structural parameters of the polypropylene but also the relationship between structural parameters and tensile properties of the fiber. The structural parameters involved are molecular weight, molecular-weight distribution, crystallinity, and orientation. All the tensile properties are affected, including tenacity, elongation at break, toughness, and modulus.

Extrusion conditions affect molecular weight, molecular-weight distribution, crystallinity, and orientation. The subsequent quenching, drawing, and annealing steps affect only crystallinity and orientation. Processing conditions and the resultant properties are both interrelated and in commercial production are difficult to control precisely. Uniformity of the heat and mechanical history of the fiber, however, is extremely important in order to obtain uniform physical and chemical properties.

Table 7 shows the effects of changing only the molecular weight while attempting to hold spinning, quenching, and drawing conditions constant (32). This table shows the overriding influence of molecular weight on mechanical properties.

Table 7. Effect of Melt-Flow Rate of Polypropylene on Fiber Properties[a]

Melt-flow rate[b]		Tenacity, g/den	Fiber density, g/ml
Resin	Fiber		
43.5	47.5	2.1	0.9118
10.7	16.1	2.8	0.9105
4.4	6.1	3.2	0.9080
3.6	5.2[c]	3.9	0.9065

[a] Fiber spun at 275°C, quenched in air, and a draw ratio of 3:1.

[b] Inversely related to molecular weight; ASTM Standards D-1238-62T, measured at 230°C. See Vol. 14, p. 288.

[c] Spun at 285°C.

The results show that tenacity increases with molecular weight at the same draw ratio, probably due to less preorientation during spinning and drawing. The observed density increases with decreasing molecular weight due to the greater mobility and faster crystallization of lower-molecular-weight polymers.

Under certain conditions of quenching, hexagonal crystals are formed but they are converted to the more stable monoclinic form by heat, especially during drawing. Rapid quenching of filaments after extrusion, as mentioned earlier, produces smectic or paracrystalline polypropylene, in which the crystals are small. These may be monoclinic or hexagonal but are also converted to the more stable monoclinic form on heating and drawing. Crystallinity is measured in many ways, and the results are not always in agreement. Orientation measurements usually contain both a crystalline and a noncrystalline component, so that separation of these variables is difficult.

Work recovery is a measure of the ability of the fiber to recover from an applied stress. Polypropylene fiber improves with higher crystallinity at low elongations (1%) but decreases at high elongations (10%). The higher the orientation the greater the work recovery at both 1 and 10% elongation (32).

Drawing. The function of the drawing operation is to orient the molecules and crystallites of the polymer in the direction of the fiber axis. The tensile properties increase with greater orientation. Figure 2 shows the effect of the draw ratio on tenacity, modulus, elongation, and density (crystallinity) of polypropylene fibers with different annealing temperatures (33). In general, tenacity and stiffness (modulus) increase with increasing draw, while elongation decreases, as might be expected from the greater molecular elongation. Density effects are more complex, with greater perfection of crystallites occurring from the high-temperature annealing. The lower draw ratios promote crystallinity, but at higher ratios there is some tendency to decrease. The effect of draw temperature and ratio on crystallinity is shown in Figure 3 (34).

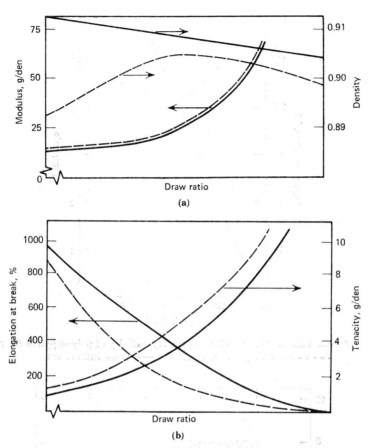

Fig. 2. Effect of draw ratio on the physical properties of polypropylene filaments: (**a**) modulus and density; (**b**) elongation and tenacity. LEGEND: - - - - annealed; ——— unannealed.

The effect of rate of draw, within the ranges used commercially, is shown in Table 8 (34). As the draw rate goes down, the crystallinity increases, presumably due to the longer exposure to the elevated temperature which in essence serves to anneal the fiber.

Table 8. Influence of Stretching Time on Fiber Crystallinity[a]

Time of stretch, sec	Crystallinity, %
4	60
37	77
41	84

[a] At 135°C; draw ratio 6:1.

The tenacity of a highly oriented fiber is higher than those of low or moderate orientation at the same elongation, as illustrated in Figure 4 (35).

Heat setting or annealing of the oriented fibers under controlled conditions imparts dimensional stability by reducing the tendency to shrink when the fiber is reheated. Heat setting should be carried out under controlled relaxation or stable ten-

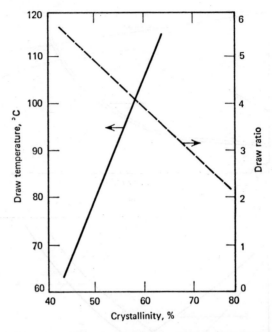

Fig. 3. Effect of draw ratio and temperature on the crystallinity of polypropylene fiber. LEGEND:
- - - - - draw temperature of 100°C; ———— draw ratio of 4:1.

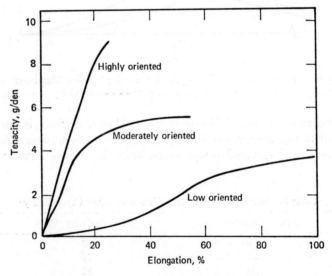

Fig. 4. Effect of orientation on tenacity of yarn.

sion conditions.   The effect of annealing on physical properties is illustrated in Figure 2.

Properties of Modified Fibers. The previous sections dealt with the physico-mechanical properties of "natural" fiber, produced from polypropylene resin containing only light and heat stabilizers.   The properties of modified dyeable or pigmented polypropylene are affected by the additives.   The data shown in Table 9 are for a family of resins containing different amounts of poly-2-vinylpyridine, a polymeric dye-site additive which renders the polypropylene fiber dyeable. The strength of fibers made from these mixtures decreases as the amount of dye-site additive increases, but for most end uses, where low levels of dye-site additives are employed, the strength losses are inconsequential.

Table 9. Properties of Modified Dyeable Polypropylene Fiber Mixed with Poly-2-vinylpyridine (36)

Composition of mixture, %		Intrinsic viscosity of polypropylene after fiber is spun, η	Elongation, %
Polypropylene	Poly-2-vinylpyridine		
100	0	1.00	27.4
96	4	1.05	32.0
92	8	1.10	27.2
88	12	1.18	29.9

Production of Fiber

Polypropylene fibers are manufactured by melt extrusion (spinning) through a multi-hole die (spinneret), followed by extension of the polymer filaments leaving the orifices. The filaments are cooled (quenched) by a perpendicular air flow or, in the case of monofilaments, by a water bath as they emerge from the spinneret. The solidified filaments are then wound on tubes in the form of "cheeses." Melt-spinning is usually followed by mechanical treatments of the fibers (drawing and/or texturizing). The three operations can be separate or continuous, ie, spin-draw-texturize.

Die-Swell. The rheological behavior of the polymer has a great effect on the process of fiber formation. It is not only the behavior of the melt or of the solidified fiber that is important but also the rheological behavior of all intermediate stages between the spinneret and the take-up device. The first problem is spinnability: a fiber-forming polymer to be melt-spun must yield stable fluid melts at practical spinning temperatures. It must form long fluid threads which support their own weight and the force of extension. During melt spinning, as the polymer leaves the spinneret, the phenomenon of die-swell (filament swelling) occurs, after which the filament is pulled into a thread about $\frac{1}{6}$ or $\frac{1}{7}$ of the diameter of the spinneret channel. Die-swell consists of the broadening of the fluid jet emerging from the spinneret the maximum radius being in extreme conditions several times as large as that of the channel. Photographic techniques have been used to determine the shape of the molten fiber.

The shape of the die-swell is dependent on melt viscosity, spinning temperatures, shear stresses, spinneret channel design, and feed rates (37,38). The ultimate linear and surface uniformity of the quenched filament is greatly affected by the die-swell phenomenon.

Excessive die-swell can cause dimensional irregularities in the thread and should surface cooling occur too fast, the surface of the filament fractures. Both effects are undesirable; therefore, careful control and design is necessary to produce a high-quality fiber (39).

High-Tenacity Polypropylene Fiber. A great deal of effort has been exerted to produce high-tenacity polypropylene fibers. High intrinsic viscosity in the spun fiber is necessary for ultrahigh tenacity. The best results have been obtained using a high-molecular-weight (400,000) resin, a low-shear extrusion system and a heated spin-way below the spinneret blanketed with nitrogen. Figure 5 illustrates the effect of fast.

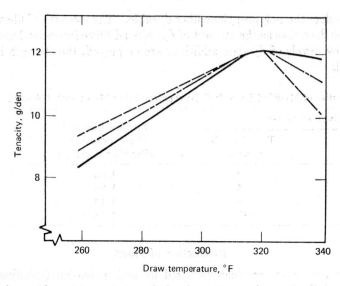

Fig. 5. Tenacity vs draw temperature and drawing rate. LEGEND: drawing rate, —— fast; — · — medium; — — — — slow.

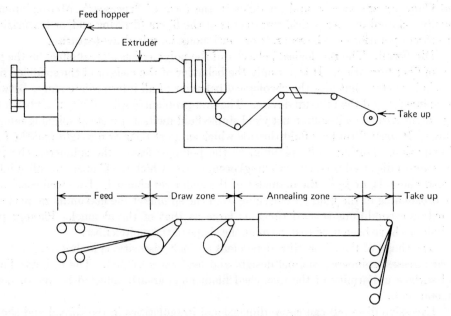

Fig. 6. Flowsheet of monofilament production.

medium and slow drawing of high-tenacity fiber at various draw temperatures. The tenacity of the drawn fiber reaches a peak at about 315°F, independent of the drawing rate (40).

Monofilament Yarns. Monofilament yarns, such as those used in outdoor chairs, vary in size from 0.003 to 0.020 in. in diam and have round, flat, or irregular cross sections. A diagram of monofilament production is shown in Figure 6. The extrusion

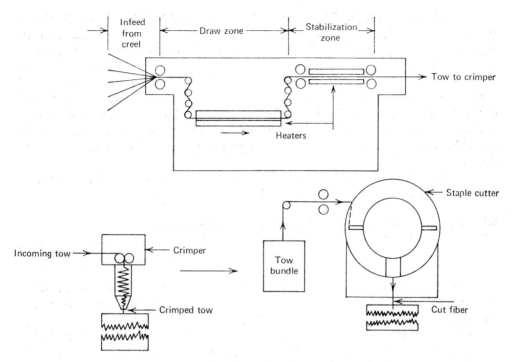

Fig. 7. Flowsheet of staple operation.

step is common to all olefin fibers and tapes. Die design, polymer heat history, and filament quench are among the parameters that must be carefully controlled.

The tenacity of the monofilament depends upon the draw ratio which varies from 4:1 to 10:1. Drawing can be carried out at elevated or at ambient temperatures, depending on the polymer. An annealing step is sometimes added in processing to stabilize the filamant against shrinkage. The stabilization is effective up to the "heat set" or annealing temperature. Monofilament yarn is wound on individual spools for further processing by the fabricator.

Staple Yarns. The manufacture of olefin fibers in the form of staple follows the technique used for polyester or nylon, but differs in several respects from those used in olefin-monofilament production. The spinning or fiber-forming operation is identical to that used in multifilament yarns. The polymer is supplied to an extruder where it is heated and pressurized at a relatively high rate. The molten polymer is then forced through carefully designed capillaries with circular or irregular cross sections. The temperature used may vary from 250 to 310°C and the fiber emerging from the spinneret is allowed to cool while being stretched by the take-up units, running at speeds up to 3,000 ft/min. A diagram of a staple-forming operation is shown in Figure 7. The incoming feed yarns, in the form of huge bundles ranging from 500,000 to 2,000,000 den, are drawn and stabilized. (Staple sizes vary from 60 den/filament to about $1\frac{1}{2}$ den/filament). The yarn bundle, or tow, is then bulked by one of several processes (see below under Bulking). The bulked yarn passes to a cutter which cuts the tow to staple, ranging in lengths from $1\frac{1}{2}$ to $7\frac{1}{2}$ in. The staple fibers are then converted to an appropriate yarn size on standard textile-spinning equipment, using a modified woolen system.

Fiber From Film (41).   Many companies are engaged in either the production or the development of fiber from polypropylene film.   Before describing the manufacturing processes, it would be worthwhile to distinguish between the two distinctly different processes for making yarn from film.   One involves making a "slit" yarn or tape from film merely by slitting the film.   This product is relatively coarse, but is useful in sand bags or carpet-backing material.   The second and more important process is the "split" or fibrillated-yarn process.   In this method, the film is reduced to a fibrillated network of fine yearns by slitting and then stretching or stretching and slitting.   This uniaxial stretching or drawing operation orients the polypropylene so that it fibrillates very easily.

The general process outlined below is believed to be the one selected by most firms for commercialization with some modifications.

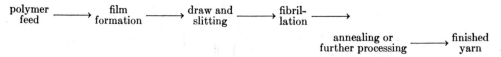

One possible modification is the initial formation of a series of ribbons employing a slotted circular die instead of extruding a wide film.   The ends of ribbons would then be treated in the manner described below for film.

Film Formation.   The film is produced by usual extrusion processes after which it is solidified by one of the three following methods: (a) water-bath quenching, (b) chill-roll quenching, and (c) air cooling of blown film.   Depending on the end use, one type of quench is preferred over the others since the quenching affects the crystallinity of the film which, in turn, has a vital influence on the quality of fibrillation.   Water cooling gives the best degree of fibrillation along with the highest tenacity.   Chill-roll quenching inherently allows better control of the gage (the thickness of the film).   Air cooling of film blown through a circular die is more economical but it produces an inferior product.   For slit tape, water cooling is acceptable but for most other uses, chill-roll cooling is more suitable.

Drawing and orientation take place between the hot and cold rolls and, if desired, the film can be reoriented by a second set of draw rolls.   The slitting is preferably done before orientation, but for some end uses the film can be slit after drawing.   Another alternative is orienting through a heated oven rather than on hot draw rolls.   Here again, the end use dictates the desired process.   In the case of oven orientation, the end-product use would most likely be carpet backing.

Fibrillation.   The most important step in the fiber-from-film process is fibrillation and once again there are several choices, such as controlled-mechanical, chemical-mechanical, and random-mechanical processes.

In the random-mechanical process, a film is fibrillated mechanically to produce a netlike random structure.   The chemical–mechanical technique, as the name suggests, involves a chemical means, such as blowing agents or water, along with mechanical means.   The chemicals produce bubbles, voids, or imperfections which are stress-concentration points facilitating mechanical fibrillation.   Controlled mechanical fibrillation produces a uniform network by mechanical means and is the one which has been most throughly investigated (42–44).   The method most commonly employed uses card clothing on rolls, in which the pins or wire cut the film into a regular network.

Properties of the untwisted fibrillated yarns vary with the process.   Table 10

Table 10. Properties of Commercial and Development Yarns

Property	Value
yarn, den	932–3800
filament, av den	8–76
slit length, in.	0.0008–0.01
tape width, in.	0.3–0.9
break strength, lb	7.8–25
tenacity, g/den	1.8–3.8
elongation to break, %	18–55

shows the ranges of properties obtained from commercial and developmental yarns made in the United States and other countries (41).

Spinbonded Polypropylene (45). Self-bonding fibers are prepared from fine-denier filaments (1–8 den/filament) at a high draw ratio which continuously orients the filaments at random. This network or "web" is heat-bonded at the filament crossover points after which a binder of lower-melting fibers or an external bonding agent, such as an acrylic or vinyl polymer, is applied. The sheet is formed and processed in a continuous operation. This semiporous, nonwoven product has found a great deal of use in carpet backing because of its dimensional stability compared to that of the woven polypropylene carpet backing.

Spin Finishes. A variety of inorganic and organic chemicals are used as processing aids in the production of yarns and fabric from synthetic fibers. These function as lubricants, antistats, and filament-cohesive agents. Usually they are applied externally (in contrast to internal lubricants which are mixed with the polymer before extrusion and lubricate after migrating to the fiber surface). The amount applied to the fiber externally varies from 0.25 to as high as 5%, but in most cases the amount is between 0.5 and 1.5%. The finish applied during spinning is called a spin finish.

A finish may also be applied at various steps in the fiber-manufacturing process and a different one may be used for the same fiber depending upon whether the end product is to be continuous filament or staple. Finish is first applied after extrusion, immediately ahead of the take-up (package builder). The finish applied at this stage is generally a fatty acid ester. It can be used for fiber destined to be either a continuous filament or staple. To protect the finish from bacterial degradation, formaldehyde or a formaldehyde donor is often added before use. For the production of drawn, untextured continuous filament it is not necessary to add another finish. When producing a draw-textured yarn some manufacturers add additional finish in the drawing and texturizing step.

The spin finish binds the filaments into a bundle and lubricates the fiber bundle as it passes over metal guides and rolls in the drawing process. It is also very important in reducing the buildup of static electricity which causes the fibers to repel each other and become entangled, causing knots and filament breaks. Some manufacturers find that additional finish increases the lubrication and reduces the static at the carpet manufacturer's carpet-tufting machine and results in improved efficiency.

When the undrawn yarn is converted to staple by drawing, texturizing, and chopping another type of finish is often applied. This is to aid in the processing of the staple at the carding operation. A fatty acid ester finish alone often causes the staple to be compacted during carding, which prevents it from passing efficiently through the card.

Therefore, during extrusion a low level of fatty acid ester is generally used and at the carding operation 1% or more of an anionic finish is applied.

Although an actual production run is best for evaluating a finish, the following five laboratory tests can be used for screening before production trials:

1. A yarn-to-metal friction test run at various speeds, angles of contact on different surfaces, temperatures, and atmospheric conditions.

2. A yarn-to-yarn cohesion test with a similar variety of testing conditions.

3. Determination of the chemical degradation of the fiber by the finish. The degradation is measured by the swelling of the fiber, amount of additives extracted, loss of tenacity, etc.

4. Wettability tests.

5. Static buildup tests.

In Table 11 a few of the popular types of finish are listed along with a rating for the five tests and an indication of the polypropylene fiber-production process for which they are suited.

Table 11. Polypropylene Finishes

Chemical type	Effect on fiber	Wetting of fiber	Yarn-to-metal friction	Yarn-to-yarn friction	Static control	Process
mixture of alkyl phosphate, fatty acid ester, and silicone	none	good	good	good	good	staple
mixture of fatty acid ester and an amphoteric	none	good	good	good	good	staple
mixture of fatty acid ester and an antistat	none	fair	good	good	fair	filament
inorganic salt of phosphated alcohol	none	good	good	good	poor	filament
butyl stearate	swelling	good	good	poor	poor	filament
salt of complex ethoxylated alcohol	none	good	good	good	excellent	filament

Bulking or Texturizing of Fibers (46,47)

Texturizing and bulking are similar but not identical processes. They are, however, the heart of any operation producing textile yarn. The number and methods are as varied as the producers and, with the continuing development of new man-made fibers, allow a great variation and selection of yarns for many consumer needs. In carpet yarn bulking gives greater resiliency and improves resistance to matting and wear. For apparel yarns, texturizing improves the yarn esthetics in terms of a softer, fuller hand and greater cover. The various processes can be generally classified into the following types: false twist, stuffer-box, fluid jet, edge crimper, and gear crimping.

False Twist. This is by far the most popular process for texturizing. Yarns are pretwisted, heat-set and then untwisted in one continuous operation. This method of bulking produces a yarn with a regular helical crimp, and is used primarily on yarns of 700 den or less.

Stuffer-Box. In this process, the filaments are compressed by feed rolls into a confined space in a heated chamber, whereby a random crimp is developed. Yarn texturized by the stuffer-box technique has essentially a two-dimensional saw-tooth crimp.

Special processes involve innovations of some system, such as "spunize," which is a variation of a stuffer-box-type crimper.

Fluid Jet (48,50).   This process uses a fluid, generally air or steam, delivered at high pressure and temperature into an area where filaments are fed at a faster rate than they are withdrawn.   The yarn contracts in length due to the heat, and the crimp and bulk are generated by the turbulent gas.   Such a method normally produces a yarn with a three-dimensional curvilinear configuration.

Edge ("Knife-edge") Crimping.   This technique consists essentially of heating the filaments and then dragging them over a sharp edge at an acute angle.   The texture produced resembles a helically coiled spring in which the direction of spiral reverses at random.

Knit-Deknit.   The process is well described by the name.   The filaments are knit, heat-set, and then unraveled and rewound.   The filaments show a wavy configuration.

Gear Crimping (49,50).   In this process the heated yarn is fed into the nip of a pair of gears, which crimps the filaments.   Mechanical variations are possible which affect the texture (51,52).

Self-Crimping Fibers.   This method of texturizing is described in great detail in the literature.   "Crimp" or texture is obtained through the use of "bicomponent" fibers.   There are filaments containing two different components.   These may be different polymers or the same polymer differing in some physical parameter, such as molecular weight.

When polymers with significant physical differences are extruded together in a laminated form and exposed to heat, the two components shrink to a different extent, causing the fiber to curl (crimp) (53).   See also Vol. 16, pp. 75–77.

Crimp Retention and Resiliency.   Crimp stability is important for texture and for the reduction of matting or "walk-out" in carpets.   A new high-resiliency polypropylene is available (52) in which the crimp is random and has rounded convolutions. Figure 8 and Table 12 illustrate the improvements in this new polypropylene yarn compared to regular polypropylene and nylon-66 yarns.   Comparable carpets made from these yarns were subjected to mechanical pounding at 1380 cph, each cycle being a pressure of 7 psi over an area of 1.25 in. in diam.   Thickness of the pile was measured initially, and after 1,000, 2,000, 10,000, and 20,000 cycles.   The pile thickness was measured with a dial gage at 0.75 psi with a 1-in.-diam "foot."

Measurement of Crimp Retention.   Crimp permanence or texture retention has

Table 12. Matting of Various Fibers After Pounding

Carpet	Initial pile height, in.	Weight, oz/yd^2	Matting[a] after cycles of pounding, %			
			1,000	2,000	10,000	20,000
polypropylene, 3900 den	0.245	30	9.0	12.6	18.4	19.6
nylon 66, 3750 den	0.253	30	5.1	6.7	8.3	10.7
high-resiliency polypropylene, 3900 den	0.231	30.8	5.2	6.5	9.9	12.1

[a] Percent matting $= \dfrac{H_i - H}{H} \times 100$, where H = pile height in in. (less backing) after matting test and H_i = initial pile height in in. (less backing).

been discussed above in relation to resiliency (54). There are several methods of measuring the permanence of crimp in a textured yarn (55,56). Table 13 gives the crimp permanence after steaming of a new high-resiliency polyproylene compared with other commercial fibers.

Table 13. Crimp Permanence of High-Resiliency Polypropylene and Other Commercially Available Fibers

Fiber	Crimp permanence,[a] %
high-resiliency polypropylene	46.0
nylon 66	50.4
nylon 6	31.0
regular polypropylene	20.0

[a] Percent crimp permanence = $\dfrac{\text{original length} - \text{length after steaming}}{\text{original length}} \times 100$.

Pigmentation (57–61)

Colored polypropylene fibers can be obtained by the "melt-dyeing" process, in which a pigment is mixed with the resin before extrusion into fiber.

The problem in coloration of polymers is the production of pigment dispersions which are essentially free of aggregates at high pigment concentration. The presence of aggregates in pigmented polymers can cause plugging of screen packs during extrusion, breaking of filaments during drawing, and loss of brilliancy in the pigmented fiber or film. The pigment can also affect the melt-flow properties of the polymer which, in turn, can cause extrusion problems due to changes in viscosity.

The use of a higher spinning temperature to compensate for these changes can likewise cause breakdowns in the resin stabilizer or pigmenting system, particularly if the stabilizer or pigment has initially only borderline stability. Highly stable pigments and pigments free from contaminants are thus necessities for uniform color and color dispersion. Some representative pigment classes are given in Table 14.

Table 14. Pigments Used for Polypropylene Fibers

Color	Pigment	Type[a]
black	carbon black	o
blue	phthalocyanine	mc
green	phthalocyanine	mc
red	quinacridone	o
	perylene	o
	naphthol	o
	cadmium	io
white	titanium dioxide	io
yellow	isoindoline	o
	benzidine	o
	cadmium	io
	nickel chelate[b]	mc
maroon and violet	carbazole	o
	quinacridone	o

[a] Organic = o; inorganic = io; metal chelate = mc.
[b] Green-gold.

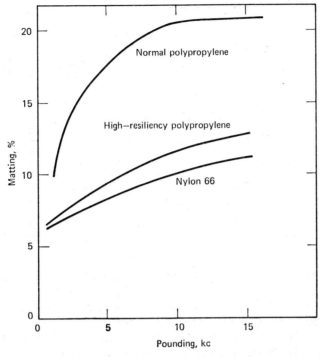

Fig. 8. Effect of pounding on matting in various yarns.

In general, the inorganic and metal-chelate types have good heat and light stability. The end-product application determines the proper level of stabilizers necessary and the type of pigment required. For example, most cadmium colors have poor outdoor stability and therefore should be avoided in any yarn to be used outdoors. The benzidine yellow has a maximum processing temperature of 525°F and this could prove to be a limitation on its use in fibers. Outdoor pigments are normally tested for as much as 900 hr using a carbon-arc, wet and dry alternating, weatherometer, the temperature and humidity being well controlled. The important pigment parameters are as follows: thermal and oxidative stability; spectral characteristics; freedom from physical contaminants; residual pigment contaminants (impure pigments); degree of pigment dispersion; and possible deleterious effect on the fiber or film.

Figure 9 illustrates the effect of various types of pigments on the aging of polypropylene fiber upon exposure to Florida sunlight (62). The results are generalized and specific pigments may better or worse than shown.

Resin Compounding. Color concentrates containing pigments dispersed in polypropylene, which can subsequently be diluted with "natural" (unpigmented) polyethylene resin, are commonly used for coloring polypropylene in the melt. The following dilution techniques are in use:

1. The color concentrate (25–50% pigment content) is diluted with natural resin, both materials being in pellet form. Dilution to a 1–2% concentration and mixing are done by simple tumble blending, followed by melt-spinning into fiber. This method, however, is not usually recommended for fibers since the high degree of color uniformity required for fiber is difficult to achieve.

2. Powdered color concentrates (pure pigment) are blended with powdered

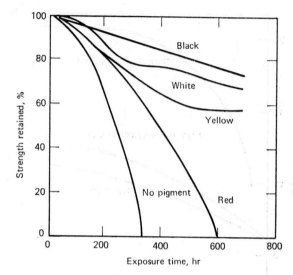

Fig. 9. Effect of various types of pigments on aging of polypropylene fiber upon exposure to sunlight.

(flake) natural resin. This operation utilizes blenders, such as twin cone and Henschel types, after which the polymer is extruded and pelletized, prior to melt-spinning. Not only is the tinctorial value enhanced by this procedure, but it also permits the use of higher dilution ratios (up to 50:1) than the previous method. The use of higher dilutions is less costly and therefore preferred.

3. Another method recommended for large-scale fiber production, is to use a completely integrated powder-concentrate system containing the natural resin, stabilizers, pigments, and all other additives. The blend is diluted to the final concentration in a single mixing step and extruded directly into fiber. This eliminates intermediate steps and allows the greatest economy. Great care in blending must be exercised in this process in order to avoid settling of higher-density stabilizers or other materials in the mixture.

4. Another method is to melt-extrude the pigment concentrate and a portion of the natural resin before dry blending it with the bulk of the natural resin.

Dyeing

The foregoing section described the solution dyeing of polypropylene fiber, where the pigment is mixed with the polymer prior to extrusion. This process lends itself to continuous production of one color or shade, but it has the disadvantage of a lack of flexibility for a mill producing a versatile range of products. It leads to a larger inventory of dyed fiber and unsold finished items than if the items could be piece-dyed when finished. It has long been recognized that it would be desirable to make polypropylene fiber amenable to the conventional processes of dyeing, to give quicker response to changes in the popularity of colors and shades. There has been no agreement, however, on how to make it dyeable. About 1500 patents on the dyeing of polypropylene are known and more are being issued constantly (63,64). About a dozen dyeable versions of the fiber have been marketed on and off with several still available. The situation is as yet unresolved, but (as of early 1971) over 90% of the polypropylene fiber being sold is colored in the melt by pigments.

Dyeability requires the presence of polar or reactive groups in the fiber which can interact with the dye molecule to bind it within the fiber. These dye sites can be, for instance, amine end groups in polyamides, hydroxyl groups in cellulose, and sulfate end groups (from the polymerization initiator) in acrylics. The additional necessity for permeability of the paraffinic matrix to dyes, particularly the water-soluble ones, has not been fully recognized (65). The water-soluble dyes diffuse into fibers only after the fibers are hydrated and, since polypropylene has essentially zero moisture regain, it resists the penetration of dyes. Modification of the polypropylene with polar groups thus almost always makes it dyeable with disperse, organic-soluble dyes, but dyeability with water-soluble dyes is more difficult to achieve.

Although numerous proposals have been advanced for dyeing the unmodified fiber, none have met the dual criteria of being applicable by conventional dyeing methods and of providing adequate fastness to light, laundering, drycleaning, and crocking. In view of the lack of both permeability and dye-binding sites within the fiber, this is not surprising and the need for modification of the fiber has been obvious. Research on modification of either polymer or fiber for dyeability has followed two paths: (a) chemical modification of the polymer, either by copolymerization or by some chemical reaction subsequent to polymerization; and (b) incorporation of additives to the fiber, which could act as dye sites, usually mixed with the polymer before extrusion.

The various proposals for modification have been reviewed in detail (66,67). Efforts at copolymerization included both copolymerization into the main chain and graft copolymerization onto the preformed polypropylene chain. Since polar monomer usually inhibits organometallic polymerization catalysts, the first type of copolymerization is difficult to accomplish. Graft copolymerization involves formation of a free-radical site, usually by abstraction of hydrogen, on the polypropylene chain. This initiates the polymerization of an added monomer to form another polymer chain or graft on the parent backbone. Many monomers have been used for grafting, including acids, amides, amines, and neutral compounds and claims have been made for improvement in dyeability with many types of dyes. Chemical reactions of the paraffin chain of the polypropylene, such as chlorination, sulfonation, phosphorylation, and even more complicated multi-step reactions have been described (63,64). It is believed, however, that there are no modified fibers of this type commercially available.

The use of additive dye receptors in the polypropylene has been very widespread. These additives have run the gamut of chemical structures. Low-molecular-weight metallic and nonmetallic compounds, such as metal salts, alcohols, amines, ketones, acids, metal complexes, and many others, have been incorporated. Polymeric materials, listed below, have been the most popular, all chemical classes being included (67).

Neutral Polymers: poly(vinyl aromatics), polyethers, polyesters, polycarbonates, polyhalides, polynitriles, polyalkylene oxides, etc.

Anionic Polymers: polycarboxylic acids and anhydrides, polysulfonic acids, etc.

Cationic Polymers: polyamines, poly(vinylpyridines), poly(vinyl-N-heterocyclics), polyamides, and polyaminoamides.

The technique of incorporating sizeable amounts, up to 10%, of any type of additive into a melt-spun fiber is fraught with many difficulties. Under the conditions required for melt-spinning, where the thread line consists of up to several hundred fine filaments at around 250°C being wound up at several thousand ft/min, almost any irregularity in the rheology of the melt can be disastrous. The additives are usually highly polar compounds mixed in a nonpolar matrix and this causes problems of compatibility, dispersion, uniformity of distribution, and chemical stability (67). It is not surprising, therefore, that although literally hundreds of additive systems have been proposed for dyeability, few have proven at all practical.

Two types of dyeable polypropylene fiber are available in the United States from Hercules, Inc.

Fiber containing a nickel-chelate dye receptor is available from Hercules. Interestingly, the use of metal compounds stems from earlier observations where it was found that metallic catalyst residues in the polypropylene imparted some dyeability with chelatable dyes. Use was then made of the nickel in the metal-chelate ultraviolet stabilizer (3) (See p. 813) as dye receptor and several dye companies have developed special chelatable disperse dyes for use with this system. Being disperse dyes, they diffuse into polypropylene, where they chelate with the nickel. The very stable bond formed between dye and metal is both a strength and a weakness of this system. The strength of the bond leads to good wash and drycleaning fastness, but also makes it difficult for the dye to equilibrate uniformly within a fabric ("leveling") and to be stripped from the fiber, if redyeing is necessary. For certain applications, however, such as printing, where leveling and strippability are not important, this type of dyeable fiber has found use.

Fiber containing cationic amine-type polymers as dye receptors is also being marketed by Hercules. A disperse-dyeable type is available from this producer and is believed to contain a vinylpyridine polymer. Such a fiber is not dyeable with anionic dyes because of its lack of permeability, as discussed previously. It can be made permeable by pretreatment with Lewis acids, which is believed to cause channels or fissures within the fiber (67,68). Anionic-dyeable fibers, also believed to contain cationic polymers have been announced at various times by both Uniroyal and Hercules, but as of early 1971, they are not commercially available. Montecatini is marketing an acid-dyeable polypropylene in Europe, but little is known of its composition.

Table 15. Polypropylene Fiber Consumption,[a] Million lb

End use	1967	1968	1969	1970[b]
upholstery				
filament and staple		2	15	
carpet				
tufted face yarns	34	48	46	
needlepunch face yarn	38	44	45	
primary backing	16	42	63	
slit film, nonwoven	2	9	14	
bags				
slit film	12	48	10	3
other[c]				
monofil and multifilament[d]	54	62	63	
total shipments				
filament and slit film	117	202	194	191
staple	39	53	62	57
grand total	156	255	256	248

[a] Data from *Textile Organon* **41** (1) (Jan. 1970), and Hercules, Inc.

[b] End-use breakdown not available.

[c] Mainly webbing, ribbon, rope, and cordage.

[d] Includes some slit film.

Table 16. End Uses of Polypropylene Fiber (69)

Fiber type	End use	Improvements due to polypropylene fibers
staple		
den 1–3	cotton and rayon blends	wear resistance; dimensional stability on washing; coverage; soft hand; strength; excellent thermal insulation
	filter and other industrial fabrics	excellent chemical resistance; strength; long life
	backing for pile fabric	coverage; dimensional stability on washing; strength
5–8	wool and acrylic fiber blends	shrinkage control on washing; strength; wear resistance
	upholstery fabrics	abrasion resistance; excellent soil resistance; excellent ease of cleaning; excellent colorfastness with pigment colors
	blankets	high bulk; excellent thermal insulation; dimensional stability on washing; soft hand
	fiberfil and pile lining	excellent thermal insulation; high bulk; resilience; low moisture absorption
15	tufted and woven carpets	excellent soil resistance; excellent ease of cleaning; low static buildup; wear resistance; pile height retention
	nonwoven fabrics	strength; wear resistance; stain resistance; coverage
cont filament		
den 15	women's hosiery	snag resistance
30–420	knit sweaters	dimensional stability on washing; high bulk; soft hand
	automotive upholstery	strength; abrasion resistance; coverage; strength; wear resistance
	socks, underwear and outerwear	coverage; strength; wear resistance
420–840	laundry bags	chemical resistance; abrasion resistance; dimensional stability
	rope and fishnets	high strength—wet or dry; light enough to float; low moisture pickup
	backing for pile fabrics	dimensional stability on washing; strength; coverage
840–3200	tufted carpets	wear resistance; pile height retention; excellent soil resistance; excellent ease of cleaning; low static buildup; excellent colorfastness with pigment colors
	carpet backings	strength; dimensional stability; rot and mildew resistance
	bag sewing thread	strength; high yield; chemical resistance; low moisture pickup
	window channel fabrics	long wear; high bulk; low moisture pickup
Fiber type	End use	Improvements due to polypropylene fibers

Economic Aspects

With the multiplicity of fibers available today, economics have a great influence on their usage. In regard to basic costs, polypropylene can be compared to either the polyester or polyamide (nylon) fibers, since all three are melt-spun, and spinning costs should be approximately the same. Bulk polypropylene resin, fully compounded with stabilizers, costs 5–10¢/lb less than polyester or the polyamides and at least this differential should carry over into the finished fiber. As discussed above, the lower specific gravity of polypropylene offers an additional advantage in covering power which could be as much as 25–50%. On a cost basis alone, therefore, without consideration of esthetic or use advantages which it might offer, polypropylene appears to be in a favorable position to maintain and expand its share in the fiber market.

The growth and consumption pattern for polypropylene are given in Table 15. Up to 1968, the fibers maintained a compounded growth rate of about 50%/yr. In 1969 and 1970, which were difficult years economically for synthetic fiber producers, the growth was flat, but forecasts predict a continuing rate of 5–10% through 1975.

End Uses. Polypropylene fiber has found its major end use in carpets. As shown in Table 15, in 1969, 64% of the fiber went into carpeting, either as the face yarn or in the backing. It is used widely as a face yarn in both conventional tufted constructions and the nonwoven needle-punch type. In regard to the latter, polypropylene was the first fiber to be used in the nonwoven "indoor–outdoor" type of carpeting, and still enjoys a large market in this application. With the introduction of more resilient and crush-resistant yarns, as discussed under Bulking and texturizing, this market should expand.

It is in the area of carpet backing that the fiber has been growing very rapidly. Its hydrophobic, mildew- and rot-resistant nature make it ideally suited for this application and its high cover factor is an added economic inducement. Although the yarn derived from slit film commands the larger share of this market, the nonwoven variety made from continuous filament by the spun-bonded process is expected to expand even faster in this use.

Almost 20% of total polypropylene fiber consumption in 1968 was in bags made from slit film. Here, of course, the high strength and rot-resistance properties are most desirable, since most of these bags were sand bags. The proportion of this use is declining, as military requirements for sand bags decrease and the other synthetic fibers move into competition with the polypropylene.

A summary of existing and projected end uses for polypropylene fiber, mainly in filament form, is given in Table 16. The good abrasion resistance, soil resistance, and ease of cleaning have suggested the use of polypropylene in upholstery fabrics and substantial growth in this area has been forecast. As mentioned before, the fiber has been recommended for underwear and hosiery because of its ability to wick out body moisture (31). Its high strength, wet or dry, resilience, and low moisture pickup recommend it for webbing, rope, and cordage, where it has to a large extent replaced polyethylene which has excessive creep under load.

Bibliography

1. N. G. Gaylord and H. F. Mark *Linear and Stereoregular Addition Polymers*, Interscience Publishers, Inc., New York, 1959.
1a. R. A. V. Raff and K. W. Doak, eds., *Crystalline Olefin Polymers*, Interscience Publishers, a div. of John Wiley & Sons, Inc., New York, 1965.
1b. V. Ehrlich and E. M. Honeycutt, "Linear Polyolefins," in H. F. Mark, E. Cernia, and S. M. Atlas, eds. *Man-Made Fibers*, Vol. 3, Interscience Publishers, a div. of John Wiley & Sons, Inc., New York, 1968, pp. 357–399.
2. Brit. Pats. 810,023 (March 11, 1959) (to Montecatini), and 828,971 (Febr. 24, 1960) (to K. Ziegler); U.S. Pats. 3,112,300 (Nov. 23, 1963), and 3,112,301 (Nov. 23, 1963), G. Natta, P. Pino, and G. Mazzanti (to Montecatini); and many others.

3. *Proc. Symp. on Polypropylene Fiber*, Southern Research Institute, Birmingham, Ala., 1964.

3a. W. P. Acton, *Market Prospects for Polypropylene Fibers*, in reference 3, pp. 53–60.

4. Reference 1a, p. 346.

5. Fr. Pat. 1,386,272 (Jan. 22, 1965) (to Mitsubishi Rayon Co.); and unpublished information of the authors.

6. M. L. Miller, *The Structure of Polymers*, Reinhold Publishing Corp., New York, 1966, p. 408.

7. Plastics Product Data Sheet, PPD-32, Hercules, Inc. Wilmington, Del., T. O. J. Dresser, *Polypropylene*, Reinhold Publishing Corp., New York, 1969.

8. F. H. Winslow and W. L. Hawkins, in reference 1a, Part I, Chap. 15.

9. W. J. Bailey, *"Mechanism of Thermal Decomposition of Polypropylene,"* in reference 3, pp. 121–136.

10. M. Farber, unpublished data, Uniroyal Inc., Wayne, N. J., 1961.

11. W. L. Hawkins and F. H. Winslow, in reference 1a, Part II, Chap. 8.

12. U.S. Pat. 3,143,584 (Aug. 4, 1964), J. F. L. Roberts and E. Walker (to Imperial Chemical Industries Ltd.).

13. Reference 11, p. 386.

14. D. A. Gordon and E. C. Rothstein, *Polymer Eng. Sci.* **6,** 231, (1966).

15. R. P. Weimer and W. P. Connor, *Textile Res. J.* **39,** 1150, (1969).

16. R. H. Hansen, *"Effects of Morphology, Antioxidants and Copper on the Oxidation of Polypropylene,"* in reference 3, pp. 137–182.

17. A. R. Burgess, *Natl. Bur. Std. (U.S.) Circ.* **525,** 149 (1953).

18. M. Farber and R. J. Sperley, unpublished data, Uniroyal, Inc., Wayne, N. J., 1966.

19. M. Heskins and J. E. Guillet, *Macromolecules* **1,** 97, (1968).

20. *Plastanox 1161 Antioxidant*, Technical Data Sheet—Plastics Additives, American Cyanamid Co., Wayne, N. J., 1966.

21. D. L. Wood and J. P. Luongo, *Mod. Plastics* **38,** 132, (1961).

22. J. G. Cook, *Handbook of Polyolefin Fibers*, Merrow Publishing Co. Ltd., Watford, Herts., England, 1967.

22a. Reference 22, pp. 84, 182.

23. S. E. Ross and Harold W. Wolf, *J. Appl. Polymer Sci.* **10,** 1557–1572 (1966).

24. G. Sussich, *Textile Res. J.* **24,** 210 (1954).

25. S. E. Ross, *J. Appl. Polymer Sci.,* **9,** 2729 (1965).

26. M. Farber, *Am. Dyestuff Reptr.* **55,** 536, (1966).

27. *Polycrest® Carpet Yarn*, Technical Information Bulletin, Fiber and Textile Division, Uniroyal Inc., Winnsboro, S. C.

28. A. V. Galanti and C. L. Mantell, *Polypropylene Fibers and Film*, Plenum Press, New York, 1965.

28a. Reference 28, p. 122.

29. Reference 22, p. 89; reference 28, p. 73.

29a. Reference 28, p. 118.

29b. Reference 28, p. 136.

30. *Man-Made Fiber Fact Book*, Man-Made Fiber Producers Assoc., Inc., New York, 1968.

31. *Marvess Olefin Yarns for Hosiery*, Alamo Industries, Inc., (now Phillips Fibers Co.), New York; *Chem. Eng.* **76,** 48, (1969).

32. G. M. Bryant, *Textile Res. J.* **37** 552–556 (1967).

33. W. C. Sheehan and T. B. Cole, *J. Appl. Polymer Sci.* **8,** 2359–2388 (1964).

34. M. Compostella, A. Coen, and F. Bertinotti, *Angew. Chem.* **74,** 618–624 (1962).

35. Reference 22, p. 76.

36. R. A. Bychkov and M. P. Zverev, *Intern. Chem. Eng.* **7**(1), 76–79 (Jan. 1967).

37. S. Kase and T. Matsuo, *J. Polymer Sci.* **3,** 2541–2554 (1965).

38. S. Kase and T. Matsuo, *J. Appl. Polymer Sci.* **11,** 251–287 (1967).

39. A. Ziabicki, *"Physical Fundamentals of the Fiber-Spinning Processes,"* in H. F. Mark, E. Cernia, and S. M. Atlas, *Man-Made Fibers*, Vol. 1, Interscience Publishers, a div. of John Wiley & Sons, Inc., New York, 1967, pp. 169–233.

40. S. W. Hong and H. P. Kato, unpublished data, Uniroyal, Inc., Wayne, N. J., 1967.

41. P. C. Condit and G. B. Johnson, *Mod. Textiles* **50,** 23–51 (1969).

42. U.S. Pat. 3,273,771 (Sept. 20, 1966), A. G. Beaumont (to Courtaulds, Ltd.).

43. U.S. Pat. 3,235,644 (Feb. 15, 1966), O. B. Rosmussen (to Phillips Petroleum Co.).
44. Fr. Pat. 1,518,108 (March 23, 1967), L. M. Guenther, G. B. Johnson, and A. L. Meader, Jr. (to Chevron Research Co.).
45. O. L. Shealy, *Textile Res. J.* **35**, 322–329 (1965).
46. *Mod. Textiles* **50**, 21 (1969).
47. R. W. Longbottom, *Mod. Textiles* **49**, 19–21 (1968).
48. U.S. Pat. 3,262,257 (July 26, 1966), B. E. Martin (to E. I. du Pont de Nemours & Co., Inc.).
49. U.S. Pat. 3,372,446 (March 12, 1968), D. Schichman and D. Siegel (to Uniroyal, Inc.).
50. U.S. Pat. 3,367,005 (Feb. 6, 1968), R. J. Clarkson (to Uniroyal, Inc.)
51. U.S. Pat, 3,457,611 (July 20, 1969), S. R. Nechvatal and W. N. Parks (to Hercules, Inc.)
52. U.S. Pat. pending, R. J. Clarkson (to Uniroyal, Inc.)
53. U.S. Pat. 2,439,814 (April 20, 1948), W. A. Sisson (to American Viscose Corp.); U.S. Pat. 3,038,235 (June 12, 1962), J. Zimmerman (to E. I. du Pont de Nemours & Co., Inc.).
54. P. Hempel, *Man-Made Textiles* **38**, 36 (1961).
55. G. M. Richardson and H. Stanley, *Mod. Textiles* **43**, 2–7 (1962).
56. A. D. Siegel, private communication, Uniroyal, Inc., Wayne, N. J., 1964.
57. Brit. Pat. 991,584 (May 12, 1965), to Hercules, Inc.
58. G. F. Sonn, *SPE (Soc. Plastics Engrs.) Tech. Papers* **15**, 525–530 (1969).
59. D. Patterson, *Pigments*, Elsevier Publishing Co., New York, 1967, pp. 105–120.
60. F. J. Hines, *Mod. Plastics* **34**, 168 (1957).
61. J. N. Scott, C. J. Silas, and J. V. Smith, *Plastics Technol.* **4**, 552 (1958).
62. Reference 28, p. 142.
63. F. Fordemwalt, "The Dyeing of Polypropylene for Textiles," *Am. Dyestuff Reptr.* **54**, 107 (1965).
64. V. Ehrlich, *Mod. Textiles* **46**, 23, 36, 76, (1965).
65. M. Farber, *Theoretical Aspects of Polypropylene Dyeing*, in reference 3, pp. 100–120.
66. Reference 22, p. 138.
67. M. Farber, *SPE (Soc. Plastics Engrs.) J.* **24**, 82, (1968).
68. U.S. Pat. 3,361,843 (Jan. 2, 1968), R. Miller, F. C. Loveless, and M. Farber (to Uniroyal, Inc.).
69. R. W. Ivett, *Am. Dyestuff Reptr.* **54**, 190 (1965).

F. C. Cesare, M. Farber,
and G. R. Cuthbertson
Uniroyal, Inc.

PROTEINS FROM PETROLEUM

The growing world shortage of dietary proteins continues to be the focus of a great deal of attention. The problem is already acute among the poor in the developing countries who make up two-thirds of the world's population and who have the highest rate of population increase. The situation is well summarized in a 1967 report of the President's Science Advisory Committee (1). A number of well-attended conferences sponsored by various professional societies and universities have dealt with the protein shortage (2–6). The relevant United Nations groups, WHO, FAO, and UNICEF have given the problem worldwide publicity and are coordinating efforts to alleviate the problem. Up-to-date information is available via the bi-annual *PAG Bulletin* (7).

The widespread publicity, coupled with drought-precipitated famine in India and North Africa in the early 1960s sparked many projects to develop alternative protein sources. Fish-protein concentrate (8), leaf-protein extract (9), protein from algae grown on municipal wastes and on carbon dioxide (10) (see also Algae cultures), and protein from yeast and bacteria grown on agricultural by-products and on various petroleum fractions, have all been evaluated. Of these, only the petroleum-based product is completely free from seasonal fluctuations and other uncertainties typical of classical agriculture. Even so, it is now evident that the application of modern agricultural methods and the increased use of high-yield varieties of the major cereal grains can provide the developing countries with sufficient protein for some years to come (11). Therefore, it is likely that the first application for the new protein sources will be in the industrialized countries where some functional property and a lower price will result in displacing a portion of the conventional proteins (11). Long-term prospects, if present trends continue, are that all available sources of dietary protein will be required.

Proteins are usually divided into two classes: those of vegetable origin and those of animal origin. For present purposes it is only necessary to state that the latter, typified by meat, milk, and eggs, are of higher nutritive value and price than the former. Table 1 contains selected prices and principal uses for some representative proteins. Although there is an upward trend in the prices, the table illustrates the range within which a new protein source has to compete. The developers of petroleum-derived protein have announced their intent to compete at both ends of this scale—with vegetable proteins in animal feeds (12) and with milk proteins in human foods (13). For human food applications, qualities such as uniformity and a bland taste are essential.

Table 1. Selected Prices and Principal Uses for Some Representative Proteins

Product	Price, ¢/lb	Protein, %	Cost of protein, ¢/lb	Principal uses
cottonseed meal	3.6	41	8.8	animal feed
soy meal	4.1	44	9.3	animal feed
peanut meal	4.5	56	8.1	animal feed
fish meal	6.8	60	11.3	animal feed
torula yeast	13.0	48	27.3	human food
skim-milk powder	18.0	36	50.0	human food
eggs	24.0	12.8	190.0	human food
fish-protein concentrate	42.0	80	52.0	proposed for human food
beef meat	70.0	15.2	460.0	human food

All of the protein-from-petroleum processes so far announced (14) involve the growing of microorganisms on various petroleum substrates and harvesting dried microbial cells as a product. Many species of both yeast and bacteria are applicable and, therefore, the product is sometimes referred to as "single-cell protein," or SCP (15). Depending upon the organism, the protein content can range from 40 to 80%; the remainder of the material consists primarily of nucleic acids, carbohydrates, lipids, and minerals. A number of petroleum hydrocarbons can serve as a source of carbon and energy for microbial growth; however, methane and the normal alkanes in the C_{10} to C_{20} range are those most commonly mentioned.

Projected manufacturing costs for SCP from petroleum range from 10 to 40 ¢/lb of SCP. The biggest unknown is whether or not the quality of SCP is sufficiently high to compete with conventional protein sources.

The remaining sections of this article summarize the state of the art of obtaining protein from petroleum hydrocarbon, beginning with a discussion of the microbiology that is fundamental to the process. The final sections describe the product and the more important aspects of the process for producing protein from petroleum hydrocarbons.

Microbial Utilization of Hydrocarbons

The utilization of hydrocarbons by microorganisms had been recognized before the turn of the century. Miyoshi, in 1895, reported that a fungus, *Botrytis cinerea*, could be responsible for the degradation of paraffin wax (16). Additional studies on the action of fungi on paraffin were reported by Rahn in 1906 (17), and during that same year, two independent reports appeared, by Söhngen (18) and by Kaserer (19), describing the utilization of methane by bacteria. Shortly thereafter, Störmer demonstrated bacterial utilization of aromatic hydrocarbons (20) and Söhngen reported on the microbial utilization of the higher paraffins (21).

The field was advanced in the 1930s and 1940s by pioneering work such as that reported by Tausson (22), Strawinski and Stone (23), Johnson et al. (24), Novelli and Zobell (25), Evans (26), and Davis (27). The work of the groups led by Stone at Pennsylvania State University and by Zobell at the Scripps Institution of Oceanography at Palo Alto, Calif., was particularly stimulated by the establishment of two major projects in petroleum and marine microbiology at these institutions.

By the late 1940s and into the 1950s, the increasing accumulation of information merited the publication of several reviews, eg those of Zobell (28,29), Shturm (30), Fuhs (31), and Foster (32,33). In addition, hydrocarbon oxidation was a major topic in *Petroleum Microbiology* by Beerstecher (34). Later reviews attempted to keep pace with the rapidly developing field, and several of these emphasized the mechanisms of microbial attack on hydrocarbons, eg, Kallio et al. (35), Evans (36), Johnson (37), McKenna and Kallio (38), Van der Linden and Thijsse (39), and Kallio (40). An updated version of *Petroleum Microbiology*, by Davis, was published in 1967 (41).

Since the early reports of microbial growth on hydrocarbons, an ever-expanding literature on this subject has developed. Even in some of the earlier reviews, a great many species of microorganisms, including bacteria, actinomycetes, yeasts, and filamentous fungi, were reported to be capable of oxidizing hydrocarbons. Although there is some confusion regarding the precise taxonomy of a few of the organisms and a degree of uncertainty as to the purity of some of the substrates used (especially in some of the earlier studies), a number of generalizations can be made as to the types of microorganisms that attack various hydrocarbons.

Methane appears to be utilized by only a relatively few species of bacteria, but these are very widely distributed in soils, water, marine muds, etc. Although many names have been given to bacteria utilizing methane, it appears that a number of these should be considered synonymous. Thus, the well-established methane-utilizing bacteria are represented by *Methylomonas (Pseudomonas) methanica*, *Methylococcus capsulatus*, and *Methanomonas methanooxidans*. Recently, several other unnamed species of bacteria have been reported to grow on methane (42,43) and there has been a description of a nitrogen-fixing methane utilizer, which has been given the name *Pseudomonas methanitrificans* (44). In addition, there is a recent report of a fungus, *Graphium* sp., that can grow on "natural gas," but it is not clear whether growth is at the expense of methane, or of ethane, or of other materials in the mixture (45). Another interesting report concerns a species of *Chlorella*, a green alga, which appeared to consume methane as a carbon source for its growth (46).

The other gaseous alkanes are also utilized predominantly by bacteria. In addition to organisms like *M. methanica*, which "co-oxidize" (see p. 840) ethane, propane, and butane while growing on methane, a variety of other bacteria have been reported to utilize these hydrocarbons. Most frequently cited are *Mycobacterium* and *Pseudomonas* species, but *Nocardia*, *Streptomyces*, *Flavobacter*, *Alkaligenes*, *Corynebacteria*, *Bacillus*, and other genera are represented. Many of these also utilize higher paraffinic hydrocarbons. Ethane- and propane-utilizing organisms are found in large numbers in soils over many oil and gas deposits, and their presence has been used as a tool in petroleum prospecting (34). In addition to the *Graphium* species mentioned above, there have been several earlier reports indicating that other fungi (eg *Fusarium*, *Acremonium*) can grow at the expense of these gaseous alkanes (47).

The lower liquid alkanes (eg C_5–C_9) apparently are also utilized predominantly by species of *Mycobacteria*, *Pseudomonas*, and *Nocardia*. These compounds are, however, relatively refractory to microbial attack. They are very poorly soluble in aqueous media and their solubility decreases markedly with an increase in chain length (48). Alkanes of still higher molecular weight are presumably emulsified as soon as a fatty acid is formed during the early stages of microbial degradation (49). "Hydrocarbon emulsifying factors" composed, for example, of peptides and fatty acids (50) or glycolipids (51) have been reported to play a role in paraffin utilization. The lower alkanes, however, may not be subject to such emulsification mechanisms. In addition, several of these compounds are quite toxic for microorganisms; their activity as solvents might be expected to be detrimental to such structures as cell membranes (33).

The longer chain *n*-alkanes (eg C_{10}–C_{18}) are those most readily utilized by microorganisms, and by the widest variety of microorganisms, which are very numerous and ubiquitous in the environment. In addition to all of the types of organisms mentioned above, many yeasts and filamentous fungi have been reported to utilize these compounds. Among the yeasts, the species perhaps most frequently encountered have been members of the *Candida*, *Torulopsis*, *Rhodotorula*, *Pichia*, and *Debaromyces*, although other genera also have representatives among the paraffin-utilizers. Since Miyoshi's observation in 1895 of a paraffin-degrading *Botrytis*, a wide variety of other fungi have been described as hydrocarbon utilizers, with frequent mention given to members of *Penicillium*, *Aspergillus*, *Fusarium*, *Mucor*, and *Cunninghamella*.

Alkenes are utilized by a fairly wide variety of microorganisms, but contrary to earlier conclusions (28), the presence of a double bond does not necessarily render a compound more susceptible to microbial attack; the opposite, in fact, is apparently true (39). Many of the more significant studies of alkene oxidation have been carried out with *Pseudomonas* species (52), *Micrococcus cerificans* (53), and *Candida lipolytica* (54,55).

Branched-chain alkanes are degraded much less readily by microorganisms than are straight-chain compounds; even a single methyl group, for example, prevents assimilation unless there is a sufficiently long unbranched chain in the molecule (56). Compounds with more than one methyl group or with branches longer than methyl are generally resistant to microbial attack. Cycloparaffins, similarly, appear to be poorly utilizable by microorganisms, although some studies with *Pseudomonas* (57,58) and with *Flavobacterium* (59) have been reported. In addition, oxidation of cyclic hydrocarbons during growth of microorganisms on *n*-alkanes (see under co-oxidation below) has been reported (60). Aromatic compounds are utilized by a wide variety of microorganisms, described in several good reviews on the subject (36,61–65).

The **mechanisms** involved in the microbial oxidation of hydrocarbons have been of interest to investigators for some time. Efforts to elucidate these mechanisms, however, have been hampered by several factors, including the elusive nature of some of the early intermediates in the pathways, and the difficulties that have been encountered in preparing appropriate cell-free systems. Nevertheless, it is possible to outline some of the general features of microbial hydrocarbon degradation. It should be noted, however, that exceptions to these generalizations have been reported for various organisms and under different conditions.

The initial reaction in the pathway is usually the **monoterminal oxidation** of a methyl group, characterized by the incorporation of molecular oxygen. It is generally believed that this reaction, catalyzed by a mixed-function oxidase, proceeds via the formation of primary free radicals. The next step has been postulated to involve the formation of hyperoxides, but there is little experimental evidence for these intermediates. In any event, primary alcohols are formed as the first stable metabolites in the pathway. These are then converted to their corresponding aldehydes and fatty acids via dehydrogenases dependent on nicotinamide adenine dinucleotide (NAD) and the fatty acids are subsequently metabolized by the usual β-oxidation mechanisms. However, **diterminal oxidation** has also been reported to occur; eg, α,ω-oxidation by species of *Corynebacterium* (66) and *Pseudomonas* (67). Methane is apparently oxidized via a pathway analogous to that found for the higher alkanes, with the production of methanol, formaldehyde, and formate as the intermediates. A diagram, showing a unified scheme for alkane metabolism, is presented in Figure 1 (40).

Co-oxidation represents another interesting route of hydrocarbon assimilation. This phenomenon involves the oxidation of an otherwise "inert" hydrocarbon, ie one that does not support growth, in a system in which a growth-supporting hydrocarbon is being oxidized. Thus, while growing on methane, *Pseudomonas methanica* is capable of oxidizing ethane, propane, butane, and other short-chain alkanes (68). Similarly, *Nocardia* sp. can co-oxidize various substituted hydrocarbons (which do not ordinarily support growth) while growing on *n*-hexadecane (69).

1-Alkenes, like alkanes in general, are apparently subject primarily to monoterminal oxidation at the saturated end of the molecule. However, attack at the double bond has also been reported, with, for example, the formation of diols by yeasts (54) and of epoxides by a *Pseudomonas* species (70). A unified scheme for the oxidation of 1-alkenes is presented in Figure 2 (40).

The energy generated by oxidation of hydrocarbons, and many of the molecules that are formed during the oxidative process, are utilized by the microorganisms for

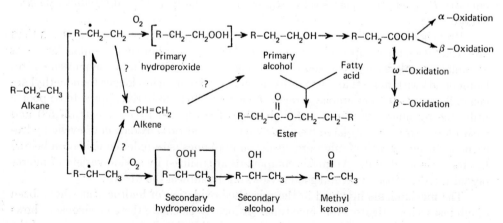

Fig. 1. Unified scheme for alkane metabolism.

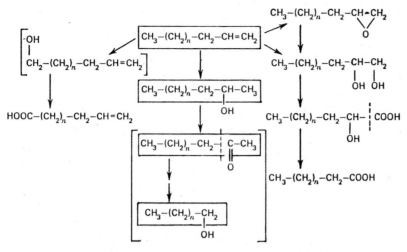

Fig. 2. Unified scheme for the oxidation of a 1-alkene.

subsequent reactions that lead to the synthesis of new cellular material. Small molecules, such as acetate and pyruvate, CH_3COCOO^-, are the starting materials for the synthesis of the amino acids, purine and pyrimidine bases, and sugars that are the building blocks for the macromolecules of the cells. A large number of simple and complex biochemical pathways are used. Proteins (enzymes) are responsible for all of these cellular activities, and most of the activities of the cell can be considered to be directed ultimately towards the synthesis of new proteins (and for maintenance of the genetic mechanisms that are responsible for specifying their structure).

The detailed mechanisms of protein biosynthesis have been the subject of a rapidly expanding research effort over the past two decades (71). These studies have made it clear that the process by which cells manufacture proteins is exceedingly complex and requires the participation of many cellular structures, specialized macromolecules, and low-molecular-weight components. The mechanisms by which the process of protein biosynthesis is regulated in cells are also under very active investigation. These appear to be subtle, exquisitely balanced systems carefully controlled during the growth of the cell.

The information for all cellular activities and, therefore, for the enzymes responsible for them, is encoded in the genetic material of the cell, deoxyribonucleic acid (DNA) which, in higher organisms, is part of more complex structures, the chromosomes. During growth, and preceding division of the cell, the entire DNA complement must be duplicated so that each of the daughter cells is supplied with a complete set of genetic information. This is accomplished by the process of DNA *replication*. Replication involves an enzymically catalyzed series of reactions, the precise mechanism of which remains quite obscure despite very intensive research efforts over the past two decades. Certainly, however, it depends upon the phenomenon of complementary base pairing, whereby the sequence of purine and pyrimidine bases that encodes the genetic information is preserved from generation to generation.

In order to transmit the instructions encoded in the DNA the cell utilizes another enzymatically mediated process known as *transcription*. With the DNA serving as a template to specify the sequence of bases, a molecule of ribonucleic acid (RNA) is synthesized, again via the complementary base-pairing mechanism. The RNA molecules thus formed are referred to as "messenger-RNA" (mRNA), because they carry the coded "message" for the structure of specific proteins.

The next step in the process is referred to as *translation*, because it is the step in which the genetic information in the "language" of sequences of purine and pyrimidine bases in mRNA is translated into the protein "language"; that is, a sequence of amino acids. Translation is carried out at the surface of ribosomes, complex subcellular particles composed of RNA and protein, which act as the site for the interaction of the many molecules involved in the process. Amino acids are brought to the site by specific RNA molecules known as transfer RNA (tRNA). The amino acids are first activated in an enzyme-mediated reaction with adenosine triphosphate (ATP), and then, in another reaction (with the same enzyme system), are attached to tRNA. These are specific tRNA molecules for each different amino acid. Each amino acid is brought into the growing polypeptide chain in its proper sequence under the direction of the mRNA, which has become bound to the ribosome. Even the binding of mRNA and aminoacyl–tRNA molecules to the ribosome are complex and incompletely understood processes, involving several specific protein factors, other molecules (eg guanosine triphosphate) and various inorganic ions (eg Mg^{2+} and K^+). Each sequence of three bases in the mRNA molecule specifies a single amino acid that is to be added to the chain. Special "triplets" of bases specify either initiation of a new chain or termination of chain growth. Thus, for each segment of DNA (ie for each gene) that has been transcribed into a molecule of mRNA, many molecules of a specific protein are synthesized. This process is repeated for each of the many proteins of the cell, in a precisely controlled sequence, during growth of the cell. Following cell division, the entire process begins again in each of the daughter cells. Thus, protein synthesis in growing microbial cells is a continuing process, which both controls, and is dependent upon, all of the other cellular activities.

Hydrocarbon-Grown Microorganisms as a Source of Protein

Early interest in the use of hydrocarbon-grown microorganisms for the production of foodstuffs emphasized lipids and vitamins (34,72,73), but as early as 1948, Just and Schnabel (74) reported feeding bacterial cells grown on paraffins to rats. Subsequently, Just et al. (75) extended these studies to include yeasts, which were cultivated to high yields on paraffinic hydrocarbons. By 1954, Beerstecher (34) and Davis and Updegraf (76) recognized the potential of hydrocarbon-grown microorganisms as a source of food protein. Hoerburger (77), however, concluded from his studies on the growth of *Candida tropicalis* on a paraffin-rich hydrocarbon mixture that industrial production was not feasible, especially in view of the high aeration rates required.

Perhaps the first really concerted effort to grow microorganisms on hydrocarbons for the purpose of producing food protein on a commercial scale was initiated in the late 1950s by Champagnat and his associates at the Société Française des Petroles BP (the French associate of the British Petroleum Company). They combined this aim with that of microbial removal of the higher *n*-alkanes from crude petroleum (78). Since that time, work in this field has been greatly expanded, with the participation of many oil companies, academic institutions, government agencies, and other interested organizations all around the world. A list of many of these is presented in Table 2.

Of the many reports in the rapidly increasing literature in this field, those referred

Table 2. Some Organizations Involved in SCP Work

United States
    Esso Research and Engineering Company (with Nestlé) Linden, N.J.
    Gulf Oil Company, Wasco, Calif., and Harmarville, Pa.
    Institute of Gas Technology, Chicago, Ill.
    Massachusetts Institute of Technology, Cambridge, Mass.
    Mobil Oil Company, Princeton, N.J.
    Phillips Petroleum Company (with General Mills)
    Standard Oil of California (Chevron)
    Standard Oil of Indiana (AMOCO), Whiting, Ind.
    Sun Oil Company, Marcus Hook, Pa.
    U.S. Bureau of Mines, Coal Research Laboratory
    University of Pennsylvania, Philadelphia, Pa.
    University of Wisconsin, Madison, Wis.
Canada
    University of Western Ontario, London, Ont.
Great Britain
    Birmingham University, Birmingham
    British Petroleum Company, Grangemouth, Scotland
    Imperial Chemical Industries, Billingham, Co. Durham
    Shell Research, Ltd., Kent
    University College, London
France
    Centre National de la Recherche Scientifique, Marseilles
    Société Française des Pétroles, Lavèra
Switzerland
    Nestlé Alimentana S. A. (with Esso), Vevey
Germany
    University of Stuttgart, Stuttgart
Sweden
    Karolinska Institute, Stockholm
Bulgaria
    Chemical Industry Research Institute, Sofia
Czechoslovakia
    Institute of Chemical Technology, Prague
    Institute of Microbiology, Czechoslovak Academy of Sciences, Prague
Soviet Union
    All-Union Scientific Research Institute of Protein Biosynthesis, Moscow
    Institute of Microbiology, Academy of Sciences of the U.S.S.R., Moscow
    Moscow State University, Moscow
Argentina
    Universidad Nacional de La Plata, La Plata
India
    Regional Research Laboratory, Jorhat, Assam
Taiwan
    Chinese Petroleum Corporation, Chi-Yee
Japan
    Institute of Applied Microbiology, University of Tokyo
    Kyoto, Osaka, Nagaya, and Ibaraka Universities
    Ajinomoto Company, Inc., Kawasaki
    Asahi Chemical Industry Company, Tokyo and Mizushima
    Dainippon Ink and Chemical Company, Gamagouri, Chiba
    Kanegafuchi Chemical Industry Company, Takasago and Kashima
    Kyowa Hakko Kogyo Company, Ltd., Tokyo and Bufo
    Toyo Kaotsu, Tokyo
    Mitsui Toatsu Chemical, Hiokoshima
    Tadeda Chemical Company, Osaka
    Hitachi Chemical Company, Yamasaki
Mainland China
    Shanghai

to in Table 3 are indicative of the types of microorganisms and hydrocarbon substrates that are being explored, and include references to work in most of the countries in which studies on SCP are being carried out.

Some representative SCP processes for which data have been published are listed in Table 4. The gross compositions of these products are listed in Table 5 along with the composition of some other protein sources (conventionally grown yeast, fish-protein concentrate, FPC, and soybean meal). The amino acid compositions of the various products are shown in Table 6.

Table 3. Hydrocarbon Substrates and Microorganisms Studied for SCP

Hydrocarbon substrate	Microorganism	Reference
methane	Methanomonas sp	(113)
	Bacillus sp	(42,114)
	bacterium	(115,116)
	bacteria (mixed culture)	(117)
higher n-alkanes		
hexadecane	Candida tropicalis	(87)
	Micrococcus cerificans	(82,83)
	Pseudomonas aeruginosa	(87)
	Bacillus thermophil.	(89)
octadecane	Candida sp	(86)
	Mycobacterium lacticolum	(84)
	M. rubrum var propanicum	(84)
	M. flavum var methanicum	(84)
	Nocardia sp	(86)
	Pseudomonas aeruginosa	(82)
C_{19}–C_{20}	Candida lipolytica	(85)
	Mycobacterium phlei.	(85)
	Nocardia sp	(85)
C_{12}–C_{15}	Candida guilliermondi	(97,98)
C_{13}–C_{19}	Micrococcus cerificans	(13)
C_{14}–C_{18}	Candida intermedia	(90)
	Torulopsis sp	(100)
C_{14}–C_{19}	Candida tropicalis, C. lipolytica, C. pelliculosa, C. intermedia	(92)
C_{15}–C_{28}	Candida intermedia plus C. lipolytica (mixed culture)	(99)
n-paraffins	Candida albicans, C. tropicalis	(93,94)
	Candida lipolytica	(3,80,81,91)
	Candida tropicalis	(95,96)
	Pseudomonas sp	(88)
oil		
gas	Micrococcus cerificans	(83)
	Candida lipolytica	(78–81,101–103)
	Trichosporum pullulans	(104–106)
	Candida intermedia plus C. lipolytica (mixed culture)	(107)
fuel	Pseudomonas sp	(108)
light	Candida tropicalis	(109)
kerosene	Pseudomonas aeruginosa	(110)
	Candida lipolytica	(100)
	Candida tropicalis	(111)
	Mycotorula japonica	(112)

Table 4. Some Representative SCP Processes

Organization	Organism	Substrate
Esso-Nestlé (E–N), United States and Switzerland	bacterium, yeast	*n*-paraffins
British Petroleum (B-P), Lavèra, France	yeast	gas oil
British Petroleum (B-P), Grangemouth, Scotland	yeast	*n*-paraffins
Regional Research Laboratory (RRL), Jorhat, Assam, India	yeast	gas oil
Chinese Petroleum Company (CPC), Taiwan	bacterium	fuel oil
Institute of Gas Technology (IGT), Chicago, Ill.	bacterium	methane

Table 5. Composition of Various Protein Sources

Source	Moisture	N × 6.25	Lipids	Ash	Carbohydrate
E-N					
bacterium		62–73	10–15	6–12	10
yeast		54	10	7	26
B-P					
Lavèra	5.0	70.5	0.45	7.9	
Grangemouth	4.2	65	8.1	6	
RRL	6.8	49.3	25.8	8.4	
CPC	10	71.2	2.1	9.3	
IGT		35–65	3–7	2.4	25–55
commercial yeast	5–8	45–55	1–6	6–10	32–40
FPC[a]	<10	<67	<0.75		
soybean meal		37–53	15–23	4–6	

[a] Fish-protein concentrate.

Table 6. Amino Acid Composition of Some Protein Sources, g/100 g Protein

Amino acid	E-N		B-P		RRL	CPC	IGT	Yeast, Torula	Fish meal	Soybean meal
	Bacterium	Yeast	Lavèra	Grangemouth						
isoleucine	3.6	3.6	5.3	4.5	6.0	3.8	4.6	5.5	3.0	2.5
leucine	5.6	5.9	7.8	7.0	3.1	6.6	8.2	7.6	4.7	3.5
lysine	6.5	7.0	7.8	7.0	4.9	4.3	5.9	6.8	4.6	2.9
phenylalanine	2.9	3.7	4.8	4.4	3.8	3.3	4.8	3.9	2.6	2.3
tyrosine			4.0	3.5		2.7	3.9		1.9	1.2
cystine	0.6		0.9	1.1		0.4	0.3	1.0	0.7	0.6
methionine	2.0	1.2	1.6	1.8	1.3	1.3	1.5	0.8	1.7	0.6
threonine	4.0	3.9	5.4	4.9	4.3	4.1	4.6	5.4	2.7	1.8
tryptophan	0.9	0.5	1.3	1.4	1.1	1.2	3.8	1.6	0.8	0.7
valine	4.5	4.0	5.8	5.4	7.1	3.5	6.6	6.0	3.4	2.3

Process for Proteins from Petroleum

Figure 3 outlines a typical continuous process for producing single-cell protein (13). The details of the various steps depend on the substrate, the type of organism used, and on the nature of the product desired. Microbial cells are produced in a fer-

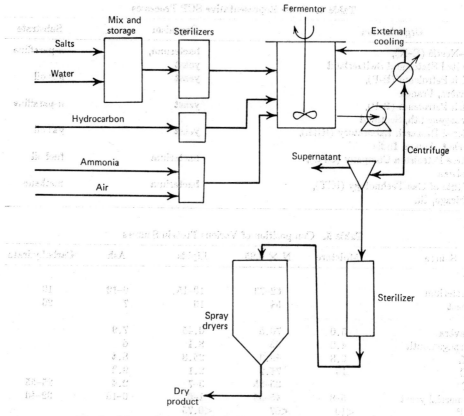

Fig. 3. Scheme for a continuous hydrocarbon-fermentation process.

mentor and are then harvested to produce a dry, stable product which needs only to be stored in moisture-proof containers to prevent spoilage.

An estimate of the raw-material requirements can be made by using $C_4H_7NO_2$ as the empirical formula for dry bacterial cells. Thus the minimum requirements for these elements can be calculated. In addition, some substrate and oxygen are required for energy and appear ultimately as CO_2, H_2O, and heat. Unless a washing step is included, a significant fraction of the salts ends up as ash in the final product. Oxygen is provided by aerating the fermentor. Nitrogen can be supplied in several forms. However, ammonia serves the additional purpose of maintaining a constant pH. The quantity (lb) and composition of the various process streams are given in Table 7, based on 100 lb of dry cells (14,128).

Microorganisms utilizing a hydrocarbon as a sole source of carbon require for growth, in addition to water and oxygen, appropriate sources of nitrogen, sulfur, phosphorus, and a number of inorganic ions. In addition, appropriate conditions of pH and temperature must be maintained. A mixed salt solution can usually be devised providing many of the growth requirements. Liquid ammonia, ammonium salts, nitrates, or urea may serve as a nitrogen source, and sodium, potassium, calcium, and magnesium salts—as sulfates, phosphates, or chlorides—can be appropriately balanced to provide proper concentrations of all of these ions, as well as to buffer the medium at the desired pH level. Other minerals, such as iron, copper, zinc, and manganese, are often

Table 7. Typical Quantities for Streams Shown in Figure 3, lb, Based on 100 lb of Dry Cells

Component	Feed to fermentor	Fermentor Off-Gas	Fermentor Broth	Centrifuge Supernatant	Centrifuge Concentrate	Dry Product
hydrocarbon, as $C_{16}H_{34}$	118	0	0	0	0	0
NH_3	25	0	12	10.8	1.2	1.2
O_2 in air	600	400	0	0	0	0
water	10,000	100	9,971	8,971	1,000	5
salts	22	0	22	16	6	6
cells as $C_4H_7NO_2$	0	0	100	0	100	100
CO_2	0	160	0	0	0	0
total	10,765	660	10,105	8,997.8	1,107.2	112.2

supplied in trace amounts. In addition, some microorganisms might also require the inclusion of small amounts of growth factors (vitamins, coenzymes, etc).

The fermentation process is initiated from a seed culture of the desired microorganism. Cultures of most microorganisms can be kept viable for several years with relatively little effort by storing at liquid-nitrogen temperatures.

A seed culture containing several ml of a liquid suspension of the organism is used to inoculate a flask containing 50–100 ml of culture media. The flask is shaken for 1–2 days at constant temperature to obtain a suspension containing 0.5–1.0% dry-weight cells. At this point the culture is usually checked for purity by spreading a diluted suspension from the flask on the suface of agar contained in a petri dish. Colonies of the organism grow readily on the agar surface and a single colony (pure culture) can be selected for further propagation. The culture volume is increased by transfer and growth in progressively larger flasks containing fresh medium. Usually a 10–100-fold increase in volume is achieved at each transfer. The final stages of inoculum preparation are accomplished in a series of mechanically agitated vessels associated with the production fermentor. In the final step the inoculum amounts to 5–10% of the production fermentor volume and contains 0.5–1% cells. The production fermentor can be brought to 1–2% cells in 10–40 hr depending on the rate at which oxygen and other nutrients are made available and on the generation time of the organisms. Maximum productivity is usually achieved by then placing the fermentor in continuous operation, as illustrated in Figure 3.

Production of cells is particularly suited to continuous operation. This is one of the major differences between a process based on recovery of biomass and one where nongrowth-associated products are important, ie the flavor elements in alcoholic beverages and some of the antibiotics. The kinetics for batch and continuous fermentation are compared in most standard bioengineering references (118) and are not presented in detail here.

A typical batch growth curve is shown in Figure 4, plotting C_f, the concentration of cells (usually expressed as grams of dry cells/liter of medium) logarithmically against time. After a short *lag phase*, whose duration depends on the size of the inoculum and the time necessary for the cells to adjust to the conditions of the medium, the linear portion of the curve starts. This is termed the *exponential phase*. In this phase the growth rate, μ, is a maximum. During this period cell propagation is described by the following first-order relationship:

$$dC_f/dt = \mu_{max} C_f \tag{1}$$

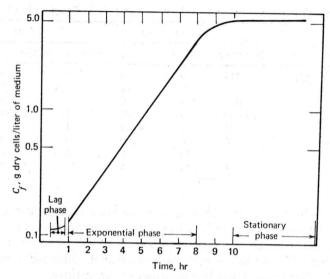

Fig. 4. Typical batch growth curve for microorganism ($\mu_{max} = 0.5$ hr^{-1}).

The maximum specific growth rate, μ_{max} (usually expresssed as hr^{-1}) is characteristic of the microorganism and the substrate. Eventually, some nutrient becomes depleted, or a product of metabolism inhibits further cell division, and this final portion of the growth curve is termed the *stationary phase*.

Continuous fermentation is started after the fermentor has been brought to the desired cell concentration by batch growth. Soluble nutrients in the aqueous solution and the hydrocarbon substrate are supplied at a constant rate. Cells and broth are withdrawn continuously to maintain a constant fermentor level. The use of ammonia to control pH ensures an adequate supply of nitrogen for cell synthesis. Air enters through a sparger and is usually further dispersed by a mechanical agitator. The agitator also disperses the hydrocarbon. Agitation is usually vigorous enough so that the fermentor behaves as a well-mixed reactor.

A material balance on dry cells for a well-mixed continuous fermentor gives the following:

$$V\mu C_f = LC_f \quad \text{or} \quad \mu = L/V \tag{2}$$

where L is the volumetric liquid feed rate to the fermentor, and V is the volume of liquid in the fermentor. The term μ is the specific growth rate as defined in equation 1, except that in equation 2 it is assumed that the substrate concentration is kept low enough to limit growth rate. Thus, for continuous fermentation equation 2 shows that μ is the reciprocal of residence time. The fermentor productivity per unit of fermentor volume, G, is then given as follows:

$$G = (C_f)(L)/V \tag{3}$$

The relationship between G and L/V is illustrated in Figure 5. As L/V is increased, a point is reached corresponding to μ_{max} beyond which cell concentration declines rapidly because the average residence time is less than that required for cell growth and division.

It is possible to increase productivity by supplying a higher concentration of the

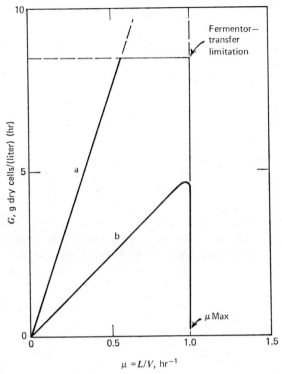

Fig. 5. Relationship between G and L/V. LEGEND: a, $C_f = 15$ g/liter; b, $C_f = 5$ g/liter.

limiting substrate, ie hydrocarbon. This results in proportionately higher cell concentration for a given L/V and is illustrated by the upper curve in Figure 5. In this case, there is an upper limit to cell concentration when the mass-transfer capability of the fermentor is reached.

The rate at which oxygen can be transferred is the factor that usually limits fermentor productivity. The oxygen-transfer rate can be increased by increasing mechanical mixing or by raising the oxygen partial pressure in the inlet air or by increasing the aeration rate in the fermentor. Once the transfer characteristics of the fermentor are known, it is easy to select the optimum productivity by balancing off the cost of higher mixing power and air rates or oxygen partial pressure against the lower fermentor volume required to yield the desired product rate. The cost of harvesting cells downstream of the fermentor dictates that the fermentor be operated at the highest possible cell concentration.

Table 8 compares cell productivity for batch and continuous fermentors. There is approximately a 10-fold increase in productivity for the continuous process and the operation of downstream equipment is simplified by eliminating the need for switching from one fermentor to another. The principal disadvantage of continuous operation is the increased probability of contamination by foreign organisms.

Sterile operation of batch fermentors for periods up to a week is now practiced in the antibiotics industry (119). However, sterility under continuous conditions depends on eliminating all organisms from large volumes of media and air for periods up to a month and it is not certain that existing technology will do this consistently.

There are a number of ways of providing the large volumes of sterile media re-

Table 8. Productivity of a 10,000-Gal Fermentor

Operating conditions	Batch	Continuous
cleaning time, hr	4	4
filling and sterilization, hr	4	4
inoculation and batch growth, hr[a]	12	12
harvesting time, hr	4	continuous
total time used for growth, %	50	88[c]
product per month,[b] lb	50,000	536,000

[a] Assumes a maximum specific growth rate of 1 hr^{-1}.

[b] Assumes cells are grown to 20 g dry wt/liter in the fermentor and at 10 g/(liter) (hr) for continuous fermentation.

[c] Based on a one-week cycle.

quired for continuous fermentation. However, heating to above 270°F and holding this temperature for several minutes is the only reliable method for killing all entering organisms. Because sterilization represents a significant operation expense, there is an incentive to recycle centrifuge supernatant back to the fermentor, provided its sterility can be maintained. This also eliminates an otherwise formidable waste-disposal problem.

With bacterial fermentation heat sterilization has the further advantage of destroying bacteriophages. Bacteriophages, ie viruses that attack bacteria, can within a matter of minutes destroy all living bacterial cells in the fermentor. It is usual practice to have many strains of the desired organism on hand so that if a bacteriophage attack does occur a resistant strain can be selected for subsequent production. In Japan improved results have been obtained for glutamic acid fermentation by planned rotation of phage-resistant strains.

The considerable heat generated during fermentation must be removed. For hydrocarbons the liberation is 13,000–14,000 Btu/lb of cells which is considerably higher than the liberation from carbohydrate substrates (120,121). The problem is unusually acute because of the small temperature differences between the fermentor and the available cooling water. If internal cooling coils are used, refrigeration is required. An alternative is to circulate the fermentor contents through an external circuit where sufficient surface area can be provided so that cooling water can be used.

Because of the cooling problem, some investigators have suggested the use of thermophilic organisms. Some thermophiles are known which can grow close to the boiling point of water (122). Therefore, it may be possible to add another 100°F to the temperature difference for cooling. Hydrocarbon-utilizing organisms have been reported which grow at 160°F (89).

Table 3 indicates that many organisms which could be used for protein production grow on n-paraffins in the C_{10} to C_{30} range. Gas oil and kerosene distillates have a C_{10}–C_{30} n-paraffin content of 10–20%. The relatively high melting point of the n-paraffins causes cloudiness and solidification at reduced temperatures. This is one of the reasons why petroleum companies have sought techniques for recovering these materials.

An alternative to using gas oil or kerosene is to separate the n-paraffins first by molecular sieve or by forming the urea adduct. The savings associated with the unpurified and, therefore, less expensive substrate are at least partially balanced by the cost of extracting unreacted hydrocarbon from the final product (123). The uncertainties in the situation are indicated by British Petroleum's proposal to construct two plants, one utilizing purified n-paraffins and the other utilizing gas oil (3). It is questionable that the latter is feasible when manufacturing a product for human consumption, where complete freedom from contamination by potentially harmful hydrocarbons is required.

Natural gas has also been evaluated as a potential fermentation substrate (42,113–117, 124). This is undoubtedly the least expensive source of carbon and is available in some locations in quantities more than adequate to supply the largest protein plants now visualized. The reduced substrate cost is offset by an apparent decrease in the quantity of cells produced per unit of substrate consumed and by the lower growth rates and cell yields obtainable with the organisms now available. In the metabolism of methane from natural gas methanol is an intermediate. Therefore, it is possible to replace natural gas with methanol in highly industrialized areas where inexpensive methanol is available.

Research on fermentor design has not kept pace with activities on the biological aspects of the field. Instead, there has been almost total reliance on conventional fermentors developed for batch propagation of yeast on various soluble carbohydrates. It is possible that significant economic savings could be achieved by developing a fermentation system solving the problems peculiar to hydrocarbons, ie immiscibility, high oxygen demand and high heat liberation. The need has been apparent for some time and references 125–129 contain data for new designs.

The nature of the phenomena involved in making immiscible hydrocarbons available to the microorganisms is still being debated (130–132). It appears that the observed growth rates on n-paraffins cannot be explained by molecular diffusion through the aqueous phase due to the extremely low solubility of the hydrocarbon (133). One possibility is that growth takes place on the surface of hydrocarbon droplets and hydrocarbon is, therefore, absorbed directly by the microorganism (134). Results suggest in some cases that the hydrocarbon and microorganisms both exist at the surface of air bubbles and that both hydrocarbon and oxygen are absorbed directly.

Despite this lack of detail, growth rate usually responds to increased oxygen availability indicating that this is the limiting factor and that if the fermentor is designed to supply oxygen at the desired rate, hydrocarbon transfer will also be adequate. A partial explanation for the latter is that hydrocarbon-utilizing microorganisms produce surfactants which emulsify the substrate (50,51).

Assuming that oxygen transfer is the limiting factor, it is possible to design a commercial-size fermentor with a reasonable degree of certainty. In fact, information is available on oxygen-transfer rates for fermentors up to a capacity of 10,000 gal (135). The uncertainty arises in extrapolating this information to the 100% increase in oxygen required for systems utilizing hydrocarbons. Further uncertainties are introduced if the design departs from the usual mechanically agitated and baffled tanks. For a good description of available fermentation equipment, including performance data, see reference 136. The available techniques for scaling up pilot-plant data to commercial size are presented in references 137 and 138.

Harvesting microorganisms can be accomplished using existing techniques. The recovery of yeast cells to produce a dried product for human and animal feed is currently practiced in the United States and Europe. Centrifugation is used as the initial concentrating step for yeast manufacture. However, bacteria are much smaller and it may be less expensive to consider some other technique, such as foam concentration (139).

Additional steps must be taken when gas oil is used as a substrate since some unreacted hydrocarbon remains with the microorganisms after centrifugation. It has been found that most of this material can be removed by several stages of washing with water containing a surfactant followed by a final extraction stage using hexane (140).

The final steps in the process consist of drying and packaging the product. Either spray or roller drying can be employed. Drying conditions must be selected to minimize loss of nutritive value and the development of off-flavors due to overheating.

Bibliography

1. President's Science Advisory Committee, *The World Food Problem*, Vols. I and II, U.S. Government Printing Office, Washington, D.C., May, 1967.
2. *World Food Supply Symposium*, American Association for the Advancement of Science, Washington, D.C., December 27, 1966.
3. D. A. B. Llewelyn, *Symposium on Microbiology, London, September 19–20, 1967*, pp. 1–19.
4. *Seventh International Congress on Nutrition, Hamburg, Germany, 1966*.
5. R. I. Mateles and S. R. Tannenbaum, eds., *Single-Cell Protein*, The MIT Press, Cambridge, Mass., 1968.
6. "Engineering of Unconventional Protein Production," in H. Bieber, ed., *Chemical Engineering Progress Symposium Ser. 93*, Vol. 65, Am. Inst. of Chem. Engineers, New York, 1969.
7. *PAG Bulletin*, FAD/WHO/UNICEF Protein Advisory Group Secretariat, United Nations, New York.
8. Anon., *Chem. Week* **105** (24), 61 (Dec. 17, 1969).
9. N. W. Pirie, *Chem. Ind. (London)*, **1968**, 864.
10. L. Enebo, in reference 6, p. 80.
11. A. A. Altschul, *Chem. Eng. News* **47** (49), 68 (Nov. 24, 1969).
12. C. A. Shaklady, *Biotech. Bioeng. Symp.* **1**, 77 (1969).
13. J. G. McNab and L. R. Rey, in reference 2.
14. D. I. C. Wang, *Chem. Eng.* **75**, 99 (Aug. 26, 1968).
15. N. S. Scrimshaw, in reference 5, p. 3.
16. M. Miyoshi, *Jahrb. Wiss. Botan.* **28**, 269 (1895).
17. O. Rahn, *Zentr. Bakt. Parasitenk. Infek.* **16**, 382 (1906).
18. N. L. Söhngen, *Zentr. Bakt. Parasitenk. Infek.* **15**, 513 (1906).
19. H. Kaserer, *Zentr. Bakt. Parasitenk. Infek.* **15**, 573 (1906).
20. K. Störmer, *Zentr. Bakt. Parasitenk. Infek.* **20**, 282 (1908).
21. N. L. Söhngen, *Zentr. Bakt. Parasitenk. Infek.* **37**, 595 (1913).
22. N. A. Marimov, ed., *Collected Works of W. O. Tausson*, Publishing House of the Academy of Sciences, U.S.S.R., Moscow, 1950.
23. R. J. Strawinski and R. W. Stone, *J. Bacteriol.* **40**, 461 (1940).
24. F. H. Johnson, W. T. Goodale, and J. Turkevich, *J. Cellular Comp. Physiol.* **19**, 163 (1942).
25. G. D. Novelli and C. E. Zobell, *J. Bacteriol.* **47**, 447 (1944).
26. W. C. Evans, *Biochem. J.* **47**, 373 (1947).
27. J. B. Davis, *Bull. Am. Assoc. Petrol. Geologists* **36**, 2186 (1952).
28. C. E. Zobell, *Bacteriol. Rev.* **10**, 1 (1946).
29. C. E. Zobell, *Advan. Enzymol.* **10**, 443 (1950).
30. L. D. Shturm, *Mikrobiologiya* **27**, 723 (1958).
31. G. W. Fuhs, *Archiv. Mikrobiol.* **39**, 374 (1961).
32. J. W. Foster, "Bacterial Oxidation of Hydrocarbons," in O. Hayaishi, ed. *Oxygenases*, Academic Press, Inc., New York, 1962, p. 241.
33. J. W. Foster and Antonie van Leeuwenhoek, *J. Microbiol. Serol.* **28**, 241 (1962).
34. E. Beerstecher, *Petroleum Microbiology*, Elsevier Press, Inc., Houston, Texas, 1954.
35. R. E. Kallio, W. R. Finnerty, S. Wawzonek, and P. D. Klimsitra, in C. H. Oppenheimer, ed., *Symposium on Marine Microbiology*, Charles C Thomas, Springfield, Ill., 1963.
36. W. C. Evans, *J. Gen. Microbiol.* **32**, 177 (1963).
37. M. J. Johnson, *Chem. Ind. (London)* **1964**, 1532–1537.
38. E. J. McKenna and R. E. Kallio, *Ann. Rev. Microbiol.* **19**, 183 (1965).
39. A. C. Van der Linden and G. J. E. Thijsse, *Advan. Enzymol.* **27**, 469 (1965).
40. D. Perlman, ed., *Fermentation Advances*, Academic Press, Inc., New York, 1969.
40a. R. E. Kallio, in reference 40, p. 635.
41. J. B. Davis, *Petroleum Microbiology*, Elsevier Publishing Co., Amsterdam, 1967.
42. B. Wolnak, B. H. Andreen, J. A. Chisholm, Jr., and M. Saadeh, *Biotechnol. Bioeng.* **9**, 57 (1967).

43. Anon., *Chem. Week* **98** (25), 89 (June 18, 1966).
44. J. B. Davis, V. F. Coty, and J. P. Stanley, *J. Bacteriol.* **88**, 468 (1964).
45. J. E. Zajic, B. Volesky, and A. Wellman, *Can. J. Microbiol.* **15**, 1231 (1969).
46. L. Enebo, *Acta Chem. Scand.* **21**, 625 (1967).
47. M. Dworkin and J. W. Foster, *J. Bacteriol.* **75**, 592 (1958).
48. C. McAuliffe, *Science* **163**, 478 (1969).
49. R. W. Stone, *Develop. Ind. Microbiol.* **4**, 5 (1963).
50. T. Iguchi, I. Takeda, and H. Ohsawa, *Agr. Biol. Chem. (Tokyo)* **33**, 1657 (1969).
51. T. Suzuki, K. Tanaka, I. Mateubara, and S. Kinoshita, *Agr. Biol. Chem. (Tokyo)* **33**, 1619 (1969).
52. G. J. E. Thijsse, A. C. Van der Linden, and Antonie van Leeuwenhoek, *J. Microbiol. Serol.* **29**, 89 (1963).
53. J. Stewart, W. R. Finnerty, R. E. Kallio, and D. P. Stevenson, *Science* **132**, 1254 (1960).
54. J. Bruyn, *Koninkl. Ned. Akad. Wetenschap. Proc. Ser. C.* **57**, 41 (1954).
55. T. Ishikura and J. W. Foster, *Nature* **192**, 892 (1961).
56. W. R. Finnerty, E. Hautrey, and R. E. Kallio, *Z. Allgem. Mikrobiol.* **2**, 169 (1962).
57. G. J. E. Thijsse, J. T. Zwilling de Vries, and Antonie van Leeuwenhoek, *J. Microbiol. Serol.* **25**, 332 (1959).
58. B. Imelik, *Compt. Rend.* **226**, 2082 (1948).
59. C. Colla and V. Treccani, *Ann. Microbiol. Enzimol.* **10**, 77 (1960).
60. J. Ooyama, J. W. Foster, and Antonie van Leeuwenhoek, *J. Microbiol. Serol.* **31**, 45 (1965).
61. M. H. Rogoff, *Advan. Appl. Microbiol.* **3**, 193 (1961).
62. V. Treccani, *Progr. Ind. Microbiol.* **4**, 1 (1963).
63. W. C. Evans in reference 40, p. 649. (See also list of general reviews in this reference.)
64. D. T. Gibson, J. M. Wood, P. J. Chapman, and S. Dagley, *Biotechnol. Bioeng.* **9**, 33 (1967).
65. D. T. Gibson, *Science* **161**, 1093 (1968).
66. A. S. Kester and J. W. Foster, *Bacteriol. Proc.* **1960**, 168.
67. M. Y. Ali Kahn, A. N. Hall, and D. S. Robinson, *Nature* **198**, 289 (1963).
68. E. R. Leadbetter and J. W. Foster, *Arch. Mikrobiol.* **35**, 92 (1960).
69. J. B. Davis and R. L. Raymond, *Appl. Microbiol.* **9**, 383 (1961).
70. A. C. Van der Linden, *Biochim. Biophys. Acta* **77**, 157 (1963).
71. P. Lengyel and D. Söll, *Bacteriol. Rev.* **33**, 264 (1969).
72. R. L. Raymond and J. B. Davis, *Appl. Microbiol.* **8**, 210 (1960).
73. H. F. Haas and L. D. Bushnell, *J. Bacteriol.* **48**, 219 (1944).
74. F. Just and W. Schnabel, *Branntweinwirtschaft* **2**, 113 (1948).
75. F. Just, W. Schnabel, and S. Ullmann, *Brauerei, Wiss. Beil.* **4**, 57 (1951).
76. J. B. Davis and D. M. Updegraf, *Bacteriol. Rev.* **18**, 215 (1954).
77. W. Hoerburger, *Research Reports of the Ministry of Trade and Transport of North-Rhine Westphalia*, No. 131, Westdeutscher Verlag, Cologne, 1955.
78. A. Champagnat, C. Vernet, B. Lainé, and J. Filosa, *Science* **197**, 13 (1963).
79. A. Champagnat, *Impact Sci. Soc.* **14**, 119 (1964).
80. B. Lainé, *Biotech. Bioeng. Symp.* **1**, 71 (1969).
81. G. H. Evans, in reference 5, p. 243.
82. R. J. Ertola, M. D. Lilly, and F. C. Webb, *Biotechnol. Bioeng.* **7**, 309 (1965).
83. R. J. Ertola, L. A. Mazza, and A. P. Balatti, *Biotechnol. Bioeng.* **11**, 409 (1969).
84. D. K. Kersten, *Prikl. Biokhimiya Mikrobiologiya* **3**, 635 (1967).
85. F. Wagner, Th. Kleemann, and W. Zahn, *Biotechnol. Bioeng.* **11**, 393 (1969).
86. R. L. Raymond, *Develop. Ind. Microbiol.* **2**, 23 (1961).
87. K. Yamada, J. Takahashi, Y. Kawabata, T. Okada, and T. Onihara, in reference 5, p. 243.
88. M. J. Johnson, *Science* **155**, 1515 (1967).
89. R. I. Mateles, J. N. Baruah, and S. R. Tannenbaum, *Science* **157**, 1322 (1967).
90. T. L. Miller, S. Lie, and M. J. Johnson, *Biotechnol. Bioeng.* **6**, 299 (1964).
91. C. A. Shaklady, *New Scientist*, **1969**, 5.
92. S. V. Chepigo, I. D. Boiko, A. D. Gololobov, A. P. Kryuchkova, G. D. Vorobeva, M. I. Rozhkova, P. N. Fisher, V. K. Pokrovskii, and N. I. Korotchenko, *Prikl. Biokhimiya Mikrobiologiya* **3**, 577 (1967); *Chem. Abstr.* **68**, 48458m (1968).
93. A. Tanaka, H. Maki, and S. Fukui, *J. Ferment. Technol.* **45**, 1163 (1967).
94. A. Tanaka and S. Fukui, *J. Ferment. Technol.* **46**, 214 (1968).
95. I. N. Pozmogova and N. S. Kuryatov, *Prikl. Biokhimiya Mikrobiologiya* **2**, 640 (1966).

96. I. N. Pozmogova, I. E. Lomova, and M. I. Lakoza, *Prikl. Biokhimiya Mikrobiologiya* **2**, 505 (1966).

97. S. Aiba, V. Moritz, J. Someya, and K. L. Huang, *J. Ferment. Technol. (Japan)* **47**, 203 (1969).

98. S. Aiba, K. L. Huang, V. Moritz, and J. Someya, *J. Ferment. Technol. (Japan)* **47**, 211 (1969).

99. T. L. Miller and M. J. Johnson, *Biotechnol. Bioeng.* **8**, 549 (1966).

100. I. Takeda, T. Iguchi, T. Kawamura, S. Horiguchi, S. Hayakawa, and S. Senoh, *Agr. Biol. Chem. (Tokyo)* **29**, 796 (1965).

101. I. Malek, in reference 5, p. 268.

102. M. Dostálek, V. Munk, O. Volfová, and Z. Fenel, *Biotechnol. Bioeng.* **10**, 865 (1968).

103. M. Dostálek, V. Munk, O. Volfová, and K. Pecka, *Biotechnol. Bioeng.* **10**, 33 (1968).

104. M. S. Iyengar, in reference 5, p. 263.

105. M. S. Iyengar and J. N. Baruah, *Brit. Chem. Eng.* **13**, 684 (1968).

106. K. Vadalkar, H. D. Singh, J. N. Baruah, and M. S. Iyengar, *J. Gen. Appl. Microbiol.* **15**, 375 (1969).

107. T. L. Miller and M. J. Johnson, *Biotechnol. Bioeng.* **8**, 567 (1966).

108. P. C. Ko and Y. Yu, in reference 5, p. 255.

109. S. Otsuka, R. Ishii, and N. Katsuya, *J. Gen. Appl. Microbiol.* **12**, 1 (1966).

110. J. Takahashi, K. Kobayashi, Y. Kawabata, and K. Yamada, *Agr. Biol. Chem. (Tokyo)* **27**, 836 (1963).

111. I. Tanabe, J. Okada, and H. Ono, *Agr. Biol. Chem. (Tokyo)* **30**, 1175 (1966).

112. T. Aida and K. Yamaguchi, *Agr. Biol. Chem. (Tokyo)* **33**, 1244 (1969).

113. G. Hamer, C.-G. Hedén, and C.-O. Carenberg, *Biotechnol. Bioeng.* **9**, 499 (1967).

114. D. L. Klass and J. J. Iandolo, *Am. Gas J.* 30–34 (1967).

115. D. W. Ribbons, *Chem. Ind. (London)* **1968**, 867–870.

116. F. Wheller, *New Scientist*, **1966**, 711.

117. P. S. Vary and M. J. Johnson, *Appl. Microbiol.* **15**, 1473 (1967).

118. S. A. Aiba, A. E. Humphrey, and N. F. Millis, *Biochemical Engineering*, Academic Press, Inc., New York, 1965.

119. H. J. Peppler, ed., *Microbial Technology*, Reinhold Publishing Corp., New York, 1967.

120. C. L. Cooney, D. I. C. Wang, and R. I. Mateles, *Biotechnol. Bioeng.* **11**, 269 (1969).

121. Z. Fencl, *Biotechnol. Bioeng. Symp.* **1**, 63 (1969).

122. T. A. Bott, and T. D. Brock, *Science* **164**, 1411 (1969).

123. D. C. I. Wang, *Chem. Eng.* **25** (18), 99 (Aug. 26, 1968).

124. V. F. Coty, *Biotechnol. Bioeng. Symp.* **1**, 105 (1969).

125. A. Kitai, H. Tone, and A. Ozaki, *Biotechnol. Bioeng.* **11**, 911 (1969).

126. E. A. Falch and E. I. Gaden, Jr., *Biotechnol. Bioeng.* **11**, 927 (1969).

127. J. C. Mueller, *Can. J. Microbiol.* **15**, 1047 (1969).

128. A. E. Humphrey, *Chem. Can.* **21** (1), 28 (1968).

129. N. Blakebrough, P. G. Shepherd, and I. Nimmons, *Biotechnol. Bioeng.* **9**, 77 (1967).

130. A. Mimura, T. Kawans, and R. Kodaira, *J. Ferment. Technol. (Japan)* **47**, 229 (1969).

131. E. J. Nyhs, J. P. Auquiere, N. Chiang, and A. L. Wiaux, *Nature* **215**, 177 (1967).

132. M. J. Johnson, *Chem. Ind.* **1964**, 1532.

133. C. McAuliffe, *Science* **163**, 478 (1969).

134. B. Erdsieck, *A Technological Study of Yeast Production With n-Alkanes as Carbon and Energy Source*, Thesis from Technical High School of Eindhoven, Netherlands, 1967.

135. A. J. C. Olsen, in *Continuous Culture of Microorganisms*, S. C. I. Monograph No. 12, Society of Chemical Industry, London, 1961.

136. J. Hospodka, in I. Malek and Z. Fencl, eds., *Theoretical and Methodological Basis of Continuous Culture of Microorganisms*, Academic Press, Inc., New York, 1966.

137. J. Y. Oldshue, *Am. Chem. Soc.*, 150th Meeting, Atlantic City, N.J., *September 14, 1965*.

138. W. H. Barthlomew, *Advan. Appl. Microbiol.* **2**, 284 (1960).

139. A. J. Rubin, *Biotechnol. Bioeng.* **10**, 89 (1968).

140. Brit. Pat. 1,168,833 (Oct. 29, 1969), B. M. Laine, J. C. Hondermark, and R. Goux (to British Petroleum).

E. R. Elzinga and A. I. Laskin
Esso Research and Engineering Co.

R

RESEARCH MANAGEMENT

This article was presented at the *Symposium of the American Institute of Chemical Engineers, St. Louis, Mo., Febr. 18–21, 1968*.

Creativity in a Systems Environment

The efficient management of large private capital enterprises is far from a hit or miss effort. But no matter how effective the management and financial-control systems of such enterprises, ultimately they flounder profit- and growthwise if the creative element disappears or becomes ineffective through improper use. Regardless of the amount of money spent on research, little return may be obtained if the process or product invented is neither fully developed in a technical and commercial sense nor made use of in an entrepreneurial sense through capital investment.

We are choosing here to define research broadly, ie, it includes research and also development, the latter encompassing the construction and operation of pilot plants together with engineering related primarily to process development and design. It also includes market development and technical services supplied by the research group. Thus, we refer to research and development (R & D) with the term "research."

This article is written primarily from the point of "petrochemicals" which are defined here arbitrarily as organic chemicals and polymers made from petroleum-based raw materials.

Creativity in a large modern business is an important research component, but seldom the controlling one in the forward movement of the corporation. To quote Reeves (1), "Research and development is only one component in the total business system." There are numerous well-known examples of companies that, although they had made the first major discoveries in new fields, either did not capitalize on these discoveries at all or succeeded far less well than other companies who licensed from the first developer or developed competing technology at a later date.

It would seem that the controlling element in maintaining profit and capital growth is the ability of the corporation to take rapid and practical advantage of creativity in all of its endeavors and in all of its functional groups that carry out the endeavors. It is too much of an oversimplification to call this good management. Such a statement is about as useful as saying that the secret of successful gambling is good luck. The question is: how do you change your odds?

The answer we suggest to changing corporate investment odds might be called "management systems engineering." By this we mean a systems approach to all aspects of capital enterprise management as opposed to the administrative approach that is implied, and very often taught, in the usual business administration school.

In the last analysis the function of management is to create a system or systems for investing and reinvesting capital that produces for the owners the desired balance among the near-term profit, long-term capital growth, and capital risk. If a system works and is legal, it really doesn't matter whether it follows conventional practice or not. Perhaps it is more likely to succeed (or fail) spectacularly if it does not.

Research Alone Is Not Enough. Let us examine this broad thesis as it may apply to the management of investments in petrochemical research. The principles developed here obviously apply to research in any industrial product field.

Money spent for research is an investment regardless of how it is treated taxwise. A return is expected and there is a limit to the amount that can be risked in view of the possible cumulative gain expected from a group of projects. Such a project group viewed as a whole should constitute a balance between defense for present businesses and a new business-venture program; the two together assist in the accomplishment of stated corporate profit and growth objectives.

In recent years increasing attention is being paid to what is often called "the efficiency of research." An article by Landau and Brown (2) is one of the most down-to-earth expositions on the subject yet to appear. In this case the authors can back up what they say with a solid record of achievement. A series of articles appeared in the *Institution of Chemical Engineers Symposium Series* (*London*) (3), including an outstanding paper by Docksey (4), who states: "A company's attitude to research will have at least as great an effect on research productivity as the competence of the Research Department itself. That attitude will find its expression in the research objectives."

Docksey's comment neatly summarizes a fact that many of us have suspected for a long time: It is not the efficiency of research workers per se that influences the cost-value ratio for corporate research but rather it is the overall system of management surrounding research and, of course, this includes research management as a part of that system, as well as a part of the research subsystem.

Merrill of Battelle Memorial Institute speaking to the Cleveland Society of Security Analysts put it this way (5): ".....the management of research and development is a complicated process. The decisions that must be made are difficult and surrounded with a great deal of uncertainty. Furthermore, if the whole system is to succeed, these decisions will involve other components of the business. The kinds of decisions that are made will reflect the corporate objectives as understood by R & D management. In my opinion, the success or failure of the R & D activity is largely dependent on: (*1*) the extent to which R & D management, as well as other managers in the corporation, understand the real corporate objectives as represented by the pattern of management decisions; (*2*) the degree of involvement of the whole structure in the research and development activity; (*3*) the degree to which the chief executive and other officers understand research and the whole process leading to research and development success."

This article is concerned with positive suggestions for improving the output of the elements supporting corporate growth research rather than with making a detailed analysis of how inefficiencies arise. Croxton (6) made a very useful analysis of the downward trends in research productivity, their possible causes, and has suggested new techniques for reversing the trend. It is sufficient to say that, in the author's opinion at least, such inefficiencies arise mainly because of the poor management systems used by research and overall management.

Purposes of Research and Research-Related Activities

The primary purpose of all research is not alike. Research projects are justified in different ways. In justifying research investments it is useful to separate research and research-related activities into five clearly distinguishable categories of purpose, as indicated in Table 1.

Table 1. Research and Research Related Activities

Research	Purpose
basic	the search for knowledge basic to corporate technical activities
defensive	improvement of present products and processes
	technical services which extend improvements to marketing, manufacturing, and engineering
growth	exploratory
	major development, including market development
related	corporate development planning and venture development (strategic software[a])
	protection and exploitation of technology through patents via licenses and/or know-how sales, exchanges, etc.

[a] Plans and programs to translate research results into profitable business system.

A generally similar categorization of research according to business purpose is used by Lenher of DuPont, a company generally acknowledged as one of the most successful ones in the efficient use of petrochemical research for corporate growth (6a).

Basic research is difficult to evaluate in dollars. It is equally difficult to decide just how much of it should be carried out. Sufficient to say that its evaluation and selection must be left almost wholly to the judgment of the research managers and scientists just as we leave to marketing managers the judgment of how much to spend on institutional advertising, the value of which they surely cannot measure quantitatively. Basic research, in the context of this article, is the search for basic information needed in the business to which a specific dollar value cannot be ascribed. One always needs a certain basic knowledge, not otherwise available, which greatly improves the cost–effectiveness of applied research. To separate basic research in a cost center is to deny to some extent its real purpose in an industrial undertaking. Separation as a cost center can be justified principally on the basis of providing data for projection of future basic-research budgets.

Some perspectives are now presented on the cost of research in relation to sales and in relation to new capital investment required to exploit research. It should be borne in mind that quoting research-cost figures is not without pitfalls due to the great variations in definitions and cost-accounting conventions related to research. To use our figures the reader must pay particular attention to the description of what the costs cover and to the overall definition given above. Even then our figures can only bracket a reasonable range of such expenditures. Such data ranges should not be used to decide how to set a particular research budget to accomplish a specific program. Instead one should work backwards from the objective desired through estimates of the time and money involved.

In the petrochemical industry basic-research costs for progressive companies are in the range of 0.2–0.4% of sales or about 5–10% of research costs. (These costs and those suggested subsequently are not the results of a detailed survey of all companies. They are, instead, selected figures based on the published expenditures of the larger, more progressive companies, and are believed to comprise the practices of the majority of the companies, making predominantly petrochemicals as defined above. These companies could truly be described as progressive in a profit- and growth-performance sense.)

The cost of *defensive research*, as defined in Table 1, is not necessarily completely under management's control, unless the corporation is the unquestioned leader in its field. Otherwise, if a company wants to keep up with competition and if there are no marked business-size, strategy, or research-efficiency disparities, the company expects to spend about the same proportionate amount on defensive research as the average of the more progressive companies in the field. For progressive petrochemical companies defensive research is generally about 2.0% of sales or roughly 40–60% of research costs, the lower spenders for research tending to do more defensive research in proportion to the total.

It is in the area of *growth research* that the systems approach takes on its greatest importance. From this point on we will deal largely with this third component of the research effort together with a closely related companion effort, the production of the "software" through which growth research should be programmed.

The growth-research cost figures for progressive petrochemical companies generally average about 1.0–3.0% of sales or 30–60% of total research over extended periods, the higher spenders for research tending to spend proportionately more on growth research. However, in some years, because extraordinary opportunities turn up, the cost of growth research could be as high as 5% or more of sales, a rate not often sustainable for longer than about a year. These peak expenditures can be magnified or hidden by the method of cost accounting used, ie, in setting the cutoff point between major developmental expenditures and what is considered as a part of early commercial operations. As indicated in Table 2, the exploratory portion of growth research runs 10–30% of the total in a reasonably balanced program.

Table 2. Research and Research-Related Expenditures of Progressive Petrochemical Companies Compared to Industry and Nation

Research	Av of ind. chemicals, 1966 net sales, %	Petrochemical companies, 1960–1970, net sales, %	1967 gross natl. prod. (7), %
basic		0.2–0.4	0.3
defensive		2	2.8[b]
growth[a]		1.0–3.0	
total	4.2[c]	3.2–5.4	3.1
related expenditures			
corporate development, and venture planning		0.2–1.0	
patent activities		0.1–0.2	
grand total		3.5–6.6	

[a] Including exploratory, at 10–30% of total in a well-balanced program.

[b] Including growth.

[c] Source: private communication, Stamford Research Institute.

The production of *software* constitutes a fourth kind of technologically oriented effort often grouped with the overall research function in companies growing rapidly through internal development but sometimes separated and placed in corporate development or some other group with a similar function.

When a corporate planning component is included with research, as we have done here, it usually has a strong mission of venture development described in an earlier article (7a), as follows: "This mission is concerned with putting together a workable concept of a complete business or business segment based on new technology or existing technology that has been adapted to the purpose at hand. In some companies the function of commercial development comes close to accomplishing this mission. At the venture development stage it is usual to select a single man as a project or program manager and this man will be charged with bringing together all of the necessary knowledge and human efforts to make the project a business success. In some companies the venture development mission is complete when the business concept has been clearly spelled out with all the necessary knowledge and strategic planning elements. In others, the venture development mission continues until the new business segment is running satisfactorily on a trial basis, after which it may be turned over to an existing operating division or serve as the basis for a new division."

While the fourth category does not involve experimental work or research "hardware," it does require significant funds and, therefore, cannot be overlooked for this and one other even more important reason. This kind of effort produces the "software" through which the systems approach to petrochemical research arises. Whether the software development takes place within the research group or outside of it, surely it is increasingly the key to effective research effort, assuming always that one is dealing with a research effort of a "critical mass" size, as well as with a research staff of at least average competence compared to competition within the petrochemical industry.

The cost of producing the increasingly important software used to optimize return on growth-research investment through good research planning and aggressive venture programming may run from 0.2–1.0% of sales, the higher figure being more likely in a company heavily oriented toward advanced applications of computers in engineering, in economic and risk evaluation, and in strategic planning through use of business models. The DuPont Company has for many years emphasized software activities in its somewhat unusual development department and has begun to adopt additional venture programming methods to create new business resulting from research.

In companies that have active and successful research programs much attention is paid to *patenting*, as well as to *licensing* in and out. Such companies recognize the futility and waste in trying to invent everything and they refuse to accept the "not-invented-here" theory as a research policy, as pointed out so forcefully by Landau and Brown (2). The cost of prosecuting patents domestically and abroad together with maintenance charges, licensing costs, litigation, etc, plus the reciprocal actions associated with taking licenses, can be an important expense item, as much as 0.1–0.2% of sales. These expenses do not include royalties paid or received as these are usually considered a direct cost of goods sold or as an item of "other income."

It is interesting to look at the cost of getting a patent. It probably costs around $10,000 (approximately one-fourth of a technical man-year with the necessary technician support and expenses) to get a reasonable idea for a patent disclosure. By the time enough exploration has been done to file a patent, an additional $50,000 to $100,000 will have been spent. Some 50–75% of the patents issued are filed by competent patent staffs after careful experimental work. Thus, it can cost $80,000–200,000 to get a single patent. In the United States the research cost per patent issued increased from $80,000 in 1956 to $170,000 in 1962 (6).

Research Investment Compared to Capital Investment. In the petrochemical industry, corporate yearly cash flow available for reinvestment after dividends is in the neighborhood of 10–15% of sales. If we consider the total research and research-related expenditure ranges in Table 2 and assume a 50% tax rate, then the ratio of cash flow available for reinvestment to these costs on an after tax basis is about 4–6, or say 5, on the average. Each new investment dollar produces on the average a dollar of sales. Thus, for every new dollar of sales produced, the industry has spent 20¢ after taxes or 40¢ before taxes on research and closely related activities. An inspection of capital spending in the petrochemical industry shows that, in fact, the industry's leaders invest approximately $2.5–3.5 for each dollar spent in research (before-taxes basis) whereas the figures developed above would indicate $2–3. The indications are that this ratio has declined rapidly from about 13 in 1956 to 5 in 1962 (6) and later to the range of 2.5 to 3.5.

The point is made to emphasize that the total research investments in our industry are large relative to the total money petrochemical companies have available for reinvestment. Therefore, it is critically important to use research expenditures in such a way that the chance of misdirecting effort is almost nil.

The Systems Approach to Research

It is difficult to give a capsule-type definition of systems approach that conveys any breadth of meaning. It is more useful to look at the probable evolution of the systems approach as a means of deriving a working definition of the term.

At the time of World War II and shortly thereafter, it began to be appreciated that technology had become so far advanced as to be able to provide on an almost certain basis two important capabilities:

1. Devices of almost any conceivable degree of complexity in relationship to their ability to carry out detailed instructions or programs upon sensing data from processes and environments; these devices could be incorporated into all manner of closed-loop control systems

2. Devices with almost unlimited power compared to any foreseeable task to be carried out.

Equipped with these two capabilities, one would think a military organization would overnight be able to overwhelm any enemy, but the military very quickly found out that these two capabilities alone did not lead to great accomplishments. To make effective use of these two previously unheard of capabilities, it was found necessary to look first at the specific mission to be accomplished. Starting with the mission, one worked backwards to define the component parts of an integrated system of devices and strategies that would work together to accomplish the mission under conditions approaching a strategic and/or economic optimum.

We will, therefore, define the systems approach to research management as one in which a corporate investment mission is clearly defined and agreed upon in the case of each proposed major developmental project in the growth category before a decision is made to undertake such major developmental effort. As Wilkinson says (8): "At Union Carbide we view a project as an overall business venture with the engineering an element of its first stages." It is understood, then, that the corporate mission is to bring into being a complete and successful business system for investing in the particular area of interest, not just to create good technology whenever possible. This means that the technological information developed must include not only sufficient information to design and build a plant, but also sufficient information to define the patent position, the marketing price-volume-time situation and all pertinent economic data needed to evaluate a 15- or 20-year business model for operating in the business area in question.

Furthermore, the systems approach includes reevaluation or stop-loss points at which a project can be aborted or deferred at the earliest time that the need for such a decision becomes evident. As phrased by Adler (9), we are talking about "a closed operating network in which the components will work together so as to yield the optimum balance of economy, efficiency, and risk minimization." This author also quotes from a definition of the systems approach given by the Rand Corporation to the U.S. Air Force (10) as follows:

"An inquiry to aid a decision-maker choose a course of action by systematically investigating his proper objectives, comparing quantitatively where possible the costs, effectiveness, and risks associated with the alternative policies or strategies for achieving them, and formulating additional alternatives if those examined are found wanting."

The systems approach to management in the chemical industry has been reviewed in some detail by Fedor (11). However, neither Fedor nor previous authors have stressed or proposed in specific detail a working systems approach to research management as related to the overall corporate-management systems.

We have emphasized the systems approach as defined above in the major development phase of the growth-research effort. In the long run, as the systems approach develops in a modern corporation, the exploratory research phase of growth research will certainly be caught up in the systems method. For example, if a well-defined corporate plan exists which is the result of a mature planning process, then the regions for exploration in research will tend to be fairly well defined as each new revision of the long-term plan is made. Also, the phasing of exploratory research along stop-loss points will be similarly made a part of the systematic procedure. For that matter, the defensive-research area, which uses a highly significant amount of corporate funds relative to net profits, will inevitably end up under systems scrutiny.

There will be those who object to the constant use of the words systems or systematic with regard to creative research. Indeed, research can be choked to death very easily by trying to put it on the basis of a set of routine procedures or project evaluation formulas. On the other hand, if we take the case of our successful mission of placing a man on the moon, we are dealing with one of the most specific missions for technological accomplishment that man has ever conceived. The moon mission incorporates every known systems approach technique. Yet hardly anyone would doubt that there was a tremendously creative technological effort in the accomplishment of this mission, in spite of the well-known systems atmosphere surrounding the project. (Ironically enough, we could go even further and say that the mission might not have been approved if it had been evaluated thoroughly in a systems analysis of national and world problems on a cost–benefit basis.)

Thus, if the wish is to stifle research, there are many ways of doing it effectively, including the overapplication of a systems approach. We are obviously not seeking a way to stifle research but a way to give it more decision-making capability and, therefore, more chance of success. By giving research more chance of success in the accomplishment of a defined mission, we do more to motivate research people than any other single factor, with the possible exception of monetary compensation. The motivational importance of accomplishment is something deeply ingrained in the experience of a seasoned and successful research director.

Project-Planning Matrix

We can structure the systems approach to research management through the use of a matrix, shown in Figure 1, of interrelated steps for treating a profitable business system around a technological development coming out of in-house research or from an outside source. These steps are carried out partly in sequence and partly in parallel. Our terms for the steps are somewhat arbitrary; hopefully they will in most cases be both acceptable and fairly obvious in meaning in the context of this article.

Clearly, a business venture starts with an idea, either a new internal one, yet to be developed, or a purchased idea already developed and more or less proven. In either case a venture has to be planned and staged for successive stop-go evaluation steps. Each idea has some chance of setting in motion three important sequences of business planning, economic evaluation, and decision making. These relate to the research area itself, to the venture-development area (an elegant name for the entrepreneurial steps leading up to a decision to invest), and to the commercialization stages necessary to translate ideas, experimental data, and venture plans into profit-making reality. This matrix of related steps is pictured in Figure 1.

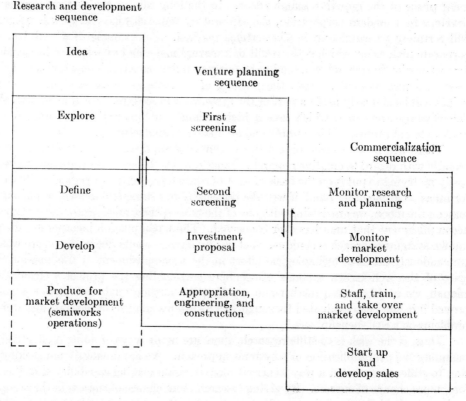

Fig. 1. Matrix of sequences of overlapping steps necessary to find a major investment project, decide on it, and put it into operation.

Before examining the properties and uses of this matrix, it is necessary to explain the meaning of the terms used. By **research and development sequence** we mean the entire sequence of steps normally carried out by a research and development group to convert a raw idea into a finished, developed product, and/or process ready for engineering and construction of a commercial plant. This sequence may include the production of material on an extended basis for market development purposes when either a relatively slow market-buildup is anticipated or when the market must be kept supplied between the end of a pilot development and the beginning of commercial production in order to keep the market alive, ie to prevent it from being taken over by competitive materials. While much additional information for engineering and process optimization may be obtained from a semiworks operation, this is not its normal or primary purpose.

At the beginning of the research and development sequence is the *idea stage*, ie the period required to crystallize an idea into a specific, identifiable, supportable project for further exploration. The idea stage does not necessarily involve new experimental work but may rely merely on previous basic research that has produced data of interest to the company. In other cases the idea may be structured entirely from information contained in the literature or it may simply come out of the combined experience of the inventor or inventors. To transform the idea into an identifiable, supportable project may require some further experimental work or it may require only analysis and calculations. Usually disclosures are carefully written up in notebooks with the view toward possible patent action, or, if the idea appears quite novel, the disclosures may be immediately acted upon by the patent group to the extent of starting searches.

The *exploration stage* is a matter of not only testing the idea, but also of trying to get a better notion of its scope. If, for example, the idea were that a certain catalyst system would produce crystalline homopolymers from a particular olefin, exploration of the idea in a laboratory could show the range of molecular weights that are apt to be produceable and could show whether the products are basically rubbery in nature or of a plastic nature. Other specific catalysts related to the first one tried would be explored in order to see if a wide number of specific catalyst systems existed. During this exploration stage much valuable information would be obtained for purposes of patent prosecution. Very likely actual patent applications would be prepared, ready for filing at certain strategic times, or, if the exploration work produced extremely promising results concerning what is obviously a basically new discovery, then patent filing might take place immediately.

At this point the **venture-planning sequence** is carried along with the research and development sequence. The venture-planning sequence is exactly what the name implies. It is a series of planning steps made in terms of specific, assumed business models to see if an embryonic idea shows promise of starting a future venture. Thus, during the exploration stage of research and development the venture-planning group may already be running a first screening of the idea to see what the costs of raw material and of building and operating a plant might be. Rather than attempting market research at this point, let alone market development, probably various levels of markets and prices would be assumed based on common-sense knowledge of the ranges in volumes of use and prices for similar materials. If the idea under exploration is simply a basically new process for producing an old material, the first screening can be done even more easily since the number of assumptions that have to be made are more limited.

If the research and development exploration and the *first venture-screening steps* have produced promising indications toward a future commercial venture, the decision may be to define a range of process conditions and a range of products which would give somewhere near optimum results for the reactions and products involved. This definition would be sufficiently specific and on a large enough scale to provide all the data within reason necessary to design a developmental or pilot unit.

In modern research the *definition stage* usually involves a "bench-scale pilot plant" or equipment often referred to as minipilot equipment. See Microplant in this volume. Because of the rapidly rising costs of research on the one hand and the greatly improved methods of analysis and experimentation on the other, there is an increasing trend toward the use of highly instrumented and automated minipilot plants to obtain most of the data needed to design a commercial plant when this is reasonably practical. In any event, the definition stage is being used to cut down the cost of reaching the next stage, whether this be through a pilot plant or directly to a commercial plant.

During the definition stage a second, more thorough screening of the project would take place. The objective of this *second screening* is to reach two very important decisions: (*1*) an in-principle decision to proceed commercially and (*2*) a decision to undertake major development in order to produce the data necessary to submit a specific investment proposal. The final decision to go ahead commercially must necessarily rest on the outcome of the development work which supports the investment proposal to be presented near the end of the development work. However, many companies make the decision to undertake major development work when they really have not thought through whether they will go ahead commercially in the near future or ever. The result is that many successful major development projects turn out to be failures insofar as investment by a particular company is concerned. In other words, for policy reasons or because of extremely poor planning, a company spends major sums of money on major development work even if there is a strong possibility that they will not use the results no matter how good they are. This kind of planning is no longer tolerable in the petrochemical industry. Therefore, our point is that the second screening of a research and development project during the definition stage should settle once and for all whether the company will go ahead commercially, provided only that the development work is technically successful and that the data confirm that an economically attractive investment can be made. It is perfectly allowable to let the second screening stage overlap the development effort if the development effort is susceptible to staging on a stop-loss basis. But if the development step requires the immediate construction of a million-dollar pilot plant, then the second screening stage had better be complete before the investment is made as it would then be too late to turn back without a serious loss.

It can be argued that availability of funds is another "subject to" that must be met. Management philosophies differ on this point. If the project is not disproportionately large, compared to the average of all projects, some management systems fund it, regardless if its return is adequately higher than the cost of capital and if the project had been selected (as it should have been) to fill out a well-planned corporate growth objective.

The *development stage* is pretty well understood as involving a pilot plant to produce engineering data, as well as to prove that a suitable product can be produced. Furthermore, this stage must produce enough of the material to test markets and to confirm the expectation that the product will have a sufficiently large market at an acceptable price. The purpose of this kind of market development is merely to verify the assumptions and predictions made previously in market research and during the first screening stage based on small amounts of material available from the laboratory. It is not normally the actual development of sales in volume because there is not sufficient material available.

Preparation of the *investment proposal* should begin as early in the development work as the data permit. To make an investment proposal we normally need preliminary engineering, costing 1–2% of the expected first cost of the first plant. The basis for this preliminary engineering will have been laid out in the second screening stage using data from the experimental defining of the process and product, but the engineering and costs of estimating cannot be done in a precise way until the data begin to flow out of the pilot plant. By combining the preliminary engineering and investment-proposal step with the development step we make sure that the development effort leads to the right data to optimize the engineering and, therefore, the investment proposal. Often the pilot plant is shut down before engineering is started and it is found that costly startups are necessary to fill in data that were forgotten.

In the ideal case of systems management of an important entrepreneurial project, the semiworks plant would start producing, if such a *semiworks stage* is necessary, just before the development unit shuts down so that there is a constant supply of product until the commercial plant starts up. If a semiworks operation is necessary for marketing reasons and if the market buildup is slow enough, it may be possible to delay bringing the commercial plant on stream deliberately in order to save money. Running the semiworks plant at a high percentage of its capacity is often cheaper than running the commercial plant at a very low capacity.

In the **commercialization sequence** the management group responsible for the profit center that will operate the project should be very much a part of the planning, and come in not later than the second screening stage of the venture-planning sequence. Preferably the commercial management group would have been contacted at the first screening stage to make sure there were no policy or prejudice reasons for not wanting to back the project if it later turned out to be a good one from a return standpoint. For that matter, the commercial group should be *monitoring the research and planning* on all growth projects, whether at the exploratory or major developmental stage. Obviously, as soon as a product is available for market development work, the commercial group should either *monitor the market development* work or participate in it. In some cases the commercial group is able to do the market development work, although often they are too busy with present products to give a new one the proper kind of market-development attention. Hence, we suggest caution in any management arrangement that turns early market development activity over to a management group that is primarily concerned with producing and selling today's products. On the other hand, it is equally unwise to leave the commercial group out entirely.

At some point, either in the late stages of market development or during the production period of the semiworks plant, the commercialization group should take over the market development and use this activity as a training base for the product manager and marketing staff. The semiworks facility or the pilot plant also provides a good opportunity to *train production supervisors* and quality-control people for use in the plant.

When the great day for the *startup of the commercial plant* finally comes, some three to fourteen years after the first faint "eureka" from the "white-coat boys," a team of very well qualified people can be put together for plant startup from the development (or from the semiworks) group, the engineering and construction group, and the already pretrained commercial group. At the same time there will exist a product manager and a number of trained marketing people who can take the first on-specification commercial product to key customers to get their earliest possible approval.

Often many months of very costly delays are experienced because not enough attention is paid to the fact that customers have to approve products from a new plant before they purchase. This is particularly true of empirical products such as polymers and much less true of a pure chemical, such as polymerization-grade butadiene. Even in the case of pure chemicals—a good case in point is polymerization-grade isoprene—the customer may want to make time-consuming polymerization runs before he orders tank-car quantities. The amount of approval time required can be staggering, when the length of time required to measure accurately the catalyst-consumption rate in the pilot-plant polymerization runs, plus the compounding studies on the product, plus the road test or other acceptance test on the manufactured article are added. If your petrochemical project has been well planned by the systems approach, all such measurable time requirements will have been figured into the project schedule so that, costly as these steps are, they will not be unanticipated costs.

Properties and Use of Planning Matrix. There are two important properties of our planning matrix (see Fig. 1) when it is picturing an actual project: (*1*) there is a continuous exchange of information back and forth horizontally across any boxes that overlap. This exchange may take place through or around the venture-planning group, but usually both communication channels are used; (*2*) the degree of overlapping of the sequences can be shifted up or down vertically. In extreme cases the ventures group may screen none of the research output until it reaches the costly major-development stage. In other extreme cases the sequences may take place for all practical purposes in series rather than in parallel. It is noted, however, that competition in our industry is forcing exactly the opposite trend. It is becoming more and more common to undertake detailed engineering (stage 4 of the venture sequence) well before development is completed. This may increase engineering cost but saves valuable time in reaching the market and may, therefore, improve the economics of the overall venture.

The step of *appropriation, engineering, and construction* has been placed in the venture-planning sequence for very compelling reasons. Often the venture planners take care of creating the production facility for all practical purposes, especially when the product is new to the company and no trained manufacturing group exists at the time of the investment decision. In such cases one group must have firm control or a rather costly hiatus can quickly develop in which capital overruns and project delays develop. Often no clear-cut responsibility can be assigned for these. It is strange that we sometimes exert the least control of an important project just when the greatest amount of money is being spent. Even a small matter, such as providing the full investment capital at the start of the project instead of as needed, can cost a half million dollars in extra interest on an 18-months project of modest size. Controlling construction expenses on a past-history basis rather than on a projected-in-advance basis can cost even more since nothing can be done to change the facilities or procedures to lower costs once the money is spent.

The cost of construction of chemical process plants in the United States is competitive with the costs in foreign countries simply because our engineering and construction management is so well organized and managed. We have the highest labor costs in the world, as well as equally high salaries for engineers and supervisory management personnel. These high labor and salary costs are reflected also in all of the labor, materials, and equipment that enter into a construction job. The systems approach of the large, high-quality U.S. engineering and construction contractor is almost surely responsible for our competitive status.

In order to get the maximum advantage in selecting and controlling the contractor, the management of this function, as suggested already, belongs more properly in the highly systems-oriented venture-planning sequence than in the normal commercialization sequence, although the situation can vary greatly from company to company. By choosing the contractor on a carefully planned basis and systematically comparing the different offerings to see which proposal has the best cost–effectiveness ratio, much money can be saved either in the plant itself or in the manufacturing costs resulting from the type of plant that is being built. Sometimes scheduling in such a way as to utilize an engineering and construction contractor at just the right time can give appreciable saving. Finally, as suggested earlier, careful control of the engineering and construction contract with advance forecasting of costs permits changes to be made in advance in anticipation of cost overruns which is the reverse procedure from that often employed. In many cases changes are made by the manufacturing staff after a contract is let with the resulting unavoidable increases in construction costs. Frequently such changes are more a matter of whim or preference on the part of the people who operate the plant than they are studied changes justified on a cost–benefit basis.

Time and Cost Experience for Planning Sequences. Fairly accurate ranges of time and cost for each of the steps in our matrix can be estimated. The assumption is made that we are dealing with the development of a basically new process to make a known product or a new process to make a new product. The newness may be relative to a company's previous knowledge and experience. We are not dealing with simple process improvements, such as the substitution of continuous reactors for batch, a new catalyst for an old reaction, a new solvent for extraction or azeotropic distillation, or anything of this kind.

Tables 3–5 present general estimates of time and cost for the project stages in the three sequences of effort. They can both be used safely to bracket the extremes that are apt to be realized in practice. If these extremes are exceeded considerably on the high side, there is serious question as to whether the overall planning has been done competently. For example, a substantial overrun in the development stage may indicate not enough effort in the definition stage. A serious construction overrun,

Table 3. Research and Development Sequence to Invest $10 Million

Sequence	Time, yr	Cost, million $
ideate	0.1–1	0.01–0.05
explore	0.3–0.5	0.05–0.1
define	0.5–2	0.25–0.5
develop	0.5–2	0.5–3
operate semiworks	1–2	self-supporting
	2.4–7.5[a]	0.8–3.7[b]

[a] Total.

[b] Total, ie 8–37% of initial fixed investment.

Table 4. Venture-Plan Sequence to Invest $10 Million

Sequence	Time, yr	Cost, million $
screening		
preliminary	0.1–1	0.01–0.02
final	0.3–1	0.1–0.2
investment proposal	0.1–0.3	0.001–0.01
appropriation, engineering, and construction	1–2	0.03–0.05[a]
	1.5–4.3[b]	0.14–0.28[c]

[a] Cost of owner's planning and controlling only; excludes know-how payments or advance royalties.
[b] Total.
[c] Total, ie. 1.5–3% of fixed investment.

Table 5. Commercialization Sequence to Invest $10 Million

Sequence	Time, yr	Cost, million $
monitor		
research and planning		0–0.01
engineering and market development	2–4	0.01–0.02
staff and train production and sales, take over		
market development		0.1–0.2
startup and sales development	0.3–2	0.5–2
	2.3–6[a]	0.6–2.2[a]

[a] Total.

unless a deliberate risk is taken on a crash basis to save time, indicates poor planning on the part of the owner's or contractor's management or both.

With regard to the times and costs for the various stages of the research and development sequence, a given company can quickly put together out of its own experience figures covering basically different types of research and development that are normally undertaken by such a company. For example, the development of new polymer products (from known monomers) that have to be market developed, shows a generally similar pattern of times and costs. On the other hand, to make known chemical intermediates from basic petrochemical raw materials establishes a different pattern of time and cost for various stages. Once these patterns have been established, they can be used very successfully for planning and estimating on proposed projects. Hughes (12) discusses the probable cost to bring a major petrochemical research project up through the definition stage.   His figures are in good agreement with those in Table 3. Hughes' article deals quite usefully with planning and evaluation methods for starting the research and development sequence.

Obviously we are not saying that the research and development sequence must cost up to 37% of fixed investment or that it is a better development if the cost is higher or lower. We are only saying that costs in the range of 10–40% of the initial fixed investment may be incurred. The research and development group should constantly strive to lower its costs through improvements of efficiency. Often one reason costs get so high is that no one expects them to be so high in advance and a program gradually gets out of control from a cost standpoint before anyone knows it. Then it is too late to do anything about the money already spent.   The decision to continue or drop the project obviously rests on the money that will have to be spent in the future, regardless of what has been spent already. But when the project is finished, the record will show the total cost and if it is unreasonably high, this will stand as a black mark against the research group's managerial and technical efficiency.

It is not of great importance whether the exact stages mentioned here are employed in research and development planning. The idea stage might be telescoped with the exploration stage or the first three stages might be telescoped together as exploration, leaving only development and semiworks as the additional stages. The degree of staging adopted will be the consequence of experience which shows what kind of stages are most helpful.

The four stages involved in venture planning are probably the minimum number of stages required. The names of the first three stages could be changed to suit a given company's definitions. The real difference between preliminary and final screening lies in the degree of precision of all economic estimates. In the final screen ing stage one is seeking that level of precision which is acceptable in an investment proposal.

The investment-proposal stage is dealing with the problem of getting a business proposition explained properly. Presumably all of the figures have been arrived at in the final screening work. In the investment-proposal stage these figures must be reprocessed and rearranged and explained so that the higher levels of management, including the Board of Directors, can fully understand what the project is about and what it will do for the company financially, as well as what it will entail in the way of risk.

As discussed below, there are some very sound reasons for putting the appropriation, engineering, and construction stage in the venture-planning sequence. The word appropriation is included in this stage because the process of expending the money, which has been committed as a fixed amount for a given project, is more than merely writing checks. The money should be taken down in such a way that the financial costs incurred are minimized. At this stage the creative assistance of competent financial people should be sought and their advice should be followed.

In many companies the commercialization sequence starts only a month or so before a new production facility is ready to start up. Then there is a last-minute rush to as semble personnel to run a plant they know nothing about to make a product that is practically unknown to the marketing group expected to handle it. This kind of last-minute planning can lead to deplorable financial losses through long drawn out startups and delays in securing customer approval.

Ideally the profit-center group that is responsible for a proposed investment should be monitoring the project proposal at an early stage of research. There can be con siderable latitude as to the stage at which this monitoring should begin, depending upon the organization and communication network in a given company. On a major project, such as the development of a new polymer requiring considerable market development to establish uses, this monitoring should begin at least a year before the commercial plant comes on stream and would be better if it begins sooner. Cine, et al. (13) and Buell (14) give a good exposition of this monitoring process during the development of Marlex (registered trade name, Phillips Petroleum Co.) high-density polyethylene. See also reference 15, covering the development of polybutadiene rubber from laboratory scale through commercial production.

However, we do not recommend using our generalized figures except for early planning estimates when no better data are yet available. It is the method that is important.   Once planning is put on a systems basis that clearly recognizes and quantifies the overall effort and coordination required to accomplish the desired results, time and cost estimates specific to the project can be made with desired precision. More precise estimates take longer and cost more; a balance must be struck between the cost and the value of precision.

If we summarize the generalized results, as shown in Table 6, we get a comparative picture of times for parallel vs series planning.   It takes at least three to four years under either planning method to put together a major project with in-house technology being developed.

Table 6. Summary of Venture-Development Times

Assumptions	Σ Time to reach breakeven, yr	
	Series planning	Parallel planning
semiworks step		
with	4.2–13.8	3.7–11.5
without	3.2–12	2.7–9.5
no semiworks and		2.1–7.8
overlap of engineering and development		

At the high end of the time requirement to put together a major project and commercialize it, the differences between parallel and series planning are much larger, about 2.5 yr as opposed to 0.5 yr at the low end.   But while the differences at the extremes are not so important, it is in the time performance on projects lying between the extremes that competitive success most often lies.   Being first into a market or being second or third instead of fifth or sixth can make a tremendous difference in the overall profitability of a venture due to market share, cost, and time for getting the market share and weighted average product price realized.

Taking the Gamble out of Research

Research is usually considered a gamble.   This is true up to a certain stage in research, but not beyond.   At the idea stage, ie ideas that are actually written up as specific disclosures, we can expect one in every ten or twenty ideas to lead to exploratory work.   At the exploratory stage perhaps one in five projects survives.   We may expect one in two or three to get beyond the definition step.   But from this point on, the success ratio should be very nearly 1.0 to 1.0.

For those who want to mitigate the gamble both as to technical result and, often more important, as to time, there is the licensing route, which may be a cheap way into a new field.   For a really valuable opportunity through license, a good price has to be paid and one should try to get the first one granted, if at all possible.   Within reason, the least important decision in licensing is the exact price; the important one is to decide if the technology is proven and competitive.   Usually the bargaining is inversely proportional to the importance of the issue involved, as in many matters of bargaining.   Licenses should not be substitutes for a good research staff; a good staff should be augmented with good licenses and faster growth and more profits will result.

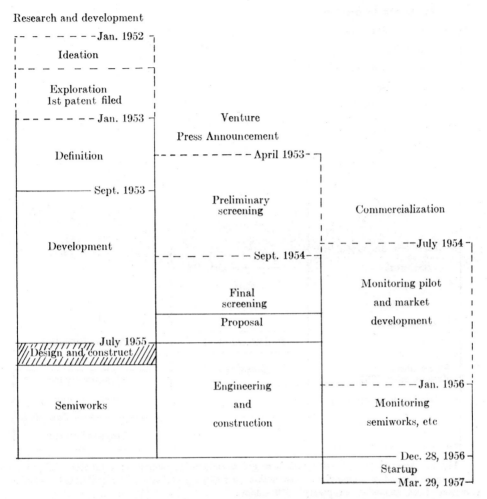

Fig. 2. Approximate planning matrix of project Marlex; total time, 5.3 yr; estimated cost—excluding engineering, construction, and startup—$4 million; estimated cost for first commercial plant, $12 million.

No large petrochemical company can afford to develop all of its technology; there is probably more waste through duplication than can be afforded indefinitely by industry.

With the modern venture-analysis methods available it should be possible to know that a major project is worth an all-out developmental effort before the money is spent. From a technical viewpoint we know at the definition stage that the process gives certain yields and qualities and we have an economics estimate that is within ±10–20% on return, making reasonable assumptions as to the market. It could be argued that there is still the market development risk in the case of a new product. This risk, however, should be limited at this stage to questions of when or how fast, not any longer a question of whether.

In its defensive and basic research, a research department is essentially trying to

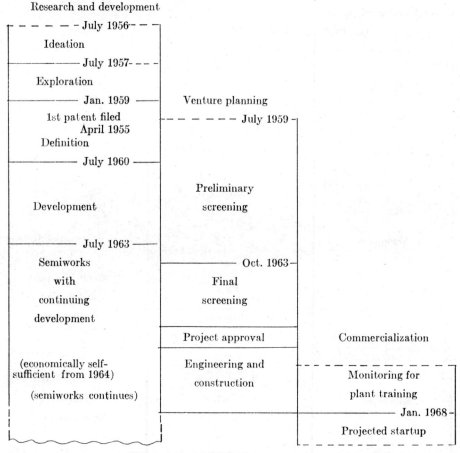

Research and development

- July 1956 -

Ideation

- July 1957 -

Exploration

- Jan. 1959 -   Venture planning

1st patent filed
April 1955   - July 1959 -
Definition

- July 1960 -

Preliminary
Development   screening

- July 1963 -

Semiworks   - Oct. 1963 -
with   Final
continuing   screening
development

Project approval   Commercialization

(economically self-   Engineering and
sufficient from 1964)   construction
                                         Monitoring for
(semiworks continues)   plant training
                                         - Jan. 1968 -
                                         Projected startup

Fig. 3. Approximate planning matrix of polybutadiene development; total time, 5.8 yr; estimated cost—excluding engineering, construction, and startup—$2–3 million; estimated cost of first commercial unit (25,000-ton capacity), $10 million.

augment the profitability of an existing business system. In growth research we are trying to create a new complete business system for making a satisfactory return on a new investment with a return-growth-risk balance which fits the entrepreneurial policy of the sponsoring company. Most of us in research do not realize that this is what we are trying to do and we have seldom had in the past a high degree of the responsibility for the complete system. Looking ahead we should do all of our research planning, project selection and progress evaluation with a complete system in mind. The systems approach to research management starts with an answer and works backward to see what component parts of a business system must be found, developed, assembled and operated to make the system produce a satisfactory return on the required investment.

Some people will argue that this is a rosy dream of how to manage research and not a reality. They will say that you can scarcely project what you can do about an idea before you know what the idea is. But ideas are not investment projects, they are just ideas. To get from an idea to a concrete proposal for a major capital in-

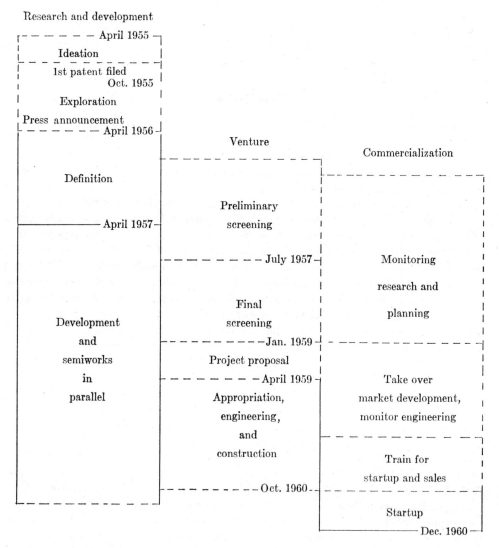

Fig. 4. Planning matrix for a family of entirely new petrochemicals; total time, approx 12 yr (8 yr to economic self-sufficiency); estimated cost—excluding engineering, construction, and startup—$3 million; estimated cost of first commercial plant, $1.35 million (with estimated sales of 5 million/yr running at capacity).

vestment requires a great deal of human effort and money as we have tried to show. In order that research pay off for an industrial concern, an investment position must be taken. The cost to develop three major new projects to the investment decision stage may be as high as the cost for the first plant needed to carry out one of these projects. It becomes amply clear, then, that one really cannot afford to carry out any major development projects unless one is quite sure that investment or sale through licensing will occur if the outcome is successful. Furthermore, one can afford very few failures on major developments out of those actually attempted. At the idea level of business-system construction one can afford nine out of ten failures for each one that is carried to the next stage. As each succeeding stage of the business-system development is reached, the proportion of failures that can be tolerated in relation to total attempts decreases rapidly.

Conclusions

The suggested rather remarkable ability to avoid costly major development campaigns that fail or go unused is certainly not possible unless a tight overall corporate planning system exists with research, venture, and commercialization planning well integrated. Otherwise the wrong product and/or process is inevitably developed now and again at very great cost.

These facts concerning the systems approach to research and venture management as a part of the overall corporate-management system are not so new as often forgotten and seldom practiced conscientiously. There is a relatively new development in a few petrochemical companies of an adequately trained staff of sufficient size to actually handle, with the aid of computers, the complex techno-economic planning effort needed to keep ahead of management's decision needs. The ability to view the whole problem as a function of its rapidly evolving and changing parts, as well as in relation to a constantly moving-target objective, is what we are after. The basic objective may, and usually does, remain the same, but the optimum strategic detail of the objective can change a great deal even in the three to five years required for a first-class R & D group to complete a development like Marlex high-density polyethylene (13) or cis-polybutadiene rubber (15). In the high-density polyethylene contest a number of companies who had bet on the homogenous catalysis approach were far outdistanced by the superb time, process, and product performance of the Phillips Petroleum Company.

It is easy to stick with platitudes about individual research creativity or to the effect that it only takes one really good research idea to create a new venture, etc. These platitudes, even though based on important truths, are largely beside the point. A well-selected, well-explored research idea, handled by a professional management team using a systems approach, is not going to be a worse idea for this. And, more important, the probability that the idea will lead to a successful commercial venture is likely to be increased from one out of ten to nine out of ten.

Figures 2–4 illustrate the planning-matrix approach, laying out the basic scheme of evaluations that must be carried out both in parallel and in series as the three main management sequences concerned with the operation on a major new product. If these evaluations are performed as a whole, even with the most primitive data and with the most drastic shortcuts, on each project that gets beyond the idea stage an ever-tightening, closed-information loop will be produced relating the evolving steps to the ultimate business objective. With a little patience and hard work we may yet produce a computer read-out in the president's office from which he can relate each new eureka emanating from his expensive laboratories to the expected financial return on the projects under study. Who knows, we may even one day reach that long sought utopia when not even the most harassed research director can any longer ascribe his harassment to the old familiar "management just doesn't understand research."

Bibliography

1. E. Duer Reeves, "Industrial Research—A Kind of Business Strategy," *Chem. Eng. News* **43** (43), 92–98 (Oct. 25, 1965).
   E. Duer Reeves, "Industrial Research as a Corporate Function," *Workshop Syllabus on Management of Industrial Research*, Sect. I, Industrial Research Institute, Inc., New York, 1968.
2. R. Landau and B. Brown, "Making Research Pay (Management Oriented Topics)," *Inst. Chem. Engrs. Symp. Ser.* **1965,** (7) 7.
3. "Productivity in Research," *Inst. Chem. Engrs. Symp. Ser.* **1963,** (13).
4. P. Docksey, *The Objectives of Industrial Research*, in reference 3.
5. R. L. Merrill, *The Wall Street Transcript* **15** (5) (Jan. 30, 1967).
6. F. C. Croxton, *New Techniques for Increased Research Productivity*, in reference 3, p. 8.
6a. S. Lenher, "Organization and Management of Science," *Res. Management* **12** (6), 425–436 (1969).
7. *Chem. Eng. News* **45** (33), 15 (Aug. 7, 1967).
7a. C. A. Stokes, *Res. Management* **9** (6), 339–349 (1966).
8. *Am. Inst. Chem. Engrs. Symp., St. Louis, Mo., Febr. 18–21, 1968.*
8a. L. A. Wilkinson, *Project Management—Getting the Job Done*, in reference 8.
9. L. Adler, "Systems Approach to Marketing," *Harvard Business Rev.* **1967** (May–June), 112.
10. E. S. Quade, ed., *Analysis for Military Decisions*, The Rand Corp., Santa Monica, Calif., 1964, p. 4.
11. W. S. Fedor, "Management by Systems," *Chem. Eng. News* **45** (36), 123–124 (Aug 28, 1967).
12. E. C. Hughes, "One Key to R & D Success: The Right Kind of Proposal," *Res. Management* **12** (1), 43–55 (1969).
13. M. R. Cine et al., "Pilot Plant Development of a Polyethylene Process," *Chem. Eng. Progr.* **54** (2), 245–254 (1961).
14. K. C. Buell, "The Development of Marlex," *Res. Management* **4** (4) 245–254 (1961).
15. D. S. Hall and J. W. Davison, *Process Development of Cis-4 Polybutadiene*, in reference 8.

C. A. STOKES
Consultant

S

SLAGCERAM

Slagceram is a material of the glass-ceramic type, produced by the fine and uniform crystallization of glass made from metallurgical slag. Slagceram was developed by the British Iron & Steel Industry Research Association (BISRA), with the aim of making slag, a major steel-industry by-product, more profitable by upgrading it into a higher-value market, and of doing so on a scale that would deal with a significant proportion of the slag output (reckoned in millions of tonnes, t) (1,2). So far, the large-scale aspects have not been realized, and the material is in commercial production only on a small scale. The smallness of the scale of production means that production costs are high, and the market is restricted to special wear-resisting shapes. Materials similar to slagceram have been reported from the U.S.S.R. (3) and Japan (4) but the scale of production is not known.

Slags and Their Utilization

Pyrometallurgical operations generally yield two molten materials: metal (or a metal-rich phase) and slag. The slag contains most of the nongasifiable impurities from the metal-bearing feed and the fuel, plus the nongasifiable part of the fluxes added mainly to obtain metal of the required purity. The metal is the main product, and it is therefore sound economic sense to make its quality and rate of production the main factor, hence the slag properties which influence its utilization are subordinate, and any changes usually have to be made after the slag has left the main metallurgical process. A wide variety of slag-utilization technologies have been developed to cope with this situation, and a review of those used for steel-mill slags has been published (5).

Though it can be made from various slags, slagceram is mainly associated with those from the iron blast furnace. This plant produces anything from about 0.25 to about 1.2 t of slag for every tonne of metal. The amount depends mainly on the purity of the iron-ore feed, the composition of its impurities, and the ash and sulfur content of the coke fuel. These factors not only have a direct effect, but also an indirect one because they govern the amount of flux (in almost all cases a lime- or magnesia-rich material) that has to be charged into the furnace to ensure that metal purity is right and that the production rate is not restricted by the viscosity of the slag at the temperatures prevailing in the critical parts of the furnace. These requirements and the growing tendency to import purer materials from large mining undertakings mean in practice that iron blast-furnace slags are rather similar in composition wherever they are produced (Table 1).

The relationship of slags to minerals in the CaO-SiO_2-Al_2O_3 system and certain other technologically important materials is shown on the liquidus diagram (Fig. 1) at 5% MgO. For U.K. slags the melilite is mainly a gehlenite–akermanite solid solution; many other phases are found, not all of which appear in Figure 1.

Table 1. Chemical Composition of Iron Blast-Furnace Slags from Different Parts of the World

Location	Composition, wt %						
	CaO	SiO$_2$	Al$_2$O$_3$	MgO	FeO	MnO	S
U.S.A., Great Lakes	40.2	38.5	7.9	11.3	not known	0.3	0.9
U.S.S.R., Siberia	39.3	37.4	12.5	5.6	0.5	0.4	0.6
Japan, Honshu	41	34	14.7	5.8	not known	0.7	0.8
U.K., Teesside	37.9	31.3	17.9	6.8	0.6	0.9	1.9

In addition to the components shown in Table 1, iron blast-furnace slags some-times contain alkali–metal oxides, derived mainly from coke, up to a maximum of a few percent.

Blast-furnace slags are occasionally (because of local economics or managerial decisions) treated as wastes and dumped; and, in very unusual circumstances they have been treated as a coproduct with iron in the sense that the attainment of the com-position needed for a particular slag use has dictated furnace operation. For the most

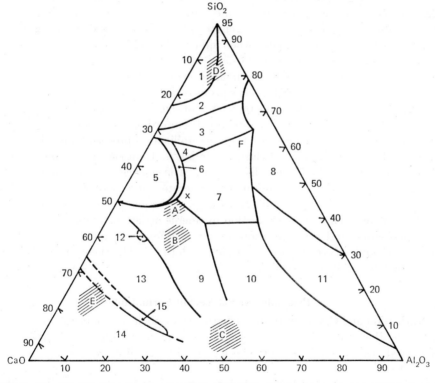

Fig. 1. The liquidus diagram for the CaO–Al$_2$O$_3$–SiO$_2$–MgO system at 5 wt % MgO. Main fields shown by numbers: (1) two liquids; (2) cristobalite, SiO$_2$; (3) tridymite, SiO$_2$; (4) clino-pyroxene, ca CaMgSi$_2$O$_6$; (5) pseudowollastonite, CaSiO$_3$; (6) wollastonite, CaSiO$_3$; (7) anorthite, CaAl$_2$Si$_2$O$_8$; (8) mullite, ca Al$_6$Si$_2$O$_{13}$; (9) melilite, Ca$_2$MgSi$_2$O$_7$(acermanite)–Ca$_2$Al$_2$SiO$_7$(gehlenite); (10) spinel, MgAl$_2$O$_4$; (11) corundum, Al$_2$O$_3$; (12) merwinite, Ca$_3$MgSi$_2$O$_8$; (13) dicalcium silicate, Ca$_2$SiO$_4$; (14) lime, CaO; (15) tricalcium silicate, Ca$_3$SiO$_5$. Position of typical slagceram shown by X; ranges (not necessarily at 5 wt% MgO) of other technologically important materials shown shaded: (A) acid blast-furnace slag; (B) ordinary (U.K.) blast-furnace slag; (C) high-alumina cement; (D) commercial glass; (E) Portland-cement clinker; and (F) copper slag.

part, however, slags are considered a by-product that the furnace operators are happy to see the last of, at a price sufficient to cover the slag-handling costs in the steelworks and with no interference with furnace operation.

Slags from the iron blast furnace already have many uses. For example, if allowed to cool in air they crystallize and can be crushed to form an aggregate suitable for use in concrete, as a roadstone, a filter medium, or a feed component in glass or Portland-cement making. Slags treated with water–air–steam mixtures form a pumice-like material for use in light-weight concrete. They can be cast into shapes, such as paving blocks, which crystallize during the annealing and slow cooling needed to prevent cracking. Finally, if a stream of molten slag is treated with a large excess of water the cooling is so rapid that a mainly glassy material is formed, which has the useful property of being easily transformed into a cement by fine grinding and addition of lime. All this can be done without changing the composition of normal iron blast-furnace slags.

With suitable composition adjustments, blast-furnace slag can be transformed into a glass so stable that it does not crystallize even with the slow cooling needed with large masses to prevent cracking, or during several hours' annealing. This is one way of raising the value of blast-furnace slags and has been used to produce glass articles of attractive, generally jet-black appearance, but rather poor mechanical properties (Mohs hardness $4\frac{1}{2}$–$5\frac{1}{2}$, rupture strength 39.2 MN/m^2) and chemical resistance (rapid formation of colloidal deposit when immersed in acid) (1).

Production of a stable glass from slag is of more interest as a step on the way to slagceram. What is needed here is virtually complete crystallization of the glass to form fine (of the order of 1–20 μm) crystals of reasonably uniform size. It is on these features that the specially desirable properties of slagceram depend. Fine and uniform crystallization is not achieved with ordinary slag or ordinary slag glass. This is mainly because in materials of such compositions crystallization proceeds from the surface or from gross discontinuities in the glassy material, ie, from crystallization centers that are relatively scarce and unevenly distributed. The essence of slagceram technology is that the slag glass has a composition that generates large numbers of crystallization centers (or nuclei) uniformly in any given region of the glass before appreciable crystal growth starts on them. This separation in time is achieved by making the two processes (nucleation and crystallization) occur at different temperatures and imposing a suitable schedule of temperature variation with time. The theory behind these processes is outlined in the next section.

Principles of Slagceram Formation

Nucleation and Crystallization. The theory of nucleation and crystallization has, along with other scientific aspects of slagceram, been treated in considerable depth by Davies et al., whose paper also provides a good bibliography (2). Only an outline will be given here.

As in any supercooled liquid, random fluctuations in slag glass continually give rise to more-ordered regions, ie, potential nuclei. The special glasses from which slag-ceram is made are designed to generate high concentrations of nuclei at a temperature (which turns out to be close to the annealing temperature) so low that the mobility of atoms and atomic groupings in the glass is insufficient to allow the considerable re-arrangements that accompany crystal growth to take place at significant rates. When the temperature is raised the mobility increases and crystals grow on the nuclei. The nucleation and crystallization processes have their own temperature ranges in which the rate rises to a maximum and then falls off. It should be noted that in nucleation the rate is measured as the number of nuclei produced per unit volume of the glass in unit time, while in crystallization it is the rate of crystal growth. The ranges overlap, but for slagceram-type crystallization to occur the maxima must be well separated in temperature.

In a supercooled (ie, metastable) glass, the separation of more-ordered regions, which can be regarded as a step on the way to the stable crystalline state, would be expected to be accompanied by a decrease in the free energy of the system. The decrease is proportional to the volume of the region, or, for a spherical region, to the cube of its radius. On the other hand, the separation of the region will produce a new surface, accompanied by a free-energy increase proportional to the surface of the region, or, for a spherical region, to the square of its radius. The netfree-energy change of the system due to the separation of the region will thus be the sum of two terms, a negative one proportional to the cube of the radius and a positive one proportional to the square. In accordance with the normal behavior of functions of this type the effect of an increase in the radius from zero will be first to increase the free-energy change (ie, the free energy) of the system to a maximum and then to reduce it. In other words, only those regions whose radii exceed that corresponding to this maximum (the critical radius) will have a tendency to grow, ie, they are nuclei. The smaller, transient regions are known as embryos. In this discussion the embryos and nuclei have been assumed to be spherical. This is reasonable because a sphere has the lowest surface–volume ratio, ie, the lowest contribution to the positive surface-dependent free-energy-change term. The general considerations would, in any case, apply to regions of other shape.

Nucleation of the type considered is called homogeneous, ie, it occurs in a homogeneous phase. There may, however, be discontinuities already present in the phase. Such discontinuities (themselves formed by a homogeneous nucleation and crystallization process) will, if their atomic arrangement is suitably related to that of the nucleating material, facilitate formation of the nuclei.

Theoretical treatment of nucleation leads to an equation giving nucleation rate as a function of temperature in which the free-energy-change maximum, corresponding to the critical radius, occurs together with the activation free energy for the assimilation of atoms or molecules across the interface of the new phase. Each of the free-energy changes is in an exponential term, the net result being that with increasing temperature the rate rises to a maximum and then falls away.

In addition to the nucleation mechanisms considered above, the new phase may separate spontaneously by spinodal decomposition, leading to glass-in-glass separation. It can occur when the normal spontaneous local fluctuations in composition result in a decrease in the free energy of the system, which is the case, eg, if a foreign network-forming ion present in the glass causes sufficient distortion of the main silicon–oxygen–silicon bonds.

To turn now to the question of the rate of growth of crystals on the nuclei. The main factor here is the rate at which the slowest-moving component involved in crystal growth moves. This factor is related to the viscosity and temperature in such a way that, as with nucleation, the crystal-growth rate increases with rising temperature to a maximum and then falls away. As already noted, slagceram formation depends on adequate separation in temperature between the nucleation and crystallization rate maxima.

Transformation of Molten Glass into Slagceram Articles. The overall transformation of the molten slagceram glass into the finished slagceram object, involving homogenization, shaping, nucleation, and crystallization, can now be discussed in terms of the nucleation and crystal-growth processes just considered. The transformation is illustrated in Figure 2, which shows how the temperature, content of glass, number of nuclei, and size of crystals (all in arbitrary units) change with time.

Before A, the batch of slag and additives (discussed later) in the right proportions have been brought into the fully molten condition. From time A to B the composition of the molten glass is being made homogeneous, an operation that, with viscous glasses, can take a long time in the absence of stirring. From time B to C, the temperature of the glass is being adjusted to that required for shaping (this temperature will depend on composition, shaping method, and shape). The shaping operation is carried out at C, and the shaped article is then cooled to the nucleation temperature range, which is reached at D. An alternative temperature schedule between C and D would be to cool the shaped article to room temperature and reheat it later to the nucleation temperature range; but such a schedule involves more danger of cracking, as well as increased process time, and would only be used in special circumstances. Nucleation starts at D and gathers speed as the temperature approaches that for the maximum rate (reached at time E). Nucleation dies away by time H, but before this has been reached crystals have started to grow (at time G) on the nuclei. Before G the material appears virtually completely glassy; after G the nuclei become increasingly enclosed in crystals. Between times F and I, the temperature is being raised to that (reached at time I) giving the maximum crystal-growth rate. At time J, when very little glassy material remains, the final cooling of the article starts; it can be carried out faster than would be possible with the corresponding uncrystallized article.

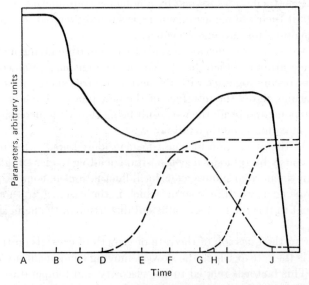

Fig. 2. Variation of temperature and other parameters during slagceram production. Legend: temperature ————; proportion of material in glassy state —·—·—; number of nuclei ——— ——; size of crystals -----.

Alteration of Slag Composition and Effects of Melting Conditions.   The changes needed in chemical composition to make slagceram from iron blast-furnace slags will now be discussed.   A general point is that, because the slag is usually the cheapest of the components and because the making of any addition involves processing costs, the change is made as small as possible.   The composition change to convert the slag into a stable glass can be implemented by adding silica and/or alumina, ie, materials that are network formers (in the glass sense).   Silica is cheaper and (possibly in combination with minor additives) generally gives a glass of better liquidus temperature for melting and assimilating additives, and better viscosity temperature-dependence for shaping by some of the methods established for ordinary glasses.   Silica addition also alters the nature of the minerals, favoring those that make the mechanical and chemical-resistance properties of slagceram better than those of slag.   Finally, silica addition increases the viscosity of the glass sufficiently to prevent the uncontrolled nucleation and crystallization characteristic of slag.   The slagceram composition to which most attention has been given is that obtained by adding about 30 parts by weight of silica sand to 100 of the "U.K., Teesside" slag listed in Table 1.

In addition to the change in the content of the main components, the transformation of slag glass into slagceram requires the presence of a few percent of minor components to produce nuclei at the right stage.   These nucleating agents can be any one, or various combinations of, a wide variety of materials.   They include transition-metal oxides and sulfides, which, since they are already present to some extent in the slag, are of special interest for slagceram.   The nucleating agents studied in greatest detail for slagceram are a combination of chrome ore (about 47% Cr_2O_3) with titania, and various forms of iron oxide.   Because iron oxide is cheap, present in slag, and plentiful in steelworks, this is the preferred nucleating agent.   Like many other nucleating agents, the above are sensitive to the state of oxidation of the glass, being most effective under reducing conditions.   For this reason, additions of coke are often beneficial, and the conditions under which the glass was melted can have a decisive effect on the extent and type of crystallization in the final product.   For example, for slagceram nucleated with iron oxide the melting conditions can, with the same nucleation and crystallization schedule, give slagceram of two distinct types or a glass that fails to crystallize properly, probably because it does not have enough nuclei.   The general effect is that with short times in the molten state a dark, fully-crystallized slagceram is obtained; as the time molten is lengthened the glass shows an increasing tendency to give an incompletely crystallized or even uncrystallized product; with still longer times molten (on a laboratory scale), a slagceram relatively light in color begins to appear; and with even longer times there is again a tendency for crystallization to be incomplete or absent.   It is both scientifically and technologically interesting that addition of carbon to the melt enables the time molten with which slagcerams can be obtained to be extended on both laboratory and larger production units.   In fact, melts held in the furnace so long that the glass shows no tendency to form slagceram can be restored by coke addition, and the over-cooking–restoration cycle can be repeated.

The mineral phases present in the dark- and light-colored slagceram are the same: clinopyroxene is the main component with, sometimes, small amounts of melilite. However, in the dark material the crystallization takes the form of spherulites, in the light it is mainly dendritic.   The nucleation in the dark material is probably heterogeneous, and homogeneous in the light.   The effect of the time the glass is held molten is most probably due to the influence it has on the state of oxidation under the normally oxidizing furnace atmosphere necessary for high fuel efficiency. The influence of changes in furnace atmosphere does not make itself felt quickly, because the high viscosity of the slag glasses retards mass-transfer. An example of this is that when the slag is taken in the liquid state direct from the highly reducing conditions of the blast furnace rather than as a solid made by crushing air-cooled slag, a very oxidizing atmosphere in the melting furnace (where the sand and nucleating agent are added) can be maintained without loss of effectiveness of nucleating agents.

The melting conditions, through their effect on nucleation, also influence another important technological factor, the ability of the shaped slagceram-glass object to maintain its shape during the nucleating and crystallizing heat treatment without mechanical support. With the right conditions, the loss of shape (slumping) is negligible, probably because a skeleton of crystallized material, with a softening temperature greatly exceeding that of the glass, is produced while some of the glass is still strong enough to resist the forces due to its own weight and surface tension.

Although a single slag composition was used for the bulk of the slagceram development work, it has also been established that other iron blast-furnace slags and slags of completely different type could be used. It is usually possible to predict what modification to the process would then be required. The slag compositions studied include at least the following approximate ranges: $CaO:SiO_2$ ratio 0.9–1.4; 15–21% Al_2O_3; 5–35% MgO; 0.6–1.1% FeO; 0.4–1.1% MnO; 1–1.8% S. With various nucleating agents, degrees of oxidation, and other factors, a considerable range of slagceram colors can be obtained, eg, orange, brown, or off-white.

Slagceram Production

Pilot Plant. The original development work on slagceram was done on melts up to about 9 kg in mass. The melts were produced from solid components in indirectly heated salamander crucibles, which, by maintaining reducing conditions, facilitated the subsequent crystallization of the glass. Conditions were in fact so reducing that there was some loss of iron oxide nucleating agent through its reduction to metallic iron.

Production on a pilot-plant scale was first aimed at producing slagceram in quantities sufficient for the reliable evaluation of its properties; later stages of the work were aimed at developing at least one technology for the commercial production of slagceram on a small scale and at getting pointers to the best technology for large-scale commercial production. The feed for the bulk of the pilot-scale work consisted of 13–19-mm pieces of cold slag (the U.K. Teesside slag of Table 1), ordinary builders' sand, and 50–15-μm nucleating agent. The mass ratio of slag to sand in most batches was 100:30, but special batches of higher sand content were occasionally made to study the effect of higher silica content on the production technology and properties of slagceram. The batch usually contained a few percent of nucleating agent, coke sometimes also being added at the rate of about 10% of the batch mass to maintain the relatively beneficial reducing conditions in the melt with oxidizing atmospheres in the direct-fired furnaces.

In the main pilot-plant work two procedures were used for melting the batch. In one, it was first charged into a cylindrical rotary furnace closed at one end (a design based on the Kaldo steel-making unit) and fired with an oxy-propane burner. The rotation of the furnace greatly accelerated the melting of the solids and homogenization of the melt.   Although a brief treatment in the rotating furnace was sometimes all that was needed for a satisfactory slagceram glass to be produced, the melt was usually transferred into a glass-tank type of furnace for a further period of homogenization and general conditioning.   The degree of homogeneity needed for an opaque, crystalline material such as slagceram is, of course, considerably less than for a clear glass.   Nevertheless, care had to be taken that no significant numbers of solid particles remained, since these would have produced uncontrolled, coarse crystallization, and that variations in the composition of the liquid should not be sufficient to lead to regions of different crystallization characteristics in the final articles, since they might then have cracked or distorted during the crystallization heat treatment.   In the second procedure the batch was charged directly into the tank (ie, nonrotary) furnace.

The mass of a batch melted varied from 0.1 to 1 t.   One of the factors was that, because the slagceram glass was dark and viscous it was difficult with normal top heating to get a uniform temperature down a deep bath without stirring (this difficulty arises in the glass industry, but not with clear, colorless glasses).   The bath depth in the tank furnaces was therefore normally limited to 75–100 mm, which is considerably less than in normal glass tank furnaces.   A greater bath depth with slagceram glass could be used in another pilot-plant furnace, operated by the Steetley Organization Research Department, Worksop, U.K., which was of the continuous type and had bottom as well as top heating.   Coke was found to be unnecessary with this furnace, probably because of the greater bath depth and consequently relatively smaller surface exposed to the furnace atmosphere.

In addition to the above procedures, based on cold slag, tests were carried out with molten slag direct from the blast furnace.   Such a technology would have many advantages for large-scale slagceram production.   The molten slag was taken from the furnace in a special insulated pot and poured into one of the rotary furnaces held upright.   No special difficulties arose in making the sand and nucleating-agent additions to the molten slag and good slagceram was obtained despite the normal variations in the composition of slag leaving the blast furnace.

The techniques used on the pilot-plant scale for shaping the slagceram glass included pressing, rolling, and casting.   These are used in ordinary glass making, but had to be modified to take into account the steeper variation of viscosity with temperature of slagceram glass (ie, its shortness) and its low thermal conductivity and dark color.   Rolling gives plate of good surface finish and flatness, but special attention is needed in the heat-treatment stage if flatness is to be preserved.   Pressing can be used for fairly complicated surface contours on articles of simple basic shape.   Casting in sectional metal molds is suitable for somewhat more complicated shapes, while for very complicated shapes, or for shapes needing rough surfaces, sand molds are best.

For the next stage of heat-treating the shaped articles to give nucleation and crystallization, the pilot plant had equipment of various types: batch gas-fired and electrically heated furnaces, and a continuous electrically heated kiln. Because of the sensitivity of the process to temperature, the uniform maintenance of the correct temperature or temperature distribution was a main design requirement. Furnace atmosphere influences the surface finish to some extent, and electric furnaces or muffle-type gas furnaces, which give a greater degree of control, would be preferable where this is an important factor.

The material nucleated with iron oxide was relatively free from distortion of the slumping or twisting type, and was treated by a simpler schedule in which nucleation was obtained without specific nucleation treatment and the rate at which the temperature was raised to the crystallization range was less critical; furthermore the crystallization temperature could be varied over a wider range and the crystallization time reduced. Since the heat-treatment stage is one of the major cost items in the overall conversion of slag to slagceram, this was an important consideration and led to the choice of iron oxide as the nucleating agent in the commercial process.

Variations in composition and heat-treatment schedule enabled a wide range of slagceram crystal sizes to be obtained. The crystal size was an important factor in deciding whether a given article distorted during heat treatment, and had a great influence on the mechanical and chemical properties of the final product.

Commercial Production of Slagceram. Slagceram is produced by C.B.P. Engineering & Construction Limited, Blackburn, Lancashire, U.K. under the registered name of Basramite. The company became interested in slagceram because one of its activities is the design, fabrication, and installation of plant components for service under highly abrasive conditions. This is a small though expanding market, and, from the slagceram point of view, still represents only a small extension of the pilot-plant scale of production. The present facilities are in fact modeled on the BISRA pilot plant, and have a melting potential of about 1 t/day.

The melting furnace is direct fired, with a bath about 1400 mm long and 760 mm wide. The design provides for operation with a bath about 13 mm deep, ie, a total charge of about ½ t, the minimum charge for a bath of adequate depth being about 300 kg. The charge is cold, crushed slag, sand, and nucleating agent. The furnace is fired with five gas–air burners directed across the top of the charge, the time to melt and homogenize a 300 kg charge being about 4.5 hr. No heat recuperation is provided, and the fuel consumption is therefore high. The temperature of the homogeneous melt is checked with an immersion thermocouple, and if it is correct for the particular shape and shaping procedure, the furnace is tilted to run the melt through the tapping hole into a lined intermediate ladle, from which it is poured by hand into the shaping facility. To prevent distortion, the more complicated shapes are left in molds during heat treatment, which adds considerably to costs. Sectional metal molds are used for flat shapes and CO_2-hardened sand–silicate molds for more complicated shapes.

The heat treatment, involving nucleation at about 700 and crystallization at about 900°C, is carried out in a gas–air-fired furnace 900 × 1200 × 1200 mm in internal dimensions. The crystallized articles are removed from the furnace at about 400°C and packed in vermiculite for the rest of the cooling period.

Basramite linings have been installed, and given service at least as good as cast basalt, in various plants: for example, in cyclones for the dirt-extraction system in a paper pulp line or for a line conveying nonpulverized ash in a boiler-firing system. Basramite has also been used as part of a venturi in a pulverized-fuel ash disposal system, and as an elbow lid for a pulverized-fuel burner at a power station.

While in many applications Basramite is a replacement for cast basalt, it is sometimes used for shapes that cannot be made in that material. As experience is gained, and the advantages of wear-resisting linings in general become better known, the market for Basramite will increase. However, it is not likely that the wear-resisting-linings market will ever rise enough to enable production costs to be reduced to what could be expected from, eg, a plant making slagceram tiles at the rate of 300 t/day.

Large-Scale Production of Slagceram. Production of slagceram on a scale large enough to bring the price into the mass-market range could be carried out in various ways. The choice would depend on the type of product and on whether the works were located near enough to the metallurgical plant for the process to be based on liquid slag.

A likely flowsheet is shown in Fig. 3. In view of the advantages of the higher production rates and lower fuel consumptions obtainable when slag is charged into the melting furnace in the liquid state, it is likely that slag will arrive molten in ladles, which will then be tipped either into a holding vessel or directly into the furnace. With a furnace of the continuous glass-tank type, slag flow from the holding vessel or ladle would be automatically controlled to give a steady flow into the furnace, the solids being dispensed by continuous weigh feeders from their bunkers. Alternatively, the tank furnace could be preceded by two or more relatively small rotating furnaces in which batches of liquid slag and the solid components would be quickly converted to a somewhat heterogeneous liquid for final homogenizing and conditioning in the tank furnace. In this alternative, batch-proportioning feed systems would be used, and the capacity of the rotary furnaces would be suitably related to that of the slag ladles. In addition to the main feed materials the melting furnace would also receive the reject material from all the stages of the production flowsheet in the absence of other uses (for which, eg, defective slagceram-glass articles could be crushed and the product heat-treated to produce slagceram aggregate). Some subdivision of the melting furnace to provide a final zone for adjusting the temperature of the molten slagceram glass to the best level for the shaping operation might be advisable. The molten glass would then be dispensed via feeders to the shaping plant. This plant would resemble a mechanized foundry if relatively complicated shapes were aimed at; pressing and rolling would be used for simpler shapes and flat products. For slagceram-aggregate production the shaping plant might consist of a granulating unit, or a foaming plant if a light-weight product were desired.

Heat treatment of the shaped articles could be carried out in a continuous kiln with suitable temperatures in different zones. For articles of specially precise dimen-

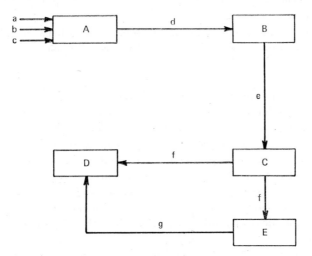

Fig. 3. A flow sheet for the large-scale production of slagceram. LEGEND: (a) slag; (b) sand; (c) nucleating agent; (d) slagceram glass; (e) shaped slagceram-glass article; (f) shaped slagceram article; (g) shaped slagceram article with special finish; (A) melting furnace; (B) shaping machinery; (C) heat-treatment furnaces; (D) shipping bay; and (E) finishing plant.

sions a shaping operation might be included at a point in the heat-treatment cycle where crystallization was not quite complete (the softening temperature of the uncrystallized material is much lower than that of the crystallized). The heat treatment could be used for simultaneously enameling articles to produce eg, specially chemically resistant surfaces or colors outside the normal range obtainable. Although the hardness of slagceram makes polishing an expensive operation, the product looks very decorative, and, since slagceram can be made in relatively thin sheets, might be competitive. The polishing would be carried out, probably with diamond paste, in a finishing shop, which would also contain the diamond wheels needed for cutting slagceram to special shapes or to specially close dimensional tolerances.

Properties of Slagceram

The main test program on the physical, mechanical, service, and chemical properties of slagceram was carried out on material nucleated with chrome ore and titania or iron oxide and made on the pilot-plant scale.

The apparent density, 2.9–3.0 Mg/m^3, is somewhat higher than that of the slagceram glass. The difference would have been greater but for the development of a small degree of porosity during crystallization. The total porosity, determined by microscopic measurements on cut sections, was about 10%, but only about 5% was open porosity (measured by the amount of water absorbed after holding of the test piece in vacuum). Very much lower values of open porosity have been observed. Observations on pore-size distribution were made on one batch of slagceram by the mercury-intrusion method at pressures up to 12.4 MN/m^2. Most pore sizes fell into the 0.1–0.3 μm and 50–100 μm ranges. These values were obtained if the pores were assumed to be cylindrical and the contact angle with mercury 140°. The specific heat at room temperature is 0.71 kJ/kg K, the coefficient of linear expansion 5 $\times$ $10^{-6}/K$ and the thermal conductivity (Lees Disc) 1.3 W/m K. The resistivity of slagceram is $10^{8.5}$ Ω-cm before, and $10^{7.9}$ after, a standard damp heat aging test in which the test piece is kept at 38–42°C and a relative humidity of 90–95% for four days.

The scratch hardness of slagceram on Mohs' scale is between 8 (topaz) and $8\frac{1}{2}$ (emery); the indentation microhardness (Vickers diamond pyramid) about 750. Scratch resistance is probably a more valuable technical index. It was found by a modification of a test method used for paints, a load of 12.8 N being applied through a pyramidal diamond point resting on the specimen sliding beneath it. The average width of scratch produced on slagceram was less than half that on either glazed or quarry tiles. The excellent resistance of slagceram to abrasion and general wear has been demonstrated in service tests, some lasting over four years, eg, in coke chutes; relatively short tests on an industrial floor area exposed to the passage of heavy, steel-wheeled trolleys, radiation from a furnace that kept the average floor temperature at about 90°C, and spillage of molten slag, showed that slagceram was greatly superior to concrete and ceramic tiles. The coefficient of friction between steel and new slagceram tiles is considerably lower than that for unpolished new ceramic tiles, but equal to that for worn polished ceramic tiles. No quantitative information is yet available on how the friction coefficient of slagceram changes with continued wear.

In addition to the service tests and the laboratory friction test, two types of laboratory tests for resistance to abrasion were used. One is the Morgan-Marshall test, devised for testing refractories, in which the mass lost by the test piece under the action of a blast of fused-alumina particles is determined. The loss with slagceram is much less than that of granite, fusion-cast alumina, and fusion-cast basalt. Even incompletely crystallized, porous slagceram, though somewhat poorer than the basalt, was better than hard-fired firebrick or china-clay brick. In the second type of abrasion test the test piece is held under load against a rotating disc onto which an abrasive is being fed; the loss in weight after a set number of disc revolutions is determined. Two abrasives, one consisting of rounded sand particles, and the other of sharp corn-emery particles, were used and gave somewhat different results. With sand the weight loss for slagceram was about 50–70% of that for fusion-cast basalt and about 31–44% of that for granite. With corn emery the average of the range for slagceram showed no significant advantage over the basalt, but retained its former advantage over granite. An important point from the service aspect is whether the measured abrasion resistance is a characteristic of the surface layer (which would eventually be worn away) or of the bulk of the material. The tests with sand showed very little difference in weight loss from a chill-cast surface and from an internal, ground surface, but both were considerably less than from a surface cast exposed to the air.

The crushing strength of slagceram, measured on a standard 76.2-mm cube of slightly irregular shape, is approximately 207 MN/m^2. This would probably have been exceeded with a regular cube. Slagceram has good resistance to concentrated static loads, no measurable indentation being produced in several weeks by a load of about 2.3 kN applied through a steel sphere (ball bearing) 12.5 mm in diameter. The resistance of slagceram to concentrated impact loads measured by a standard method, in which a 4.54-kg weight with a rounded end is dropped repeatedly onto the test piece from increasing heights, was equal to that of ceramic floor tiles (failure at 50 mm). In general, the resistance of slagceram to impact is relatively good by ceramic, but not by metal, standards.

The modulus of rupture (bending test) of slagceram depends considerably on the method of preparation of test pieces as well as on the slagceram itself. For example, three-point-loading tests on pieces cut from a tile of annealed slagceram nucleated with iron oxide gave values of 107 ± 22 MN/m^2, those for annealed individually-cast rods being 135 ± 18 MN/m^2. The poorer values and large scatter for machined test pieces are in line with experience in the testing of glasses and ceramics, which are very liable to develop stress-concentrating surface imperfections during the machining process. The values for cast test pieces can therefore be taken as more representative of what can be expected from slagceram articles in service. In fact, with ceramic-type materials there is no completely satisfactory alternative to the use of complete articles as the test piece.

The properties quoted refer to slagceram in the massive state. Those of light-weight (foamed) slagceram have not been properly evaluated yet, but published values for the corresponding U.S.S.R. product (6) suggest that densities of 300–700 kg/m^3, compression-strength values of 6–14 MN/m^2 and thermal-conductivity values of about 0.13 W/m K would be obtainable.

The properties of slagceram specifically for building applications were also determined. The impervious nature of smooth slagceram makes adhesion to ordinary cement mortar rather poor; better results are obtained with rough surfaces. With a filled epoxide adhesive, however, a very strong bond is obtained even with smooth slagceram, failure occurring in the epoxide rather than at the interface. Slagceram has excellent long-term constant-temperature stability, the expansion observed being at the limit of sensitivity of the test method. Room-temperature tests lasting 12 weeks at 100% relative humidity on slagceram tiles that had been sprayed with suspensions of the spores of four of the more common molds affecting buildings showed that only isolated growths, which do not impair appearance, were present. Slagceram specimens have been exposed for over five years at a variety of atmospheric corrosion test sites covering the main aggressive types of atmosphere (urban, industrial urban, industrial marine) and at a test site where the specimen is immersed at high tide and exposed at low. In no case has any significant deterioration been observed.

The resistance of slagceram to various liquids has been compared with that of earthenware tiles. In concentrated and 50% sulfuric acid there is no difference between the materials; in 10% sulfuric and in concentrated and dilute (10%) nitric, hydrochloric and acetic acids the resistance of slagceram was less. In concentrated and 5% caustic soda and distilled water there was no difference between the two materials, and in 10% sodium carbonate, 5% ammonia, tap water, and 20% magnesium sulfate, slagceram had the higher resistance. The tests lasted two years for slagceram nucleated with chrome ore and titania and 6 months for slagceram nucleated with iron oxide. Long-term tests have shown that slagceram has good resistance to spillage of milk and beer.

It is impossible to compare the properties of slagceram precisely with those of the parallel products (slag sitalls) developed in the U.S.S.R. because test conditions have generally not been specified and discordant values have been quoted (possibly because they refer to different grades, or even to material made not from slag but from the expensive special glasses used for glass-ceramics). According to a publication (6), the mechanical properties appear to be similar to those of slagceram, except that the crushing strength of slag sitalls is said to be higher; slag sitalls have been formed into various articles, including tiles, sheet, corrugated sheet, pipe, electrical insulators, sanitary ware, and light-weight blocks; a range of colors can be produced. Production is believed to be on a large pilot-plant scale for tiles and sheet, and on a smaller scale for other shapes. The reported cost of slag sitalls, about $39–$67/tonne of sheet (7), are difficult to interpret because they depend on the doubtful meaning of the official ruble rate of exchange and because the rate of production they refer to—a dominant factor—is not specified.

Comparison with the Japanese materials is also difficult, but it appears that their bending strength is higher than those of either slagceram or slag sitalls (4).

Appendix 1. Conversion Factors

To convert	Multiply by
tonne (t) to short ton	1.10231
MN/m^2 to lbf/in^2 (psi)	145.04
N to lbf	0.22312
mm to in.	0.03937
μm to in.	0.03937×10^{-3}
kg to lb	2.20462
Mg/m^3 to lb/ft^3	62.43
kg/m^3 to lb/ft^3	62.43×10^{-3}
kJ/kg K to Btu/(lb)(°F)	0.23885
W/m K to Btu/(hr)(ft²)(°F/ft)	0.5778

See Units in this volume.

Bibliography

1. S. Klemantaski and B. Kerrison, *Chem. Ind.* **15**, 1745 (1966).
2. M. W. Davies, B. Kerrison, W. E. Gross, M. J. Robson, and D. F. Wichall, *J. Iron Steel Inst.* **208**, 348–370 (April 1970).
3. I. I. Kitaigorodskii, *Zh. Vses. Khim. Obshchestva im. D. I. Mendeleeva* **8**(2), 192 (1963) T. E. Goliuf et al., Proizvodstvo shlakositallov, Vol. II, MPSM, Ukr.S.S.R., 1968.
4. U.S. Pat. 3,170,780 (Feb. 23, 1965), T. Takahera and A. Tsuji (to NGK Insulators Ltd.).
5. S. Klemantaski, *Steel Times Ann. Rev.* **1969**, 158.
6. I. I. Kitaigorodskii, 'Sitalls' in A. T. Tumanov, ed., *Encyclopedia of Modern Techniques*, Vol. 3 II, Izdatel'stvo Sovetskaya Entsiklopediya, USSR, 1965, pp. 169–171.
7. *Chem. Proc.* **12**, 78 (June 1966).

S. Klemantaski
British Steel Corporation
(Corporate Laboratories)

SOLUBILITY PARAMETERS

Solubility parameter concepts have found wide and increasing use in many areas of industrial and academic endeavor because of the simplicity with which significant predictions can be obtained. These concepts are generally applied to solvent selection in the industrial community, while the calculation of solubilities and thermodynamic properties have concerned the more theoretical workers. Hildebrand's initial work was based on the solution of nonelectrolyte solids in nonpolar solvents, although such topics as gas-in-liquid solubility, liquid–liquid miscibility, metallic solutions, polymer solutions, and correlations with surface phenomena and critical properties were discussed (1, 2). Burrell (3–6) applied the solubility parameter to polar solvents and polar polymers, and Hansen (7–12) has described relationships with organic and inorganic pigments, proteins, and biological materials, and even inorganic salts. Based on these results, it appears that a solubility parameter study can provide systematic information on physical interactions for any material which interacts suitably (dissolves, swells, or absorbs) when contacted with a sufficient number of solvents (energy probes). It is assumed that there is a close similarity between the cohesive energy densities of the interacting, well-defined solvents and that of the substrate material, and thus a solubility parameter may be assigned to the material.

Historical Background

Hildebrand and Scott designated the energy of vaporization per cubic centimeter as the *cohesive energy density* (*ced*) and its square root as the *solubility parameter*, δ. Thus,

$$\delta = \left(\frac{\Delta H_V RT}{V}\right)^{1/2} = \left(\frac{\Delta E_V}{V}\right)^{1/2} = (ced)^{1/2} \tag{1}$$

where ΔH_v and ΔE_v are the heat and energy of vaporization, respectively, and V is the molar volume. As suggested by Crowley (13) the unit $(cal/cm^3)^{1/2}$ is designated as a "hildebrand." This parameter is important in the estimate of the heat of mixing for two nonpolar liquids, given by Hildebrand as:

$$\Delta H^M \approx \Delta E^M = \phi_1\phi_2(x_1 V_1 + x_2 V_2)(\delta_1 - \delta_2)^2 \tag{2}$$

The heat of mixing ΔH^M and the energy of mixing ΔE^M are equal when there is no volume change on mixing. The ϕ's are the volume fractions of the liquids, and the x's are their mole fractions.

Consideration of the free energy equation

$$\Delta G^M = \Delta H^M - T\Delta S^M \tag{3}$$

quickly shows that the negative ΔG^M values necessary for solution to occur can be achieved by reducing ΔH^M, which in turn means that δ_1 and δ_2 should be similar in value. The entropy of mixing ΔS^M can be assumed to be positive, and generally does not receive much attention, at least from the practical approaches to using solubility parameter theory.

Burrell (3–6) was the first to apply the solubility parameter to practical (polar) systems. He grouped a large number of solvents into three classes according to their "low," "medium," and "high" hydrogen bonding capacities, and used these groupings together with the solubility parameter itself to aid in solvent selection in the paint industry. Following this lead, various refinements were proposed to quantify a hydrogen bonding parameter (14, 15), and ultimately a three-parameter system using the solubility parameter, the dipole moment, and a hydrogen bonding parameter (based on shifts in the 4-micron band for methyl deuteroxide) was proposed (13, 16).

Other approaches to account for polar bonding have been developed along the lines proposed by Van Arkel (17) and Hildebrand (17a), and particularly by Prausnitz and co-workers (18–20). The basis of this approach is that the cohesive energy arises from both the permanent dipole molecular interactions and the London "dispersion" type atomic interactions. The latter have been estimated as being equal to the energy of vaporization of a homomorph at the same reduced temperature, T/T_c where T_c is the critical temperature. The homomorph of a polar molecule is a nonpolar molecule having very nearly the same size and shape as those of the polar molecule. Each solvent is assigned a polar solubility parameter and a nonpolar solubility parameter. This division has been used to estimate solubilities (18, 20), to aid in solvent selection for extractions (19), and to calculate activity coefficients (21). A somewhat similar approach to division of the cohesive energy was described by Gardon (22) in which a fractional polarity was estimated.

In any of these systems, as well as the one proposed by Hansen, described in more detail below, a proper estimate of the nonpolar contribution is important. The homomorph concept appears to be the current best choice, since use of ionization potentials in various potential equations does not account for the effects of inner shell electrons. On the other hand, this approach tacitly assumes that the hydrocarbon homomorph's entire cohesive energy is due to London forces, which is not exactly true. This is an area for future research.

If it is assumed (7–12) that the cohesive energy, ΔE, arises from contributions from hydrogen bonding ΔE_H, as well as permanent-dipole–permanent-dipole interactions, ΔE_P, and nonpolar interactions, ΔE_D, the following equation can be written:

$$\Delta E = \Delta E_D + \Delta E_P + \Delta E_H \tag{4}$$

Dividing this equation by the molar volume of a solvent, V, gives:

$$\frac{\Delta E}{V} = \frac{\Delta E_D}{V} + \frac{\Delta E_P}{V} + \frac{\Delta E_H}{V} \tag{5}$$

or

$$\delta^2 = \delta_D{}^2 + \delta_P{}^2 + \delta_H{}^2 \tag{6}$$

where

$$\delta = (\Delta E/V)^{1/2} \tag{7}$$

is the usual equation for the solubility parameter,

$$\delta_D = (\Delta E_D/V)^{1/2} \tag{8}$$

is the dispersion component of the solubility parameter,

$$\delta_p = (\Delta E_P/V)^{1/2} \tag{9}$$

is the polar component of the solubility parameter, and

$$\delta_H = (\Delta E_H/V)^{1/2} \tag{10}$$

is the hydrogen bonding component of the solubility parameter. Permanent dipole-induced dipole interactions are generally small compared to the other forces (24), with all errors being largely grouped into the δ_H component. These parameters are given in Table 1 for a number of solvents. The parameters listed in Table 1 were developed through independent calculations for the individual values where data were available and have been checked by numerous solubility evaluations (7, 8, 10–12) and compared to other systems for their accuracy (25). The nonpolar contribution was estimated from homomorph considerations; the hydrogen bond values agree well with ΔH_V measurements of about 4,650 cal for each OH group, and the polar contribution was calculated from a slight modification of Böttcher's equation (26):

$$\delta_P{}^2 = \frac{12{,}108}{V^2} \cdot \frac{\epsilon - 1}{2\epsilon + n_D{}^2} (n_D{}^2 + 2) \, \mu^2 \tag{11}$$

where V is the molar volume, ϵ is the dielectric constant (static value), n_D is the index of refraction for D light (sodium), and μ is the dipole moment expressed in Debye units $(10^{-18} \, (\text{esu})(\text{cm}))$.

It must be emphasized at this point that "hydrogen bonding" is being used rather loosely in this article, and that some more ambiguous term such "weak chemical bonds," or perhaps "association bonds" might be better. However, historical considerations favor continuation of this loose usage, at least for the present article, with the understanding that some π-bonds, quadrupole and octapole interactions, and probably other yet unnamed forces are included in δ_H and ΔE_H.

The energies calculated as described fit equation 4 or 6 very well where all four terms can be estimated independently. These quantities can also be estimated from the parameters in the other systems described above by use of the simplified equations of Beerbower (25), such as

$$\delta_P = 18.3 \, \mu/\sqrt{V} \tag{11a}$$

but parameters so calculated may be in error by ± 1.7 hildebrand. A better solution is to extend the "group contributions" mentioned above for —OH to most of the common functional groups.

The group concept was first applied to total parameters by Small, but his work was updated and extended by Hoy (23). They felt that $V\delta$ contributions from por-

Table 1. Solubility Parameters of Various Liquids at 25°C

Class	Code	Name	Molar volume V	Parameters hildebrands, δ_D	δ_P	δ_H
paraffin hydrocarbons	1	*n*-butane	101.4	6.9	0	0
	2	*n*-pentane	116.2	7.1	0	0
	3	*i*-pentane	117.4	6.7	0	0
	4	*n*-hexane	131.6	7.3	0	0
	5	*n*-heptane	147.4	7.5	0	0
	6	*n*-octane	163.5	7.6	0	0
	7	2,2,4-trimethylpentane	166.1	7.0	0	0
	8	*n*-nonane	179.7	7.7	0	0
	9	*n*-decane	195.9	7.7	0	0
	10	*n*-dodecane	228.6	7.8	0	0
	11	*n*-hexadecane	294.1	8.0	0	0
	12	*n*-eicosane	359.8	8.1	0	0
	13	cyclohexane	108.7	8.2	0	0.1[a]
	14	methylcyclohexane	128.3	7.8	0	0.5
	14.1	*cis*-decahydronaphthalene	156.9	9.2	0	0
	14.2	*trans*-decahydronaphthalene	159.9	8.8	0	0
aromatic hydro-carbons	15	benzene	89.4	9.0	0[a]	1.0
	16	toluene	106.8	8.8	0.7	1.0
	16.1	naphthalene[b]	111.5	9.4	1.0	2.9
	17	styrene	115.6	9.1	0.5	2.0
	18	*o*-xylene	121.2	8.7	0.5	1.5
	19	ethylbenzene	123.1	8.7	0.3	0.7
	19.1	1-methylnaphthalene	138.8	10.1	0.4	2.3
	20	mesitylene	139.8	8.8	0	0.3
	21	tetrahydronaphthalene	136.0[a]	9.6[a]	1.0	1.4
	21.1	biphenyl	154.1	10.5	0.5	1.0
	22	*p*-diethylbenzene	156.9	8.8	0	0.3
halohydrocarbons	23	methyl chloride	55.4	7.5[a]	3.0	1.9
	24	methylene dichloride	63.9	8.9	3.1	3.0
	24.1	bromochloromethane	65.0	8.5	2.8	1.7
	25	chlorodifluoromethane	72.9	6.0	3.1	2.8
	26	dichlorofluoromethane	75.4	7.7	1.5	2.8
	27	ethyl bromide	76.9	8.1	3.9	2.5
	27.1	1,1-dichloroethylene	79.0	8.3	3.3	2.2
	28	ethylene dichloride	79.4	9.3[a]	3.6	2.0
	28.1	methylene di-iodide[c]	80.5	8.7	1.9	2.7
	29	chloroform	80.7	8.7	1.5	2.8
	29.1	1,1-dichloroethane	84.8	8.1	4.0	0.2
	29.2	ethylene dibromide	87.0	9.6	3.3	5.9
	30	bromoform	87.5	10.5[a]	2.0	3.0[a]
	31	*n*-propyl chloride	88.1	7.8	3.8	1.0
	32	trichloroethylene	90.2	8.8	1.5	2.6
	33	dichlorodifluoromethane	92.3	6.0	1.0	0
	34	trichlorofluoromethane	92.8	7.5	1.0	0
	35	bromotrifluoromethane	97.0	4.7	1.2	0
	36	carbon tetrachloride	97.1	8.7	0	0.3
	37	1,1,1-trichloroethane	100.4	8.3	2.1	1.0
	38	tetrachloroethylene	101.1	9.3	3.2[a]	1.4
	39	chlorobenzene	102.1	9.3	2.1	1.0
	39.1	*n*-butylchloride	104.9	8.0	2.7	1.0
	39.2	1,1,2,2-tetrachloroethane	105.2[a]	9.2	2.5	4.6
	40	bromobenzene	105.3	10.0	2.7	2.0
	41	*o*-dichlorobenzene	112.8	9.4	3.1	1.6
	42	benzyl chloride	115.0	9.2[a]	3.5	1.3

Table 1 (*continued*)

Class	Code	Name	Molar volume, V	Parameters hildebrands,		
				δ_D	δ_P	δ_H
	42.1	1,1,2,2-tetrabromoethane[c]	116.8	11.1	2.5	4.0
	43	1,2-dichlorotetrafluoroethane[c]	117.0	6.2	0.9	0
	44	1,1,2-trichlorotrifluoroethane	119.2	7.2	0.8	0
	45	cyclohexyl chloride	121.3	8.5	2.7	1.0
	46	1-bromonaphthalene	140.0	9.9	1.5	2.0
	47	trichlorobiphenyl[d]	187.0	9.4	2.6	2.0
	48	perfluoromethylcyclohexane	196.0	6.1	0	0
	49	perfluorodimethylcyclohexane[d]	217.4	6.1	0	0
	50	perfluoro-*n*-heptane	227.3	5.9	0	0
ethers	51	furan	72.5	8.7	0.9	2.6
	51.1	epichlorohydrin	79.9	9.3	5.0	1.8
	51.2	tetrahydrofuran	81.7	8.2	2.8	3.9
	51.3	1,4-dioxane	85.7	9.3	0.9	3.6
	51.4	methylal[c] $CH_2(OCH)_2$	88.8	7.4	0.9	4.2
	52	diethyl ether	104.8	7.1	1.4	2.5
	53	bis(2-chloroethyl) ether	117.6	9.2	4.4	2.8[a]
	53.1	anisole[c]	119.1	8.7	2.0	3.3
	53.2	di-(2-methoxyethyl) ether	142.0	7.7	3.0	4.5
	53.3	dibenzyl ether[c]	192.7	8.5	1.8	3.6
	53.4	di-(2-chloro-*i*-propyl) ether[c]	146.0	9.3	4.0	2.5
	54	bis-(*m*-phenoxyphenyl) ether	373.0	9.6	1.5	2.5
ketones	55	acetone	74.0	7.6	5.1	3.4
	56	methyl ethyl ketone	90.1	7.8	4.4	2.5
	57	cyclohexanone	104.0	8.7	3.1	2.5
	58	diethyl ketone	106.4	7.7	3.7	2.3
	58.1	mesityl oxide	115.6	8.0	3.5	3.0
	59	acetophenone	117.4	9.6[a]	4.2	1.8
	60	methyl *i*-butyl ketone	125.8	7.5	3.0	2.0
	61	methyl *i*-amyl ketone	142.8	7.8	2.8	2.0
	61.1	isophorone	150.5	8.1	4.0	3.6
	62	di-(*i*-butyl) ketone	177.1	7.8	1.8	2.0
aldehydes	63	acetaldehyde[c]	57.1	7.2	3.9	5.5
	63.1	furfuraldehyde	83.2	9.1[a]	7.3	2.5
	64	butyraldehyde	88.5	7.2	2.6[a]	3.4[a]
	65	benzaldehyde	101.5	9.5	3.6	2.6
esters	66	ethylene carbonate	66.0	9.5	10.6	2.5
	66.1	γ-butyrolactone	76.8	9.3	8.1	3.6
	66.2	methyl acetate	79.7	7.6	3.5	3.7
	67	ethyl formate	80.2	7.6	4.1	4.1
	67.1	propylene carbonate	85.0	9.8	8.8	2.0
	68	ethyl chloroformate	95.6	7.6	4.9	3.3
	69	ethyl acetate	98.5	7.7[a]	2.6	3.5[a]
	69.1	trimethyl phosphate	99.9	8.2	7.8	5.0
	70	diethyl carbonate	121.	8.1	1.5	3.0
	71	diethyl sulfate	131.5	7.7	7.2	3.5
	72	*n*-butyl acetate	132.5	7.7	1.8	3.1
	72.1	*i*-butyl acetate	133.5	7.4	1.8	3.1
	72.2	2-ethoxyethyl acetate	136.2	7.8	2.3	5.2
	73	*i*-amyl acetate	148.8	7.5	1.5	3.4
	73.1	*i*-butyl *i*-butyrate	163.	7.4	1.4	2.9
	74	dimethyl phthalate	163.	9.1[a]	5.3[a]	2.4
	75	ethyl cinnamate	166.8	9.0	4.0	2.0
	75.1	triethyl phosphate	171.0	8.2	5.6	4.5
	76	diethyl phthalate	198.	8.6	4.7	2.2
	76.1	di-*n*-butyl phthalate	266.	8.7[a]	4.2	2.0
	76.2	*n*-butyl benzyl phthalate	306.	9.3	5.5	1.5

(*continued*)

Table 1 (*continued*)

Class	Code	Name	Molar volume, V	Parameters hildebrands,		
				δ_D	δ_P	δ_H
	77	tricresyl phosphate	316.	9.3	6.0	2.2
	78	tri-*n*-butyl phosphate	345.	8.0	3.1	2.1
	79	*i*-propyl palmitate[c]	330.	7.0	1.9	1.8
	79.1	di-*n*-butyl sebacate	339.	6.8	2.2	2.0
	79.2	methyl oleate[d]	340.	7.1	1.9	1.8
	79.3	dioctyl phthalate	377.	8.1	3.4	1.5
	80	di- - -butyl stearate[c]	382.	7.1	1.8	1.7
nitrogen compounds	81	acetonitrile	52.6	7.5	8.8	3.0
	81.1	acrylonitrile	67.1	8.0	8.5	3.3
	82	propionitrile	70.9	7.5	7.0	2.7
	83	butyronitrile	87.0	7.5	6.1	2.5
	84	benzonitrile	102.6	8.5	4.4	1.6
	85	nitromethane	54.3	7.7	9.2	2.5
	86	nitroethane	71.5	7.8	7.6	2.2
	87	2-nitropropane	86.9	7.9	5.9	2.0
	88	nitrobenzene	102.7	9.8	4.2	2.0
	89	ethanolamine	60.2	8.4	7.6	10.4
	89.1	ethylene diamine	67.3	8.1	4.3	8.3
	89.2	1,1-dimethylhydrazine[c]	76.0	7.5	2.9	5.4
	89.3	2-pyrrolidone	76.4	9.5	8.5	5.5
	90	pyridine	80.9	9.3	4.3	2.9
	91	*n*-propylamine	83.0	8.3	2.4	4.2
	92	morpholine	87.1	9.2	2.4	4.5
	93	aniline	91.5	9.5	2.5	5.0
	93.1	*N*-methyl-2-pyrrolidone	96.5	8.8	6.0	3.5
	94	*n*-butylamine	99.0	7.9[a]	2.2[a]	3.9[a]
	95	diethylamine	103.2	7.3	1.1	3.0
	95.1	diethylenetriamine	108.0	8.2	6.5	7.0
	96	cyclohexylamine	115.2	8.5	1.5	3.2
	96.1	quinoline	118.0	9.5	3.4	3.7
	97	di-*n*-propylamine	136.9	7.5	0.7	2.0
	98	formamide	39.8	8.4	12.8	9.3
	99	dimethylformamide	77.0	8.5	6.7	5.5
	99.1	*N,N*-dimethylacetamide	92.5	8.2	5.6	5.0
	99.2	tetramethylurea	120.4	8.2	4.0	5.4
	99.3	hexamethyl phosphoramide[c]	175.7	9.0	4.2	5.5
sulfur compounds	100	carbon disulfide	60.0	10.0	0	0.3
	101	dimethyl sulfoxide	71.3	9.0	8.0	5.0
	101.1	ethanethiol[c]	74.3	7.7	3.2	3.5
	102	dimethyl sulfone[b]	75.	9.3	9.5	6.0
	103	diethyl sulfide	108.2	8.3	1.5	1.0
acid halides and anhydrides	104	acetyl chloride	71.0	7.7	5.2	1.9
	104.1	succinic anhydride[b]	66.8	9.1	9.4	8.1
	105	acetic anhydride	94.5	7.8[a]	5.7[a]	5.0[a]
monohydric	120	methanol	40.7	7.4	6.0	10.9
	121	ethanol	58.5	7.7	4.3	9.5
	121.1	ethylene cyanohydrin (hydracrylonitrile)	68.3	8.4	9.2	8.6
	121.2	allyl alcohol[c]	68.4	7.9	5.3	8.2
alcohols	122	1-propanol	75.2	7.8	3.3	8.5
	123	2-propanol	76.8	7.7	3.0	8.0
	123.1	3-chloro- - -propanol	84.2	8.6	2.8	7.2
	124	furfuryl alcohol	86.5	8.5	3.7	7.4
	125	1-butanol	91.5	7.8	2.8	7.7
	126	2-butanol	92.0	7.7	2.8	7.1

Table 1 (*continued*)

Class	Code	Name	Molar volume, V	Parameters hildebrands,		
				δ_D	δ_P	δ_H
	126.1	2-methyl-1-propanol	92.8	7.4	2.8	7.8
	126.2	benzyl alcohol	103.6	9.0	3.1	6.7
	127	cyclohexanol	106.0	8.5	2.0	6.6
	128	1-pentanol	109.0	7.8	2.2	6.8
	129	2-ethyl-1-butanol	123.2	7.7	2.1	6.6
	129.1	diacetone alcohol	124.2	7.7	4.0	5.3
	129.2	1,3-dimethyl-1-butanol	127.2	7.5	1.6	6.0
	130	ethyl lactate	115.	7.8	3.7	6.1
	130.1	n-butyl lactate	149.	7.7	3.2	5.0
	131	ethylene glycol monomethyl ether	79.1	7.9	4.5	8.0
	132	ethylene glycol monoethyl ether	97.8	7.9	4.5	7.0
	132.1	diethylene glycol monomethyl ether	118.0	7.9	3.8	6.2
	132.2	diethylene glycol monoethyl ether	130.9	7.9	4.5	6.0
	133	ethylene glycol mono-n-butyl ether	131.6	7.8	2.5	6.0
	133.1	2-ethyl-1-hexanol	157.0	7.8	1.6	5.8
	134	1-octanol	157.7	8.3	1.6	5.8
	134.1	2-octanol	159.1	7.9	2.4	5.4
	134.2	diethylene glycol mono-n-butyl ether	170.6	7.8	3.4	5.2
	135	1-decanol	191.8	8.6	1.3	4.9
	136	"tridecyl alcohol"[d]	242.	7.0	1.5	4.4
	136.1	"nonyl" phenoxy ethanol[d]	275.	8.2	5.0	4.1
	137	oleyl alcohol[d]	316.	7.0	1.3	3.9
	137.1	triethylene glycol mono-oleyl ether	418.5	6.5	1.5	4.1
acids	140	formic acid	37.8	7.0	5.8	8.1
	141	acetic acid	57.1	7.1	3.9	6.6
	141.1	benzoic acid[b]	100.	8.9	3.4	4.8
	142	n-butyric acid[c]	110.	7.3	2.0	5.2
	142.1	n-octoic acid[c]	159.	7.4	1.6	4.0
	143	oleic acid[d]	320.	7.0	1.5	2.7
	143.1	stearic acid[b]	326.	8.0	1.6	2.7
phenols	144	phenol	87.5	8.8	2.9	7.3
	144.1	1,3-benzenediol[b]	87.5	8.8	4.1	10.3
	145	m-cresol	104.7	8.8	2.5	6.3
	145.1	o-methoxyphenol[c]	109.5	8.8	4.0	6.5
	146	methyl salicylate	129.	7.8	3.9	6.0
	147	"nonyl" phenol[d]	231.	8.1	2.0	4.5
water	148	water[c]	18.0	7.6[a]	7.8[a]	20.7[a]
polyhydric alcohols	149	ethylene glycol	55.8	8.3	5.4	12.7
	150	glycerol	73.3	8.5	5.9	14.3
	150.1	propylene glycol	73.6	8.2	4.6	11.4
	150.2	1,3-butanediol	89.9	8.1	4.9	10.5
	151	diethylene glycol	95.3	7.9	7.2	10.0
	152	triethylene glycol	114.0	7.8	6.1	9.1
	153	hexylene glycol	123.0	7.7	4.1	8.7
	154	dipropylene glycol[d] (mixed isomers, see Vol. 10, p. 651)	131.3	7.8	9.9	9.0

[a] Altered from previously published value.
[b] Solid, treated as supercooled liquid.
[c] Values uncertain.
[d] Impure commercial product of this nominal formula.

tions of a molecule would be additive, and obtained good precision. However, hydrogen bonding is usually additive on an energy $(V\delta^2)$ basis (28). The near-constancy of μ for each group in McClellan's (27) Appendix B, along with equation 11a led to correlating both $V\delta_P$ and $V\delta_P{}^2$. The former showed greater precision and freedom from hydrocarbon portion effects, and so was used in Table 2 while the hydrogen bonding columns use $V\delta_H{}^2$. The precision shown is the full range for the data (about ± 2 standard deviations).

Table 2. Group Contributions to Partial Solubility Parameters

Functional group	Polar parameter, $V\delta_P$, $(cal \cdot cc)^{1/2}/mol$	H-bond parameter, $V\delta_H{}^2$, cal/mol	
		Aliphatic	Aromatic
—F	225 ± 25^a	~ 0	~ 0
—Cl	300 ± 100	100 ± 20^a	100 ± 20^a
>Cl$_2$	175 ± 25	165 ± 10^a	180 ± 10^a
—Br	300 ± 25	500 ± 100	500 ± 100
—I	325 ± 25^a	1000 ± 200^a	
—O—	200 ± 50	1150 ± 300^b	1250 ± 300^{ab}
>CO	390 ± 15	800 ± 250^b	400 ± 125^a
—COO—	250 ± 25	1250 ± 150	800 ± 150^a
—CN	525 ± 50	500 ± 200^b	550 ± 200^a
—NO$_2$	500 ± 50	400 ± 50^b	400 ± 50^a
—NH$_2$	300 ± 100^a	1350 ± 200^c	2250 ± 200^{cb}
>NH	100 ± 15	750 ± 200	
—OH	250 ± 30	4650 ± 400^c	4650 ± 500
(—OH)$_n$	$n(170 \pm 25)$	$n(4650 \pm 400)$	$n(4650 \pm 400)^a$
—COOH	220 ± 10	2750 ± 250	2250 ± 250^a

[a] Two or less compounds tested, confidence limits by analogy.
[b] Unpublished infrared data included in correlation.
[c] Data from (28), corrected to 25°C and $V\delta_P{}^2$ subtracted. For important steric shielding effects, see his Tables 7.6 and 7.7 (page 205).

Most of the data were taken from Table 1, using compounds having only one functional group. In addition, excess heats of vaporization from Bondi (28) and Weimer (19), and from gas-liquid chromatography by Martire (29), were corrected for dipole interaction and used for hydrogen bonding. An unpublished infrared method similar to that cited by Crowley (13) was also used. Some δ_P values from equation 11a were used where Table 1 data were sparse (ie, on —F).

The reader is cautioned against indiscriminate addition of functional groups as is permitted in Small's system. For —OH, δ_H is additive and δ_P nearly so; but the effect of adding a second chlorine reduces δ_P and may or may not double δ_H. Most spectacular is the effect of ortho —COO— groups in phthalate; they combine to quadruple δ_P. Addition of an ether group causes such complex effects that Hoy (23) calls the products "chameleon"; some of the benefits are discussed below under emulsions, but mathematical prediction requires further study.

Practical Use of the Solubility Parameter

Solvent Selection for Coatings. The most widespread practical use of the solubility parameter has been within the paint and related industries since these are intimately associated with solvent selection. Indeed, most of the practical developments outlined in the previous section were by workers in the paint field. The usual procedure is to perform a solubility-parameter study by contacting the solute (polymer) in question with a limited number of solvents chosen specifically to examine behavior at all levels of the parameters concerned. These data are then plotted in a suitable manner and a region of solubility is defined by those solvents found to dissolve the particular polymer. Plotting the data is a straightforward procedure when only two solvent parameters are used, but requires more effort when the three-dimensional systems are employed (Fig. 1). Various means to plot three parameters have been suggested including projections along each of the three axes (12, 25), use of triangular coordinates (30), and contour plotting (16). It has also been suggested that the δ_P vs δ_H plot in the Hansen system is sufficiently accurate for most practical purposes (Fig. 2). It should be remembered, however, that cyclic, halogenated, and a few other special solvents have relatively high δ_D components, as do most polymers, and are, therefore, somewhat more potent than indicated by this plot. Fig. 1 also has the advantage that the solubility region is a circle rather than an irregular shaped body as is found in the other systems. A computer can be very useful in calculations and in plotting.

Having defined a region of solubility, one can proceed to use it in solving practical problems. Solvent selection can be systematically worked out according to the requirements of the solvent for evaporation rate, flash point, toxicity, etc, and finally the requirement that the solvent or solvent blend chosen lie within the region of solubility. Many practical solutions to this problem involve boundary solvent mixtures, since hydrocarbon diluents are used as much as possible for economic reasons. A rule for the average solubility parameter of a mixed solvent based on the volume fractions of the solvents is sufficiently accurate in practice. The effect of diluents (nonsolvents) is seen since the average solubility parameter approaches a boundary as their concentration increases. One can also systematically choose a mixed, good solvent composed exclusively of nonsolvents, by choosing nonsolvents located, respectively, on opposite sides of the region of solubility. It is possible to make use of combinations of alcohols and hydrocarbons in such situations, perhaps including a third, slow, good solvent as insurance that the last solvent leaving the film is a good one. Plasticizers can contribute to the average solubility parameter of a system and should not be neglected in calculations or graphic solutions to problems.

In general, one can quickly determine all possible combinations of solvents which will solve a particular solubility problem. It may be useful to remember that the solution viscosity at high polymer concentration can be decreased by selectively using solvent blends where the solvent viscosity itself is low, and where the solubility parameter of the solvent approaches that of the polymer. Returning to the example of an alcohol–hydrocarbon mixed solvent, it is well known that additions of 1-butanol (viscosity = 2.96 cP) to xylene (viscosity = 0.87 cP) will produce this viscosity reduction effect in spite of the greater neat viscosity of the 1-butanol. Had ethanol been chosen instead of 1-butanol, the effect would have been more pronounced because of its lower viscosity and higher δ_H. Similar examples can be found by considering solubility parameter plots, such as Fig. 1 or 2.

Selection of Other Coating Ingredients. In addition to solvent selection one can use solubility-parameter (energy) concepts to help understand and solve other types of practical problems. Burrell's articles are filled with examples. Liquid miscibility plots can be constructed, if desired, and problems concerning polymer compatibility

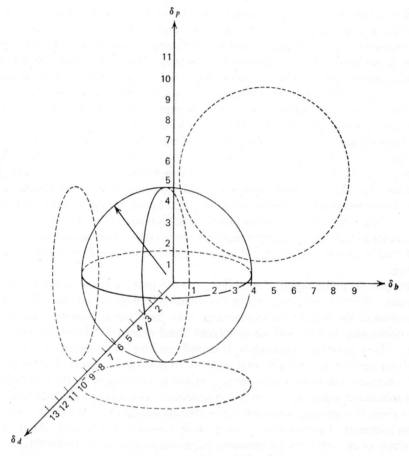

Fig. 1. Solubility plot for poly(methyl methacrylate) based on solution in solvents of different delta values. The circles represent areas within which the solubility is 10% or more.

can be systematically approached since polymers having essentially the same solubility parameters (dissolve in the same solvents) are more likely to be compatible because of their physical similarity. Crystallinity and high molecular weight may far outweigh these factors, however. Other examples include the formulation of thixotropic systems where (in alkyd systems) one customarily reacts a small amount of hydrocarbon insoluble material into the system late in the synthesis of the vehicle. These hydrocarbon insoluble portions form loosely bound domains in hydrocarbon solvent; these domains provide body to the system while at rest and are easily broken by shear (brushing) to allow even flow during application. Small additions of alcohol will also destroy the domains and the thixotropic behavior, illustrating that one does not always want good solvents.

Some work on the relation of solubility parameters to pigment dispersion has been reported, but this has not been explored as much as the importance of the process warrants (31–33). In general, if a pigment suspends for prolonged periods in the liquids used in a solubility-parameter study of its surface properties, that pigment will be easily wet by a suitable binder. The most suitable binder from this point of view

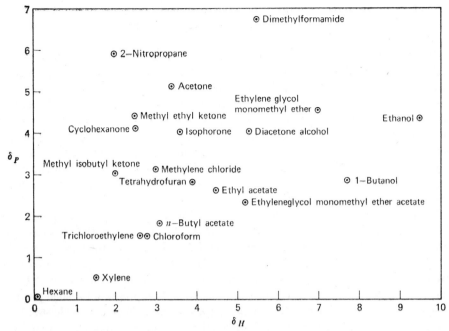

Fig. 2. Solubility parameter plot for common solvents.

would be one dissolving in the same solvents that suspend the pigment. Adsorption seems to be greater in a poor solvent than in a good one, but stability may be greater in a better solvent since the polymer molecules apparently extend more in the better solvent maintaining greater interparticle distances (31–34). Adsorption of polymers as well as surface-active agents is better considered in terms of nonsolubility rather than solubility, since the Gibbs principle requires that the total sytem free energy become stabilized at the lowest possible value. According to the particular situation this may be arranged to occur with high energy portions being adsorbed on a high energy solid surface, or perhaps in a water phase. Low energy portions may remain in an organic vehicle, or if they are not compatible therein (eg hydrocarbon, silicone), they will appear at the lowest energy surface available, the air–liquid interface.

Dispersion-type coatings can also be analyzed from a solubility parameter point of view. The general principle is to distribute the film former in a stabilized manner, in a relatively fast evaporating medium, be it water or hydrocarbon solvent. Film formation from the dispersed state requires the flowing together of the dispersed particles. This intimate intermingling of the particles is effected by a liquid known as a *coalescing solvent*, which is added to impart the required mobility to the polymer molecules. To be effective, the slowly evaporating, coalescing solvent must be such that the solubility parameter of the last solvent to volatilize is located within the region of solubility for the film-forming material. Organosols are formulated on similar principles, with a boundary solvent mixture in the initial stable system. The solvent improves with the loss of the poorer solvent and a film is formed, aided by the application of heat in most cases.

In general, visual observations of 10% "solutions" are suitable for a solubility parameter study. Higher or lower concentrations may be used in particular problems.

Low degrees of swelling (solution) in noncrosslinked polymer systems essentially define concentric regions surrounding those usually described as "soluble" on a solubility parameter plot.

Other Studies on Polymers. Beerbower (25) has systematized selection of crosslinked elastomers for use in contact with various types of liquids. This is illustrated in Figure 3, where the swelling of polysulfide rubber has been plotted on the plane obtained by opening out the three-dimensional corner of Figure 1 along the δ_D axis and flattening it. Each liquid appears in each quadrant, so that this presentation is 50% redundant. The 25% swelling contours are presented here as rectangles as a simplification to permit expressing them as "pass or fail" limits, but could have been shown as the projections of two ellipsoids. This figure is of special interest since it unexpectedly revealed that the rubber consisted of a block copolymer—a finding which was later verified by independent investigation.

A third method of presentation is shown in Figure 4. This is a computer procedure, as it requires simultaneous evaluation of δ_D, δ_P and δ_H for the elastomer, two weighting factors for the differences in δ_P and δ_H, the maximum possible swelling, Q_{max}, and a constant related to the relative molar volumes of the liquid and elastomer (between crosslinks). As there is some question as to the true constancy of the last factor, it is suggested that investigators develop their own program for such problems, and especially for copolymers. Only vulcanized natural rubber was evaluated by the computer procedure, but results on twelve other elastomers were correlated by the flattened three-dimensional approach. The results were successful in terms of predicting "pass" or "fail" on the 25% swell criterion in 97% of over 1000 data points.

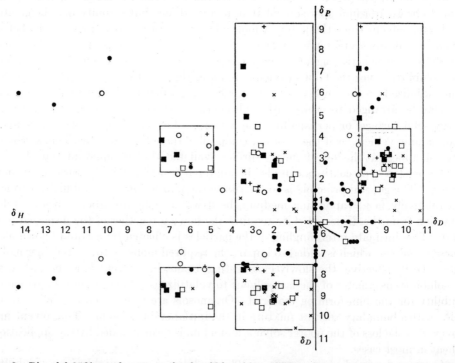

Fig. 3. Bimodal 25% sweel contour of polysulfide rubber (CST). Legend: ■, greater than 350% swell; □, = 101 to 350% swell; ✕, 51 to 100%; +, 26 to 50%; ○, 11 to 25%; and ● 0 to 10%.

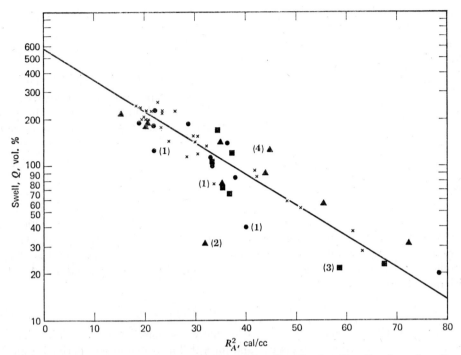

Fig. 4. Correlation of swell of natural rubber with radius of spheroid; all values of swell were normalized for vulcanization level of 2.75 pph sulfur. The equation of the line is $\log_{10} Q = \log_{10} Q_{max} - 0.08\ R_A^2$; $R_A^2 = (\delta_D - 8.8)^2 + 0.19\ (\delta_P + 3.9)^2 + 0.19\ (\delta_H - 3.4)^2$. LEGEND: ✕, binary mixtures from ref. 35; ●, pure compounds from ref. 35; ▲, pure compounds from ref. 36; and ■, pure compounds from ref. 37. (1) indicates hexane–ethyl acetate system; (2), aniline; (3), CCl_2F_2; and (4), benzaldehyde.

Another important property of a polymer is its wettability. This has been characterized by Zisman (38) in a *critical surface tension*, γ_c, defined as the surface free energy of the most energetic nonhydrogen-bonded liquid to wet the polymer completely (ie, contact angle = 0°). Wu (39) has been able to correlate these γ_c values with the solubility parameters of the polymers as calculated by Small's (40) method. His preferred equation is dimensionally unbalanced, but he also offers a second, balanced equation which gives about the same results. As an example, Wu calculates γ_c for polyisoprene in the following way:

The monomer is considered in simple groups, with the double bond which enters into polymerization disregarded. "Force constants" according to Small are tabulated, multiplied by the number of groups of this class, and summed up:

$$
\begin{array}{lll}
-CH_3 & 1 \times 214 & = 214 \\
CH_2 & 1 \times 133 & = 133 \\
CH- & 1 \times 28 & = \ \ 28 \\
-CH=CH- & 1 \times 222 & = 222 \\
H & 1 \times 90 & = \ \ 90 \\
\Sigma F & & = 687
\end{array}
$$

This is substituted into the equation

$$\gamma_c = 0.229(\Sigma F)^2 d^{1.67}/x^{0.33} M^{1.67} \tag{11b}$$

where d is the polymer density, x the number of atoms in the monomer and M the monomer molecular weight. The result of this calculation is $\gamma_c = 30.7$, compared with 31 by actual measurement. Presumably, the constants more recently computed by Hoy (23) would give approximately the same value.

An alternative approach was published by Hansen (40a), in which the cosine of the contact angle is used in place of the solubility on a plot similar to Figure 1. The circles are then drawn to enclose all liquids which spread on the surface. The result is a set of three partial parameters to characterize the surface, rather than a γ_c value. The technique, like Zisman's, may be applied to metallic and other surfaces as well as plastics.

Surface Free Energies. Hildebrand (2) established the relationship between solubility parameter and surface free energy as a simple quadratic equation, but unfortunately was unable to provide a theoretical value for the constant in it. Even more unfortunately, he then set up a dimensionally unbalanced equation which has been widely used, with confusing results (see preceding section). Beerbower (41) has carried the analysis through on a three-dimensional parameter basis, and was able to correlate the surface free energies of most organic liquids, fused salts, and liquid metals with one equation:

$$\gamma = 0.0715 V^{1/3} [\delta_D{}^2 + 0.632(\delta_P{}^2 + \delta_H{}^2)] \tag{12}$$

Special equations were required for aliphatic alcohols, for alkali halides, for five metals roughly grouped as "irregular," and for γ_c. The constant was derived from the number of nearest neighbors lost in surface formation, assuming that the molecules tend to occupy, on the average, the corners of regular octahedra. This postulate has other justifications, but the greatest is that it yields a value of 0.07152, while empirical fit of the data on organic solvents had previously given 0.07147.

Hildebrand (2) suggests that the solubility parameters of blends may be estimated by summing the parameters of the components multiplied by their volume fractions. This works well enough for polymer interactions (7, 25) but cannot be applied to surface free energies of blends due to enrichment at the surface in accordance with the Gibbs-Duhem principle of minimizing the free energy of the system. This approach presumably gives the instant free energy of a freshly formed surface, which is useful in such fast-moving processes as fractional distillation. Hildebrand's solution to this problem is not entirely satisfactory, though Clever (41a) has done a great deal of work on evaluating it and has developed a computer program for the purpose. The predictions are quite accurate but are made so at the cost of using the molar surface areas of the components as adjustable parameters. The deviation from the "real" areas as expressed by a $V^{2/3}$ function is minor in regular liquids but becomes sizable with increasing irregularity. An alternative approach was worked out by Shain (42) and applied by Sprow (43) with good success, again for simple mixtures. Beerbower (25) reported use of the volume blending rule along with chromatographic separation for the solubility parameters of petroleum fractions, and more recently has used equation 12 to estimate these from the surface free energies. This again falls into the regular solution category, and there is still need for much work in prediction of surface free energies from three-dimensional parameters for blends of irregular liquids. In addition, the rate of attaining the Gibbs-Duhem equilibrium has not been adequately predicted.

Liquid–Liquid Interactions. One of the factors often overlooked in the use of solubility parameters is the vital importance of the molar volumes when predicting solubilities, and such rules-of-thumb as "liquids differing by 2 hildebrands are incompletely miscible" can be quite misleading. The reason is that disparity of molar volume plays a duel role here, as it builds up not only $\Delta\delta$, but also the entropy. Hildebrand's equation (ref. 1 (43a) (eq. 10.3) shows this very clearly, and has been used by Beerbower (25) to correlate the aniline point (ASTM Method D-611) with the solubility parameters and molar volumes at 25°C of hydrocarbon solvents. Assuming that the "consolute temperature" (CST) comes at the 50%-by-volume point, which Francis (44) shows is usually true, and using 10.6 as the empirical solubility parameter of aniline (approximately $\delta_P{}^2 + 0.25[\delta_P{}^2 + \delta_H{}^2]$) he arrived at the relation

$$\delta = 10.6 - \left[\frac{4R}{1.8}\left(\frac{A + 460}{V + 91.1}\right)\right]^{1/2} \tag{13}$$

where $R = 1.9864$, the gas constant in cal/(°C)(mole). This expression fits the aniline point (A, in °F) and molar volumes of 41 hydrocarbon solvents within ±0.8 hildebrand. However, the relationship fails for olefins and esters, where the CST does not fall near 50%-by-volume point. Hildebrand's equation contains means for adjusting to other consolute volumes, but these were not tested.

It will be noted that the above example uses the single parameter, with a somewhat arbitrary adjustment for δ_P and δ_H. For liquid–liquid extractions, this is not adequate, and Weimer (19) has developed methods for handling polar–nonpolar interactions. Helpinstill (21) extended this to polar–polar systems. Unfortunately, both articles contain misprints, and (19) in particular needs correction. Figures 1–3 in this article actually plot cal/cm³ rather than cal/g-mol as stated, and equation 9 lacks the factor "RT" in the last two terms. Worst of all, the homomorph charts in these articles yield δ_D values that are higher than those from Blanks (18) which were the basis for successful correlations (8, 10, 11, 25, 38, 45). Even more unfortunately, Beerbower (25) propagated the problem by extending the same charts to higher molar volumes, but he did not make use of them. In order to take advantage of the values in Table 1, it is necessary to continue use of the Blanks chart.

Despite these difficulties, the two articles on liquid–liquid extraction make a very important point. Both use a two-part parameter, the polar and hydrogen-bonding forces being lumped together in the following expression:

$$\tau^2 = \delta_P{}^2 + \delta_H{}^2 \tag{14}$$

This parameter, τ, is used with a correlation factor, or as defined by Weimer, a correction term which in effect becomes a factor. The need for this has been attributed to failure of real systems to meet one of Hildebrand's assumptions (19), and to the directional nature of the polar and hydrogen-bond forces (38). In any case, the need for this correction is very real. The values found for various situations are as follows:

Correction Factor, b	Liquid Interacting With	Reference
0.250	polymers, surfactants, pigments	11
0.191	vulcanized polyisoprene	25
0.632	its own vapor	38
0.208, 0.202	paraffins	19, 21
0.170, 0.224	olefins	19, 21
0.100, 0.106	aromatics	19, 21

Since the last three categories were evaluated on the basis of the homomorph charts questioned above, they are not quite comparable with the others. It is to be hoped that resolving this problem will tend to reduce the scatter of the liquid–liquid factors.

The selectivity of an extraction solvent "1" for a mixture of A and B is defined as the ratio of their activity coefficients at infinite dilution in 1. This is equal to the mole ratio of A to B in the extract obtained by treating an equimolar mixture of A and B with an infinite amount of solvent. Each of these infinite dilution activity coefficients "a_2^∞" may be obtained by the following equation:

$$\ln a_2^\infty = V_2[\delta_{D1} - \delta_{D2})^2 + b(\tau_1 - \tau_2)^2]/RT + 1 - (V_2/V_1) + \ln(V_2/V_1) \quad (14A)$$

where b is the correction factor (see above). While greater accuracy might be obtained by use of the three individual parameters, this has not been demonstrated and the example cited (21) indicates little need for improvement.

The last three terms of equation (14A) represent the Flory-Huggins entropy correction. Since V_2 appears in almost every term of this equation, selectivity depends both on the differences in the partial parameters and on the molar volumes of the two components to be separated. Because of this, it is possible to separate chemically similar liquids of unequal molar volumes, as well as dissimilar liquids of equal molar volumes. If both these factors vary, it is possible for the two effects to enhance or cancel each other; this is in agreement with the experimental evidence.

Emulsions. Winsor (46) predicted that the properties of emulsions could be related to the "ratio of the dispersing tendencies on the oil and water faces of the surfactant region." He was unable to quantify these forces, but Beerbower (45) did so by equating them to the cohesive energies of the mixtures of oil with the lipophile tail of the surfactant and of water with the hydrophile head. Both mixtures were calculated on the basis of three-dimensional solubility parameters, though this was only a formality where the oil was a paraffin hydrocarbon ($\delta = \delta_D$). Making the logical assumption that the volume swelling of the surfactant film was equal on both sides, he was able to produce an expression of these forces meeting all of Winsor's requirements.

However, this equation still contains ϕ, the volume fraction of each liquid which swells the surfactant layer, and this cannot be precisely evaluated at present. One method used to bypass this problem is to consider only those emulsions in which a perfect "chemical match" has been made (ie, δ_D, δ_P, δ_H are identical for oil versus lipophile, and for water versus hydrophile). The equation then reduces to a form independent of ϕ, for this special case of Winsor's ratio R:

$$R_0 = \frac{V_L \delta_{*L}^2}{V_H \delta_{*H}^2} \quad (15)$$

where V_L and V_H are the partial molar volumes of the lipophile tail and hydrophile head; δ_{*L}^2 and δ_{*H}^2 are defined by

$$\delta_*^2 = \delta_D^2 + 0.25(\delta_P^2 + \delta_H^2) \quad (16)$$

the 0.25 correction factor being based on Hansen's work (11).

This permits relation of R_0 to the well-known hydrophile–lipophile balance (*HLB*, see Vol. 8, p. 131) which Becher (47) showed correlates much of the data on nonionic emulsions. Since HLB is defined as $20M_H/(M_L + M_H)$ where M is molecular weight,

$$R_0 = \frac{\delta_{*L}^2}{\delta_{*H}^2} \left(\frac{20}{HLB} - 1 \right) \frac{d_H}{d_L} \tag{17}$$

where d_H and d_L are the densities of head and tail.

This valuable relationship helps to validate both the Winsor theory, which lacked numerical data, and the HLB theory, which was entirely empirical. Another approach to the swelling fraction problem was to assume that $\phi = 0.5$. This resulted in an equation which correlated the data on emulsions made in water, formamide, and mixtures of these, but not those made in glycols.

Use of these equations for the design of O/W (oil-in-water) emulsions made with ethoxylated surfactants requires only the assumption that the supply of emulsifier is adequate to cover at least 50% of the droplet surface. The steps are as follows:

1. Determine V_O and δ_{*O} for the oil to be emulsified. Unless the oil is exceptionally polar or hydrogen-bonded, the value of δ or δ_D may be used for δ_*. If a surface free energy is available, equation 12 may be used as an approximation.

$$\delta_{*O} \cong \sqrt{\gamma/0.0715 \, V_O^{1/3}} \tag{17a}$$

2. Correlation of literature data for the optimum value of R_0 for oil in water emulsions leads to the working version of equation 17:

$$HLB_0 = 20 \, \delta_{*O}^2/(\delta_{*O}^2 + 38.4) \tag{17b}$$

where HLB_0 is the required HLB value for the emulsifier.

3. An emulsifier is selected which meets the above criteria of HLB_0 and $\delta_{*L} = \delta_{*O}$. The term δ_{*L} is determined by Small's method (37), calculating the $\Sigma \, F$ values down to but not including the first ether or ester (—O—) linkage. A third criterion, based on experience, is that $V_L = V_O$. Rarely is a single emulsifier available which meets all three criteria, and it is customary to blend two or more. This practice is especially beneficial when different types of lipophile are blended (47), probably because of increased entropy.

4. All that remains is to set the percentage of emulsifier. Becher (47) provides some calculation methods, but it is probably best to make a test series to determine the balance of economy versus stability.

Solubility of Gases. Hildebrand (1) gave a chart which is reasonably accurate for predicting the solubility at 25°C of simple gases in regular liquids with solubility parameters from 6 to 10. This work has been greatly extended by Prausnitz (48), who removed not only the temperature limitation but also other limitations. Their approach is basically that of "condensing" the gas to a hypothetical state having a liquid-like volume. This hypothetical fluid is then blended with the solvent on essentially a liquid miscibility basis. The key information is the molar volume and solubility parameter of the gas as "condensed" at 25°C. Appropriate values for common gases are listed in Table 3. These are used in the following equation:

$$\frac{1}{X_2} = \frac{f_2^L}{f_2^g} \exp \frac{V(\delta_1 - \delta_2)^2 \, \phi_1^2}{RT} \tag{17c}$$

where X_2 is the mol fraction of the gas in solution, f_2^g is the fugacity of the pure gas at initial conditions (taken as one atmosphere partial pressure) and $f_2{}^L$ is the fugacity of the hypothetical liquefied gas. The latter is obtained from Fig. 5, adapted from Prausnitz (48). The critical temperature (T_c) and pressure (P_c) of the solute gas are also required. For gases of ordinary low solubility, ϕ_1 (the volume fraction of solvent) may be taken as unity.

Table 3. "Liquid" Volumes and Solubility Parameters for Gaseous Solutes at 25°C[a]

Gas	V, cc/g-mol	δ, (cal/cc)$^{1/2}$
N_2	32.4	2.58
CO	32.1	3.13
O_2	33.0	4.0
Ar	57.1	5.33
CH_4	52	5.68
CO_2	55	6.0
Kr	65	6.4
C_2H_4	65	6.6
C_2H_6	70	6.6
Rn	70	8.83
Cl_2	74	8.7

[a] J. M. Prausnitz and F. H. Shair, *A.I.Ch.E.J.* **7,** 682 (1961); also reference 48.

Special methods are required for the light gases H_2, He, and Ne, which require corrections based on quantum mechanics, and for reactive gases such as HCl, SO_2 and NH_3. Hydrogen-bonding gases are given special treatment (48).

Effects of Temperature on Solubility Parameters. The success cited above in handling miscibility and gas solubility problems at various temperatures from the parameters at 25°C is due to a feature of the regular solution model, cited by Prausnitz (48). This is that the value of the complex functions

$$V_2\phi_1{}^2(\delta_1 - \delta_2)^2 \text{ and } V_1\phi_2{}^2(\delta_1 - \delta_2)^2 \tag{18}$$

are independent of temperature (as long as the composition remains constant). Since ϕ_1 and ϕ_2 vary only slightly with temperature, $(\delta_1 - \delta_2)$ is often nearly temperature in-

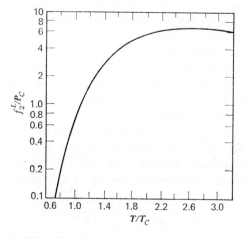

Fig. 5. Fugacity of hypothetical liquid at 1 atmosphere.

dependent. Hildebrand (2) gave an estimate of the variation of individual solubility parameters of nonpolar liquids

$$\frac{d\delta_D}{dT} = -1.25\alpha\delta_D \tag{19}$$

where α is the temperature coefficient of expansion, $d(\ln V)/dT$. This is not very exact, as he warns the reader, and he suggests a more sophisticated method. However, it is possible to derive an even more exact relationship from the well-known Watson equation for variation of ΔH_V with temperature:

$$d\delta_D/dT = -\delta_D[\alpha/6 + 0.6\ T_c^{1.2}/\delta_D^2(T_c - T)^{2.2}] \tag{20}$$

It is now evident that the "constancy" of $(\delta_1 - \delta_2)$ is true only when the critical temperatures of the two materials are comparable, or a happy combination of α, T_c and δ_D exists.

The polar parameter may be handled more simply, since μ is independent of temperature. Differentiation of equation 11a gives

$$d\delta_P/dT = -\delta_P\alpha/2 \tag{21}$$

There is no rigorous way of arriving at values of the temperature coefficient of the hydrogen bonding parameter, but Bondi (28) has provided empirical values at 100°C along with some of the ΔE_H values cited in Table 2. Assuming as above that $d(\Delta E_P)/dT = 0$, his numbers should reflect only $d(\Delta E_H)/dT$. Dividing them by the excess heats of vaporization and averaging the four results leads to

$$d\delta_H/dT = -\delta_H(1.22 \times 10^{-3} + \alpha/2) \tag{22}$$

Processing some of Weimer's data (19) the same way gives several more results of about the same magnitude, though averaging slightly lower.

By way of example, the rates of change for two liquids are shown in Table 4.

Table 4. Rates of Change for Two Liquids

Liquid	Equation		
	19, $d\delta_D/dT$	21, $d\delta_P/dT$	22, $d\delta_H/dT$
acetone[a]	-11.1×10^{-3}	-3.0×10^{-3}	-6.1×10^{-3}
1-propanol	-9.3×10^{-3}	-1.6×10^{-3}	-14.5×10^{-3}

[a] The value for $d\delta_D/dT$, as calculated by equation 20, would be -10.7×10^{-3}, an insignificant improvement.

This points up the importance of the level of hydrogen bonding, since it is generally believed that these bonds weaken rapidly with temperature. Actually, this is true only for alcohols and is due to equation 22 being the sum of the two.

Effects of Pressure on Parameters. Large increases in pressure tend to increase all the solubility parameters because of the decrease in V, and may be considered in a general way to be equivaent to reductions in temperature. Compressibility measurements afford a means to study cohesive energy, as pointed out by Hildebrand (2), and currently by Bagley (49).

A very interesting extension of the solubility parameter concept has been made by

Giddings (50) who applied it to supercritical gases compressed to liquid-like densities. The results have been useful in predicting the correct gas to use in high-pressure gas chromatography, and also in other problems relating to solubility in these peculiar fluids.

The above examples should be sufficient to demonstrate how various types of physical-chemical problems can be analyzed systematically and simply in terms of the energy concepts made possible by suitable interpretation of the solubility parameter. Understanding physical phenomena in terms of energies allows analysis of how materials can be expected to interact, a prime requisite for solving everyday industrial problems.

Theoretical Implications of the Solubility Parameter

The theoretical implications of an understanding of energy interactions among materials are too numerous to relate here. Prausnitz (48) has gone into this in some detail, and has demonstrated the interchangeability of solubility parameters, Flory-Huggins interaction parameters, and activity coefficients. In doing so, he emphasizes a point often overlooked, that the definition of δ in equation 1 describes the energy of vaporization required to expand the vapor isothermally to infinite volume. He also relates this type of correlation to the more general Prigogine and corresponding states theories (51). However, there is still work needed to tie in Hansen's work with Maron's (52), and Patterson's (53). The notable absence here of numbers related to acceptor–donor interactions has disturbed numerous people, but this arose only in the surface-free-energy work (41) and could be easily handled by correction factors. The success of solubility parameter concepts in explaining the data as completely as they do has been said to rest upon compensating errors; if so, the compensation is excellent. It has also been suggested (54) that the Hansen solubility-parameter system should be inverted, the solvents being represented as spheres having radii proportional to $(RT/V)^{1/2}$, thus leading to reducing radii with increasing molecular weight (ie, polymers as points helping to explain incompatibility more readily). This last consideration has generally been resolved in an arbitrary manner by treating the material concerned as the volume on solubility parameter plots, since this is generally what is of greatest concern in a given situation. The success of the solubility parameter in the (partial) characterization of inorganic salts and other materials in terms of the properties of organic liquids, suggests that terms can be included in equations 4 and 6 to include the energies arising from ionic and metallic type interactions. Work on surface-active agents and also bearing materials is being continued. Questions concerning entropy are yet to be resolved, but we do know that the free energy must be close to zero in a boundary region on a solubility plot. The Flory-Huggins parameter should also be close to 1/2 in the same region.

In spite of these many questions, some significant progress has been made in the area of relating surface phenomena to bulk liquid properties. The correlation of Hildebrand and Scott has been rewritten in terms of the Hansen solubility parameters with excellent correlation for most liquids (41).

Conclusion. It is hoped that this brief exposition of the past performance and the expected future of a very useful practical tool will stimulate more interest and action on the part of practical and theoretical workers alike. There is much to be done and, hopefully, the three-parameter nature of the solubility parameter will not impede progress. If there are three (or more) independent effects, quite simply, three (or more) parameters are required to describe them. Certainly there are other effects in the solubility question, but the δ_D, δ_P, and δ_H parameters have demonstrated significance, with molar volume as a necessary fourth parameter in most cases.

The challenge to understand the physical interactions among all types of materials in terms of their energy properties should be recognized and met, not only in bulk systems, but also at interfaces.

ACKNOWLEDGMENT: The work reported in this article was supported in part by Army Contract No. DAHC19-69-C-0033, administered by the Research Technology Division, Army Research Office, Arlington, Va.

Bibliography

1. J. Hildebrand and R. Scott, *Regular Solutions*, Prentice-Hall, Englewood Cliffs, N.J., 1962.
2. J. Hildebrand and R. Scott, *Solubility of Non-Electrolytes*, 3rd ed., Reinhold Publishing Corp., New York, 1949.
3. H. Burrell, *Am. Chem. Soc., Division of Organic Coatings Plastics Chemistry, Preprints* **28** (1), 682–708 (1968).
4. H. Burrell, *Offic. Dig.* **27** (369), 726 (1955).
5. H. Burrell, *Offic. Dig.* **29** (394), 1159 (1957).
6. H. Burrell, *VI Federation d'Associations de Techniciens des Industries des Peintures, Vernis, Emaux et Encres d'Imprimerie de l'Europe Continentale*, Congress Book, 1962, p. 21.
7. C. M. Hansen, *Ind. Eng. Chem. Prod. Res. Dev.* **8**, 2 (1969).
8. C. M. Hansen, doctoral dissertation, Technical University of Denmark, Danish Technical Press, Copenhagen, 1967.
9. C. M. Hansen, *Farg Lack* **14** (1), 18–22; (2), 23–25 (1968).
10. C. M. Hansen, *J. Paint Technol.* **39** (505), 104 (1967).
11. C. M. Hansen, *J. Paint Technol.* **39** (511), 505 (1967).
12. C. M. Hansen and K. Skaarup, *J. Paint Technol.* **39** (511), 511 (1967).
13. J. D. Crowley, G. S. Teague, and J. W. Lowe, *J. Paint Technol.* **38** (496), 296 (1966).
14. E. P. Lieberman, *Offic. Dig.* **34** (444), 30 (1962).
15. M. Dyck and P. Hoyer, *Farbe Lack* **70**, 522 (1964).
16. J. D. Crowley, G. S. Teague, and J. W. Lowe, *J. Paint Technol.* **39** (504), 19 (1967).
17. A. E. Van Arkel and S. E. Ules, *Rec. Trav. Chim.* **55**, 407 (1936); A. E. Van Arkel, *Trans. Faraday Soc.* **42B**, 81 (1946).
17a. Reference 1, p. 167.
18. R. F. Blanks and J. M. Prausnitz, *Ind. Eng. Chem. Fund.* **3**, 1 (1964).
19. R. F. Weimer and J. M. Prausnitz, *Hydrocarbon Proc. Petr. Ref.* **44**, 237 (1965).
20. H. G. Harris and J. M. Prausnitz, *Ind. Eng. Chem. Fund.* **8**, 180 (1969).
21. J. G. Helpinstill and M. Van Winkle, *Ind. Eng. Chem. Proc. Res. Dev.* **7**, 213 (1968).
22. J. L. Gardon, *J. Paint Technol.* **38** (492), 43 (1966).
23. K. L. Hoy, *J. Paint Technol.* **42** (541), 76 (1970).
24. R. J. Good, in *Treatise on Adhesion and Adhesives*, R. L. Patrick, ed., Marcel Dekker, Inc., New York, 1967.
25. A. Beerbower and J. R. Dickey, *A.S.L.E. Trans.* **12**, 1 (1969).
26. C. J. F. Böttcher, *Theory of Electric Polarization*, Elsevier, New York, 1952, Chap. 5.
27. A. L. McClellan, *Tables of Experimental Dipole Moments*, Freeman, Inc., San Francisco, 1963.
28. A. Bondi, *Physical Properties of Molecular Crystals, Liquids, and Glasses*, John Wiley & Sons, Inc., New York, 1968.
29. D. E. Martire and P. Riedl, *J. Phys. Chem.* **72**, 3478 (1968).
30. J. P. Teas, *J. Paint Technol.* **40**, 19–25 (1968).
31. P. Sorensen, *J. Oil Colour Chemists' Assoc.* **50**, (3), 226 (1967).
32. K. Skaarup, *Farg Lack* **14**, (2), 28–42; **14**, (3), 45–56 (1968).
33. A. Vinther and A. Peterson, *Verfkroniek* **40**, 286–9 (1967).
34. W. D. Schaeffer, *Am. Ink Maker* **43** (5), 54 (1965).
35. G. Gee, *Trans. Inst. Rubber Ind.* **18**, 266–281 (1943).

36. B. J. Eiseman, Jr., *Refrigeration Eng.* **57**, 1171 (1949).

37. Anonymous, *Enjay Butyl Rubber Chemical Resistance Handbook*, Enjay Chemical Co., New York, 1964.

38. W. A. Zisman, in *Contact Angle, Wettability and Adhesion, Advances in Chemistry Series No. 43*, American Chemical Society, Washington, D.C., 1964, pp. 1–54.

39. S. Wu, *J. Phys. Chem.* **72**, 3332 (1968).

40. P. Small, *J. Appl. Chem.* **3**, 71 (1953).

40a. C. M. Hansen, *J. Paint Tech.* **42** (550), 660 (1970).

41. A. Beerbower, *J. Coll. Interf. Sci.*, **35**, 126 (1971).

41a. H. L. Clever, *J. Coll. Interf. Sci.*, awaiting publication.

42. S. A. Shain and J. M. Prausnitz, *A.I.Ch.E.J.* **10**, 766 (1964).

43. F. B. Sprow and J. M. Prausnitz, *Trans. Faraday Soc.* **62**, 1105 (1965).

43a. Reference 1, p. 143.

44. A. W. Francis, *Critical Solution Temperatures, Advances in Chemistry Series No. 31*, American Chemical Society, Washington, D.C., 1961.

45. A. Beerbower and J. Nixon, *Am. Chem. Soc. Petrol. Div. Preprints* **14** (1), 62 (1969).

46. P. Winsor, *Solvent Properties of Amphiphilic Compounds*, Butterworth Scientific Publications,, Ltd., London, 1954.

47. P. Becher, *Emulsions, Theory and Practice*, 2nd ed., *Am. Chem. Soc. Monograph Series No. 162*, Reinhold Publishing Corp., Inc., New York, 1965.

48. J. M. Prausnitz, *Molecular Thermodynamics of Fluid-Phase Equilibria*, Prentice-Hall, Englewood Cliffs, N.J., 1969.

49. E. B. Bagley, T. P. Nelson, J. W. Barlow, and S-A. Chen, *Ind. Eng. Chem. Fundamentals* **9**, 93 (1970).

50. J. C. Giddings, N. M. Myers, L. McLaren, and R. A. Keller, *Science* **162**, 67 (1968).

51. J. M. Prausnitz, *Chem. Eng. Sci.* **20**, 703 (1965).

52. S. H. Maron and C. A. Daniels, *J. Macromol. Sci.-Phys.* **B2** (3) 449–461 (1968); **B2** (3), 463–477 (1968); **B2** (4), 591–602 (1968); **B2** (4), 743–767 (1968); **B2** (4), 591–602 (1968).

53. D. Patterson, *J. Polymer Sci. Part C Polymer Symp.* No. 16, 3379 (1968).

54. T. Kahler and S. L. Knudsen, Student Report, Technical Univ. of Denmark, 1967.

CHARLES HANSEN
PPG Industries, Inc.

ALAN BEERBOWER
Esso Research and Engineering Co

STYRENE–BUTADIENE SOLUTION COPOLYMERS

Commercial production of butadiene styrene rubber, SBR, by emulsion polymerization (see Vol. 7, p. 679) foreshadowed corresponding copolymers from the solution catalyst systems which had been evolving for several decades.

Alkali metal homopolymerization of dienes was reported first in 1910 by Matthews and Strange (1). Sodium and potassium were subsequently used in German and Russian plants for production of polybutadienes (2a). In 1946, Marvel, Bailey, and Inskeep (3) reported copolymers of butadiene with styrene obtained by initiation with metallic sodium in hydrocarbon solvent; but the process and products were not followed up commercially. These developments and other early work on homopolymerization and copolymerization of butadiene and styrene initiated by alkali metals and their organo derivatives have been extensively reviewed (2,4). In 1948, copolymerization of butadiene with styrene was reported (5) using a sodium-based alfin catalyst discovered in 1945 by A. Morton (6). This type of copolymer has been developed to commercial production and is discussed here.

Catalysts based on transition elements rather than on alkali metals have been described for solution copolymerization of butadiene with styrene (14), but they have not been developed commercially.   The field has been left essentially to the derivatives of alkali metals and particularly lithium.

Polymerization of isoprene by means of metallic lithium to an elastomer of very high *cis*-1,4 structure (7), and commercial production of alkyllithium-initiated polybutadiene (8) established alkyllithium polymerization as an important production process.

Early work on copolymerization of butadiene with styrene by alkyllithium was reported by Chesnokova and Korotkov (9).   Subsequent work established that the alkyllithium system was remarkably effective for tailoring copolymers with respect to composition, structure, and properties.   Commercial production of technologically important butadiene–styrene copolymers followed in a short time (10,11).   Copolymers are now available in the United States under trademarks Solprene (trademark of Phillips Petroleum Company), Kraton (trademark of Shell Chemical Company), and Stereon (trademark of The Firestone Tire & Rubber Company).

Because of the commercial and technological significance of butadiene–styrene copolymers prepared with alkyllithium, these elastomers are the main subject of this article.

Alkali metals other than lithium or sodium have been involved in very limited work (4).   Alkoxides of the various alkali metals, however, may participate in the alkyllithium system to control the relative rate of entry of styrene into the copolymer, and the microstructure of the polybutadiene units (12,13);   they will be discussed later in this article.

Butadiene–styrene rubbers made in solvent systems have been designated SBR rubbers by analogy to the much older emulsion SBR.   This terminology, however, is not entirely satisfactory since it does not emphasize the distinct difference in certain important aspects between solution and emulsion elastomers.

Copolymers by Alkyllithium Catalysis

COPOLYMERIZATION OF BUTADIENE WITH STYRENE

Reactivity Ratios and Copolymer Composition.   Alkyllithium initiation of dienes and active olefins such as styrene generates anions which propagate with monomer to produce polymer anions.   There is usually no spontaneous termination, and no chain transfer or crosslinking reaction of these anions.   In these respects alkyllithium polymerization differs significantly from free radical polymerization.   Because the polymer chains remain active, they have been described as "living."   Further discussion of the unique chemical characteristics of this polymerization system, and their consequences, is given below.

Copolymerization of butadiene, B, with styrene, S, occurs between polymer anions and monomer by the following homo- and cross-propagation steps:

1. $\bar{B} + B \xrightarrow{\ k_{BB}\ } B\bar{B}$

2. $\bar{B} + S \xrightarrow{\ k_{BS}\ } B\bar{S}$

3. $\bar{S} + S \xrightarrow{\ k_{SS}\ } S\bar{S}$

4. $\bar{S} + B \xrightarrow{\ k_{SB}\ } S\bar{B}$

where $\bar{B}$ and $\bar{S}$ indicate polymer anions of terminal butadiene and styrene units, respectively. The equation originally developed for free-radical copolymerization has been found to apply also to the above anionic copolymerization by proper consideration of the kinetics (15,16):

$$\frac{db}{ds} = \frac{B}{S} \frac{r_B B + S}{r_S S + B}$$

where r_B and r_S are the relative reactivity ratios of, respectively, butadiene and styrene, defined by $r_B = k_{BB}/k_{BS}$ and $r_S = k_{SS}/k_{SB}$, and

b = moles of butadiene entering the copolymer,
s = moles of styrene entering the copolymer,
B = moles of butadiene in the monomer mixture, and
S = moles of styrene in the monomer mixture.

Some recent values of the relative reactivity ratios for butadiene and styrene follow:

r_B	r_S	Solvent	Temp., °C	Ref.
15.0 ± 1.4	0.025 ± 0.080	hexane or heptane	50	17
17	0.017	benzene	30	75

Mochel (17) considered the question of the validity of reactivity ratios determined from copolymer composition data in an alkyllithium system and inferred that, since no statistically significant trend in value was observed with increasing conversion, the r values are effectively constant.

The absence of spontaneous termination in alkyllithium polymerization results in relatively narrow distribution of chain length and few short chains. Since there is no transfer reaction the polymer chains are linear (unbranched). The typically linear polymers of narrow molecular-weight distribution are in contrast with the branched, broad distribution polymers produced by free-radical emulsion polymerization. However, chain branching and molecular-weight distribution are effectively controlled by proper utilization of the reactivity of the polymer anions. The live anions also furnish an efficient route to block copolymers through further polymerization with a different monomer.

With butyllithium initiation in hydrocarbon solvent, butadiene homopolymerizes more slowly than styrene. In copolymerization, however, the reverse order of reactivities applies, with the result that butadiene enters the copolymer at a much greater rate than styrene. The large difference in relative reactivities leads to copolymers rich in butadiene while this monomer is still present in the reaction mixture. After butadiene has polymerized, the remaining styrene rapidly adds to the live polymer chain as a block.

Block polystyrene (P.S.) content is usually determined by the chemical method of Kolthoff (76). The copolymer is oxidatively degraded at the double bonds of the polybutadiene part. Polystyrene blocks are not attacked and are isolated and determined gravimetrically.

Numerous aspects of alkyllithium-initiated polymerization have been comprehensively and critically reviewed by Hsieh and Glaze (16) with emphasis on kinetics.

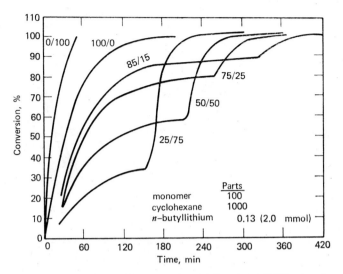

Fig. 1. Copolymerization of butadiene with styrene in cyclohexane at 50°C, at various initial weight ratios of butadiene/styrene (16a). *Courtesy Rubber Chem. Technol.*

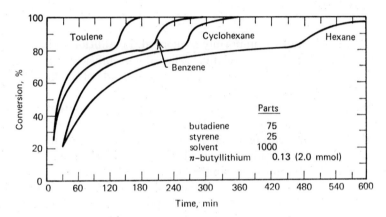

Fig. 2. Copolymerization of butadiene with styrene at initial weight ratio of butadiene/styrene-75/25 in different solvents at 50°C (16a,78). *Courtesy Rubber Chem. Technol.*

Characteristics of copolymerization of butadiene with styrene are well illustrated in Figures 1, 2, and 3. The reversal of relative rates of butadiene and styrene in copolymerization, as compared with homopolymerization, and the two stages of copolymerization are exhibited in Figure 1. The effect of different hydrocarbon solvents on rate is shown in Figure 2. Total styrene content and block polystyrene content as functions of conversion are given in Figure 3 for copolymerization in four hydrocarbon solvents. It is seen that in cyclohexane, benzene, and toluene, similar bound styrene results are observed, while in hexane slightly lower styrene values are found.

Copolymer composition with respect to butadiene and styrene units can be controlled, ranging from exclusively blocked structures to uniformly distributed monomer sequences, by regulation of monomer concentrations, use of polar modifiers, and conditions of polymerization. Methods of preparation of copolymers are described below.

Thus, anionic "live" polymerization is capable of yielding two distinct types of

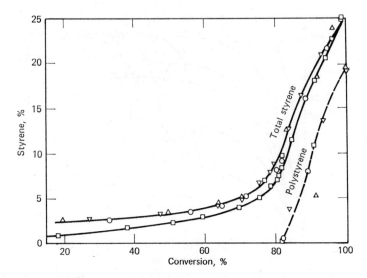

Fig. 3. Copolymerization of styrene from a butadiene/styrene 75/25 initial weight ratio in different solvents at 50°C (16a). LEGEND: □, hexane; △, cyclohexane; ▽, benzene; ○, toluene. Courtesy *Rubber Chem. Technol.*

copolymer, (a) block, and (b) uniformly sequenced, in addition to intermediate products. Both are produced commercially. They differ sufficiently in viscoelastic and mechanical properties that they are used in separate fields of application. Details of their preparation are also quite different, as discussed below.

Monomer Sequence Distribution. Block polystyrene content is usually determined by the chemical method of Kolthoff (76). The copolymer is oxidatively degraded with *tert*-butyl hydroperoxide in the presence of osmium tetroxide at the double bonds of the polybutadiene part. Polystyrene blocks are not attacked; they can be isolated and determined gravimetrically.

A method has been developed by Mochel and Johnson (17) for determining styrene sequence distribution in butadiene–styrene copolymers. Resolution of overlapped peaks in the styrene aromatic proton NMR spectrum was accomplished by means of an analog computer. Application of the method to solution copolymers resulted in quantitative distinction between "short blocks" of 2 and 3 styrene units, and "long blocks" of 4 or more units. Distribution of styrene-centered triads (SSS, SSB, BSB), and styrene sequence weight distribution for sequence lengths of 1, 2, and 3 were determined. From either of these experimental quantities all other sequence-related properties can be calculated. Differences between the NMR spectra for emulsion and solution copolymers were attributed to greater isotacticity of the latter.

A convenient method for graphically evaluating NMR styrene sequence distribution results has been devised by Mochel (18). Experimental values of the amount of styrene of given sequence length are compared with theoretical curves calculated for a perfectly random copolymer (ie, for the case $r_B = r_S = 1$). The amount of vertical displacement of a point from the corresponding theoretical curve is a measure of departure from uniform sequence distribution.

Molecular-Weight Distribution. Solution copolymers from alkyllithium systems are characteristically linear and of narrower molecular-weight distribution (MWD) than their emulsion counterparts. Chain length and number-average molecular weight (M_n) are controlled by the ratio of alkyllithium to monomer. A chain termination step is normally absent. In commercial production at high temperatures and in continuous operation, there is an opportunity for the live ends to react with impurities, for branching to increase, and for the molecular-weight distribution to broaden beyond that of laboratory counterparts.

Linear elastomers of narrow MWD exhibit Newtonian viscosity behavior, and, consequently, cold flow in storage. This undesirable property has been eliminated by introducing a controlled small degree of nonlinearity by adding a modifying comonomer having at least two terminal $=CH_2$ groups (19). Increased breadth of MWD may also be realized by solution mixing of polymers of various chain lengths.

Chain branching contributes to departure from Newtonian rheological behavior and improves the processability of solution copolymers, as discussed below. Branching can be introduced by coupling of reactive chain ends to a multivalent center (methyl trichlorosilane or silicon tetrachloride) (20), and by other methods such as graft copolymerization and special conditions of polymerization (21,22).

Molecular-weight distribution of alkyllithium-initiated solution polymers has been studied extensively by Johnson and his associates by means of the relatively fast method based on gel-permeation chromatography (23,24).

Microstructure. The polybutadiene part of copolymers contains cis-1,4-, trans-1,4- and 1,2-polybutadiene structures. Polymerization in hydrocarbon solvents in absence of polar compounds produces these structures in relative proportions which vary only slightly with temperature of polymerization (25) and with styrene content (Table 1) (26).

Table 1. Microstructure Variation with Styrene Content (26)

styrene, %	polybutadiene portion, %		
	cis-1,4-	trans-1,4	1,2-
0	36.0	55.0	9
18	34.1	57.0	9
23	31.2	58.4	10.4
32	28.8	60.8	10.4

The amount of cis-1,4 in polybutadiene remains fairly constant with increase of MW up to solution viscosity of about 6, beyond which the cis-1,4 content has been reported to increase steeply to 60% and higher (4b,25), while trans-1,4 decreases by a comparable amount, and 1,2- decreases by only about 4 percentage points. This conflicts with reports that the increase in cis content is linear with the increase in inherent viscosity (40,78).

Effect of Polar Modifiers. Polar compounds such as ethers, amines, and alkoxides increase the rate of homopolymerization of butadiene and of styrene, and alter the microstructure of polybutadiene (27–29). Changes are produced in copolymerization (12,30–34) by: (a) increased relative rate of copolymerization of styrene accompanied by reduction or elimination of block styrene, (b) increased over-all rate of copolymerization, and (c) increased amount of 1,2-polybutadiene structure in copolymers accompanied by comparable decrease of cis- and trans-1,4-polybutadiene units.

Table 2 illustrates the influence of two active nonionic polar modifiers on co-

Table 2. Effect of Nonionic Polar Modifiers on Copolymers: Initial Charge of B/S = 65/35 in Hexane, *n*-Butyllithium Initiator (34)

Modifier	Molar ratio modifier/BuLi	Polymerization temp, °C	Initial-bound styrene, %	Block styrene,[c] %	1,2-PBD, %
none	0	32	5.5	ca 20	9.1
		65	6.0	ca 20	9.3
diglyme[a]	0.1	32	13.8		32–36
		65	11.2		18–20
	1	32	25.7	0	76–77
		65	21.2	5	54–56
	3	32	27.3	0	77–80
		57	27.3	0	70–71
TMEDA[b]	0.1	32	12.1	7.3	25–27
		65	9.0	16	14–15
	1	32	28.8	0	64–66
		65	26.0	0	50–51
	2	32	29.2	0	67–72
		65	29.2	0	58–61

[a] Dimethyl ether of diethylene glycol.
[b] *N,N,N',N'*-tetramethylethylenediamine.
[c] Determined by the chemical method of Kolthoff and co-workers (76).

polymer composition. Tabulated is the effect of temperature and amount of modifier on initial-bound styrene, block styrene, and 1,2-polybutadiene content in the final copolymer. Initial styrene content is increased by dimethyl ether of diethylene glycol at a 1:1 mole ratio, for example, to about 26% (from 5.5%), and block styrene is correspondingly eliminated from the final copolymer. This effect is accompanied by an increase of 1,2-polybutadiene content to 76% (from 9%). Increase of temperature is seen to diminish the effect of polar modifiers. Dialkyl ethers, R_2O, and trialkylamines, R_3N, are much less effective.

Alkoxides of sodium, potassium, rubidium and cesium in alkyllithium copolymerization also strongly influence the rate of polymerization, styrene incorporation, and 1,2-polybutadiene content (12,33). Lithium alkoxide is an exception in that it decreases the rate and is without effect on styrene copolymerization and 1,2-polybutadiene content. Effects of the alkali metal alkoxides have a negative temperature coefficient, as in nonionic polar modification.

Interaction of temperature and kind and amount of alkoxide produces a broad range of effects on styrene incorporation and microstructure. Potassium *tert*-butoxide is reported to be, in general, the most effective of such modifiers. By adjusting the ratio of alkali metal *tert*-butoxide to butyllithium, and the temperature, copolymers can be produced with, (a) constant styrene content at all conversions, (b) no block styrene, (c) content of 1,2-polybutadiene from high (above 50%) to low value (9%).

Preparation of Block Copolymers. A detailed review of various methods of synthesis of block copolymers by homogeneous anionic polymerization has been published by Fetters (35). The fact that the polymer anions are "living" is the basis for preparation of block polymers. Sequential addition of different monomers maintains polymerization upon the active polymer anions and results in formation of block copolymers. It is important that terminating impurities (air, moisture, alcohols, acids, ketones, aldehydes, esters, etc) be at a minimum in sequential addition of monomers. Such impurities may produce by-product homopolymer, and in the preparation of three-block copolymers, may give rise to some two-block polymer. Contamination of the end product with these unwanted polymeric species generally leads to inferior properties as shown by Morton et al. (64b).

Synthesis of two-block polymers has been described (36), based on use of monolithium initiator RLi. A mixture of butadiene and styrene (eg, B/S = 75/25) in hydrocarbon solvent is initiated by organolithium such as n-butyllithium. Polymerization to complete conversion of monomers proceeds at ordinary temperatures, the monomers entering the copolymer according to the copolymerization equation. The final polymer of B/S–S type contains all of the initial styrene in bound form, or 25%, of which about 68% (or 17% of the copolymer) is polystyrene block. No homopolystyrene is produced. The other block consists of a butadiene–styrene copolymer containing about 8% of non-block styrene.

Copolymers containing two pure blocks of, respectively, butadiene and styrene may be prepared by first polymerizing one of the monomers to completion, and then polymerizing the second monomer onto the live polymer anion of the first monomer (37). Block copolymerization may be terminated at this stage to yield an ideal two-block S–B polymer.

Three-block S–B–S polymers may be prepared by the above process by polymerizing styrene onto the live S–B polymer in a procedure which has been described in some detail (37).

Dilithio initiators, also, have been proposed for synthesis of S–B–S polymers (38). Thus, 1,2-dilithio-1,2-diphenylethane was employed as initiator of butadiene polymerization to produce, first, a terminal dianion of polybutadiene. This in turn was polymerized with styrene to produce terminal polystyrene blocks on polybutadiene.

Three-block S–B–S polymer may also be prepared by coupling polymer anions of S–B– type by means of difunctional reagents such as bis(chloromethyl) ether (39) and other reagents.

Preparation of graft block copolymers was described by Minoura and Harada (21). Cis-1,4-polybutadiene was first lithiated by means of n-butyllithium activated by N,N,N',N'-tetramethylethylenediamine (TMEDA), and styrene was block polymerized on the chain at the lithium anionic sites. Polystyrene branches grafted onto the polybutadiene amounted to as high as approximately 500% by weight. Grafting efficiency (proportion of total styrene charged which was converted to grafts) was as high as 72%.

Tate et al. (77) extensively studied TMEDA–butyllithium metalation of polybutadiene and polyisoprene, and grafting of styrene and other monomers onto the lithiated substrate. Metalation levels were in the range of 2–24 mmol/100 g polymeric substrate, in contrast with much higher levels (1850 mmol/100 g polymer) reported earlier (21). As high as 95% of the styrene employed appeared as blocks grafted on the substrate. Metalation was accompanied by chain scission.

Cunningham and Treiber (40) found that sec-butyllithium gave S–B–S block polymers of better stress-strain properties than obtained with n-butyllithium. The improvement was attributed to absence of low tensile two-block S–B polymers by reason of utilization of all sec-butyllithium in the first step of formation of polystyryllithium. Use of n-butyllithium, in contrast, may furnish initiator at later stages of polymerization, with consequent formation of butadiene–styrene diblock. Butadiene block polymers, S–B–S, were reported to give better stress-strain properties than the corresponding isoprene polymers.

Preparation of Copolymers Containing Non-Block Styrene. Large-scale preparation of solution copolymers is similar to production of polybutadiene, but requires, in addition, consideration of factors peculiar to copolymerization. Thus, in addition to problems inherent in (a) the high viscosity of the reaction mixture, and (b) the large heat of reaction, there are chemical and engineering consequences of (c) the large difference between the relative reactivity ratios of the two monomers.

Due to the high viscosity of the polymer solutions, adequate engineering measures are required in order to effect mixing of ingredients, and to handle the heat of reaction so as to control temperature.

The problem of producing copolymers containing non-block styrene is one of maintaining butadiene and styrene in the monomer mixture at the constant ratio required to yield a copolymer of specified constant differential composition db/ds as expressed by the copolymerization equation (see p. 911).

Various processes have been proposed for controlling these parameters of copolymerization.

Control of composition to produce uniformly spaced styrene units is proposed (41) by a continuous process in which the monomer ratio is maintained by addition of faster polymerizing butadiene. By rigorous control of monomer ratio in this way the resultant styrene content of the copolymer can be controlled to any desired constant value at all values of conversion.

A process is described (42) which is claimed to produce random copolymer with an arbitrarily small end block of styrene. Monomer mixture in solvent, and catalyst, are charged continuously into a reaction zone at the relatively high temperature of 90°C (or up to 150°C), and product mixture is withdrawn continuously into a finishing reactor or tubular zone. Polymerization is very fast and residence time is less than two hours. Concentration of unreacted monomer in the reaction zone is maintained at less than 3%, and any remaining monomer is completely polymerized in the final reaction zone. End block of styrene is said to be of such small proportion as to have no adverse effect on properties of the copolymer. A variation of the process employs some tetrahydrofuran, which has a randomizing effect, but increases the amount of 1,2-polybutadiene.

A process is described (43) by which butadiene and styrene at a fixed ratio are charged to a reaction zone "at a rate less than the normal polymerization rate of the system under the conditions employed." Rate of addition is governed by the temperature of the reaction mixture. Polymerization is reported to be very fast at the preferred temperature range of 100–150°C, and is described as taking place "almost instantaneously upon contact of the monomer mixture with the catalyst." Typical copolymerizations in a one-gallon reactor of a ratio of butadiene/styrene of 77/23, using 300 g of monomer, were reported to be completed to 90–100% conversion in 12–20 minutes. Block styrene determined by the chemical method (76) was reported to be 1.5%.

Polar modifiers are the basis of patented processes (30,32,33) for avoiding block styrene in copolymers. The use of ethers and amines for this purpose (30) entails an increase of the 1,2-polybutadiene microstructure above the low value (approximately 9%) characteristic of alkyllithium polymerization. Ionic modifiers of the alkali metal alkoxide type, however, are the basis of a process (12) which purportedly avoids block styrene without increasing the 1,2-polybutadiene content.

Properties of Solution Copolymers

Solution copolymers of butadiene and styrene are amorphous elastomers and have a range of properties which is extremely wide due to the broad spectrum of composition and structure. Two classes of copolymer are recognized, the basis of distinction being whether or not the styrene is in block form.

Copolymers with no chemically detectable blocks of polystyrene constitute a distinct class. Some authors have employed the term "random" to describe such copolymers. This terminology is not entirely satisfactory since small blocks of polystyrene may themselves be randomly distributed in a copolymer. Less ambiguous is the term "non-block," it being understood that styrene is the monomer referred to. Such random or non-block copolymers have properties that are optimum for automobile tires and general rubber applications.

Block copolymers, in contrast, in which the styrene is present in the form of pure blocks, as in S–B and S–B–S, are at the opposite extreme. Mixed chain block copolymers, B/S–S, are intermediate in character. The polystyrene blocks aggregate into domains which impart heterogeneity of structure. Two-block copolymers, S–B and B/S–S in raw form behave as uncured elastomers and require crosslinking for service under stress. Three-block polymers S–B–S have properties of self-cured elastomers which are processed by techniques suitable for thermoplastics, and do not require vulcanization of the polybutadiene block.

Glass-Transition Temperature. This molecular parameter, T_g, is important in consideration of an amorphous elastomer since it defines the lower limit of the rubbery state, and therefore, of practical application of the elastomer (44). In the case of block copolymers, two glass transitions are observed, the upper one corresponding to the styrene blocks, the lower to the butadiene part (45). Anderson, Weissert and Hunter (46) determined T_g by differential thermal analysis for a series of solution copolymers, and reported values from approximately $-90°C$ for very low styrene content to $-36°C$ for 51% styrene. From the data was developed, by treatment according to the Gordon, Taylor and Wood equation, a method for determining block styrene content.

In studies of correlation of structure and properties of elastomers, Weissert and Johnson (47) have proposed that T_g is probably the most important single molecular parameter, as discussed below.

Kraus, Childers and Gruver extended the original Gordon and Taylor formula relating T_g and binary copolymer composition to four terms, which correspond to the three microstructures of polybutadiene (cis-1,4-, trans-1,4- and 1,2-polybutadiene) plus polystyrene, and found good correlation between calculated and observed values of T_g for solution copolymers (45). This study included a useful comparison of the dynamic properties of four types of butadiene–styrene solution copolymer which were described as "uniformly random" (composition does not vary along the chain), "random" (composition may change along the chain, and with conversion), "block" and "ideal block" (all block sequences are uniform in composition). Some results are exhibited in terms of storage modulus in Figure 4, and in terms of damping (loss tangent) in Figure 5.

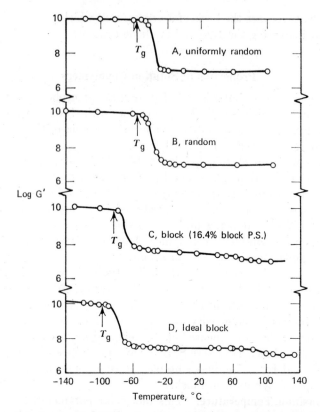

Fig. 4. Storage moduli of gum vulcanizates of random and block copolymers of butadiene–styrene of 25% total styrene content, plotted as log of storage modulus against temperature (45).

Glass-transition temperatures (Figure 4) have appreciably higher values (by 20–25°C) for random than for block copolymers. This difference reflects the two-phase character of block polymers, in which the polybutadiene is the continuous phase, and the polystyrene consists of incompatible colloidal domains. A further difference is the occurrence, in the case of block copolymers, of a second, but less distinct, glass transition at 40–100°C corresponding to the polystyrene blocks. Block copolymers lose their self-cured character at the polystyrene glass transition. Damping curves (Figure 5) distinguish sharply between random and block copolymers by exhibiting a distinct peak at the glass transition of polystyrene in the case of block copolymers. Damping peaks also reflect extent of styrene blocking and broadened molecular-weight distribution.

Properties of Non-Block Copolymers. The copolymers containing non-block styrene have properties suitable for tire treads and other tire parts, and for rubber applications generally.

Relationships between structural features and properties of these solution copolymers have been studied by Alliger and Weissert (11), Kraus and his co-workers (45), Weissert and Johnson (47), and by Hoffman, Pampus and Marwede (48). Discussion of the results was simplified (11,47) by relating such properties as processability, heat buildup of vulcanizates in service, traction of tire treads, and abrasion resistance, to mainly two measurable molecular parameters, namely, macrostructure (molecular-

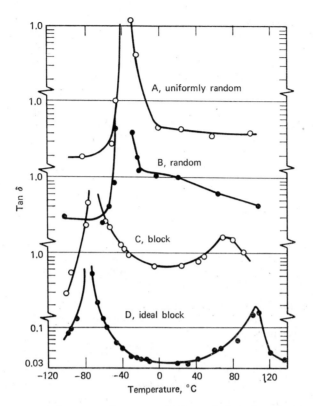

Fig. 5. Loss tangents of the gum vulcanizates of Figure 4 plotted against temperature (45).

weight distribution and branching), and glass-transition temperature. Young's modulus index (YMI) (49) was employed (11,47) as an equivalent, but somewhat more relevant substitute for T_g in discussion of vulcanizates. YMI is defined as the temperature at which Young's modulus becomes 10,000 psi; as the temperature is lowered and the rubber approaches the glass-transition region, YMI is the temperature at which the polymer becomes too stiff for many applications. A comparison of two solution copolymers with solution polybutadiene and emulsion SBR, Table 3, illustrates effects of certain structural features on properties (47).

YMI is a function of microstructure at a given styrene content. The copolymers of Table 3, compared with respect to microstructure of the polybutadiene part, are seen to exhibit significant differences. Stereon and Diene (trademarks of The Firestone Tire & Rubber Company) rubbers, polymerized by ether-free alkyllithium catalyst, have a large content of 1,4-polybutadiene structure and only 9% 1,2-polybutadiene units. The ether-modified solution copolymer has a large amount of 1,2-polybutadiene and correspondingly lower 1,4-structure. These features are reflected in glass-transition temperature and in YMI. It should be noted that the commercial polymers were significantly more narrow in molecular-weight distribution than was the emulsion polymer. In laboratory preparations with this system it is possible to achieve an even more narrow distribution.

Table 3 shows that tread wear rating and rebound increase while the coefficient of friction and the YMI values decrease.

Table 3. Solution Copolymers Compared with Polybutadiene and Emulsion SBR (47)

Condition or properties	Emulsion SBR with free radical[a]	Solution copolymers		
		High 1,2- with ether/ alkyl-Li[a]	Stereon with alkyl- lithium[a]	Diene rubber with alkyllithium[a]
medium	aqueous	hydrocarbon	hydrocarbon	hydrocarbon
molecular-weight distribution	very broad	broad[b]	broad[b]	broad[b]
styrene[c], %	23.5	25	21	0
microstructure[d]				
cis-1,4-, %	10	23	33	36
trans-1,4-, %	70	49	58	55
1,2-, %	20	28	9	9
rebound (steel ball), %				
73°F	31	33	42	52
212°F	54	61	62	63
Young's modulus index, °C	−39	−42	−55	−70
coefficient of friction on wet concrete	100	100	98	85
tread wear rating	100	100	135	145

[a] Polymer type catalyst.

[b] Especially marked by absence of low-molecular-weight fraction.

[c] Non-block styrene by the chemical method of Kolthoff and co-workers (76).

[d] Of polybutadiene part.

The tire wear rate in terms of miles per mil of tread loss is plotted against ambient temperature of road test in Figure 6. Solution copolymers (Stereon) exhibit relatively little loss in miles per mil with increase of ambient temperature in contrast with treads containing polybutadiene or emulsion SBR. Increase of miles per mil is seen at 18% styrene compared with 24% styrene.

Wear index is seen in Figure 7 to vary inversely with Young's Modulus Index.

Similar correlations of service performance with T_g have been reported in the case of other elastomers: brittle fracture at high rate of deformation and tensile failure pattern (50), arbasion resistance and resistance to tensile failure at high rate of deformation (51), and coefficient of friction (52).

High-speed testing of some solution copolymers has been studied by Weissert and Johnson (47) and by Weissert (55), as a means of more nearly approximating the actual physical situation of tire rubber in service. These results translated into tensile product, which is related to energy of breaking, and plotted against speed of testing, yield the curves of Figure 8. At high test speed of about 10^2 in./min, solution copolymer has considerably greater tensile product than solution polybutadiene, whereas, emulsion SBR has declined to a low value. At still higher test speed, above 10^4 in./min, the greater tensile product of polybutadiene than of solution copolymer reflects the high elasticity and low hysteresis of the homopolymer. (The alkyllithium-catalyzed solution polybutadiene used in the above quoted tests is Diene, trademark of The Firestone Tire & Rubber Company.)

The ether-free alkyllithium copolymer of Table 3 has macrostructure in which the molecular-weight distribution is broad, but is characterized by absence of very low-molecular-weight chains. The other two solution polymers are similar in these respects. Emulsion SBR, in contrast, has considerably broader molecular-weight distribution which includes low-molecular-weight fractions and a high degree of branching.

These aspects of macrostructure relate mainly to processing characteristics. Rheological studies of solution polymers were first made in relation to polybutadienes (23, 47,53–56) and were extended to copolymers (47,55,56). Some of the results of these studies are the following: (a) alkyllithium-initiated polymers are remarkably New-

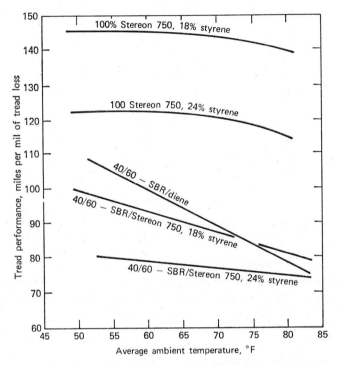

Fig. 6. Effect of ambient temperature of tire test on tread wear performance of Stereon tread compounds and mixed polymer tread compounds containing Stereon (79).

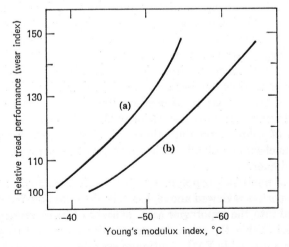

Fig. 7. Relative tread performance versus Young's modulus index for tread compounds containing, (**a**) 43 and (**b**) 31 parts of oil for 100 parts elastomer. Range of YMI in each series obtained by variation of only the polymer (47,79).

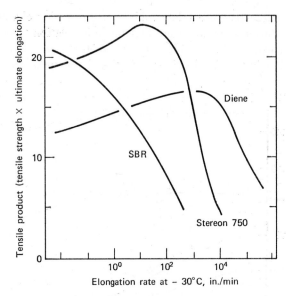

Fig. 8. Tensile product (related to breaking energy) plotted against speed at −30°C, comparing emulsion SBR, solution polybutadiene, and solution copolymer ($^1/_8$ in. specimen) (47,49).

tonian in exhibiting relatively constant bulk viscosity over a wide range of shear rates, as a result of the strict linearity of the molecules and the narrowness of the molecular-weight distribution (53); (b) introduction of branching by coupling of polymer anions (54), and otherwise broadening molecular weight while avoiding low-molecular-weight molecules (47), is an effective means of imparting non-Newtonian behavior to solution polymers. By this means the apparent bulk viscosity can be reduced to a small fraction (as low as 0.001) of the zero shear stress viscosity over a large range of shear stress. The result is greatly improved processability in contrast with linear, narrow MWD polymer, as illustrated in Figure 9, in a generalized graph for the range of shear stresses comparable to those occurring in factory processing. More detailed discussion of apparent viscosity in relation to macrostructure, with graphical comparison of solution copolymer with other elastomers has been given by Weissert (55).

Non-Block Copolymers in Automotive Tires. The largest use of non-block solution copolymers is in automotive tires. The excellent performance of this relatively new type of rubber in tires has been discussed in detail by Willis and Barbin (57). A good balance of tread wear resistance and traction on wet pavements has been achieved. Tread wear resistance is superior to that of emulsion SBR, and traction is superior to that of solution polybutadiene. A single polymer tread compound as distinguished from elastomer blends is, therefore, practical through use of alkyllithium-polymerized copolymer.

Application of non-block copolymer to tire service, employing the correlations of structure and properties reviewed above, has been discussed by Willis and Barbin (57). Features designed into the copolymer are: absence of block styrene to avoid decline of some properties (Table 4); microstructure with maximum 1,4- and minimum 1,2-polybutadiene for a favorable YMI; optimum styrene content of about 18% to retain the high wet traction of emulsion SBR (S-184) (Figure 10); macrostructure of broad MWD without the low-molecular-weight fraction typical of SBR (Figure 11) with

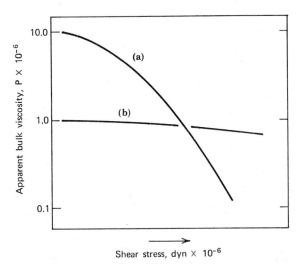

Fig. 9. Apparent bulk viscosity of solution copolymer versus shear stress, in a generalized graph, in the range encompassing factory processing shear stresses; (**a**) branched, broad MWD; (**b**), linear, narrow MWD.) (47,55,79). See reference 55 for detailed treatment and graphs.

proper branching for good processability (Figure 9). These factors combine to give tire-tread rubber of superior wear resistance, wet traction and cut growth resistance as exhibited in Figure 12.

The non-block copolymers have applications in many areas of rubber usage, as discussed in technical brochures on Solprene 1204 (Phillips Petroleum Co.) and Stereon 750 (The Firestone Synthetic Rubber & Latex Company).

Properties of Block Copolymers. A review of block copolymers with emphasis on those derived from butadiene and styrene has been published by Zelinski and Childers (58). A comprehensive symposium on anionic preparation and properties of block copolymers deals largely with butadiene–styrene block copolymers (59).

Block copolymers of butadiene with styrene, in which the proportion and molecular weight of polystyrene blocks are of sufficient magnitude, exhibit a two-phase structure (60). Polybutadiene constitutes the continuous phase in which colloidal aggregates or domains of polystyrene are dispersed. These domains of polystyrene function as particles which impart reversible self-cure to S–B–S block polymers. This heterogeneity of structure is clearly revealed by electron micrography (60–62,66); the polystyrene domains are approximately spherical and 100 Å in diameter.

Table 4. Effect of Block Styrene on Tread-Rubber Properties (57)

Properties	Styrene	
	Block-free	All-block
bound styrene, %	25	25
tensile strength, psi	3000	1700
steel ball rebound, %	42	40
running temperature, °F	280	440
YMI, °C	-50	-32
tear strength, 212°F, lb/in.	360	176
hardness, Shore A	59	71

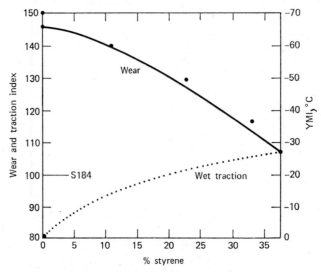

Fig. 10. Wear and traction indices, and YMI, of tire tread compounds, as functions of styrene content of non-block solution copolymers of butadiene with styrene (57).

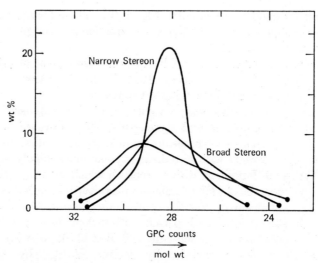

Fig. 11. Molecular-weight distribution of Stereon 750 solution copolymers in comparison with emulsion SBR. Vertical axis is weight percent of polymer of molecular weight indicated on horizontal axis in terms of gel-permeation chromatograph counts, GPC (57).

Block copolymers of S–B–S type of optimum composition exhibit high resilience, high tensile strength, reversible elongation, and good abrasion resistance. In contrast, B–S–B and S–B copolymers behave as unvulcanized elastomers, even though they exhibit polystyrene domain formation.

Block length and proportions of butadiene and styrene in S–B–S copolymers are important in realizing elastomer performance. Minimum styrene block molecular weight of 5000–10,000 is required for domain formation, corresponding to a minimum polybutadiene molecular weight of the order of 40,000 (60,63). The minimum for polybutadiene is the value required to form a continuous rather than a domain phase

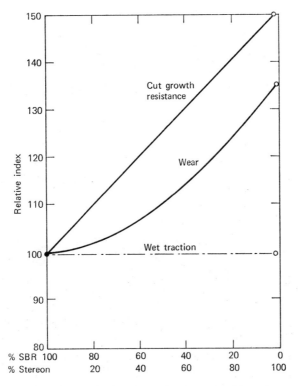

Fig. 12. Performance indices of tire tread compounds of blends of butadiene-styrene solution copolymer Stereon 750 with emulsion SBR (57).

of polybutadiene. The useful range of block molecular weights is about 10,000–20,000
for polystyrene, and 40,000–80,000 for polybutadiene (64). The upper limit corresponds to the region of high viscosity of both polystyrene and polybutadiene, which
would interfere with domain formation.

Within the above limits of molecular weight of blocks, stress-strain properties
are dependent mainly on polystyrene content (40,60,64), and very little on molecular
weight. Figure 13 shows stress-strain results for styrene contents from 13–80%. At
13% styrene the block copolymer behaves like rubber at very low state of cure. At
28% styrene, stress-strain behavior approaches that of vulcanized rubber. At 39–53%
styrene the copolymers exhibit a yield stress followed by cold draw and finally elastic
extension. Above these values of styrene content yield stress increases to large values
and elastic extension vanishes.

Above the glass transition of the end blocks the S–B–S copolymers flow as thermoplastics. Upon cooling, the self-cured behavior is fully recovered through formation of
styrene domains (60).

Melt viscosities of the copolymers are much greater than those of either homopolymer of the same total molecular weight, reflecting the energy of transfer of the
end block from one aggregate to another through the elastomeric matrix (60).

The nature of the network of S–B–S polymers was studied by Bishop and Davison
(65), on the basis of swelling experiments. It was found that the molecular weight between crosslinks, M_c, was much smaller than the molecular weight of the polybutadiene

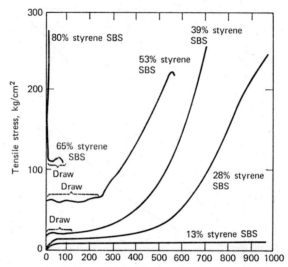

Fig. 13. Stress-strain curves for S–B–S block copolymers of various styrene contents. Specimen length, 1 in.; rate of elongation, 2 in./min. (60).

block. Thus, M_c, dependent on both polystyrene domains and points of permanent entanglement of polybutadiene chains, ranged from $\frac{1}{13}$ to $\frac{1}{4}$ of the value of molecular weight of the middle polybutadiene block in a representative series of copolymers. Also, M_c decreased appreciably with increase of volume fraction of styrene, which is equivalent to increase of crosslink density as in the case of conventional vulcanizates containing reinforcing filler. Reinforcing activity of the polystyrene domains was found to be approximately equivalent to that of reinforcing carbon black.

Variations of morphological details of S–B–S polymers as influenced by solvent, temperature and deformation were studied by Beecher, Marker, Bradford and Aggarwal (66) by means of electron microscopy. Solvents representing a wide range of polarity and solubility parameters used for solution casting of specimens were shown to have a great effect on the morphology of the polymers. Corresponding variations in damping versus temperature, in stress-strain results, in size of polystyrene domains, and other effects were observed.

Applications of Block Copolymers. Three-block S–B–S copolymers of the Kraton series have been summarized by Higginbottom and Hendricks with respect to properties and applications (67). Five series of types varying from soft to hard are proposed for applications in adhesives, caulks, sealants, coatings, food packaging, toys, tubing, sheeting, molding equipment, belting, shoe soles and heels, and other uses. A variety of processing methods are indicated: solution or hot-melt techniques, extrusion, injection molding, blow molding, thermoforming, calendering, and Banbury or other high shear mixing techniques.

Adhesives applications of Kraton block polymers have been discussed in detail by Bailey (68), in terms of solvents, resins and antioxidants in the processing and compounding of contact, pressure-sensitive, and hot-melt adhesives.

Alfin Copolymers of Butadiene with Styrene

The alfin catalyst for solution polymerization, composed of sodium isopropoxide, allylsodium, and sodium chloride was discovered by A. A. Morton in the mid 1940's.

It was studied in considerable detail by the discoverer and his co-workers during the next decade (2b,2c). The name alfin was coined from the first and last syllables of respectively, alcohol and olefin, two of the four reactants used in preparation of the catalyst. Much fundamental and developmental work was done on the catalyst and the polymers and copolymers in the Rubber Reserve Company synthetic rubber program until its termination in 1955.

Copolymers of butadiene with styrene were studied in the early program and were tested in tires where they were reported (2b) to exceed emulsion copolymers in tread wear rating (117 compared to 100).

Molecular weight of the early alfin polymers at typical dilute solution viscosities of 8–10 was characteristically too high for satisfactory processing by conventional factory methods. Consequently, interest in alfin elastomers lagged until recent discovery by Greenberg and Hansley (69) of a method for controlling molecular weight. It was found that 1,4-dihydronaphthalene (DHN) is a very effective regulator of chain length in all alfin polymerizations, making available for the first time a series of processable polymers and copolymers of this class (70,71). These elastomers have been named Hytrans, a trademark of National Distillers and Chemical Corporation. Approximately 1.5% of DHN on the monomers produces polymer having molecular weight of about 300,000, and Mooney viscosity of about 40. Processing characteristics have been reported to be satisfactory.

Commercial production of a series of alfin elastomers has been reported to be scheduled for late 1970, by Nippon Alfin Rubber Company, Ltd., Tokyo (72), a licensee of National Distillers. Capacity of the plant is to be 30,000 tons per year. Butadiene–styrene copolymers of a 5 and 15% styrene content and oil extended counterparts of these are among the polymers to be produced.

The microstructure of the polybutadiene part of the butadiene–styrene copolymers was reported to contain 1,4-*trans*, 1,4-*cis*, and 1,2-polybutadiene in the ratio of 70:10:20, as in alfin polybutadiene.

The crystallinity of the alfin elastomers is particularly noted by Sato (72) who refers to this property as "the most outstanding feature of alfin rubber." Transition is observed between 40 and 90°C from stiff to soft polymer. At the upper temperature alfin rubber is said to process very nearly like emulsion SBR. Stiffness at room temperature eliminates cold flow, which is advantageous in storage. Sato notes that due to crystallinity the green strength of alfin rubber compounds is the greatest of all rubbers (149 psi for B/S 85/15 copolymer, against 116 psi for natural rubber RSS No. 1, and 34 psi for emulsion SBR).

Compounding, processing, physical properties, and performance in automotive tires have been discussed in some detail in the references given. Performance rating of tire treads of alfin copolymer containing 85% butadiene and 15% styrene in comparison with a control containing a mixture of 65% emulsion SBR and 35% *cis*-polybutadiene and rated at 100, has been reported (173) as follows,: tread wear 132; dynamic traction on packed snow 100 to 103, on ice (dry) 123, on wet asphalt 120; static starting traction on ice (dry) 109, on wet asphalt 113; braking rating (distance to stop) on ice (dry) 110, on dry asphalt 102, on wet asphalt 105.

PLANT CAPACITIES

As of 1970 the production of butadiene–styrene solution rubbers is included in production figures of solution polybutadiene, and many of the plant capacities for making the two products are presented as combined figures.   The following copolymer information, however, is available (74).

Solution butadiene–styrene plants in the U.S.	*Capacity, long tons*
Firestone, Lake Charles, La.	80,000
Phillips, Borger, Texas	23,750

Bibliography

1. Brit. Pat. 24,700 (1910)—F. E. Matthews and E. H. Strange.
2a. R. L. Bebb and L. B. Wakefield, "German Synthetic Rubber Developments," in G. S. Whitby, ed., *Synthetic Rubber*, John Wiley & Sons, Inc., New York, 1954, Chap. 26.
2b. W. K. Taft and G. J. Tiger, "Diene Polymers and Copolymers other than GR-S and the Specialty Rubbers," *ibid.*, Chap. 21.
2c. A. A. Morton, "Alfin Catalysts," in *Encyclopedia of Polymer Science and Technology*, Vol. 1, Interscience Publishers, a division of John Wiley & Sons, Inc., New York, 1964, pp. 629–638.
3. C. S. Marvel, W. J. Bailey, and G. E. Inskeep, *J. Polymer Sci.* **1**, 275–88 (1946).
4a. Erik G. M. Törnqvist, "The Historical Background of Synthetic Elastomers with Particular Emphasis on the Early Period," in J. P. Kennedy and Erik G. M. Törnqvist, eds., *Polymer Chemistry of Synthetic Elastomers*, Part I, Interscience Publishers, a division of John Wiley & Sons, Inc., New York, 1968, Chap. 2.
4b. L. E. Forman, *ibid.*, Part II, 1969, Chap. 6.
5. J. D. D'Ianni, *Ind. Eng. Chem.* **40**, 253–6 (1948).
6. A. A. Morton, *Ind. Eng. Chem.* **42**, 1488 (1950).
7. F. W. Stavely and co-workers, *Ind. Eng. Chem.* **48**, 778 (1956).
8. G. Alliger, B. L. Johnson, and L. E. Forman, *Kautschuk Gummi* **4**, 48, 248 WT (1961).
9a. N. N. Chesnokova and A. A. Korotkov, *Theses of Reports to the Ninth Conference on the General Problems of Chemistry and Physics of High Molecular Compounds, (Moscow, 1956)*, p. 32.   This reference is cited in the following reference and is stated to contain information on the inversion of reactivities of butadiene and styrene in copolymerization by butyllithium.
9b. G. V. Rakova and A. A. Korotkov, *Rubber Chem. Technol.* **33**, 623 (1960).
9c. A. A. Korotkov, *International Symposium Macromolecular Chem., Prague, Sept., 1957, Paper 66; Angew. Chem.* **70**, 85 (1958).
9d. A. A. Korotkov and co-workers, *Vysokomolekul. Soedin.* **2**, 356, 1811 (1960); **5**, 212 (1963).
9e. S. P. Mitsengendler and co-workers, *Vysokomol. Soedin.* **5**, 212 (1963).
10. W. W. Crouch, *Rubber Plastics Age* **42**, 276 (1961).
11. G. Alliger and F. C. Weissert, *Rev. Gen. Caoutchouc* **43**, 1321–8 (1966).
12. U.S. Pat. 3,294,768 (Dec. 27, 1966), C. F. (Wofford to Phillips Petroleum Co.).
13. C. F. Wofford and H. L. Hsieh, *J. Polymer Sci. A1*, **7**, 461–469 (1969).
14a. German Pat. 1,225,391 (Sept. 22, 1966), Herbert Mueller (to BASF).
14b. French Pat. 1,458,322 (Nov. 10, 1966), Bridgestone Tire Co.
14c. German Pat. 1,245,130 (July 20, 1967), Herman Winter and co-workers (to Chemische Werke Huels, A-G.).
15a. K. F. O'Driscoll and I. Kuntz, *J. Polymer Sci.* **61**, 19–24 (1962).
15b. Herman Mark and co-workers, "Copolymerization Reactivity Ratios" in J. Brandrup and E. Immergut, eds., *Polymer Handbook*, Interscience Publishers, New York, 1966, II–141.
16a. H. L. Hsieh and W. H. Glaze, *Rubber Chem. Technol.* **43**, 22–73 (1970).
16b. Maurice Morton, "Anionic Copolymerizations" in G. E. Ham, ed., *Copolymerization*, Interscience Publishers, New York, 1964, Chap. 7.
17a. V. D. Mochel and B. L. Johnson, *Fourth International Synthetic Rubber Symposium, London, Sept. 30–Oct. 2, 1969, Issue No. 3*, pp. 74–79 (Dec., 1969).
17b. V. D. Mochel, *Rubber Chem. Technol.* **40**, 1200–11 (1967).
18. V. D. Mochel, and W. E. Claxton, *J. Polymer Sci. A-1* **9**, 345–362 (1971).
19. U.S. Pat. 3,363,659 (Jan. 16, 1968), N. F. Keckler and B. L. Johnson (to The Firestone Tire & Rubber Co.).
20. R. P. Zelinski and C. F. Wofford, *J. Polymer Sci. A-3*, 93 (1965).

21. Yuji Minoura and Hiroshi Harada, *J. Polymer Sci. A-1*, **7**, 3–14 (1969).

22. British Pat. 1,177,787 (Jan. 14, 1970), Asahi Kasei Kogyo Kabushiki Kaisha, Osaka, Japan.

23. B. L. Johnson, H. E. Adams, F. C. Weissert, and K. Farhat, *The Proceedings of the International Rubber Conference, Brighton, England. 1967*, pp. 29–43.

24. H. E. Adams, *Paper Presented at 159th National American Chemical Society Meeting, Houston, Texas, February, 1970.*

25. E. W. Duck, D. P. Grieve, and M. N. Thornber, *Fourth International Synthetic Rubber Symposium, London, Issue No. 3*, 88–91 (Dec., 1969).

26. Unpublished Results, The Firestone Tire & Rubber Co., Akron, Ohio.

27. V. A. Kropachev, B. A. Dolyoplask, and N. I. Nikolaev, *Doklady Akad. Nauk. S.S.S.R.* **115**, 516 (1957).

28. U.S. Pat. 3,301,840 (Jan. 31, 1967), R. P. Zelinski (to Phillips Petroleum Co.).

29. H. L. Hsieh and C. F. Wofford, *J. Polymer Sci. A-1*, **7**, 449–460 (1969).

30. U.S. Pat. 2,975,160 (Mar. 14, 1961), Robert P. Zelinski (to Phillips Petroleum Co.).

31. Irving Kuntz, *J. Polymer Sci.* **54**, 569–86 (1961).

32. C. F. Wofford and H. L. Hsieh, *J. Polymer Sci. A-1*, **7**, 461–469 (1969).

33a. U.S. Pat. 3,496,154 (Feb. 17, 1970), C. F. Wofford (to Phillips Petroleum Co.).

33b. U.S. Pat. 3,498,960 (Mar. 3, 1970), C. F. Wofford (to Phillips Petroleum Co.).

34. T. Antkowiak, A. E. Oberster, A. F. Halasa, and D. P. Tate, in press, The Firestone Tire and Rubber Co., *J. Polymer Science, A-1* (1970).

35. L. J. Fetters, *J. Polymer Sci. C* **26**, 1–35 (1969).

36. Brit. Pat. 817,693 (Aug. 6, 1959), The Firestone Tire & Rubber Co.

37. U.S. Pat. 3,265,765 (Aug. 9, 1966), G. Holden and R. Milkovich (to Shell Oil Co.).

38. U.S. Pat. 3,251,905 (May 17, 1966), R. P. Zelinski (to Phillips Petroleum Co.).

39. U.S. Pat. 3,078,254 (Feb. 19, 1963), R. P. Zelinski and H. L. Hsieh (to Phillips Petroleum Co.).

40. R. E. Cunningham and M. R. Treiber, *J. Appl. Polymer Sci.* **12**, 23–34 (1968).

41. Canadian Pat. 769,096 (Oct. 10, 1967), The Firestone Tire & Rubber Co.

42. Brit. Pat. 1,136,189 (Dec. 11, 1968), to Shell International Research.

43. U.S. Pat. 3,094,512 (June 18, 1963), J. N. Short (to Phillips Petroleum Co.).

44. A. V. Tobolsky, *Properties and Structure of Polymers*, John Wiley & Sons, Inc., New York, 1960, pp. 71–78.

45. C. W. Kraus, C. W. Childers, and J. T. Gruver, *J. Appl. Polymer Sci.* **11**, 1581 (1967).

46. J. N. Anderson, F. C. Weissert, and C. J. Hunter, *Rubber Chem. Technol.* **42**, 918–923 (1969).

47. F. C. Weissert and B. L. Johnson, *Rubber Chem. Technol.* **40**, 590–601 (1967).

48. M. Hoffman, G. Pampus, and G. Marwede, *Kautschuk Gummi*, **22** (12), 691–706 (1969).

49. "Young's Modulus Index," *ASTM D797-58.*

50. T. L. Smith, *J. Appl. Phys.* **35**, 27 (1964).

51. K. A. Grosch and A. Schallamach, *Trans. Inst. Rubber Ind.* **41**, T80 (1965).

52. K. A. Grosch, *Proc. Roy. Soc. (London)* **A274**, 21 (1963).

53. J. T. Gruver and G. Kraus, *J. Polymer Sci. A 2*, 797 (1964).

54. Gerard Kraus and J. T. Gruver, *J. Polymer Sci. A 3*, 105 (1965).

55. F. C. Weissert, *Rubber Chem. Technol.* **42**, 903–917 (1969).

56. G. Kraus and J. T. Gruver, *Transactions of the Society of Rheology* **9** (2), 17 (1965).

57. J. M. Willis and W. W. Barbin, *Rubber Age* **100** (7), 53–56 (1968).

58. Robert Zelinski and C. W. Childers, *Rubber Chem. Technol.* **41**, 161–181 (1968).

59. J. Moacanin, G. Holden, and N. W. Tschogel, *J. Polymer Sci. C* (**26**); *Polymer Symposia, Block Copolymers*, edited by above, Interscience Publishers, New York, 1969.

60. G. Holden, E. T. Bishop, and N. R. Legge, *J. Polymer Sci. C* **26**, 37–57 (1969).

61. H. Hendus, K. H. Illers, and E. Ropte, *Kolloid-Z.* **216/217**, 110–119 (1967).

62. E. B. Bradford and E. Vanzo, *J. Polymer Sci. A-1* **6**, 1661–1670 (1968).

63. D. J. Meier, *J. Polymer Sci. C* **26**, 81–98 (1969).

64a. Maurice Morton, James E. McGrath, and Peter C. Juliano, *J. Polymer Sci. C* (**26**), 99–115 (1969).

64b. M. Morton, L. J. Fetters, F. C. Schwab, C. R. Strauss, and R. F. Kammereck, *Fourth International Synthetic Rubber Symposium, Issue No. 3*, 70–73 (London, Dec., 1969).

65. E. T. Bishop and S. Davison, *J. Polymer Sci. C* **26**, 59–79 (1969).

66. J. F. Beecher, L. Marker, R. D. Bradford, and S. L. Aggarwal, *J. Polymer Sci. C* **26**, 117–134 (1969).

67. Brian Higginbottom and W. R. Hendricks, "Styrene–Butadiene" in S. Gross, ed., *Modern-Plastics Encyclopedia*, Vol. 46, No. 10A, McGraw-Hill, Book Co., Inc., New York, 1969, pp. 241–242.

68. J. T. Bailey, *J. Elastoplastics*, **1**, 2 (1969).

69. U.S. Pat. 3,067,187 (Dec. 4, 1962); U.S. Pat. 3,223,691 (Dec. 14, 1965), H. Greenberg and V. L. Hansley (to National Distillers and Chemical Corp.).

70. V. L. Hansley and H. Greenberg, *Rubber Chem. Technol.* **38**, 103–111 (1965).

71. R. G. Newberg, L. D. Grinninger, and H. Greenberg, *Rubber World* **161** (2), 67–70 (1969).

72. T. Sato, *Rubber Age* **102** (1), 64–71 (1970).

73. *Chem. and Eng. News* **47**(44), 46 (1969).

74. *Rubber Plastics Age* **50** (11), Card No. 402, 403 (1969).

75. M. Morton and R. Sanderson, *Seminar at Akron University, Akron, Ohio, May 14, 1968*.

76. I. M. Kolthoff, T. S. Lee, and C. W. Carr, *J. Polymer Sci.* **1**, 429 (1946).

77. D. P. Tate, A. F. Halasa, F. J. Webb, R. W. Koch and A. E. Oberster, *J. Polymer Sci. A-1* **9**, 139–145 (1971).

78. H. L. Hsieh, *Rubber Plastics Age* **46**, 394–401 (1965).

79. *Stereon 750, A Stereospecific Copolymer*, Technical Publication of Firestone Synthetic Rubber & Latex Company, Akron, Ohio, April 1, 1968.

R. L. Bebb
E. L. Carr
Firestone Tire & Rubber Company

T

TEXTILE TECHNOLOGY

The following topics are discussed:

ADHESIVES FOR CARPET BACKING AND APPAREL

The subject of adhesives used in the textile industry covers an extremely broad field. Emphasis here will be directed toward carpet backing and bonded fabrics for apparel. Many of the compounds discussed could also be used for flocking adhesives, pile adhesives for backing upholstery fabrics, seaming compounds, edging compounds, threadless sewing, etc.

Application Techniques

Before considering the adhesives themselves, it is well to review briefly the various methods by which the adhesives may be applied. Probably the oldest and simplest method of lamination is by so-called wet lamination where the adhesive is applied by a rotating applicator roll dipping into a tray of the adhesive and applying it to the fabric which passes over it. A knife or scraper bar may be employed to either level off or meter the amount of coating applied. Immediately, or after partial drying, (depending on the adhesive properties), the coated fabric is brought into contact with the second fabric of the laminate. The two fabrics are then passed together either through squeeze rolls or simply over a series of rotating, heated cans where intimate contact is maintained and drying accomplished. Alternatively, after passing through the squeeze rolls, the fabric could be carried on a pin tenter frame over a bank of steam coils or other heat source to accomplish drying.

A modification of the system using a gravure printing roll or a transfer roll permits the adhesive to be applied to the fabric in either a print pattern or in stripes. This type of system offers the possibility of a patterned application of the adhesive or the application of adhesive with intermittent bonding producing softer, more conformable, and more pliable combined fabrics. Although it is not commonly practiced, it is also possible to apply the adhesive by spray, either continuously or in a pattern, followed by the same lamination and drying procedures as above.

Finally, under wet lamination, we should consider the application of adhesive by a spreader bar or knife. In this operation, an adhesive of a much higher viscosity is employed. The adhesive is spread behind a knife which scrapes against the fabric and applies an even coat of adhesive. Variously, the knife may be over a roll, over a moving blanket or the fabric may be supported only by tension. These three methods are appropriately called knife over roll, knife over blanket, and knife over air. Lamination to the secondary fabric by squeeze rolls and drying over steam coils or on dry cans is accomplished as noted above.

A second type of adhesive system is the hot melt. Properly considered, hot melts are those applications where the adhesive is applied either from a water system, or a solvent system, by any of the methods already noted, after which the adhesive is dried. At a later stage, the fabric with the adhesive is brought in contact with a secondary fabric and adhesion is accomplished by passing through heated calender rolls. A modification of the hot-melt system which has grown in importance and volume is the use of powdered adhesives which are distributed over the fabric by a rotating brush, vibrating screens or even electrostatic action after which the adhesive and fabric are heated to a point where the adhesive powder softens and adheres to the fabric. At this point, a second fabric may be introduced and lamination completed or the fabric with the powdered adhesive adhered to it may be rolled up and later bonded as described above.

The third type of adhesive application is extrusion. The heated molten adhesive is extruded from a trough either by gravity or, more commonly, under pressure as a thin film which falls and is picked up by the fabric passing under it. The combined fabric and adhesive film may then be passed over a chill roll for later lamination, or alternatively, a second fabric may be introduced prior to the chill roll using the film as the laminating adhesive.

The fourth and final type of adhesive system is flame lamination using urethan foam as the binding mechanism. Although when first introduced, flame lamination was beset by many difficulties, it has in the past few years been greatly improved and today is a very popular and successful system. Flame lamination is generally confined, however, to applications where a foam-to-fabric assembly is desired or perhaps where two fabrics may be laminated together with the foam in the middle of the sandwich. In any case, the foam is passed through an oven containing carefully controlled and positioned gas flames which actually melt the surface of the foam, at which point the foam and the fabric are brought into immediate contact. Upon cooling, the foam and fabric are securely bonded together. By carefully controlling the heating, the pressure, and the foam cell size, it is possible to develop a considerable degree of discreet particle lamination and extremely soft, pliable, and conformable laminates can be produced. It is also possible to repeat the process, with the foam laminated to one fabric, and laminate a second fabric to the other side of the foam. In fact, in some applications, an extremely thin layer of foam is used and after the lamination is completed, little, if any, foam still remains, it having served only as the adhesive. Although the process of flame lamination was originally developed as a means of bonding foam to fabric, its use in the double flame process for the lamination of two fabrics with a very thin, if any, foam layer left between them has now made it necessary to consider foams as adhesives.

Adhesives for Carpet Backing

The tufting of carpets has become a multibillion dollar development with rapid growth from 1960 to 1970. Much of the success has been due to the tuft anchoring power of the adhesives which serve simultaneously to bond secondary backings. Many physical and chemical properties of the adhesive used in bonding or laminating a secondary backing to a carpet are important and must be considered in the selection of the adhesive. Among these are the type of backing fabric and face or pile yarns, since the adhesive used must be adherent to both the pile fiber and the backing, to provide adequate adhesion of the backing fabric as well as to lock the pile fiber securely in the completed carpet. The "hand," or resilience, of the finished carpet as affected by the adhesive backing must also be taken into account. Many otherwise satisfactory materials from an adhesive point of view are too dead or lacking in resilience with the result that a carpet which has been rolled up will not lie flat when unrolled. It is of special importance in the case of outdoor carpet but is also important for indoor carpets to have an adhesive with adequate water resistance, to withstand the normal processes of carpet cleaning. A degree of solvent resistance is sometimes required for protection against spot removers as well as the possibility of the carpet absorbing finishing materials from the floor which may cause a deterioration of the adhesive. The ageing properties of the adhesive must be given careful consideration to avoid the pitfalls of an unsatisfactory product as the result of either a drying up or stiffening of the adhesive. Conversely a breakdown of the adhesive to a soft tacky mass could result in poor bond as well as sticking to a finished wood floor with damage to the floor and loss of the carpet. Flame resistance is also extremely important.

After choosing a satisfactory adhesive for all of the above chemical and physical requirements, cost becomes the most important deciding factor and indeed may in many cases necessitate a compromise in some of the desired properties to permit the manufacturer to maintain a competitive position. The caseins and the starches and some other natural adhesives were tried in the very early stages of carpet development, but failed to meet the strict specifications. The first and most satisfactory adhesive for carpet backing was natural rubber latex. See Vol. 17, p. 674.

For certain purposes the natural latex as received could be considered an adequate adhesive without further processing. However, to obtain satisfactory ageing, antioxidants and inhibitors are added as well as additional stabilizers, curing agents, and viscosity modifiers. Finally, in an attempt to reduce the cost of the adhesive, it is common practice to add fillers or extenders.   These consist of natural clays, carbonates, and silicates which are dispersed in water with suitable dispersing agents prior to their addition to the latex. However these fillers do not necessarily reduce the cost of the adhesive as much as one might expect. There are two prime reasons for this, the first being that the addition of the filler generally raises the unit weight or weight per gallon of the adhesive; thus the cost per pound of the adhesive may have been reduced, but the adhesive is applied on a volume basis, and the cost per gallon is the important factor. The second is that a certain amount of the adhesive or binding power of the natural rubber must be employed to bind the filler together and therefore some adhesive value is lost for the prime purpose of binding the backing to the carpet. As a result, more adhesive has to be used to get the required binding power, and often the cost has not been reduced. In this regard, one outstanding property of natural latex is that it has probably the highest "loading tolerance" of any of the elastomeric materials. Loading refers to the percentage of extender or filler on a solids basis that may safely be added without undue deterioration of the properties.

Natural latex dominated the carpet-backing field for many years dating back to the period before tufted carpets. Eventually the natural oils in the wood finishes, the contamination from copper and manganese either from the rug processing equipment, or copper-containing dyestuff, began to cause increasing numbers of complaints that the backing of the rugs was becoming soft and sticky. Unfortunately, natural rubber is very susceptible to oxidation, catalyzed by trace amounts of copper and manganese. For some time rubber backing on carpets became unpopular. However, improvements in the processing and the development of new copper and manganese inhibitors which could be incorporated in the compounds made possible the production of satisfactory material. Progress was further spurred by the rapidly increasing market for secondary backed carpeting with a satisfactory flexible secure bond. Thus the use of rubber backing began to grow again and natural latex began to enjoy a greater demand.

Almost simultaneously, synthetic latexes made their appearance, based on styrene butadiene, and referred to as SBR (see Vol. 7, p. 679). These latexes can be compounded in much the same manner as natural latex. They do not have as high a susceptibility to copper and manganese and are a domestically produced product and therefore free from vagaries of wars and internal strife in the producing areas. However, probably the greatest inducement to the development and growth of the synthetic latexes was the fact that they could be produced at a lower cost than natural latex and that, more importantly, being a synthetic product, they were available at a stable price, whereas natural latex being a natural commodity continually varied in price, depending on the productivity of the plantations and the immediate market demand, together with a variety of political and domestic situations in the producing areas. Volumes could be and indeed have been written on the various styrene–butadiene and other synthetic latexes and those interested in a detailed study are referred to the literature for the complete information. Briefly, however, the SBR latexes are divided into two classes, differentiated by the temperature of the original polymerization. They are the "hot latexes" which were the first ones produced and later the "cold latexes." Speaking in general terms the cold latexes tend to exhibit better wet gel strength, and less odor, and are available in higher solids content. Generally, too, they have better tensile strength without a sacrifice in flexibility, particularly at low

Table 1. General Properties of SBR 2001 and SBR 2105

Property	SBR 2001	SBR 2105
solids, %	37–39	60
monomer ratio, B/S	50/50	70/30
pH	10.5–11.5	10.5
free styrene, %	0.19	0.1
bound styrene, %	44–48	25
total soap, %	7	5–7
type of soap	rosin acid	rosin acid and fatty acid
surface tension, dyn/cm	48-60	45
Mooney viscosity, ML-4	20–40	140

temperatures. The SBR latexes can be additionally classified into two groups called the *rubber latexes*, which contain 50% or more butadiene and 50% or less styrene, and the *resin latexes*, which contain less than 50% butadiene and more than 50% styrene. For rug backing purposes two latexes have been most commonly used; the first of these being of the hot type, SBR 2001, the general properties of which are tabulated in Table 1. A second common hot SBR is type 2000 which is almost identical to the type 2001 except that the Mooney viscosity is 60–90. The Mooney viscosity of a latex is a measure of the plasticity of the unvulcanized rubber made from it. The difference in the Mooney viscosity of the two latexes above indicates that the unvulcanized film of type 2001 is very soft and plastic and therefore will offer better adhesion and maintain better tear strength in the applications where it is used, whereas the type 2000 has somewhat better cohesive strength.

Of the cold SBR latexes the commonest one today in the rug backing field is type 2105, the general properties of which are also listed in Table 1.

A wide range of butadiene to styrene ratios exists all the way from 100% butadiene (SBR-2004 and 2104) to a latex containing 85% styrene and 15% butadiene. All of the SBR latexes of the classes above discussed require compounding in a manner very similar to that needed for natural rubber and indeed the reason for this is not surprising considering that they were originally synthesized to be a substitute for natural rubber. Butadiene (qv) is closely related to isoprene (qv), which is the basic monomer of natural rubber. Therefore, the addition of antioxidants, sulfur, accelerators, stabilizers and the like follow very closely the compounding of natural rubber. There are, however, a few differences, some of which have already been noted above. The SBR latexes are not subject to catalyzed oxidation by copper and manganese. Further, if they do oxidize, in contrast to natural rubber, they go only to a less flexible dry film. They do not revert to a soft tacky material. It is also common practice in the compounding of adhesives from the SBR latexes to add tackifying resins. This is often necessary because of one further difference between the synthetic and the natural rubber latex. The synthetic rubber latexes do not exhibit the same degree of tack or pressure sensitivity in their wet state as does natural rubber latex.

Taking all of the factors of serviceability, cost, physical properties and others, as discussed in the foregoing, into account, it becomes the chemist's responsibility to formulate a satisfactory adhesive. The type of latex, the filler content, and solids can be varied considerably, but the formulas in Table 2 are typical of those in commercial use.

Table 2. Three Typical Carpet Backing Formulations

Components	Parts solids		
	1	2	3
Natural Rubber Latex 60-64TS	100		
SBR 2105 (curing type)		100	
SBR resin latex (self curing)			100
zinc oxide	3	5	
sulfur	2	1.0	
accelerator[a]	0.5–1.0	1.5	
antioxidant[a]	0.5–1.0	1.0	0.5–1.0
clay and whiting (CaCO₃)	50–300	25–150	100–200
thickener[b]	to desired viscosity	to desired viscosity	to desired viscosity

[a] For detailed information on accelerators, antioxidants and other compounding ingredients, the reader is referred to the *Vanderbilt Latex Handbook* (1).

[b] Thickeners used may include various types, such as polyacrylates, casein, ethyl and/or methyl cellulose or natural gums.

For many years, the butadiene–styrene latexes represented in Table 1 were the only ones available. However, demands for improved solvent resistance resulted in the development of a new series of synthetic latexes still based on butadiene but having acrylonitrile as the second monomer in place of styrene. These have been made available as is the case in the SBR latexes in a variety of ratios of butadiene to acrylonitrile. Again, the compounding of these is similar to that for the SBR latexes or natural latex. A still later improvement in the butadiene–acrylonitrile latexes was the development of the reactive or carboxylic modified butadiene–acrylonitriles. These latexes could be made to cure or vulcanize in the presence of small amounts of zinc or aluminum salts in a slightly alkaline medium. This reaction would take place either rapidly at elevated temperatures or would take place in a period of 24–48 hours at room temperature, thus eliminating the need for the longer cure, time delay and the larger ovens required to process backings made from early materials. The higher cost of the butadiene–acrylonitrile latexes was a deterrent to their acceptance in the carpet backing field. However, in those special applications where solvent resistance was required they began to make some inroads. This progress was, however, rather short-lived due to the later development of the acrylic latexes which offered many advantages in addition to solvent resistance and were available initially at a price equivalent to the butadiene–acrylonitriles and are now (1971) available at prices considerably below them. Today many acrylic latexes are available, at prices competitive with some of the medium to lower cost styrene–butadiene latexes, from a number of manufactureres including the Chemical Division of Goodyear Tire and Rubber, the Chemical Division of B. F. Goodrich Company, Uniroyal, Inc., and Firestone Tire and Rubber Company. The acrylic latexes, particularly with the advent of lower prices, have been looked at in the past few years much more carefully as adhesives for carpet backing. They offer some distinct advantages. They have excellent ageing properties; they do not yellow or discolor and, especially with the advent of the reactive types, can be made highly water and solvent resistant. Curing times can be shortened materially without a sacrifice in properties, leading to an increase in production speed. The methods of application are identical with those for the other types of water-based latexes.

The final adhesive system to be considered for carpet backing is that of hot melts. Originally, the term hot melt adhesive denoted thermoplastic adhesives which were applied in the molten form largely in the paper industry for packaging and for book binding. Recently, attempts have been made to adapt this system of adhesion to the secondary carpet-backing application. There are essentially two methods for applying hot melts. The first is to extrude the material from a slot in the molten form as a thin film onto the carpet after which the adhesive must be reheated to develop sufficient penetration into the pile yarns. At the time of this reheating, the secondary backing is also applied and the complete structure passed through chilled squeeze rolls to complete the bond.

The second method of application is very similar to that used for latex application except that the reservoir trough under the kiss roll is heated in order to melt the adhesive. The adhesive is then picked up by the kiss roll and applied to the carpet, after which the secondary backing is immediately brought into place and again the two are passed through chilled squeeze rolls. This second method offers the advantage that a lower viscosity adhesive can be used and therefore adequate penetration is obtained without the necessity of a secondary heating.

Both of these systems offer some very distinct advantages to the carpet producer. There is no water or solvent to be evaporated and removed, and no extended drying or curing oven is needed. This offers not only a reduction in cost and a speed-up in operation but also, the very fact that the carpet does not have to be passed through a hot zone means that the pile is not subjected to potential damage from the heat.

The present hot melt systems are based primarily on ethylene–vinyl acetate copolymers and these materials compared to latex are relatively expensive. It is possible to reduce the cost by the addition of some extender resins such as low-melting polyolefin waxes. It is difficult to incorporate satisfactorily the usual type of clay and carbonate fillers used with latex. However, the type of extenders used have a lower specific gravity of approximately 1.0, which is considerably less than that of the clay-filled latex adhesives so that although the adhesive may cost somewhat more per pound, the total weight applied is less. It is claimed that satisfactory results are obtained with hot melt adhesives using between 12 and 16 oz/yd^2. More precise data are not available.

Table 3 summarizes the salient properties of the five major hot melts in use today.

Table 3. Properties of Five Major Hot Melts

	Polyamide	Polyesters	Polyethylene	Polypropylene	Ethylene–vinyl acetate
tensile strength, psi	7–12,000	1–6,000	1500–5000	4–5000	1500–3000
hardness, Shore D	50–80	75–85	30–40	50–70	17–38
specific gravity, polymer	1.14	1.38	0.95	0.91	0.94
adhesion to fabric	good	good	good	good	good
tear resistance	fair	good	fair	fair	fair
rebound, cold	good	good	fair	fair	good
solvent resistance					
aliphatics	excellent	excellent	excellent (cold)	excellent (cold)	good
aromatics	excellent	excellent	good (below 100°F)	good (below 100°F	good
drycleaning	excellent	excellent	fair	fair	good
ageing	good	good	good	good	very good

Apparel Fabric Lamination and Bonding

A laminate is by present definition a structure consisting of one or two fabrics with foam either on one side of one fabric or sandwiched between the two fabrics, whereas a bonded fabric is one consisting of two fabric webs which are adhered together without foam. A survey of today's bonded fabric market will show five types of adhesives predominating: acrylics, hot melts, fusible adhesives, polyurethans, and foam.

In the past, a number of other adhesives have been used in attempts to make bonded fabrics and, indeed, in some cases, have been and still are successful. These include neoprene, natural latex, polyvinyl acetate, and styrene–butadiene latexes, as well as butadiene–acrylonitrile latexes. However, these have already been discussed in the section on carpet backing adhesives. Consistent with the definition of laminates and bonded fabrics, foam is the only member of our series that can be considered in the lamination classification. Because the process actually involves the melting and decomposition of at least part of the foam, the foam itself can be considered as an adhesive. The process of lamination or bonding with foam by heat is called *flame lamination* and the process is precisely that. The foam, in a continuous web, is carried over a roll with carefully controlled gas burners impinging on the foam. By adjustment of the speed and the flame height, it is possible to melt a controlled amount of foam, at which point the fabric to be bonded or laminated to the foam is introduced and the completed structure is then carried either through a light pressure or a controlled nip or alternatively over a chill roll where, upon cooling of the molten foam, adhesion is completed. Where it is desirable to adhere a fabric to both sides of the foam, it is possible to carry the foam and bonded fabric over a second roll and set of gas burners and apply a second fabric to the back side, repeating the rest of the process, thereby producing a laminated fabric consisting of a face fabric, a foam, and a backing fabric.

By the use of very thin foams, it is possible to melt essentially all of the foam and use it strictly as an adhesive for the two fabrics, in which case we now have a bonded fabric structure in contrast to a lamination. In the double flame process, approximately 50 mils of foam are consumed in the lamination, so that a foam of approximately this thickness is required to end up with a bonded fabric with no foam remaining in the finished product. If foam is desired as the sandwich in a lamination, then whatever thickness of foam is desired in the final lamination must be added to the approximately 50 mils which will be consumed.

There are two general types of polyurethan foams, depending on the type of polyol resin which is used: the polyether foams and the polyester foams. The polyether foams have found their largest market in the cushion and mattress industry because of their lower cost. However, for the laminating and bonding applications, the higher price of the polyester foams has not been a deterrent to their use because the polyester foams have a much higher degree of resistance to softening and resistance to the usual drycleaning solvents. They are also far more resistant to the destructive effects of oxidation from heat, light, and air.

It is also possible to make laminates using the several adhesive systems to be discussed below, as well as using natural and synthetic latex foam in place of the polyurethan. Indeed, in the early attempts to produce foam-backed fabrics, the natural and synthetic latex foams were used and adhered with water-based adhesives. However, this practice has largely lost favor due to the low degree of solvent resistance and relatively poor ageing properties over an extended period of time for these types of foam. In a sense, the hot melt adhesives and the fusible adhesives (both described below) are related to the flame-foam lamination or bonding in that they all depend on the use of a thermoplastic material which creates a bond by melting to a liquid form in which a controlled degree of penetration is possible and then cooling to set the material in the desired position. In fabric bonding with hot melt adhesives, two distinct types have dominated the market. Not surprisingly, they are closely related to the predominant synthetic fibers, namely, the polyamides and the polyesters. In the early development of hot melt adhesives, many thermoplastic resins were tried and, indeed, can be used with limited success. However, when the completed bond was separated, usual experience showed that adhesive remained on both of the fabric surfaces and that failure was the result of a parting of the adhesive itself. This implies inadequate cohesion or cohesive strength. It was, therefore, not unreasonable to look to the fiber field where thermoplastic resins had been specifically developed with extremely high cohesive strength in order to give strong fibers.

The other distinct advantage that both the polyamide and polyester resins offered was their high resistance to solvent action, especially with any of the common dry-cleaning solvents. In fact, this high solvent resistance was the reason that they had to be considered for application as hot melts. Both the polyamide and polyester resins require some modification in order to obtain adequate adhesive strength and this is generally proprietary information of the adhesive manufacturer.

Hot melt adhesives can be applied by many different systems. They are available in a variety of forms, such as chips or granules, powders, and suspensions or dispersions of fine particles in water. They may also be obtained as films, in rods, or as a loose nonwoven structure. As chips or granules they can be heated and applied by extrusion, either as a film or discreet particles or droplets. As powder, they can be applied either by a flour sifter system or a brush roll after which they can be heated by infrared and bonded to another fabric or passed through heated calender rolls or squeeze rolls. The material in dispersed form can be applied by kiss rolls, roll coaters, spray, knife applicators and spreaders. If a particulate deposit in a pattern is desired, it is possible to use the hot melt in the dispersed form, applying it with a gravure roll in any desired pattern, thus improving the conformability and flexibility of the finished bonded fabric. A film may be applied between the two layers of fabric and then bonding accomplished again by the use of heated rolls as is also the case with the nonwoven web adhesive where the advantage of discontinuous adhesion can be realized. Hot melt adhesives may be obtained in rod form for use in equipment designed to take the specific size and shape of the rod, where it is melted and extruded in a pattern form or stripes generally on the backing fabric, which is then combined with the face fabric by means of a further heating.

Because of the already mentioned advantages, the polyamide and polyester resins have dominated this field. They also offer good ageing and can be modified to obtain any degree of softness or stiffness and any degree of adhesion required. However, where less strict quality requirements exist, it is possible to use many other thermoplasticre sin ssuch as polyethylene, plasticized poly(vinyl chloride), and copolymers of ethylene and vinyl acetate.

The fusible bonding systems, while they might be considered to be part of the hot melt systems, have another implication. The additional possibility is the inclusion of a thermoplastic fiber as an integral part of one of the fabrics to be bonded, generally the backing fabric. All that is required is to soften the thermoplastic fibers to create a durable bond. For this purpose, the polyamides and polyester fibers, along with acetate fiber and perhaps even plasticized poly(vinyl chloride) fiber, may be used depending on the service requirements to be met.

The acrylic adhesives for good reason have enjoyed a very sizeable part of the total market for bonded fabric. They have excellent stability, and the adhesive will not yellow with passing time. Reactive acrylics can be made so that they are resistant to most drycleaning systems, and are resistant to delamination on washing. The cost of the adhesive is comparatively low on a square yard basis. Material cost is approximately one cent per square yard. The acrylic adhesives have excellent storage stability. There is no hazardous or toxic solvent involved and the clean-up of equipment is relatively easy. The absence of solvent eliminates air pollution which is becoming an increasing concern to the users of solvents. These latexes are currently being produced in large quantities by the B. F. Goodrich Chemical Company, Rohm & Haas, Union Carbide, National Starch and Chemical Corporation and others (2, 3, 4).

Generally speaking, the reactive or carboxylated acrylic latexes have found the greatest favor in the bonded fabric field because they can be cured at lower temperatures (275–300°F) and indeed may require the addition of no further catalyst or compounding ingredients. However, if a higher degree of solvent resistance or wash resistance is required, crosslinking may be accomplished by the addition of melamine formaldehyde and/or urea formaldehyde resins. B. F. Goodrich Chemical Company has developed several acrylic latexes for the adhesive field, which can be made highly solvent resistant by the addition of their Carbopol, an extremely high-molecular-weight, hydrophilic carboxy vinyl polymer. Carbopol serves not only as a curing agent but also as a thickener for the adjustment of viscosity. Interestingly, the curing does not take place until the removal of all of the water, so that an adhesive can be compounded, ready for application, which has a long shelf or pot life without the danger of premature curing. For the fabric bonder the basic systems of compounding are readily available to him. Probably the most important property which he must adjust and control is the rheology of his coating system as this will have the greatest effect on the location of the adhesive within the fabric and therefore the type of hand, adhesion, and bond strength that he will obtain. The acrylic thickeners are based on polyacrylic acid. Fortunately, polyacrylic acid, when neutralized with alkali, forms a very effective thickener. Neutralized polyacrylic acids, for example, Acrysol GS of Rohm & Haas, are readily available and can be added to the acrylic latex adhesive system to develop any degree of viscosity desired. The neutralized polyacrylic acids are extremely high viscosity materials and are sometimes very difficult to mix or blend into the adhesive system. Therefore, they are also offered as the unneutralized polyacrylic acid which may be added to the latex adhesive system as a low-viscosity material, and thickening results in situ. All that is necessary is to add a predetermined amount of alkali, generally ammonia, to the adhesive system to compensate for the acidity of the polyacrylic acid. If a fugitive alkali such as ammonia is used, it will be eliminated from the adhesive system and the fabric during drying and curing. Thus the remaining polyacrylic acid will become water insoluble and add to the adhesive properties of the system. Various neutralized and unneutralized polyacrylic acids from variously substituted monomers are available so that by the proper selection a viscosity or rheology of any desired type can be obtained from one of a very smooth paste to one that develops long stringy legs.

The acrylic latexes are most commonly applied by any of five systems, namely, reverse transfer roll, transfer roll, kiss roll, spray, or a doctor blade spreader, and the viscosity and rheology properties will have to be adjusted differently for each of these systems. It should be particularly noted that to obtain satisfactory soft and textile-like hand for the bonded fabric it is generally necessary to apply the adhesive in a discreet particle pattern, and for this reason either the reverse transfer roll or transfer roll systems are the most commonly used although a similar effect can be obtained by spray application.

The urethan adhesives in the field of fabric bonding and laminating have had a rapid growth and indeed stand with the acrylics as the two primary adhesive systems for fabric bonding and laminating. Four classes of urethan adhesive systems have been considered and evaluated. These are: (1) solvent solutions of thermoplastic polyurethans; (2) emulsions of thermoplastic polyurethans; (3) solvent solutions of blocked polyurethans; and (4) solvent solutions of two-package urethan, prepolymer–isocyanate moisture-cure urethans. Of these four to date only the latter two have enjoyed real commercial acceptance. However, the emulsions of polyurethans have been improved considerably in the recent past and may enter the picture more actively. It is possible to make a stable one-part urethan system which consists of a urethan prepolymer wherein the functional hydroxyl group of the polyol is partially reacted with an isocyanate containing a phenol group. This phenol group prevents the complete curing of the system and so makes possible a material which is stable at room temperature. However, if the temperature is raised to approximately 300°F the phenol is released from the system, the isocyanate is regenerated, and the crosslinking is completed with the remaining hydroxy groups in the polymer. This system yields a material which has good shelf life. Fabric treated and cured is immediately ready for shipment due to complete, rapid cure.

The second popular system, namely the two-package urethan prepolymer–isocyanate system, consists of an adhesive which is shipped in two parts. The first part contains a prepolymer, a partially reacted polyester, rich in active hydroxyl groups, whereas the other part of the system contains the reactive isocyanate group. When these two materials are mixed in the proper proportion, crosslinking of the polymer proceeds through the catalyzing action of a small amount of moisture. Treated fabrics need only be heated to 175°F to remove solvent. However, there is an offsetting disadvantage. In this system the cure is initiated by the presence of moisture but is not completed during the drying period. Indeed the cure is not complete for 24 to 48 hours. Although this takes place in the fabric roll, the producer is unable to check his finished goods for adequacy of bond for some time after production. Mistakes in production are discovered therefore belatedly. The adhesive formula also has a short pot life.

The proponents of the solvent systems claim that the existence of solvents offers some advantages over the water-based systems. First, a solvent system tends to wet synthetic fibers more readily than water and so a satisfactory bond is more readily obtained. Secondly, it is claimed that by modification of the type and therefore activity of the solvent, together with the diluent used, the viscosity can be controlled so as to position the adhesive more readily. Also an adhesive with a high degree of wet tack can be developed whereby the initial bond is made more rapidly and securely, thereby reducing any tendency of the fabric layers to shift or delaminate.

The sensitivity of the urethan system to reaction with water blocked the development of emulsion systems for a long time. The Wyandotte Chemical Company has

Table 4. Adhesive Properties[a]

Properties	Natural rubber	Styrene-butadiene	Butadiene-acrylonitrile	Acrylic	Polyurethan
tensile strength, psi	over 3000	below 1000	below 1000	2–3,000	over 4000
hardness, Shore A	30–90	40–90	40–95	50–70	10–99
specific gravity,	0.93	0.94	1.00	1.14	1.06
adhesion to fabric	excellent	fair	good	good	excellent
tear resistance	good	fair	fair	good	excellent
rebound (cold)	excellent	good	good	fair	fair
solvent resistance to					
aliphatics	poor	poor	excellent	poor	excellent
aromatics	poor	poor	good	poor	good
drycleaning	poor	poor	good	good	excellent
ageing	fair	fair	good	excellent	excellent

[a] Due to the myriad formulations and polymer modifications possible in any one group, the data must be considered as representing only averages from which wide deviations may and do exist within and between various suppliers. For brevity only those polymers of significant current volume have been included.

worked very actively in this field and is now having a degree of success. These urethan latexes are available at solids of approximately 50% or higher and are offered in a range of hardness from Shore A 40 to 95. Many of the same advantages as are claimed for other water-based materials pertain to the urethan latexes, namely, the lack of flammable solvents, ease of application, and easy clean-up, together with freedom from limitation on the working life of the adhesive and the fact that a completely precured system simplifies the control of the finished product as no polymerization is required. However, it is necessary to reach a temperature of 300°F to obtain the maximum properties of strength and solvent resistance with these materials and therefore the same limitation on heat-sensitive fibers and fabrics exists as does with the blocked polyurethan solvent systems (5).

Table 4 is offered as a guide to the selection of the proper adhesive.

Bibliography

1. G. G. Winspear, *The Vanderbilt Latex Handbook*, R. T. Vanderbilt Co., Inc., New York, 1954.
2. A. C. Nuessle, "Acrylics in Textile Application," *Chem. Ind. (London)* 1966, 1500–1594.
3. G. C. Kantner, "Adhesives for Textiles," *Adhesive Age*, June 1967.
4. G. C. Kantner, *Resin Review, Vol. XVIII #2*, Rohm & Haas, Philadelphia, 1968.
5. J. M. McClellan, *Rubber Age, 1968*.

General References

"Hot Melts & Foam Latex," *Textile Month*, June, 1969.
M. B. Brodbeck, "Flame Bonding for Laminates," *Textile Chemist and Colorist*, Dec. 31, 1969.
D. K. Smith, "Fusible Systems for Bonding," *Textile Chemist and Colorist*, Dec. 31, 1969.
J. P. Shealy, Jr., "Bonding with Solvent-Based Urethane Adhesives," *Textile Chemist and Colorist*, Dec. 31, 1969.
J. M. McClellan, "Urethane Latices," *Rubber Age*, March, 1968.
A. C. Brown, "Fabric Laminating Flame and Adhesive," *Textile Manufacturer*, April, 1967.
P. G. Cook, *Latex—Natural and Synthetic*, Reinhold Publishing Corp., New York, 1965.
P. Weiss, *Adhesion and Cohesion*, Elsevier Publishing Corp., New York, 1962.
I. Skeist, *Handbook of Adhesives*, Reinhold Publishing Corp., New York, 1966.

THEODORE E. LANNEFELD
Fabric Research Laboratories, Inc.

FIRE-RESISTANT TEXTILES

Since the publication in 1966 of the review of fire-resistant textiles (1), flammability and its relationship to textiles of all types has had worldwide attention. Industry, government, and university researchers have broadened their outlook and have put more emphasis on ways to impart flame resistance to textile products. This research has involved fundamental and applied approaches with some emphasis being placed on the development of test methods. Chemical producers are looking at ways to produce chemicals that can be used to impart flame resistance either as additives for fibers or as finishes for use by finishing plants. Mills are also more cooperative and willing to evaluate new chemical finishes and fibers to improve the flame-retardant properties of their products.

Two of the major driving forces for this increased emphasis were (a) the Conference on Burns and Flame Retardant Fabric which was held in New York in December 1966 (2), and (b) the passage by the U.S. Congress in December 1967 of a bill which amended the Flammable Fabrics Act of 1953 (3).

The purpose of the flammability conference, which was held under the auspices of various medical groups, the U.S. Public Health Service, and also the textile industry, was to stimulate the interest of the public and industry in the seriousness of the subject and also to aid in promoting legislation for the control of flammable textiles, thus reducing serious burn injuries from clothing and other fabric fires. It is believed this conference had an effect on the passage by the U.S. Congress of the amendment to the Flammable Fabrics Act (3). The amendment authorized the Secretary of Commerce to establish and modify flammability standards for wearing apparel and interior furnishings when he determines that such standards are needed to protect the public against unreasonable risk of fire. Certain procedures are imposed for the exercise of this authority. All interested parties can participate in the development of flammability standards or other regulations established under this act, and it requires that the Secretary consult with the National Advisory Committee for the act before standards can be set. It also authorizes research on flammability, on related materials and products; studies of the feasibility of reducing their flammability; development of test methods and devices; and training in their use. Required also is a continuing study and investigation by the U.S. Dept. of Health, Education, and Welfare in cooperation with the Dept. of Commerce, of deaths, injuries, and economic losses resulting from the accidental burning of fabrics and related material. The National Bureau of Standards has been assigned the responsibility for development of test methods. As of 1971, the flammability test which applies under the amendment is CS191-53 (4). This test was originally designed to eliminate dangerously flammable cellulosic garments from the market. See also Halogenated fire retardants in this volume.

Development of Test Methods

On December 3, 1970, a notice of findings was published in the Federal Register (33FR1792) that a flammability standard, which should include labeling, may be needed for carpets and rugs. On December 17, 1970, the U.S. Dept. of Commerce issued the first proposed standard under the amendment to the Flammable Fabrics Act (5). The test method is a modification of Federal Specification DDD-95, carpets and rugs, wool, nylon, acrylic, and modacrylic. The method tests the resistance to flammability of various rugs and carpets under draftfree conditions by requiring a maximum specified dimension of charred area when subjected to a controlled standard ignition source.

AATCC Fire-Resistance Test.   AATCC Test Method 34, Fire Resistance of Textile Fabrics (Revised), is a standard vertical test, but it was not applicable to some synthetic fabrics which melt or shrink away when exposed to a flame.   Three changes or additions in the test method were made so that it could also be used in the evaluation of these fibers (6,7).   Prior to being tested thermoplastic fabrics must be stitched with three rows of glass thread in the long direction.   In addition, a 3-sec exposure to the flame, as well as a 12-sec exposure, was incorporated into the test in order to screen out the marginally treated fabrics which would pass the 12-sec exposure but would fail the 3-sec exposure to the flame source.

Oxygen Index Test Method.   Considerable attention has been given to the interpretation of flammability in terms of the oxygen index (OI).   (This has sometimes been referred to as limiting oxygen index, LOI.)   This test was originally designed by Fenimore and Martin (8) at the research laboratories of the General Electric Company for use with self-supporting plastic specimens.   The reproducibility of the results of this test are reported to be very good.   The apparatus consists of two sections, a gas-metering system and the test column.   In the gas-metering system the volumetric flow of both oxygen and nitrogen is accurately determined before the streams are mixed and fed into the base of the test column.   In the test column the gas mixture flows upward past the burning specimen, which is ignited at the top to burn in a candle-like manner.   By adjusting the flow in each line to vary the oxygen concentration in the mixture, it is possible to accurately determine the oxygen index, OI, ie the minimum oxygen concentration which just supports combustion of the material (see below).   This test has gained widespread use throughout the plastics industry.   It is now an ASTM standard (D2863).   More detailed information concerning the usefulness of this test and results obtained was reported by Isaacs (9).

Tesoro and Meiser (10) extended the use of this test method to textiles.   They evaluated the flammability of textile material as a function of chemical composition and showed that the OI is primarily governed by chemical composition with only a small effect attributed to the weight and construction of the fabric.   As shown by Tesoro et al., fabrics with reduced flammability had higher OI values.   Some of these values are listed in Table 1.

Willard and Wondra (11) reported on the quantitative evaluation of the flammability characteristics of cotton and flame-retardant cotton using the OI technique.   According to these authors, the synergistic interaction of nitrogen and phosphor can be described and measured.   They found that reduced flammability was dependent on increasing values of nitrogen or phosphor and no single definite nitrogen–phosphor

Table 1.   Oxygen Indexes of Various Fabrics

Fabric	OI	Fabric	OI
acrylic	0.182	nylon	0.201
acetate	0.186	polyester	0.206
polypropylene	0.186	wool	0.252
rayon	0.197	flame-retardant cotton	0.270
cotton	0.201	Nomex[a]	0.282

[a] Registered trademark, E. I. du Pont de Nemours & Co., Inc. See p. 960.

ratio produced the best synergistic effects. Some relationship of the OI value to the standard vertical-flame test was established. Generally, an OI value of 0.26 was shown to be equivalent to a 5-in. char length when measured by the standard vertical-flame test.

Some emphasis is now being placed on obtaining flame retardants for textiles which do not produce smoke or toxic gases during combustion.

The Michigan Chemical Company designed a smoke densitometer which can be used in combination with the General Electric Flammability Index Tester. They also installed an additional pyrometer in the chamber of the smoke densitometer to measure the temperature of the gases rising from the combustion chimney while the sample was being burned in the OI apparatus (12,12a).

Circular Feed Flame-Propagation Method. Although not an official test, Miller (13) has shown this test to have features lacking in other test methods. Two wheels, $5\frac{1}{2}$ in. in diam are placed parallel, about 2 in. apart, on a horizontal axis. Part of the cylinder surface thus formed is covered by the fabric to be tested. The fabric is ignited at the highest point of the cylinder surface; the flame then spreads downward, but there are arrangements to rotate the wheels at variable speed, which is adjusted so that it exactly balances the downward spread of the flame, and so that the flame remains at the highest point. This gives the rate of flame propagation. The wheel apparatus is mounted during the testing inside a 7-in. diam chimney which is supplied with a metered oxygen–nitrogen mixture, so that the OI can also be determined. The temperature of the flame can also be measured by means of a thermocouple.

Semicircular Test Method. Some interest, though limited, has been shown by Tesoro (14) in a semicircular test method which was the basis of an earlier British Standard for evaluating flame resistance of fabrics (15). Schon (16) has commented on this test, and it was further developed by Hilaire et al. (17). In this test, a semicircular frame, 7 in. in diam, is used for holding a 10-in. strip of fabric. The fabric is ignited at one end and the rate of burning can be measured.

Theory of Flame-Retardant Action

No new theories for the action of flame retardants have been proposed since 1954, when Schuyten, Weaver, and Reid (18) proposed the chemical theory that flame retardants for cotton were based on a dehydration process by Lewis acid or base formation through a carbonium ion or carbanion mechanism. Investigators have conducted research to further clarify these theories.

Earlier theories suggested that flame-retarded cellulose decomposed at high temperatures to levoglucosan which in turn broke down to form other volatile products which were highly flammable. Kilzer and Broido (19) proposed a different mechanism for the pyrolysis of fabric if bases are present in the fabric during burning. In their work levoglucosan was not formed and dehydrocellulose was formed by a base-catalyzed dehydration of cellulose which was followed by a char formation. Mack and Donaldson (20) proposed that base-catalyzed dehydration prevents the formation of levoglucosan by propagating structural changes at an energy level below that required to convert the coformers of the glucopyranose ring.

Hendrix et al. (21) suggested that fabrics, treated with phosphorus compounds to impart flame resistance when exposed to a heat source, undergo phosphorylation during decomposition as a first step, probably at the C-6 hydroxyl, and thus prevent the formation of levoglucosan. The second step was the acid-catalyzed dehydration and thermal decomposition of the cellulose.

Phosphorus-containing materials are by far the most important class of compounds used to impart durable flame resistance to cellulose. These usually contain either nitrogen or bromine and sometimes both. In 1947, Little pointed out that a combination of urea and phosphoric acid imparted flame resistance to cotton fabrics at a lower add-on than when the acid or urea was used alone (22). He also reported that other nitrogenous compounds, such as guanidine or guanylurea, could be used instead of urea.

Reeves et al. (23) studied some of the chemical and physical factors influencing flame retardancy. They suggested that the proper selection of the nitrogenous polymer or compound to be used with phosphorus-containing flame retardants is very important because they can aid flame resistance, have a neutral effect, or reduce flame resistance. Amide and amine nitrogen generally aid flame resistance, whereas nitrile nitrogen can detract from the flame resistance contributed by phosphorus. Amide nitrogen from nylon fiber is unusual in that the nylon detracted from flame resistance. Several factors may contribute to this effect. Perhaps the most important reason for the nylon effect is that the amide is part of a thermoplastic polymer which has a high percentage of combustible hydrocarbon. Substances such as fatty amide and fatty ammonium chlorides can destroy flame resistance in cotton fabric also. Cyanamide, which contains an amine and also a nitrile nitrogen, contributed flame resistance much the same as amides. This is probably due to hydrolysis of the cyanamide to urea and other nitrogenous products during treatment of the fabric. Infrared data on the treated fabric support this view in that only weak absorption was observed for the nitrile group.

Nitrogen contributes most efficiently to phosphorus-containing flame retardants at the lower concentrations relative to the phosphorus. An atomic ratio of nitrogen: phosphorus $\sim$1 in the fabric contributes maximum flame retardancy per unit weight of nitrogen. This does not mean that larger amounts of nitrogen should not be used in a flame retardant. Nitrogen is effective at atomic ratios of at least 14. It is just not as efficient at the high ratios. Much of the nitrogen lost during charring must contribute flame resistance by acting in the vapor phase, otherwise the efficiency of nitrogen would drop rapidly as the atomic ratio of nitrogen:phosphorus in the fabric is increased. In deciding the amount of nitrogen to use with phosphorus, many factors should be taken into consideration, such as cost, ie nitrogenous agents may be much less expensive than the phosphorus being replaced, and also hand and strength of the fabric.

Small amounts of phosphorus contribute more flame resistance per unit weight of phosphorus than large amounts. If complete flame resistance is desired, it is usually necessary to use large and less efficient quantities of phosphorus. All flame retardants examined decrease in effectiveness per unit weight of retardant as the add-on of retardant is increased. Thus, the first 5% of flame retardant added to a fabric is more efficient, as determined by the match test, than the second or third 5%. This and other data indicate that the most efficient flame-retardant system contains two retardants, one acting in the solid and the other in the vapor phase.

In the absence of nitrogen, essentially all of the phosphorus in a flame-resistant fabric can be accounted for in the char produced by pyrolyzing the fabric in air. The phosphorus could also be accounted for in the char when nitrogen was present, provided it was in the form of an amide, pseudo amide, or amine. Nitrile nitrogen caused a significant reduction in percent phosphorus accounted for in the char. The amount of nitrogen accounted for in the char is dependent upon the atomic ratio of nitrogen to phosphorus in the flame-resistant fabric. High ratios in the fabric are decreased substantially during the charring while ratios of about one are reduced to very small amounts. The most stable ratio is one. Based on atomic ratio and insolubility in water, acids, and alkali, the thermally most stable residual compound may be phosphorus oxynitride, PON.

Bromine in flame-resistant fabric escapes from the tar to the vapor phase during pyrolysis in air. It appears to have little or no effect on the amount of phosphorus remaining in char. Bromine contributes flame resistance to phosphorus-containing flame retardants although it acts independently of the phosphorus. To do this it must act almost completely in the vapor phase.

Tesoro and co-workers (24–26) have also studied synergistic effects in flame retardancy of nitrogen when used in conjunction with phosphorus compounds. They also showed that the phosphorus content could be reduced without changing the efficiency of the flame retardant by addition of nitrogen to the system. An explanation for these effects was offered by Hendrix et al. (21). They believed that the interaction of the phosphorus and nitrogen compounds produces a more effective catalyst for the degradation of the cellulose and that the nitrogen base could react directly with the products of the decomposition.

Flame-Retardant Textile Treatment

Weather-resistant flame-retardant fabrics for outdoor use are available and are being used. Certain flame-retardant apparel and household items are also available to a limited extent. The largest market today for flame-retardant textiles is the military.

SEMIDURABLE FLAME RETARDANTS

Cyanamide–Phosphoric Acid Process. Although Ward (27) had previously reported research on a flame-retardant process based on cyanamide and phosphoric acid, it was O'Brien (28) who refined the finish, making it commercially feasible. This finish appears attractive since cyanamide is relatively inexpensive and is now commercially available as a 50% aqueous solution; phosphoric acid is also very cheap.

The cyanamide–phosphoric acid formulation, using a ratio of 3 parts cyanamide to 1 part phosphoric acid can be applied to fabric using a pad-dry-cure technique. During the drying and curing of the fabric a very rapid exotherm appears. Temperature increases of about 120°C have been observed shortly after the dry-cure operation begins. The hand of the fabric is very little affected. The durability of the finish to laundering is dependent on the hardness of the water. The harder the water, the less the durability. The treated fabrics are dimensionally stable and exhibit rot- and crease-resistance. Since the finish is subject to ion-exchange, treatment with ammonium salts improves the flame resistance. However, the ammonium is easily converted to sodium or calcium in the laundering process, especially if basic tap water and detergents are used. When these sodium or calcium salts are formed, the fabrics burn, although still containing the flame-retardant group. The flame retardancy can generally be restored if, after an acid sour, the fabric is treated with a water solution containing ammonium hydroxide, and dried. One of the major faults of this finish is that 40–45% of the fabric strength is lost. This finish has found some commercial acceptance, especially for use on drapery fabrics.

DURABLE FLAME RETARDANTS

Miles and Delasanta (29) reported on a durable nonreactive flame retardant for cotton textiles. It can be applied to fabrics from existing plant equipment designed for solvent applications. In addition, it can be easily applied to garments as paints or sprays or using drycleaning equipment. Tris(2,3-dibromopropyl) phosphate is combined with small amounts of poly(vinyl chloride), poly(vinyl acetate), or acrylic polymers, applied to the fabric from solvent and merely dried. With an add-on of 26–35% on an 8-oz fabric (8 oz/yd^2) the flame resistance is durable to fifteen accelerated mobile launderings. A typical formulation is the following:

Flame retardant	Parts
perchloroethylene	80
acrylic polymer	1.5
tris(2,3-dibromopropyl) phosphate	20

The treating solution is prepared by adding the bromine compound to the solvent, followed by the addition of the acrylic polymer, and allowing to stand for 24 hr at room temperature.

One of the outstanding features of this finish is the high retention of tear strength. Other solvents, such as xylene or methyl ethyl ketone, can be used in place of halogenated solvents.

Sanderson, Muller, and Swidler (30) conducted research to impart flame resistance and crease resistance to cotton textiles in one operation. It was based on guanidine, dimethyl phosphite, and formaldehyde; the reaction product can be expressed as shown below:

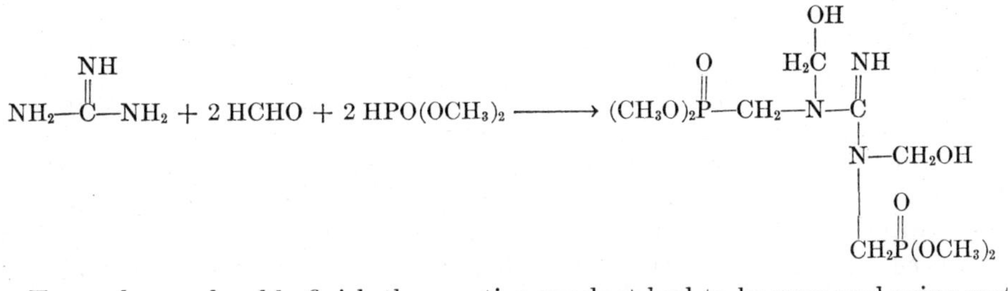

$$
\underset{\substack{\| \\ NH}}{NH_2\text{—}C\text{—}NH_2} + 2\ HCHO + 2\ HPO(OCH_3)_2 \longrightarrow
$$

$$
(CH_3O)_2\overset{O}{\underset{\|}{P}}\text{—}CH_2\text{—}\underset{\substack{| \\ N\text{—}CH_2OH \\ | \\ O \\ \| \\ CH_2P(OCH_3)_2}}{N}\text{—}\overset{\substack{OH \\ | \\ H_2C \quad NH \\ | \quad \|}}{C}
$$

To produce a durable finish the reaction product had to be prepared using methanol in place of water. When this product was applied to cotton a reaction time of 45 min was required. Excessive strength losses and poor reproducibility seriously affected the usefulness of this finish.

A second system, reported by these same authors, was based on methylphosphoric acid (MPA) and cyanamide. Fabrics were treated by a pad-dry-cure technique. At an add-on of 10% this flame-retardant finish was durable to 40–50 laundry cycles, had dry-wrinkle recovery angles of 200–220, and wet-wrinkle recovery angles of 220–270. (The wrinkle recovery angle reported is the sum of the recoveries in the warp and fill directions, W + F; thus, the maximum possible wrinkle recovery is 360°.) The same finish gave tensile-strength retention of 60–80%, and tear-strength retention of about 50%, and raised the moisture regain of the fabric about 3%. A disadvantage of this finish is that smoke is evolved during curing. Some of the reactions that can take place are as follows:

$$2\ CH_3\overset{O}{\overset{\uparrow}{P}}\!-\!OH \underset{\diagdown OH}{} \longrightarrow CH_3\overset{O}{\overset{\uparrow}{P}}\!-\!O\!-\!\overset{O}{\overset{\uparrow}{P}}CH_3 + H_2O$$

MPA   MPA dimer

One or more of the hydroxyls in MPA or in its dimer can react with cellulose as follows:

$$CH_3\overset{O}{\overset{\uparrow}{P}}\!-\!OH \underset{\diagdown OH}{} + R_{cell}\!-\!OH \longrightarrow CH_3\overset{O}{\overset{\uparrow}{P}}\!-\!O\!-\!R_{cell} \underset{OH}{} + H_2O$$

The water shown in these equations is taken up by the cyanamide, forming urea:

$$H_2NCN + H_2O \longrightarrow H_2N\overset{O}{\overset{\|}{C}}NH_3$$

The system shows high tolerance for calcium.

A new flame retardant for cellulosic textiles, Pyrovatex CP, was introduced in the United States by the Ciba Chemical and Dye Company in March of 1968. It is based on the reaction product of a dialkyl phosphite and acrylamide (31). The resulting product is methylolated with one mole of formaldehyde per mole of the dialkyl-phosphonopropionamide.

$$(CH_3O)_2\overset{O}{\overset{\|}{P}}\!-\!H + CH_2\!=\!CH\!-\!\overset{O}{\overset{\|}{C}}\!-\!NH_2 \longrightarrow (CH_3O)_2\overset{O}{\overset{\|}{P}}\!-\!CH_2CH_2\!-\!\overset{O}{\overset{\|}{C}}\!-\!NH_2$$

$$\Big\downarrow \text{HCHO}$$

$$(CH_3O)_2\overset{O}{\overset{\|}{P}}\!-\!CH_2CH_2\!-\!\overset{O}{\overset{\|}{C}}\!-\!NHCH_2OH$$

Use of larger quantities of formaldehyde causes its release during fabric processing and by using an acid catalyst it reacts with cotton. This finish is usually used in conjunction with a crosslinking agent, such as trimethylolmelamine, TMM, which improves its efficacy and durability. It is nonirritating to the skin and does not adversely affect the hand of the treated fabric. This finish is durable to 30–50 launderings and drycleanings. Fabrics treated with it have tensile-strength losses of 20–30% and tear-strength losses of 30%. Add-ons required for cotton textiles are about 20–35%. A typical treating solution for cotton is shown in Table 2.

Fabric is padded through the solution to a wet-pickup of 70–80%, dried below 250°F, and cured for $4\frac{1}{2}$ min at 330°F. This is followed by an alkaline afterwash.

Tesoro, Sello, and Willard (32) also prepared cellulosic derivatives resembling very closely those based on the dialkylphosphonopropionamides. Fabric was treated with three N-hydroxymethylhaloacetamides (chloro, bromo, and iodo) in a solution in dimethylformamide (DMF) by a pad-dry-cure technique using zinc nitrate as the catalyst. These derivatives were then reacted in solution with trimethyl phosphite

Table 2. Treating Solution for Cotton

Component	Parts
Pyrovatex CP	30–60
triazine resin[a]	10.0
nonionic wetting agent	0.05
prediluted polyethylene softener[b]	2.00
NH_4Cl[c]	0.40
an amine hydrochloride[c]	3.00
$MgCl_2$ hexahydrate phosphoric acid[c]	1.00

[a] Containing 50% solids, such as Aerotex 23 Special (American Cyanamid Co.).

[b] Solids, 25%.

[c] Any of these compounds may be used to adjust to pH 4.

at about 140–150°C employing the Arbuzov reaction shown below. The reaction rates decreased in the order iodo > bromo > chloro.

$$R_{cell}OH + HOCH_2NHCOCH_2I \xrightarrow{DMF} R_{cell}OCH_2NHCOCH_2I$$

$$\downarrow (CH_3O)_3P$$

$$R_{cell}OCH_2NHCOCH_2\overset{O}{\overset{\uparrow}{P}}(OCH_3)_2 + CH_3I$$

With phosphorus contents above 1.5% good flame resistance durable to laundering was obtained without noticeable loss in fabric-strength properties.

Chance and Moreau (33,34) conducted research also related to some extent to the dialkylphosphonocarboxyamides, as did Aenishänslin and co-workers (31). They attached the dialkoxyphosphinyl group to the triazine ring rather than to an alkyl group. The 2,4-diamino-6-diethoxyphosphinyl-1,3,5-triazine (DAPT) was prepared by the reactions of 2,4,6-tris(diethoxyphosphinyl)-1,3,5-triazine with ammonia in ethanol, as shown below:

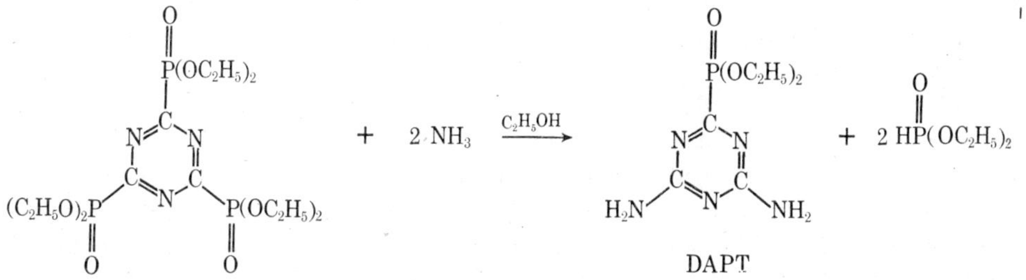

DAPT reacts with formaldehyde to form a derivative which polymerizes readily to an insoluble crosslinked polymer. Fixers, such as the methylol triazines, are therefore not needed. The fabric was treated by a pad-dry-cure procedure. Fabrics were wetted with the solution to a wet-pickup of about 100%, dried for 5 min at 85°C, cured for 5 min at 150–170°C, washed, and dried. Best results were obtained by using a solution at pH 6.6 (no catalyst). Fabrics containing from 17.5–20% resin add-on passed the standard vertical-flame test even after thirty-five laundry cycles. Tear-strength losses were about 35% and tensile-strength losses about 18%. Although the treated fabrics did not yellow on chlorine bleaching and scorching, some strength loss resulted, indicating chlorine retention.

N-METHYLOLAMIDES OF PHOSPHINES AND PHOSPHINE OXIDES

A new flame retardant, tris(2-carbamoylethyl)phosphine, was synthesized by the reaction of ammonium hydroxide with the ethyl or methyl ester of tris(2-carboxy-ethyl)phosphine (35).

$$P(CH_2CH_2COOR)_3 + 3 NH_3 \longrightarrow P(CH_2CH_2CONH_2)_3 + 3 ROH$$

Tris(2-carbamoylethyl)-phosphine oxide (TCPO) was prepared by the method of Rauhut and others (36). The methylol derivatives of these two compounds were prepared and applied to cotton fabric by conventional padding procedures to a wet-pickup of 80–90% on print cloth, dried for 5 min at 85°C, cured for 3–5 min at temperatures ranging from 140 to 170°C, rinsed, and air dried. Zinc nitrate and magnesium chloride catalysts were used. High wrinkle resistance and moderate flame resistance were simultaneously imparted to the fabric. Strength losses were comparable to those produced by the commonly used methylolamide finishing agents for cotton. Fabrics treated with either of the compounds were damaged in the chlorine-retention test. Both of the fabric finishes were more resistant to acidic than to alkaline hydrolysis, but the phosphine oxide finish was more resistant to both acidic and alkaline hydrolysis than the phosphine finish.

This work was further extended by Morris and co-workers (37,37a). TCPO was prepared by adding KOH to a mixture of acrylamide and white phosphorus.

$$P_4 + 2 KOH + 4 H_2O + 9 CH_2=CH-CONH_2 \longrightarrow K_2HPO_3 + 3 O=P(CH_2CH_2CONH_2)_3$$

The product was methylolated and fabric was processed with it using 0.5–2% of a catalyst of citric acid and $MgCl_2 \cdot 6H_2O$ in a 1:1 molar ratio. The wetted fabric was dried at 85°C and cured for 3–5 min at 150–170°C to produce an add-on of about 21%. The fabric was flame resistant and would pass the standard vertical flame test after twenty but not thirty, laundry cycles. By raising the solids content more resin was deposited in or on the fabric; therefore the finish was durable to more than forty laundry cycles. The fabric retained 78% of its breaking strength and 65% of its tear strength. Initial stiffness imparted to the fabric was largely removed after one laundry cycle. Replacement of some of the TCPO by trimethylolmelamine did not improve the process.

THPC-Based Flame Retardants. Flame retardants based upon tetrakis(hydroxy-methyl)phosphonium chloride (THPC) are used more than any other for apparel and household goods, and for certain military items, such as tent-liner fabrics. Processes based upon THPC are used in the United States, Europe, and other countries (39,40).

THPC is a water-soluble, crystalline compound that is produced in high yield by the reaction of formaldehyde with phosphine and HCl (38). It is sold in the United States by Hooker Chemical Co. and Aceto Chemical Co. and in Europe by Albright and Wilson Ltd. of England.

The methylol groups in THP react with amines (or amides) in the following manner:

$$(HOCH_2)_4PCl + RNH_2 \longrightarrow RNHCH_2PCl(CH_2OH)_3 + H_2O$$

One or more methylol groups are replaced by the $RNHCH_2$— group. The ionic chlorine is hydrolyzed:

$$(RNHCH_2)_3PCl(CH_2OH) + H_2O \longrightarrow HCl + CH_3OH + (RNHCH_2)_3PO$$

Thus, the final product contains no chlorine and the phosphorus is in the form of phosphine oxide, a structure which is very stable to hydrolysis. If the nitrogen compounds are di- or polyfunctional, the product is a highly insoluble polymer.

THPC also reacts with cellulose, but it is very slow when using processing conditions associated with the finishing of cotton textiles.

The original THPC–amide flame-retardant formulation has been modified in several ways. The objective was to reduce cost and to improve the properties of the treated fabric.

Antimony Oxide and Organic Chlorine Compounds. Lynrus Finishing Co. and Hooker Chemical Co. have developed modified THPC–amide formulations containing antimony oxide and organic chlorine compounds (41,42), generally poly(vinyl chloride) or a chlorinated paraffin. Although the antimony oxide and organic chlorine compounds are cheaper than THPC, they are less effective on a weight basis. When they are substituted for part of the THPC–amide formulation, greater total add-ons must be applied to the fabric to give any specific degree of flame resistance.

THPOH-Based Flame Retardants. New reactive methylol phosphorus compounds can be made from THPC. One method is the reaction of 1 mole of THPC with 0.8–1 mole of sodium hydroxide. The product of this reaction in aqueous solution has been referred to as THPOH (43).

It should be pointed out that THPOH is not yet adequately characterized. Some researchers consider it to be mainly an equilibrium mixture of tetrakis(hydroxymethyl)-phosphonium hydroxide, THPOH, and tris(hydroxymethyl)phosphine, THP (44), shown in equations 1 and 2. Others have evidence that the solution consists of a mixture of THP and a hemiacetal of THP (45), shown in equations 3 and 4.

$$(HOCH_2)_4PCl + NaOH \longrightarrow (HOCH_2)_4POH + NaCl \tag{1}$$

$$(HOCH_2)_4POH \rightleftharpoons (HOCH_2)_3P + HCHO + H_2O \tag{2}$$

$$(HOCH_2)_4PCl + NaOH \longrightarrow (HOCH_2)_3P + HCHO + NaCl + H_2O \tag{3}$$

$$(HOCH_2)_3P + HCHO \rightleftharpoons HOCH_2OCH_2P(CH_2OH)_2 \tag{4}$$

Ellzey and co-workers (46) studied the reaction of THPC with one equivalent of sodium hydroxide. Using data from proton and phosphorus NMR spectra, they concluded that there was little evidence for the formation of $(HOCH_2)_4\overset{+}{P}\ \overset{-}{O}H$. Species definitely identified in solution were THP and THPO. Evidence for two other phosphorus-containing species was obtained. Although their structures were not definitely proved, both appear to result from the reaction of formaldehyde with THP. A likely structure for one product is $(HOCH_2)_3\overset{+}{P}CH_2\overset{-}{O}$, which may form reversibly from THP and formaldehyde.

An important point to remember when reacting THPC with sodium hydroxide or other bases to produce THPOH is that the pH of the solution must not exceed 7.5–7.8. In this pH range the THPOH solution is stable. THP, like most other phosphines, can be oxidized to tris(hydroxymethyl)phosphine oxide (THPO). This does not occur appreciably in the THPOH solution as long as the pH is below about 7.8, possibly because of the stabilizing effects of the —CH$_2$OH groups. THPOH can be converted to THPO by an excess of sodium hydroxide, even in the presence of formaldehyde. The excess alkali may be in catalytic amounts, thus it is very important that an excess of the base be avoided to minimize the production of THPO, a substance which reacts very slowly with amides and amines.

THPOH reacts with amides which contain two or more NH groups to produce insoluble polymers containing nitrogen and phosphorus. In the final reaction product, the phosphorus is in the form of a phosphine oxide, the same structure that results when THPC reacts with amides to form insoluble polymers. THP also reacts with amides to form polymers containing a phosphine oxide structure. Since the final product in each case is phosphine oxide, it is highly probable that a methylol phosphine structure is an intermediate in all of these reactions.

THPOH–NH₃ Flame Retardants. The retardant with the least complex formulation based upon THPOH is the THPOH–NH₃ flame retardant (47). It is applied by padding fabric with a solution of THPOH and various auxiliaries, then partially drying the fabric and finally exposing the partially dried fabric to ammonia gas. A typical formulation for flameproofing an 8-oz cotton fabric contains 30% THPOH, and wetting and softening agents. After padding the fabric with the solution, it is dried to about 10–20% moisture retention as measured by a moisture meter. If the fabric is thoroughly dried the THPOH decomposes into much less reactive compounds. It is important to maintain moisture in the fabric until it is exposed to ammonia. Another important processing step is the application of ammonia to the fabric. A preferred technique is illustrated in Figure 1. In this arrangement the ammonia is forced directly through the fabric. When the ammonia treatment is carried out this way, reaction is complete within a few seconds. On the other hand, if the partially dried fabric is merely passed into an atmosphere of ammonia, several minutes are required for the ammonia to diffuse into the fabric and react with the THPOH. The reaction of ammonia with THPOH produces water which combines with ammonia to form ammonium hydroxide. Since ammonium hydroxide can further react with THPOH to form water-soluble products instead of an insoluble polymer, it is necessary to have a good exhaust system in the reactor to remove as much of the water and ammonium hydroxide as possible.

Since the THPOH–NH₃ flame retardant does not stiffen the fabric, the process is applicable to most cotton fabrics. Fabrics weighing as little as 2 oz/yd² have been satisfactorily flameproofed by this process. Another outstanding feature is the high breaking strength of treated fabric. The strength is usually greater, sometimes as much as 25%, than that of the untreated fabric. This is particularly true when softeners have not been used. If softeners are used, however, the tear strength is reduced about 30%. With the proper amount of softening, tear strength can be increased essentially to 100% of the untreated fabric, while maintaining about 100% breaking strength. The phosphorus-to-nitrogen ratio in fabrics treated by this process is about 3.5 to 1.

THPOH–TMM–NH₃ Flame Retardant. A third flame retardant based on THPOH is the THPOH–TMM–NH₃ flame retardant (48). In applying this retardant, the fabric is padded with the reagents, partially dried, then exposed to ammonia, and finally heated at 150°C for 3 min. A typical formulation of this retardant contains 18.5% THPOH, 11.5% trimethylolmelamine, plus wetting and softening agents as desired. Such a formulation is adequate for an 8-oz cotton fabric, and will enable it to pass the standard vertical-flame test. TMM has been effectively substituted for about one-third of the THPOH required in the THPOH–NH₃ process discussed above.

The properties of fabrics treated by this process are about the same as those reported above for the THPOH–NH₃ flame retardant, except for two main differences: (1) Fabrics treated by this process exhibit breaking-strength values up to 100%, but usually not greater than 100%, and (2) the cost of the chemicals is lower.

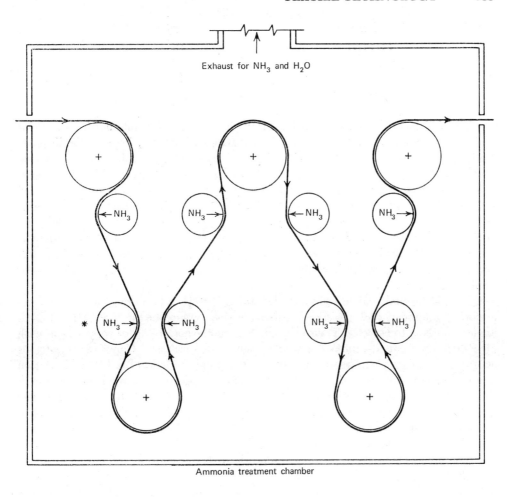

Exhaust for NH$_3$ and H$_2$O

Ammonia treatment chamber

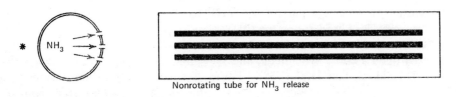

Nonrotating tube for NH$_3$ release

Fig. 1. Application of ammonia to fabric.

When THPOH is used alone, the chemical cost is about 12¢/yd^2 of fabric treated. When the molar ratio of THPOH to TMM is 2:1, the cost drops to about 8.7¢/yd^2. The incorporation of still greater amounts of TMM does not reduce cost any further.

THPOH–Amide Flame Retardant. A fourth new flame retardant based on THPOH is the THPOH–amide flame retardant (49). In applying this retardant, the reagents are padded onto the fabric, then dried and cured at about 150°C for 3 min. The typical formulation required on 8-oz cotton fabric is given below.

Flame retardant	Parts
THPOH	16
urea	10
TMM	10
auxiliaries	1.5

THPOH has been substituted for THPC in the THPC–amide finish on a molar basis. The new flame retardant based on THPOH, however, imparts significantly different properties to fabrics. With the THPOH–amide retardant, fabrics retain about 80–90% of their original breaking strength. Stiffness imparted by the process is less than that imparted by the THPC–amide process. Because of the reduced stiffness, this retardant is applicable to a wider variety of fabrics, sheeting for example. Wrinkle recovery (W+F) is about 285°. This finish, like THPC–amide, gives a high degree of rot resistance. Another particularly important feature of this retardant is that treated fabrics have a reduced tendency to yellow when exposed to sodium hypochlorite bleach. Most other durable flame retardants cause more yellowing under similar conditions.

Donaldson and Daigle (50) modified the THPOH–NH_3 curing process and reported a simplified pad-dry-cure process for the application of the THPOH–NH_3 flame retardant to cotton. They utilized the complexing ability of copper salts with phosphorus compounds, ammonia, and amines in this process. Copper salts, such as cupric nitrate, cupric sulfate, or cuprous chloride, when added to the THPOH solution in a mole ratio of copper salt to THPOH of 1:4, produce a system which is stable in the presence of ammonium hydroxide. This stabilization is probably due to complex formation between the copper and phosphorus atoms. Without the copper salt, the ammonium hydroxide reacts immediately with the THPOH on mixing to form a white, insoluble polymeric material.

The process consists of padding the fabric with the solution and curing at about 150°C for 3 min. The finish is durable to laundering and has very little effect on the hand or strength of the fabric. Because of the copper present a slight bluish color is imparted to the fabric. Methylol compounds, such as TMM, can be added to the treating solution to replace a part of the THPOH, thereby producing a lower-cost durable flame-retardant finish for cotton (51).

THPC–Cyanamide Flame Retardant. A new, durable flame-retardant finish for cotton, based upon THPC, cyanamide, and phosphoric acid, has been developed by Normand, Donaldson, and Drake (52). Fabric is treated by padding it through a water solution of the three components, then drying and curing at elevated temperatures. The flame-retardant formulation imparts a high degree of flame resistance to fabric.

An 8-oz sateen fabric with as little as 8% add-on passed the standard vertical-flame test after thirty laundering cycles. About 15% add-on was required for print cloth to have this durability. Treated fabrics have a good hand and appearance. Losses in breaking and tear strengths associated with this treatment were about 25 and 50%, respectively. Chlorine bleaching alone did not discolor any of the treated fabrics. There was very slight yellowing after chlorine bleaching and scorching. The flame-retardant finish did not impart any color to the fabric and when treated samples were exposed to a flame very little odor or smoke was produced. This last property might be of great benefit in confined areas where fumes are harmful or fatal during a fire.

Unpublished work by Normand et al. has shown that by substituting Na_2HPO_4 in place of H_3PO_4 in the THPC–cyanamide finish flame-retardant fabrics are produced with much less strength loss.

Research by Yeadon, Danna, Cooper, and Reeves (53) has shown that significant changes in the fire-resistant characteristics of flame-retardant finished fabric can occur when exposed to sunlight, followed by laundering even though repeated washing and tumble drying of samples of the same specimen did not indicate any significant changes, especially in the durability of the finish. Mazzeno, Robinson, McCall, and Morris (54) also showed that dry heat alone, followed by laundering or autoclaving could have a deleterious effect on the flame-retardant properties of some flame-retardant finished fabric.

Application of Flame Retardants from Solvent Systems

With pressures being applied from various sources to prevent stream pollution, a limited amount of research is underway to find flame retardants that can be applied to textiles from solvent systems. Symm (55) used chlorinated solvents to apply flame retardants like APO (see Vol. 9, p. 309), brominated hydroxyl-containing compounds (such as tribromopentyl alcohols), and phosphonates. The compounds were applied in solvent systems to fabric and cured at 160–170°C to produce flame-retardant fabrics with less add-on than is usually required from aqueous systems.

Flame-Retardant Rayons

FMC Corporation has marketed flame-retardant acetate yarns since 1963, a semipermanent flame-retardant rayon since 1966, and, in December 1967, announced a durable flame-retardant rayon fabric (56,57). A brominated organic phosphate is added to the acetate spinning dope in order to obtain fire resistance. The flame resistance is reported to be durable to laundering and drycleaning since the organophosphorus compound is insoluble in water and the yarns do not swell in solvents. The flame retardancy is also durable to drycleaning. FMC has also released a rayon containing 2–3% phosphorus under the trade name Avisco PFR rayon. It is reported to contain a nonhalogenated phosphorus compound (58,59). The hand and appearance of Avisco PFR rayon in fiber or fabric form are reported to be similar to regular rayon. It withstands normal boil-off and bleaching procedures used in mills, and the flame-retardant properties are little affected. The durability to laundering and drycleaning is reported to be excellent. The flame-retardant rayon is not sensitive to uv light.

Patents were also issued to Courtaulds, Ltd. (60,61) wherein flame resistance was imparted to viscose rayon by incorporating 15–30% of tris(2,3-dibromopropyl) phosphate into the viscose dope.

Noncellulosic Manmade Fibers

The thermoplastic fibers, such as nylon and polyester, have very different burning characteristics than the cellulosic fibers. These manmade fibers tend to shrink away from the source of ignition or melt and carry away the flame. This flaming molten polymer can be a potential source of danger.

Most manmade fibers have low melting points. Reported values for polyester, nylon, and polypropylene are 255–290, 210–260, and 150°C, respectively.

Flameproofing of these thermoplastic manmade fibers presents a somewhat different problem than that encountered with cotton and rayon. Although many of the same flame retardants which are effective on cotton are also effective on the manmade fibers, generally a greater amount of retardant is needed on the manmade fiber. It appears that flame retardants must be specially designed for the synthetic fibers if they are to be efficient. Flame retardancy of the synthetic fibers is obtained in two ways: (1) by mechanically blending the retardant with the polymer before it is drawn into a fiber, and (2) by chemically modifying the polymer itself. The flame retardants must be developed specifically for each fiber because the effectiveness of the retardant depends upon the chemical structure of the polymer from which the fiber is made. The burning rate of the fabric depends upon the physical form of the fabric initially and during combustion, the thermal stability of the material, the composition of the pyrolysis products, and the accessibility of the products to oxygen. Flame retardants for synthetic fibers can produce their effects in either the substrate or in the volatile phase. Those acting in the substrate do not function as a dehydrating agent as is the situation with cellulosic fibers. The flame retardant must act by changing the nature of the volatile products and reducing the concentration of the flammable vapors. Suitable techniques for flameproofing manmade fibers of the thermoplastic types, that are now being produced commercially, have not yet been found.

Chemical modification of the polymer is a promising approach for flameproofing fibers. For example, a limited number of the manmade fibers mass-produced at low cost are considered self-extinguishing. Fibers made from copolymers of acrylonitrile and vinyl chloride, or acrylonitrile and vinylidene chloride are good examples. Even greater resistance to burning is exhibited by fibers made entirely of vinyl chloride or vinylidene chloride (62). Because bromine is a better flame retardant than chlorine, vinyl bromide has been used in copolymers with acrylonitrile (62).

Flame-Resistant Blend Fabrics

Many of the more popular and prevalent apparel and household fabrics are made by blending two or more fibers. Frequently these textiles are made by blending cotton and polyester or cotton and nylon fibers, or by blending rayon with these thermoplastic fibers. Combination of the thermoplastic and cellulosic fibers gives products which may be more hazardous with respect to burning than products made of a single-fiber type. When nylon 6, nylon 66, polyester, or acrylic or polypropylene fibers are blended with rayon or cotton and woven into a fabric, the fabrics burn with great vigor. Such blends pose a real hazard which is caused, to some extent at least, by the fact that the cellulosic fibers serve as a grid or wick for the thermoplastic fibers when they are heated and melt.

Because of the importance to the general public of blend fabrics, considerable effort is being made to develop satisfactory flame retardants for them. Some progress has been made. It is now feasible to produce flame-resistant blend fabrics which contain about 65% or more cellulosic fibers. Before additional significant advances can be made, it is necessary to develop flame retardants for the thermoplastic fibers. Flame retardants are already available for the cellulosic fibers. The most practical approach may be to produce flame-resistant thermoplastic fibers by altering the chemical structure of the polymers and, after blending these fibers with cotton or rayon, treating the finished textile with an appropriate flame retardant for the cellulose.

The gaseous products given off when manmade fibers are pyrolyzed between 500–800°C vary, depending on the type of fibers. Nylon gives off water, ethanol, carbon dioxide and monoxide, hydrocarbons, and cyclopentanone. Acrylics produce alcohols, hydrocarbons, ketones, HCN, and black polymer. Polypropylene produces pentane, pentene, hexene, butane, propylene, and ethylene. Fibers based on poly(vinyl chloride) or poly(vinylidene chloride) yield HCl and hydrocarbons.

As of 1971, no really effective durable flame-retardant finish for nylon has been discovered. The usual flame retardants suitable for the cellulosics are not applicable for nylon. Numerous references appear in the literature describing methods for imparting flame resistance to nylon. Most of these are based on the use of thiourea–formaldehyde.

Research to obtain flame retardants for use on polyester and polyester–cotton blends is increasing. Poly(vinyl chloride) and its mixtures with antimony oxide, natural rubbers, etc, have been studied (63,64). A satisfactory flame retardant for polyester fibers has not been found.

Polyolefin fibers, of which polypropylene is probably the most widely used, especially in indoor and outdoor carpeting, is a low-melting fiber and burns readily. Flame retardancy is reported to be imparted to these fibers by dispersing halogen-containing compounds within the polymer (65,66). Phosphorus compounds have also been reported to impart some flame resistance to polypropylene fibers. See also Polypropylene fibers in this volume.

Some Heat- and Flame-Resistant Manmade Fibers

Considerable progress has been made in making both inorganic and organic fibers that are remarkably resistant to heat. However, there are problems that remain to be solved, particularly the dyeing of these fibers.

INORGANIC FIBERS

Glass fibers are apparently the most extensively used textile fibers which are highly resistant to heat and flame. They are available at a modest cost and are extensively used in drapery fabrics. Their primary limitations is lack of aesthetic properties and low resistance to abrasion. A new innovation in glass is the so-called beta glass fibers. Chemically these fibers are the same as the older and more widely used ones. The main difference is in the small diameter of the fiber. The denier (weight in g of 9000 m of the fiber) is about 0.25. Beta glass fibers are much more expensive than the older fibers but are more suitable for apparel goods.

Carbon fibers have become of great interest for the aerospace program. One method for making carbon fibers is to impregnate a cellulosic yarn with a flame retardant, then heat it at relatively low temperatures, usually about 300°C, to produce a carbonaceous product. This product weighs about one-half as much as the original yarn. Subsequently, the charred cellulosic yarn is heated at about 1400°C or higher and stressed to orient the carbon structure. During the increase of the temperature, there is a gradual formation of aromatic ring structures with a loss of hydrogen and resultant enrichment of carbon. After this high-temperature heating, the product is about 95% or more pure carbon. Part of the carbon is usually in the form of graphite. The resulting fiber resists temperatures as high as 3000°C. The carbonized fibers, although generally made from cellulosic fibers, can also be made from other fibers, such as those made of polyacrylonitrile. The carbon fibers are very expensive and brittle, and have very little abrasion resistance but have exceedingly high tensile strength. Such fibers, at least at this stage of technology, have very little utility in apparel and household goods.

A new **ceramic fiber** under the trade name Fiberfrax is advertised by the Carborundum Company. They report it to be a soft, pliable, strong, resilient, light, white fiber which can be used in the manufacture of structures of various types, such as cloth, rope, blankets, etc. It is resistant to continuous heat at 2300°F.

HIGH-TEMPERATURE ORGANIC FIBERS

There are five types of organic polymers which have received attention as high-temperature fibers. All of these are aromatic or heterocyclic in nature. They are copolyamides, polybenzimidazoles, polyoxadiazoles, polyimides, and highly fused ring systems.

Copolyamides. About 1960 Du Pont introduced one of the first high-temperature organic fibers. It is a polyamide and was named HT-1, now known as Nomex. These fibers contain an abundance of aromatic structures and a minimum of aliphatic character. The aromaticity increases heat resistance considerably. Fibers made with such chemical structures do not shrink or melt, even at temperatures above 500°C. Thus, ordinary flames, which burn at about 500°C, do not adversely affect the product. A typical polyamide structure, such as the polyamide obtained from isophthaloyl chloride and *m*-phenylenediamine, is shown below.

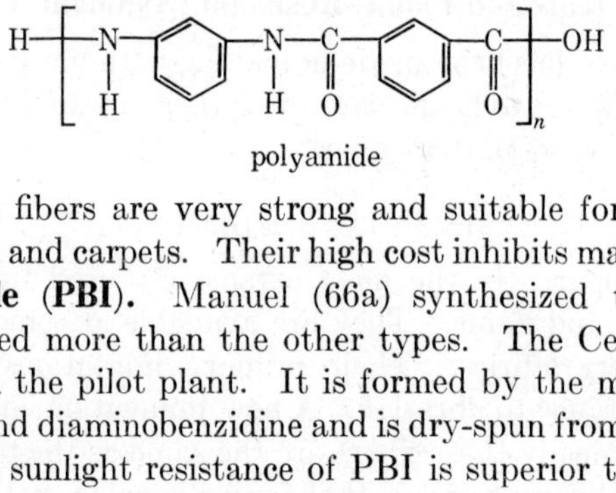

polyamide

These polyamide fibers are very strong and suitable for use in household and apparel goods, drapes, and carpets. Their high cost inhibits mass production.

Polybenzimidazole (PBI). Manuel (66a) synthesized the PBI-type polymer which has been studied more than the other types. The Celanese Corporation has produced this fiber in the pilot plant. It is formed by the melt condensation of diphenyl isophthalate and diaminobenzidine and is dry-spun from a solution in dimethylacetamide (67). The sunlight resistance of PBI is superior to Nomex. When compared to other high-temperature fibers, PBI was best with respect to difficulty of ignition and burning rate. Its structure is shown below.

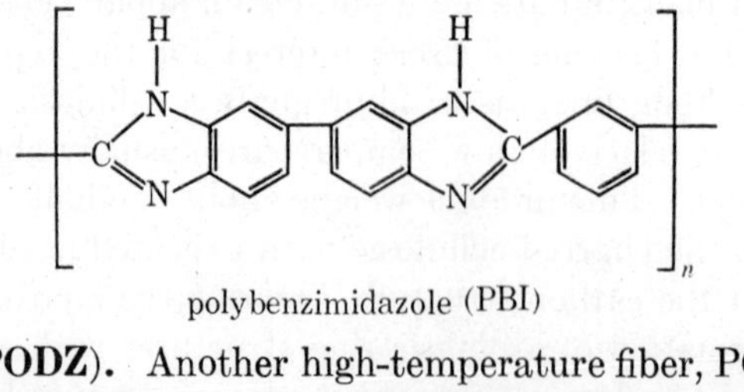

polybenzimidazole (PBI)

Polyoxadiazole (PODZ). Another high-temperature fiber, PODZ, was developed by reacting terephthaloyl chloride and isophthalic dihydrazide, $m\text{-}C_8H_4(CONHNH_2)_2$, to form an alternating polyhydrazide. It is dry-spun from solution to dimethyl sulfoxide (68). The polyhydrazide is thermally cyclodehydrated to form the oxadiazole structure shown below.

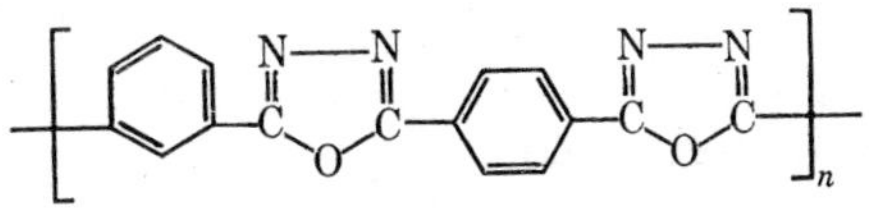

polyoxadiazole (PODZ)

Although flame retardancy is good, uv resistance and flex life are reported to be poor.

Polyimides (Polypyromellitides). By condensing the dianhydride of pyromellitic acid (1,2,3,4,5-benzenetetracarboxylicacid) with an aromatic diamine, Du Pont produced a polyimide high-temperature fiber (69). Above 500°F polyimides have a thermal resistance superior to that of polyamides. A typical polyimide structure is shown below.

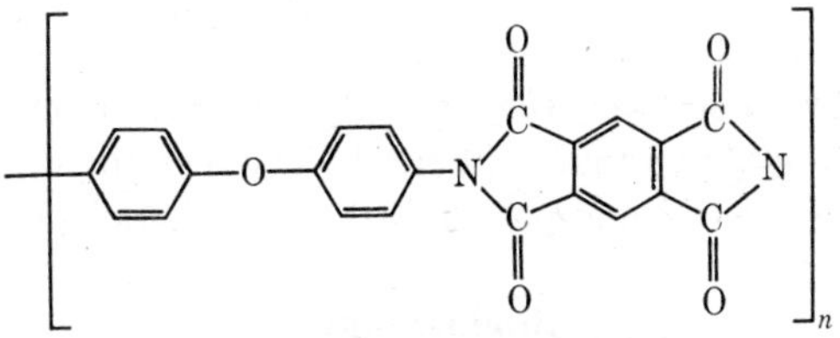

polypyromellitimide of *p*-phenylene diamine

Hirsch (71) has shown that the degradative reactions of thermostable polymers at low temperatures can be attributed to aromatic hydrogen atoms. He prepared a polyimide by reacting pyrazinetetracarboxylic dianhydride with 2,5-diamino-1,3,4-thiodiazole, which is void of hydrogen. The structure of the product is shown below.

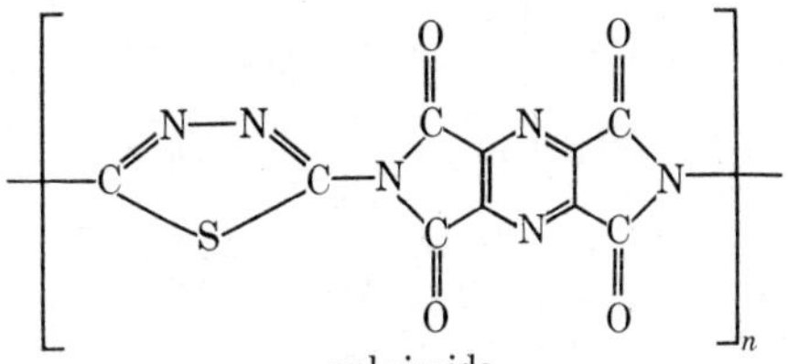

polyimide

This polymer has high-temperature oxidation stability, being stable up to 592°C. Although a film of this material ruptured at this temperature, no charring resulted. The corresponding polymer which was prepared from pyromellitic dianhydride and which contained two hydrogen atoms per repeating unit, began to char at 320°C. See also Polyimides in this volume.

Fused-Ring Systems. Van Deusen (70) discovered one of the newer high-temperature fibers by reacting 1,4,5,8-naphthalenetetracarboxylic acid with 3,3'-diaminobenzidine to form poly(bisbenzimidazobenzophenanthroline) (BBB). A typical structure is shown below.

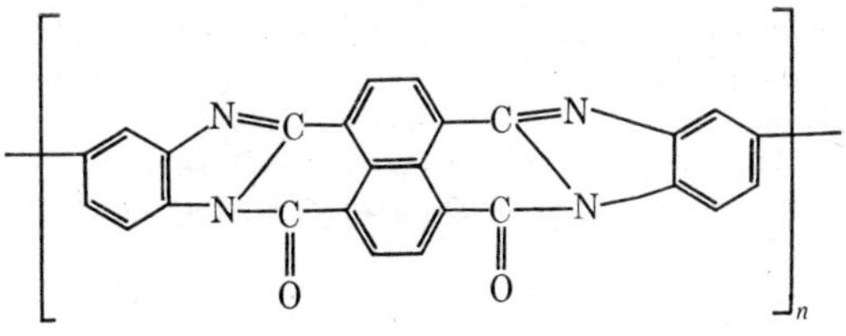

polybisbenzimidazobenzophenanthroline (BBB)

The fiber is wet-spun from a concentrated sulfuric acid solution into a bath containing 70% or less of sulfuric acid. The yarn, after washing and neutralization, is drawn at a temperature of 1000–1100°F. It retains 60% of its room-temperature tenacity when tested at 1100°F for one-min exposures. It has excellent resistance to uv degradation.

Dyeing of all of these fibers presents somewhat of a problem.

In April 1969, the Carborundum Company announced a new generic textile fiber called Kynol (72). Chemically the new fiber is a highly crosslinked phenolic polymer containing only carbon, hydrogen, and oxygen. Because of its highly crosslinked structure the polymer is amorphous. It has a glassy appearance and a golden brown color. Kynol is a flame-resistant fiber, resisting flames of 2500°C. It is practically inert to all organic solvents and nonoxidizing acids. It burns in a 100% oxygen atmosphere. In a flame the fiber converts to a carbon fiber giving off water, and carbon monoxide and dioxide; the fiber retains its integrity with only slight shrinkage. Suggested uses for this fiber are in the aerospace industry, as protective clothing, filtration medium for corrosive liquids and gases, household linens for use in hospitals, dormitories and hotels, and in blends for apparel fabric. See Phenolic fibers in this volume.

Bibliography

1. George L. Drake, Jr., "Fire-Resistant Textiles," in A. Standen, ed., *Encyclopedia of Chemical Technology*, 2nd ed., Vol. 9, Interscience Publishers, a div. of John Wiley & Sons, Inc., New York, 1966, pp. 300–315.
2. "Conference on Burns and Flame-Retardant Fabrics, New York, 1966," *Bull. N.Y. Acad. Med.* **43** (8), 615–769 (1967).
3. *Public Law 90-189, S 1003*, 90th Congr., Sect. 4, Dec. 14, 1967, U.S. Govt. Printing Office, Washington, D.C., 1967.
4. *Commercial Standard 191–153*, U.S. Dept. of Commerce, Bur. of Foreign and Domestic Commerce, 1953.
5. "First Proposed Flammability Standard as Issued by Dept. of Commerce," *Textile Chemist Colourist* **2** (1), 13–16 (1970).
6. A. S. Endler and M. L. Hurwitz, *Am. Dyestuff Reptr.* **56** (19), 694–697 (1967).
7. R. B. LeBlanc, *Textile Chemist Colourist* **2** (3), 47–50 (1970).
8. C. P. Fenimore and F. J. Martin, *Mod. Plastics* **43**, 141, 146, 148, 192 (1966).
9. J. S. Isaacs, *J. Fire Flammability* **1**, 36–47 (1970).
10. G. C. Tesoro and C. H. Meiser, Jr., *Paper TRI Ann. Meet. New York, April 1969; Textile Res. J.* **40**, 430–436 (1070).
11. J. J. Willard and R. E. Wondra, *Textile Res. J.* **40** (3), 203–210 (1970).
12. *Polymer Conf. Ser., Univ. of Detroit, 1970*, Detroit Coll. Eng., Polymer Inst., Detroit, Mich., 1971.
12a. H. Stepniczka and J. DiPietro, *Smoke Density and LOI Studies of Polymeric Systems*, in reference 12, 38 pp.
13. B. Miller, *New Approaches in Flame Propagation*, in reference 12, 17 pp.
14. G. C. Tesoro, *Inform. Council Fabric Flammability Proc. 2nd Ann. Meet.* 1968, pp. 73–181.
15. *Brit. Standards 467*, Part 2, Brit. Standards Inst., London, 1955.
16. G. Schon, *Melliand Textilber*, **48**, 215–217 (1967).
17. P. St. Hilaire, K. Knoettner, and L. E. Rossiter, *Am. Dyestuff Reptr.* **57**, 942–945 (1968).
18. H. A. Schuyten, J. W. Weaver, and J. D. Reid, "Fire Retardant Paints," *Advan. Chem. Ser.* **9**, 7–20 (1954).
19. F. J. Kilzer and A. Broido, *Pyrodynamics* **2**, 151–163 (1965).
20. C. H. Mack and D. J. Donaldson, *Textile Res. J.* **37**, 1063–1071 (1967).
21. J. E. Hendrix, J. E. Bostic, Jr., E. S. Olson, and R. H. Barker, *J. Appl. Polymer Sci.* (to be published).

22. R. W. Little, *Flameproofing of Textile Fabrics*, Reinhold Publishing Corp., New York, 1947.
23. W. A. Reeves, R. M. Perkins, B. Piccolo, and G. L. Drake, Jr., *Textile Res. J.* **40** (3), 223–231 (1970).
24. G. C. Tesoro, *Textilveredlung* **2**, 435–440 (1967).
25. G. C. Tesoro, S. B. Sello, and J. Willard, Jr., *Textile Res. J.* **38**, 245–255 (1968).
26. *Ibid.*, **39**, 180–190 (1969).
27. F. J. Ward, *J. Soc. Dyers Colourists* **71**, 569–578 (1955).
28. S. J. O'Brien, *Textile Res. J.* **38**, 256–266 (1968).
29. T. D. Miles and A. C. Delasanta, *Textile Res. J.* **38**, 273–278 (1968).
30. W. A. Sanderson, W. A. Muller, and R. Swidler, *Textile Res. J.* **40** (3), 217–222 (1970).
31. Fr. Pats. 1,395,178 (April 9, 1965) and 1,466,744 (Jan. 20, 1967) to Ciba Ltd.; U.S. Pat. 3,374,292 (March 19, 1968), A. C. Zahir (to Ciba Ltd.). R. Aenishänslin, C. Guth, P. Hoffman, A. Maeder, and H. Nachbur, *Textile Res. J.* **39** (4), 375–381 (1969). Tech. Bull. 081-4B (270M), Ciba Chemical and Dye Co., Toms River, N.J.
32. G. C. Tesoro, S. B. Sello, and J. J. Willard, *Textile Res. J.* **38** (3), 245–255 (1968).
33. J. P. Moreau and L. H. Chance, *Am. Dyestuff Reptr.* **59** (5), 37–38, 64 (1970).
34. L. H. Chance and J. P. Moreau, *Paper Am. Chem. Soc. 159th Meet., Div. of Cellulose, Wood, and Fiber Chemistry, Houston, Texas, Feb. 22–27, 1970.*
35. L. H. Chance, W. A. Reeves, and G. L. Drake, Jr., *Textile Res. J.* **35** (4), 291–298 (1965).
36. M. M. Rauhut, R. Bernheimer, and A. M. Semsel, *J. Org. Chem.* **28** (2) 478–481 (1963).
37. *Proc. 10th Cotton Utilization Res. Conf., New Orleans, La., Sept. 1970*, USDA-ARS 72–83.
37a. C. Morris, L. H. Chance, G. L. Drake, Jr., and W. A. Reeves, in reference 37, p. 76.
38. A. Hoffman, *J. Am. Chem. Soc.* **43**, 1684–1688 (1921). U.S. Pat. 2,743,299 (April 24, 1956), F. F. Flynn, W. A. Reeves, and J. D. Guthrie (to U.S. Dept. Agr.).
39. W. A. Reeves and J. D. Guthrie, *U.S. Dept. Agr. Ind. Chem. Bull.*, **364** (1953).
40. J. D. Guthrie, G. L. Drake, Jr., and W. A. Reeves, *Am. Dyestuff Reptr.* **44** (10), 328–332 (1955).
41. R. B. LeBlanc, *Textile Ind. (Atlanta)* **132** (10), 274, 294, 296, 298 (1968).
42. U.S. Pat. 3,243,391 (March 29, 1966), G. M. Wagner (to Hooker Chemical Corp.).
43. J. V. Beninate, E. K. Boylston, G. L. Drake, Jr., and W. A. Reeves, *Textile Ind. (Atlanta)* **131** (11), 110–114 (1967).
44. N. Filipescu, L. M. Kindley, H. E. Podell, and F. A. Serafin, *Can. J. Chem.* **41**, 821–825 (1963).
45. W. J. Vullo, *J. Org. Chem.* **33** (9), 3665–3667 (1968).
46. S. E. Ellzey, Jr., et al., private communication, 1970.
47. J. V. Beninate, E. K. Boylston, G. L. Drake, Jr., and W. A. Reeves, *Am. Dyestuff Reptr.* **57** (25), 74–78 (1968).
48. J. V. Beninate, R. M. Perkins, G. L. Drake, Jr., and W. A. Reeves, *Textile Res. J.* **39** (4), 368–374 (1969).
49. J. V. Beninate, E. K. Boylston, G. L. Drake, Jr., and W. A. Reeves, *Textile Res. J.* **38** (3), 267–272 (1968).
50. D. J. Donaldson and D. J. Daigle, *Textile Res. J.* **39** (4), 363–367 (1969).
51. D. J. Daigle and D. J. Donaldson, *Textile Chemist Colourist* **1** (24), 34–36 (1969).
52. F. L. Normand, D. J. Donaldson, and G. L. Drake, Jr., *Textile Ind. (Atlanta)* **134** (6), 169–170, 176, 186, 188 (1970).
53. D. A. Yeadon, G. F. Danna, S. A. Cooper, Jr., and W. A. Reeves, in reference 37, p. 70.
54. L. W. Mazzeno, Jr., H. M. Robinson, E. A. McCall, and N. M. Morris, in reference 37, p. 72.
55. R. H. Symm, *Textile Chemist Colourist* **1** (6), 42–45 (1969).
56. J. W. Schappel, *Mod. Textiles Mag.* **49** (7), 54–60 (1968).
57. U.S. Pat. 3,266,918 (Aug. 16, 1966), to FMC Corp.
58. Brit. Pat. 1,153,955 (June 4, 1969), to FMC Corp.
59. U.S. Pat. 3,455,713 (July 15, 1969), L. E. A. Godfrey (to FMC Corp.).
60. Can. Pat. 769,630 (Oct. 17, 1967), Madhu P. Godsay (to Courtaulds (Canada) Ltd.).
61. Fr. Pat. 1,495,909 (Sept. 22, 1967), to Courtaulds Ltd.; U.S. Pat. 2,763,631 (Sept. 18, 1956), H. W. Coover, Jr., and J. B. Dickey (to Eastman Kodak Co.).
62. Neth. Pat. Appls. 6,517,131, 6,517,132, and 6,517,074 (1966), to Monsanto Co.
63. G. Pastuska, *Gummi, Asbest, Kunstoffe* **19** (3), 275–277 (1966); *Chem. Abstr.* **65**, 4016f, (1966).
64. Ger. Pat. 1,150,044 (June 12, 1963), E. Hilscher (to Farbwerke Hoechst A.G.).

65. Brit. Pat. 1,126,478 (1968), to Johnson & Johnson.

66. Fr. Pat. 1,484,485 (1967), to Johnson & Johnson.

66a. C. S. Marvel, *J. Macromol. Sci. Part A* **1** (1), 7–28 (1967).

67. W. H. Gloor, *Am. Dyestuff Reptr.* **57** (13), 59–64 (1968).

68. A. H. Frazer and T. A. Reed, *J. Polymer Sci. C* **19**, 89–94 (1967).

69. R. S. Irwin and W. J. Sweeney, *J. Polymer Sci. C* **19**, 41–48 (1967).

70. R. L. Van Deusen, O. K. Goins, and A. J. Sicree, *Paper Am. Chem. Soc. 152nd Meet., New York, Sept. 12, 1966.*

71. S. S. Hirsch, *J. Polymer Sci. A-1* **7**, 15–22 (1969).

72. J. Economy, L. C. Wohrer, and F. J. Frechette, "Kynol—A New Flame-Resistant Fiber," *Paper 39th Ann. Meet. Textile Res. Inst., New York, April 7–11, 1969. A Major Breakthrough in Flame-Resistant Fibers,* Bull. A-2113, Carborundum Co., Niagra Falls, N. Y., April 1, 1969.

George L. Drake, Jr.

U.S. Dept. of Agriculture

SOIL-RELEASE FINISHES

Soil-release finishes are a class of textile treatments which are used to improve the response of soiled textiles to cleaning. More specifically, soil-release (or stain-release) finishes are film-forming, polymeric materials which function by imparting to the fibers of a textile substrate new surface characteristics which facilitate the release of oily stains and soils during conventional laundering.

The past two decades have witnessed remarkable changes in textile technology which have served to provide the consumer with a variety of fabrics having certain substantially improved characteristics. These changes in technology have involved both the use of complex new finishing formulations and the large-scale substitutions—in whole, or in part—of synthetic fibers for the cellulosic fibers (ie cotton and rayon) which had accounted for essentially all washable fabrics prior to 1950. The most noteworthy recent innovation has been the introduction of "durable-press" fabrics which require little, if any, ironing during their lives. These fabrics generally comprise a blend of cellulosic (usually cotton) and synthetic fibers (usually polyester, ie, polyethylene terephthalate) in a ratio, cotton:polyester ranging from 20:80 to 65:35, respectively. A typical single-bath finishing formulation for "durable press" would involve the application of 10% of a given aminoplast resin, 2% of a resin-curing catalyst, 2% of an acrylic or vinyl polymer and 0.5% polyethylene, or various derivatives of animal and vegetable fats and oils. (The stated percentages of aminoplast resin and catalyst are dry-weight percent of reactants based on cotton content; while the other percentages are based on total fiber content.) The functions of these additives are: the aminoplast resin acts as a crosslinking agent for cellulose within the cotton fibers to confer adequate crease-recovery properties to the fabric; the acrylic or vinyl polymer serves as a builder to impart fullness of hand or feel; and the polyethylene or fat derivative acts to soften the hand and serve as a lubricant during the high-speed sewing of the finished garment.

As textile technology has changed, so have the inherent soil-release characteristics of fabrics changed. It is not surprising to find that the laundering procedures and textile detergent formulations which were developed for cleansing the traditional, essentially unfinished cellulosic fabrics of yesterday are usually inadequate for cleansing the highly finished, composite-fiber fabrics of today, unless auxiliary soil-release agents are applied during fabric finishing.

Nature of the Problem

A soil is considered to be any nontransitory agent which alters the appearance of a textile in an undesirable fashion. Most common soils fall into one of four general categories: aqueous-borne stains and soils, oil-borne stains and soils, dry particulate soils, and composite soils involving fluid and particulate matter.

Aqueous-borne stains generally do not present serious release problems for the simple reason that the coloring matter present on the fabric is frequently soluble in the wash liquor. The major exception to this rule occurs when proteins are present, eg, in blood, glue, egg, and many other food stains. A major recent change in commercial detergent formulation has been the addition of proteolytic enzymes to improve the release of protein stains during laundering (1,2). The nature of this release appears to be largely independent of the fabric substrate. (See Enzyme detergents in this volume.)

Oil-borne stains are a very important and troublesome category of soils. This class includes mineral and lubricating oils and greases, food fats and oils, and sebum— the omnipresent, complex mixture of fatty minerals exuded by human skin.

Oil stains bond to fibers by a "sorptive" mechanism and the probability of achieving satisfactory release of these stains on laundering depends on the ability of the detergent solution to overcome the sorptive forces which operate at the oil–fiber interface. (Sorptive bonding is simply the adhesion which often results when two dissimilar materials are brought into intimate contact.) As might be expected, the incorporation of proteolytic enzymes in detergents has little, if any, effect on the release of oil stains.

Dry particulate soils are a rather limited category and include such materials as flour, carbon black, clay, etc. Compton and Hart carried out comprehensive studies on the particulate soiling of textiles (3,4). These workers distinguished between "geometric" and "sorptive" bonding and concluded that geometric bonding was the principal mechanism for dry-particle retention in the fabric. (Geometric bonding may be considered to be the physical capture of particulate matter by any of the following mechanisms: embedment in soft-finish films present on the fibers; entrapment of particles within the largely submicroscopic crevices of natural fibers; and entrapment of particles both between fibers in the yarns and between yarns in the weave.) Kling and Mahl (5), and Tripp, Clayton, and Porter (6) demonstrated that sorptive bonding, similar to the bonding of oil to fiber, can be an appreciable factor in the retention of particles by fabrics.

The probability of releasing dry particulate soils during laundering appears to depend on two factors: the ability to provide sufficient mechanical energy to overcome the geometric bonding of the particles, and the inherent ability of the detergent solution to overcome the sorptive bonding of the particles to the textile fibers. Soil embedded in a soft finish is almost impossible to remove.

Composite fluid–particle systems in which the fluid is an oil are a very important class of soils. This class includes such diverse materials as lipstick, dirty motor oil, printing ink, atmospheric soot, and deposits from foot traffic (7). In many instances the oily component of the composite soil acts as the carrier or cement which bonds the particle to the textile fibers by a sorptive bonding mechanism (4,8). It has been suggested that the major problem of releasing such soils is simply the problem of removing the oil carrier (8).

In summation, the problem of effecting the release on laundering of many soils (and most especially the oil-rich soils) is associated with the ability of the detergent solution to overcome sorptive bonding and displace the oil from the fiber surface. Satisfactory release of any given oil from textiles is highly dependent on the surface properties of the component fibers. Soil-release agents are used to impart a set of surface properties to the fibers which favor the spontaneous release of oil on laundering. The fiber surface properties of many of today's fabrics (the "durable-press" fabrics, in particular) are of such a nature that spontaneous oil release during washing is extremely difficult (if not impossible) to achieve, in the absence of a suitable soil-release finish.

In the laundering of soiled fabrics, one is normally concerned with two processes: soil release and soil redeposition. The latter term refers to a process in which soil is released from certain fibers and then redeposited from the wash liquor onto other fibers. Soil redeposition is normally evidenced by a progressive graying of a fabric as a result of repeated laundering. Soil redeposition is recognized to be a special problem on most fabrics containing synthetic fibers (9). Soil-release agents generally effect improvements in both the soil-release and soil-redeposition characteristics of fabrics. The general subject of soil redeposition, however, is largely ignored in the present article for two reasons: reliable test methods for studying the problem have yet to be developed, and redeposition is perhaps as dependent on the specific detergent formulation used as it is on the surface properties of the fibers.

Theory of Oil Release

General Theory of Oil–Fiber Interactions. The Young equation describes the basic interaction between a liquid and a solid (10).

$$\gamma_S - \gamma_{SL} = \gamma_L \cos \theta \tag{1}$$

where γ_S, γ_{SL}, and γ_L are the surface free energies per unit area (equivalent to surface tensions) at the solid–air, solid–liquid, and liquid–air interfaces, respectively, and θ is the contact angle assumed by a sessile drop of the liquid on the solid surface (see Vol. 9, p. 709).

The thermodynamic work of adhesion (W_A) required to separate a liquid from a solid in a reversible process is given by the Dupré equation (11):

$$W_A = \gamma_S + \gamma_L - \gamma_{SL} \tag{2}$$

(W_A is identical to the sorptive bonding parameter discussed previously and is simply the free energy change for a reversible unbonding process.)

Combination of equations 1 and 2 yields the familiar Young-Dupre equation:

$$W_A = \gamma_L(1 + \cos \theta) \tag{3}$$

The manner in which the surface energies of solid and liquid control the degree of wetting of the solid (ie, the value of θ) has been reviewed by Zisman (12). In general, liquids having surface energies lower than a given solid completely wet that solid (ie $\theta = 0°$). The surface-energy relationship existing between all commercial unfinished fibers ($\gamma_S > 30$ erg/cm^2) and virtually all oil-bearing soils (γ_L ranges from 20 to 35 erg/cm^2 for most mineral oil and fatty compounds), is such that complete wetting of the fibers usually occurs on contact. This is universally true for all oily soils which contact the yarns of unfinished fabrics, provided the viscosity of the soil is low enough to permit an approach to the stable, equilibrium distribution of soil within the yarns. Smith and Sherman have reviewed the surface-energy, geometric, and viscosity factors which control capillary-flow processes in yarns with regard to fluid penetration rates and equilibrium states of fluid distribution (13). When oily soil completely wets the fiber, the sorptive bonding is shown in equation 3 to be at its maximum value, $2\gamma_L$.

Zisman has shown that organic compounds containing long-chain perfluoroaliphatic groups (eg C_8F_{17} groups) have the lowest surface energy known (range of about 8–12 erg/cm^2) (12). Conventional water- and oil-repellent fabric finishes are based on the uniquely low surface energy of such fluorochemicals (14–16). The oil-repellent finishes function by imparting to the fiber substrate a sufficiently low surface energy so that, on contact with an oily soil, a negative capillary pressure results which prevents the spontaneous wicking of the soil into the contacting yarns (13). Fabrics containing such fluorochemical finishes are, however, susceptible to oily soiling if external pressure is applied to overcome the negative capillary pressure. In such instances the sorptive bonding of the soil to the fibers is considerably smaller (ie less than $2\gamma_L$) than it would be in the absence of the fluorochemical finish, since θ is considerably greater than 0° (perhaps exceeding 90° in some instances).

Oily Soil Release. We are concerned here with the factors which influence the probability that a given washing procedure will succeed in overcoming the sorptive bonding of the oily soil to fibers.

Adam discovered that a detergent solution causes oil release by a "rolling up" mechanism wherein the surface forces generated at the three-phase boundary of fiber–detergent solution–oil result in a progressive retraction of the oil along the fiber surface until it assumes a θ value of 180° (W_A then equals 0), a point at which displacement is complete (17). The free energy change for the oil release process can be calculated from a form of the Dupré equation in which an aqueous environment has been substituted for the air environment assumed in equation 2 and the deformation of the oil during displacement is neglected:

$$\Delta G = \gamma_{OW} + \gamma_{WF} - \gamma_{OF} \tag{4}$$

where γ_{OW}, γ_{WF} and γ_{OF} are the free energies of the oil–detergent solution, detergent solution–fiber and oil–fiber interfaces, respectively. Since the criterion of any spontaneous process is a negative change in free energy, the following inequality must be realized if oily soil release is to be achieved:

$$\gamma_{OF} > \gamma_{OW} + \gamma_{WF} \tag{5}$$

It seems worthwhile here to consider the factors which control the magnitude of each of these terms.

The value of γ_{OW} is determined by the oil, the specific detergent used, and its concentration. Under normal circumstances γ_{OW} is very small relative to the other terms and can be neglected.

With regard to the desirability of realizing a small value of γ_{WF} relative to the value of γ_{OF}, a few general considerations of factors influencing interfacial energy should be reviewed. A perfect match of the attractive force fields operating between the molecules of one species and the molecules of a second species at an interface would yield an interfacial energy of zero. (It is questionable whether such a situation has ever been realized, but an interfacial tension of zero is theoretically possible for a crystalline solid in equilibrium with its melt, if the two phases have equal densities.) As the nature of the attractive force fields diverges, the interfacial energy increases. When one component at an interface is capable of interacting by hydrogen bonding as well as by dispersion bonding forces, higher interfacial energies result if the other component is capable of interaction only through dispersion forces, rather than through both hydrogen bonding and dispersion forces (18). For example, inherently hydrophilic fibers such as cotton and rayon give relatively low values of γ_{WF}, largely as a result of the hydrogen-bonding capacities of water and these cellulosic fibers. (It is unfortunate that interfacial energies are not susceptible to direct measurement when one phase is a solid.) Polyester fiber, on the other hand, is hydrophobic, does not hydrogen bond with water (19) and, as a consequence, exhibits relatively high values of γ_{WF}.

Although unfinished fibers of cotton and polyester are both completely wetted by all oily soils, the γ_{OF} value for any given oil is much higher on cotton than it is on polyester, since hydrocarbons interact only by dispersion force bonding (18). (Although not all oils are hydrocarbons in the strict sense, they are all hydrocarbon-like in their energies of interaction.)

When film-forming finishes are applied to fabrics, the fibers assume the surface characteristics of the finish. Thus hydrophobic finishes, such as silicones, waxes, polyethylene, and oil-repellent fluorochemical polymers of the type discussed by Grajeck and Petersen (14), serve to increase markedly the values of γ_{WF} for otherwise hydrophilic fibers such as cotton.

At the same time these hydrophobic finishes generally tend to reduce the γ_{OF} values of hydrophobic fibers. (Fluorochemicals are an exception to this rule, since their inherently low surface energy still provides rather large values of γ_{OF}, even though still larger values of γ_{WF} are simultaneously realized.)

For purposes of clarification, the following scale of ascending relative surface free energies may reasonably be assumed to exist for the fibers, fluids, and finishes of concern: fluorochemicals < silicones < waxes ~ oils ~ polyethylene ~ normal detergent solutions < polyester fibers < nylon fibers < cotton ~ rayon fibers < water. For any two materials, the closer they are within this scale, the lower is the interfacial energy between them.

In the light of the foregoing discussion, one would expect that unfinished cellulosic fabrics would inherently be better oil-releasing substrates than unfinished fabrics based on hydrophobic fibers. Similarly, hydrophobic film-forming finishes should detract from the oil-releasing properties of hydrophilic fibers; while very hydrophilic film-forming finishes (eg carboxymethylcellulose, acrylic acid polymers) would be expected to improve the oil-releasing characteristics of most fabrics. Considerable work in this field has demonstrated that these expectations are indeed realized (20–29).

Two papers have reported that certain fabrics based on uncrimped, continuous-polyester-filament yarns showed oil release which is superior to that shown by cotton fabrics (30,31). Their findings also showed that oil tended to be retained in the fine crevices of cotton fibers and fiber cross-over points in all yarns. They further reported that any complication of the polyester fabric construction, eg crimped filaments, polyester staple versus filament yarns and tighter yarn twists, tended to affect oil release very adversely and render such fabrics considerably less oil releasing than cotton fabrics. (All yarns comprising blended fibers are staple yarns.) Smith and Sherman have attempted to account for these results by invoking a theory concerning the manner in which purely geometrical factors of fabric construction control the hysteresis of the dynamic contact angles of fluids on fibers, thus influencing the rates of the capillary-flow processes involved in oil release (13). Briefly, these authors claim that all factors tending to increase the roughness, or irregularity, of the fibers and yarns should retard oil release.

It should be stressed that geometric factors affect only the kinetics of the detergency process, and not the thermodynamics. (The thermodynamics of the process, as discussed above, determines only the feasibility of achieving oil release.) Since soil-release agents exert their major effect on the thermodynamics of the oil-release process, further consideration of the specific effects of geometric factors on fabric detergency does not seem warranted in this article.

Commercial Soil-Release Agents

A soil-release agent designed for the finishing of durable-press fabrics was introduced by Imperial Chemical Industries Ltd. shortly after the commercial introduction of durable-press fabrics (Cirrasol PT, see below). The Deering-Milliken Co. shortly thereafter announced the availability of proprietary soil-releasing, durable-press fabrics, which apparently were based on emulsion polymers containing carboxylic acid groups (25). The Deering-Milliken fabrics (identified by the trade name, Visa) were finished using a treatment which was claimed to be proprietary to this textile firm. Subsequently a large number of chemical suppliers made available to the textile industry a wide variety of soil-release agents.

The volume usage of soil-release agents has never been disclosed. It is safe to say, however, that usage was very high on durable-press fabrics for a significant period and has recently declined. One estimate was made that about one-half of all durable-press fabrics marketed during early 1968 contained a soil-release agent (32).

The reason for the declining usage is very puzzling, since the problem of oily soil release on durable-press fabrics is universally recognized throughout the textile industry and widely recognized by the consumer. Many independent sources have attested to the significant contribution that soil-release agents, in general, have made toward solving the problem of oily-stain release on conventional laundering (32–35). Some of the reasons which have been offered by the textile industry for the declining utilization of soil-release agents have included the following: their general effectiveness did not live up to the claims made for them; the effectiveness tended to deteriorate with prolonged wear and repeated launderings; certain soil-release agents (in particular, the "acrylics") presented problems in formulation, sewing, dusting of fabrics, and dye changes; and, finally, the increased cost of soil-release finishing was not justified by the advantages.

Soil-release agents are durable film-forming polymers containing very polar groups which are capable of hydrogen bonding with water. Their effectiveness derives from their ability to impart new surface energy characteristics to fibers which result in a net reduction of γ_{WF} value when fibers interact with water and a net increase of the γ_{OF} value when they interact with an oily soil. The overall effect of these changes in interfacial energies is to produce a more negative value of ΔG in the detergency process, as seen in equation 4, thus enabling oil release to proceed at a larger rate than would otherwise be realized (13).

There are four broad classes of soil-release finishes currently available: *(1)*

fluorochemical; (2) "co-crystallizing," (3) emulsion polymers containing carboxylic acid groups; and (4) water soluble polymers containing carboxylic acid groups. (The latter two classes are often referred to as "acrylic" soil-release agents.)

In general, all suppliers claim an improved oily-soil release (see section on Test method) for textiles—particularly durable-press fabrics—treated with their compositions. (No supplier claims that his finish is a universal panacea for all oily stains.) The effectiveness is claimed to persist through many launderings. In addition, most suppliers claim that their soil-release agents improve the antistatic and soil-redeposition qualities of fabrics containing synthetic fibers.

The general natures of the different classes of soil-release agents are discussed below. Since suppliers normally do not furnish information regarding chemical composition, any precise identification of the chemical nature of specific materials is precluded. Attention, however, is given to certain chemical, physical, and application characteristics which tend to differentiate the various classes. No attempts are made to judge the relative performance merits or application costs for the different materials. (In general, the chemical cost for the soil-release agent varies from about 2 to 7¢/lb of textile treated.)

Many textile mills have adopted trade names identifying their fabrics which contain soil-release treatments. Since these finishes are, for the most part, furnished by unidentified chemical suppliers, no listing of these trade names is made here.

Fluorochemical Soil-Release Agents. As mentioned previously, conventional fluorochemical oil- and water-repellent treatments are incapable of functioning as soil-release treatments. In fact, the adverse effect of these agents on the oily-soil-releasing properties of cotton has been reported (22).

Sherman, Smith, and Johannessen have described the surface properties of films and fabrics treated with a new class of hybrid polymers comprising segments based on both polyoxyethylene and acrylate polymers containing long-chain perfluoroaliphatic groups (36). These hybrid polymers are unique in their ability to confer both oil-repellent and soil-releasing properties to textiles. These authors showed that these hybrid polymers are capable of exhibiting reversible surface conformations which are controlled solely by the polarity of the environment. Thus, the hybrid polymer film exhibits oil-repellent characteristics in air (a situation where the fluorochemical component dominates the surface) and oily-soil-releasing characteristics in water (a situation where the polyoxyethylene component dominates the surface).

A particularly noteworthy aspect of fluorochemical soil-release agents is the contribution that the fluorochemical component makes to the oil-releasing properties, presumably by reducing the sorptive bonding of the oil to the fibers—the magnitude of this sorptive bonding being independent of the aqueous environment.

Minnesota Mining and Manufacturing Company is the only supplier of a fluorochemical soil-release finish: FC-218 (Scotchgard brand "Dual Action Fabric Protector"). This finish is the only soil-release agent which confers oil repellency to fabric. The supplier recommends the application of 0.3–0.4% of active solids to the fabric. The finish is compatible with virtually all normal treating bath additives and has little, if any, effect on the hand of the fabric.

"Co-Crystallizing" Soil-Release Agents. This class refers to polyester finishes containing long, recurring segments of polyoxyethylene as the hydrophilic component as well as short blocks of polyethylene terephthalate units. This type of composition is claimed to co-crystallize with the polyester fiber components of fabrics, thereby conferring oily-soil-release properties (24,37). The co-crystallization phenomenon is highly specific (demanding a partial match in chemical composition between finish and fiber) and is alleged to render the treatment durable to multiple launderings.

The co-crystallizing soil-release agent is normally applied to deposit 1–2% solids on the fabric. (Its use is, of course, restricted to fabrics containing polyester fibers.) The effect of the treatment on fabric hand is believed to be minimal. The agent has excellent compatibility with normal finishing-bath ingredients.

Co-crystallizing soil-release agents are available under the trade name Cirrasol (Imperial Chemical Industries Ltd.).

Emulsion Polymers Containing Carboxylic Acid Groups. This subclass of "acrylic" soil-release agents refers to water-insoluble polymers containing carboxylic acid groups as the hydrophilic component (either in acid or salt forms). The acid groups generally derive from either acrylic or methacrylic acid. A typical polymer composition is 70:30 ethyl acrylate:acrylic acid.

Many suppliers offered "acrylic" emulsion soil-release agents during 1967 and early 1968. As of 1970, however, it is believed that the only "acrylic" emulsion soil-release agents which are offered are Perapret D, a product of BASF A.G. (29), and certain products of the Sylvan Chemical Division of Magnolia Industries.

Water-Soluble Polymers Containing Carboxylic Acid Groups. These are "acrylic" polymers which are closely related to the previous class. They generally contain a higher concentration of carboxylic acid groups (in acid or salt form) to assure water solubility. This class of materials depends on crosslinking during textile finishing for its subsequent durability to laundering. (The crosslinking reaction occurs during the normal curing of the aminoplast crease-proofing resin at 150–175°C. It probably involves a partial condensation of the aminoplast resin with some carboxyl groups of the polymer.)

Acrylic soil-release agents of both the emulsion and water-soluble types are generally used at a level of 1.5–2.5% solids on the fabric. These treatments tend to make the hand of fabrics harsher, and a higher concentration of softener may be required to offset this effect.

The reactivity and anionic character of "acrylic" soil-release agents impose definite limitations on the formulation of the finishing bath, particularly with regard to obtaining satisfactory compatibility with specific softeners and salt catalysts to be used in conjunction with aminoplast resins. It is usually important to follow closely the supplier's recommendations concerning procedures for formulating treating baths based on his particular soil-release agent.

Commercial water-soluble acrylic soil-release agents include the following trade-name products: Rhoplex 528 (Rohm and Haas Co.); Prym 47 and Prym 100 (Sun Chemical Co.); Astro-Clean 770 (Glo-Tex Chemical Co.); and Seyco 11-2820 (Seydel Wooley Co.)

Test Methods

The subject of developing methods which are suitable for testing the efficacy of soil-release agents to a broad spectrum of representative stains and soils has been somewhat controversial.

Two general test methods of rating oily-soil release have been widely used by investigators: (1) determination of the weight percent of the soil which is retained following laundering; and (*2*) reflectance observations of the laundered fabric by visual or instrumental means.

Although the first general method can be very precise, serious objections to its exclusive use can be raised. The consumer is certainly more concerned with the visual effect that residual soil exerts, rather than its intrinsic persistence. Schott has shown that cotton is a unique fiber in that it possesses a hollow lumen, which can easily be penetrated by oil (38). If this occurs, the lumen acts to prevent oil release on subsequent laundering. Oil trapped within the cotton lumen should have no effect on fabric appearance.

Reflectance testing of laundered fabrics by visual or instrumental means is now the generally accepted method of rating soil release. Prescott et al. favor instrumental reflectance measurements because they contend that it is more precise and can be more readily adapted to rating differently colored fabrics than visual observation (39,40).

The American Association of Textile Chemists and Colorists (AATCC) has recently adopted a standard test for the evaluation of oily-stain release (41). It involves the visual rating, using a 1–5 scale, of the laundered test fabric in comparison with a set of photographic standards. The test prescribes the exact procedures for staining (Nujol, a refined mineral-oil stain is specified), laundering (with a standard detergent at temperatures of 41, 49, and 60°C), drying, and rating the samples. The basis for the test is the assumption that results obtained on Nujol release relate to the release of other common oily stains. This assumption seems to be fairly well founded, at least for nonoxidizing oils which are free of particulate matter.

Composite soils, such as dirty motor oil, are of particular concern in the case of work clothes. The AATCC test can be readily adapted for rating composite soil release as well. Many soil-release agents are effective in improving the release of dirty motor oil—a soil which has been heretofore almost impossible to release from common fabrics, even using repeated launderings.

The AATCC test method for oily-soil release has been almost universally adopted by the industry.

Bibliography

1. Anon., *Chem. Eng. News* **47**, 16, 17 (Feb. 3, 1969).
2. R. L. Liss and R. P. Langguth, *J. Am. Oil Chemists' Soc.* **46**, 507–510 (1969).
3. J. Compton and W. J. Hart, *Textile Res. J.* **23**, 158–163, 418–423 (1953).
4. J. Compton and W. J. Hart, *Textile Res. J.* **24**, 263–264 (1954).
5. W. Kling and H. Mahl, *Melliand Textilber.* **35**, 640–645 (1954).
6. V. W. Tripp, R. L. Clayton, and B. R. Porter, *Textile Res. J.* **27**, 340–342 (1957).
7. N. F. Getchell, *Textile Res. J.* **25**, 150–194 (1955).
8. T. Fort, Jr., H. R. Billica, and C. K. Sloan, *Textile Res. J.* **36**, 7–12 (1966).
9. S. Shimauchi and N. Mizushima, *Am. Dyestuff Reporter* **57**, 462–469 (1968).
10. T. Young, *Trans. Roy. Soc.* (*London*) **95**, 65 (1805).
11. A. Duprê, *Théorie Mécanique de la Chaleur*, Gauthier-Villar, Paris, 1869, p. 369.
12. W. A. Zisman, "Contact Angle, Wettability, and Adhesion," *Advances in Chemistry Series No. 43*, Amer. Chem. Soc. 1964, pp. 1–51.
13. S. Smith and P. O. Sherman, *Textile Res. J.* **39**, 441–449 (1969).
14. E. J. Grajeck and W. H. Petersen, *Textile Res. J.* **32**, 320–331 (1962).
15. F. J. Philips, L. Segal, and L. Loeb, *Textile Res. J.* **27**, 369–378 (1957).
16. R. E. Read and G. C. Culling, *Am. Dyestuff Reporter* **56**, 881–887 (1967).
17. N. K. Adam, *J. Soc. Dyers Colourists* **53**, 121–129 (1937).
18. F. M. Fowkes, "Contact Angle, Wettability, and Adhesion," *Advances in Chemistry Series No. 43*, Amer. Chem. Soc. 1964, pp. 99–111.

19. A. H. Ellison and W. A. Zisman, *J. Phys. Chem.* **58**, 503–506 (1954).

20. J. V. Beninate, E. L. Kelly, G. L. Drake, Jr., and W. A. Reeves, *Am. Dyestuff Reporter* **55**, 37–41 (1966).

21. J. Berch, H. Peper and G. L. Drake, Jr., *Textile Res. J.* **34**, 29–34 (1964).

22. J. Berch, H. Peper, and G. L. Drake, Jr., *Textile Res. J.* **35**, 252–260 (1965).

23. T. Fort, Jr., H. R. Billica, and T. H. Grindstaff, *Textile Res. J.* **36**, 99–112 (1966).

24. D. A. Garrett and P. N. Hartley, *J. Soc. Dyers Colourists* **82**, 252–257 (1966).

25. U.S. Pat. 3,377,249 (April 9, 1968), F. W. Marco (to Deering-Milliken Research Corp.).

26. H. Peper and J. Berch, *Am. Dyestuff Reporter* **54**, 863–869 (1965).

27. S. Smith and P. O. Sherman, *Textile Chem. Colorist* **1**, 105–109 (1969).

28. W. P. Utermohlen, M. E. Ryan, and D. O. Young, *Textile Res. J.* **21**, 510–521 (1951).

29. H. E. Bille, A. Eckell, and G. A. Schmidt, *Textile Chem. Colorist* **1**, 600–607 (1969).

30. R. Tsuzuki and N. Yabuuchi, *Am. Dyestuff Reporter* **57**, 472–476 (1968).

31. C. B. Brown, S. H. Thompson, and G. Stewart, *Textile Res. J.* **38**, 735–742 (1968).

32. Anon., *Textile World* **118**, 112–118 (May 1968).

33. L. D. Queen, F. F. Schrum, Jr., and H. M. Lewis, *Am. Dyestuff Reporter* **57**, 846–849 (1968).

34. R. T. Hunter and R. C. Roga, *J. Am. Oil Chemists' Soc.* **46**, 199–201 (1969).

35. B. W. Terry and W. L. Groves, paper presented at the *Spring Meeting of the American Oil Chemists' Society*, San Francisco, 1969.

36. P. O. Sherman, S. Smith, and B. Johannessen, *Textile Res. J.* **39**, 449–459 (1969).

37. U.S. Pat. 3,459,590 (Aug. 5, 1969), W. M. Corbett and D. Harrison (to Imperial Chemical Industries, Ltd.).

38. H. Schott, *Textile Res. J.* **39**, 296–298 (1969).

39. W. B. Prescott and E. J. Stearns, *Textile Chem. Colorist* **1**, 64–78 (1969).

40. G. B. Aspelin, W. B. Prescott, and R. R. Krammes, *Textile Chem. Colorist* **1**, 231–233 (1969).

41. *AATCC Test Method 130-1969*, AATCC Technical Manual 45, 1969, pp. 223–224.

SAMUEL SMITH
Minnesota Mining and Manufacturing Company

SOLVENT DYEING

Up until the last decade, textile operations such as sizing, desizing, bleaching, prescour, dyeing, afterscour and application of finishing agents were carried out exclusively in aqueous media. In the 1960s organic-solvent-based processes for bleaching and prescour and for the application of finishing agents have been commercialized. Although these solvent processes account for only a minor portion of the total textiles processed, their use is growing. The fact that these processes have been accepted at the expense of existing water-based processes has stimulated the interest to explore the potential of an organic-solvent-based dyeing process. At the present time solvent dyeing is not practiced commercially but is under development in a number of industrial laboratories in the U.S. and Europe.

Solvent dyeing is the substitution of organic liquids for water in the process of application and fixation of dyes to textile fibers and constructions. The mechanics of solvent dyeing are similar to aqueous dyeing and involve contacting the fiber with a measured quantity of an organic solvent solution or suspension of the dye and subjecting the fiber, wet with dye solution or suspension, to conditions to establish equilibrium diffusion of the dye between the fiber and organic solvent. The distribution ratio of dye between fiber and solvent at equilibrium will be determined by such previously recognized factors governing dye affinity for fibers as salt formation, hydrogen bonding, or chemical reactivity. The rate at which equilibrium is reached is a function of temperature and is generally more rapid in organic solvent systems than in aqueous systems.

In the development of a solvent dyeing process there are many factors to be considered; some of the most important are:

1. Selection of organic liquids as solvent.
2. Selection of dyes.
3. Type of fiber and construction.
4. Dye bath additives.
5. Fiber preparation.
6. Method of dye application and fixation.
7. Equipment.

Selection of Organic Liquids as Solvent

A great variety of organic liquids have been proposed for the solvent in a solvent dyeing process (1). These include aliphatic and aromatic hydrocarbons, their chlorinated and oxygenated derivatives, and other more sophisticated products. Ideally the solvent should meet the following requirements to be useful in a solvent dyeing process:

1. It should be nontoxic.
2. It should be stable and nonflammable under conditions employed.
3. It must be a solvent for the dye at fixation temperatures.
4. It should have a swelling, but nondestructive, action on the fiber.
5. The boiling point should be high enough to permit accelerating dye fixation to a commercially acceptable rate.
6. It must be readily recoverable at low cost without significant loss.
7. The initial cost must be economically acceptable.

The chlorinated aliphatic hydrocarbons most nearly meet the stated requirements. Trichloroethylene and 1,1,1-trichloroethane serve best as dye solvents, but their boiling points, 87°C and 74°C respectively, are too low for rapid dye fixation. At higher temperatures the solvent flashes off and dye fixation occurs only at conventional thermofixation temperature. Perchloroethylene, bp 121°C, generally provides a dye solution at temperatures conducive to rapid dye fixation but it is a less effective dye solvent at ambient temperatures. The difficulty can be overcome by the addition of a cosolvent to solubilize the dye (2). Materials proposed as cosolvents include dimethylformamide, cyclic ethers and esters, glycols, and glycol ethers. These cosolvents solve dye solubility problems but introduce other problems relating to flammability, toxicity, recovery, and cost.

Selection of Dyes

It appears that all dye classes or dye structures are useful which can be dissociated from a solvent suspension or dispersion to the nonaggregated molecular state. Diffusion of dye molecules into the fiber occurs at dyeing conditions. The dye classes currently being studied include acid, basic, direct, and dispersed dyes. The term dispersed is a misnomer in the solvent system because such dyes are generally solvent-soluble at the dyeing or fixation temperature. Not all dyes of each class have the required solubility in a given solvent to be useful in a solvent dyeing system. Therefore the latitude in the selection of dyes is critically dependent upon the choice of the solvent vehicle; the use of cosolvents greatly increases the latitude of dye selection.

Commercially available dyes for aqueous dyeing are generally not suitable for solvent dyeing because of the inorganic diluents used to standardize the dyes for strength. In the manufacture of dyes for use in the solvent system it will be necessary to produce them as the concentrated color, free of inorganic salts. If standardization is necessary, solvent-soluble diluents will be required because insoluble components are extremely inconvenient in a textile mill. In many cases a chemical modification of the dye molecule is required to enhance its solubility in the solvent.

Type of Fiber and Construction

All fiber classes are dyeable in a solvent dyeing system with the possible exception of polypropylene, which is subject to dimensional distortion in the commonly proposed solvents at the temperatures required for dye fixation. Man-made fibers are more amenable to dyeing in solvent than in water because the swelling effect of the solvent enhances the permeability to dyes. Natural fibers can be dyed from solvent if the vehicle incorporates a few percent (based on weight of fiber) of water or possibly other suitable swelling agents (analogous to the use of carriers for man-made fibers in the aqueous system). The dye acceptance of man-made fibers can be varied by process modifications introduced during the production of the fiber to provide differential dyeing yarns. These yarns produce similar desired tone on tone shade differences in the solvent dyeing system as in aqueous dyeing systems. Barre streaks due to differences in dye acceptance caused by unintentional fiber variations are evident in the solvent system as in the aqueous system. In the present state of development, it has not been established whether one system is superior to the other in this respect. The dyeability of man-made fibers in the solvent system is modified by prior heat setting to stabilize fabric dimensions, similar to the effect obtained in aqueous systems.

Dye Bath Additives

An outstanding property of solvent dyeing systems is the rapidity and thoroughness with which the dye solution penetrates and is distributed through any textile construction. Surfactants and leveling agents do not appear to be needed to aid distribution. The addition of thickeners, such as cellulose ethers, to the dye liquor may help control migration, in pad-vapor methods where evaporation or condensation might cause uneven coloration.

In cross dyeing, the dyeing of dissimilar fibers in contrasting colors, and union dyeing, the dyeing of dissimilar fibers to the same shade, dyes of different dye classes are present in the dye bath. In aqueous systems an anticoprecipitant is frequently employed to inhibit the interaction between dyes of different classes, such as acid and basic dyes. Since the solvent is a nonionizing medium, the acidic or basic character of the dyes is not significant during application and all classes can be conveniently combined in the same dye bath without the addition of anticoprecipitants. The affinity between dye class and fiber class bears the usual relationship, ie, dyes containing acid or basic groups will be fixed on fibers containing oppositely charged groups. When using mixtures of dyes of different classes in the solvent system, it is useful to add a relatively nonvolatile cosolvent to assist in the redistribution of the dyes to the appropriate fiber for maximum dye efficiency.

Fiber Preparation

Fabric or fiber preparation prior to solvent dyeing may require scouring and/or bleaching. Present aqueous or solvent emulsion methods of preparation are generally not compatible for economic integration with a solvent dyeing system. Drying to remove water prior to dyeing would be required (3). However, it can be expected that in many procedures, this pretreatment will either be eliminated or be integrated into the solvent dyeing system as a solvent-based pretreatment. Many soils, lubricants, sizes and identification tints do not interfere with solvent dyeing procedures and are effectively removed in the dyeing process. Discriminating selection of additives used for fabric construction and identification is necessary but it is not necessarily true that they must be solvent soluble.

Method of Dye Application and Fixation

Economics and pollution control dictate that consumption of the vehicle in a solvent system must be kept to a minimum. Assuming 95% recovery, then, if the total solvent used for dye application, fixation and afterwash is ten parts on weight of fiber, one half pound of solvent would be lost per pound of fiber. Most batch dyeing methods will require 15–25 parts liquid for the dye bath and additional material for washing. With continuous procedures, however, the liquid required to apply the dye is usually about one part on woven goods and three parts on pile fabrics. This consideration largely discourages the development of batch methods, except for specialty products, and directs attention toward continuous pad-vapor procedures. It has also been established that in exhaust dyeing from solvent, 5% or more of dye may be left in the bath; in contrast, the pad-vapor fixation process can achieve 100% dye efficiency, even with dispersed dyes. This may have even greater economic significance. Nevertheless, it must be noted that because aqueous dyeing of textured knit fabrics has unresolved problems, much interest is directed toward development of an exhaust solvent dyeing process for these materials even at a higher cost (4).

Most advances toward commercialization of solvent dyeing utilize a continuous pad procedure. A method described by DuPont in 1949 (5) used a pad-drain technique to apply a solution of dye in a cyclic ester to acrylic fiber, followed by aqueous steaming. The Vapocol process proposed by Imperial Chemical Industries in 1957 applied aqueous dye suspensions to polyester fiber by padding and drying (6). When passed into refluxing trichloroethylene vapors, condensed vapors dissolve the dye which diffuses into the fiber. In 1966 the J. R. Geigy Company applied for patents (7,8), utilizing as the dye vehicle chlorinated hydrocarbons mixed with water-soluble cosolvents. The dye solution is applied to cellulose acetate and other fibers by padding and is air dried at low temperature. The dye is subsequently thermofixed. An alternative procedure described by Institut für Textil Technologie der Chemiefasern in 1964 (9) dyes polyester from an exhausting solvent bath below the boiling point, followed by aqueous soaping. None of these processes is a fully integrated solvent system comprising application, fixation, and washing in solvent. None of them describes an efficient solvent-recovery system.

In 1966 The Dow Chemical Company filed for a patent on a process for heating and drying solvent-wetted material by means of superheated solvent vapors (10). The volatilized solvent is airfree and is recovered by simple condensation. Using this technology, Allied Chemical Corporation and The Dow Chemical Company, in a joint effort, have developed procedures by which fabric is continuously impregnated with dye solution, heated in superheated solvent vapor to fix the dye, washed with the condensed solvent and reheated in superheated solvent vapor to remove residual wash liquor (11). The dyed fabric emerges in the dry state. Dye fixation time in this system is measured in seconds at 100–120°C. The process is amenable to application of lubricants or other finishes after washing prior to drying; also, using appropriate temperatures and fabric handling, heat setting can be achieved during drying. The wash liquor is purified for reuse by distillation to eliminate dye bath assistants and additives removed from the greige goods. These materials thus removed constitute the sole residue of the process.

Equipment

The equipment presently used for aqueous dyeing processes is not adaptable to a solvent dyeing process. New equipment must be developed and will follow as the requirements of solvent dyeing processes become better defined.

Evaluation of Various Proposed Solvent Dyeing Systems

Availability of suitable equipment and chemicals will determine feasibility of the system. They are now in commercial development.

Various methods have been proposed for heating textile materials impregnated with dye-solvent solution. Hot-air systems volatilize the solvent before it reaches dye diffusion temperature; thermofixation is then required. Systems utilizing carbon absorption for recovery of solvent vapor from air are complex and difficult to maintain. Steam systems which volatilize the solvent for recovery hybridize the method and leave a water-wet fabric. Systems which heat with solvent vapors at reflux temperature allow liquor condensation on the fiber resulting in uneven dyeing. Use of superheated vapor, of the same solvent as used in the dye bath and washing, provides a homogeneous system free of condensate, effective low-cost recovery, and integrated operation from greige goods to finished fabric. This latter method is expected to improve substantially the economic feasibility of solvent dyeing methods.

The preparation of dye-solvent solutions, for uniform distribution on textiles, limited initial development to the use of dispersed dyes. The development by Allied Chemical Corporation of dye-solvent compositions, utilizing ionic dyestuffs, has accelerated interest in solvent dyeing. These dyes overcome the application and performance limitations inherent in disperse dyes. They broaden the range of fibers and textiles amenable to solvent dyeing. Identification of these dyes by Colour Index Numbers discloses they are familiar products with well-known performance properties. Utilization of these dye classes enhances the technical feasibility of solvent dyeing.

Advantages of the System

There are many potential advantages in a solvent dyeing system. Dye fixation can be accomplished in a few seconds at temperature, and this short residence time permits compact equipment and high production rate. The compact units with limited in-process material permit short runs previously possible only by batch operation. Capital costs for floor space and equipment are minimal. Clean-out of equipment between runs is very simple.

The process is adaptable to integration of operation from prescour through dyeing, washing, finishing, and drying. Operating and chemical simplicity is conducive to automation. High capacity and automated integrated operation offer maximum labor savings.

The heat capacity of chlorinated hydrocarbon solvents is only about a tenth that of water. Energy requirements for process heating and solvent recovery can be very low. Airfree systems, which recover the solvent by condensation rather than by carbon absorption or steaming and phase separation, promise easier operation and economic advantage.

Suitable water resources are becoming increasingly scarce. During the 1960s the cost of water and subsequent effluent treatment increased about eight times. The solvent system eliminates the need to rely on water resources and produces essentially no waste, whereas in the aqueous system the residue from the solvent recovery is the only waste and comprises lubricants, sizes, dye bath additives and other materials used in fabric production. This waste can be removed in a concentrated form which can be either burned or buried in the ground.

In aqueous dyeing systems the amount of water required per unit of finished product is much larger than the amount of solvent required in the solvent dyeing system. This is due to the much faster dye fixation time and the more efficient wetting properties of the solvents compared to water. Also the aqueous system requires more additives in the dye bath, thus the amount of contaminants in the effluent water is greater than that in the effluent solvent. It is doubtful that methods to treat the effluent water to make it suitable for reuse can compete economically with the distillation recovery systems for the reuse of the solvent.

All these advantages can be translated into improved economics. They must be balanced against the cost of solvent, as determined by its effective recovery, in commercial operation.

Bibliography

1. G. Siegrist, *Teintex* **9**, 575–593 (1969).
2. Brit. Pat. 1,128,989 (July 8, 1966) (to J. R. Geigy A.G.).
3. R. E. Ritter, *J. Am. Assoc. Tex. Chem. and Color.* **1**, 234–235 (1969).
4. Charles Reichman, *Knitted Outerwear Times*, March 9, 1970, 33–34.
5. U.S. Pat. 2,654,652 (Oct. 6, 1953), L. G. Ray (to E. I. du Pont de Nemours & Co., Inc.).
6. D. A. Garrett, *J. Soc. Dyers Colourists* **73**, 365–374 (1957).
7. French Pat. 1,505,677 (Dec. 8, 1966); 1,507,460 (January 4, 1967) (to J. R. Geigy A.G.).
8. U.S. Pat. 3,510,243 (May 5, 1970), M. Seuret, W. Leutenegger, and H. E. Wegmuller (to J. R. Geigy A.G.).
9. British Pat. 1,048,878 (March 17, 1964), E. Wunsch et al. (to Institut für Textiltechnologie der Chemiefasern).
10. U.S. Pat. 3,408,748 (Nov. 5, 1968), J. L. Dunn (to The Dow Chemical Co.).
11. F. L. Sievenpiper et al., *J. Am. Assoc. Tex. Chem. and Color*, **3**, 69–71 (1971).

FREDERIC L. SIEVENPIPER
AND CHARLES E. McGINN
Allied Chemical Corporation

TEXTILE WASTE TREATMENT

The pollution of lakes, rivers, and other water courses by both domestic and industrial wastes is very much a matter of public concern. Present-day activity by citizens groups, however, tends to overlook the fact that studies of treatment methods for both classes of wastes have been going on for many decades. Not all of the technical problems can be solved immediately, but much has been accomplished in research and experimental studies. In the textile industry many reports have been published in special monographs and articles in trade journals. The American Association of Textile Chemists and Colorists has a task committee (RA58 Stream Sanitation Technology) that actively follows the progress of textile-waste treatment in the industry. It provided a pertinent bibliography to interested agencies many years ago. A more recent one, covering modern references (1954–1968), has been prepared by Livengood (1).

Much has been written of the complexity of textile wastes and indeed with justification. There is no comparable industrial segment that uses so many diverse materials in manufacture. The industry is also widely scattered and heterogeneous in its makeup due to the complexity of fabric types and fiber raw materials. Some textile mills handle fiber through spinning only, others go on to weaving or do weaving only. These are often "greige" operations, that is to say, performed upon the undyed fiber. Others may do these greige operations and also dye and finish cloth, while still others only dye and finish. The mills which do all the processing from fiber to finished cloth are called vertical organizations and they have the advantage of better control of waste products.

Major Types of Textile Mills and Their Wastes.

Spinning Mill (cotton, synthetics): Very small volumes, if any, of liquid wastes (other than sanitary sewer).

Weaving Mills (spun yarns and continuous filament): Small-volume residues of size (starch, gelatin, synthetic polymers) and tints.

Dyeing and Finishing Plants: Desizing liquors (enzyme-converted starch and gelatin solutions of synthetic sizes).

Scouring liquors and rinse water, containing natural fiber waxes, spinning oils, size residues, alkali, detergents, tints, etc.

Bleach liquors, containing spent bleach (sodium hypochlorite, hydrogen peroxide) and alkali (caustic soda), etc.

Mercerizing liquors, containing spent caustic.

Finishing wastes, ie remnants of unused finish formulas (resin precondensates, softeners, high-polymer finishing materials).

Dye wastes, ie residues from exhausted dye baths, dye rinses, salt, dye additives, dye carriers, etc. Printing operations discharge colors and print-paste materials such as dextrin.

Any consideration of waste treatment is generally confined to the dyeing and finishing plants since the others produce very little waste of consequence. This would appear to unscramble the problem of diversity mentioned above, but there are still wide variations in dyeing and finishing plants, not only in the types of cloth processed, but also in the wide variety of chemicals used in processing and in the fabric-fiber residues that constitute the waste.

The work of Masselli (2) and his colleagues at Wesleyan University, dating from the mid-1930s up to the present, have gone a long way toward a simplification of textile-waste-treatment problems. The work was based on ingenious techniques for analysis of a given mill's waste potential and led to an approach to possible treatment procedures.

The extent to which textile wastes contribute to stream pollution is measured by the same analytical method as is used for domestic sewage. The quantitative measure is expressed as biochemical oxygen demand (BOD), as it is the depletion of oxygen by organic matter in the water courses that endangers marine life and produces malodorous residues in stream bottoms and along the banks. See Vol. 21, p. 700. The BOD values of typical textile-waste materials are given in Table 1 (3), the materials chosen are a partial listing of over 400 chemicals and proprietary products used in scouring, dyeing, printing, and finishing, or result from wet finishing processes. The values given are parts of 5-day BOD per 100 parts of the waste material (pollutant); thus, each pound of gelatin textile waste requires one pound of oxygen, and one pound of starch requires half a pound.

In waste-water analysis BOD values are commonly expressed as ppm. The dissolved oxygen in the water of a water course under normal conditions is about 7–8 ppm. This range of oxygen content prevails in water at temperatures from 70 to 50°F with higher values approaching 10 ppm near freezing temperature. In earlier waste-treatment technology, the major issue was the dilution factor. For example, one million gal of a 300-ppm BOD waste could be adequately handled by a stream flow of 43 million gal with 7 ppm dissolved oxygen. It was assumed that it would take five days to deplete the stream's oxygen, but depletion would not occur since there would be a continuous regeneration of oxygen as the stream became re-aerated. The average domestic sewage has a 5-day BOD of about 250 ppm. But it can be seen from Table 1 that 1% starch in the effluent has a BOD of 5000 ppm, a very high value.

It should be noted that the 5-day incubation period used in the test is to some extent arbitrary; 10-, 20-, or 30-day values would be higher and more meaningful for materials of slow biodegradability. For such materials the test merely measures the rate of oxidation, rather than the total oxygen demand.

Starch is cited as an example, even though a number of other materials in Table 1 have higher ratings, because starch is present in textile wastes generally in much higher concentrations. The use of starch as a warp-sizing material on a large portion of cotton

Table 1. BOD Values of Typical Textile-Waste Materials

Pollutant	5-day BOD per 100 parts pollutant	Pollutant	5-day BOD per 100 parts pollutant
gelatin	100	acetic acid, 56%	33
pine oil	108	formic acid, 85%	2
starch (corn)	50	o-phenylphenol	138
stymer (styrene maleic salt)	1	lauryl sulfate	125
CMC (carboxymethylcellulose)	3	poly(vinyl acetate)	1
hydro (sodium hydrosulfite)	22	poly(vinyl alcohol)	1
wheat starch	55	ethyl alcohol	125
dextrin	50	phenol	200
tallow	152	salicylic acid	141
soap	155	sodium chloride	0
dyes	0–10	urea	
melamine resin	14–23	derived resin	3–20
alkylarenesulfonate	0–4	kerosene	53

and cotton-blend fabrics at concentrations of 8–12% of the warp weight implies a major waste constituent. In the waste waters most of the starch is converted to sugars by the enzyme treatment required to remove the starch, but this does not alter the potential pollution load. Some mills have changed over from starch to carboxymethylcellulose (CMC) to enjoy a lower 5-day BOD rating even at higher cost. This substitution formerly made sense but in today's world of intensified concern, the reduction in BOD by use of CMC is insufficient, and actually turns out to be a delusion.

CMC is very slowly biodegradable, and although its 5-day BOD is low, the 10-, or 20-day BOD would perhaps approach that of starch, which means that it has the same polluting potential but with a longer period of digestion. Thus, untreated CMC would pollute a stream for many miles and many days of downstream flow.

An anomaly in textile-waste treatments is the question of color. Much is made of this aspect as it poses primarily aesthetic questions. The BOD is very low, yet color is hard and therefore expensive to remove. Carbon-black absorption or chemical coagulation is possible. The real surprise, however, is the fact that most color contamination comes not from the dyehouse, but from the removal of identification tints on the greige goods from the weaving mill.

Liquid Wastes from Textile Mills

It has been noted above that spinning and weaving mills produce little if any liquid wastes. These mills are putting materials, such as the spinning oils, sizes, and tints, onto fibers, yarns, and cloth, but are removing none of these. Only in the case of wool fiber in the worsted division of that industry is a thorough scour applied prior to spinning. This wool-scouring waste is high in grease and in concentrated form is usually handled separately to recover the wool grease for its lanolin content.

The materials listed in Table 1 are typical and represent generic groups; for example, the first seven items (except hydro and pine oil) are warp sizes. Hydro is used to reduce vat dyes. Pine oil, tallow, and soap are kindred materials and are used as detergents, penetrators, and softeners. Lauryl sulfate and alkylarenesulfonate are typical synthetic detergents for scouring, dye leveling, and wetting. Acetic and formic acid and, of course, mineral acids such as sulfuric, are used in dyeing, neutralizing, and carbonizing (of wool). o-Phenylphenol, phenol, and salicylic acid are typical synthetic fiber-dye carriers, especially for polyester fibers. The use of dyes is obvious, and sodium chloride (and other salts) are used in large quantities in dyeing. The dyes are exhausted onto the fibers, and so little of them is discharged. The salts, however, even though they have a low BOD, none the less can upset the stream balance, as do alkalis with high pH's or acids with low pH's.

Poly(vinyl acetate) and poly(vinyl alcohol) are used in finishing to add body and stiffness to fabrics. Their presence in wastes is limited except for the poly(vinyl alcohol) which is also used in warp sizing. As with CMC, it may also have a latent BOD not determined in the 5-day test. Textile resins for durable press are present in minute amounts in waste waters and pose no problems in treatment.

Table 2 gives the average wastes of a few substances in dyeing- and finishing-plant effluents. There are, of course, hundreds of dyes and scores of chemicals in use, but not necessarily every day, nor in every plant. It is also obvious that interactions can occur among these wastes where acids meet alkali and oxidizing agents meet reducing agents.

Table 2. Average Waste in Dyeing- and Finishing-Plant Effluents

Pollutant	Ppm	5-Day BOD/ppm
sucrose (from starch)	400	300
oils, fats, waxes (natural and mfd)	100	150
detergents, surface-active agents	60	60
spent dyes	20	5
caustic alkali, other alkali salts	400	0
mixed acids	40	10
salts	1000	0
greige goods tints	40	10
dye auxiliaries (carriers, levelers, etc)	50	75
dextrin (print pastes)	1000	500
hydrogen peroxide	10	0
sodium hydrosulfite	45	11
finishing resins	15	15

The volume of wastes from a typical plant are 25–30 gal/lb of cloth; thus, a dye plant processing 200,000 yards a day, equivalent to 100,000 lb of cloth, would discharge 2.5–3.0 million gal of a waste averaging 1100 BOD.

Treatment Methods. In general, textile wastes can be treated with domestic sewage by the conventional oxidation methods of the activated-sludge process and the trickling-filter process. Problems arise only when shock loads occur from the dumping of high BOD wastes in concentrated batches. This problem is circumvented by the use of detention tanks or lagoons which mix the various textile wastes and release them to sanitary sewers in even amounts over a 24-hr period. Reductions of BOD in the various aeration or oxidation processes are usually in the 90–95% range. Higher degrees of treatment can be accomplished with extended treatment time. Treatment-plant effluents can be "polished" by filtration through sand or activated carbon, the latter yielding effluents of low color content. In many instances mills have contracted with city sanitary-treatment plants to handle their wastes after lagooning to even out shock loads.

pH Control. The inorganic materials of Table 1 (low to no BOD) are generally innocuous to rivers and streams except for extremes of pH. Strong acidity is particularly damaging, much more so than alkalinity. It is obviously preferable to hold to a more or less neutral pH but this would be difficult for a cotton-finishing plant with its large amount of caustic waste from boil-off and mercerizing. Again lagooning and proportioning of waste minimize the need for neutralization. It has been established that streams can stand fairly high pH's (10–11), provided they are relatively steady and not in heavy concentration of buffered alkalinity.

Toxic Materials. Many authorities had early expressed concern with the phenolic materials and other aromatics used in polyester dyeing. In contrast with concentrations encountered in disinfecting systems, the amounts in textile waste are much too low for toxicity and the organisms of the activated sludge process and trickling filters consume them. The heavy metals copper and chromium do not hinder these processes but do inhibit the anaerobic processes in sludge digestion, a separate treatment of the solids settled from the final liquid by clarification.

Copper salts are used as dye fixatives, sometimes in the form of organic complexes. Chrome salts are used in wool dyeing for color fixation and also as oxidizing agents in vat dyeing (as bichromates). The use of phenolic materials in carrier dyeing of polyester fibers has increased year by year as these fibers have grown in importance. Pressure dyeing has sometimes eliminated or minimized the use of carriers, but its total usage is on the rise. These agents assist in dye penetration by virtue of the oleophilic nature of the fiber and an oiliness with slight water solubility on the part of these carriers. Thus, the dispersed dyes at the fiber interface are assisted in penetration and accompany the carriers into the fiber. The carriers are subsequently rinsed or scoured out of the cloth.

Solvent Materials. Solvents should be handled separately from water-borne wastes. The alcohols have such a high BOD that they can put a waste-treatment plant out of commission. Nonmiscible solvents should be skimmed off or recovered in catch basins if they are heavier than water. Inflammable solvents should also be segregated for other disposal.

Wool Waste. Wool wastes from a scouring plant are a special category. The amount of grease and suint is so great as to require primary treatment at the mill. Lanolin grease in impure form is separated by calcium chloride treatment or acidification and collected in a centrifuge. There is a limited market for the lanolin but it does not constitute a boon to the wool scourer. The balance of the waste is still very concentrated and must be further treated by itself in oxidation processes or in conjunction with sanitary sewage.

The early separation of wool wastes poses an example of considerable significance to all industrial-waste engineers and chemists. When wastes are concentrated, they should be kept that way and dilution avoided. Masselli (4) counsels the segregation of starch wastes both at the greige mill and the dye plant and their concentration by evaporation, filtration, or other means, followed by the collection of the solid waste for disposal by ignition or burial. This would lighten the burden on waste-treatment facilities, for it is so much more difficult and costly to handle a dilute waste. Print pastes and solvents, especially alcohols, fall in this category also.

Bibliography

1. C. D. Livengood, *Textile Wastes*, a Bibliography, North Carolina State University, School of Textiles, Raleigh, N.C., 1969.
2. J. W. Masselli, N. W. Masselli, and M. G. Burford, *A Simplification of Textile Waste Survey and Treatment*, New England Interstate Water Pollution Control Commission, Boston, Mass., 1959, 68 pp.
3. Committee RA58 Report, *Am. Dyestuff Reptr.* **55,** 685–688 (1966).
4. J. W. Masselli, *Paper New England Regional AATCC Convention, Portsmouth, N.H., May 1970.*

Francis K. Burr
Fabric Research Laboratories, Inc.

U

UNITS

The manuscript of this article was completed in May, 1969, it does not describe developments later than that date.

Measurement

Measurement is counting. Although we talk loosely of "measuring the value" of a particular length, or electric current, or temperature, we have no means of doing it. The only kind of physical quantity which we can measure (that is to say count) is one that is a number, such as the number of peas in a bottle or the number of fringes in an interferometric experiment. For any other kind of physical quantity the best we can do is to count the number of times by which the physical quantity is greater or smaller in one instance than in another instance. For example, we can measure the ratio (a pure number) I_2/I_1 of two particular electric currents I_2 and I_1 by using a specified method to count the number of times by which I_2 is greater or smaller than I_1. A complete specification of the method of counting serves to define the physical quantity called electric current, and is indeed our only way of saying exactly what we mean by "electric current."

Units

Similarly, we can measure the ratios I_1/I^*, I_2/I^*, .., of each of several electric currents I_1, I_2, .., and the particular electric current I^*. We may then, if we wish to do so, treat I^* as a *unit* of electric current by giving it a name of its own and denoting it by a special symbol.

It follows that, if we think it useful to do so, we may treat *any* physical quantity as a unit. It also follows that it is never necessary to treat any physical quantity as a

984

unit. The sole criterion for judging the usefulness of a unit should be its effectiveness as a means of making the results of measurements as immediately and unambiguously intelligible as possible, with as little explanation as possible, to all who may need to use them, regardless of the field or of the country in which they happen to work. According to that criterion we must deplore any unnecessary proliferation of units; the more there are, the more difficult it becomes to remember or to find out how they are defined.

If I were to tell the reader the value of the ratio $l/$"stg" of the length l of my desk, and the length of my standard piece of string which I treat as a unit and denote by the symbol "stg", then he would be little the wiser; the "stg" may be useful to me personally, but it is a *noncommunicable* unit. If I were to tell him the values of the ratios $l/$"stg", $b/$"stg", and $h/$"stg", where l, b, and h denote the length, breadth, and height of my desk, then he could calculate the ratios l/b and l/h (which it would have been more sensible to have given him in the first place) which determine the *shape* of my desk, but he would still not know whether it is a large desk or a small one. If, however, I were to tell him the values of the ratios $l/l^\ominus$, $b/l^\ominus$, and $h/l^\ominus$, where $l^\ominus$ is a length equal to a specified number of wavelengths of some specified spectral line, then if he were determined enough he could make himself a desk of exactly the same size as mine. There is still no particular advantage to be gained from treating the length $l^\ominus$ as a unit by giving it a special name and symbol, but if I did so, then the unit would be a *communicable* one. Treating it as a unit would not, however, absolve me from the duty of defining it in every publication in which I used it. Nor would the unit, though communicable, be a very useful one, implying as it does easy access to the elaborate spectrometric and interferometric apparatus which would be needed to enable the reader to make a copy of my desk.

To be useful a unit must not only be communicable but must also be accessible; it must be *practical*. Practical units must satisfy three requirements. Firstly, they must be unambiguously defined. Secondly, they must be reproducible (and must be regularly reproduced) with the highest accuracy at least in specialized laboratories. Thirdly, they must be internationally accepted so as to ensure (a) that they need not be defined every time they are used, and (b) that practical meters are widely available for measurements ranging from the crudest to the most accurate.

My $l^\ominus$ satisfies the first two of these requirements but not the third. To make it accessible as well as communicable I should have to give a value of the ratio of $l^\ominus$ and some internationally accepted unit such as the centimetre (symbol: cm). But then I should hope that my editor would insist that I save each of my would-be desk-copiers from having to do the calculations for himself by giving the values of $l/$cm, $b/$cm, and $h/$cm.

Ease of communication demands a sufficient, but no larger, set of internationally accepted units. A sufficient set comprises one unit (called a base unit) for each physical quantity which is regarded as being a dimensionally independent physical quantity (for which see below). Such a set now exists. It is called the International System of Units (Système International d'Unités) and is denoted by the cipher SI. For the sake of easy communication among scientists it is greatly to be hoped that all non-SI units will progressively disappear from scientific work.

The International Authorities

The international authority on units and in particular on SI units is the General Conference on Weights and Measures (CGPM). The CGPM was set up under the

Metre Convention of 1875 to make international decisions about the definitions of metric units. Its most recent meetings were in 1948, 1954, 1960, 1964, and 1967. The work of the CGPM is prepared by the International Committee on Weights and Measures (CIPM) which meets annually. The CGPM maintains the International Bureau of Weights and Measures (BIPM) at Sèvres near Paris. It also sponsors the international journal *Metrologia*.

It may be noted that the use of metric units in the U.S. was legalized by Congress in 1866 (more than a century ago!) and that the U.S. was one of the seventeen nations which signed the Metre Convention in 1875. The U.K. did not sign the Metre Convention until 1885; the use of metric units in the U.K. was legalized in 1897. Interesting historical accounts of the metric system can be found in references 1–3.

The international authority on the names and symbols for, and the definitions of, units other than metric units (as well as on the standardization of names and symbols for physical quantities, and on the rules for the expression of relations between physical quantities, units, and numbers) is the International Organization for Standardization (ISO), and in particular its Technical Committee ISO/TC 12 with headquarters in Copenhagen. ISO/TC 12 is engaged in the preparation and publication of a series of documents (4) called "ISO Recommendation R 31" as a "comprehensive publication dealing with quantities and units in various fields of science and technology". ISO subunits its draft documents to, and revises them in the light of comments from (*1*) the various national standards organizations which are its "Member Bodies", and (*2*) the international organizations representing the several disciplines of science and technology (for physics the International Union of Pure and Applied Physics, IUPAP, through its Commission on Symbols, Units and Nomenclature, SUN; for chemistry the International Union of Pure and Applied Chemistry, IUPAC, through its Commission on Symbols, Terminology, and Units, STU; for electrotechnology the International Electrotechnical Commission, IEC, through its Technical Committees IEC/TC 24 and 25). Before a part of ISO/R 31 is published it will have been approved by an overwhelming majority of the forty or so subscribing countries. When finally approved the parts are published in English, French, and Russian. They can be purchased in any country from the "Member Body".

The international authorities on quantities and units not (or not yet) dealt with by ISO are: for physics, IUPAP through its SUN Commission (5); for chemistry, IUPAC through its STU Commission (6); and for electrotechnology, IEC through its technical committees IEC/TC 24 and 25 (3). The IUPAP, IUPAC, and IEC documents are all in virtually complete agreement with one another and with ISO/R 31.

Dimensionally Independent and Derived Physical Quantities

Seven physical quantities are regarded by international agreement as being dimensionally independent (4–6). These are length, mass, time, electric current, thermodynamic temperature, luminous intensity, and amount of substance. There is nothing fundamental about the particular choice of the number of quantities which are regarded as dimensionally independent; it is simply a matter of convenience. Indeed, in the obsolescent "three-quantity" system of equations for electricity and magnetism, only three of the quantities, ie length, mass, time, and electric current were regarded as being independent. Even when the *number* of them has been fixed, there is nothing fundamental about the particular choice of the set of quantities which are to be regarded as dimensionally independent; again it is simply a matter of convenience. For example, instead of the subset length, mass, time, and electric current, the subset length, time, electric current, and electric potential difference might have been chosen.

All other physical quantities are regarded as being derived from, and as having dimensions derived from, the seven dimensionally independent physical quantities by definitions involving only multiplication, division, differentiation, and/or integration. For example, volume is derived from lengths by double integration, specific volume is volume divided by mass, molar volume is volume divided by amount of substance, and partial molar volume is the partial differential of volume with respect to amount of substance.

Amount of Substance

One of the internationally agreed set of dimensionally independent physical quantities, amount of substance, calls for further comment because, although it is of special importance to chemists and chemical engineers, it is not yet understood by all of them.

1. The amount of a substance is not the same as its mass. The amount of a substance and its mass, unlike its volume for example, do share the property that each of them is independent of temperature and pressure. It is also true that the amount of a *particular* substance is proportional to its mass. Any resemblance between amount of substance and mass ends there, however, and in general the amounts of several substances are not proportional to their masses.

2. Just as the dimension of mass is simply that of mass, so the dimension of amount of substance is simply that of amount of substance; that is what is implied by the words "dimensionally independent".

3. The definition of amount of substance, as of all other physical quantities, has nothing to do with any choice of unit, and in particular has nothing to do with the particular unit of amount of substance called the mole. It is as wrong to call an amount of substance n the "number of moles" as it would be to call a mass m the "number of kilograms" or a length l the "number of metres."

4. The amount of a substance is proportional to the number of specified entities of that substance. The proportionality factor is the same for all substances, is called the Avogadro constant, and is denoted by L or N_A. (Avogadro's constant should not be referred to as Avogadro's number. It is not a number, but is a number divided by an amount of substance and so has dimension (amount of substance)$^{-1}$.) The specified entity may be an atom, a molecule, an ion, a radical, an electron, a photon, etc., or any specified group of such particles. The ratio of any two amounts of substance can be measured (L cancelling) by any method which can be used to count the number of the specified entities in each case.

Example. A solution containing $N(C)$ atoms of carbon, $N(H)$ atoms of hydrogen, and $N(O)$ atoms of oxygen *may* be regarded as a mixture of the entities H_2CO_3 and H_2O if $N(C)$, $N(H)$, and $N(O)$ satisfy the relation:

$$N(O) = \tfrac{1}{2} N(H) + 2 N(C)$$

In a solution which satisfies that relation and is so regarded, the amounts $n(H_2CO_3)$ of H_2CO_3 and $n(H_2O)$ of H_2O are given by

$$n(H_2CO_3) = N(C)/L$$

$$n(\text{H}_2\text{O}) = \{\tfrac{1}{2} N(\text{H}) - N(\text{C})\}/L$$

When the same solution is regarded instead as a mixture of $\tfrac{1}{2}\text{H}_2\text{CO}_3$ and H_2O the amount $n(\tfrac{1}{2}\text{H}_2\text{CO}_3)$ of $\tfrac{1}{2}\text{H}_2\text{CO}_3$ is twice as large, while the amount $n(\text{H}_2\text{O})$ of H_2O is unchanged. When the same solution is regarded instead as a mixture of H_2CO_3, HCO_3^-, CO_3^{2-}, H_3O^+, and H_2O, then the amounts of those five substances are inter-related by

$$n(\text{H}_2\text{CO}_3) + n(\text{HCO}_3^-) + n(\text{CO}_3^{2-}) = N(\text{C})/L$$

$$2\,n(\text{H}_2\text{CO}_3) + n(\text{HCO}_3^-) + 3\,n(\text{H}_3\text{O}^+) + 2\,n(\text{H}_2\text{O}) = N(\text{H})/L$$

$$3\,n(\text{H}_2\text{CO}_3) + 3\,n(\text{HCO}_3^-) + 3\,n(\text{CO}_3^{2-}) + n(\text{H}_3\text{O}^+) + n(\text{H}_2\text{O})$$
$$= \{\tfrac{1}{2} N(\text{H}) + 2\,N(\text{C})\}/L$$

The two further relations needed to solve for the five amounts must be provided by physicochemical theory (for example, expressions for two equilibrium constants).

Coherent Systems of Units

A system of units based on a chosen set of base units (one for each of a chosen set of dimensionally independent physical quantities) is said to be coherent when the units for all derived physical quantities are obtained from the base units by multiplication or division without the introduction of any numerical factors (not even powers of ten). As long as all derived units are written explicitly as products and quotients of the base units no question of non-coherence arises.

The Choice of a Set of Base Units for the SI

In view of some confusion about the arguments which led to the particular choice of the set of base units for the SI, the reader is reminded that there is no question of coherence or non-coherence among the units chosen for the selected set of dimensionally independent physical quantities. That is what the word "independent" means. Questions of coherence affect the choice of base units only when it is wished to keep some pre-existing units for *derived* quantities as part of a coherent system based on that choice.

For mechanics there was little to choose between the system based on cm, g, and s (CGS system) and that based on m, kg, and s (MKS system). The pre-existing units denoted by dyn, erg, St, and P (see Table 5, p. 993) are coherent with the former, while those denoted by N, J, and W (see Table 2, p. 992) are coherent with the latter. For mechanics plus electricity and magnetism, however, the pre-existing units C, V, Ω, F, Wb, H, and T, as well as N, J, and W (see Table 2, p. 992) are all coherent with a system based on m, kg, s, and A (MKSA or Giorgi system), but not with any system based on cm, g, s, together with any one electrical unit, preexisting or otherwise. That was the reason for the adoption of the MKSA system based on m, kg, s, and A, which was eventually expanded into the SI.

No question of coherence arose over the choice of base units for the remaining three dimensionally independent quantities—K for thermodynamic temperature, cd for luminous intensity, and mol for amount of substance—because no pre-existing units for derived quantities were involved. This last point has been persistently misunderstood by those who, because the base unit of mass has been changed from the gram to the kilogram, think that the base unit of amount of substance "ought" to be changed from the mole to the kilomole. There is simply no "ought" about it; the choice of the base unit of amount of substance is entirely one of convenience. The argument that the kilomole would be a more *convenient* choice than the mole was, by contrast, worth treating with respect. Since it is clear, however, that those who thought that the kilomole would have been a more convenient base unit than the mole were far outnumbered by those who did not, there would have been no point in choosing as basic some unit other than that already in almost universal use (for "lb mol" see footnote r to Table 6, p. 995) namely the mole. Moreover, the mole having been chosen as the base unit, the kilomole is also a unit of the SI, as are the megamole and the millimole and so on, and can be freely used within the SI by those who find it convenient. The choice of the mole, rather than the kilomole or other unit, as the base unit of amount of substance implies only one restriction, namely, that if a special name and symbol is at some future date proposed for the unit of a derived quantity containing amount of substance among its dimensions, then that unit should be coherent with the mole and the other base units. Thus a proposal might be entertained (say) that the name "mark", symbol Mk, be used to denote the unit of molality mol kg^{-1} and be added to the list in Table 2 below, while a proposal that the name "standen", symbol Sd, be used to denote the unit of concentration mol dm^{-3}, and so add yet another entry to the list in Table 5 below, should be strongly resisted.

SI Units

The SI Base Units are those shown in Table 1.

Table 1. The SI Base Units

Physical quantity	Name of SI base unit	Symbol for SI base unit
length	metre	m
mass	kilogram	kg
time	second	s
electric current	ampere	A
thermodynamic temperature	kelvin	K
luminous intensity	candela	cd
amount of substance	mole [a]	mol [a]
SI Supplementary Units [b]		
plane angle	radian	rad
solid angle	steradian	sr

[a] Although these are the internationally recommended (4–6) names and symbol for the base unit of amount of substance, they have not (yet) been adopted by the CGPM as part of the SI.

[b] The SI Supplementary Units are those for which it is not decided whether they are SI Base Units or SI Derived Units.

DEFINITIONS OF THE SI BASE UNITS

The following definitions are the English-language versions authorized by the CGPM.

Metre. "The metre is the length equal to 1 650 763.73 wavelengths in vacuum of the radiation corresponding to the transition between the levels $2p_{10}$ and $5d_5$ of the krypton-86 atom."

As originally conceived the metre was intended to be exactly one ten-millionth part of the earth's quadrant on the meridian through Paris. In fact, however, and until 1960 the metre was defined as the distance between two lines engraved on a certain platinum–iridium bar, kept at the BIPM at Sèvres, when the bar was supported in a specified way at the temperature of melting ice and at standard atmospheric pressure. That definition was replaced in 1960 by the one given above in terms of a spectral wavelength. The redefinition did not change the length of the metre but considerably improved the accuracy with which it can be realized and ensured that it would no longer slowly change with time.

Kilogram. "The kilogram is the unit of mass; it is equal to the mass of the international prototype of the kilogram." The international prototype of the kilogram is a certain piece of platinum–iridium kept at the BIPM at Sèvres.

It may reasonably be expected that the present definition will eventually be replaced by one which depends, like the definitions of the metre and second, on some atomic phenomenon, so as to ensure that the mass of the kilogram no longer slowly changes with time. The name kilogram and the symbol kg for the SI Base Unit of mass are a little unfortunate, because they falsely suggest a decimal multiple of a base unit, and because they lead to a slight difficulty in the construction of decimal fractions and multiples of the base unit by use of the SI Prefixes (see below). Several new names and symbols have been proposed for the unit now called the kilogram, but in the author's opinion the difficulty is so slight as not to justify any change. The rule for the formation of decimal fractions and multiples is that these should be constructed by adding the SI Prefixes (see below) not to kg but to g, in spite of the fact that kg and not g is the SI Base Unit.

Examples: mg not μkg for 10^{-6} kg

Mg not kkg for 10^3 kg

Second. "The second is the duration of 9 192 631 770 periods of the radiation corresponding to the transition between the two hyperfine levels of the ground state of the caesium-133 atom."

Ampere. "The ampere is that constant current which, if maintained in two straight parallel conductors of infinite length, of negligible circular cross-section, and placed 1 metre apart in a vacuum, would produce between these conductors a force equal to 2×10^{-7} newton per metre of length."

Kelvin. "The kelvin, unit of thermodynamic temperature, is the fraction 1/273.16 of the thermodynamic temperature of the triple point of water."

The kelvin was formerly called the "degree Kelvin" and was denoted by the symbol °K, or in the case of thermodynamic temperature interval, sometimes by the symbol deg. In October 1967 the CGPM recommended that the kelvin, symbol K, be used both for thermodynamic temperature and for thermodynamic temperature interval.

Examples: $T = 305.53$ K $T_{ice} = 273.15$ K $T - T_{ice} = 32.38$ K

$R = 8.3143$ J K^{-1} mol^{-1}

Thermodynamic temperature interval will be mentioned again below in connexion with the "degree Celsius", symbol °C.

Candela. "The candela is the luminous intensity, in the perpendicular direction, of a surface of 1/600 000 square metre of a black body at the temperature of freezing platinum under a pressure of 101 325 newtons per square metre."

Mole. The following definition of the mole is that recommended by ISO, IUPAP, IUPAC, and CIPM. "The mole is the amount of substance of a system which contains as many elementary entities as there are carbon atoms in 0.012 kilogram of carbon-12. The elementary entity must be specified and may be an atom, a molecule, an ion, an electron, etc., or a specified group of such particles."

Units such as the "gram-molecule", "gram-equivalent", "equivalent", "gramion", "gram-atom", and "gram-formula" are all obsolete.

Examples: 1 mole of H_2SO_4 not   1 "gram-molecule" of H_2SO_4

1 mole of $\frac{1}{2}H_2SO_4$ not   1 "equivalent" of H_2SO_4

1 mole of SO_4^{2-} not   1 "gram-ion" of SO_4^{2-}

1 mole of Hg   not   1 "gram-atom" of Hg

1 mole of HgCl has a mass equal to 0.236 04 kilogram

1 mole of Hg_2Cl_2 has a mass equal to 0.472 08 kilogram

1 mole of Hg^+ has a mass equal to 0.200 59 kilogram

1 mole of Hg_2^{2+} has a mass equal to 0.401 18 kilogram

1 mole of $\frac{1}{2}Hg_2^{2+}$ has a mass equal to 0.200 59 kilogram

1 mole of CuZn has a mass of 0.128 92 kilogram

1 mole of $Cu_{0.5}Zn_{0.5}$ has a mass of 0.064 46 kilogram

1 mole of $Fe_{0.91}S$ has a mass of 0.082 88 kilogram

1 mole of e^- has a mass of 5.4860×10^{-7} kilogram

1 mole of a mixture containing 78.09 moles per cent of N_2, 20.95 moles per cent of O_2, 0.93 mole per cent of Ar, and 0.03 mole per cent of CO_2, has a mass of 0.028 964 kilogram

SI DERIVED UNITS

The SI Derived Units are those derived by appropriate multiplication and division of the SI Base Units.

Examples: velocity: $m\ s^{-1}$

force: $kg\ m\ s^{-2}$

electric field strength: $kg\ m\ s^{-3}\ A^{-1}$

specific heat capacity: $m^2\ s^{-2}\ K^{-1}$

molar heat capacity: $kg\ m^2\ s^{-2}\ K^{-1}\ mol^{-1}$

Some of the SI Derived Units have been given the special SI names and SI symbols shown in Table 2. Two candidates for admission to Table 2, the pascal and the siemens, are given later in Table 4.

SI PREFIXES

The SI prefixes given in Table 3 have been approved by the CGPM to indicate decimal fractions or multiples of the SI Base Units or of the SI Derived Units with special names and symbols. A symbol formed by combining a prefix and the symbol for a unit is regarded as a single symbol which may be raised to a power without the use of parentheses.

Example: $Mg\ km^2\ \mu s^{-2} = 10^3\ kg\ (10^3\ m)^2\ (10^{-6}\ s)^{-2} = 10^{21}\ kg\ m^2\ s^{-2}$

Table 2. SI Special Names and Symbols for Derived SI Units

Physical quantity	Name of SI Unit	Symbol for SI Unit	Definition of SI Unit
frequency	hertz	Hz	s^{-1}
energy	joule	J	$kg\ m^2\ s^{-2}$
force	newton	N	$kg\ m\ s^{-2} = J\ m^{-1}$
power	watt	W	$kg\ m^2\ s^{-3} = J\ s^{-1}$
electric charge	coulomb	C	$A\ s$
electric potential difference	volt	V	$kg\ m^2\ s^{-3}\ A^{-1} = J\ A^{-1}\ s^{-1}$
electric resistance	ohm	Ω	$kg\ m^2\ s^{-3}\ A^{-2} = V\ A^{-1}$
electric capacitance	farad	F	$A^2\ s^4\ kg^{-1}\ m^{-2} = A\ s\ V^{-1}$
magnetic flux	weber	Wb	$kg\ m^2\ s^{-2}\ A^{-1} = V\ s$
inductance	henry	H	$kg\ m^2\ s^{-2}\ A^{-2} = V\ A^{-1}\ s$
magnetic flux density (magnetic induction)	tesla	T	$kg\ s^{-2}\ A^{-1} = V\ s\ m^{-2}$
luminous flux	lumen	lm	$cd\ sr$
illumination	lux	lx	$cd\ sr\ m^{-2} = lm\ m^{-2}$

Table 3. Prefixes for SI Units

Fraction	Prefix	Symbol	Multiple	Prefix	Symbol
10^{-1}	deci	d	10	deca	da
10^{-2}	centi	c	10^2	hecto	h
10^{-3}	milli	m	10^3	kilo	k
10^{-6}	micro	μ	10^6	mega	M
10^{-9}	nano	n	10^9	giga	G[a]
10^{-12}	pico	p	10^{12}	tera	T
10^{-15}	femto	f			
10^{-18}	atto	a			

[a] Not B; the word "billion" means 10^9 to some and 10^{12} to others.

Notwithstanding recommendations (notably by certain bodies in the U.K. in effect trying to be more Catholic than the CGPM-Curia) that the use of the first two prefixes on each side of Table 3 should be restricted, and in spite of the fact that units formed by use of the prefixes will not in general be coherent with units formed from the SI Base Units alone, the CIPM has recommended that the name "International System of Units" and its abbreviation SI apply to the whole ensemble consisting of the SI Base and SI Supplementary Units, of the coherently derived units having special names and symbols, *and* of any of the decimal fractions and multiples of any of those units formed by use of any of the SI Prefixes.

Non-SI Units

SPECIAL NON-SI NAMES AND SYMBOLS FOR UNITS COHERENTLY DERIVED FROM THE SI BASE UNITS

The units shown in Table 4 are coherent with the SI Base Units, but the special names and symbols, though recommended by the CIPM, have not (yet) been adopted by the CGPM.

The case for the adoption of the pascal as an SI Unit has been urged by many of those concerned with practical questions involving hydrostatic pressures or stresses in solid materials, and by those who think that the use of some special name and symbol for some unit of pressure is inevitable, and fear that unless the pascal is given

Table 4. Special Non-SI Names and Symbols for Units Coherently Derived from the SI Base Units

Physical quantity	Name of of unit	Symbol for unit	Definition of unit
pressure	pascal	Pa	$kg\ m^{-1}\ s^{-2} = N\ m^{-2}$
electric conductance	siemens	S	$kg^{-1}\ m^{-2}\ s^3\ A^2 = \Omega^{-1}$

the blessing of CGPM the unit used in practice will be the non-SI and non-coherent unit called the bar.

The case for the adoption of the siemens as an SI unit has been urged among others by those who wish finally to dispose of the monstrous "mho" which has been used for S and of the even more monstrous "gemmho" which has been used for μS.

Table 5. Decimal Fractions and Multiples of SI Units Having Non-SI Special Names and Symbols

Physical quantity	Name of unit	Symbol for unit	Definition of unit
length	ångström	Å	10^{-10} m
	micron [a]	μ [a]	10^{-6} m $=$ μm
	millimicron [a]	mμ [a]	10^{-9} m $=$ nm
area	are	a	10^2 m^2
	barn	b	10^{-28} m^2
volume	litre [b]	l	10^{-3} m^3 $=$ dm^3
acceleration	gal	Gal	10^{-2} m s^{-2}
mass	tonne	t	10^3 kg $=$ Mg
force	dyne	dyn	10^{-5} N
	sthène	sn	10^3 N
pressure	bar [c]	bar [c]	10^5 N m^{-2}
	pièze	pz	10^3 N m^{-2}
energy	erg	erg	10^{-7} J
diffusion coefficient, kinematic viscosity	stokes	St	10^{-4} m^2 s^{-1}
dynamic viscosity	poise	P	10^{-1} kg m^{-1} s^{-1}
electric current	biot	Bi	10 A
magnetic flux	maxwell	Mx	10^{-8} Wb
magnetic flux density (magnetic induction)	gauss	G	10^{-4} T
concentration [d]		M [d]	mol dm^{-3}

[a] The names micron and millimicron are bad enough; the symbols μ for μm and mμ for nm are indefensible.

[b] By decision of the CGPM in 1964 the old definition of the litre (which led to 1 litre $\approx$ 1.000 028 dm³) was rescinded and the word litre was reinstated as a special name for the cubic decimetre. Neither the word litre nor its symbol l should now be used to express results of high precision.

[c] The microbar, μbar, is also called the "barye". The millibar, mbar, is widely used in meteorological barometry, and is then often denoted by "mb".

[d] A solution with a concentration of 0.1 mol dm^{-3}, say, is sometimes called a "0.1 molar" solution. In view of the agreed use of the word "molar" with the meaning "divided by amount of substance" its use as an abbreviation for mol dm^{-3} must be deprecated. In view of the likelihood of confusion between mol dm^{-3} and mol kg^{-1} it is recommended that the symbol M standing for mol dm^{-3} should be used if at all only for rough values in aqueous solutions.

DECIMAL FRACTIONS AND MULTIPLES OF SI UNITS, HAVING NON-SI SPECIAL NAMES AND SYMBOLS

These units are not SI units and are not coherent with SI units. Their use is to be progressively discouraged and eventually abandoned. The time-scale implied by the word "progressively" need not, however, be the same for all units, nor for any unit need it be the same in all fields of science. In the meantime it is to be hoped that any author who thinks that he has some good reason for continuing to use these units will define them in terms of SI units once in every publication in which he uses them. The list given in Table 5 is not exhaustive.

OTHER NON-SI UNITS NOW EXACTLY DEFINED IN TERMS OF THE SI UNITS

These units are not SI units and are not coherent with SI units. Their use is to be progressively discouraged and eventually (the sooner the better) abandoned. Most of them are former "Zanzibar" units which, as a man may be shriven before he is executed, have been made less disreputable as the first step toward their abandonment, by redefining them by international agreement in terms of SI units. The term "Zanzibar units" refers to the following story:

"A certain retired sea captain made his home in a secluded spot on the island of Zanzibar. As a sentimental reminder of his seafaring career he still had his ship's chronometer and religiously kept it wound and in good operating condition. Every day exactly at noon, as indicated on his chronometer, he observed the ritual of firing off a volley from a small cannon. On one occasion he received a visit from an old friend who inquired how the captain verified the correctness of his chronometer. 'Oh,' he replied 'there is a horologist over there in the town of Zanzibar where I go whenever I lay in supplies. He has very reliable time and as I have fairly frequent occasion to go that way I almost always walk past his window and check my time against his.' After his visit was over the visitor dropped into the horologist's shop and inquired how the horologist checked his time. 'Oh,' replied he, 'there's an old sea captain over on the other end of the island who, I am told, is quite a fanatic about accurate time and who shoots off a gun every day exactly at noon, so I always check my time and correct it by his.'" This story is told by Cohen, Crowe, and Dumond (7) who attribute it to Professor George Harrison.

In view of the various meanings which have been attached to these non-SI units in the past, it is important that any author who thinks that he has some good reason for continuing to use them should use them only with the internationally agreed meanings given in Table 6; and it is essential that he gives their definitions in terms of SI units once in every publication in which he uses them. The list given in Table 6 is by no means exhaustive. Each of the definitions given without qualification in the fourth column is exact. Additional values are sometimes given after the sign $\approx$; these are accurate only to six significant figures.

The author spent a good deal of time compiling Table 6. He will think that his time was not wasted only if he has succeeded in making manifest the absurdity of these units, nearly all of which are still used but only in the English-speaking world, and if he has thereby brought closer the day when Table 6 will be of only historical interest.

NON-SI UNITS NOT DEFINABLE IN TERMS OF THE SI UNITS

These "units" are not SI units, are not coherent with SI units, and can not even be exactly defined in terms of SI units. They are physical quantities and best treated as such. The ratios of these "units" to the corresponding SI units are subject to change in the light of new experimental measurements of the physical quantities

Table 6. Other Non-SI Units Now Exactly Defined in Terms of the SI Units

Physical quantity	Name of unit	Symbol for unit	Definition of unit
angle	right angle	L	$(\pi/2)$ rad
	grade	g	$(\pi/200)$ rad
	degree	°	$(\pi/180)$ rad
	minute	′	$(\pi/10\ 800)$ rad
	second	″	$(\pi/648\ 000)$ rad
length	yard	yd	0.9144 m [a]
	foot	ft	0.3048 m [b]
	inch	in	0.0254 m
	rod, pole, or perch		5.0292 m
	chain		20.1168 m
	furlong		201.168 m
	mile	mile	1609.344 m
	nautical mile	n mile	1852 m [c]
	fathom		1.8288 m
area	rood		$1210 \times 0.9144\ \mathrm{m}^2 \approx 1011.71\ \mathrm{m}^2$
	acre		$4840 \times 0.9144\ \mathrm{m}^2 \approx 4046.86\ \mathrm{m}^2$
volume	gallon(US)	gal(US)	$231 \times 0.0254^3\ \mathrm{m}^3$ [d,e] $\approx 3.785\ 41 \times 10^{-3}\ \mathrm{m}^3$
	dry barrel(US)	bbl(US) (dry)	$7056 \times 0.0254^3\ \mathrm{m}^3 \approx 115.627 \times 10^{-3}\ \mathrm{m}^3$
	bushel(US)	bu(US)	$2150.42 \times 0.0254^3\ \mathrm{m}^3$ [f] $\approx 0.035\ 239\ 1\ \mathrm{m}^3$
mass	metric technical unit of mass		9.806 56 kg
	pound (avoirdupois)	lb	0.453 592 37 kg [a]
	slug		$(980.665 \times 0.453\ 592\ 37/30.48)$ kg ≈ 14.5939 kg
	grain	gr	$6.479\ 891 \times 10^{-5}$ kg
	ounce (avoirdupois)	oz	$(0.453\ 592\ 37/16)$ kg $\approx 0.028\ 349\ 5$ kg
	hundredweight	cwt	$112 \times 0.453\ 592\ 37$ kg [g] ≈ 50.8023 kg
	ton	ton	$2240 \times 0.453\ 592\ 37$ kg [g] ≈ 1016.05 kg
	short hundredweight	sh cwt	45.359 237 kg [g]
	short ton	sh ton	907.184 74 kg [g]
	troy ounce	oz t (in U.S.) / oz tr (in U.K.)	$(480 \times 0.453\ 592\ 37/7000)$ kg [h] $\approx 0.031\ 103\ 5$ kg
	apothecaries' ounce	oz ap (in U.S.) / oz apoth (in U.K.)	
time	minute	min	60 s [i]
	hour	h	3600 s [i]
	day	d	86 400 s [i]
force	kilogramme-force / kilopond	kgf / kp	9.806 65 N [j]
	poundal	pdl	$0.453\ 592\ 37 \times 0.3048$ N $\approx 0.138\ 255$ N
	pound-force	lbf	$0.453\ 592\ 37 \times 9.806\ 65$ N [k] $\approx 4.448\ 22$ N

(continued)

Table 6 (*continued*)

Physical quantity	Name of unit	Symbol for unit	Definition of unit
pressure	atmosphere	atm	101 325 N m^{-2} [l]
	torr	Torr	(101 325/760) N m^{-2} [m] $\approx$ 133.322 N m^{-2}
	technical atmosphere	at	98 066.5 N m^{-2}
	pound-force per square inch	lbf in^{-2} [n]	(9.806 65 $\times$ 4535.9237/6.4516) N m^{-2} $\approx$ 6894.76 N m^{-2}
	conventional millimetre of mercury	mmHg	13.5951 $\times$ 9.806 65 N m^{-2} [m] $\approx$ 133.322 N m^{-2}
	conventional inch of water	inH$_2$O	0.002 54 $\times$ 98 066.5 N m^{-2} $\approx$ 249.089 N m^{-2}
energy	kilowatt hour	kW h	3.6 $\times$ 10^6 J
	I.T. calorie	cal$_{IT}$	4.1868 J [o]
	thermochemical calorie	cal$_{th}$	4.184 J [p]
	British thermal unit	Btu	1055.06 J [q]
power	metric horsepower, cheval vapeur		75 $\times$ 9.806 65 W $\approx$ 735.499 W
	horsepower (British)	hp	550 $\times$ 0.3048 $\times$ 0.453 592 37 $\times$ 9.806 65 W $\approx$ 745.700 W
thermodynamic temperature	degree Rankine	°R	(5/9) K
radioactivity	curie	Ci	3.7 $\times$ 10^{10} s^{-1}
amount of substance	pound-mole	lb mol	453.592 37 mol [r]

NOTE: The monstrosity "e.u.", standing for "entropy unit", is not recognized by any authority as having even the standing of a unit whose use is to be progressively discouraged. To say that an entropy has a value of so many entropy units is as stupid as it would be to say that the height of a man is so many height units. The carelessness of those who use the "e.u." is revealed by the fact that they use it for entropies but never for heat capacities or for the gas constant which have the same dimensions.

[a] This definition is now the legal one in Australia, Canada, New Zealand, South Africa, the United Kingdom, and the United States.

[b] The "US Survey foot", used by the U.S. Coast and Geodetic Survey, is defined as (1200/3937) m.

[c] The "UK nautical mile" is defined as 1853.184 m.

[d] The gal(US) is used only for liquids. In addition these units are used:
barrel(US) (for petroleum, etc.) = 42 gal(US); liquid quart(US) = gal(US)/4;
liquid pint(US), liq pt(US) = gal(US)/8; gill(US) = liq pt(US)/4;
fluid ounce(US), fl oz(US) = gill(US)/4; fluid dram(US) = fl oz(US)/8;
minim(US), min(US) = fluid dram(US)/60.

[e] The gallon(UK), gal(UK), is used for liquids and for dry goods. It is still defined in terms of a weight of water measured under specified conditions. Its value correct to six significant figures is 4.546 09 $\times$ 10^{-3} m^3. In addition the following units are used:
bushel(UK) = 8 gal(UK); peck(UK) = 2 gal(UK); quart(UK) = gal(UK)/4;
pint(UK), pt(UK) = gal(UK)/8; gill(UK) = pt(UK)/4;
fluid ounce(UK), fl oz(UK) = gill(UK.)/5; fluid drachm(UK) = fl oz(UK)/8;
minim(UK), min(UK) = fluid drachm(UK)/60.
The word "bushel" is also used with other meanings in the U.K.

(*table footnotes continued on next page*)

involved. The use of these "units", *qua* units, should be abandoned. Since every physical quantity is a potential "unit" of this kind, only a few examples are given in Table 7. The conversion factors given in the fourth column of Table 7 are not, and can never be, exact.

The "unified atomic mass unit" is not really a unit at all, but is a physical quantity denoted by m_u and defined as $\frac{1}{12}$ of the mass of an atom of ^{12}C. Alternatively it is the product L^{-1} g mol^{-1} of a physical quantity L^{-1}, the reciprocal of the Avogadro constant, and the unit g mol^{-1}. Similarly the "electronvolt" is not really a unit at all, but is the product eV of a physical quantity e, the charge of a proton, and the unit V.

Other physical quantities which have often been used as "units" in this way include the Bohr radius a_0, the modified Rydberg constant $R_\infty hc$, and the Bohr magneton μ_B.

Nothing that has been said about the use of these "units" should be taken to reflect in any way against the often convenient, and sometimes necessary, practice of recording the results of measurements as ratios of two physical quantities rather than as ratios of a physical quantity and a unit. For example the ratios $m(A_2)/m(A_1)$ of the atomic masses m of two nuclides A_2 and A_1 can at present be measured more

---

f The bushel(US), bu(US), is used only for dry goods. In addition these units are used: peck(US) = bu(US)/4; dry quart(US), dry qt(US) = peck(US)/8; dry pint(US), dry pt(US) = dry qt(US)/2.
The word "bushel" is also used with other meanings in the U.S.

g In the U.S. when the word "ton" is used alone it usually refers to the short ton of 2000 lb unless there is specific reference to the long ton or gross ton. The ton of 2240 lb and the hundredweight of 112 lb are also used to some extent in the U.S. They are then called "long ton" and "long hundredweight."

h The troy pound is not a legal unit in the U.K., but is legalized in the U.S., where it is defined as 5760 grains or 12 troy ounces. In addition other units are:
dram ap(US) = oz ap(US)/8; scruple(US) = dram ap(US)/3;
drachm(UK) = oz apoth(UK)/8; scruple(UK) = drachm(UK)/3.

i It is not suggested that these units will cease to be used for ordinary purposes. It is their use in numerical values of physical quantities, such as values of rate constants of chemical reactions, which is to be discouraged in favour of the second.

j This unit must be distinguished from the (inconstant) local weight of a body having a mass of 1 kg.

k This unit must be distinguished from the (inconstant) local weight of a body having a mass of 1 lb. This would be called "pound-weight."

l The symbols "atma" and "atmg" are sometimes used to distinguish values respectively, of the pressure of a system, and of the excess of the pressure of a system over that of the surroundings of a pressure gauge.

m The conventional millimetre of mercury, symbol mmHg (not mm Hg), is the pressure exerted by a column exactly 1 mm high of a fluid of density exactly 13 595.1 kg m^{-3} in a place where the acceleration of free fall is exactly 9.806 65 m s^{-2}. The difference between 1 mmHg and 1 Torr is less than 2×10^{-7} Torr.

n The symbols p.s.i. and its variants psi, psia, and psig (see footnote *l* above), are sometimes used.

o The Fifth International Conference on Properties of Steam (London 1956) adopted this definition of the I.T. calorie (International Table calorie).

p This definition is widely used by thermochemists.

q This is the "international table British thermal unit" adopted by the Fifth Conference on Properties of Steam (London 1956).

r The "pound-mole," symbol "lb mol," is not equal to lb $\times$ mol as is implied when it is given that name and that symbol. Its name should be the pound mole per gram, symbol lb mol g^{-1}.

Table 7. Non-SI "Units" not Definable in Terms of the SI Units

Physical quantity	Name of unit	Symbol for unit	Conversion factor
length	light year	l.y.	l.y. $\approx 9.4605 \times 10^{15}$ m [a]
	astronomic unit	AU	AU $\approx 1.49600 \times 10^{11}$ m [b]
	parsec	pc	pc $\approx 3.086 \times 10^{16}$ m [c]
mass	unified atomic mass unit	u	u $\approx 1.6604 \times 10^{-27}$ kg
time	year	a	a $\approx 365.242\,198\,78 \times 86\,400$ s [d]
energy	thermie	th	th $\approx 4.1855 \times 10^{6}$ J
	15 °C calorie	cal_{15}	$cal_{15} \approx 4.1855$ J
	60 °F British thermal unit	$Btu_{60/61}$	$Btu_{60/61} \approx 1054.5$ J
	mean British thermal unit	Btu_{mean}	$Btu_{mean} \approx 1055.8$ J
	electronvolt	eV	eV $\approx 1.6021 \times 10^{-19}$ J
quantity of electricity	franklin	Fr	Fr $\approx 3.335\,64 \times 10^{-10}$ C [e]

[a] A light year is the distance traversed in 1 year by electromagnetic waves in a vacuum.

[b] An astronomic unit is approximately equal to the mean distance between the earth and the sun. A full definition is given in *Annuaire du Bureau des Longitudes*, Paris, 1966, p. B22.

[c] A parsec is the distance from which 1 AU appears under the parallax angle of 1 second.

[d] At January 1900.0; decreasing at the rate of $0.005\,30$ s a^{-1}.

[e] Electrical units belonging to three-quantity systems of equations are discussed below.

accurately than the ratios $m(A)/kg$, so that some hard-won accuracy would be lost in the process of converting measured values of $m(A_2)/m(A_1)$ to values of $m(A)/kg$. It is the treating of such physical quantities as units by giving them special names and symbols which is deplored.

The Degree Celsius

For the purpose of this section we shall consider two particular thermodynamic temperatures, firstly that of the equilibrium of solid sodium sulfate decahydrate, solid sodium sulfate, and aqueous sodium sulfate saturated with air at a pressure of 101 325 N m^{-2}, which we denote by T_t, and secondly that of the equilibrium of solid and liquid water saturated with air at a pressure of 101 325 Nm^{-2}, which we denote by T_{ice}. We have seen that the kelvin, symbol K, is used without distinction for thermodynamic temperature and for thermodynamic temperature interval. We then have

$$T_t = 305.53 \text{ K}$$

$$T_{ice} = 273.15 \text{ K}$$

$$T_t - T_{ice} = 32.38 \text{ K}$$

The degree Celsius, symbol °C, is a unit of thermodynamic temperature interval identical with the kelvin. (Celsius not centigrade. One reason is that the word "centigrade" is used in some non-English-speaking countries as a unit of angle (see Table 6). The ° sign and the letter following form one symbol and there should be no space between them. Thus 25 °C, but not 25° C.) (See also Temperature measurement.) We then have

$$T_t = 305.53 \text{ K} \qquad \text{but not} \qquad T_t = 305.53 \text{ °C}$$

$$T_{\text{ice}} = 273.15 \text{ K} \qquad \text{but not} \qquad T_{\text{ice}} = 273.15 \text{ °C}$$

$$T_t - T_{\text{ice}} = 32.38 \text{ K} \qquad \text{or} \qquad T_t - T_{\text{ice}} = 32.38 \text{ °C}$$

If we define a physical quantity θ_C called the Celsius thermodynamic temperature interval, or more briefly the Celsius temperature, by the relation

$$\theta_C = T - 273.15 \text{ K}$$

then we have

$$T_t = 305.53 \text{ K}$$

$$T_{\text{ice}} = 273.15 \text{ K}$$

$$\theta_{C,t} = 32.38 \text{ K} \qquad \text{or} \qquad \theta_{C,t} = 32.38 \text{ °C}$$

It is now clear that the degree Celsius is an unnecessary unit. Although it may continue to be used in everyday life, it is to be hoped that it will gradually disappear from science and technology. In the meantime a statement such as "The temperature of the sodium sulfate transition is 32.38 °C" must be regarded as a permissible colloquialism in which the word "temperature" is used loosely for the excess of the thermodynamic temperature of interest over 273.15 K, that is to say for the quantity which we have called the Celsius thermodynamic temperature interval, or more briefly the Celsius temperature.

The Degree Fahrenheit

The degree Fahrenheit, symbol °F, is defined in a parallel way to the degree Celsius. It is a unit of thermodynamic temperature interval equal to $(5/9)$ K, that is to 1 °R. Thus,

$$T_t = 549.95 \text{ °R} \qquad \text{but not} \qquad T_t = 549.95 \text{ °F}$$

$$T_{\text{ice}} = 491.67 \text{ °R} \qquad \text{but not} \qquad T_{\text{ice}} = 491.67 \text{ °F}$$

$$T_t - T_{\text{ice}} = 59.28 \text{ °R} \qquad \text{or} \qquad T_t - T_{\text{ice}} = 58.28 \text{ °F}$$

If we define a physical quantity θ_F called the Fahrenheit thermodynamic temperature interval, or more briefly the Fahrenheit temperature, by the relation

$$\theta_F = T - (5 \times 459.67/9) \text{ K}$$
$$= T - 459.67 \text{ °R}$$

then we have

$$T_t = 549.95 \text{ °R}$$

$$T_{\text{ice}} = 491.67 \text{ °R}$$

$$\theta_{F,t} = 58.28 \text{ °R} \qquad \text{or} \qquad \theta_{F,t} = 58.28 \text{ °F}$$

$$\theta_{F,\text{ice}} = 32.00 \text{ °R} \qquad \text{or} \qquad \theta_{F,\text{ice}} = 32.00 \text{ °F}$$

It is now clear that the degree Fahrenheit is an unnecessary unit. Although it may continue to be used in everyday life (though it is to be hoped that even there it will be replaced by the degree Celsius) it is greatly to be hoped that both it and the degree Rankine will disappear from science and technology.

The International Practical Temperature Scale

The practical difficulties associated with the direct realization of thermodynamic temperatures by gas thermometry led to the adoption in 1927 of an International Temperature Scale designed to lead to values as nearly as possible equal to the corresponding values of thermodynamic temperature. The Scale was revised in 1948 and has recently (8) been extensively revised again. The International Practical Temperature Scale of 1968 (IPTS-1968) has been chosen so that the temperatures measured on it are identical, within the bounds of the present accuracy of measurement, with the corresponding values of thermodynamic temperature.

Temperatures measured on the IPTS-68 are referred to as the International Practical Kelvin Temperature, symbol T_{68}, or as the International Practical Celsius Temperature, symbol $\theta_{C,68}$. The relation between T_{68} and $\theta_{C,68}$:

$$\theta_{C,68} = T_{68} - 273.15 \text{ K}$$

is identical to the relation between θ_C and T already given.

The IPTS-68 is based on values assigned to the temperatures of ten examples, chosen for their reproducibility, of an equilibrium state between two or three phases of a pure substance ("fixed points") together with the value 273.16 K assigned by definition (of the kelvin) to the triple-point of water, and on standard instruments calibrated at those temperatures. Interpolation between the fixed-point temperatures is provided by specified formulae. Details of the IPTS-68 have been published in *Metrologia* (8).

The Quantity pH

For ionically dilute solutions the quantity denoted by pH is defined approximately by the relation

$$\text{pH} = -\log_{10}\{[\text{H}^+]/\text{mol dm}^{-3}\}$$

where $[\text{H}^+]$ is the concentration of H^+. That definition is inadequate as a general measure of "acidity" and has been replaced (6,9) by an operational one.

Operational Definition of pH. The electromotive force E_X of the galvanic cell

Pt, H$_2$ | solution X | concentrated KCl solution | reference electrode

is measured, and likewise the electromotive force E_S of the cell

Pt, H$_2$ | solution S | concentrated KCl solution | reference electrode

both cells being at the same temperature throughout and the reference electrodes and bridge solutions being identical in the two cells. The pH of the solution X, denoted by pH(X), is then related to the pH of the solution S, denoted by pH(S), by the definition:

$$\text{pH(X)} = \text{pH(S)} + \frac{E_X - E_S}{(RT \ln 10)/F}$$

where R denotes the gas constant, T the thermodynamic temperature, and F the Faraday constant. Thus defined the quantity pH is a number.

Table 8. Values of pH(S) for Five Standard Solutions [a]

$\theta_C/°C$	A	B	C	D	E
0		4.003	6.984	7.534	9.464
5		3.999	6.951	7.500	9.395
10		3.998	6.923	7.472	9.332
15		3.999	6.900	7.448	9.276
20		4.002	6.881	7.429	9.225
25	3.557	4.008	6.865	7.413	9.180
30	3.552	4.015	6.853	7.400	9.139
35	3.549	4.024	6.844	7.389	9.102
38	3.548	4.030	6.840	7.384	9.081
40	3.547	4.035	6.838	7.380	9.068
45	3.547	4.047	6.834	7.373	9.038
50	3.549	4.060	6.833	7.367	9.011
55	3.554	4.075	6.834		8.985
60	3.560	4.091	6.836		8.962
70	3.580	4.126	6.845		8.921
80	3.609	4.164	6.859		8.885
90	3.650	4.205	6.877		8.850
95	3.674	4.227	6.886		8.833

[a] The compositions of the standard solutions are:
A: KH tartrate (saturated at 25 °C)
B: KH phthalate, $m = 0.05$ mol kg^{-1}
C: KH$_2$PO$_4$, $m = 0.025$ mol kg^{-1}; Na$_2$HPO$_4$, $m = 0.025$ mol kg^{-1}
D: KH$_2$PO$_4$, $m = 0.008695$ mol kg^{-1}; Na$_2$HPO$_4$, $m = 0.03043$ mol kg^{-1}
E: Na$_2$B$_4$O$_7$, $m = 0.01$ mol kg^{-1}
where m denotes molality.

To a good approximation, the hydrogen electrodes in both cells may be replaced by other hydrogen-ion-responsive electrodes, e.g., glass or quinhydrone. The two bridge solutions may be of any molality not less than 3.5 mol kg^{-1}, provided they are the same.

Standards. The difference between the pH of two solutions having been defined as above, the definition of pH can be completed by assigning at each temperature a value of pH to one or more chosen solutions designated as standards. A series of pH(S) values for five suitable standard reference solutions is given in Table 8.

If the definition of pH given above is adhered to strictly, then the pH of a solution may be slightly dependent on which standard solution is used. Such unavoidable deviations are caused not only by imperfections in the response of the hydrogen-ion electrodes, but also by variations in the liquid junctions resulting from the different ionic compositions and mobilities of the several standards and from differences in the geometry of the liquid-liquid boundary. In fact such variations in measured pH are usually too small to be of practical significance. Moreover, the acceptance of several standards allows the use of the following alternative definition of pH.

The electromotive force E_X is measured, and likewise the electromotive forces E_1 and E_2 of two similar cells with the solution X replaced by the standard solutions S$_1$ and S$_2$ such that the E_1 and E_2 values are on either side of, and as near as possible to, E_X. The pH of solution X is then obtained by assuming linearity between pH and E, that is to say

$$\frac{pH(X) - pH(S_1)}{pH(S_2) - pH(S_1)} = \frac{E_X - E_1}{E_2 - E_1}$$

This procedure is especially recommended when the hydrogen-ion-responsive electrode is a glass electrode.

Electrical and Magnetic Quantities and Units

There is space here for only a brief introduction to the vexed subject of electrical and magnetic quantities and units. The following three aspects of the subject must be distinguished:

(A) Four systems of electrical and magnetic equations have been used.

(B) The equations belonging to each of the four systems have been written sometimes in "rationalized" and sometimes in "non-rationalized" forms.

(C) Several systems of electrical and magnetic units have been used.

When all scientists make the same choice from each of (A), (B), and (C), such an account as the present one will no longer be needed. That choice has already been internationally agreed; it is the system of equations founded on four dimensionally independent quanties (length, mass, time, and electric current), written in rationalized forms, and with numerical values expressed in terms of the SI units. Unfortunately, however, many writers of elementary text-books, and many physicists, still use one of the other, obsolescent, systems.

SYSTEMS OF ELECTRICAL AND MAGNETIC EQUATIONS

The first of the four systems of equations mentioned in the preceding section is:

1. The internationally recommended rationalized "four-quantity" system of equations in which the permittivity of a vacuum ϵ_0, and the permeability of a vacuum μ_0, appear as physical quantities having dimensions.

Examples: In the four-quantity system the equation for the force F and energy Fr between two electric charges Q_1 and Q_2 separated by a distance r in a vacuum is (in rationalized form):

$$Fr = Q_1Q_2/4\pi\epsilon_0 r$$

so that, the electric charge Q having dimension (time)(current), the permittivity of a vacuum ϵ_0 has dimension:

$$(\text{length})^{-3}(\text{mass})^{-1}(\text{time})^4(\text{current})^2$$

In the four-quantity system the equation for the force F and energy $\frac{1}{2}Fd$ between two electric currents I_1 and I_2 in two parallel rectilinear conductors of length l separated by a distance d in a vacuum is (in rationalized form):

$$\tfrac{1}{2}Fd = \mu_0 I_1 I_2 l/4\pi$$

so that the permeability of a vacuum μ_0 has dimension:

$$(\text{length})(\text{mass})(\text{time})^{-2}(\text{current})^{-2}$$

The product $\epsilon_0\mu_0$ which thus has dimension $(\text{length})^{-2}(\text{time})^2$ is equal to c_0^{-2} where c_0 is the speed of light in a vacuum.

The following three distinct systems of equations founded on three dimensionally independent mechanical quantities have also bee used. (Length, mass, and time have often been chosen as the three quantities, but other choices such as length, time, and energy, or length, time, and force have also been made.) Examples of these are given only in the non-rationalized forms in which they have most often been used.

2. The "electrostatic" system of equations in which the electric charge Q_E is so defined that the permittivity of a vacuum $\epsilon_{0,E}$ is a dimensionless quantity having the value unity.

Examples: In the electrostatic system the equation for the force F and energy Fr between two electric charges $Q_{E,1}$ and $Q_{E,2}$ separated by a distance r in a vacuum is (in non-rationalized form):

$$Fr = Q_{E,1}Q_{E,2}/\epsilon_{0,E}r = Q_{E,1}Q_{E,2}/r$$

so that the electric charge Q_E has dimension:

$$(\text{length})^{3/2}(\text{mass})^{1/2}(\text{time})^{-1}$$

and the electric current I_E has dimension:

$$(\text{length})^{3/2}(\text{mass})^{1/2}(\text{time})^{-2}$$

3. The "electromagnetic" system of equations in which the electric current I_M is so defined that the permeability of a vacuum $\mu_{0,M}$ is a dimensionless quantity having the value unity.

Example: In the electromagnetic system the equation for the force F and energy $\frac{1}{2}Fd$ between two electric currents $I_{M,1}$ and $I_{M,2}$ in two parallel rectilinear conductors of length l and separated by a distance d in a vacuum is (in non-rationalized form):

$$\frac{1}{2}Fd = \mu_{0,M}I_{M,1}I_{M,2}l = I_{M,1}I_{M,2}l$$

so that the electric current I_M has dimension:

$$(\text{length})^{1/2}(\text{mass})^{1/2}(\text{time})^{-1}$$

and the electric charge Q_M has dimension: $(\text{length})^{1/2}(\text{mass})^{1/2}$.

4. The "symmetrical" or "Gaussian" system of equations using the electrical quantities from the electrostatic system (2) and the magnetic quantities from the electromagnetic system (3). (Electric current is treated as an electrical and not as a magnetic quantity.) As a result of combining equations from the two sets the speed of light in a vacuum c_0 appears explicitly in some of the equations.

Examples: In the symmetrical system the equation for the force F and energy Fr between two electric charges $Q_{S,1}$ and $Q_{S,2}$ separated by a distance r in a vacuum is (in non-rationalized form):

$$Fr = Q_{S,1}Q_{S,2}/\epsilon_{0,S}r = Q_{S,1}Q_{S,2}/r$$

so that the electric charge Q_S has dimension:

$$(\text{length})^{3/2}(\text{mass})^{1/2}(\text{time})^{-1}$$

and the electric current I_S has dimension:

$$(\text{length})^{3/2}(\text{mass})^{1/2}(\text{time})^{-2}$$

In the symmetrical system the equation for the force F and energy $\frac{1}{2}Fd$ between two electric currents $I_{s,1}$ and $I_{s,2}$ in two parallel rectilinear conductors of length l and separated by a distance d in a vacuum is (in non-rationalized form)

$$\tfrac{1}{2}Fd = \mu_{0,s}I_{s,1}I_{s,2}l/c_0{}^2 = I_{s,1}I_{s,2}l/c_0{}^2$$

confirming that the electric current I_s has dimension:

$$(\text{length})^{3/2}(\text{mass})^{1/2}(\text{time})^{-2}$$

It follows from the examples used to illustrate the rationalized four-quantity system and the three non-rationalized three-quantity systems, that the electric charges and the currents in the four systems are related as follows:

$$Q/(4\pi\epsilon_0) = Q_S = Q_E = c_0 Q_M$$

$$I/(4\pi/\mu_0) = I_S/c_0 = I_E/c_0 = I_M$$

or, when we use the relation $\epsilon_0\mu_0 = c_0{}^{-2}$,

$$I/(4\pi\epsilon_0) = I_S = I_E = c_0 I_M$$

RATIONALIZATION

The "rationalized" and "non-rationalized" systems of equations differ in the places where factors 4π or 2π appear. In rationalized equations those factors appear only where they are expected from the geometry. In non-rationalized equations they appear when not expected, and fail to appear when expected, from the geometry.

In the preceding section the four-quantity system of equations in the rationalized form, and the three three-quantity systems each in the non-rationalized form were discussed. These are the forms in which the four systems have most often been used. Scientists all over the world are thus engaged in carrying out two transitions in their thinking, teaching, and writing:

non-rationalized equations → rationalized equations
three-quantity equations → four-quantity equations

There is no necessary relation between these two transitions; it is a historical accident that they are being carried out at the same time. As a matter of fact the third transition,

"CGS" units → SI units

is also being carried out at the same time, but this is the subject of the next section.

SYSTEMS OF ELECTRICAL AND MAGNETIC UNITS

The International System of Units (SI) is based, as far as electricity and magnetism are concerned, on the subset of independent base units: metre, kilogram, second, and ampere. The units based on that subset were formerly called MKSA units. The SI units are appropriate only to four-quantity systems of equations and are recommended for use with the recommended rationalized four-quantity system of equations.

The transition from three-quantity to four-quantity equations implies a transition from a unit-system based on three mechanical quantities such as length, mass, and time, to a unit-system based on four quantities of which at least one must be an electrical or magnetic quantity. The unit-system based on four quantities need not, however, be the SI, and in fact two other four-quantity unit-systems have been used. These other systems are:

1. The system in which the four base units are the centimetre, gram, second, and franklin. The franklin, symbol Fr, is a unit of electric charge, sometimes called the "electrostatic unit of charge" and denoted by e.s.u., having the value

$$\text{Fr} = (10/c_0) \text{ C cm s}^{-1} \approx (10/2.997\,925) \times 10^{-10} \text{ C}$$
$$\approx 3.335\,640 \times 10^{-10} \text{ C}$$

2. The system in which the four base units are the centimetre, gram, second, and biot. The biot, symbol Bi, is a unit of electric current, sometimes called the "electromagnetic unit of current" and denoted by e.m.u., having the value:

$$\text{Bi} = 10 \text{ A}$$

We now turn to the unit-systems based on three mechanical units which are used with the three-quantity systems of equations dealt with above. The three base units need not be units of length, mass, and time, but they usually have been so chosen. Nor when length, mass, and time have been chosen need the three base units be the cm, g, and s, but they usually have been so chosen. The unit-system based on cm, g, and s is called the CGS system. A system based on m, kg, and s (MKS) would have served as well but has seldom been used.

We now see at once how to use the CGS system of units with any of the three-quantity systems of equations. For example it is clear that the CGS unit of the electric charge Q_E or Q_S is $\text{cm}^{3/2} \text{ g}^{1/2} \text{ s}^{-1}$ or $\text{erg}^{1/2} \text{ cm}^{1/2}$, while that of the electric charge Q_M is $\text{cm}^{1/2} \text{ g}^{1/2}$ or $\text{dyn}^{1/2} \text{ s}$.

Table 9. Names and Symbols for CGS Electrical and Magnetic Units

Name and symbol for physical quantity	Name of CGS unit	Symbol for CGS unit	Definition of CGS unit
magnetic field strength H_M	oersted	Oe	$\text{cm}^{-1/2} \text{ g}^{3/2} \text{ s}^{-1} = \text{dyn}^{1/2} \text{ cm}^{-1}$
magnetic flux density B_M	gauss [a]	G	$\text{cm}^{-1/2} \text{ g}^{1/2} \text{ s}^{-1} = \text{dyn}^{1/2} \text{ cm}^{-1}$
magnetic flux Φ_M	maxwell [b]	Mx	$\text{cm}^{3/2} \text{ g}^{1/2} \text{ s}^{-1} = \text{dyn}^{1/2} \text{ cm}$

[a] The name gauss, symbol G is also used for the corresponding unit of magnetic flux density B in the four-quantity system and is then given by

$$G = 10^{-4} \text{ kg s}^{-2} \text{ A}^{-1} = 10^{-4} \text{ T}.$$

[b] The name maxwell, symbol Mx, is also used for the corresponding unit of magnetic flux Φ in the four-quantity system and is then given by

$$\text{Mx} = 10^{-8} \text{ kg m}^2 \text{ s}^{-2} \text{ A}^{-1} = 10^{-8} \text{ Wb}.$$

Some derived CGS units for quantities in the electromagnetic and electrostatic systems of equations are given the special names and symbols shown in Table 9. The CGS unit for electric dipole moment p_E in the electrostatic system is $\text{cm}^{5/2} \text{ g}^{1/2} \text{ s}^{-1}$. The special name debye, symbol D, is used with the meaning

$$D = 10^{-18} \text{ cm}^{5/2} \text{ g}^{1/2} \text{ s}^{-1}$$

The name debye, symbol D, is also used for the corresponding unit of electric dipole moment p in the four-quantity system and is then given by

$$D = 10^{-18} \text{ Fr cm} \approx 3.335\,640 \times 10^{-30} \text{ C m}$$

Metrication

Metrication is the name given in the United Kingdom to the programme, which is now (1969) well under way, of at last abandoning the ill-defined collection of folk-lore hopefully called the "Imperial System of Units" in favour of metric units, and in particular of SI units, throughout the whole of the nation's industry, commerce, and daily life. As a preparation for this, the SI is already being rapidly adopted for the teaching of science and engineering in schools, technical colleges, and universities, where the student is now being taught about the old non-SI units merely as quaint fossils, the definition of which in terms of SI units he will need when he reads old or old-fashioned books.

It is greatly to be hoped that a similar movement will soon gather momentum in other English-speaking countries and particularly in the United States.

Bibliography

Parts of this article are reproduced from a monograph (10) by kind permission of the Royal Institute of Chemistry, and from an article (11) by kind permission of the Institute of Physics and the Physical Society.

1. M. Danloux Dumesnils, *Étude Critique du Système Métrique*, Gauthier-Villars & Cie., Paris, 1962; *Esprit et Bon Usage du Système Métrique*, Librairie Polytechnique Béranger, Paris, 1965.
2. U. Stille, *Messen und Rechnen in der Physik*, Friedr. Vieweg & Sohn, Braunschweig, 1955.
3. *Recommendations in the Field of Quantities and Units Used in Electricity*, International Electro-technical Commission, 1st ed., 1964.
4. ISO Recommendation R 31 will, when complete, form a comprehensive publication dealing with quantities and units in various fields of science and technology. The following parts have so far been published:

   Part I: *Basic quantities and units of the SI*, 2nd ed., December 1965.
   Part II: *Quantities and units of periodic and related phenomena*, 1st ed., February 1958.
   Part III: *Quantities and units of mechanics*, 1st ed., December 1960.
   Part IV: *Quantities and units of heat*, 1st ed., November 1965.
   Part VII: *Quantities and units of acoustics*, 1st ed., November 1965.
   Part XI: *Mathematical signs and symbols for use in physical sciences and technology*, 1st ed., February 1961.

   Parts drafted but not yet published are: Part 0: *General principles concerning quantities, units, and symbols;* Part VI: *Quantities and units of light and related electromagnetic radiation;* Part VIII: *Quantities and units of physical chemistry and molecular physics;* Part IX: *Quantities and units of atomic and nuclear physics;* Part X: *Quantities and units of nuclear reactions and ionizing radiations;* Part XII: *Dimensionless parameters.*

5. *Symbols, Units and Nomenclature in Physics*, Document U.I.P. 11 (S.U.N. 65-3), published by IUPAP, 1965. This document supersedes Document U.I.P. 9 (S.U.N. 61-44) with the same title, which was published by IUPAP in 1961.
6. "Manual of Symbols and Terminology for Physicochemical Quantities and Units," *Pure. Appl. Chem.* **21**, 1 (1970). Also published for IUPAC separately bound in hard covers by Butterworths Scientific Publications, London, 1970. This Manual supersedes that published under the title Manual of Physicochemical Symbols and Terminology by IUPAC in 1959 and reprinted in *J. Am. Chem. Soc.* **82**, 5517 (1960).
7. E. R. Cohen, K. M. Crowe, and J. W. Dumond, *Fundamental Constants of Physics*, Interscience Publishers Inc., New York, 1957.

8. *Metrologia*, **5,** 35–49 (1969).
9. R. G. Bates and E. A. Guggenheim, *Pure and Appl. Chem.* **1,** 163 (1960).
10. M. L. McGlashan, "Physicochemical Quantities and Units," *Monograph for Teachers*, No. 15, 2nd ed., Royal Institute of Chemistry, London, 1970.
11. M. L. McGlashan, *Physics Education*, **4,** 1 (1969).

M. L. McGlashan
Department of Chemistry
The University, Exeter, U.K.